AMERICAN HANDBOOK OF PSYCHIATRY

Volume Five

AMERICAN HANDBOOK OF PSYCHIATRY

Silvano Arieti, EDITOR-IN-CHIEF

Volume One
The Foundations of Psychiatry
EDITED BY SILVANO ARIETI

Volume Two
Child and Adolescent Psychiatry, Sociocultural and Community Psychiatry
EDITED BY GERALD CAPLAN

Volume Three
Adult Clinical Psychiatry
EDITED BY SILVANO ARIETI AND EUGENE B. BRODY

Volume Four
Organic Disorders and Psychosomatic Medicine
EDITED BY MORTON F. REISER

Volume Five
Treatment
EDITED BY DANIEL X. FREEDMAN AND JARL E. DYRUD

Volume Six
New Psychiatric Frontiers
EDITED BY DAVID A. HAMBURG AND H. KEITH H. BRODIE

AMERICAN HANDBOOK OF PSYCHIATRY

SECOND EDITION

Silvano Arieti · Editor-in-Chief

VOLUME FIVE

Treatment

DANIEL X. FREEDMAN AND JARL E. DYRUD · *Editors*

BASIC BOOKS, INC., PUBLISHERS · NEW YORK

Library of Congress Cataloging in Publication Data (Revised)
Main entry under title:

American handbook of psychiatry.

 Includes bibliographies.
 1. Psychiatry—Collected works. I. Arieti,
Silvano, ed. [DNLM: 1. Mental disorders. WM100
A503]
RC435.A562   616.8'9'008   73-78893
ISBN 0-465-00147-5 (v. 1)

CONTRIBUTORS

C. Knight Aldrich, M.D.
Professor of Psychiatry, University of Virginia School of Medicine, Charlottesville; Director, Blue Ridge Community Mental Health Center, Charlottesville.

Robert L. Arnstein, M.D.
Chief Psychiatrist, Division of Mental Hygiene, Yale University Health Services, New Haven; Clinical Professor of Psychiatry, Yale University School of Medicine, New Haven.

William A. Bellamy, M.D.
Associate Clinical Professor of Psychiatry, School of Medicine, University of California at San Francisco.

Lauretta Bender, M.D.
Clinical Professor of Psychiatry, retired, College of Physicians and Surgeons, Columbia University, New York; Clinical Professor of Psychiatry, Department of Child and Adolescent Psychiatry, University of Maryland, Baltimore.

Sidney W. Bijou, Ph.D.
Professor, Department of Psychology, Child Behavior Laboratory, University of Illinois, Champaign.

Peter Blos, Jr., M.D.
Psychiatric Consultant, Child Development Project, Department of Psychiatry, University of Michigan School of Medicine, Ann Arbor.

Murray Bowen, M.D.
Clinical Professor and Director, Family Programs, Department of Psychiatry, Georgetown University Medical Center, Washington, D.C. Clinical Professor and Chairman, Division of Family and Social Psychiatry, Virginia Commonwealth University, Medical College of Virginia, Richmond.

Francis J. Braceland, M.D.
Editor, American Journal of Psychiatry; Clinical Professor of Psychiatry, Emeritus, Yale University School of Medicine, New Haven.

Dexter M. Bullard, Jr., M.D.
Medical Director, Chestnut Lodge, Rockville, Maryland.

Robert N. Butler, M.D.
Research Psychiatrist and Gerontologist, The Washington School of Psychiatry, Washington, D.C. Associate Clinical Professor of Psychiatry, Howard University School of Medicine, Washington, D.C.

Justin D. Call, M.D.
Professor and Chief of Child Psychiatry Division, Department of Psychiatry and Human Behavior, School of Medicine, University of California at Irvine; Analyzing and Supervising Instructor, Los Angeles Psychoanalytic Society and Institute.

Pietro Castelnuovo-Tedesco, M.D.
James G. Blakemore Professor of Psychiatry, Vanderbilt University School of Medicine, Nashville.

Sharon Chaiklin, D.T.R.
Dance Therapist, Gundry Hospital, Baltimore; Dance Therapist, Silver Spring Day Treatment Center, Silver Spring, Maryland.

Jonathan O. Cole, M.D.
Psychiatrist, McLean Hospital, Belmont, Massachusetts; Lecturer, Harvard Medical School, Boston.

Laurence A. Cove, M.D.
Research and Faculty Associate and Attending Psychiatrist, Children's Hospital National Medical Center, Washington, D.C. Assistant Clinical Professor of Child Health and Development, and of

Psychiatry and Behavioral Sciences, George Washington University School of Medicine, Washington, D.C.

Robert S. Daniels, M.D.
Dean, University of Cincinnati College of Medicine.

John M. Davis, M.D.
Director of Research, Illinois State Psychiatric Institute, Chicago; Professor of Psychiatry, University of Chicago Pritzker School of Medicine.

Thomas P. Detre, M.D.
Professor and Chairman, Department of Psychiatry, University of Pittsburgh School of Medicine; Director, Western Psychiatric Institute and Clinic, Pittsburgh.

Jarl E. Dyrud, M.D.
Professor and Associate Chairman, Department of Psychiatry, University of Chicago Pritzker School of Medicine.

Stuart M. Finch, M.D.
Lecturer in Psychiatry, University of Arizona College of Medicine, Tucson.

Jerome D. Frank, M.D., Ph.D.
Professor Emeritus of Psychiatry, The Johns Hopkins University School of Medicine, Baltimore.

Daniel X. Freedman, M.D.
Louis Block Professor of Biological Sciences and Chairman, Department of Psychiatry, University of Chicago Pritzker School of Medicine.

Lawrence Friedman, M.D.
Clinical Assistant Professor of Psychiatry, Cornell University Medical College, New York; Assistant Attending Psychiatrist, New York Hospital-Cornell Medical Center.

Eugene T. Gendlin, Ph.D.
Department of Psychology, University of Chicago.

Samuel Gershon, M.D.
Professor of Psychiatry, New York University School of Medicine, New York; Director, Neuropsychopharmacology Research Unit, New York University Medical Center.

Milton Greenblatt, M.D.
Professor of Psychiatry, School of Medicine, University of California at Los Angeles; Chief of Psychiatry, Veterans' Administration Hospital, Sepulveda, California.

Marguerite J. Holmes, M.N.
Lecturer, College of Nursing, Arizona State University, Tempe; Counselor, Phoenix Family Life Center, Phoenix.

Howard F. Hunt, Ph.D.
Chief, Psychiatric Research (Psychology), New York State Psychiatric Institute, New York; Professor of Psychology, Columbia University, New York.

Lothar B. Kalinowsky, M.D.
Clinical Professor of Psychiatry, New York Medical College, New York.

Chase Patterson Kimball, M.D.
Professor of Psychiatry, Medicine, and Behavioral Science, University of Chicago Pritzker School of Medicine.

David J. Kupfer, M.D.
Associate Professor of Psychiatry, University of Pittsburgh School of Medicine; Director of Research, Western Psychiatric Institute and Clinic, Pittsburgh.

H. Peter Laqueur, M.D., F.A.P.A.
Associate Professor of Psychiatry, University of Vermont Medical College, Burlington; Director, Family Therapy, Vermont State Hospital, Waterbury.

William C. Lewis, M.D.
Professor of Psychiatry, University of Wisconsin Medical School, Madison.

Morton A. Lieberman, Ph.D.
Professor, Departments of Behavioral Science (Human Development) and Psychiatry, University of Chicago Pritzker School of Medicine.

Kenneth E. Livingston, M.D., F.R.C.S.
Associate Professor of Surgery, University of Toronto, Ontario; Chief of Neurosurgery, The Wellsley Hospital, Toronto.

Reginald S. Lourie, M.D., Med.Sc.D.
Professor Emeritus of Child Health and Development, and of Psychiatry and Behavioral Sciences, George Washington University School of Medicine, Washington, D.C.; Senior Consultant, Psychiatric Institute of Washington.

Arnold M. Ludwig, M.D.
Professor and Chairman, Department of Psychiatry, University of Kentucky, Lexington.

David F. Musto, M.D.
Associate Professor of Psychiatry (Child Study Center) and Associate Professor of History, Yale University, New Haven; Associate Director, National Humanities Institute, New Haven.

John C. Nemiah, M.D.
Psychiatrist-in-Chief, Beth Israel Hospital, Boston; Professor of Psychiatry, Harvard Medical School, Boston.

Joseph D. Noshpitz, M.D.
Clinical Professor of Psychiatry, George Washington University School of Medicine, Washington, D.C. President (1973–75), American Academy of Child Psychiatry, Washington, D.C.

William Offenkrantz, M.D.
Professor of Psychiatry, University of Chicago Pritzker School of Medicine; Faculty, Institute for Psychoanalysis, Chicago.

Martin T. Orne, M.D., Ph.D.
Director, Unit for Experimental Psychiatry, Institute of the Pennsylvania Hospital, Philadelphia; Professor of Psychiatry, University of Pennsylvania Medical School, Philadelphia.

Helen Harris Perlman, M.S., D. Litt.
Samuel Deutsch Distinguished Service Professor Emeritus, School of Social Service Administration, University of Chicago.

Arthur J. Prange, Jr., M.D.
Professor of Psychiatry, University of North Carolina School of Medicine, Chapel Hill.

William H. Redd, Ph.D.
Associate Professor of Psycology, University of Illinois, Urbana-Champaign.

Bernard Rubin, M.D.
Professorial Lecturer, University of Chicago Pritzker School of Medicine and the Law School; Attending Psychiatrist, Michael Reese Hospital and Medical Center, Chicago.

Edward C. Senay, M.D.
Associate Professor, Department of Psychiatry, University of Chicago Pritzker School of Medicine; Director, Illinois Drug Abuse Program, Illinois Department of Mental Health and Developmental Disabilities, Chicago.

Frida G. Surawicz, M.D.
Associate Professor of Psychiatry, University of Kentucky College of Medicine, Lexington; Chief of Psychiatry, Veterans' Administration Hospital, Lexington.

Arnold Tobin, M.D.
Research Associate in Psychiatry, University of Chicago; Fellow, Center for Psychosocial Studies, Chicago.

Gary J. Tucker, M.D.
Professor of Psychiatry, Dartmouth Medical School, Hanover, New Hampshire.

Edward A. Tyler, M.D.
Associate Dean and Professor of Child Psychiatry, Northwestern University School of Medicine, Chicago.

Eberhard H. Uhlenhuth, M.D.
Professor of Psychiatry, University of Chicago Pritzker School of Medicine.

Lewis R. Wolberg, M.D.
Clinical Professor of Psychiatry, New York University School of Medicine; Chairman, Board of Trustees, Postgraduate Center for Mental Health, New York.

Israel Zwerling, M.D., Ph.D.
Professor and Chairman, Department of Mental Health Sciences, Hahnemann Medical College and Hospital, Philadelphia.

CONTENTS

Volume Five

PART THREE: *The Somatic Therapies*

PART FOUR: *Management and Care of the Patient*

PART FIVE: *Psychiatry and General Medicine*

PART SIX: *Legal Psychiatry*

PART SEVEN: *Psychiatry for the Seventies*

PART ONE

Introduction

CHAPTER 1

PSYCHOTHERAPY IN CONTEMPORARY AMERICA: ITS DEVELOPMENT AND CONTEXT*

Martin T. Orne

THE PRACTICE of medicine has sometimes been described as the art of making the right decision without sufficient knowledge. While great clinicians often intuitively transcend what is definitely known, the

* The substantive research upon which the theoretical outlook presented in this paper is based was supported in part by grant #MH 19156 from the National Institute of Mental Health and by a grant from the Institute for Experimental Psychiatry.

I am deeply indebted to Henry Gleitman for his many conceptual contributions and extensive editorial comments as well as some particularly apt descriptive metaphors and to A. Gordon Hammer and Lester B. Luborsky for their detailed criticisms and incisive suggestions, and to Frederick J. Evans, Merton F. Gill, John F. Kihlstrom, J. Martin Myers, Emily Carota Orne, and Sydney E. Pulver for their helpful comments in the preparation of this paper.

effectiveness of a field as a whole nonetheless depends upon the state of scientific knowledge. In order to illustrate the relationship of science to art in the context of psychotherapy, I ask my residents to imagine that they need their gall bladder removed and could somehow choose their surgeon from among Hippocrates, Paré, Billroth, or a second-rate surgical resident from a second-rate medical school in a second-rate hospital today. I then ask them to contrast *this* choice with the choice they would make if selecting their psychotherapist, given the option of Hippocrates, Rush, Freud, or Adler, or a second-rate resident in psychiatry from a second-rate medical school in a second-rate hospital today.

Needless to say, their choice for the gall bladder operation is invariably in favor of today's medicine. Their choice of a psychotherapist, however, rarely favors contemporary practice.

In all healing professions the great clinician is preferred to the mediocre practitioner. Nonetheless, the measure of what is really known in a field is whether the midget of today can stand on the shoulders of the giant of yesterday, thereby becoming more effective than the great practitioner of the past. Though the role of art is likely to remain important in all healing professions, it is fair to ask why psychotherapy (which after all is ofttimes described as old as man himself) has failed to develop a readily transmitted body of cumulated knowledge that can ensure the competence of its average practitioner. Perhaps some of the reasons will become clear as we reexamine the nature of psychotherapy, its historical development and underlying assumptions, its role both as a form of treatment and as a social force in contemporary American society. We will examine some of the forces in the development of psychotherapy that have ultimately led to inherent contradictions and to a number of crises, and, finally, we will consider the dilemma faced by the individual psychotherapist as he studies the therapeutic process, tries to evaluate its effectiveness, and seeks to integrate systematic observations into the practice of the clinical art.

⟮ Background

The Context of Treatment

Since time immemorial, man has sought to develop means of coping with maladies that afflict him. To the extent that the treatment of priest, shaman, or other primitive physician equivalents does not depend upon specific physiological effects acting upon the true cause of the illness but nonetheless leads to improvement, the process is often considered a primitive form of psychotherapy (belonging to the general category of faith healing). How a condition is treated in any society depends upon the group's relevant concepts of causality. Primitive cultures recognize simple injuries and can identify some fractures; most have some concept of immobilization and even the setting of bones. On the other hand, primitive cultures vary widely in the degree to which they accept naturally occurring disease as an explanatory mechanism to account for the symptoms of illness. The Hopi, for example, explains symptoms primarily as due to witchcraft.[63] To him, diagnosis is thus a matter of identifying the kind of witchcraft, and therapy is the practice of some appropriate and counteractive magic. Not surprisingly, the culturally defined categories of affliction also determine whether the individual perceives himself as suffering from a malady. Thus, a large number of individuals in many primitive cultures suffer low-grade parasitic infections without being aware that they have a problem. The possibility of *healing* arises only when there is a realization that there is something out of the ordinary to which some cause must be ascribed. While the explanatory principles evoked by folk medicine often seem quaint or naive, if not ludicrous, some primitive treatments contain potent drugs as active ingredients (e.g., quinine, rauwolfia).

The same principles that determine how a physical malady is to be treated, or whether for that matter it is even categorized as such, apply to functional disorders. The same set of behavioral symptoms that one culture ascribes to spirit possession and treats with toleration are explained by another culture as witchcraft that requires the immediate attention of a shaman. Yet another culture might consider the behavior as deviant and unacceptable and punish it severely. What matters is how a culture interprets behaviors that we regard as manifestations of functional disorders. Depending upon how the culture explains their occurrence, they will be dealt with by either some therapeutic intervention, by social sanctions, or perhaps by benign neglect. If treatment is called for, the healing process (whether it "works" or not) invariably depends on a generally agreed upon diagnosis, verified and legitimized by an individual whose skill in such matters is generally recognized and is usually based on extensive and arduous training. Frank[15] has emphasized a number of important similarities among the broad range of techniques employed to treat functional disorders in a wide variety of social settings. These include the importance of a socially defined treatment, usually of a dramatic nature, often accompanied by a heightened state of arousal, and a shared belief system that provides a rationale for both the disorder and the treatment, making possible renewed hope for relief.

The Nature of Psychotherapy

It is difficult to arrive at an acceptable definition of psychotherapy. *Dorland's Illustrated Medical Dictionary*[1] defines it as "the treatment of emotional and mental problems" without specifying the remedy, and therefore it is clearly too broad: it includes psychopharmacology, psychosurgery, as well as Christian Science and faith healing. Somewhat more circumspect, Webster[20] and Noyes and Kolb[46] define psychotherapy as "the treatment of emotional and mental problems by psychological means." This definition specifies that *both* the disorder and the techniques of therapy be *psychological* which, while more satisfying in some ways, tends to exclude the treatment of organic illnesses such as ulcerative colitis, peptic ulcers, asthma, and so on, in which psychological factors may play significant roles. In another sense, one might well want to define psychotherapy as the treatment of disorders by psychological means, focusing only on the modality of treatment rather than on the disorder itself. This has generally been the definition implicitly accepted by psychiatrists who treat psychosomatic as well as psychiatric problems.

None of these definitions is truly adequate since they are overinclusive in some regards and fail to make important distinctions in other regards. For example, the application of psychotherapeutic techniques has been extended to helping individuals deal with psychological components of physical illness, habit disorders, deviant but not necessarily ill behavior, and facilitating emotional growth and development.

In actual practice psychotherapy does not define itself solely either by the nature of the disorder it tries to treat or by the specific procedures it employs in so doing. In contrast to all other medical-treatment procedures that are defined by *what* is done to the patient, psychotherapy is defined more by *who* does it—by the role relationship and the training of the therapist. An appendectomy is an appendectomy regardless of who performs it, whether a surgeon, a general practitioner, or a paraprofessional. On the other hand, interactions that are behaviorally indistinguishable from those which occur during psychotherapy are referred to as "good teaching" if they occur between a student and his teacher, a "heart-to-heart talk" if between a child and its parent, "rapping" if among college students, and "good business" if between a bartender and his customer. It is not the specifics of the interaction but the context, the purpose, and the social infrastructure that in fact define it as *psychotherapy.*

Specific and Nonspecific Factors

One attribute not emphasized in most definitions but nonetheless crucial is the therapist's belief that his method has *specific effects* on the underlying disorder that is treated. Such effects must have their roots in some systematic, causal-belief system about the nature of the disorder and its therapy. This point has been important to physicians since medicine first became a legitimate field of study. Physicians distinguished themselves from quacks on the basis of their rational approach as opposed to the faith-healing aspects of the quacks' endeavors.* Though the effectiveness of faith healing was often recognized by the physician, and the importance of nonspecific factors was already recognized by Hippocrates, these were differentiated from specific treatments.

---

* Unfortunately, while it is easy to recognize someone else's treatment as faith healing, it is extremely difficult to recognize such components in one's own practice. The chiropractor readily dismisses his patient's former treatment by a Christian Science practitioner as faith healing as he manipulates the spine and administers megavitamins to "definitively" treat his patient's complaint of fatigue.

The practicing physician was generally willing to take advantage of the beneficial effects associated with the patient's faith in him and his treatment, but he saw such factors as ancillary to the specific treatment itself.

The distinction between specific and nonspecific treatment factors is particularly crucial to the development of psychotherapy and well illustrated in the history of hypnosis. Franz Mesmer was highly successful in treating a broad range of disorders. He also showed an intuitive awareness that appropriate patient expectancies, and suggestion, were important factors in treatment. He believed, however, that his cures were the consequence of a specific therapeutic agent, which he called "animal magnetism," and he vehemently rejected the possibility that "suggestive mechanisms" (that is, nonspecific factors) played a major role in his treatment. Indeed, it has been documented that Mesmer was aware of somnambulism (as later described in detail by his student, the Marquis de Puységur), but refused to concern himself with this and related phenomena because he wished to study the scientific aspects of animal magnetism—in other words, what he viewed to be the specific therapeutic agent.[9,41]

Similarly, the Royal Commission which investigated Mesmer's claims focused exclusively on the question of whether animal magnetism was real, a claim that it appropriately rejected. In the process of the investigation it was recognized that many patients derived a great deal of relief from the procedure and that their ailments were often greatly ameliorated. Furthermore, it was acknowledged that Mesmer was at times able to induce anesthesia; however, both the cures and the anesthetic effects were explained as the consequence of "mere imagination"; in other words, not different in kind from other forms of faith healing. Since the theory of animal magnetism was thus refuted, the effects of the treatment were rejected as "mere imagination"—the eighteenth-century equivalent of nonspecific factors. It is no doubt relevant that eighteenth-century science ("the Age of Reason") in an effort to free itself from religion and mysticism, considered causality exclusively in phys-

ical terms, and could not ascribe causal status to psychological phenomena.

Two hundred years later we know only too well that the empirical distinction between nonspecific faith-healing effects (which in psychopharmacology are conveniently subsumed under the concept of the *placebo effect*) and specific therapeutic effects is difficult to draw. One needs to be as much on guard against the possibility of being deceived by a placebo response as against rejecting a treatment that is in fact specific.

Imagine a nineteenth-century scientific inquiry into the treatment of dropsy by a witch's brew that includes such choice ingredients as bat wings but also an extract of foxglove (albeit picked at the new moon). Such an inquiry might well have rejected all claims of the potion's effectiveness because the rationale of why it worked could not stand up to close scrutiny. Yet many years were required before the active ingredient was identified, and much has yet to be learned about the mechanisms of action of digitalis. In fact, in this instance the question of therapeutic effectiveness—so carefully skirted in the investigation of Mesmer—provided the basis for continued interest.

In other cases, later analysis showed that despite a very plausible rationale, there was no specific treatment after all. Consider the widespread use of internal mammary artery ligation in the treatment of angina pectoris as recently as 1958. This by no means innocuous surgical intervention was based on an eminently reasonable rationale and initially yielded dramatic results. It was only after a careful, systematic double-blind study[8] was carried out that it became clear that the therapeutic effects could be totally accounted for as a placebo response.*

It is difficult to fully appreciate the ubiquitous nature of the placebo effect. Recently Evans[11] reanalyzed a large number of studies that had compared active analgesic drugs and placebos. In several double-blind studies

* It is worth noting that with the current regulations governing medical research it would be extremely difficult if not impossible to carry out such a study, and it is likely that a great many more patients would have been exposed to a great many more risks with this procedure.

where aspirin had been compared with placebos, the effectiveness of a placebo was found to be roughly 54 percent that of aspirin. On the other hand, when a far more potent drug —morphine—was compared with a placebo, again in double-blind studies, placebos still turned out to have approximately 54 percent of the effectiveness of morphine. Thus it seems that the strength of the placebo response depends in large part upon the physician's belief in the effectiveness of the active drug being administered. Thus, the placebo given in a double-blind study along with morphine proved to be a far more powerful placebo than that given in a double-blind study with aspirin. The effectiveness of the placebo in other studies was determined by the context of physician expectations in which it was administered.

An individual's response to a placebo is incidentally quite independent of his response to hypnotic suggestion. Thus, a hypnotic suggestion of analgesia administered to hypnotizable individuals leads to a considerable increase in the pain threshold, but this increase is uncorrelated with the same individual's placebo response. On the other hand, the hypnotic suggestion of analgesia administered to *un*hypnotizable individuals will also lead to an increase in the pain threshold that, while smaller, is nonetheless significant: in this group the increase *is* highly correlated with their response to placebos.[40,50] It may therefore be appropriate to speak of a placebo response that occurs in the context of hypnosis but is independent of and separable from the specific effect of hypnotic suggestion. Thus, hypnotic suggestion, usually conceived of as a nonspecific effect, can be quite specific after all.

The difficulty in distinguishing between placebo effects and specific pharmaceutic action in physical medicine is great enough, but it becomes immense when we try to evaluate the effects of psychotherapy.* In part, the problem lies in the prior difficulty of defining

both psychotherapy and the disorders to which this form of therapy tries to address itself. Thus, any meaningful test of the distinction between specific and nonspecific factors presupposes some initial decisions on these crucial but unresolved issues. To see these problems in perspective it will be helpful to consider how our modern concept of psychotherapy has evolved, and the extent to which we can meet a minimal requirement: to specify what psychotherapy is *not*. Until we can do at least this, it will be well-nigh impossible to answer questions about specific psychotherapeutic effects.

Though no definition of psychotherapy is currently shared by all those who claim to practice it, it is clear that the term, however, is clearly used both in a broad and in a more restricted sense. In the broadest sense, the term can be used to describe all forms of nonphysical treatment, and in this generic sense it includes procedures ranging from advice, habit training, coercion, and persuasion to interpretation, the analysis of associations and dreams, the ventilation of feelings, abreaction, and all those procedures generally subsumed under behavior therapy as well as suggestive therapeutics and faith healing. In contrast, most psychotherapists use the term psychotherapy in a more narrow and more technical sense—at least some of the time. To them, psychotherapy refers to a method designed to alleviate specific difficulties through the use of specific therapeutic procedures practiced by highly skilled professionals. Psychotherapy seen in this fashion did not evolve until the end of the nineteenth century, and it is with the ramifications of this development that we are most concerned in this chapter.

⟨ Psychotherapy Within Medicine

The Origins and Legitimization of Psychodynamic Therapy

While the importance of psychological factors and their effects on disease were recognized by the ancient Greeks and had been

---

* Placebo effects will of necessity play a role in the psychotherapeutic process, as they do in any other form of treatment (an issue that has been discussed by Shapiro[62]).

commented upon by physicians through the ages, reassurance, support, and even counseling about personal problems were seen as an ancillary part of medical treatment. The practice of psychotherapy could not become a medical specialty in its own right until it was seen to go beyond these general common-sense principles. The study of hypnotic phenomena in the early nineteenth century came close to providing a specific method of treatment, and the increased recognition of functional disorders helped identify the maladies to which it could most appropriately be applied. However, despite a flurry of interest occasioned by such controversies as those of the Salpêtrière and Nancy schools, the apparent similarities of hypnosis and suggestive therapy to faith healing probably prevented their widespread acceptance by medicine. Though some few neurologists enjoyed good reputations and seemed to have considerable success in the treatment of functional disorders, the practice of psychotherapy as a truly independent enterprise could not develop until it was conceived of as a specific treatment, based on principles other than suggestion and not readily inferred through common sense. The formulation of such principles required, in turn, the evolution of the concept of psychological causality. It remained for Sigmund Freud to develop the rationale necessary to make psychological treatment a specific therapy.

Freud and Josef Breuer's early psychotherapeutic efforts employed hypnosis in a novel way as a means of exploring unconscious memories. The existence of such memories and their effects had been recognized previously and had played an important role in the thinking of several of Freud's contemporaries.[73] What was crucial about Freud's studies in hysteria from our point of view was the emphasis on a specific mechanism: in his view the effect of psychotherapeutic treatment was caused not by suggestion but rather by the recall of unconscious repressed material and its interpretation.

Hypnosis had proved to be an effective technique to facilitate the recall of material; nonetheless, Freud eventually abandoned it in favor of free association. The reason he originally gave was the difficulty of inducing hypnosis in all patients, an explanation that hardly explains why the procedure ought not to be used for those individuals who are able to enter trance. Undoubtedly his decision was determined by various additional factors such as a growing awareness of the mechanisms of transference and countertransference. Contrary to some assertions, Freud was highly sophisticated and skilled in the use of the hypnotic technique,[28] but whatever his reasons for abandoning hypnosis, his decision to do so was probably crucial for the eventual acceptance of psychoanalysis as a specific form of therapy. The sole reliance on free association as an apparently rational procedure for investigating repressed memories made it more plausible that his results were due to a specific therapeutic effect, and this clearly distinguished them from the therapeutic success of others who relied on "suggestion." He developed a theory, couched in the mechanistic metaphors of the day, that discussed the effect of psychic energy—libido—and tried to show how these energies would be appropriately reallocated as repression was lifted. He outlined a developmentally oriented rationale for the etiology of neurosis, analogous to the characterization of physical anomalies of development by the emerging discipline of embryology. Though his insistence on the sexual etiology of all neuroses caused great controversy, he nonetheless succeeded in distinguishing between the enterprise of psychoanalysis, on the one hand, and either faith healing or common-sense advice and persuasion on the other. This distinction is crucial to the concept of psychotherapy as it has evolved over the years, and by drawing it Freud created a new discipline.

These comments should not be taken to deny the substantive merit of his incisive clinical observations, particularly as they relate to the analysis of transference,[18] the recognition of countertransference, the mechanisms of defense, and the significance and multidetermined causality of symptoms. Nor do we minimize his contribution in adding a new form of clinical inquiry as a primary data source. The intention here is neither to question nor to evaluate critically the contribution of psychoanalysis, but rather to indicate its crucial historical importance for the acceptance of psychotherapy as a specific treatment —quite independent of its scientific validity.

Though the medical profession was slow to recognize the significance of Freud's contributions, his theories provided a radically new framework for perceiving man. The impact on the arts and the humanities was rapid and dramatic. Psychodynamic concepts address themselves to the nature of man and his basic motives. These concerns are central to the writer, to the artist, to the anthropologist, and also to the historian and the social philosopher; though the psychological causation of illness had long been recognized by the great poets, it now became the focus of much artistic work and literary criticism. The acceptance of psychodynamic thinking had profound consequences for the artist's view of man, and changed the focus of interest from what an individual does to why he does it. These same insights helped to brand many of the values, beliefs, and perceptions of the Victorian era as false and artificial. Thus, altruism became self-serving, patriotism an excuse for a variety of infantile feelings, loyalty became suspect, and so on—a reevaluation of attitudes that undoubtedly gained enormous impetus from the general disillusionment that followed World War I. The influence of Freud's ideas outside of medicine was probably even greater than that within it; we are probably too close as yet to fully appreciate their effect. If Marx created Economic Man, Freud created Psychological Man.[56]

The impact of psychoanalysis on society at large was probably of considerable import for the development of psychotherapy itself. The medical establishment refused to bestow its recognition, but this recognition was accorded by significant segments of the public so that until the Second World War most patients who sought psychoanalytic aid did so directly without referral by other physicians. Indeed, Freud seriously contemplated establishing psychoanalysis as a separate discipline, undoubtedly influenced by the hostile attitudes of many of his medical colleagues in Austria. It is interesting to note that only in the United States was psychoanalytic training limited almost exclusively to physicians, and it was here that psychoanalytic thinking was most readily integrated into psychiatry.

Freud's impact on contemporary American psychiatric thought has been so great that it is difficult to imagine how there could have been any American psychiatry without him. It is worth remembering, however, that until the 1940s the practice of psychotherapy—in the sense of *dynamic psychotherapy*—hardly played a significant role in the day-to-day work of either the state hospital psychiatrist or the neuropsychiatrist. Psychoanalysis was taught outside of academic channels in separate institutes, and psychotherapy was, with a few notable exceptions, largely taught by psychoanalysts. Most residencies in psychiatry included no formal training in psychotherapy, and the practice of psychotherapy did not become the principal occupation of psychiatrists until relatively recently.

The Basic Tenets of Psychodynamic Therapy

This is not the place to discuss the details of psychoanalytic thinking or techniques, but only those views about the nature of the psychotherapeutic process that have become generally accepted by virtually all psychodynamically oriented therapists (that is, by psychotherapists who, whatever their different theoretical persuasions, accept the notion that psychopathology, and indeed many facets of normal personality, are rooted in the "dynamic" conflicts of intrapsychic forces). These beliefs are, for the most part, shared by the patients who seek psychotherapy; they have, in fact, become part of the belief system of those subcultures within contemporary society from which the overwhelming bulk of patients for psychotherapy are drawn. These views contrast sharply with the concepts underlying the practice of other branches of medicine. Most psychodynamic therapists feel that these beliefs must be understood and accepted to make psychotherapy a meaningful and rational enterprise.

An admittedly incomplete list of such basic tenets might include the following assertions (whose validity, or for that matter even testability, are not at present under discussion):

1. An individual is never fully aware of the reasons for his feelings and actions.

2. All behavior is multidetermined and motivated.

3. Symptoms are expressions of important psychological needs and motives. They satisfy these motives in a variety of ways but usually without the patient's awareness. While often initially obscure, when understood they generally turn out to be important and meaningful communications by the patient to those around him.

4. Symptoms are an expression of an underlying difficulty and ought, therefore, not to be suppressed. Instead, what requires treatment is the underlying problem.

5. Appropriate treatment involves making the patient aware of those unconscious motives which play a dynamic role in his adjustment. This growing awareness will ultimately lead to psychological growth and development on the one hand and the elimination of specific symptoms on the other.

6. The process of treatment requires the patient to honestly express his feelings and thoughts to his therapist. He must not hold them back or censor them, regardless of how unacceptable, demeaning, or frightening he may find them. These feelings and thoughts often include some that could not be expressed under other circumstances. They must be shared with the therapist even if, or rather especially if, they concern the therapist.

7. The therapist's role is to help the patient understand, but not to suggest or to give advice. He is to help the patient grow by helping him become aware of what he really wants by bringing into consciousness motives, feelings, and ideas that were not previously available.

8. Among the various techniques that are used to facilitate the therapeutic process are encouragement of free expression, free association, the interpretation of dreams, appropri-

ate inquiry into feelings and thoughts associated with various experiences and events, and the analysis of discrepancies between what individuals do and the reasons they provide for their behavior.

9. The process of therapy is seen as a mutual enterprise, analogous to a learning experience rather than to other forms of medical treatment. Its effects are dependent upon the active participation of the patient and the changes within his awareness that follow insights derived from treatment.

10. The process of therapy will involve considerable effort and some suffering on the part of the patient. He is likely to feel worse before he feels better, and some sessions will involve the experience of intense dysphoric affects.

The Concept of a Definitive Treatment

In addition to these general beliefs about treatment (for a more extended discussion, see Orne and Wender[51]) there are also various shared beliefs about the nature of psychological difficulties. According to most psychodynamic therapists, various symptoms reflect basic underlying personality problems that, in turn, are best understood developmentally. Psychoanalysis is usually seen as that process by which these developmental difficulties can be *definitively* cured, analogous to the way a surgeon is able to treat physical anomalies. It is important to recognize that the (psychodynamically oriented) psychotherapeutic ethos postulates not only the mechanism that produces the malady and the process that heals it, but further asserts that its treatment is definitive rather than supportive and that, when cured, the patient is, in principle, cured once and for all.

The view of therapy as a definitive, once-and-for-all treatment was probably very significant in leading to its acceptance by both the lay public and the medical profession in the United States.[49] It would seem that such a view of man was highly consonant with the Protestant ethic[72] at a time when fundamental religion had ceased to be an active force in many lives. A value system that holds that change is basically good, that man is infinitely adaptable and capable of growth, that everyone can and indeed should grow up to be successful and prosperous, and that the failure to achieve in such a manner is sinful, provides a ready climate for a therapeutic system that ascribes problems to faulty development and promises to rectify such faults definitively once and for all. It hardly seems accidental that psychoanalysis and psychodynamic psychotherapy became accepted in those areas where the Protestant ethic had been firmly established, but was largely ignored in those areas which held to a more traditional Catholic view of the world. After all, if man is seen as unchangeable and his job is to find his proper place in a fixed universe and make his peace with God, if poverty and illness are givens and accepted, to be bravely endured with proud humility, and if character is seen as largely predetermined at birth, it hardly seems reasonable to expect psychotherapy to be effective.

It is interesting to note that the same country that supports the greatest number of psychotherapists *per capita* is also the country that, more than any other, believes in man's infinite capacity for self-improvement, be it through higher education, correspondence courses, or primers on "How to Win Friends and Influence People." This same claim of nearly limitless human plasticity is a cardinal tenet of early behaviorism, a theoretical posture that took America by storm during the twenties and thirties and is still a dominant force today:

"Give me a dozen healthy infants, well-formed, and my own specified world to bring them up in and I'll guarantee to take any one at random and train him to become any type of specialist I might select—doctor, lawyer, artist, merchant-chief and, yes, even beggar-man and thief, regardless of his talents, penchants, tendencies, abilities, vocations, and race of his ancestors." [p. 82][71]

Watson and American psychodynamically oriented therapists undoubtedly disagree about the means whereby man can be altered, but

that he is alterable both believe, and believe without question. The fact that America so readily accepted both behaviorism and the psychoanalytic view seems related to this one basic tenet that both views share.[*]

Given the Protestant ethic, it was important that psychotherapy was seen as leading to a genuine change, for it could then be conceptualized as a definitive treatment rather than as some kind of crutch. The former seems worth suffering for; the latter is seen as degrading and leading nowhere. The promise that psychotherapy, however long, can ultimately produce a person who is truly well seemed to justify whatever was required.

A different view of psychotherapy was recently put forward by Frank, who suggested that the problems might be conceived of as analogous to the common cold.[16] If this were so, it would not prevent the patient from catching another cold at a later time, even if the treatment was originally effective. This position readily explains the difficulty of documenting the effectiveness of treatment, and such a view is congruent with many clinical observations, but most therapists find it unacceptable, probably due in part to discomfort at the thought of practicing anything other than definitive treatment. Indeed, many therapists believe that most patients share their own bias: that they would prefer a course of treatmen that extends over several years, but results in a definitive cure, to an intermittent form of therapy that produces equal symptomatic relief but requires them to consult a therapist three or four times a year for the rest of their lives. This is not a matter of faith in the efficacy of a relatively small number of ongoing visits—even if both patient and therapist were to believe that both procedures are fully and equally effective, the two forms of treatment must inevitably produce two different ways in which both participants see the patient. In the one case, the patient is defined as a person with a continuing and never-end-

---

[*] Freud himself was far less sanguine about man's ultimate plasticity, but environmental determinism became dominant within psychoanalysis as it was transplanted to the United States.

ing need for the therapist; in the other, the patient is defined as someone who will eventually become well. The implications of these attitudes for the practice of supportive therapy are considerable.

Psychotherapy and the Medical Model

We have noted that the tenets of psychodynamic psychotherapy make it a procedure that, in many respects, is radically different from other forms of medical practice. Over the years considerable controversy has developed as to whether the medical model is appropriate for psychotherapy. Both the theoretical and pragmatic importance of who shall practice psychotherapy, how, and why, can hardly be overrated. The question of whether it is a medical treatment, a form of education, a method of behavioral engineering, a religious practice, or simply a personal service (in effect, a commodity) are issues where the conceptual model, scientific fact, the societal value system, and pragmatic public policy must intersect. While these various factors often seem independent, they are not. The kind of research that is carried out will modify the conceptual model, the kind of practice that exists may modify the kinds of research, and the patterns of both practice and research will necessarily be affected by public policy. Both the underlying rationale and the practice of psychotherapy have broad implications; in consequence, it will be carried out differently in different social systems. In our own society, it has been profoundly affected by political considerations as well as by the value systems of various social groups.

THE HISTORICAL RELATIONSHIP BETWEEN PSYCHOTHERAPY AND MEDICAL PRACTICE

We must consider the role of the physician in society to understand why it was so important that psychotherapy was originally perceived in a medical context. In modern society, illness is defined as a medical problem, diagnosed and treated by physicians. A broad range of deviant behaviors are treated rather than punished, if it can be demonstrated that they were the direct consequence of a physical malady. For example, extremely violent behavior is not prosecuted, given the diagnosis that it is consequent to a brain tumor; and it is medical opinion that determines whether the tumor does explain the patient's behavior. Similarly, if a soldier falls asleep on guard duty or refuses to fight, he is excused, if accepted medical opinion holds that his actions are the result of illness. Again, it is a physician who decides whether an individual is ill enough so that he cannot work, when he is ready to return to work, and so on. Just as medical decisions affect the attitude of our social institutions, so they do our own: medical opinion forms the basis for our decision to view a particular behavior, in others as well as in ourselves, as reprehensible or as sick.

The physician's role as the final arbiter of when an individual is ill, and of what actions can be explained and excused because of this illness has long extended to psychiatry. Indeed, one of the alienist's major responsibilities was to advise the courts whether an individual was suffering from mental illness, to help determine competence, and, finally, to arrange for commitment if this seemed necessary. The profound legal and social implications of the psychiatrist's decisions were as readily accepted as the pronouncements of any other medical specialist. His competence was legitimized by his medical training and experience and by his adherence to the approach of medical science in reaching his conclusions. While, in retrospect, one can undoubtedly see many inadequacies, it is probably fair to say that his judgment was the best available, and its probability of error was no greater than that of other medical judgments, a point easily overlooked in present-day criticisms of past (and perhaps present) psychiatric practice.

A further factor is the patient's belief in the therapist's competence, a belief more readily accorded to physicians than "laymen." The importance of this belief in the therapist's competence to provide help is, after all, a common thread in all psychological healing. That this competence derives from scientific rather than from religious credentials has been crucial to the further development of the field, especially since psychotherapy was accepted most eagerly by those segments of society for whom religion had ceased to be of preeminent significance.

Finally, the medical role provided a tradition of ethics for the therapist that was generally very helpful. The medical tradition demanded that the physician treat all sick individuals, even those society might have condemned. Regardless of his personal attitude he was expected to provide the best care he was able to give. Within such a framework it was accepted by the physician and society at large that it was his obligation to alleviate suffering and preserve life. This ethos allowed the psychotherapist to avoid explicit value judgments about his patients and to develop a point of view that holds moral judgments in abeyance and seeks to evaluate causality, an approach often held to be particularly conducive to the psychotherapeutic process. This attitude was facilitated by the already widely accepted view that transactions between doctor and patient are confidential, and that the physician's first responsibility lies with the patient.

The uncritical acceptance of the medical model ultimately involved psychotherapy in some contradictions. Since treatment was carried out by physicians, the person treated was by definition a patient, resulting in a doctor–patient role relationship with all of its sociological implications. It soon became clear in the context of psychotherapy that it was the patient's responsibility to participate actively in the process of treatment. But the therapist nonetheless accepted responsibility for the procedure, since the age-old tradition of medical responsibility was taken for granted by all concerned—the patient, the therapist, and the community. On the one hand, the ethos of psychotherapy emphasized that it was vital that the patient make decisions, accept responsibility, decide what is best for him; on the other hand, the physician never abrogated *his* obligation to look out for the patient's best interests and never really abandoned the implicit assumption that *he* knew what was in the patient's best interests. These inherent contradictions have been eloquently emphasized by Szasz.[69]

THE CONCEPTUAL IMPLICATIONS OF THE MEDICAL MODEL FOR PSYCHOTHERAPY

Psychotherapy evolved not by way of the alienist and the mental-hospital psychiatrist but rather through the treatment of psychoneurosis by "nerve specialists." These were neurologists to whom patients with unexplainable disorders were referred, and they developed the criteria by which functional illness was distinguished from neurological problems. They tried to describe psychopathology in a manner analogous to the description of organic pathology. In so doing they provided a medical model not only for the initial evaluation of the patient's symptoms but also for the schemata by which the therapist might understand the nature of the underlying disease. Much of the appeal of psychoanalysis derived from its assertion that it was the science that sought to do for psychopathology what organic medicine had so successfully done for the treatment of organic pathology. Freud made extensive use of structural metaphors in the development of his theories. The descriptions of the id, the ego, the superego, the conscious, the unconscious, and the preconscious have a quality that might lead a naive reader to localize them within the brain. Similarly, in discussing psychic development he writes as if he had discovered psychobiological processes analogous to those which were being discovered in embryology. Again, he discusses the organs of ego functioning as though these were analogous to the physical organ system; the libido theory is discussed in a manner analogous to hemodynamics. Yet another example of this postulated parallelism between mental and biological mechanisms is the implied analogy between unacceptable, and unconscious, ideas that fester until brought into the light of day, and infections by foreign bodies that are handled by surgical incision and drainage.

Thus, Freud and his followers saw themselves developing a scientific basis for specific treatments of psychopathology, and this view remained largely unchallenged by other dynamic psychologists regardless of the technical differences between theories that engendered so much affect within the field.*

By the end of the nineteenth century the extension of the medical approach to the treatment of functional ailments was unquestioned. Even the rather virulent disagreements among schools of psychotherapy had an acceptable historical analogue in disagreements between medical authorities about physical ailments, which did not in and of themselves undermine the prestige of the various medical practitioners.

One often overlooked consequence of this historical development is that psychotherapy based its legitimacy not on its outcome but rather on its scientific rationale. The early disputes among the various psychodynamic views are polemics about the nature of the postulated mechanisms, hardly ever about the more concrete issues of technique or outcome. Only rarely did the parties to the disputes refer to the success of their treatment as evidence for the validity of their theories. The early history of psychodynamic psychotherapy clearly reflects the peculiar dual attitude of medicine: on the one hand, it is an empirical art whose practitioners use their best judgment to employ whatever treatments have been shown to be effective; on the other hand, it is a scientific discipline whose members try to identify the underlying mechanisms of disease in a rigorous scientific fashion.

---

* Freud stayed closer to the biological theories than neo-Freudians who focused more on social factors and the here-and-now. Nonetheless, these were differences of degree. Even Harry Stack Sullivan,[68] who focused very heavily on environmental factors and rejected much of the biological metaphor, nonetheless describes the identification and resolution of parataxic distortions much in the manner used in describing some physical disorder that required resolution. The medical model shared by these workers seemed so ingrained as to have been a background phenomenon largely outside of awareness. It is likely that Adler was least biological in the infrastructure of his views, and this may account for his disproportionate impact on educational thinking, and the tendency for psychiatry, until very recently, to have largely ignored his contributions.

It was an ambitious undertaking indeed to build a science of psychopathology by constructing the mental analogues of physical processes. The resulting system was familiar to medical practitioners who recognized the analogies to the biological and physical sciences of the day. Interestingly enough, the link to psychobiology was not kept up to date; it was a link to scientific conceptions of the late nineteenth and early twentieth centuries that was never abandoned and inevitably became a fettering chain. While the brain sciences evolved and developed less ambitious but testable formulations that facilitated and, in turn, were facilitated by continuing laboratory research, the conceptual categories of psychodynamic therapy remained rooted in the late nineteenth century. This surely is one major reason why it has been so difficult to integrate new findings from other sciences that deal with brain and behavior with the constructs upon which psychotherapy was based.

In sum, psychodynamically oriented psychotherapy has been rooted in medical traditions and has continued to work with a translation of the conceptual framework that dominated medicine at the turn of the century while (with the notable exception of the psychosomatic movement) it became increasingly alienated from physical medicine, on the one hand, and relevant biopsychological research on the other.

⟨ Beyond the Medical Model

The last three decades have seen a series of major challenges to the whole system of beliefs and practices that constitute the core of psychodynamically oriented psychotherapy. These eventually led to the development of several alternate models of therapy. Historically, these challenges began as two questions were raised ever more insistently during the forties and fifties: (1) who should practice psychotherapy, and (2) does this practice have any effect?

We will begin our discussion by considering

these issues as they were treated during the two decades following World War II.

Who Should Practice Therapy?

Within the psychoanalytic movement it was soon recognized that the technical aspects of the therapeutic method had no direct relationship with other forms of medical practice and that medical training, oriented as it was toward organic pathology, might even interfere in some ways with the development of an appreciation for subtle psychological factors. Furthermore, it was evident that some highly gifted nonmedical individuals were eminently capable both as practitioners and theorists in the new discipline. This potential readiness to accept lay practitioners was strengthened by the fact that psychoanalysis was taught outside of universities and did not depend upon other medical specialties for referrals or consultation. It was only the integration of psychoanalysis into the mainstream of American psychiatry during the 1940s that kept it, and thus psychotherapeutic practice, within the confines of medicine for many years. Much the same happened in Europe when psychodynamically oriented psychotherapy was subsequently reintroduced there under American auspices, but eventually a number of forces combined that served to legitimize psychotherapists with other professional backgrounds.

With the increasing acceptance of psychotherapy as the appropriate form of treatment for psychological difficulties, it soon became clear that the number of therapists was insufficient to meet the demand. As long as psychotherapists were expected to be psychiatrically (and preferably psychoanalytically) trained physicians, the problem simply could not be solved. The relative shortage of physicians in the United States provided a limited pool from which potential medical psychotherapists could be drawn. However, the increased emphasis on psychiatry in medical schools, the ready availability of training stipends for residents, and the greatly enhanced social and economic prospects of future psychiatrists served to attract many young physicians to this specialty. Furthermore, special training stipends for established physicians made it possible for them to acquire specialty training, an option a good many physicians availed themselves of later in life. While the number of psychiatrists rose, the public demand for their services rose yet more. If one considers the relatively small number of patients who can be seen by psychiatrists in long-term treatment, a continuing scarcity of medical psychotherapists was well-nigh assured.

In child psychiatry, nonmedical therapists had long been accepted as competent practitioners—largely due to the orthopsychiatric movement. Treatment was typically carried out in collaboration among psychiatrists, psychiatric social workers, and psychologists. Well-trained psychiatric social workers were recognized as competent therapists. Initially, there was considerable conflict about the appropriateness of psychologists as psychotherapists. Some highly respected medical psychotherapists did, however, emphasize the competence of nonmedical professional workers and, despite official pronouncements to the contrary, there was a progressive inclination toward their acceptance, especially in institutional settings with a surfeit of patients and a shortage of staff.

Independent of medical psychotherapy, a different psychotherapeutic tradition evolved by way of the guidance-counseling movement in schools. Academically trained guidance counselors had credentials as scientific experts based on their work with objective tests that were designed to help individuals choose appropriate professional careers. The acceptance of this group initially came by way of the educational establishment and the widespread use of psychological tests in both school and industry. In the context of adjustment to various difficulties in school, many counseling psychologists had long carried on psychotherapeutic activities with troubled students. The work of Carl Rogers represented a major change of focus. Initially called "non-directive therapy"[59] and subsequently "client-centered therapy,"[60] it was rooted in entirely different, largely humanistic, traditions from those of psychodynamic therapy. Rogers argued that man is essentially healthy and that to help the "client"—not the patient—recognize and effectively deal with his difficulties, it was necessary only that the therapist create a context of positive regard in which to reflect the client's feelings. Rogerian therapists saw themselves as contributing to the client's growth and development, as strengthening his feelings of self-worth and helping him to better cope with his problems. In sharp contrast to the medical psychotherapists, Rogerians neither attempted to diagnose the underlying pathology nor did they feel called upon to take medical responsibility.

More or less concurrent with the growth of the Rogerian movement (just after World War II) there was a general upsurge of interest in clinical psychology. Many academic psychologists became interested in applying both psychological techniques and theories to clinical problems. The problems that interested this group were different from the earlier traditions of clinical psychology, which had applied laboratory methods to the diagnosis of special deficits. In principle, these academic clinical psychologists were sympathetic to many (though certainly not all) of the basic premises of the psychodynamic approach. Their object was to put dynamic psychology on a rigorous scientific basis. As a consequence, several gifted scientists in outstanding academic settings made serious efforts to relate psychoanalysis to facts and theories developed by academic psychology and by the social sciences, using methods and concepts from each of these.*

These academically trained clinical psychologists also had applied interests. Initially they concerned themselves with the development of various diagnostic tests, especially projective techniques, that were quite different from the aptitude and intelligence tests created and

* For example, the Department of Human Behavior at Yale, where the work of Miller and Dollard[43] represented a concerted effort at synthesis; the Department of Social Relations at Harvard, only slightly less psychoanalytically oriented, resulting in the close collaboration of Kluckhohn and Murray,[29] and "the new look in perception"[7] that focused on dynamic factors in what had previously been seen as traditional areas of psychology; at Columbia the work of Kardiner and Linton,[26] and so on.

perfected by the American testing movement between the two world wars. These projective methods (such as the Rorschach, the Thematic Apperception Test, sentence completion, and so on) were widely used as a means of rapidly evaluating the interplay of dynamic forces within the patient. Their focus was not so much on traditional descriptive diagnosis but rather on diagnosis in psychodynamic terms that were directly relevant to the psychotherapeutic process. Considering this focus it is hardly surprising that the interest in and emphasis on projective tests came to the fore in the period following World War II. Ultimately, however, these clinicians wanted to do more than help in diagnosis: they wanted to participate in the therapeutic process itself. With progressive insistence they sought training as psychotherapists. The eventual acceptance of psychotherapists who were clinical psychologists rather than physicians was partially based on the value many medical therapists attached to the contribution of clinical psychology to diagnosis in what was seen as a quasi-objective evaluation of psychodynamic factors. Many therapists hoped that psychological tests would ultimately provide them with information analogous to that which the pathologist gives to the surgeon. Because of these contributions, the psychologists' demands to take clinical training in institutional settings were progressively met (though with varying degrees of enthusiasm). It was a relatively small step from the practice of psychotherapy in institutional settings to psychotherapy in private practice.

The importance of clinical psychology for present views about psychotherapy can hardly be overrated. In contrast to social workers, some of whom became practitioners and accepted a secondary role within the medical setting, psychologists had their own tradition and derived both respectability and power from their own academic discipline. Most important, the traditions of psychology were entirely different from those of medicine. Trained in scientific analysis and often highly articulate, some clinical psychologists recognized the apparent contradictions in the medical orientation of the psychotherapist and had both the intellectual and social skills to make their own views heard. Their success in asserting their right to be practitioners is evidenced by the licensure or certification of psychologists in many states, specifying that psychotherapy is part of the practice of psychology.

Though psychologists were critical of the difficulties encountered in testing various aspects of psychoanalytic theory, and different individuals questioned one or another aspect, we should reiterate that on the whole they accepted the psychoanalytic approach and that this approach formed the basis for the theory and practice of post-World War II clinical psychology. While effectively questioning the need for medical training, there was, with the exception of the work of Rogers, still no serious challenge to the medical model that formed much of the conceptual basis for the practice of psychotherapy.

Some Comments on Training Requirements

There is no doubt that a dispassionate analysis of the actual activities of a traditional analytically oriented psychotherapist will reveal few instances where his medical training is directly relevant. What alternative academic training, however, is relevant to the actual day-by-day tasks of the therapist? Psychological training, probably most widely cited as a specific alternative form of background, is hardly more relevant to activities of the psychotherapist (and only slightly more so to those of the behavior modifiers to be considered later). Perhaps the only curriculum that focuses primarily on training that is directly relevant to the practice of traditional psychotherapy is that of some schools of psychiatric social work. Such a curriculum would, however, be rejected by many as too brief, too applied, and lacking in sufficient depth and breadth.

It is easy to overlook the fact that all professions require training that is not necessarily relevant to the practitioner's day-to-day activity. As professions are upgraded, the amount of education not directly relevant but nonetheless required inevitably increases. For example, it was once possible to become a physician as an apprentice to a practitioner. Later,

medical school became a requirement, then an internship was added. Subsequently two years of college training were required for admission to medical school; more recently, practically all students complete college prior to entering medical school, and some residency has become all but mandatory. It is only when a profession has achieved a very high status and there is a shortage of practitioners that it voluntarily (under much social and political pressure) revises this trend and questions the relevance of some of the requirements.

In fact, neither medical schools nor graduate schools in psychology qualify the graduate as a practitioner of psychotherapy; rather, they provide a general background of information, some fraction of which may prove useful. More important, however, they provide the graduate with a legitimacy that is helpful both in terms of his self-image and the ease with which he will be accepted as a competent member of the healing professions.

With the development of community mental health centers that tried to provide psychotherapeutic help to all who desired it, it was soon evident that there were simply not enough trained mental health workers. In response to this need (justified partly by the work of Rioch[58]) as well as in response to other social pressures, mental health aids became the providers of primary care in most mental health centers. Similarly, many programs sought to provide mental health training to members of the community without "appropriate" prior education. Thus, while up until the late 1950s psychotherapy was practiced almost exclusively by individuals with some formal advanced degree augmented by further supervision and training, the stated need for such training in order to practice within recognized institutional settings decreased dramatically and inevitably affected the ease with which totally untrained individuals could lay claim to mental health skills.

Does Psychotherapy Have an Effect?

Up until the fifties the issue was, as we have seen, not *how* psychotherapy should be practiced, but *who* should practice. During the last two decades a much more basic question was raised even more sharply: does this practice have any effects, and, if so, what exactly are they?

THE ATTEMPT TO EVALUATE OUTCOME

If previously we have sometimes used the terms *psychotherapy, psychoanalysis, dynamic psychology*, and even *psychiatry* almost interchangeably, it merely reflects the tremendous influence of psychoanalysis upon post-World War II psychotherapy. It was hardly conceivable to speak of a well-trained psychotherapist without implying that he was a dynamic psychologist, which, in turn, implied that he was psychoanalytically oriented. To be sure, there were disagreements between different psychoanalytic points of view and between psychodynamically oriented therapists and more orthodox analysts, but these were minor family quarrels, for there was a broad set of shared assumptions that formed the basis of psychotherapeutic practice, and none of these assumptions was more central and none more unchallenged than the assertion that, if properly practiced, psychotherapy works.

An early attempt to address this issue was made by Rogers and his students whose work was characterized by an emphasis upon research. By using verbatim tape recordings, reasonably sized samples of patients, and independent judges to analyze and objectify the interview protocols, they sought to clarify the mechanisms of the therapeutic process. Their efforts were made somewhat easier by the relatively brief duration of the Rogerian treatment process and by the relatively mild problems it seeks to treat, but this fact does not diminish the historical importance of these studies which were the first serious attempts to evaluate the outcome of psychotherapy and to understand and document some of the factors that affect it. The great impact of the Rogerian movement upon academic psychologists was partially due to the fact that Rogers and his students tried to verify the change they sought to obtain.

Rogers had demonstrated that it was possible to study the psychotherapeutic process, but his work was largely outside of the thera-peutic mainstream. Rogerian treatment presented an alternative to the medically oriented model of psychotherapy, but it was not considered appropriate for the treatment of serious pathology and had relatively little impact on the practice of clinical psychology and practically none on medical psychotherapists. However, there was a gradually increasing dissatisfaction with the unwillingness of psychotherapists to take a hard look at their results, and to subject the therapeutic process to more rigorous analysis.

Far and away the most widely publicized and devastating attack on psychotherapy was launched by Eysenck,[12] who argued that there was no evidence to show that psychotherapy had any effect whatever. He summarized the few outcome studies, pointing to the lack of controls of most and the negative findings of those few which were controlled, and concluded that there was no scientific evidence for any effect of psychotherapy let alone a beneficial one. Other studies, most notably the work of Frank and his associates[17] had shown that it was difficult to demonstrate specific therapeutic effects, that individuals who were treated in outpatient clinics did not improve significantly more than controls who were awaiting treatment, and that the relatively sparse improvement that could be seen initially failed to persist over time.

It was possible, of course, to deny in each instance that psychotherapy was given a fair test: to argue that the investigators had failed to evaluate truly skilled psychotherapists, that they employed unreasonably brief periods of treatment, that they evaluated symptomatic improvement rather than the resolution of the underlying illness. But mere argument was obviously not enough, and there was an increasing willingness by psychotherapists to subject their treatment efforts to systematic inquiry.[27] For an excellent summary of outcome-evaluation studies of psychotherapy, see Strupp and Bergin,[67] Bergin and Garfield,[6] and for a careful and sympathetic review of psychoanalytically oriented studies, see Luborsky and Spence.[38]

It is not possible here to review the work that has been carried out and is yet in progress in this area. Suffice it to point out that reviewers conclude that some treatment effects have been documented. Bergin[5] concludes that outcome measures evaluated after psychotherapy show considerably greater variability than those taken from control patients, which suggests that psychological treatment makes some patients better and leaves others worse. This conclusion is not exactly comforting, but at least it suggests that there is some effect rather than none at all as Eysenck had claimed. In a careful recent review Luborsky[36] was able to document that in long-term therapy the therapist's training turns out to be of considerable importance; furthermore, that the bulk of outcome studies support the effectiveness of psychotherapeutic treatment.

SOME DIFFICULTIES IN EVALUATING THE EVALUATIONS OF THERAPY

There are serious problems in conducting appropriate research on the outcome of psychotherapy. These include the highly variable natural history of the difficulties under treatment, the importance of apparently unrelated patient attributes and resources, and the myriad of adventitious concurrent events that affect the psychological status of the individual. Furthermore, while each of a number of different indices that have been employed to evaluate outcome has some face validity, they correlate poorly with each other, which creates difficulties of method and interpretation. However, the most serious problems are conceptual and hinge on the definition of the psychotherapeutic process. What is the proper control group, the group that did *not* receive therapy? Can we possibly specify an appropriate control without a clear conception of the precise phenomenon under investigation? To specify a control group we must at least be able to specify what psychotherapy is *not*. Much of the difficulty with outcome research is that it has not squarely faced this issue: it has sought to determine whether a technique works without properly specifying either the technique or the outcome to be evaluated. A test of the specific effects of psychotherapy is not equivalent to tests that try to determine, say, whether a meaningful human relationship can lead to emotional growth. (For a more extensive discussion of these issues, see Fiske, Hunt, Luborsky et al.[14])

It is not surprising that many of the implicit questions about the nature of the psychotherapeutic enterprise become especially clear when one attempts to do meaningful research on psychotherapy. Only then are we forced to confront the lack of consensus about what constitutes psychotherapy; once given this lack, we have to face the fact that we can specify neither the nature of the treatment, the appropriate outcome measures, nor the appropriate controls. These difficulties are hardly novel and have often been commented on, but it is interesting that until fairly recently concerted efforts to deal with these issues did not occur.

It is worth noting that when outcome studies ask a reasonably specific and modest question, they may get a specific answer. For example, several studies have shown that in hospital settings a certain kind of patient tends to be selected for psychotherapy: the so-called YAWIS patient—young, attractive, white, intelligent, and successful.[23] Other studies have shown that the therapist's empathy and warmth are positive factors affecting outcome.[70] Again, a specific hypothesis was proposed[47,51] that suggested that successful dynamic therapy depends partially upon whether there is a set of psychodynamic assumptions that both patient and therapist share (see also Goldstein[19]). Since most patients in private psychotherapy have friends in treatment, it was argued that persons who know no one else in treatment might well encounter difficulties: their therapists might mistake an unfamiliarity with the psychodynamic point of view for a negative attitude and an inability to verbalize. Accordingly, an anticipatory socialization interview was developed by Orne and Wender,[51] specifically designed to overcome this potential handicap. In two studies,[22,64] a single anticipatory interview of this kind produced a significant positive effect on the outcome of therapy. In both instances, the therapists were unaware that some randomly selected patients had received special anticipatory socialization instructions.

Nonetheless, the salutary effects of this pre-treatment session could be demonstrated some months after termination.

The difference between these and most other psychotherapy studies is that they focused on the effects of a clearly specifiable factor upon the psychotherapeutic process. Unfortunately, such specificity is very difficult to achieve regarding precisely those variables which most therapists view as particularly important for treatment outcome.

⟪ An Alternate Model: Behavior Therapy

Some of the effectiveness of Eysenck's[12] attack on psychotherapy as a treatment procedure was probably due to his forceful attempt to propose a viable alternative: behavior therapy. The behavioral approach to psychological problems, based on principles of conditioning and learning, dates back to the work of Pavlov[54] and Watson.[71] It met with considerable success in the treatment of specific symptoms, such as in the case of enuresis by Mowrer.[45] But this approach has received wide attention and gained increasing acceptance only within the last fifteen years. Like psychoanalysis it proposes a meaningful rationale for the development of symptoms: they are learned responses that must be unlearned and replaced by other, more adaptive reactions. Certain earlier theorists such as Miller and Dollard[43] had tried to create a theoretical bridge between psychodynamic thinking and their current versions of Hull's[24] S-R (stimulus-response) reinforcement theory: in effect, they tried to interpret various psychodynamic mechanisms in terms derived from the animal conditioning laboratory, with particular emphasis on avoidance learning. But to the modern behavior therapist (e.g., Wolpe,[75] Yates,[76] Krasner and Ullman[30]) the focus is on the symptoms, for in his view the symptoms as such *are* the pathology. Here was a radical change from the medical model of disease that views symptoms only as an external manifestation of an underlying process. If symptomatic difficulties are seen as maladap-

tive learning, then the learning process itself becomes sufficient to explain the symptom. Further, from such a point of view, if the symptom is unlearned, nothing more remains to be treated.

While psychotherapy took its legitimacy from its medical roots, behavior therapy saw its legitimacy in its scientific roots. It looked to rigorous laboratory research with animals and man for its scientific underpinnings, and developed a number of treatment techniques that sought to modify maladaptive behavior. These techniques were at least said to derive from animal research. Thus, examples are systematic desensitization[75] based on classical conditioning, a wide variety of techniques using shaping procedures,[13,35] implosive therapy,[39,66] aversive conditioning,[55] the token economy for the treatment of hospitalized patients,[2] and a wide range of related techniques to manipulate overt and covert behavior.[30,57,76] These and others became part of a burgeoning literature that showed much of the excitement that characterized the early years of psychoanalysis.

In some regards the development of behavior therapy is curiously reminiscent of the early years of psychodynamic therapy, and it appears to recapitulate some of its growing pains. For example, there are a number of competing approaches within the behavior-modification movement, some more strident than others in claiming to be the only truly scientific approach. Different approaches are often based on different theoretical positions within the field of learning (some leaning on I. P. Pavlov, others on E. R. Guthrie, still others on neo-Hullian views, many on B. F. Skinner), and sometimes opposite techniques, both of which seem to take their rationale from the same theory and to yield good results (implosion therapy versus systematic desensitization). Again, there is considerable divergence of opinion on whether theory derived from laboratory studies should take precedence over the clinical facts observed during therapy itself. Some therapists argue that the empirical findings evolved in the process of behavior therapy are the most relevant and should be used to clarify the theoretical for-the psychiatrist: respectability and a general world view.

It is somewhat unfortunate that the diague between dynamic psychotherapists and behavior modifiers has been characterized by lack of understanding of each other's position, a tendency to criticize the most poorly ormulated aspects of the other's view, and a eluctance to come to terms with some of the genuine points of disagreement. While a detailed consideration of the relationship between psychotherapy and behavior modification is beyond the scope of this discussion, some similarities as well as some differences deserve emphasis.

There are certainly some genuine differences. One concerns the basic conceptual model from which the therapy is said to derive. As previously noted, dynamic therapists share certain convictions. These include an emphasis on unconscious motivation, the dynamic meaning of symptom formation, the use of the transference relationship, the importance of insight, and the working through of basic conflicts in order to modify the mechanisms underlying maladaptive psychopathology. Behavior therapists share a set of different convictions. In their view, symptoms must be understood in terms of learning and any attempt to modify them must ultimately be based on learning principles. Given this belief, they regard it as crucial to explore in detail the environmental contingencies that aggravate or suppress the occurrence of symptoms (recognizing full well that more than one antecedent event may elicit a given symptomatic behavior and that a number of different environmental contingencies may serve to suppress it). Their efforts to modify symptoms may be based on breaking the link between certain environmental events and symptomatic behavior by deconditioning or counterconditioning procedures, by establishing competing operant-response patterns, or by modifying the environment to prevent certain contingencies from occurring. Finally, they believe that one can transfer the control over undesirable behavior (broadly defined) to other contexts and place it within the control of the individual himself.

Another difference concerns the professed goal. Stated in extreme form, the dynamic therapist wants to cure the underlying problem of which the symptom is but an external manifestation; the behavior therapist wants to remove the symptom that, in his view, is the illness itself.

When considered more closely, the actual differences between the two groups are not as large as they appear in polemics. This holds for their goals as well as the means by which these goals are implemented. Some of the similarities are obscured by the enormous difference in the language each group employs. [64a] In fact, there have been some attempts at translation. Thus, Miller and Dollard have tried to account for many of the events that occur in dynamic therapy from a learning theory point of view.[43] Analogously, it may be possible to analyze much of what occurs in behavior therapy in dynamic terms.[74] Similarly, the distinction between the focus on the underlying illness as opposed to the symptom is in actual practice rarely clear-cut. Many dynamically oriented psychotherapists show little concern for dynamic diagnosis, while virtually all behavior therapists carry out a detailed assessment of the contingencies associated with the symptom, which, in fact, provides much of the data upon which clinical diagnoses are ultimately based. Much has been made of another difference: the interest of many behavior therapists in discovering the natural history of a patient's symptoms in his everyday environment as contrasted with the dynamic therapist's preference for exploring the patient's problems retrospectively, far removed from the actual event. Even here exceptions abound: dynamic, conjoint family therapy is based on bringing the conflicts into the therapeutic session so that they may be studied and dealt with as they occur, and the pioneering work of analysts such as Spitz[65] and Engel[10] was also based on systematic observation of primary data. In contrast, Wolpe's behavior therapy is practiced exclusively in an office setting.

Similar comments can be made about several other distinctions that are often raised in debates, but that on closer inspection turn out mulations based on laboratory research. Finally, there is considerable disagreement about the evaluation of therapeutic results: some insist on outcome studies with statistical comparisons between treated persons and appropriate controls, while others insist with equal vigor on the systematic study of single cases in which specific interventions can be shown to have systematically altered specific kinds of behavior.

The initial appeal of behavior therapy was based in large part on what seemed a striking clinical effectiveness. Thus, Wolpe[75] reported that 188 of 210 neurotic patients seen in his practice recovered or were greatly improved after an average of thirty treatment sessions, a truly remarkable cure rate approximating 90 percent. A further factor was the assertion that behavior therapy involved a specific form of treatment unlike the "talking cures" of psychodynamic therapy, which were attacked as "nonspecific"—an ironic recapitulation of the controversy between Freud and the French hypnotists in which *he* laid claim to specificity for his procedure. A number of controlled studies sought to show that therapeutic techniques such as systematic desensitization are specific and that the results could not be accounted for in terms of subject expectancies, therapeutic relationships, and similar nonspecific factors. One of the most influential studies of this type[52] compared the results of systematic desensitization with those of short-term psychotherapy in an elegant experimental design. A number of dynamically trained therapists, committed to psychotherapy, were trained to carry out systematic desensitization. Each therapist treated randomly assigned individuals—students with stage fright who were patient volunteers—with either dynamic psychotherapy or systematic desensitization. A third group of subjects was exposed to a placebo pseudotreatment. Finally, this study also included yet two more control groups. One was a group of students with stage fright who were contacted about participating in the study, and after having agreed to do so were placed on a waiting list. Another group was made up of students who were matched for the severity of stage fright but were never

contacted until after the study an inert control group to evaluate change over time.

The surprising findings were the presumed psychodynamic bia apists, systematic desensitization significantly more effective in reli fright than any other method. I enough, subjects treated by dynar therapy expressed more positive vie their treatment, though according t behavioral criteria this method wa effective than the placebo control o matter, the waiting-list control group all three of these groups changed n the uncontacted inert controls). Th ally well-controlled study certainly document that systematic desensitiza therapeutic intervention that has specific effects above and beyond the cific components of subject expectatio related placebo elements. A follow-up indicated that, far from suffering from tute symptoms, persons who received ioral treatment for stage fright also show general improvement on a number of tionnaire measures, which suggests that specific effects of behavior therapy may eralize to other fears and difficulties.

The impact of such studies on psycho was prompt and dramatic. Within a few years the focus and training veered sha from psychodynamic psychotherapy and sonality assessment toward an interest in havior therapy.

It is, of course, too soon to evaluate be ior therapy. Some aspects, however, are v noting. The remarkably high cure rates nally reported[75] have never since been tained by these authors or others. Despit emphasis on scientific principles and tl the relationship between therapeutic pr and theory is often tenuous. London[33] I cently pointed out that behavior therapy fact, a clinical art, and while it derives tific legitimacy from scientific psycholo procedures cannot rigorously be adduce commonly accepted theory. One may w whether academic psychology only p for the behavior therapist what medici to be quite blurred in actual practice. Contrary to some early characterizations (both by the behavior therapists and their dynamically oriented adversaries) most behavior therapists are *not* naive peripheralists who look only at gross, overt motor actions; today their concerns extend to all sorts of private, covert behaviors as well; similarly for the assertion that behavior therapists do things *to* the patient while dynamic therapists try to help the patient do things *for* himself. This, too, is a caricature. Some dynamic therapies—especially the briefer ones—are at least as manipulative as behavior therapy; an example is the use of "paradoxic intention."[21] Nor is there a dearth of behavior therapists who explicitly see their task as helping the patient gain control over his own behavior: among others, therapists whose conceptual roots are in social learning theory (e.g., Bandura,[3] Kanfer and Karoly,[25] Mischel[44]) do exactly that. In these cases, even the techniques are not as different as are the terms in which they are described. The behavior therapist insists on the detailed analysis of the contingencies that evoke certain kinds of behavior to help the patient gain control over his own behavior; the dynamic therapist tries to help the patient become aware of why he does certain things in the psychotherapeutic context in the hope that this will increase ego control. Isn't there a parallel? Some behavior therapists (notably Lazarus[31]) are trying to make some of these underlying similarities explicit and, with varying degrees of success, have begun to build bridges, both conceptually and in technique. Only too often, unfortunately, their efforts are rewarded by severe attacks for departing from orthodoxy, reminiscent of the vehement polemics during the early days of psychoanalysis.

This is not to deny that there are some genuine differences in points of view that transcend mere semantic issues but rather to emphasize some of the useful points of contact. In any case, all practitioners of whatever persuasion should applaud the behavior therapist's demand for the precise contingencies under which certain behavioral events occur; likewise his concern about specifying exactly what is to be done and why and how; and,

similarly, his attempts to make the research effort an integral part of clinical practice. Of course, it still remains to be seen how effectively the scientific ideals of the present generation of behavior modifiers will be retained in the face of increasing clinical responsibility. Only time will tell how effectively this movement will resist the pressure of increasing professionalization, codification, and a concurrent decrease in the concern with the whys and wherefores of therapeutic results.

⟨ Alternate Goals: Cure or Happiness

Recent Trends Toward Increasingly Broader Goals

As stated before, many of the controversies between adherents of different psychotherapeutic approaches hinged on different conceptions of the goal. Again and again the pendulum has swung from goals that were narrow and precise (get rid of the symptom) to goals that were much broader, more ambitious, and correspondingly imprecise (remove the underlying disorder). The psychodynamic therapists argued that the behavioral approach was too superficial. But if they are right (which symptom-oriented therapists, of course, would not concede), they face the immense task of specifying what this underlying disorder is and how one can know for certain that it is no longer there. There is an unpalatable trade off: as the goal becomes broader and more ambitious, it becomes progressively more difficult to define.

The tendency toward a broadened definition of therapy's goal is virtually built into the dynamic approach, given its assumption of a rather general, underlying disorder. But recently a similar trend can be seen in behavior therapy as well, though justified on different theoretical premises. One manifestation is a growing interest in the modification of behavior patterns that are so pervasive that one might well describe them as general personality characteristics, such as assertiveness,[75] self-control,[25] and depression.[4]

This widening of goals was probably most pronounced in the actual day-to-day clinical practice of both groups, whether dynamically oriented or based on behavioral models. Both groups gradually broadened the scope of their activities to encompass increasingly vague and diffuse complaints. While initially they treated only those persons with readily defined problems, whose need for help was clear and self-evident, therapists increasingly lent their services to anyone who asked for them (on the assumption that if the patient asks for treatment he probably needs it, even if the clinician does not really know why).

In part, the extension of the therapeutic goals seems forced upon the practitioners by the realities of the clinical situation since the number of patients with clear-cut, specifiable focal complaints is limited, whereas most troubled individuals present themselves with a variety of difficulties, none of which is necessarily that which prompted the visit. Regardless of the clinical realities, however, the extension of goals exacts an inevitable price: as the definition of what one wants to achieve becomes increasingly vague, it becomes ever more difficult to determine whether one has achieved it.

Many dynamically oriented therapists, perhaps in response to some of these difficulties, had gradually changed their criteria of whom to treat; the concern was less with whether someone needed treatment and more with whether he would be likely to benefit from treatment. Concurrently, the therapeutic emphasis shifted from the cure of disorders that cause pain and suffering (and interfere with an individual's ability to effectively function in his environment) to the more ambitious goal of helping an individual to achieve his potentialities and increase his personal satisfaction. In a sense these ultimate goals were defined much in the way Freud defined the ultimate goals of analysis: to enable the person successfully to love, work, and play. But these goals are radically different from those of traditional medicine, which is concerned with the treatment and prevention of disease and illness. In general medicine there is concern for physical fitness, but the analogy is superficial at best,

for the physician's concern about fitness focuses on its importance for preventing illness rather than on what this fitness may contribute to an individual's happiness and the healthy gratification of his wishes as ends in themselves. Thus, psychotherapy, while continuing to use medical metaphors, progressively moved from goals consistent with those of other medical disciplines to goals that were more characteristic of the educator, the philosopher, and the moralist.

The ever-increasing scope and ambition of the therapeutic purpose is most dramatic in those therapeutic movements which have explicitly abandoned either of the two conceptual models that served to set some limits, the medical model or the learning–theoretic one. One such movement is existential therapy whose adherents explicitly seek to deal with ultimate questions of meaning and purpose, questions that—at least explicitly—had rarely been raised by traditional psychotherapists.

Existential therapists were not primarily concerned with either unconscious conflicts or with symptoms; instead, they tried to deal with the feeling of aimlessness, purposelessness, anomie, and ennui that had become widespread. In many ways their concern was in response to problems that had become especially common during the post-World War II period. Long-established values were widely challenged, and never before had such large segments of the population enjoyed material comforts and security without corresponding responsibilities. The combination of leisure and security, and a limited number of obligations and commitments in the absence of either meaningful challenges or a guiding value system, led many persons to ask themselves what they really wanted to do and whether it was really worth it. Such "existential" concerns undoubtedly contributed to a wide range of aberrations in individuals—the widespread use of hallucinogens and other sensation-seeking behavior are excellent examples of behaviors related, at least in part, to these issues. But, except for those individuals who suffered from true depressions, these problems were different in kind from the incapacitating symptoms, the inability to function, or the acute suffering that had previously characterized most individuals seeking therapy. There was a new kind of patient population, some of whom sought out a new therapy: they typically lacked focal symptoms and they were generally able to cope with their environment. As often as not there was a surfeit of resources, physical and mental, rather than a lack, and the patients sought help not to escape pain but to escape ennui. Existential therapists argued that they were dealing with a new kind of difficulty, where neither the concept of disease nor that of focal symptoms was really relevant. They saw their task as helping people to seek their own solutions to their own problems—not by trying to resolve them historically but by dealing with "where they are at."

A similar shift had taken place in the focus of group psychotherapy, which, during the forties, had become strongly dynamically oriented and had been widely used as an alternative or an adjunct to dyadic therapy. Extensive training was required of group therapists that, in addition to the usual credentials of qualified therapists, included much supervision in group experience. Group therapy was seen as clearly health-related, both in terms of its goals and in terms of the orientation and training of its practitioners.

Competing models of group psychotherapeutic efforts, however, also developed concurrently from other traditions. Especially influential was the work of Kurt Lewin on group dynamics, which led to sensitivity training or the "T-group." Conceptions such as "feedback," the giving and receiving of interpersonal perceptions, and "participant observation" were some of the techniques used by the group leader to help the group learn the dynamics of its functioning. The T-group was seen as a means of enhancing interpersonal understanding, modifying prejudice in a variety of areas, and facilitating productive creative interactions. In contrast to traditional group therapy, however, it was practiced primarily by individuals trained in group dynamics, with group members who defined themselves as normal. The settings as well were far removed from the healing context,

ranging from industry to schools, hospitals, and even police departments. While using some dynamic insights and much of the technology of behavioral science, the goals tended to orient around specific problem areas. Initially, at least, group leaders were trained with considerable care and for the most part felt responsible in helping to prevent any serious difficulties arising from interactions. A further focus and direction with these groups was usually provided by the institutional aegis under which they were organized.

Under the stimulus of the humanistic tradition, the T-group, renamed by Carl Rogers the "basic encounter group," became increasingly prominent in the early sixties. Now the purpose had become the search for a meaningful experience on the part of the individual participant, a growth experience that need not be either health related or important for the achievement of some greater group goal. The basic encounter group, which proved to be a powerful but by no means totally harmless method of modifying experience,[32] is then a particularly clear example of the shift away from psychotherapy toward experiences with the avowed purpose of growth. Once having made this shift, the practitioner of the new method found it progressively easy to disclaim all responsibility for the client's welfare. He was not responsible to an institution nor did he have culturally defined responsibility as a healer. Quite to the contrary, the Hippocratic view that the healer should not only strive to help his patient but that above all else he "must do no harm" was explicitly and purposively rejected as inappropriate and harmful paternalism.

The practice of any form of psychotherapy inevitably must come to terms with some of these broader issues of goals. Many thoughtful psychotherapists talked of providing emotional-corrective experiences, and many likened the process to other forms of education. Clinicians often saw how the resolution of various conflicts helped release previously blocked creative forces and recognized that the process of psychotherapy must involve emotional growth as it seeks to alleviate symptoms and alter those patterns of behavior which most of us would characterize as psychopathology. Nonetheless, as much as the therapist and patient might strive to release the latter's creative potentials, such a goal was accomplished in the context of treating an underlying disorder (or, in terms perhaps more palatable to at least some behavior therapists, the modification of behavior patterns defined in exceedingly molar terms). On the face of it, it seems extremely reasonable and appropriate to move only a small step further and think of the therapeutic process exclusively in positive terms. Would it not seem best to abandon the authoritarian vestiges of medical tradition and the pretense of treating mental illness—especially if it is only a myth? Instead of the role of patient, repugnant to many, the role of an individual seeking fulfillment would seem acceptable to all. With this apparently small step therapists began to promise not merely the relief of symptoms or the treatment of underlying disorders, but a far more ambitious goal. The terms varied, but in essence they now offered the hope that individuals could obtain that ultimate (and most impossible to define) of all gifts—happiness.

However reasonable the shift of emphasis might seem, the consequences have been both unexpected and troubling. Freed from the constraints of medical and professional traditions, a myriad of new therapies, each stridently asserting its effectiveness and superiority over more traditional procedures (and over each other) suddenly emerged. The range of "therapies" or "growth experiences" available to all comers expanded from encounter groups to marathons, to nude marathons, to sensory experiences. Still different techniques are now advocated to help "let it all hang out," from Gestalt therapy to extreme forms of Reichian treatment, screaming, Rolfing, energetics, sex therapy, and brutality therapy. Similarly, the meditative disciplines that were once practiced in highly structured settings were now widely popularized in an "instant" form, whether as transcendental meditation and its variants or in the use of biofeedback to achieve instant *samadhi* (see London[34]). All of these various procedures (should they still be called *therapies*?) are characterized by an emphasis on rapidly achieved experiential change, by the rejection of traditional concepts of illness, and by the explicit abrogation of responsibility for the consequences of treatment. The purpose of treatment is simply to make the individual "happier." If the process happens to precipitate serious difficulties—*caveat emptor*. The patient who had become a client was now simply a consumer, and as such it is he who decides whether he is in need of the treatment —the therapist merely "does his thing" for a fee. For the instant therapies the justification for the treatment's effectiveness is no longer in its theories, in the scientific evidence, or even in the reflected glory of the medical or psychological doctorate of its practitioners. To the contrary, there is a common theme of anti-intellectualism and a rejection of science and what is sometimes called the "engineering approach," often expressed with mystical overtones and an emphasis upon feeling, on "vibes," and the free expression of instinctual needs.

We have previously stressed the difficulty of evaluating whether therapy "works." In great part this reflects the difficulty of defining the therapeutic goal. As this goal is defined ever more broadly, its definition becomes correspondingly vague and the difficulty of evaluating outcome increases in turn. When the purpose of treatment expands to the wide horizons sought by the new therapies, the determination of whether the treatment works has become more than difficult . . . it is impossible. We can, therefore, say little or nothing about the effectiveness of the new treatments. We can only suggest some of their sociopsychological roots.

Some Implications of the Broadened Goals: When Is Treatment Necessary?

We have argued that as the therapeutic goals of therapy become increasingly broadened it becomes increasingly difficult, if not impossible, to evaluate whether they have been met. This does not deny the desirability of goals, such as emotional growth, or the possibility that they may be approached in a responsible fashion. Suppose one grants, for the purpose of discussion, that goals such as growth and even happiness can be defined so that their attainment can be determined. Suppose one also grants that a given treatment can indeed achieve these effects, and that this can be documented. If so, we will still face a variety of social and even political issues that hinge upon the question of when such treatment is necessary—and what do we really mean by necessary. These issues tend to come most sharply into focus as one considers the availability of therapy and who shall bear its cost.

Whether treatment is indicated and how much treatment is enough has always been a difficult matter to decide. However, as long as the financial cost was borne by the patient, the financial sacrifice itself helped minimize the problem. The question of whether treatment was really necessary hardly seemed relevant as long as the therapist was prepared to offer it and did not see it as detrimental and so long as the patient himself sought the treatment. This question becomes more thorny, however, when the financial burden is borne not by the patient himself but by others (e.g., his family). In the past, therapists considered such issues ethical matters, to be resolved on an individual basis in line with their own integrity while trying to take into account the needs of all persons involved. As long as psychotherapy functioned within the framework of the medical model, it could rely on traditional guidelines of how such matters might be resolved. Questions about the burden an individual's medical needs impose upon his family were by no means new and have been of considerable concern to thoughtful physicians for a long time. A reconsideration of this issue, however, is necessitated by the increasingly widespread view that adequate medical treatment is a right and should be freely available to all. This view has gained general acceptance throughout the world and various forms of third-party payment now account for the overwhelming bulk of medical expenses even in the United States.

Third-party payment systems such as medical insurance have serious implications for the practice of all forms of psychotherapy. In recent years, psychotherapists have increasingly come to accept the patient's decision that he requires treatment as an adequate justification for administering it. But this approach is altogether different from the way in which medical, third-party payment systems determine the kind and duration of treatments whose costs they are willing to pay. The patient asks for medical assistance, but it is the physician's responsibility to establish the nature of his illness and to determine whether there is a viable procedure for its cure or alleviation. If such a procedure is available, but in limited supply (e.g., long-term dialysis treatment for kidney failure), its allocation is generally based on some rational principle that considers both need and prognosis.

An analogous set of decisions may ultimately have to be made about the need for psychotherapy. The question of whether someone should receive psychotherapy will have to be considered in terms of the patient's needs, the likelihood of achieving the therapeutic goal, and the availability of appropriate treatment resources. This will require us to identify those psychological problems which are sufficiently serious to be analogous to those physical problems which urgently require treatment. We will undoubtedly find that for other psychological problems treatment is desirable (as a matter of health) but not urgently so, analogous to physical disorders that should be treated on an elective basis. We will finally note a set of problems that may trouble the patient and for which he seeks treatment, but for which treatment is not a health necessity. Such problems also have a clear analogue in medicine—cosmetic (as opposed to reconstructive) plastic surgery. Interestingly enough, the question that determines whether a procedure is paid for by health insurance is not whether the procedure is a medical one but only whether it is necessary for health. Thus some problems of appearance may be so disfiguring as to interfere with the individual's normal functioning and thus justify cosmetic surgery for reasons of health, but this is probably true in only the most extreme cases. On the other hand, an individual whose nose is well within the norm may ardently wish to change the shape; he does not as a consequence suffer from a health-related problem, no matter how intense his desire may be. Under the circumstances, no health insurance will pay the cost. There is, of course, nothing that prevents the patient from making a private arrangement with a plastic surgeon, to modify his appearance at his own expense.

A similar distinction may be useful for psychotherapy. Such a distinction would have to establish when psychotherapy may be considered health-related (and thus appropriately reimbursed by third-party payments) and when it is essentially elective or "cosmetic" in nature. Growth experiences that fall in the latter category do not thereby become any less desirable, but must still not be confused with health necessities. If health professionals choose to provide such experiences as a personal service, they are not, in so doing, carrying out a function vital to an individual's health. Once the distinction is clearly drawn, both the public and other health professionals are likely to show a similar ambivalence toward such treatment as that often seen toward the practice of cosmetic plastic surgery. Such a distinction may also have implications for determining criteria of outcome effectiveness. If we are considering psychotherapy for health, the criteria should probably be similar to those used to judge health-related procedures: the person's ability to function and the prevention of dire consequences that might otherwise occur. But if we are considering psychotherapy, not as a health-necessity but as a form of psychic self-improvement, the criteria may well be similar to those whereby cosmetic surgery is judged almost exclusively: the patient's satisfaction with the procedure.

Another analogy with medicine may help clarify the role of the psychotherapist in the development of programs of mental hygiene and other forms of prophylaxis. There are certain safe and effective prophylactic procedures against serious diseases; it is the public-health physician's responsibility to ensure actively that such procedures are carried out. He has a clear-cut responsibility to treat communicable diseases and to prevent their spread. The public-health physician may also be concerned with various measures to improve the population's physical fitness insofar as these have profound effects on matters of health. But this does not mean that the public-health physician feels called upon to become a physical-education teacher, nutritionist, or environmental engineer, though he recognizes his responsibility to bring relevant matters to the attention of each of these. Indeed, he will carry out the necessary epidemiological studies to help clarify the relationship between physical fitness and illness, and will identify procedures that may have potential application. Preventive medicine has made great strides because its programs were based upon a firm scientific foundation; its advance was due to this rather than any premature activism on the part of its practitioners. Preventive medicine has long since given up the goal of making Olympic athletes of us all. Its effectiveness increased as it assumed more modest goals. Psychotherapy would do well to adopt an analogous point of view, devoting less effort to merchandising its knowledge and more effort to acquiring and to validating it.

Some Final Comments

The psychodynamic approach seemed to provide a new way of studying mental phenomena by way of dreams, free associations, and parapraxes that led to the discovery of such basic clinical phenomena as transference and countertransference, the meaning of symptoms, and the various defenses. It seemed as though a new scientific way had been found by which great universal truths could be identified with relevance to all aspects of human life and experience. The theoretical foundations for dynamic psychotherapy were formulated at the turn of the century, but the acceptance of the psychodynamic view followed neither from the accumulation of hard evidence nor the demonstration of effectiveness in clinical practice; rather, it was more the result of a fortuitous link between a novel view toward man and the prevailing *Zeitgeist* of the American culture. Psychodynamic ideas did not find broad public, scientific, and medical acceptance until the early forties. The fact that these ideas were promulgated under medical/scientific auspices in no small part contributed to their acceptance.

The degree to which the psychodynamic viewpoint had been accepted in the United States was invariably commented upon by European psychiatrists, surprised by the influence that the ideas of their American colleagues had on the general public. The general awe in which psychiatric opinion was held led psychiatrists to assume the role of social philosophers, using the credentials of medicine and science as their justification for commenting upon everything from the consequences of rock music to the suitability of presidential candidates. The limitations of psychotherapy as a treatment, however, were obscured by the respect accorded to psychiatrists' comments about matters far removed from medical practice.

The last fifteen years have witnessed the gradual erosion of consensus within psychiatry about the conceptual models underlying psychotherapy, the kind of training required to practice it, the procedures by which it is carried out, and the ethical responsibilities the therapist assumes in undertaking treatment. A concurrent change in attitude within academic medicine, the scientific community, and among the public at large has gradually taken place, resulting in a decline of esteem from that in which the theory and practice were once held. It gradually became clear that psychotherapy was unable to live up to the promises made for it by its most enthusiastic protagonists. Its claim to be a scientific discipline is no longer undisputed, and even when accepted is no longer universally seen as an undisputed good. On the one hand, serious challenges from within the scientific community deny the validity of these claims. On the other hand, ironically enough, some segments of the public are prepared to reject the psychodynamic approach (and no doubt the behavior therapist's as well) because they see it as too scientific, too rational, and not sufficiently concerned with feelings, emotions, and love.

Psychotherapy had become widely accepted in contemporary society, largely because of its claim to scientific legitimacy on the one hand, and the fact that it was practiced by highly skilled practitioners, members of the traditional healing profession who had completed rigorous and arduous training. But the legitimacy based on training is rapidly eroding, nor is membership in the established healing professions any longer accepted as an essential prerequisite for psychotherapeutic practice. The rapid proliferation of more or less bizarre therapeutic procedures creates the serious risk that the public will come to regard them all as equally effective or ineffective. Some acceptable basis must be found for choosing among them and rejecting some while accepting others.[37] This will require a widespread concern for relevant empirical information among practicing therapists, which has thus far been largely lacking. Instead, psychotherapists have tended to become alienated from their own conceptual base and have shown little concern for the potentially relevant literature in psychological or psychiatric journals. (In this regard, psychotherapy is very different from other medical disciplines, where reports of relevant new findings rapidly affect both the conceptual models and clinical practice.) In some instances, psychotherapeutic practice has tended to ignore solidly based clinical research with obvious relevance for practice.

If these trends continue, psychotherapy will become a discipline unto itself, essentially unrelated to psychology or medicine, and functionally autonomous from efforts to elucidate issues that are obviously crucial to an understanding of the psychotherapeutic process (from any point of view other than the parochial one adopted by the therapist himself).

Psychotherapy thus finds itself at a crossroad. We must begin to recognize that the original enthusiastic reception accorded to psychodynamic views was based on a promissory note—the clinical and scientific evidence promised for later delivery. It happens to be the present author's conviction that the major insights derived from the dynamic view are basically sound and have to be incorporated into whatever (health-related) psychotherapies will evolve in the future. Unfortunately, such affirmations of personal credo are no longer enough. Even if shared by virtually all practitioners (as they were a few decades ago) they can never provide the firm platform on which a solid future can be developed. We have to begin to recognize the limitations of the data obtained from the private, dyadic relationship upon which the bulk of our theory has been based. Interesting as they may be, such data are inevitably obtained under special circumstances in which neither patient nor therapist is a truly objective, disinterested observer, and while this allows for the study of transference and countertransference, it also introduces the problems of self-fulfilling prophecies,[41] experimenter-expectancy effects,[61] and demand characteristics,[48] well-documented in other areas of research. Observations obtained in a psychotherapeutic context can be uniquely important in formulating hypotheses, but they cannot provide a rigorous test of these hypotheses until they are objectively evaluated.

Of the crises in psychotherapy that we are now facing, perhaps the most serious is the proliferation of therapies—many of them increasingly implausible and irresponsible—without any objective means for discriminating among them. In an increasingly egalitarian society, pronouncements from authorities and legal regulations become increasingly ineffective in preventing abuses, and we will be compelled to develop reasonable means by which objective evaluations can be carried out.* Unfortunately, meaningful outcome studies are both very expensive and extremely difficult to execute. Worse yet, judging by present events, the proliferation of new techniques will undoubtedly exceed the rate at which they can be evaluated, nor will any negative study, regardless of merit, serve to

* The establishment of the Society for Psychotherapy Research has been a recent salutary development in the effort to share information and develop meaningful methods by which various treatments can be evaluated.

convince the protagonists of any new treatment to abandon the procedure. Such an approach will not as such do much to advance our understanding. It is analogous to executing outcome studies on every new combination of drugs that any individual claims to be effective in the treatment of some disorder. The science of pharmacology did not advance in this manner. Instead, it depended on an understanding of how different groups of active ingredients function *in vivo, in vitro,* and in the presence of different kinds of pathology. In clinical pharmacology, outcome studies become relevant only after a great deal of pharmacologic information is already known; they are rarely, if ever, considered in the absence of any plausible pharmacologic mechanism. Unfortunately, the basic science that underlies psychotherapy remains to be developed. There is reason to believe that this development will occur only if psychotherapy resumes contact with the psychological sciences in general and with those relevant biological disciplines that may shed light on the relationship between brain, behavior, and experience. For the only way in which psychotherapy can become truly effective will be by recapturing the zest for learning that characterized its early years while acquiring a new-found eagerness to disprove—if possible—its own pet beliefs.

We are not a new discipline any longer. Modern psychotherapy antedates modern physics, biochemistry, molecular biology, behavioral genetics, and many other highly developed disciplines. We can no longer excuse the lack of hard clinical and scientific data either by the newness of the field or by the complexity of its problems. Our task is to build an applied science upon the foundations of the relevant basic sciences, to incorporate the lore of our art (and some of its beliefs that have stood the test of time will probably also stand the test of rigorous, empirical scrutiny) within a solid discipline that truly fulfills Freud's promise to create a rational science of the irrational. Only when this is accomplished will we be able to boast, along with other cumulative disciplines: we can do what yesterday's giants could not . . . because we stand on their shoulders.

(Bibliography

1. AREY, L. B., W. BURROWS, J. P. GREENHILL et al., eds. *Dorland's Illustrated Medical Dictionary*, 23rd ed. Philadelphia: Saunders, 1957.
2. AYLLON, T. and N. H. AZRIN. *The Token Economy: A Motivational System for Therapy and Rehabilitation*. New York: Appleton, 1968.
3. BANDURA, A. *Principles of Behavior Modification*. New York: Holt, Rinehart and Winston, 1969.
4. BECK, A. T. *Depression: Clinical, Experimental, and Theoretical Aspects*. New York: Harper & Row, 1967.
5. BERGIN, A. E. "The Effects of Psychotherapy: Negative Results Revisited," *J. Consult. Clin. Psychol.*, 10 (1963), 244–250.
6. BERGIN, A. E. and S. L. GARFIELD, eds. *Handbook of Psychotherapy and Behavior Change: An Empirical Analysis*. New York: Wiley, 1971.
7. BRUNER, J. S. "Personality Dynamics and the Process of Perceiving," in R. R. Blake and G. V. Ramsey, eds., *Perception: An Approach to Personality*, pp. 121–147. New York: Ronald, 1951.
8. COBB, L. A., G. I. THOMAS, D. H. DILLARD et al. "An Evaluation of Internal-Mammary-Artery Ligation by a Double-Blind Technic," *N. Engl. J. Med.*, 260 (1959), 1115–1118.
9. ELLENBERGER, H. F. *The Discovery of the Unconscious*. New York: Basic Books, 1970.
10. ENGEL, G. L. and F. REICHSMAN. "Spontaneous and Experimentally Induced Depression in an Infant with Gastric Fistula," *J. Am. Psychoanal. Assoc.*, 4 (1956), 428–452.
11. EVANS, F. J. "The Placebo Response in Pain Reduction," in J. J. Bonica, ed., Advances in Neurology, Vol. 4., *Pain*, pp. 289–296. New York: Raven, 1974.
12. EYSENCK, H. J. "The Effects of Psychotherapy: An Evaluation," *J. Consult. Clin. Psychol.*, 16 (1952), 319–323.
13. FERSTER, C. B. "Positive Reinforcement and Behavioral Deficits of Autistic Children," *Child Devel.*, 32 (1961), 437–456.
14. FISKE, D. W., H. W. HUNT, L. LUBORSKY et al. "Planning of Research on Effectiveness of Psychotherapy," *Arch. Gen. Psychiatry*, 22 (1970), 22–32.
15. FRANK, J. D. *Persuasion and Healing: A Comparative Study of Psychotherapy*. Baltimore: The Johns Hopkins Press, 1961.
16. ———. "The Role of Hope in Psychotherapy," *Int. J. Psychiatry*, 5 (1968), 383–395.
17. FRANK, J. D., E. H. NASH, A. R. STONE et al. "Immediate and Long-Term Symptomatic Course of Psychiatric Outpatients," *Am. J. Psychiatry*, 120 (1963), 429–439.
18. GILL, M. M. "Hypnosis as an Altered and Regressed State," *Int. J. Clin. Exp. Hypn.*, 20 (1972), 224–237.
19. GOLDSTEIN, A. P. *Therapist-Patient Expectancies in Psychotherapy*. New York: Pergamon, 1962.
20. GURALNIK, D. P., ed. *Webster's New World Dictionary*, 2nd Coll. ed. New York: World, 1970.
21. HALEY, J. *Strategies of Psychotherapy*. New York: Grune & Stratton, 1963.
22. HOEHN-SARIC, R., J. D. FRANK, S. D. IMBER et al. "Systematic Preparation of Patients for Psychotherapy: 1. Effects on Therapy Behavior and Outcome," *J. Psychiatr. Res.*, 2 (1964), 267–281.
23. HOLLINGSHEAD, A. B. and F. S. REDLICH. *Social Class and Mental Illness*. New York: Wiley, 1958.
24. HULL, C. L. *Principles of Behavior*. New York: Appleton, 1943.
25. KANFER, F. H. and P. KAROLY. "Self-Control: A Behavioristic Excursion into the Lion's Den," *Behav. Ther.*, 3 (1972), 398–416.
26. KARDINER, A. and R. LINTON. *The Individual and His Society*. New York: Columbia University Press, 1939.
27. KERNBERG, O. F., E. D. BURSTEIN, L. COYNE et al. "Psychotherapy and Psychoanalysis: Final Report of the Menninger Foundation's Psychotherapy Research Project," *Bull. Menninger Clin.*, 36 (1972), entire issue.
28. KLINE, M. V. "Freud and Hypnosis: A Reevaluation," *Int. J. Clin. Exp. Hypn.*, 20 (1972), 252–263.
29. KLUCKHOHN, C. and H. A. MURRAY. *Person-*

ality in Nature, Society, and Culture. New York: Knopf, 1949.

30. KRASNER, L. and L. P. ULLMAN, eds. *Research in Behavior Modification.* New York: Holt, 1965.

31. LAZARUS, A. *Behavior Therapy and Beyond.* New York: McGraw-Hill, 1971.

32. LIEBERMAN, M. A., I. D. YALOM, and M. B. MILES. *Encounter Groups: First Facts.* New York: Basic Books, 1973.

33. LONDON, P. "The End of Ideology in Behavior Modification," *Am. Psychol.*, 27 (1972), 913–920.

34. ———. "The Psychotherapy Boom: From the Long Couch for the Sick to the Push Button for the Bored," *Psychol. Today*, 8 (1974), 62–68.

35. LOVAAS, O. I. "A Program for the Establishment of Speech in Psychotic Children," in J. K. Wing, ed., *Early Childhood Autism*, pp. 115–144. Oxford: Pergamon, 1966.

36. LUBORSKY, L. "Another Reply to Eysenck," *Psychol. Bull.*, 78 (1972), 406–408.

37. LUBORSKY, L., B. SINGER, and L. A. LUBORSKY. "Comparative Studies of Psychotherapies: Is it True that 'Everybody Has Won and All Must Have Prizes'?" *Arch. Gen. Psychiatry*, 1975, in press.

38. LUBORSKY, L. and D. SPENCE. "Quantitative Research on Psychoanalytic Therapy," in A. E. Bergin and S. L. Garfield, eds., *Handbook of Psychotherapy and Behavioral Change*, pp. 408–437. New York: Wiley, 1971.

39. MARKS, I. M. "Perspective on Flooding," *Semin. Psychiatry*, 4 (1972), 129–138.

40. McGLASHAN, T. H., F. J. EVANS, and M. T. ORNE. "The Nature of Hypnotic Analgesia and Placebo Response to Experimental Pain," *Psychosom. Med.*, 31 (1969), 227–246.

41. MERTON, R. K. "The Self-Fulfilling Prophecy," *Antioch Rev.*, 8 (1948), 193–210.

42. MESMER, F. A. *Mémoire sur la découverte du magnétisme animal. (Précis historique écrite par M. Paradis en mars 1777.)* Paris: Didot, 1779.

43. MILLER, N. E. and J. DOLLARD. *Social Learning and Imitation.* New Haven, Conn.: Yale University Press, 1941.

44. MISCHEL, W. *Personality and Assessment.* New York: Wiley, 1968.

45. MOWRER, O. H. *Learning Theory and Personality Dynamics.* New York: Ronald, 1950.

46. NOYES, A. P. and L. KOLB. *Modern Clinical Psychiatry*, 5th ed. Philadelphia: Saunders, 1959.

47. ORNE, M. T. "Implications for Psychotherapy Derived from Current Research on the Nature of Hypnosis," *Am. J. Psychiatry*, 118 (1962), 1097–1103.

48. ———. "On the Social Psychology of the Psychological Experiment: With Particular Reference to Demand Characteristics and Their Implications," *Am. Psychol.*, 17 (1962), 776–783.

49. ———. "On the Nature of Effective Hope," *Int. J. Psychiatry*, 5 (1968), 403–410.

50. ———. "Pain Suppression by Hypnosis and Related Phenomena," in J. J. Bonica, ed., *Advances in Neurology*, Vol. 4., *Pain*, pp. 563–572. New York: Raven, 1974.

51. ORNE, M. T. and P. H. WENDER. "Anticipatory Socialization for Psychotherapy: Method and Rationale," *Am. J. Psychiatry*, 124 (1968), 1202–1212.

52. PAUL, G. L. *Insight versus Desensitization in Psychotherapy: An Experiment in Anxiety Reduction.* Stanford, Calif.: Stanford University Press, 1966.

53. ———. "Insight versus Desensitization in Psychotherapy Two Years after Termination," *J. Consult. Clin. Psychol.*, 31 (1967), 333–348.

54. PAVLOV, I. P. *Conditioned Reflexes.* London: Oxford University Press, 1927.

55. RACHMAN, S. and J. TEASDALE. *Aversion Therapy and Behavior Disorders: An Analysis.* Coral Gables, Fla.: University of Miami Press, 1969.

56. RIEFF, P. *The Triumph of the Therapeutic: Uses of Faith after Freud.* New York: Harper & Row, 1956.

57. RIMM, D. C. and J. C. MASTERS. *Behavior Therapy: Techniques and Empirical Findings.* New York: Academic, 1974.

58. RIOCH, M. J., C. ELKES, A. A. FLINT et al. "National Institute of Mental Health Pilot Study in Training Mental Health Counselors," *Am. J. Orthopsychiatry*, 33 (1963), 678–689.

59. ROGERS, C. R. *Counseling and Psychotherapy.* New York: Houghton, 1942.

60. ———. *Client-Centered Therapy.* Boston: Houghton, 1951.

61. ROSENTHAL, R. *Experimenter Effects in Behavioral Research.* New York: Appleton, 1966.

62. SHAPIRO, A. K. "The Placebo Effect in the

History of Medical Treatment: Implications for Psychiatry," *Am. J. Psychiatry*, 116 (1959), 73–78.

63. SIMMONS, L. W. *Sun Chief.* New Haven: Yale University Press, 1942.

64. SLOANE, R., A. CRISTOL, M. PEPERNIK et al. "Role Preparation and Expectation of Improvement in Psychotherapy," *J. Nerv. Ment. Dis.*, 150 (1970), 18–26.

64a. SLOANE, R. B. "The Converging Paths of Behavior Therapy and Psychotherapy," *Int. J. Psychiatry*, 8 (1969), 493–503.

65. SPITZ, R. A. "Hospitalism," in *The Psychoanalytic Study of the Child*, Vol. 1, pp. 53–74. New York: International Universities Press, 1945.

66. STAMPFL, T. G. and D. J. LEVIS. "Essentials of Implosive Therapy: A Learning-Theory-Based Psychodynamic Behavioral Therapy," *J. Abnorm. Psychol.*, 72 (1967), 496–503.

67. STRUPP, H. H. and A. E. BERGIN. *Research in Individual Psychotherapy: A Bibliography.* Washington: NIMH, 1969.

68. SULLIVAN, H. S. *The Interpersonal Theory of Psychiatry.* New York: Norton, 1953.

69. SZASZ, T. S. *The Myth of Mental Illness.* New York: Hoeber, 1961.

70. TRUAX, C. B. and R. R. CARKHUFF. *Toward Effective Counseling and Psychotherapy: Training and Practice.* Chicago: Aldine-Atherton, 1967.

71. WATSON, J. B. *Behaviorism.* New York: People's Institute, 1924.

72. WEBER, M. *The Protestant Ethic and the Spirit of Capitalism.* Translated by Talcott Parsons. London: Allen & Unwin, 1930.

73. WHYTE, L. L. *The Unconscious before Freud.* New York: Basic Books, 1960.

74. WILKINS, W. "Desensitization: Social and Cognitive Factors Underlying the Effectiveness of Wolpe's Procedure," *Psychol. Bull.*, 76 (1971), 311–327.

75. WOLPE, J. *Psychotherapy by Reciprocal Inhibition.* Stanford: Stanford University Press, 1958.

76. YATES, A. J. *Behavior Therapy.* New York: Wiley, 1970.

CHAPTER 2

THERAPEUTIC
INTERVENTION AND
SOCIAL FORCES:
HISTORICAL PERSPECTIVES

David F. Musto

THERAPEUTIC INTERVENTION rests on widely-accepted responses to abnormal behavior, psychiatric institutions sanctioned by society, and social forces that influence where that intervention is focused. This usual harmony between social forces and scientific institutions has not been sufficiently analyzed, probably because concord seems natural (at least to contemporaries), and to dissect it may be not only uncomfortable, but seem pointless as well. Historically, however, the most severe distortions of professional objectivity arise from the unquestioned beliefs that permeate society in a particular era. For example, if various minorities are generally thought to be a source of intergroup tensions

or antisocial activity, they may prompt explanation or treatment by the psychiatric profession. Not infrequently, public officials or community leaders call upon psychiatrists to explain and sometimes to modify a subgroup's "inherently" dangerous, recalcitrant, or abnormal state. (In the United States these groups have included such disparate categories as Negroes, the Irish, Communists, and drug addicts.) Psychiatrists who shared these dominant social fears of certain subgroups have at times found themselves providing the appearance of scientific support for what are merely widely held and often transitory public attitudes.

Nevertheless, the profession's integration

with broad social forces is not necessarily destructive; its response to current social reality makes effective delivery of service and communication with patients possible. A profession is part of society, not an isolated observer. In the tension between conformity and the acquisition of new knowledge lies both the chance for progress and the possibility of holding a mirror to contemporary culture.

The Dangers of Social Forces

The danger of social forces to the profession arises from the ease with which the necessary integration with society induces practitioners to confirm current, powerful prejudices rather than to question them. An example from the 19th century concerns psychiatric opinion about American Negroes: because of manipulated 1840 census statistics, Southern Negroes appeared to have the lowest rate of insanity in the nation.[7,16] Some experts argued that their low insanity rate must be due to the institution of slavery, since the rates ranged from lowest to highest almost along ascending parallels of latitude, from Louisiana to Maine. Ex-president John Quincy Adams, then a representative in Congress, vigorously challenged the census, as did other antislavery critics. Medical statisticians and psychiatrists such as Edward Jarvis of Massachusetts also presented convincing objections.[11,12] Nevertheless, officials of the federal government, popular American writers, and European specialists continued to use the census for what would now be termed racist purposes.

Although the change in rate of insanity between slave and free states was a new twist in the debate over slavery, that Negroes had a naturally lower insanity rate than Caucasians was generally accepted. The relatively high rate of insanity found in Western nations in the nineteenth century had been attributed by authorities to a correspondingly high level of civilization, and it seemed appropriate, therefore, that American Negroes, considered savages, would have a low rate of insanity. Yet after the Civil War, when the recorded insanity rate of Negroes began to rise, medical writers did not describe this as a sign of prog-

ress toward a higher civilization. Rather, these new statistics were interpreted as further proof of the Negro's inherent deficiency as he unsuccessfully struggled with freedom's responsibilities. The mainstream of psychiatry concurred with society's assumption that Negroes were intellectually and morally inferior, and wondered whether elevation of a Negro's psychological state was possible.[22] One physician in a southern asylum opined that a Negro's cranial sutures closed more quickly than a Caucasian's, thereby naturally limiting intellectual development.[4] It is not surprising that these assertions met little professional resistance, for psychiatrists were reared and trained in a conforming milieu. Eventually, scientific and educational leadership rejected such explanations and asserted that, given equal opportunity and social experience, the races are equal.

Blacks have not been the only group subject to a cultural denigration supported by leading medical authorities. Prominent American psychiatrists, now revered, advocated separate but equal mental-health facilities for the Irish in the mid-nineteenth century. Ironically, one advocate of this policy was the same Edward Jarvis who had angrily attacked suspicious census statistics dealing with the Negro insanity rate. Jarvis, a Massachusetts resident, was as impressed by the apparent deficiencies of the nearby Irish immigrants as he was doubtful of claims for slavery's benefits to Negro mental health in the South. Irish immigration to Massachusetts in the 1840s added many patients to the state's charitable institutions, which had previously claimed as much as a 90 percent cure rate. The Irish, however, did not seem to trust the "Yankee" hospital staff. For that reason (or other reasons such as a rising patient/doctor ratio) they did not respond favorably to the "moral therapy" that had appeared to be so efficacious for earlier immigrants to New England. After surveying the "Irish problem," along with other retardation and psychiatric questions for the state, Jarvis concluded that the Irish were constitutionally inferior and subject to mental derangement from the vicissitudes of civilization.[13] Following publication of Jarvis' report, Isaac Ray, a

pioneer of American forensic psychiatry, recommended separate but equal facilities in
order to isolate the Irish in familiar surroundings. Ray hoped this scheme would create an
affinity between staff and patients that would
make moral therapy effective. His suggestion
was not adopted; a new hospital would have
been expensive.[17]

These episodes from the nineteenth century
illustrate a profession's difficulty in maintaining an objectivity able to transcend the surrounding cultural milieu, even when that
profession is concerned with the study of environment and its effects on mental processes.
A more recent example illustrates another way
in which psychiatry may be drawn into areas
of broad social concern as an instrument of
society's will. Those who recall the 1950s will
appreciate the difficulty psychiatrists would
have felt in refusing aid to a fearful nation, particularly since such a request was an affirmation of professional expertise. And during the
late 1940s and early 1950s, most Americans
believed communism to be the greatest direct
threat to their way of life. In order to understand this threat, leading psychoanalysts in
various parts of the United States were enlisted in the "Appeals of Communism Project"
based at Princeton University.[2] The project
directors hoped that these therapists, selected
"by reputation, position, or published papers
. . . in social science research," would be able
to explain the role of communist beliefs in the
defensive structure of their analysands who
had been attracted to that ideology. The study
also sought to define the typical family constellation that bred left-wing analysands.
Based on thirty-five psychoanalytic cases, the
study concluded that communism permitted
the individuals to "express hostility or submission without feelings of guilt." Further research was planned on "those aspects of
family structure—sex-role conflict and intel-
lectuality—that have been highlighted in the
discussion of the psychoanalytic data . . . Such
an investigation . . . would . . . provide some
germane hypotheses about the susceptibility
to Communism of intellectuals." Of the psychoanalysts asked, about half declined to participate, but it was not always clear "whether
their refusal was based on lack of pertinent
case records or on lack of willingness to cooperate."[15]

(Characteristics of Eighteenth-
Century Medicine

Psychiatry in the mid-twentieth century holds
some similarities to general medicine around
1850. The transition from a theoretical harmony in 18th-century medicine to a more rigorous experimental and scientific medicine a
hundred or more years later developed after
several generations of painful chaos. During
that difficult time medicine was assailed from
within and without, and critics demanded its
abolishment, an end to chemical therapies,
surgery, and theory-making. Revulsion to experimentation and even vaccination threatened a profession that had lost the serenity of
concensus and was not yet firmly established
on an effective and optimistic foundation. Research that eventually laid the groundwork for
modern medicine had to persevere quietly
while the waves of extremism found temporary popularity and power. Physicians today
owe a great debt to those who a century ago
could tolerate uncertainty while responsibly
building scientific medicine and humanely
responding to their patients.

During the eighteenth century the leadership of American medicine concurred on general principles of theory, treatment, and education. Usually disease was conceptualized as
a general imbalance in the body's functions,
perhaps located either in the solid or the
liquid parts or else in a specific system such as
the circulatory or nervous systems. Treatment
consisted of phlebotomy (the withdrawal of
blood from a patient), or of purges brought
on by calomel (a mercury preparation) or
botanicals such as jalap. These and other
treatments such as blistering were designed to
restore health by rebalancing the body's disharmony. Greek and Roman authors were
quite relevant to the educated physician.
Without a familiarity with, say, Celsus or
Hippocrates, a physician lacked important

information useful in daily practice. The ideal physician required formal training to prescribe effective treatment and to interpret properly the theory under which he functioned. In order to protect the public from the untrained, the educated physicians persuaded most states to adopt a system of licensure. Graduation from a chartered medical school or examination by a medical society generally conferred the legal right to practice.

Benjamin Rush (1746–1813) illustrates the general characteristics of eighteenth-century medicine. A controversial public figure, a signer of the Declaration of Independence, and one of the four original professors at the University of Pennsylvania medical school, he is now acclaimed as the "Father of American Psychiatry." Like a number of his contemporaries, he established his own system of medicine. He postulated that all disease has as its fundamental dysfunction the constriction of the arterioles in a part, or in all, of the body. Treatment consisted of purges and bleedings to reduce the arterioles' tension and reestablish a healthy balance. Although Rush felt he had put medicine on a new footing, his theory was deeply rooted in the medical ideology of the 18th century.

The psychological role of medical theory in practice was apparent in letters he wrote during Philadelphia's catastrophic yellow-fever epidemic of 1793. During that year, about 10 percent of the population of the nation's then largest city died from a disease that had no known pathology, origins, or effective treatment. Yet theory gave Rush a basis for action, verified the need for a highly trained professional, and rewarded him with a sense of hard work well done. (These results were achieved, in fact, by a theory and a practice that undoubtedly weakened the victim's natural resistances.) At the height of the epidemic Rush wrote to his wife Julia:

Alive! and though I slept but three or four hours last night, am still through divine goodness in perfect health. Yesterday was a day of triumph to mercury, jalap, and bleeding. I am satisfied that they saved, in my hands only, nearly one hundred lives. . . . [p. 663][19]

❨ Attacks on the Profession

During the next several decades, such professional confidence came under attack on three levels: from social movements; from research; and from rival theories. The success of these attacks caused the 18th-century framework to collapse. This in turn ushered in a period of transition and confusion in the medical profession that was similar in a number of ways to the mental health professions in our own time.

Egalitarian Movements

The first heresies to confront the medical profession, Thomsonianism and Eclecticism, were denounced by medical leaders as "mere empiricism."[14] Samuel Thomson (1769–1843) stressed botanical treatment as opposed to the mineral and bleeding techniques in medical vogue. He advocated simple theories that would allow anyone to be his own physician, eliminating any requirement for an organized medical profession, an elaborate medical education, and state licensure. Thomson patented his own system of medicine and sold rights to those who would practice it. He suggested that ideally the mother should be physician to her family, the family being his key unit in the practice of medicine. This suggestion combined feminism, opposition to the highly trained physician, and self-reliance of the family unit—an important element in a migratory society. He opposed physicians of the academy, whom he termed "learned quacks." His movement as a whole reacted against the overdevelopment of theory that characterized the eighteenth century. As an empirical reaction to theory it had features in common with many such movements in the history of medicine, dating back to the Hippocratic School itself. The Thomsonians and their simple methods found a widespread response among the lower and middle classes of America in the early decades of the 19th century.

This botanical trend was also fostered by a Connecticut physician, Wooster Beach (1794–

1868), who founded a school of medical thought termed Eclecticism. Again it was chiefly botanical, but it was even more associated with political radicalism than the Thomsonian school. Beach wrote extensively in newly founded journals against "King-Craft, Priest-Craft, Lawyer-Craft and Doctor-Craft." Both movements were deeply involved with such causes as equal rights for women and the plight of the common man, and stood against the establishment represented by the educated physician.

These movements, like not a few of those within the mental health professions today, appeared in the guise of rival medical theories. In fact, they were not just attacks on the medical profession but were a part of popular social protests. "Regular" physicians, as the traditionally-educated termed themselves, went on the defensive under these egalitarian assaults. Contemporary physicians angrily commented on this turn of events, as in the following statement by a New York physician:

> Empiricism is everywhere rife, and was never more arrogant, and the people love to have it so. That restless agrarian spirit, that would always be leveling down, has so long kept up a hue and cry against calomel and the lancet, that the prejudices of the community are excited against it: and their confidence in the medical profession greatly impaired . . . [p. 316][20]

The lay movement was not confined to journals. It expanded into associations and to the establishment of homes where these principles were carefully followed and one could be assured of the absence of regular physicians. These homes, reminiscent of some current therapeutic communities, conducted life in a most healthy manner, emphasizing hygienic and often vegetarian foods, regular hours, exercise and uplifting conversation. One of the great leaders of the lay hygiene movement was Sylvester Graham (1794–1851), who was quite successful in promulgating his views on health foods and natural cures for illness and moral defects. Today his memory is perpetuated by a humble cracker, which represents the kind of food that was once provided in the "grahamite" houses scattered about the land.

The Paris School

The second blow to the medical profession's unity in the United States was the arrival from Paris of research findings that arose from new instruments and a new methodology.[1] The most unsettling results of the Paris research and observations were not any particular theories attached to them but the very facts themselves, bereft of theory, which did not seem to fit established ideas. For example, the perfection of the stethoscope, which seems so rudimentary to us, revolutionized the diagnosis of chest diseases. Prior to the use of the stethoscope, pulmonary diseases were classified according to generalized reactions of the body such as pulse, fever, chills, and so on. The stethoscope made possible a diagnosis based on conditions actually prevailing within the chest; this supported the concept of local disease (as opposed to a general body imbalance), as well as permitting detection of internal bodily processes.

The Paris School also introduced the statistical method. Although this often meant nothing more than counting, nevertheless it permitted some objective testing of rival therapies. For example, such studies suggested that blood-letting was not a generally effective treatment for disease.

Reevaluation of traditional treatments, a growing conviction that disease was often localized, and a realization of how extremely complicated physiological processes must be, all encouraged a distaste for broad explanatory theories. Grand theories, it seemed, must be wrong, since there was so little certain knowledge upon which one could construct any theory. Not only theorizing, however, was endangered by these new findings: the medical profession's special contribution to society —therapeutics—was also put in doubt. A prevailing skeptical attitude maintained that the physician should support nature by prescribing light food and a warm bed, rather than by employing some treatment that was unproven and perhaps harmful.

The research and skepticism of the Paris hospitals were extremely disquieting to the

American medical profession. These new ideas could not be ridiculed as popular frenzy, as could those of the Thomsonians, for they came from revered centers of medicine.

Homeopathy

The third attack on the medical profession in the early 19th century came from a new but incompatible medical theory, homeopathy.[9,14] The inspiration of Samuel Hahnemann (1755–1843), homeopathy differed from the antiestablishmentarian botanical systems and the new data and therapeutic skepticism of the Paris School in that it was an all-encompassing theory like Rush's. Homeopathy favored vitalism—a conviction that the body has a nonmaterial ability to change food into body parts—and was associated with a broader definition of "soul." The best known feature of Hahnemann's system was the belief that one should use drugs that evoked the same symptoms as the disease one wished to treat. In addition, it was believed that the more dilute the drug, the more powerful the effect on the body. Dilutions of millions, billions, and even trillions of a particular drug would be carefully administered.

One of the most remarkable actions of the homeopaths was to discount the whole tribe of regular professionals by giving them a new name with a negative connotation—and almost making it stick. There had been something reassuring about a "regular" physician; but the homeopaths announced that non-homeopaths were in reality "allopaths," practitioners who might try anything and who lacked the unity of therapy that came with a true theory encompassing the whole of medical practice. Traditional physicians were enraged but confounded by this turn of events. Although homeopathy seemed laughable, it had attracted the endorsement of respectable people such as Emerson and the Beechers. Unlike the social attitudes that were part of the lay-led botanical systems, homeopathy was something of an elitist movement. The homeopathic practitioner required education for the careful interpretation of an involved system.

Since the therapy employed by the homeopaths was usually without physiological effect, and since it was applied with complete confidence, the results compared favorably with the best treatments of the regular physicians, who favored what they termed the "heroic" method of treatment: massive doses of mineral and plant medicine, bleeding, and blistering. Some physicians recognized that this heroic style might seem excessive, but they argued that America was a young, vigorous land with tough diseases that required measures of equally heroic proportions. Traditional medical treatment, therefore, helped create a willing clientele for those who instead treated mildly and supportively.

Other Nineteenth-Century Changes

By the mid-nineteenth century, licensure of medical practitioners was no longer effective in the United States.[21] Social movements, research, and rival theories had destroyed the system in force since the eighteenth century. The legislatures could do no better than the patients in distinguishing sects and cults from true science, and thought it best not to try. Anyone could claim to be a practitioner and set up practice. Although malpractice suits remained a possibility, they were difficult to pursue.

A corollary to the confusion among practitioners was the layman's increased activity in medical matters. Aside from the Graham movement and other hygienic associations, great strides were made in psychiatry by nonphysicians, particularly in the development of "moral treatment" and the establishment of asylums. Through their enthusiasm for the idea that the insane could be cured if treated by moral therapy in special institutions, they urged on the asylum movement. These mental institutions were built in state after state, with the promise of great rewards for society. Legislators being asked to put up money for an institution were assured that they would be saving money as well as behaving humanely, because lives would be rescued and returned to productive work. Almost all new cases, it was maintained, could be cured if they were caught in time, treated with dignity, and encouraged along the principles of moral therapy. Upon these arguments money was appropriated and the institutions built.

Perhaps this would be an appropriate place to mention a problem that eventually dampened some of the enthusiasm for the asylum movement. It became increasingly apparent that as each asylum functioned, it gradually built up a population of chronic patients, either as permanent or repeated residents. Because the program was sold to legislatures on a very optimistic forecast of the efficacy of psychiatric treatment in the asylums, such a turn of events was discouraging both to those who put up the money and those who staffed the institutions. Therefore when St. Elizabeth's Hospital opened in the mid-1850s, the Board of Visitors decided to warn the public that an accretion of chronic patients would occur and reach levels of, say, 30–40 percent.[3] They had recognized that initially extravagant therapeutic optimism would at first seem to be vindicated, but that later statistics could lead to a damaging pessimism on the part of the hospital's supporters.

In fact, the pessimism that eventually gripped the asylum movement had occurred earlier among regular physicians and medical students. A student's thesis in 1842 contained these dour words:

Writers have indulged in various speculations, but we are, I apprehend, in the present state of knowledge most profoundly ignorant, and more than this I see no reason to believe that it will ever be otherwise. [p. 2.][8]

Two years later, a leading practitioner addressed a State Medical Society on the gloomy topic: "The Respect Due to the Medical Profession and the Reasons that It Is Not Awarded by the Community." He complained that:

Never have the opinions of the people been so thoroughly unsettled in regard to different remedies and modes of practice; and the remark is heard every day, even from men of intelligence, 'in medicine I know not what to believe.' [pp. 22–23.][10]

How was the crisis in nineteenth-century medicine resolved? The confusion in the pro-

fession was cleared away by the gradual transference of confidence from the broad theories of the 18th century to the rigidly organic models arising from chemistry, histopathology, and bacteriology—a far swing of the pendulum, which later had to be balanced by an appreciation of psychological and social factors in disease. The regular medical schools were transformed into essential centers of teaching and research and were reestablished as the key element in medical education. Once again society agreed that esoteric knowledge obtained from the academy was the hallmark of the reputable physician.

The above comments on nineteenth-century medicine have been, of necessity, brief and simplified. Detailed analyses of specific periods and issues can be greatly enlightening and should be sought out by the reader. Increasingly, such studies have been undertaken by qualified historians; their perspective on present issues in psychiatry ought not to be ignored. John C. Burnham's excellent studies of physicians and paramedical personnel in American psychiatry, as well as his illuminating description of the introduction of psychoanalysis to America, clarify the immediate past that is responsible for so much of psychiatry's current goal and style.[5,6] Also valuable is Charles E. Rosenberg's presentation of forensic psychiatry and politics in the late 19th century, as seen in the trial of the presidential assassin Guiteau.[18] These and many other studies (which are described in greater detail in Vol. I of this *Handbook*) speak to our own time in a language of rational perspective, not claiming to offer answers to our present questions, yet suggesting a broader spectrum against which to judge contemporary alternatives.

(Concluding Remarks

The path of medicine, although it eventually led to enormous practical benefits for individual patients as well as whole communities, was often obscured by shifting popular social and political movements. This observation is made easily in retrospect, but could any methodology at the time have disclosed such extrascientific influences on a profession? The question inescapably arises: how much does contemporary psychiatric judgment reflect scientific "truth," and how much does it merely reflect beliefs and attitudes already held by general society? Following the halcyon days of the 1960s, this question has been raised with vigor and increasing harshness, both from within and without the psychiatric profession.

Recent distrust of therapeutic intervention grows out of an awareness that the definitions of mental illness and the criteria for commitment and observation are affected by social forces that are using psychiatry, so to speak, instrumentally. The attack on psychiatry for using these biased standards coincided with the changes in attitude toward civil rights and liberties that marked the 1960s. In a climate of public opinion becoming more aware of injustices to the person, critics have also found instances where arbitrary social forces such as racial prejudice or bureaucratic laziness lead to discriminatory treatment or prolonged incarceration. With the intimate relationship between psychiatric practice and contemporary mores thus being made manifest—and nineteenth-century American psychiatry is also a rich field for instances of the close and (at the time) unrecognized connection between the two—it is small wonder that the profession's social role can be assailed. Perhaps psychiatrists should be among the first to expect that the attack would become broader than the base of actual injustices upon which it rests.

The best antidote to an excessive influence by society on the scientific aspect of psychiatry is a recognition of that influence, rather than a mere hope that the mental health professions can somehow be exempt from it. One wishes to believe that Jarvis, who reported that the Irish were constitutionally inferior beings, would have been delighted to discover his mistake and would have worked diligently to understand how his error occurred. Naturally, objective evaluations of social pressures are not popular when they place the science of psychiatry at odds with psychiatry's expedient social interests as a practicing profession. Yet despite present and anticipated turbulence within the profession, the dispute over the extent to which social forces affect psychiatric intervention can be one of the healthy episodes in the history of American psychiatry. In many instances during the last two centuries, psychiatrists have espoused "medical" or "psychological" insights as their own that in fact were merely the norm of the dominant culture. No one would defend a specious professional belief discovered to have existed in the 19th century; where a similar congruence of a professional belief with contemporary social prejudices is found to exist now, it should also be so described. The outcome may be an alteration in practice and in professional goals.

Growing doubts, among the public and the profession, of psychiatry's claims to preeminence in social reform could return the model practice of psychiatrists to a more strictly medical style of individual treatment, supported by recent advances in organic psychiatry as well as by attainments in the dynamic tradition. Those who remain in the larger social arena may become better able to contribute to the resolution of community problems through an increased sensitivity to cultural influences on their own professional judgments. Perhaps we should view society's influence on therapeutic intervention as the individual's unconscious, powerful but unnoticed, and the recognition of it as a humbling and painful step toward maturity.

⟦ Bibliography

1. ACKERKNECHT, E. H. *Medicine at the Paris Hospital: 1794–1848*, p. 129. Baltimore: The Johns Hopkins Press, 1967.
2. ALMOND, G. A. *The Appeals of Communism.* Princeton: Princeton University Press, 1954.
3. BOARD OF VISITORS OF THE GOVERNMENT HOSPITAL FOR THE INSANE. "Minutes of the Meetings, July, 1855," Archives, St. Elizabeth's Hospital, Washington, D.C.
4. BUCHANAN, J. M. "Insanity in the Colored Race," *N.Y. Med. J.,* 44 (1886), 67–70.

5. BURNHAM, J. C. "Psychoanalysis and American Medicine, 1894–1918: Medicine, Science, and Culture," *Psychol. Issues*, 5 (1967), Monograph no. 20.

6. ———. "The Struggle between Physicians and Paramedical Personnel in American Psychiatry: 1917–1941," *J. Hist. Med.*, 29 (1974), 93–106.

7. DEUTSCH, A. "The First U.S. Census of the Insane (1840) and Its Use as Pro-slavery Propaganda," *Bull. Hist. Med.*, 15 (1944), 469–482.

8. HAILE, A. B. "On the Causes of Diseases." Unpublished doctoral thesis, p. 2. New Haven: Yale Medical College, 1842.

9. HOLMES, O. W. "Homeopathy and Its Kindred Delusions," in *Medical Essays: 1842–1882*. Boston: Houghton Mifflin, 1891.

10. HOOKER, W. *Dissertation on the Respect Due to the Medical Profession and the Reasons that It Is not Awarded by the Community*, pp. 22–23. Norwich, Conn.: Cooley, 1844.

11. JARVIS, E. "Statistics of Insanity in the United States," *Boston Med. Surg. J.*, 27 (1842), 116–121, 281–282.

12. ———. "Insanity among the Colored Population of the Free States," *Am. J. Insanity*, 8 (1852), 268–282.

13. ———. (1855) *Insanity and Idiocy in Massachusetts: Report of the Commission on Lunacy*. Cambridge, Mass.: Harvard University Press, 1971.

14. KETT, J. F. *The Formation of the American Medical Profession*, p. 97. New Haven: Yale University Press, 1968.

15. KRUGMAN, H. E. "The Role of Hostility in the Appeal of Communism in the United States," *Psychiatry*, 16 (1953), 253–261.

16. PRUDHOMME, C. and D. F. MUSTO. "Historical Perspectives on Mental Health and Racism in the United States," in C. V. Willie, B. M. Kramer, and B. S. Brown, eds., *Racism and Mental Health: Essays*, pp. 25–57. Pittsburgh: University of Pittsburgh Press, 1973.

17. RAY, I. "Review of E. Jarvis 'Insanity and Idiocy . . .'," *N. Am. Rev.*, 82 (1856), 95–96.

18. ROSENBERG, C. E. *The Trial of the Assassin Guiteau*. Chicago: University of Chicago Press, 1968.

19. RUSH, B. "Letter of Rush to Julia Rush, 13 September 1793," in L. H. Butterfield, ed., *Letters of Benjamin Rush*, Vol. 2, p. 663. Princeton: Princeton University Press, 1951.

20. SHRYOCK, R. H. "Public Relations of the Medical Profession in Great Britain and the United States: 1600–1870," *Ann. Med. Hist.*, 2 (1930), 308–339.

21. ———. *Medical Licensing in America: 1650–1965*, pp. 41–42. Baltimore: The Johns Hopkins Press, 1967.

22. WITMER, A. H. "Insanity in the Colored Race in the United States," *Alien. Neurol.*, 12 (1891), 19–30.

CHAPTER 3

ELEMENTS OF INFLUENCE
IN PSYCHOTHERAPIES

William C. Lewis

THIS CHAPTER is concerned with what all psychotherapists *have* to be doing, whether they say so or not. It attempts to tease out their unstated premises and the operations based on them. It adduces, in summary form, some scientific knowledge about these unstated therapeutic operations. Particular schools will be mentioned only in passing, as they are amply covered elsewhere in this *Handbook*.

Here we try first to supply some answers to a puzzle. The puzzle is how one person can move another. That one can do so shows the mutability of humans, while the fact that the change can last shows their permanent aspect. But why *do* changes last? Living protoplasm, seen under the microscope, is in constant flux —all bubbly ebb, flow, fusion, and division. On the other hand, the configuration of an individual human and his behavior has remarkable constancy and fixity, as we recognize when we meet an old friend. Most of the

molecules in our friend's body (and our own) may have been replaced many times since we last saw each other. Yet moments after the reunion we find that the friend remains, to be enjoyed once more. And we move each other afresh to joy or sorrow, through mutual encounter, despite the apparent fixity of each of us.

Corresponding to the mutability of individual friends is the mutability of groups—which is, of course, what group therapies depend upon. The temporary impact of a great dramatic or artistic performance is striking, as is the power of an individual charismatic demagogue. But the permanent ties that bind those who have shared an important group experience in the past have a power that is wondrous to behold. College class reunions may be the object of cynical carpings by the class skeptics; but to witness the welding of a group of sour, dispirited, individual military men— most of whom tried desperately to use any and every escape route out of the unit in question in the beginning—into a group sufficiently cohesive to bring them thousands of miles to be together twenty-five years later, is to evoke a sense of awe at the constancy of a structured allegiance, a shared experience. This is no romantic fantasy. In one ship's crew known to me from the day of the ship's commissioning, the group spirit went from disunity (expressed in the first month in requests for transfer by sixty percent of the crew), through a welding-together process during seven amphibious landings, to a unity expressed by an annual reunion and an ongoing active correspondence among crew members. And this is but one example of the constancy typical of many such groups of military comrades.

Structure, Change, and Creative Advance

Rigidity and pliability, flux that becomes structure—all psychotherapies depend on these qualities of human behavior. All of them seek change, but not fleeting change. Some human behavior has well-nigh incredible rigidity and obduracy: for example, addiction; or the life-dance of a long marriage in which the partners move like the figurines of a Swiss clock despite what had seemed to be a curative change, years before, as a result of therapy. History abounds with examples of both constancy in the face of overwhelming pressure (our own and others' martyred heroes) and incredibly pliable gullibility (Hitler's seduction of previously decent burghers into genocide and suicide). It also abounds with the active creative advances of geniuses in every field of human endeavor.

Any theory of influence will be incomplete that does not account for both obduracy and pliability, stubborn resistance and open reception, constancy and creative advance. The settled past, with its determining limits; the unsettled present; and the hope of the novel future—any theory must consider these as struggling partners in the processes of therapy. And yet a curious feature of theories of

psychotherapy is their proponents' myopia to one or another of these dimensions.

Some Blind Spots in Theories of Therapy

The school of psychotherapy most concerned with the settled past is, of course, psychoanalysis. Concepts such as fixity, psychic determinism, infantile genesis, instinct theory, transference, and so forth loom large in all psychoanalytic theories. And there can be no doubt that pervasive patterns of feeling, thinking, and acting that derive from the patient's earliest life do intrude into the therapeutic operation. Freud, extrapolating backward from child or adult behavior, first outlined the main patterns of infantile life, which can be discerned in derivative but powerfully determinative forms both in children and adults. His daughter Anna Freud continued to consolidate and carry forward this pioneering work, along with many students and colleagues. With the advent of play therapy, Melanie Klein and her followers were able to draw back the curtain that failing memory has closed, for most of us, upon the preverbal phases of our lives. The Kleinians were able to assemble evidence, derived from play behavior, that permits a heuristic hypothesis concerning the mental operations of early life. Some therapists regard these formulations as settled conclusions; other therapists are far more tentative, or even reject them. In any case, analysts agree that play- and consultation-room behavior provides convincing evidence of powerful rules, guiding both internal and external behavior, that stem from earliest life—rules that require modification if therapy is to succeed, and that impede the therapeutic process in the form of resistances and defenses. Soft protoplasm often seems more like steel in its resistance to change in the therapeutic process.

Yet as Franz Alexander often pointed out in his teachings and writings, psychoanalysis as a treatment would fail totally were this conclusion to hold sway in the consultation room. Treatment rests on the premise that fixity is only relative and change is possible. If new learning could not take place, therapy would founder. If present actions were not having their effect, how justify hundreds or thousands of analytic treatment hours? If hopes for future relief and increased novel enjoyment had only a trivial role to play, how account for the arrival of a patient in the first place, or his continuing participation in analysis?

Another example of prevalent myopia: many schools of psychotherapy strive to be "ahistoric." This means that they deplore the psychoanalytic emphasis on events in the patient's ancient past. These schools include the Rogerians, many transactionalists (but this is changing rapidly), and the behavior therapists (this is also changing with each passing year). They emphasize the "here and now" and leave aside the intrusion of transference reactions into the therapeutic relation, although they may concern themselves with past reactions to things and situations (as do behavior therapists, even of such single-minded purity of purpose as Wolpe).[29] It is in fact possible to conduct a great many therapies without examining the curious compliance most of us show toward authority figures. Only when this compliance is absent does its relative universality become obvious—as when a well-planned program of desensitization, given in a most benign fashion, rips out its keel on the rock of a patient's stubborn, defiant, negative transference to the therapist of reactions to authority figures of the patient's past.

Therapies that emphasize future growth, unrealized potentialities, new experiences, and the jettisoning of the fetters that trouble people—as gestalt therapies do—also ignore that which gives therapists the leverage to achieve their objectives: that is, they ignore the positive attitudes that the patient brings to the treatment situation from the past. These therapists are free-loaders on the earlier positive experiences that their patients have had with authorities. If not for these experiences, why would patients come, listen to therapists, do as requested—and come back again?

Myopia concerning one or another aspect of human change afflicts laymen as well as professionals. Leaving aside current controversies

raging on the printed page, as to whether claims made for the effectiveness of psychotherapies (or psychiatric ministrations in general) have been overweening, it is still an everyday experience to confront patients and families who believe people cannot change as a result of psychotherapy. Yet these same individuals learned in some measure what love is about, as infants with their mothers; learned the English language, as previously inarticulate toddlers; learned mathematics and all manner of special skills in school; learned and adopted the customs, laws, fads, and fripperies of their youth and the prejudices of their communities; and accommodated to the idiosyncratic needs of their spouses and relatives. They forget the problems they have solved, the struggles they have won. It seems never to occur to these skeptics that the psychotherapeutic situation is only a specially structured occasion for similar new experiences that in fact are often aimed at correcting faulty past learning or at opening new avenues out of the cages built from the accidents of a patient's circumstances.

Confusion about stability, change, and active creativity is thus common among both professionals and the general public.

Conflicting Premises in Theories of Therapy

Reduced to its essence: there is a paradox abroad, which on the one hand asserts that people can persist and resist change (a view held by all defenders of the status quo—for example, by church fathers of every faith), but on the other hand asserts that people can't help changing or being changed (a view held by all who wish to mold behavior—parents, teachers, therapists, politicians, statesmen, and so forth). Contained within this paradoxical antinomy are many premises and assumptions. Some are as follows:

1. The individual human has autonomy and freedom of choice. We are ultimately our own masters, and no one can change us unless we voluntarily comply.

2. The above is not true. The young are un-

formed, and one can teach standards to children (and sometimes enforce them) that will endure a lifetime in guiding their behavior. The standards include one's mother tongue (with its uses and abuses), moral laws, religious beliefs, patriotism, and heroic loyalties that may have life-or-death force. And adults are not unchangeable; they are subject to brainwashing and other forms of coercion against their will.

3. The contradiction between the above two statements is resolved by two further assumptions: (a) humans are receptive to influence, and at least something is known of the mechanisms of interaction between people; and (b) though there are "givens" of behavior that are fixed by biology, such as instinctive and reflexive behavior, there is in all species—and especially our own—a margin of mutability (such as conditioning of reflexes, or learned behavior in general) that can supply the basis for therapeutic work.

4. Whatever the "givens" of behavior, one may confidently count on the individual organism's active capacity to synthesize, categorize, and act upon *new* experience in a fashion that is novel to its prior usage. We are not mere collections of reflexes, but are active in the creation of our own experience.

5. Influence on an individual or a group tends to become structuralized, in those influenced, as a permanent pattern of behavior. Otherwise therapy would be bankrupt.

These statements may strike the reader as excessively abstract and formal. Let the reader join in dialogues with therapists of various schools, however, and various derivative slogans will be heard. "The past is irrelevant: only the present counts," is met with "Memory is essential for change"—as Santayana said, "those who cannot remember history are condemned to repeat it." The statement "We care nothing for what we can't observe—those theoretical constructs about what the contents of the Black Box are—we will stick to what we can record on videotape,"—or, in another form, "Beliefs, prejudices, transferences are all irrelevant: behavior is what counts," may be contrasted with "A change in the patient's internal dialogue—his beliefs about himself, the world, and others—will work change most effectively," or "Interpretation of the transference neurosis is the 'pure gold' of psychoanalysis."

Some therapies play down cognitive change and stress emotional experience; others stress changes in belief as crucial to therapy; still others equate the two in that they are deemed inextricable. Some therapies stress "modeling behavior" as a potent factor. Others consider imitative behavior in a patient as trivial and transient. Some therapies concentrate on one level of experiencing at the expense of others; other therapies stress confusion between levels of experiencing and communications as being the proper focus of therapy. And there are therapies that count upon expansion and creative advance almost exclusively: for example, those based on Zen Buddhism. Indeed, the catalog of slogans and emphases has filled many books.

Practical Impact of These Conflicts

The practicing therapist, and more essentially the student of therapies, is left with the task of trying to find order and reason among competing claims for varying techniques. At its worst the contention may impress the observer as a sort of Tower of Babel. This present discussion does not deal with the scientific evidence regarding the relative efficacy of one sort of therapy or another in treating any particular psychopathologic state, except to assert that such research is at a very early stage indeed. Because of the staggering complexity of the problem of evaluating outcomes—or even of descriptively comparing the differing therapeutic processes, therapists, and patients—research in this area often seems primitive. (There *are* some recent accounts that offer the promise of solid knowledge, at the empirical level, of the results of various types of therapy.)[18,3] In this chapter we instead seek light on how one theory can relate to another by means of knowledge of the mechanisms that underlie all types of therapy. Happily, there are glimmers from diverse sources that indicate some reconciliation among contending factions.

❰ The Role of Reflexes and Signaling Systems in Influence

The conflicting premises outlined above concerning autonomous free will, on the one hand, and the fixity of instinct and reflex, on the other, have long occupied the thought of philosophers; while throughout recorded history, those persons who wish to influence others have proceeded to do so unencumbered by concern over this debate. Just how these persons were and are able to accomplish their ends has become more comprehensible with the help of science.

We take for granted here the exploration of varieties of instinctual drives, the conflicts between them, their vicissitudes in development, and the defenses against them. All of these matters were studied by Freud and are still under scrutiny by his followers and by students of child development, primate behavior, and the behavior of lower mammalian or lower-order animals—that is, researchers who have many different theoretical orientations. Such work expands constantly. Freud's study of psychosexual development aided us in viewing certain deviant behaviors as products of the interactions of instinctual drives with cultural or familial norms, rather than as incomprehensible sins, but enlightenment has not stopped with the Freudians. Early psychic development and the processes by which it can be modified have been studied, in very young children, by Melanie Klein's group[14] and, in the regressions seen in psychoses, by a variety of pioneering therapists (for example, Rosen).[23] We can hope for further enrichment of our humanistic understanding from work with primates and other animals. Such work has already provided insights into instinctual drives of curiosity and problem solving, the desire for contact-comfort, and the vital role of infant–infant affectional systems. (See Harlow[11] and Ardrey,[1] to mention only two examples.)

All these developments most likely are within the reader's experience, and they are further described elsewhere in this *Handbook*. Psychoanalysis has supplied the main *Weltanschauung* in the theory and practice of psychotherapy for the last several decades, especially in the United States; and it is assumed here that the reader is familiar with the enormous enrichment and power it gives to the theory of influence. The reader may even have shared with the writer the great human satisfaction obtained by both patient and analyst from its use. The following discussion aims at augmenting the range and flexibility of this predominant mode of influence by sketching out theoretical, clinical, and laboratory research that may not yet have come to the reader's attention.

Reflex Behavior

A reflex, such as the familiar knee jerk that follows the physician's tap on the quadriceps tendon, is a response to a particular sensory stimulus. In contemporary terms it is preprogramed, occurring outside conscious volition. Thought is short-circuited. Any instinctual drive involved—say, self-preservation—is also short-circuited. In fact, an awareness of drives and analysis of whether or not a stimulus holds promise of satisfying a drive tends to inhibit reflex behavior (discussed below). Reflexes are biological "habits" that offer the economic gain of saving vital time, as in the righting reflex of a dropped cat, or the blinking reflex of a threatened eye. It is best not to have to think what one needs to do when one drops some distance to the ground unexpectedly, and the stretch reflex (the one that the knee jerk demonstrates) has kept many a human from breaking a bone. Reflexes are a form of instinct, but they differ from the haunting urges that persist in organisms as diverse as the insect drawn to its death by a pheromone (the external analogue of a hormone) and the human driven for years by persistent passions of love, rage, fear, or simple hunger. If being "driven" by instinct is compared to the sensation of being on a roller coaster (as distinct from driving one's car through traffic), then reflex is typified by that instantaneous complex of responses we show when we trip on a step.

Commonly we lump all reflexes together, but science has shown that reflex behavior has at least three main classes of response. One is of especial relevance to psychotherapies, though all three underlie any school of psychotherapeutic intervention. These classes have been studied for many decades in Russian laboratories, and the distinctions used here are those used by Russian theorists and experimenters. The classes are: firstly, the *defensive*; secondly, the *specific adaptive*; and thirdly, the *orienting* reflexes.

CLINICAL APPLICATIONS OF ADAPTIVE AND DEFENSIVE REFLEXES

Defensive reflexes protect us (and all animals) against injury. For example, the eyeblink reflex protects the cornea.

Specific adaptive reflexes keep stimuli within physiologically tolerable limits. When we emerge from our offices into blinding sunlight, the reflex contraction of the pupils of our eyes aids our vision. And, on a hot day, we are kept more comfortable by perspiring and by vasodilation, both of which increase heat loss from our skins.

These two classes may seem to the reader to be hardly worth discussing in relation to psychotherapy; they are "givens," unworthy of notice. But this is not so. All behavior therapies lean heavily on the work of Pavlov, who showed how these classes of reflex can be "conditioned" by experience so as to produce a changed response. When we place a patient on a couch in psychoanalysis, we gradually condition him to relax the level of vigilance of his defensive and adaptive reflexes; and when we suggest relaxation and ease in hypnotherapy or in the desensitization maneuvers of behavior therapy, we are conditioning the defensive and adaptive reflexes of our patients in much the same way that Pavlov "taught" the dog to salivate to a bell instead of the sight and smell of food. More subtle interventions by a therapist, such as friendly support in place of the outrage the patient expects the therapist to show (on the model of previous conditioning), have unavoidable effects on the patient's defensive and adaptive reflexes.

These two kinds of reflex behavior, together with the conditioning or deconditioning of their levels of activation, are so pervasive in all psychotherapeutic encounters that one might expect far greater mention of them in the literature of psychotherapy than is the case. Reflex behavior in fact is not foreign to psychoanalysis. Pavlov remarked in conversation that the idea of conditioning came to him from Freud's work, and the two fields may lie closer than the literature of either modern psychoanalysis or reflexology and behavior therapy might suggest.

THE ORIENTING REFLEX AND ITS IMPLICATIONS FOR THERAPY

The third family of reflexes consists of the orienting reflexes (usually shortened to "reflex" for simplicity of reference, though there is actually a rich variety of responses). The orienting reflex is the automatic response to external or internal changes. We notice difference whether it is a loud noise or sudden silence, a bright flash or sudden darkness. Our organism responds quite automatically in ways that might be characterized as increased vigilance, alertness, or fine-tuned awareness. This hypervigilance and readiness for flight or fight varies in its bodily expression, depending on the sensory modality through which the change is perceived. First there is a general alarm, then a focused attention expressed in increased responsivity, depending on whether the alerting signal is auditory, olfactory, visual, or tactile, and so forth. The alerting signal may even be internal: for example, one responds with alarm to anginal pain or even to an extrasystole (which may be experienced as a "skipped" heart beat). The patterns of response characteristic of differing sensory systems have been mapped out in considerable detail in the laboratory.

The orienting reflex differs from other families of reflex in important respects: it is set off by change in the world, whether positive or negative; and it subsides rapidly when signals recur in a steady fashion. These qualities contribute to the importance of orienting in all forms of therapy, since orienting responses occur in the first moments of therapeutic encounter and continue in both therapist and patient until the end of therapy. They are set off by silence as well as by words or gestures. They are automatic; and without mentioning them as such, we therapists use them to guide our work, both in diagnosing and in every hour of therapy. We note a pause in dialogue or an anxious rush of speech. In turn, a patient will orient to our silence or to our reassuring comment if either response differs from what is expected as a result of past experience. This is a source of therapeutic leverage; it can be lost, if the therapy is led into monotonous stalemate by monotonous repetition without inventive variation.

An example may make the above clear to those who are unfamiliar with orienting. If one desires to make contact with some small wary animal, say a squirrel, one will approach very quietly and expose some appetizing object—perhaps a cracker spread with peanut butter—that will alert the squirrel and attract his interest. He orients to both the odor and sight of the cracker and also to the approach of a potentially dangerous large animal, a human. If one remains perfectly still, the squirrel may approach, most tentatively. He will risk a foray—a scouting expedition, as it were—but remains ready to scamper at the slightest warning. If one is patient and persistent, it takes only a short time for the squirrel to learn that it is safe to eat out of one's hand. In the intervening period, any change—even a loudly enunciated "Boo!"—will send the squirrel up a tree.

We humans are not qualitatively different from the squirrel in our approach to new and potentially dangerous situations. Therapy is always sensed as such; and though we have more complex cognitive capacities than small animals possess, the preciseness of the orienting reflex is astonishing in all vertebrates (see Sokolov).[24] Humans orient precisely when they perform a symphony or play a football game, but the coordinated orienting of a flock of birds in migratory flight is hardly less intricate, despite the lack of the planning and discussion that is characteristic of human activity. And as our knowledge of events at the molecular level expands, we find that intricate and precise processes of response, adjustment,

and accommodation seem to pervade all organisms—from simple bacterial cells recognizing dangerous foreign protein molecules, to patients in analysis responding to expectant silence as if it were a mortal peril, or to heads of state assessing the events of foreign affairs. The three classes of reflex seen in physiological experiments and in clinical observations reveal modes of influence that have very general significance not only in all psychotherapeutic interventions but also in life processes of all kinds.

THE INTERNALIZATION OF REFLEX RESPONSE PATTERNS IN INDIVIDUAL DEVELOPMENT

Drives and reflexes can largely explain the behavior of lower organisms in response to influences from within and without. But even in lower organisms we require for our explanation a malleability of response that leads to regular change in behavior, rather than simple stimulus-and-response patterns. While our habitual modes of thought restrict the use of "concept formation" to higher organisms or even solely to humans (Webster on "concept[11]:" . . . a generic mental image abstracted from percepts . . ."), these modes of thought have been challenged in the many philosophical writings of Alfred North Whitehead (see Lowe[19] for a summary and references). Whitehead proposed that all organisms possess a mental pole of existence, however faintly we may discern it. For the present argument, suffice it to say that modern molecular biology (see Watson)[27] demonstrates conclusively that immunological and genetic processes possess capabilities closely analogous to (if not identical with) memory, and that even in the simplest bacterial cells this "memory" rests on the ability to form "a generic [mental?] image abstracted from percepts." Fine definitions must be left to extended analysis at another time; the central point to be made is that patterns of behavior are acquired—learned—in organisms far below man in the evolutionary ladder, and acquired in humans long before they possess the speech with which to tell anyone about them.

We need a clear idea of how such patterns change over time in the development of an individual organism. An egg (say a feline ovum) responds to a sperm in complex ways not characteristic of the suckling animal (the kitten) that results from the development of the fertilized egg. Still later, the nurtured kitten develops into a fine-tuned predator on birds and an expert exploiter of human vulnerabilities toward purring or meowing cats. As kitten turns into cat, we see the emergence of a new mode of influence: the cat's internalized map or plan of the way the world works, which overrides any simple hunger or fear responses. Cats learn their territories, the habits of their masters, their order in the hierarchy of other pets, the permissable rules of the household and its prohibitions, the proper use of a cat box, and so on. As cats slip slowly into senility, any cat owner can see the cat's increasing rigidity, irritability at change, and love of comfortable tranquility. At any age, then, the cat forms internalized models—syntheses of drive, reflex, and perception of the surrounding world—that endure for long periods and that guide behavior, depending on the cat's developmental stage. Ordinary experience, not sophisticated experiment, led to the conclusion that one has difficulty teaching an old cat new tricks.

Thus in our analysis of the underpinnings of all therapies we must consider two additional factors besides the influence of drive and reflex: (1) the developmental stage of the organism that is to be influenced; and (2) the modification of instantaneous response into enduring regulatory patterns. Therapeutic interventions with very young children must be appropriate to the child's repertoire. The same can be said of adolescents, adults, and the very old. In all cases we must take cognizance of what was given the individual at birth, what has developed, and what has been learned. We entertain the notion that it is a mismatch between internalized models of the world and the experience of the therapeutic encounter (of whatever variety) that gives the therapist leverage, using the orienting reflex and the active synthetic processes that the mismatch sets going.

LEVELS OF AWARENESS OF RESPONSE PATTERNS

There is a further complication that modifies all therapeutic interventions. We know now that our organisms are arranged in many levels. The perception, orienting, and rearrangement of models occurs even in peripheral receptors like the cochlea or retina, let alone the levels of the central nervous system, from spinal cord to cortex. Further, we know that all levels of perception, comparison, rearrangement, and recording respond to qualifying influences such as drugs, different levels of arousal, circadian rhythms, and the toxic disease processes that are responsible for deliria. Such influences occur accidentally, spontaneously, and regularly in life outside the consultation room. When used intentionally they supply a powerful set of tools and contribute in turn to many schools of psychotherapy, as in narcosynthesis, encounter experiences using adjuvant psychoactive drugs like LSD and peyote, and so forth. The orienting reflex in particular is sensitive to such drugs; that is, the tendency toward a decrease in response when an unusual experience is repeated is partially blocked when cortical activity is decreased by drugs or by drowsiness.

These complications ramify into diverse expressions. Orienting occurs and modifies behavior by means of forms of influence that we do not recognize consciously. One famous example will serve: the horse called Clever Hans, who appeared able to perform mathematical operations such as adding, subtracting, multiplying, and dividing. Only after very careful study by learned scientists did it become apparent that the horse was guided by minute cues given it by its trainer, who was himself unaware of his influence. Subliminal cues can similarly guide our own behavior—a fact known to advertisers and one used by all therapists, whether they are aware of it or not. In like manner, the use of the couch by the psychoanalyst deprives the analysand of many subliminal cues while simultaneously dulling the cortical suppression of the initial "general-alarm" phase of the orienting reflex. The net effect is to make the patient more responsive to internal cues and less able to test whether the analytic situation is safe or not, thus contributing to the development of what analysts call the *regressive transference neurosis*—a state of childish vulnerability that permits the examination of long-buried modes of coping, with the aim of correcting these patterns.

TIMETABLES OF THEORY-BUILDING, INCLUDING LANGUAGE ACQUISITION

New knowledge illumines sequences of orienting and rule-building from birth on. Clinical observation of the behavior of mothers with their newborn babies led to the increasing prevalence of the rooming-in practice, which allows mothers continuous contact with their babies in hospitals (instead of the practice, still followed in many places, of separating the two for a period of days or weeks). Clinical hunches have been backed up by sophisticated instruments that record the cries of newborn babies, even in the delivery room, and that will make possible an understanding of a baby's earliest communicational efforts. Thus far it is clear that in the first few days of the baby's life a mother-baby dialogue develops that goes far beyond such vague concepts as "mother instinct." Ingenious research has also been able to prove that babies only fifty days old can receive complicated messages, sort them out, reach conclusions concerning their meaning, and alter their own behavior in accordance with what this proto-communication or proto-language tells them. (This refers to the astonishing research of Bower,[5,6] using the peekaboo game with young babies. See Beadle[2] for a summary of this and similar research.) Babies can process symbols in the first weeks of life; our prevalent conceptions of them as creatures that are almost solely occupied with surviving and growing and that lack abstractive, cognitive capacities have been demolished. We still write articles that would have conceptual capacity appearing only at one, two, or three years of life; but such writings seem clearly wrong, as are our earlier visions of the inner life of the newborn. The new knowledge afforded by recent research alters the content of our conceptions of the early months and years of life not so much as it provides assurance that categorizing and at least proto-concept-forming in infants have been demonstrated. The long controversies that beset psychoanalysis as to "whether the suckling child can be credited with the mentality of the four-year-old"—to paraphrase Glover[8] in criticizing Melanie Klein's formulations—have at least in principle been laid to rest. Glover himself, with his concept of ego nuclei, acknowledged early structure; from there it is but a small step to concepts such as splitting, introjection, projection and the paranoid or depressive positions, and a variety of Klein's still-controversial ideas.[13] Any current formulation of any single mental mechanism of infantile life may be in error, but it is now clear that complex discriminations, classifications, and operational theories do develop in the first weeks of life. Nor is this of only passing intellectual interest: the early defenses also appear closely intertwined with physiological and pathophysiological processes in later life.[16]

It is myopic to assign the beginnings of language acquisition to the second year of life. Complex nonverbal languages are well developed by then, and by the age of three or four, children can already have mastered the working use of three or four verbal languages—a mere refinement of their earlier virtuosity. In fact at least one expert, Joos, asserts[12] that our estimates of the age at which a child masters grammar in any given language are similarly distorted, judging from our schools; he maintains that it is not "normal" to learn *any* grammar after the age of eight. We may later engraft refinements of grammar for "schoolroom" use, but our conversation will remain essentially unchanged beyond this age. (See also Bloom[4] for abundant evidence of the early flowering and subsequent waning of many assimilative talents and of the openness to influence.)

The assertion that nonverbal communicational rules (and proficiency with these rules) can be put in the same category as verbal performance gains support from studies of the congenitally deaf children who learn to manipulate symbols without the use of language.[15] It is difficult to test their categorizing cognitive capacities, but the available evidence indicates that while thought processes may be hampered by the lack of language, thought is nevertheless clearly present in children who do not have the assistance of verbal language.

Today it is also clear that the influences resulting in language acquisition are thrust along by developmental processes that unfold both a desire for synthetic creation and an open receptiveness, of the sort embodied in the Freudian concept of the libido and served concretely by the lowly orienting reflex. The thrust toward conceptualizing can survive a massive physical insult (such as a hemispherectomy of the child's dominant lobe) and go on to push the injured child into acquiring nonverbal and verbal languages by the same sure steps made earlier, resulting in the re-acquisition of the whole gamut of symbols and the whole of the child's native tongue. (For reasons still obscure, however, the limit of this reacquisition coincides with puberty.) This thrust toward creative symbolization can also survive environmental deprivations that one might think would be almost as crippling as a neurologic injury. For example, the children of totally deaf parents learn to talk quite as well as children immersed in the chatter of parents who can hear and talk; and those foundling-home children whose main source of language models is the lowly television set can gain a surprising grasp of language in spite of the barren institutional setting in which they are raised and the mentally retarded attendants who may be the only models available for them to mimic.

The Influence of Speech, the Second Signaling System

The reader may ask himself what all this has to do with influence in psychotherapies. True, the studies cited reveal a very early categorizing and synthetic thrust in children— earlier than we had thought, before this work was available to guide us. But the link between this work and any essential aspect of any psychotherapy needs further explication. Such explication, once more, is provided by an immense amount of information, for which we are in the main indebted to Russian researchers. This work is available in lucid, summary form in a small volume entitled *The Role of Speech in the Regulation of Normal and Abnormal Behavior*,[20] which puts forth the thesis underlying many separate pieces of research. Its author, A. R. Luria, himself one of the guiding lights of many Russian laboratories, may be destined to assume a stature comparable to that of Freud or Piaget; and in this volume he gets to the meat of his own and his colleagues' work.

The work follows a thought of Pavlov: we humans have the same sort of signaling system possessed by the famous salivating dog, and we can lay down rules in our brains that will guide subsequent behavior just as the dog was "conditioned" to salivate to the bell instead of to the sight and smell of food. *But we also have a second signaling system, with its own regularities and stored rules that guide our behavior: and this system is speech.* The first signaling system is the one possessed by the babies with whom Bower played the peekaboo game, the system to which children who never learn to speak remain confined. Primates too, without speech, can store memories of many complex sequences of events as they occur, place them in their "files" of past occurrences, and guide their future behavior accordingly. But with the acquisition of speech, a new dimension opens.

If a three- to four-year-old baby is given a fairly complex task to perform by verbal instruction, it is easy to find limits on his powers to comply. An example from the Russian studies will serve: if a child is asked to watch a display panel on which various signals can be displayed, then told to squeeze a bulb (attached to a recording manometer) when a certain light goes on, and, finally, to release his squeezing pressure when the light goes off, the child fails. Persevering, random, uncoordinated behavior results. Yet if the same child is told, "When the light goes on, please squeeze the bulb and say out loud the word 'Go,' and when it goes off, stop squeezing and say 'Stop,'" the child quickly masters the task. The act of speaking made the difference. Russian laboratories have mapped out the sequences by which the child progressively masters more complex tasks. Their evidence demonstrates that verbal processes are of immense importance in the regulation of all behavior, providing a control that is unattainable without them.

This persists into adult life, as two examples will show. First, let the reader recall looking up a number in a telephone book and then turning to the phone to dial: is it not well-nigh universal to find ourselves saying the number aloud? This is also the process involved when we say rote arithmetic facts aloud (or at least *sotto voce*) to aid ourselves in adding, multiplying, and so forth. Second, the Russians have discovered that the consequences of diseases that impair motor performance can be combatted by instructing patients to use just this route in order to regain control. Thus sufferers from Parkinson's disease, unable to perform repetitive motions, can regain that power if instructed to count—either aloud or silently—as each motion is completed.

The Two Signaling Systems in Psychotherapy

The two signaling systems just described supply the underpinning of any type of psychotherapy. The messages in the two are not always congruent and consistent; this will be explored below. It is also possible to do psychotherapy by nonverbal messages alone, as Frieda Fromm-Reichman demonstrated through the many hours she would spend sitting wordlessly and tranquilly beside a mute schizophrenic. (Many of our "newer" schools of therapy stress nonverbal types of contact— physical manipulations, nude therapy in swimming pools, and so forth.) Nevertheless all therapies make use of both signaling systems, striving by one means or another to work a change in the guiding rules that patients bring to therapy. Millimeter by millimeter a psychoanalyst, using the second signaling system predominately, bends the rails on which the patient's engine runs. An exhortatory, evangelistic therapist strives to supply new guiding rails. So does a therapist expert in confrontational techniques. Even a nondirective therapist like Carl Rogers, while seeming to stay very close to what a patient is trying to say, will introduce inevitable minor changes in the patient's verbal messages with each such "reflection," since his "client" will hear the reflection coming from another person—and one who does not merely parrot the patient's statement.

The vital role of the second signaling system is further demonstrated in the developmental processes revealed by the studies both of Russian workers and of Jean Piaget and his group. Children four or five years old talk aloud to themselves. Piaget showed that nearly a third of what they say to themselves consists of instructions, injunctions, threats, prohibitions, and so on. They say "Johnny, if you touch that, mommy will spank you," or "Patty, if you eat that, you'll get fat." Russian data indicate that by the age of seven or eight, the role played by vocalized speech in the regulation of behavior begins to be taken over by internalized speech: the child in the transitional age period will not speak aloud, but recordings from glottal muscles show that the child speaks silently to himself. Thereafter, all through adult life, we humans carry on an internal dialogue in our heads, using *words* as we argue the pros and cons of a course of behavior. These words have extraordinary force for us all—as the reader can demonstrate by searching the lexicon of shibboleths surrounding any prejudice, including those that have driven humans to war, pillage, lynching, and massacres throughout recorded history. Even today one need not search hard to find some of these slogans guiding people to heroic self-sacrifice or to bestial, uncaring slaughter.

The reason why words have such power to guide us in our daily rounds (including our lapses toward mad behavior) remained a puzzle until Piaget studied the process of speech internalization and its regulatory power. He showed that children make judgments about the nature of the world before they possess sophisticated scientific understanding; they enunciate these judgments to themselves, and thereafter they almost never examine the premises on which these judgments are based.

Parents of seven-year-old children seldom bother to explore what their children are saying to themselves about the world. By eight or nine years of age such statements are no longer available for study, since by then they are *silent* instructions. A four-year-old child who concludes that the moon is following him, on the evidence of the movement of the moon's image behind a line of trees or houses as the child walks a twilit street, may tell his parents of his hypothesis (akin to the theory-building he may engage in later if he becomes a scientist). But this same child, at age eight or nine, will incorporate his conclusions outside his parents' awareness and thereafter be guided by what, essentially, a psychiatrist would label a delusion.

These arbitrary commands in one's internal dialogue make up what Freud collected under the rubric of the superego. Freud stressed the earliest, archaic forms of the internal dialogue rather than the seven- or eight-year-old's statements; these latter forms are recognized as determinative of behavior by various religious groups, including the Catholic Church. But whatever the age to which one assigns the origin of the magic mischief of childhood's dicta, it is of interest that these dicta recur in hallucinatory form in deliria and psychoses. As Freud recognized, it is as if we could hear once more the things our parents told us and warned us against, and could hear our own instructions, on their model, scolding ourselves.

Albert Ellis[7] has been foremost in making the modification of these verbal regulations of behavior the core target of psychotherapeutic operations. His views have solid scientific foundation, as sketched above. Many parents whose eyes have been opened by Ellis' writings regret that their child's irrational self-instructions were not explicitly teased out of him as they were forming, instead of when these same self-instructions led the child into misery during adolescence or young adulthood. He could have been saved this suffering. The long, slow remodeling of such pronunciamentos that occurs in a psychoanalysis, or the labor of learning to talk to one's self more reasonably—the direct focus of such psychotherapies as Ellis' Rational Emotive Therapy

and, to some extent, transactional analysis—could be rendered superfluous if parents attended to what their children say silently, over and over, to themselves and condition themselves to accept as gospel, so that they become capable of righteous indignation and single-minded zealotry toward themselves and other people.

THE INTERPLAY OF SIGNALING SYSTEMS

This is not to say that conditioning in the first signaling system is superseded by self-conditioning in the second system. Both systems guide behavior, and modifications of both systems form the focus of various therapies and of the influences of life outside the consulting room.

For example: most of us have some secret fascination with bloody mayhem, its infliction, and its results. This fascination, curbed by parental prohibitions, can re-emerge in our enjoyment of movies, television, or fiction, all of which often depict violent events foreign to our daily lives. Has the reader ever come upon a bloody accident? Some years ago, when train travel was more common, I spent some hours observing the behavior of men, women, and children who flocked to the front end of a train on which I was traveling when it collided with a car at a country crossing. Word had spread to a town several miles distant that three people had been killed. The train passengers sat waiting for order to be restored and discussed the grisly event, on the report of those who ventured forward to see the car and a decapitated man. The car was, as it were, caught in the jaws of a Diesel-powered version of a giant serpent, and a parade of spectators began to approach from miles around. All seemed furtive, excited with some guilt-ridden and macabre passion. Mothers holding babies in their arms hurried to see what had happened.

This urge to view bloodletting is as old as mankind. Roman games exploited this desire. We try to train our children out of indulging it, but the nonverbal, first-signaling-system urge remains. It can be modified by parents, and it can be gradually modified again in adult life by training procedures serving very different uses. Medical schools, for example, gradually prepare civilized adults to be able to cut open a chest and expose the heart of a living human; this is accomplished by a progressive desensitization over several years through exposure to dissected lower animals, followed by living mammals, and eventually by draped (and thus isolated) portions of human beings. The verbal, second-signaling-system messages that accompany these graded exposures are couched in scientific terms, and medical students show gradually lessening reactions as they pass through their studies. This has social utility. However, a similar course designed for evil purposes was part of the Nazi S.S. "training" of decent Germans, who were gradually encouraged to define progressively more brutal treatment of fellow humans as a "patriotic" service "for the Fatherland." The end result was the freedom to commit the atrocities of a Belsen or a Buchenwald. Such interplay of definition with behavioral response appears in laboratory experiments[25] in which physiological responses to horrendous motion pictures vary with the tenor of the soundtrack describing the scenes: they are less pronounced with surgical, detached descriptions; more pronounced with "human," empathic involvement.

At any rate, this is not the place to explore the neuroanatomical and neurophysiological findings that have flooded into the scientific world in recent years, regarding an organism's coding, recoding, and recording of the nature of experience in persistent reference form for the guidance of future behavior. Fortunately, this body of findings has recently been summarized in the remarkable volume entitled *Languages of the Brain.*[22] Its author, the neurosurgeon-turned-neuropsychologist Karl Pribram, sets forth the evidence that over the years persuaded him that any stimulus–response, reflex-arc model of brain function simply will not do. Instead, he proposes a sophisticated cybernetic theory of feedback and feedforward mechanisms that have memory functions at their core. These functions are themselves very complex. Some are sharply localized in the brain, such as the receptors in the visual cortex for discerning contrast,

edges, slant, and so on. Others, as Karl Lashley showed years ago, are widely distributed and are scarcely impaired by ablations of neural tissue, irrespective of anatomical location—for example, learned, complex behavior. Wherever it is stored in multiple locations, however, memory mediates behavior according to context and past experience. Pribram suggests that we should look to the holograph for our model of memory, rather than to the file-cabinet model that earlier concepts of memory invoked. Whatever the model, the organism absorbs and processes experience in order to supply itself with guiding plans of temporal sequences of events (including its own behavior in relation to these events). Many signaling systems and many processing, intervening operations—including comparisons of the "now" with the "was," and a projection of "what might be in the future"—as well as many effector systems interact in the guiding of behavior.

Whether or not the reader's tastes and interests will take him into the exciting world that is unfolding daily in the laboratory, as the above suggests, it is implicit in any psychotherapeutic operation that the therapist has a plan, temporally organized, to change his patient's plans. This change in the directed plans guiding the patient's behavior involves the implicit assumption that events in the consulting room will become encoded as a persistent message in the languages of the patient's brain, guiding his future behavior by their import. For the convenience of exposition, the subsequent discussion simplifies the actual multiplicity of signaling systems, languages, memories, and plans. The reader will perhaps grant me this violence to the richness of any moment of experience—a handclasp, a kiss, a vehement denunciation—in the service of ordering the confusion that threatens attempted descriptions of the psychotherapeutic scene.

CLINICAL APPLICATIONS OF BOTH SIGNALING SYSTEMS

Various therapies attack the guiding program, the plans, that a patient brings to therapy, in both the first and the second signaling systems—those plans to which the patient has been conditioned in the past.

Behavior therapies, for example, provide the richest and most obvious variations of tactics. Messages in the second signaling system —verbal instructions—enable the therapist to induce a state of relaxation. Therapy may stop there, simply training a patient to relax rapidly whenever he feels tense. Or, after inducing relaxation, verbal signals may be used to suggest progressive hierarchies of frightening situations, from "least scary" to "most scary," all the while promoting easy calm and tranquility by means of other second-system messages. The extreme variation, once physical relaxation is achieved, would be for the therapist to use the verbal signaling system to evoke the most horrid experiences imaginable —a sort of extrapolation of what the patient says is *most* feared and avoided ("implosive therapy").[26] The objective of all these techniques is for the patient to achieve a realistic and stoic acceptance of the world of the adult, stripped of the delusional exaggerations characteristic of childhood terrors.

The above serves as a paradigm for many other types of therapy. Thus in psychoanalysis the couch supplies an implicit tranquilizer, obviating the training in relaxation that the behavior therapist first gives his patient. Repeated calm, interpretive remarks serve to reduce the fears that the patient brings to therapy concerning his behavior and thoughts and the responses of an authority to these events. The pattern of influence, however, is in all important respects shared by behavior therapies and psychoanalysis.

THE RELATION OF SIGNALING SYSTEMS TO AFFECTS

The above discussion and examples from therapeutic operations stress cognitive elements. The literature and practice of therapy, on the other hand, have long stressed affect as the actual main target of mutative interventions. Signals in either of the two main signaling systems can evoke affective responses. For example, the sight of a raging fire may pro-

duce fear; but a verbal warning of an approaching tornado, given on the radio, can do likewise.

When we encourage a bereaved patient or a friend to talk of the death of a loved one, we are not surprised if lachrymal glands respond by secreting tears that accompany the thoughts expressed in words. So also with other "emotion-laden" recountings of past important events; indeed, we would regard a lack of any sign of rearoused emotion as an indicator of psychopathology. We expect some immediate evidence of emotional response if we intentionally slap someone hard across the face, but we tend to forget that long-sustained affects owe their life to the link between feelings and words (or some equivalent cognitive apparatuses, in those who lack speech). Internalized verbal thoughts carry with them affective components that may be low-keyed (as in a memorized shopping list) or may have life-or-death power (as prejudices do). In these times of reason and science, battle cries and marching slogans still arouse the most primitive emotions to which we are prey.

Words become linked with feelings and with bodily processes in general, in ways that have as yet received little study except by psychoanalysts. That these linkages have unsuspected force and permanence can no longer be doubted. The work of Graham[9] and others has demonstrated highly specific bonds between verbal statements about stressful life events, which are characteristic of and uttered in common by the sufferers from "psychosomatic" diseases. We do not call weeping a disease, or grieving after bereavement; neither do we label as an illness the muscular tension and the flushed face of the man describing an insulting encounter. Yet the statements of ulcer patients about life events preceding the onset of their illnesses are as characteristic as those of grievers or ragers, and as different from the statements of asthmatics as grievers differ from ragers in recounting what disturbed them.

The Graham studies shed light on an implicit influence and offer an exciting promise for future lines of therapeutic exploration.

People suffering from ulcers, asthma, hives, ulcerative colitis, migraine, eczema, and so forth appear to have conditioned themselves to their own utterances about and definitions of life events in the early years of their lives (as in "The moon is following me," described above). Thus the ulcer-prone man who defines a job loss as "Those S.O.B.'s gypped me out of what belongs to me and I'd like to chew them out!" generates bodily reactions appropriate for digestion. In any system of psychotherapy, efforts to influence this patient toward a more adult view of misfortune will change the automatic primitive response he keeps making to the loss of his job. The asthma-prone individual will define the same job loss as "being shut out in the cold," and his bronchial tubes behave as if he were in fact exposed to frigid air. Efforts of his psychotherapist to help him find more adaptive ways to view his predicament and the options that remain to him will implicitly change his way of defining the job loss. But ulcer-prone patients, it now appears, keep conditioning themselves by attending to their own pronouncements about the job loss, and in this process they keep activating pathological bodily responses. Psychotherapeutic influences toward more realistic responses will help, but it appears possible that interventions directed at this pathogenic self-signaling can offer a more rapid and effective therapeutic route.

Wider influences on patterns of interaction between words and feelings—the influences of family, group, culture, and native language—affect the individual's capacity to define, in his second signaling system, what occurs in his feelings. We know little of this type of influence as yet, though it must creep unnoticed into the psychotherapeutic operation: Frenchmen know what "liver trouble" means; people from America's Deep South talk of "ague and fever;" and we know now that Tahitians cannot describe depression, nostalgia, grief, and loneliness.[17] But psychotherapy of any type, in any land or language, implicitly tinkers with the patient's description of his feelings, offering new labels and new ways to think about the life of the emotions.

THE INCORPORATION OF SIGNALING AND COPING MODES BY MODELING

Children acquire language, our most developed signaling system, by a mysterious process that seems almost akin to osmosis. As yet we know very little about how to facilitate this acquisition or to repair any damage to its spontaneous development.

Children acquire nonverbal languages (voice tones, expressions, gestures, styles of walking, swimming, or skiing, and so on) in a similar mysterious way. We see our children copy us, but there our understanding stops. How can they mimic us down to the tiniest mannerisms? This area remains clouded with problems that we are only beginning to examine.[21] For example, if you call an old friend on the telephone, you might easily be gulled into launching an intimate discussion by the incredible similarity of the voice of a postadolescent son of your friend to his father's (your friend's) voice. This imitative and incorporated process persists into adulthood. Our patients may not learn our verbal and nonverbal languages as readily as they once might have, but the capacity for imitative behavior pervades the consulting room. We may not choose to include identification as one of the recognized items of our therapeutic armamentary, but it serves us nonetheless. Identification with our teachers both aids and obfuscates the process of learning the technique of psychotherapy; is there a reader who has not "tried on" the style of the latest visiting expert, or the most recent author the reader has read?

(Concluding Remarks

The preceding material bears upon the basic operations of therapy of any type. We begin with the heuristic assumption that a normal human being delights in revealing himself or herself to another person for the sheer joy of sharing an encounter. This is not a one-sided barrage of self-revelation, such as a caricature of a prototypical Hollywood character might produce. Rather, it involves the rapid sensing of one another by patient and therapist, and the joint revelation and experience that supplies both of them with one of the great joys of the psychotherapeutic enterprise.

All therapists watch for interruptions in this process. They collect an inventory of barriers, then begin guessing what produced them in past experiences with a patient and what might help to remove them as they intrude into the present. Injuries? Scoldings? Threats? Scars of some blighted reaching-out? Desertions? Disappointments? In other words, all therapists are in a sense like obstetricians, who count on the natural progression of events and who are alert to any interruptions, moving into activity when progress slows and working to remove the dystocia—the barrier to progress—as rapidly and effectively as they can.

Barriers may have originated at preverbal or nonverbal levels or in an enormous variety of experiences of a verbal nature. And—a *big* and—barriers can also originate in conflicts of feelings at all levels of experience, in conflicts of cognitive knowledge, and in conflicts between knowledge of the world coming from the first signaling system and knowledge of the world coming from the second signaling system. Therapists concern themselves with all these varieties of barriers and conflicts.

The raw data are available to the general public, but conventions of manners and habits of thought blind the originally perceptive eye of the average citizen. Training in psychotherapeutic technique strives to restore fresh awareness. Some gifted nonprofessionals retain this awareness all their lives, making them the people we seek out in times of trouble: the comforting parent, the sainted aunt, the gentle uncle, the cherished friend. Some people have an ear for music or an eye for line, others are tone-deaf or can draw nothing more complex than a stick figure. Similarly, a talent for empathy, for tactful exploration of barriers to encounter, for skillful facilitation—such gifts bless people in all walks of life, outside of any formal profession. What writing such as this tries to do is to assist in the process of discovering or recovering sensitive awareness and sensitive assistance.

Imagine a therapeutic session. Our patient pauses. Why? After a silence the patient starts out on (it seems) an entirely new tack. We conjecture. Our patient deluges us with a rush of detail. Why? Then our patient blushes. We search for connections, and some coherence looms. We listen with our "third ear," as Theodore Reik advised; we make hypotheses of the sort we might make when we were newborn infants; we also apply all the sophisticated scientific knowledge we can muster. The patient wants to make contact with us. What blocks the effort, then, and his efforts elsewhere?

It is easy to engrave inhibitions on the plans of humans, as on lower animals. All one need do is impose punishment reliably; and the earlier and more impressionable the age at which this is done, the more effective. But the higher the organism in the evolutionary scale, the more possibilities there are for contradictory and paradoxical inhibitions, prohibitions, conditions, and demands to be engraved. To be sure, some ambivalences come with the genes and with the drives that are governed thereby. Observe two sibling kittens. One moment they groom each other and curl up together amicably; the next moment, when food is to be shared and divided, they fight. Ambivalence is inescapable in nature, but with our elaborately structured plans we humans have the capability of raising nature's given ambivalences to exponentially expanded levels. All therapies focus on inappropriate inhibitions and use various means of reducing the force these retain from childhood days.

To survive in a world of other humans, we require what psychoanalysts have called defenses. These are, of course, familiar to the reader. But in the context of this chapter they can seem as styles of recoding the raw data of experience, with the result that certain data are lost to the synthetic, cognitive efforts our patients make. For example, in the "isolation" defense, the data of feelings associated with an event or a thought undergo censoring; in "denial," portions of sensory inputs are elided; in "repression," some of the data of experience are denied access to consciousness. Compulsions can be compared to railroad sidetracks, in that the real objective of the wish or drive is, as it were, diverted from the main track of motivation onto a substitute motor activity (or, in the case of obsessions, cognitive activity). Thus the patient's plan is diverted into a discharge that is safer than a discharge on the main track. Obviously it is safer to beat a rug than to beat one's husband, or to wash one's hands than to feel unbearable reproaches of guilt. But such recodings of experience are damaging—even crippling—to sensitive coping. All therapies therefore implicitly attack these editing processes to some degree, if only to gauge how desperate is the need they fulfill. A successful therapy will leave the patient's plans for dealing with experience in a more effective state, either by sluicing off disturbing conflicts or drives into harmless substitute activities that control panic better, or by finding a resolution to needs previously deemed irreconcilable in the codings of past experience.

Defenses imply an organism divided against itself. This in turn involves paradox. One plan says "Feel this" while another says "You must not feel this." The best-studied paradoxes are those disclosed in a long psychoanalysis, and those interactions that are immediately obvious in family therapy. In psychoanalysis, one gradually comes to hear the irrational contradictions coded in the patient's memories, as disclosed in free association and in behavior during the analytic situation. In family therapy one can observe the absurd contradictions imbedded in a family's dialogue. A wife says to her husband, in commanding, imperious, dictatorial tones, "Be spontaneous!"—a command that defeats itself even as it is uttered, since the imbedded paradox is "Do as I say" as well as "Do what you want on your own." Such paradoxical dilemmas have been exposed and analyzed in many writings—particularly in those of Haley[10] and other members of the group known in professional circles as the "Palo Alto Group," whose major leaders were Gregory Bateson and Don D. Jackson. A most penetrating analysis of the distorted logic of the guiding plans found in human interactions can be found in *Pragmatics of Human Communication*.[28]

Paradoxes have their therapeutic uses. Behavior therapies of all types implicitly use the incompatability of safety, security, protection, and reasonableness (all of which the behavior therapist generates in one way or another) with the wild, unreasoning terror involved in many patients' symptoms. Once a patient learns to trust the therapist, he can relax the defenses used to ward off panic and, bit by bit, begin to undo the connection between some past traumatic experience and his feelings of helplessness. What seemed horrendous gradually becomes tolerable and even comfortable. This paradigm can be seen to underlie many other therapeutic strategies and tactics, especially the "working-through" process of psychoanalysis. One simply cannot feel abandoned, annihilated, or maimed in an atmosphere providing respect, understanding, and the sense of being cherished. The loving aspect of the superego, expressed as good-humored acceptance of the reality of one's self and one's surroundings, comes to supplant the ancient Talmudic eye-for-an-eye law.

However, in perusing discussions devoted to different types of therapeutic influences, there are some caveats to be observed. These caveats center on the fact that therapists from various schools usually fail to mention many of the operations in which they engage but rather leave them implicit, in their wish to emphasize the particular element of therapeutic influence that is the focus of their special technique. Why—so they might argue—why mention ordinary tact or politeness, or a sense of humor? Of *course* these can be assumed. Why mention ground rules of therapy such as the freedom to call the therapist on the telephone, or at home? What influence does a brief encounter on the street exert, or a friendly visit when intercurrent illness leads to the hospitalization of the patient? What does a brief chat matter during the intermission of a play? In this latter context, spouses may well be included, and the whole gestalt of therapy will change accordingly. And what does one do with the influence deriving from encountering one's patient in the shower room of a university gymnasium, or at a private club, or in some other intimate, if casual, setting? We ignore such side operations; but they are often of crucial importance.

The effort to subject therapies to scientific scrutiny tends to involve taking the data of therapeutic sessions and evaluating them by rating scales, numbers, and other measures that can be fed into a computer. This practice is in the long run necessary if we are ever to make a science of the art of psychotherapy— which outcome we may reasonably doubt on the evidence currently available. But if such an objective is ever to be achieved, some way of measuring the hardly tangible dimensions of devotion and commitment—in short, the dimensions of what is meant by the Greek word *caritas*—will have to be devised. This capability may elude the scientist at present, but patients have no trouble at all in telling one therapist from another. They know whether the therapist in question gives a damn or not about what happens to them, or how much work the therapist is willing to exert to make a therapeutic intervention. (An unmentionable dimension that belongs in this discussion is money. In passing, I wish only to point out that the dollar intrudes into every type of therapeutic setting, for better or worse, and that in this respect all therapists tend to practice the defense of denial when they come to write about what they do in practice.)

As the reader strives to understand the efforts humans devote to influence other humans, in myriad ways, I make a plea for compassion toward therapists. They strive for the expansion of experience and for vividness of life, and this may at times require disciplined resistance to chaotic avoidance in the destructive behaviors their patients often exhibit. Perhaps, in reading various accounts of therapeutic endeavors, the reader can listen for the melody rather than a specific note, and can confidently assume the real desire for creative advance that all therapists hold in common.

❲ Bibliography

1. ARDREY, R. *The Territorial Imperative*. New York: Atheneum, 1966.

2. BEADLE, M. *A Child's Mind*. Garden City: Doubleday, 1970.

3. BERGIN, A. E. and S. L. GARFIELD. *Handbook of Psychotherapy and Behavior Change*. New York: Wiley, 1971.

4. BLOOM, B. J. *Stability and Change in Human Characteristics*. New York: Wiley, 1964.

5. BOWER, T. G. R. "The Visual World of Infants," *Sci. Am.*, 215 (1966), 80–92.

6. ———. "The Object World of the Infant," *Sci. Am.*, 225 (1971), 38–47.

7. ELLIS, A. *Reason and Emotion in Psychotherapy*. New York: Lyle Stuart, 1962.

8. GLOVER, E. *On the Early Development of Mind*. London: Imago, 1956.

9. GRAHAM, D., R. M. LUNDY, L. S. BENJAMIN et al. "Specific Attitudes in Initial Interviews with Patients Having Different 'Psychosomatic' Diseases," *Psychosom. Med.*, 24 (1962), 257.

10. HALEY, J. *Strategies of Psychotherapy*. New York: Grune & Stratton, 1963.

11. HARLOW, H. F. "Motivation as a Factor in the Acquisition of New Responses," in M. R. Jones, ed., *Current Theory and Research in Motivation*, pp. 24–49. Lincoln: University of Nebraska Press, 1953.

12. JOOS, M. "Language and the School Child," *Harvard Educ. Rev.*, 34 (1964), 203–210.

13. KLEIN, M. *The Psychoanalysis of Children*. London: Hogarth, 1932.

14. KLEIN, M., P. HEIMANN, and R. E. MONEY-KYRLE, eds. *New Directions in Psychoanalysis*. New York: Basic Books, 1957.

15. LENNEBERG, E. H. *Biological Foundations of Language*. New York: Wiley, 1967.

16. LEWIS, W. C. "Some Observations Relevant to Early Defenses and Precursors," *Int. J. Psychoanal.*, 44 (1965), 132–142.

17. ———. *Why People Change*. New York: Holt, Rinehart & Winston, 1972.

18. LIEBERMAN, M. A., I. D. YALOM, and M. MILES. *Encounter Groups: First Facts*. New York: Basic Books, 1973.

19. LOWE, J. *Understanding Whitehead*. Baltimore: The Johns Hopkins Press, 1962.

20. LURIA, A. R. *The Role of Speech in the Regulation of Normal and Abnormal Behavior*. New York: Liveright, 1960.

21. MUSSEN, P. "Early Socialization, Learning and Identification," in *New Directions in Psychology*, vol. 3, pp. 51–105. New York: Holt, Rinehart & Winston, 1970.

22. PRIBRAM, K. *Languages of the Brain*. Englewood Cliffs, N.J.: Prentice-Hall, 1971.

23. ROSEN, J. N. *Direct Analysis.* New York: Grune & Stratton, 1953.
24. SOKOLOV, E. N. *Perception and the Conditioned Reflex.* New York: Macmillan, 1963.
25. SPIESMAN, J. C. "Autonomic Monitoring of Ego Defense Process," in N. S. Greenfield and W. C. Lewis, eds., *Psychoanalysis and Current Biological Thought,* pp. 227–244. Madison: University of Wisconsin Press, 1965.
26. STAMPFL, P. G. and D. J. LEWIS. "Essentials of Implosive Therapy: A Learning-Theory Based Psychodynamic Behavioral Therapy," *J. Abnorm. Psychol.,* 72 (1967), 496–503.
27. WATSON, J. D. *Molecular Biology of the Gene,* 2nd ed. Menlo Park, Calif.: Benjamin, 1970.
28. WATZLAWICK, P., J. H. BEAVIN, and D. D. JACKSON. *Pragmatics of Human Communication.* New York: Norton, 1967.
29. WOLPE, J. *Psychotherapy by Reciprocal Inhibition.* Stanford: Stanford University Press, 1958.

CHAPTER 4

THE PRESCRIPTION OF TREATMENT FOR CHILDREN

Lauretta Bender

⟦ Introduction: Every Child Is Unique and Imperfect

EVERY CHILD is the sum total of all the interrelationships between his physical being and his personal experiences in an environment. There is a trend at present to see all behavior in terms of social–cultural factors. Problem-behavior patterns are too easily explained away in terms of the child's experiences and his environment; and any endogenous problems—those connected with his body and its organs, or even his individual identity as a person—are ignored and even denied. The medical model is in low repute.

Social–cultural influences do exist, and they have always been recognized in form similar to the present influences in the communities we know. Poverty, downgrading of minority groups, anomie, inner-city or rural deprivation, and antagonisms between peoples have been observed through history; and violence,

taboos, religious conflicts, and identity crises occur in all societies.[59,108] These things alone do not make the child, however. They merely focus on a given child who has his own phylogenetic and ontogenetic history, his own person and body and medical record. The possibilities of deviations or simple differences from other persons—of pathologies, of defects, of unique functionings—are infinite, and they are always present in everyone. In some persons they may be accentuated or distorted or especially vulnerable to external stresses. But in any case the two areas—internal and external—cannot be separated; and this interrelationship does more to support and advance the individual than it does to inhibit, disturb, or destroy him, since it offers more opportunities for compensation and growth. The individual is unique and remains uniquely himself in all his relationships throughout his life. This is true regardless of and indeed because of the family social–cultural influence and also because of such medical and psychiatric (treatment) influences as Dubos[58] has emphasized.

It behooves a professional to whom a child has been referred, because of behavioral or emotional or neuropsychiatric problems, to determine as much as he can about the unique combination of endogenous problems in the child, as well as the exogenous ones that always exist. He may quickly find some obvious problem, but he should never feel satisfied that this will lead to an easy solution. For the one child referred to him with this problem, there are undoubtedly many others with the same condition and from a similar social–cultural environment who are not being so referred because the condition in itself does not necessarily lead to problem behavior.

Every child has deviations in every area of functioning, but has stronger drives for normal development and compensations. When a child is referred for professional attention, it must be assumed that there is something wrong in every area of functioning: at the level of congenital or developmental organic brain impairment; of minimal or gross brain damage; of maturational lags; of neurotic defense mechanisms; of situational stresses in the family; and of the school or social–cultural environment. What is also true is that every child called "normal" also has defects, deficiencies, pathologies, or disorders in all these areas. However, most children are still able to cope and function within the normal range of behavior. The severity of the disorders is a factor determining this ability, as is the child's innate capacity to develop so that he can function and compensate. The drive for normalcy tends to overcome the ever-existing interrelated disorders. In some children the disorders are not evident; other children may cope with, compensate for, or "outgrow" their difficulties with or without help. Needless to say, these processes may be facilitated by a more positive environment, situational support, or an enriching rather than a depriving culture.

Different schools of thought tend to emphasize one area of disorder and its possible compensations while ignoring others. Thus a psychodynamic school may see the following case from the point of view of a sick mother who infantalizes her child: A four-year-old child of a schizophrenic mother is still being carried by her. He walks clumsily, is spoon-fed, is not toilet trained, and does not talk. If we assume that this sick mother has infantalized a potentially normal child, we may fail to note that the child shows real signs of organic defect, such as a head circumference of 19 inches (48.26 cm.), simian folds in the hands, general small size, and poor muscle tone. Though there is a lack of speech, there is some understanding of simple and pertinent language. The child cuddles up for attention and responds to smiles: although he is retarded, even mentally defective, he is not autistic.

Thus, while in fact the mother is mentally sick and—without a husband or father for the child—dependent on public support, she may nonetheless be giving the child good care for his special needs. Further, she might well be able to continue to do so for some time, under psychiatric and social welfare supervision of both herself and her child, thus making institutionalization unnecessary. The child will probably gain speech, be classified as a high-grade defective, and be able to do simple routine work as an adult in a protected situation. But before this social and educational and psychiatric treatment is prescribed, there needs to be a mobilization of facilities that will afford knowledge and experience in the fields of pediatrics, neurology, psychiatry, electroencephalography, psychopharmacology, and social welfare; and there needs to be an availability of opportunities for both mother and child in the community and in education and recreation. The program may need to be changed at each developmental epoch in the child's life (school age, puberty, adolescence, adulthood), or when there is a change in the mother's condition, or at such time as society changes its attitude and programing for its deviate members.

Thus, while we emphasize that some degree of pathology may be expected to be present in every area and cannot be ignored, it must also be realized that positive developmental trends, compensations, and coping mechanisms always exist as well, and that they can be appreciated and utilized. For the majority of human beings these positive factors outweigh the negative. This is evolution.

Each child is unique in spite of his pathology and because of it. No treatment will change the uniqueness of the individual. It is striking that if one has known and remembered a disturbed child, one will still recognize him and know how to communicate with him in a follow-up visit when he is an adult, however sick he may have been throughout his life or however well he may have responded to treatment and life experiences.

We must conclude that there are no cures for personality disorders and psychiatric ills. We have learned this from many long-time follow-up or longitudinal studies of patients, treated or untreated, including those known from childhood. It is a universal experience that about one third of all psychiatric patients do quite well most of their life as functioning and satisfied persons; another third tend to be dependent but do fairly well part of the time; and the final third do not improve or may even regress, regardless of treatment, care, or neglect (though some of these also make a pretty good adjustment to a well-regulated institutional environment). This is true whether the treatment has been nonspecific psychological, physiological, or milieu therapy, or some specific therapy for a pathology that is only a part of the total problem.*

Almost anyone who has ever successfully tried a treatment or therapy has experienced the conviction that it is their treatment that works, and they experience an almost omnipotent feeling that they can help another human being—especially a child in his troubles. But what is due the child is overlooked; it is forgotten that children are alive, plastic, and in a process of development and growth. The strongest drive in the human child or any young living thing is the drive toward growth, learning, repair, coping, compensating, and responding to the environmental stimuli with endogenous processes of all kinds. Children are quick to accept every offer of help, every clue, every stimulus that will promote their

tendency toward normalcy. *There are no cures for personality or psychiatric disorders, but there are strong processes for self-adjustment and coping.* This is part of the evolutionary process that can not be denied.

(The Goal for Treatment in Children

The goal for treatment in children should be to enable them to respond within the normal developmental pattern as quickly as possible, and to live as rich and full and normal lives in the here and now as they can. Childhood should not be seen as a preparation for adulthood. Childhood should never be sacrificed for the future. Immediate time and what can be done with it is the most precious possession of a child. Any experience that is missed in childhood is lost forever. If there is a quick method of treatment, it should always have preference over methods that require a longer time. Since drugs facilitate speed in treatment, they should be used as aids in tutoring, psychotherapy, or an institutional experience away from home. Two months of residential treatment in an institution is often preferable to one hour of psychotherapy a week while staying at home. An intensive residential tutoring program or a special class in a community school is preferable to only an hour a day from a "home teacher." Hospital care should not be prolonged; rapid discharge should be planned, even if it requires readmission for other short stays.[44,38] Every opportunity should be used to take advantage of the child's natural tendency toward growth, changed behavior, or even remissions at certain developmental epochs such as latency, puberty, and adolescence. It may be assumed that each of these epochs represents a new period—not of stress but of growth, adaptation, positive responses, and a renewed organization of vital forces.

The Numerous but Nonspecific Prescriptions for Treatment

How are we to arrive at a prescription for treatment? How can we make rules or pat-

* See references 92, 96, 97, 27, 31, and 32.

terns for such prescriptions? Not only is each child and each form of behavior disorder or psychiatric disturbance unique, but also each diagnostician, therapist, or consultant. Therefore the methods for prescriptions for treatment are almost as numerous as the individuals using them.

Winnicott,[135] before he died, gave us a splendid description of his special form of therapeutic consultation. His background was psychoanalysis, and his special technique was the "squiggle game" in which he and the child contributed to an ongoing drawing as they related to each other and talked. Winnicott observed the child and made elaborate notes. A pediatrician before he was a psychoanalyst, he claimed that he remained a pediatrician always. He also emphasized that he was always conscious of the social pressures of the times in which he and the child lived. Winnicott was a creative and empathic man who could evaluate the whole child physically and psychically, in a social situation and a living relationship, and keep careful records. His contribution is important not because of the special technique he used but because his work emphasizes the value of a lifetime of experience.

The inexperienced must gain experience from observation, reading, and supervised work. To begin with, no examiner, consultant, therapist, or diagnostician—especially at the learning stage—should ever interview a child or mother while keeping an outline or list of medical terms, in effect, between himself and the child. To begin with, there is no outline or list that can do justice to this process. More importantly, the adult who likes such things will always relate to and observe and be creative about the outline, but will be incapable of relating himself to the child or of drawing the child into a relationship with him. He will be utterly unable to observe the child while the outline is there. A trainee needs, firstly, to have the confidence that he can relate to a child, give the child something of himself, and get something from the child in return. Secondly, he needs to have as much knowledge about children and their problems as will make it possible for him to arrive at some conclusions about the child in question as a deviate from other children. Such knowledge can be gained only from life itself, from his professional education, from observing other experienced interviewers, from wide reading, and from repeated experiences in observing children under all conditions.

Some trainees, of course, may be in or have had a personal analysis; if so, the experienced analyst should have widened the vision, experiences, and knowledge of the student. Many beginners are under the supervision of an experienced child psychiatrist, psychologist, or other professional who, of course, enriches the beginner's experiences. Such a supervisor should interview children in the presence of the student, be present when the student conducts his own interviews, and discuss cases with him.

Groups of observers may be present when a child is interviewed, diagnostically and therapeutically, by an experienced professional. In my experience this is always accepted well by the child; it even enhances the relationship, the social experience, and therapeutic effects. But it sometimes traumatizes inexperienced students, unless they are warned in advance that it is good for the child and the total professional and educational experience.

Examination Procedures

One can, of course, go to the extreme of utilizing every possible test for deviations from the normal functioning of the child's central nervous system and brain. One can use clinical, electrical, X-ray, chemical, and chromosomal methods; psychological, intelligence-quotient, personality, educational achievement, and perception tests; psychiatric interviews, play observation (individually and in peer and family groups), and observation of the child in his normal environment or separated in a residential institution; and histories from the child's birth record and other hospital, home development, school, and community-activity records. But however valuable it might seem to collect everything possible, it should never be forgotten that such procedures may be very expensive for some, may interrupt the lives of people more than is justified, and may become too voluminous ever to be usable.

It is nevertheless true that any child who is disturbed enough to be referred for professional consideration is entitled to a comprehensive history, interview, and observation and to appropriate test procedures. Every child psychiatrist should be trained to take his own histories, do his own mental-status and neurological examinations, do some simple psychological testing (usually of the paper–pencil type, such as drawing a person, or some simple school work), and observe some behavior. Every disturbed child should be seen in some relationship by more than one professional.

The psychiatric interview should explore the child's problem that led to his referral, and also his interpersonal relationships with family members and peers, school teachers and schoolmates, and community friends. It should explore his concepts of his body image, self image, and sex identity. It should explore his fantasy life through dreams, story-telling, television and movie stories, and spontaneous drawing. Causes for anxiety, especially, should be explored, as well as trends toward negativism. The child should be observed in action or motion in a play room or waiting room or as he enters the office. His body should be manipulated, at least during a neurological or physical examination, as far as the social relationship and the child permit. Experience alone makes it possible to know what to emphasize and what to neglect. An interview may be completed in twenty minutes, or it may go on for an hour and a half and still not be completed. Every such interview should be a therapeutic or learning experience for the child. It is usually desirable for the mother or referring adult to be partly involved in the interview.

A child psychiatrist should be able to evaluate such common psychological tests as Wechsler's Intelligence Scale for Children (WISC),[132] the Stanford–Binet or similar tests, the Vineland Social Maturity Scale,[56] and some of the paper–pencil tests:[87] the drawing of persons;[81] drawings of the family;

the House-Tree-Person (HTP)[49] test; and the Visual Motor Gestalt Test.[7] There should be an interpretive understanding of personality projection tests such as the Rorschach test and the Thematic Apperception Test (TAT) and, possibly, the Children's Apperception Test (CAT) and Sentence-Completion tests. None of these tests should be left to the interpretation of another person—i.e., a psychologist— unless one knows the interpreter in question. A test of this type is no better than its interpretation. Unfortunately the same has to be said of a neurological examination and electroencephalograms (EEG), especially in children, unless there are very specific pathological signs that can be demonstrated—such as the intelligence level, on psychometrics; reflex or focal gross neurological signs, on the neurological examination; and focal or seizure signs, in the EEG.

Values of Repeated Interviews and Examinations

Every interview with a child should be a therapeutic and learning experience. This is a good reason why no child who has been referred for professional evaluation should be deprived of it, especially if he has been removed from his usual routine and taken to a clinic or teaching center. He should never be left in doubt as to the reason for the trip and interview and tests.

There are reasons for the psychiatric interview, examination, and evaluation beyond the immediate diagnosis and prescription for treatment. It may be assumed in our modern medical practices that the child will return again to the same clinic or to some other similar setting, or that some member of his family will. The record becomes more valuable with each additional visit. One may even say that one sequence of examination, interview, psychological testing, EEG, and neurological examination is only of relative value, whereas two or more such sequences give us a developmental scheme or progressive pathological or improvement trend—an on-going pattern— to which time has added another element. The additional visits also, of course, give us some view of the child's normal capacities to cope and need of and response to treatment, thus adding a great deal to the prescription for treatment. This is true whether the treatment is specifically medical, pharmaceutical, or psychotherapeutic, and whether it involves manipulation of the home, school, or social situation. Needless to say, the careful (but not necessarily too wordy) preparation of records and their preservation and availability are important for the future management of the patient as well as for evaluating past diagnoses and treatment, for teaching professionals, and for research.

(Diagnostic Classifications

The prescription for psychiatric treatment might appear to be best made through a classification or diagnostic evaluation based on etiological or causative factors. Such is the statement from the Committee on Child Psychiatry of the Group for Advancement of Psychiatry (GAP). In their 1957 report, "The Diagnostic Process in Child Psychiatry,"[83] it is said: "Comprehensive treatment evolves directly from the diagnostic formulation which gives purpose and direction to therapeutic goals, prognostic speculation, and appropriate plans to ameliorate or correct the child's emotional disability."

However, with our present state of knowledge, we find that diagnostic evaluation does not actually contribute to the goal of prescribing a treatment that will cure the psychiatric, emotional, mental, or behavioral problems of childhood. This is because the child is continually developing (or failing to develop) within an interplay of given constitutional, experiental, and environmental factors and within an embedded (and also developing) capacity to integrate and evolve compensatory and coping mechanisms that change at each developmental stage.[12] There are no cures, but at the same time there are multiple capacities in the child to experience reality responses and compensations, as well as to utilize therapeutic endeavors in ameliorating unhealthy, painful, and disruptive symptoms

and behavior. The child benefits most from therapeutic programs that aim at current, immediate results, at healthy and happy life experiences in the here and now. For future needs we must trust to the life course to correct itself with the same or similar corrective mechanisms—or to fail to do so.

The Classification of the American Psychiatric Association

There have been great difficulties in the diagnostic classification of childhood psychiatric disorders. The *Diagnostic and Statistical Manual of Mental Disorders*, (DSM-II) 2nd ed.,[2] prepared by the American Psychiatric Association, includes children's diagnoses under each adult classification.[95] This cannot be satisfactorily used for the treatment of children. It does not allow for the developmental deviations and compensations that occur in children. The classification was formulated for the purposes of improving communication between psychiatrists and other medical clinicians, between disciplines, and between geographical states and nations; providing a medium for statistics; making results of research more readily understood; and classifying issues in psychiatry. It does not imply judgments aboout the cause and nature of disorders and their treatment.[85]

The GAP Classification

A most comprehensive and useful classification of children's psychopathological disorders has been prepared by the Committee on Child Psychiatry of GAP.[83,84] An additional valuable contribution of the report is a review of all previous classifications, (twenty-four in number) in the appendix. The committee's proposed classification is based on three propositions: (1) the psychosomatic concept involving unity of mind and body and the interrelatedness of mind and body; (2) the developmental dimension, so essential to the study of the child; and (3) the psychological aspects of the child's existence in the family and society.

Their classification runs as follows: (1)

healthy responses; (2) reactive disorders; (3) developmental deviations; (4) psychoneurotic disorders; (5) personality disorders; (6) psychotic disorders; (7) psychophysioloical disorders; (8) brain syndromes; (9) mental retardation; and (10) other disorders. It will be seen that this classification is based on a "hierarchy ranging from healthy responses, through milder to more severe psychological disorders, to syndromes in which somatic syndromes predominate." The committee also offers a list of subcategories and of symptoms that can be used in a diagnostic formulation.

The emphasis on healthy responses to stress is noteworthy, as is that on the child's capacity to spontaneously correct some of the reactive disorders, developmental deviations, and psychoneurotic disorders, especially in a new phase of development. The committee found that an effort to seek a clinical-dynamic-genetic-etiological scheme and indication for therapy was unrealistic at this time.

A Modification of the DSM-II Classification by Fish and Shapiro

Barbara Fish and Theodore Shapiro[68,69] worked out a "Typology of Children's Psychiatric Disorders," based on current functioning of the child and to be used in controlled, and especially psychopharmacological, studies of treatment. They had found the DSM-II nomenclature inadequate for treatment research in children because it gives no specific subdivisions of childhood problems. Therefore they emphasized the importance of diagnostic categories[66] evaluated by severity of disturbance, and they objected to the trend toward giving a specific drug (or other treatment) to one target symptom—for example, a stimulant for hyperkinesis—rather than treating the child for the severity of the disturbance. Their analysis of their own work and that of others reported in the literature (such as Bradley[47,48] and Bender and Cottington)[36] justifies these claims.

They classify disorders into three types, based on grade of severity, prognosis, and ability to respond to treatment. These are re-ally subgroups of classical diagnostic categories, which could be used in controlled studies in an institutional setting—such as Bellevue, where they were working.

Type 1. Autistic-Disjunctive. Severely impaired schizophrenic children with autistic and symbiotic features.

Type 2. Immature-Labile. Better-integrated children, but inadequate and labile, with borderline impairment of integrative functions; fragmentary, autistic, and neurotic paranoid features. May develop into one of the following features, but current functioning was the criteria.

Type 3. Anxious-Neurotic. Labile, with relatively intact personality organization and predominantly neurotic and anxiety adaptation, ranging from mild neurotic reactions to pseudoneurotic schizophrenia.

Type 4. Sociopathic-Paranoid. Well-patterned, organized, manipulative, antisocial, and negativistic, denying anxiety and dependency needs.

Fish and Shapiro also show that they include the categories of many other workers. They mention Bender's[18] pseudodefective, pseudoneurotic, and pseudopsychopathic schizophrenics; Mahler's[106,107] symbiotic psychosis; Kanner's[100] early infantile autism; the British group's[53] childhood psychosis; and Goldfarb's[80] "organic" and "nonorganic" schizophrenia.

Wender's Minimal Brain Dysfunction (MBD): A Denial of Classification

According to Paul Wender,[133] MBD is extremely common and includes conditions that have both psychological and neurological bases, such as: (1) motor disorders; (2) attention, perception, and cognition dysfunctions; (3) learning difficulties; (4) disorders of impulse control; (5) difficulties in interpersonal relationships; and (6) a variety of emotional types. Neuroses, delinquencies, and schizophrenia may be included, or MBD may be at least a forerunner or early manifestation of schizophrenia. It may be safely assumed that any preadolescent child in a child guidance clinic may be put in the category of MBD until proved otherwise. The exceptions Wender would allow are those childhood conditions that are too bizarre in behavior and fantasy, or too retarded mentally, or too brain damaged, or who have recently been disturbed by a noxious environment.[133]

In the diagnostic evaluation, Wender finds most useful the mother's and teacher's complaints and the therapeutic tests with drugs. He does not find of much use the psychiatric interview of the child, the psychological or educational tests (except to help in school placement), the neurological examination, or the EEG. He also says that even if the child shows organic brain disease, the MBD may be independent of it. He feels that there is no need for a diagnosis in an outpatient service. His main emphasis is on a management program with drugs on a trial basis, counseling of parents, or casual forms of psychotherapy and educational programing. He anticipates a good prognosis, with disappearance of symptoms in puberty. [p. 96][133]

Wender's chapter on management with description of available drugs and their use and effectiveness, is very useful. His first drug choices are the stimulants, amphetamines, and methylphenidate, but he also discusses the antidepressants, phenothiazines, diphenhydramine (Benadryl), and anticonvulsants. [p. 105ff][133] His results would indicate that he has seen only the milder cases in out patient services, such as those in Types 3 and 4 described by Fish.

Undoubtedly Wender's management program will work in many cases—at least until puberty, when a change (usually improvement) may be anticipated even in many untreated cases. It will save time for the child, the family, and the clinic, and thus it will also save money. But it leaves the more difficult children uncared for, and a certain number of children will not be adequately evaluated or treated; whereas a careful diagnosis and selective treatment might anticipate and prevent more serious problems such as a psychotic decompensation, adolescent epilepsy, some progressive neurological disease, or a situational crisis.

Anna Freud's Diagnostic Profile

Anna Freud[73,74] has formulated a diagnostic profile aimed at prediction, which she claims is "not only . . . a tool for completion and verification of diagnosis but also an instrument to measure treatment results, [and to make a] prediction [of] chances for spontaneous recovery and response to treatment." It has been productive of considerable response in the literature (see Thomas[128] and Laufer),[104] but there has not yet been time enough to assess its value on long term follow-ups. The diagnostic profile is based on developmental and genetic assessments.

Her classification of symptoms includes the following headings: (1) the initial nondifferentiation between somatic and psychological processes; (2) compromise formation between id and ego; (3) corruption of id deviations into ego; (4) change in libido economy or direction of cathexis; (5) change in quality or direction of aggression; (6) undefended regression; and (7) organic changes.

Rutter's Triaxial Classification

Michael Rutter[119] argues against a classification based on etiology, because of the inadequacy of our knowledge of etiologies, because many children are inadequately evaluated, because of the lack of differentiation between clinical syndromes that have different clinical pictures and apparent causes, and particularly because of the usual implication of "one cause for one condition" in such a classification. Working with the World Health Organization (WHO) in a series of international seminars on psychiatric diagnosis and classification,[120] he has become convinced that a multiaxial approach to classification is the logical development to a multicategory scheme.

Four axes are suggested. The first specifies the clinical psychiatric syndrome; the second, the intellectual level; the third, any associated or etiological-biological factor; and the fourth, any associated or etiological-psychosocial influences. However, Rutter actually uses a tri-axial classification to discuss the first axis in the psychiatric syndrome: the intellectual level; biological factors; and psychosocial influences. He divides the psychoses of childhood into autism, schizophrenia, and the disintegrative psychoses (usually organic), arguing that they are three different and unrelated conditions. Concerning treatment, he says, "It should not be thought that there is one treatment for one syndrome. We are dealing with individuals suffering from disorders, not with disembodied disease states." [p. 332][119]

Bender's Classification

My own classification of the psychiatric disorders of childhood is based on an organic substratum, developmental trends, and environmental influences, all of which effect every child. Thus I suggest: (1) organic brain defects or damages; (2) minimal brain damage; (3) maturational lags (including schizophrenia and learning disabilities); (4) neurotic disorders; and (5) emotional-cultural deprivation and situational stress.

Every child (and adult) has defects or disorders or pathology of some degree in all these areas. The rule of parsimony, which holds that a single diagnosis should be used to account for a medical complaint or ailment—or, as it has been stated by Menninger,[109] "Each patient has one and only one disorder"—is certainly not true of the neuropsychiatric problems of childhood, and it is not a law that can be used in the prescription of treatment for children. The ideal of a perfect human being developing and living normally in a perfect environment is an unreality. Every child has inherited physical and personality and intellectual characteristics that are unique and to some degree anomalous. There is probably always some organic deviation, slight or gross. The child always reacts with some defenses and neurotic patterns, unless grossly defective or grossly deprived. There are always situational problems. Not all children have the specific maturational lags of schizophrenia or language disabilities, but they may have some

nonspecific maturational lag. If we consider a child diagnosed as schizophrenic, we must expect to find: (1) the specific characteristics of the schizophrenic processes; (2) the stress (usually organic and with minimal brain damage in children) that decompensated the otherwise latent schizophrenia into whatever clinical picture is presented; (3) anxiety; (4) the defenses—autistic, neurotic, psychopathic, or psychotic; (5) the child's unique constitutional organic being and personality; and (6) his situational or social and family problems.

Every disturbed child must be examined in every area for evidences of pathology and problems and how the child is reacting to them. We must never be content, for example, to know only that there is evidence of a birth injury, epilepsy or mental deficiency, a situational stress, or a rejecting mother; or that the child belongs to a minority group, is socially outcast, living in poverty, or without a father. Even if we know that a single condition is gross and overwhelming the child, we must remember that some problems exist in all other areas as well. Other children with similar overwhelming problems in some areas may be coping. The child in question may or may not be able to develop within the normal range if help is given in one area or, alternatively, in several areas. It cannot be assumed that specific treatment applied to one obvious condition will solve the child's problems, but on the other hand it may indeed be sufficient to enable the child's normal adjustment capacities to function and pull the child out of his morass of difficulties.[12,20]

(Prescribed Treatment for Classified Diagnostic Disorders

Organic Brain Disorders

Many kinds of organic brain defects or damages occur, including perceptual defects of sight or hearing (peripheral or central) and motor disorders, such as cerebral palsies, hemiplegias, choreas, extrapyramidal disorders, and cerebellar agenesis. These may be combined with each other, and they may be severe or very slight. It is the very slight conditions, left unrecognized, that are most important in the child with a behavior or mental problem. Mental retardation of every grade, psychoses, epilepsies, and various behavior disorders may be associated with conditions that are either congenital or developed in utero, perinatally, or in the early postnatal period.*

The natural history of individuals who survive early brain damage varies enormously.[77] However, only a very few of even the most severely structurally damaged children do not show some capacity toward normal development or compensations and coping mechanisms. The mentally defective child does develop physically, mentally, and emotionally (even if more slowly than expected), and he often makes a better adult adjustment than would be anticipated.[20] Unless he is severely mentally defective, the child with prenatal or perinatal damage (before the age of two) to the brain areas associated with language development does develop language and does not show the type of aphasias seen in adults with later-acquired pathology.[113] Children with cerebellar agenesis tend to outgrow most of both the neurological and the reactive psychiatric signs that are present in early development, but they retain special personality characteristics.[8]

Many efforts have been made to find specific treatments for various organic problems associated with mental, emotional, and behavioral disorders. Some given specific treatment has often been possible, but even when it has been successful and the specific condition cured, the child often remains disturbed in his development and behavior. Most congenital disorders—whether inherited or of unknown origin, whether acquired in utero from the mother (such as maternal rubella, at a critical embryonic stage of development) or postnatally from the environment (such as encephalitis)—have already injured the child and interfered with the usual pattern of development.

Premature birth creates its own problems, usually for the lifetime of the individual.[50,54] These problems may not be overwhelming, but they may be added to whatever condition precipitated the premature birth. (Often the condition is pathology in the mother in early pregnancy.)[35] And birth itself is associated with its own threats of pathology, such as the hemolytic diseases (erythroblastosis foetalis), hemolysis with kernicterus, congenital syphilis, or (more common in the 1970s) heroin addiction of the newborn. Each condition needs its own treatment at the time of birth; thereafter the child may or may not need treatment of a nonspecific type and, indefinitely, training.

The infectious processes that later attack the brain lead to the same requirements for care. The medical profession has contributed to preventive programs with antibiotics, serums, and vaccines. But it is still true that even when there are specific treatments that may cure the original disease, most of the organic causes for cerebral damage leave scars and tend to change the lifetime pattern of the child's development, behavior, mentality, and emotional responses in interpersonal relationships. We must emphasize again that one illness alone is never the only factor in the individual's total life experiences.

The following can serve as an example. In the 1930's a number of cases with Sydenham's chorea, with psychosis or behavior disorder, were observed in the children's psychiatric service at Bellevue. Some were referred from the pediatric service of that institution, where they had been under treatment for rheumatic fever in one or another of its multiple forms and had been found unmanageable. Others were referred from community resources as behavior disorders, the rheumatic fever and even the typical choreiform motility having gone unrecognized. Neurological evaluations identified the typical features of the chorea in these children. Otherwise their behavior, intellectual levels, and emotional responses varied in every way. Fever therapy was the treatment of choice at that time for all forms of the rheumatic fever complex, including the chorea. Thirteen of twenty such children, eight to fourteen years of age, received fever therapy

---

* See references 6, 9, 14, 17, and 122.

on the psychiatric children's ward. This was part of the larger treatment program, which included sedation (barbitals and bromides, in the 1930s), education, socialization, psychotherapy, and a wide range of activity therapies (puppetry, art, music, dance, and so forth).[15] They all showed an immediate improvement in all aspects of their rheumatic fever, the chorea, and their behavior; afterwards the children were sent to convalescent homes for months of care. However, a follow-up after nine years, on the average, when they were twenty-two to thirty-one years old, showed that most of both the treated and untreated cases had made a poor adjustment. Only three of the twenty had made a satisfactory one. Poor adjustments occurred in particular where there were maladjustments before the recognized rheumatic fever. These early maladjustments included: gross emotional and cultural deprivation through institutionalization in infancy; encephalitis in infancy; mental retardation; and learning difficulties in school (dyslexia). Three cases proved later to be schizophrenic, as well. There was also evidence of chronic brain damage in some cases investigated, apparently as a result of the rheumatic fever process in the brain.[101]

The convulsive or seizure disorders of children or of epileptics suggest themseves at once as good examples of disorders that respond to specific pharmacological agents.[55] It is of some interest to recall that phenobarbital, the first anticonvulsant, was only incidentally found to control convulsions when it was given as a sedative to institutionalized epileptics to control their poor sleeping and their restlessness, especially in their sexual behavior. After that the deliberate effort to find drugs that would effectively control convulsions led to the discovery of other barbiturates, such as Amytal Sodium and Mysoline; the hydantoins, such as Dilantin; the succinimides, such as Zarontin (especially for petit mal); and the oxazolidines, such as Tidione. Often drugs are given in combination to reduce the toxicity of each, such as a barbiturate with Dilantin, and sometimes adjuvants are added, such as Diamox or Dexedrine. Other drugs are added to relieve symptoms other than the

convulsive disorder itself, such as anxiety or hyperkinesis; these may include the tranquilizers and antidepressants.

These practices only emphasize the fact that children with convulsive disorders have problems separate from the convulsions, and that even if the convulsions are controlled, these other problems will most likely still need attention. We may always assume that such children show signs of minimal brain damage at least (if not gross damage) and of neurotic responses and situational stress, and that they often have maturational lags such as learning problems. On the other hand, many children will be able to cope with their incidental problems if the major problem of the convulsions is controlled. There are other children who have all the features of a convulsive disorder, including EEG changes, without having had a convulsion (at least up to that time), and whose behavioral symptoms will improve if treated like a convulsive disorder with anticonvulsive drugs, especially Dilantin. (See Kennard,[102] denied by Pasamanick.)[112] Sometimes such behavior and EEG signs may anticipate convulsions occurring later at puberty. Hopefully, treatment may not only control the disorganized and unruly behavior, but also prevent the occurrence of the convulsions; but this is difficult to document.

Minimal Brain Damage*

Minimal brain damage is due to intrauterine or perinatal or early postnatal damage to the immature brain, with no necessarily demonstrable structural damage to the cortex. Fine changes in and damages to the periventricular vascular bed, involving the cerebral germinal matrix, have been demonstrated by Banker[4] and Towbin.[130] I have described the syndrome in children,[13,14] and Greenacre[82] has described the lifelong effects and the response to psychoanalytic therapy in adults.

The symptomatology of the minimally brain-damaged child, as I see it, is fairly specific. The damage creates problems in the maturation and organization of perceptual, impulse,

* I use the term "minimal brain damage" to distinguish my concepts from Wender,[133] and I never use the abbreviation MBD except in quoting Wender.

and motor patterns. Consequently, though borderline hard neurological signs may occur, more often soft neurological signs are present. The soft neurological signs described by Schilder[122] refer to the immaturity of patterned reflex behavior. These soft signs include the retention of the Moro reflex or the tonic neck or postural reflexes beyond their usual time of disappearance, the slow maturation of cortical dominance, and the inadequate maturation of vestibular tonic responses and ocular–motor control (especially of convergence). Consequently there may be motor awkwardness without motor neurone signs. Disorganized and impulsive behavior is common. Lack of or retardation in patterning of perceptual experiences is as important as the motor and impulsive disorders and contributes maximally to the hyperkinesis.[13] It reveals itself in immature visual motor gestalt patterns and immature human figure drawings and, significantly, in an immature body image (and consequently a poor self-image or identity).[7,9]

Anxiety is a common feature, together with an increased infantile demand for security in the mother–child relationship or such behavior as clinging and demanding of attention. Often hard to gratify, this demand leads to irrational feelings of rejection and (along with the identity difficulties) to paranoid attitudes. The hyperkinesis seems in part to serve the function of seeking more perceptual experiences and a better organization of them.[14] Since this is an immaturity in organization and not a neurone defect, it tends to correct itself with development. It responds to increased mothering or interpersonal relationships and to all kinds of motor and perceptual experiences, and it suffers from a lack of them. It may pretty well disappear by puberty, with or without treatment. But as Greenacre has shown, some adults may still be seriously handicapped by it.

Some degree of minimal brain damage must be very common, if not universal. What individual can survive the vicissitudes of intrauterine life, birth, and early infancy without some likelihood of damage of some degree? That most individuals do not show clinical signs is due to the mildness of the disorder,

the strong drive for maturation, and the compensatory mechanisms, usually of an obsessive-compulsive nature. (Of course, every major organic brain disorder will also be associated with all the signs of minimal brain damage, although the latter symptoms may not be as prominent as those due to the major damage.)

The treatment for minimal brain damage should aim at stimulating maturation, organizing patterned perceptual, motor, and impulse experiences, and relieving anxiety and distrust. The hyperkinesis will respond accordingly. Treatment should include intensive mothering of the infant, with substitutes to relieve the unbearable demands on the mother; this may take the form of psychotherapy or some other kind of structured activity within an interpersonal relationship. Stimulating (rarely sedative) drugs are a great help. Wender's management of MBD is certainly appropriate for such cases. The main emphasis, however, should be on life experiences, interpersonal relationships, and the exploitation of every opportunity for patterned behavior (which is certainly facilitated by drugs).

Maturational Lags

What I have called maturational lags in children include schizophrenia and the specific learning disabilities such as dyslexia.[19,21,111,129] Both conditions are believed by many to be hereditary (see Kallmann,[98] Rosenthal and Kety,[118] and Heston[90] in schizophrenia, and Orton,[111] Hallgren,[86] and Bender[21] for dyslexia).

I see childhood schizophrenia[27,31] as a psychobiological entity determined by an inherited predisposition. This has recently been confirmed by many others (see Rosenthal and Kety,[118] and Bender.[31,34]) This entity is decompensated into a childhood clinical disorder by a physiological or organic stress (usually perinatal), with both a failure in adequate defense mechanisms against the core anxiety, and disorganization. These results in turn add to the symptomatology. Schizophrenia persists for the lifetime of the individual. It is manifested by different clinical, behavioral, or psychiatric features at different epochs in the individual's life, and in relationship to compensating defenses and environmental stress or support. There are autistic[99] and symbiotic[107] features in infancy and early childhood, psychoses in mid- and late childhood, remissions in latency or puberty, pseudoneurotic and pseudopsychopathic features in adolescence, and a wide range of regressive, psychotic, and remitted states in adulthood.

The specific features of childhood schizophrenia are maturational lags and embryonic plasticity. There is a lack of differentiation of pattern formation and of boundaries in every area of functioning, such as the autonomic nervous system, motor behavior (with soft neurological signs), perception, cognition, affect, and social behavior. Anxiety is at the core of the problems and calls forth a variety of autistic, neurotic, psychopathic, and psychotic defenses. Because of these characteristics of early schizophrenia—the plasticity, the maturational lags, and defensive and coping responses—spontaneous remissions are very common, especially in puberty in boys and latency in girls. They often lead to a change in diagnosis or an overvaluation of therapeutic efforts, if the follow-up time is too short.[18] Later in adolescence or adulthood the schizophrenic illness may again become too evident, even if in some other form.

BIOLOGICAL TREATMENTS

Specific treatments in both the biological and psychological areas have been sought in childhood as well as in adult schizophrenia. These have included Metrazol, electric and insulin convulsive therapies, hormones, orthomolecular therapy and many of the psychopharmacological therapies.[97] My own experience with the biological treatments for childhood schizophrenia has probably been the most extensive.[65] Metrazol convulsive treatment was used in Bellevue from 1938 to 1942.[24,51] Electric convulsive treatment was given to more than 500 children at Bellevue from 1942 to 1956,[10,16,32] and at Creedmoor State Hospital children's service from 1956 to 1969.[37,64] In the 1940s insulin therapy was sometimes combined with electric therapy. Annel[3] of Sweden had more experience with

insulin therapy. Subcoma insulin has also been used.[64]

The first five-year follow-up report on 100 schizophrenic children treated with electric convulsive therapy[10] led to the conclusion that the essential schizophrenic process did not seem to have been modified. With twenty-five years more experience, these same conclusions hold.[32] Convulsive therapy in childhood does not cure schizophrenia. Neither has it changed the life course of schizophrenia when children who have received Metrazol convulsive therapy from five to fourteen years of age, or electric convulsive therapy from two to twelve years of age, are followed into their fourth and fifth decade.[32] Kalinowsky and Hippius imply that the same results are found in adults when they say, "The difference between the outcome of shock treated and untreated schizophrenics may not be too striking, but the number of years spent outside the hospital is certainly higher in shock treated patients." [p. 241][97] This apparently refers to the remissions that in many cases follow early shock treatment.

Children also seemed to benefit from both Metrazol and electric convulsive treatment, immediately and for some time thereafter. In the case of the Metrazol treatment, it was concluded[24] that treated children who had shown an early autistic development became more manageable and could be habit-trained, and many went home in a partial remission. But they had to return to an institution and the chronic course was not changed. Boys who were psychotic in mid-childhood and had Metrazol near puberty responded with a remission, and could be discharged; most of them maintained a favorable but dependent life in the community. Boys who had an onset of schizophrenia in puberty responded, in some cases, with a remission; this made possible a community and educational program for several years and, for a few of the boys, indefinitely. Most of them returned to hospitals for a chronic course, but some again responded in the 1950s to the tranquilizing drugs and were able to make a dependent adjustment in the community.[31]

Our early conclusions[10] in 1947 concerning

electric shock treatments were that although the schizophrenic process was not modified, the children benefited by an improvement in their ability to deal with symptoms—especially anxiety—secondary to the schizophrenia. We found that the development of the intelligence and the IQ remained stable, and that the EEG tended to maturate normally; in some cases it even seemed to accelerate, if maturation had been slow before the treatment.[102] Our last follow-up studies[32] in 1971 showed that although none of the convulsive therapies—Metrazol, electric shock or insulin coma—significantly modified the life course of individuals treated in childhood, children treated with Metrazol convulsions did have significantly more puberty remissions (87.3 percent) than children with electric convulsive therapy (63.6 percent) or children with no convulsive therapy (50 percent).

PHARMACOLOGICAL THERAPIES

Pharmacological agents have been looked to hopefully, as a specific treatment for schizophrenia that would produce a cure. Eisenberg,[61] in a discussion on childhood problems, said that the goal of drug research was to find an agent that would cure mental illness. However, Kalinowsky and Hippius[97] have stated that "the early claims of some workers for the new drugs have not been fulfilled and it is realized that they improve symptoms only, rarely producing a deep-seated effect on the fundamental aspects of the illness. The main value of neuroleptic drugs to patients, other than the stimulus for more research, appears to be twofold; the tranquilizing of acutely disturbed patients otherwise uncontrollable, and symptomatic improvement in chronic patients enabling them to have and use more freedom and participate in more activities." This applies to adults. Actually, more has been accomplished with the psychopharmacology of childhood; nevertheless no drug has been found that will cure childhood schizophrenia.

Pharmacological therapy was an important part of our regime at Bellevue beginning in 1935, when we first recognized schizophrenia in children.* Using a wide range of available

* See references 70, 18, 23, 37, and 40.

drugs, we aimed at reducing anxiety, stimulating maturation, and organizing unpatterned homeostasis, behavior, and interpersonal relationships. We started with the amphetamines,[30,36] which Bradley[47,48] had first recommended for brain-damaged children. We eventually found amphetamine the most useful for schizophrenic children who exhibited frank anxiety and inhibitions in interpersonal relationships, along with maturational lags such as learning disabilities; it also seemed to be specific for reducing excessive sexual drives and preoccupations. We used the anticonvulsant drugs, especially Dilantin, in those schizophrenic children with impulsive behavior and EEG dysrhythmias. (This was not confirmed by Pasamanick.)[112] We found that Dilantin and Benzedrine could be effectively combined in some children. In the 1940s, when we became aware of the immature homeostatic patterning often described as allergic in young schizophrenic children, we started the use of antihistamines. Benadryl proved most effective in stimulating better-patterned maturation of the autonomic, or homeostatic, function. We went on to use Mephenesin derivatives (Meprobamate), the rauwolfia alkaloids (Serpasil), and the phenothiazines (Thorazine, Compazine, Stelazine, and Mellaril). Except for the emergency control of an acutely disturbed child, as on admission to a hospital, these drugs were not used to sedate or tranquilize children. We found that they would organize disorganized behavior, relieve anxiety, and facilitate interpersonal relationships. Reductions in overactivity and aggression appeared to be secondary benefits, as were an improvement in learning ability, better concentration, and better peer relationships.

However, there is no specific effect of any of these drugs on schizophrenic children. Other disturbed children who were not schizophrenic also responded. In other words, pharmacotherapy is prescribed not for the disease but for the child, and for his reaction to whatever pathological processes or experiences he may have.

A special research program for D-lysergic acid diethylamide (LSD-25) and its methylated derivative, Methylsergide (UML-491), was carried out at Creedmoor in 1961–1966, with the hope that these agents might be a specific treatment for schizophrenia in children. The hope was based on: (1) evidence that they had a serotonin-inhibiting and stabilizing effect on the autonomic and central nervous system; and (2) their effect in arousal and then increasing responsiveness to sensory stimuli, with a preponderance of sympathetic activity and increase in skeletal muscle tone and tone of the vascular bed of the brain.[25] We found that young schizophrenic children responded to the agents with considerable improvement in general well-being, in autonomic nervous system patterning (which tended to normalize),[63] and in habit training and behavior. This was true even in cases with severe behavior disorders, such as self-mutilation and head-banging, that had not responded to other therapeutic measures. In addition, a group of prepuberal schizophrenic boys improved in over-all behavior and attitude and reality contact; decreasingly bizarre fantasies were replaced, with considerable insight, with some paranoid and depressive trends. Mental testing showed improved maturity and better organization in the boys, and this was reflected in better school work. Improvement was maintained for one and a half years. Boys that had a suitable home were able to leave the hospital and be maintained at home. Subsequent follow-up has not been done.

In 1968, following a report of chromosome damage in LSD-25 users,[93] chromosomes were examined in children who were still available in the hospital and who had received 100 to 150 micrograms of LSD-25 daily for five and one half to thirty-five months. No chromosome damage was found.[41] The use of LSD-25 and related agents still offers some hope for the treatment of schizophrenic children, even if only at the symptomatic level.

PSYCHOTHERAPIES

Psychotherapy has been extensively used as a specific treatment for schizophrenic children.

Even more commonly, however, psychotherapy is used with disturbed children nonspecifically, without a recognized diagnosis.[103,72,115] There are also outstanding specific therapeutic endeavors. Bruno Bettelheim, in *The Empty Fortress*,[44] reported on the results of "the most intensive and sustained therapy we were able to provide" on forty-six autistic children. (This was residential therapy combined with individual, psychoanalytically-focused therapy.) He claimed seventeen good results and fourteen fair results; fourteen either had poor results or were excluded because of insufficient treatment. These results do not differ much from the 31.5 percent adequate social adjustment out of 759 cases summarized[28] from twelve reports from the international literature for a twenty-year period. There is no evidence in Bettelheim's report that any of the treated children were cured as adults, although several did well in college. But Bettelheim certainly demonstrates that these very sick children benefited from the therapeutic program to which they were exposed. Their lives were enriched, they had a great deal of happiness, and they contributed to the world's fund of knowledge and human warmth through the relationship with the adults who were dedicated to their care and treatment. These things are important too. Bettelheim figured that at least three years was needed in the residential treatment of each child.

Rudolf Ekstein[62] reported on children treated psychoanalytically on an outpatient basis at the Reiss–Davis Child Center. He speaks of cures, but no cures are recorded. The fifteen-year-old adolescent most extensively reported had nearly ten years of treatment, but she relapsed and entered a hospital with a psychotic episode for two months. Still, her ability to cope with her schizophrenia showed continuous improvement in organization and maturation, both in the life test of living in the community and in her responses to psychological tests.

In the 1930s, our earliest years at Bellevue, psychoanalytical therapy was emphasized[27] and carried out by many whose names have become well known. Rapoport,[116,117] Cottington,[52] Paul Schilder,[121] and many others were especially active, hoping to help the children they treated and hoping also that the analysis of childhood cases would reveal evidence for early trauma or deprivations that would help account for the disorder. Such evidence had not been uncovered in analyses of adult cases. We were disappointed in these hopes, however, whether from our own work or from that reported in the literature.

Later Gurevitz[39] attempted a modification of psychoanalytic treatment that aimed at activating the neurotic symptomatology, relieving anxiety, and promoting identification processes, thus helping a group of young schizophrenic children to cope with their symptoms and maturate in behavior. To some degree he adapted Sechehaye's[123] method of symbolic fulfillment. Treatment lasted from two to four years, beginning in residence and continuing on an outpatient basis with the same therapist. All the children showed marked improvement in observable behavior related to homeostatic, vasovegetative, and neurological functions; in body image and self-concept; in anxiety; in intellectual function; and in school and home or boarding-home adjustment. This improvement lasted through latency and early puberty, after which various schizophrenic symptoms recurred: one child committed suicide, one was lost to follow-up, and the rest had chronic hospital care as adults.

Tutoring schizophrenic children who had a reading disability proved, in the hands of Ilse Goldberg,[78] to improve both conditions symptomatically. This occurred in both boys and girls in the prepuberal and adolescent periods. Effective remissions in the schizophrenia occurred, and the learning of reading advanced. All this contributed to our own observations that both conditions are maturational lags. Many specific language disabilities, such as dyslexia, are also best understood as maturational lags in the (evolutionally) recently acquired functioning of cortical areas that serve language and symbol formation and the tool-and-pencil-using hand.[19,21] In addition there is (often disputed) evidence of an inherited familial pattern.[86,111] Many other maturational lags occur in the areas of personality, perception, cognition, and motor organization (soft neurological signs).[54] Of course there are many children with slow learning who may appear not to belong to this specific category but, instead, to be effected by cultural deprivation.[114] As in all disorders in children, there is a wide range in the severity of learning disabilities, and it is probable that the less vulnerable child may be able to compensate (if he is not culturally deprived) whereas the culturally deprived child will not.

Early—preferably preschool—prediction of reading failure is feasible[54,94] and is certainly the desired method for saving the child from school failure and behavioral disorders. (It is also more economical for the educational system.) Otherwise, after the child has failed for several years, the more difficult course may have to be followed—providing remedial training and therapy for the reactive personality problems.

Dyslexia and all the other learning disabilities have been the subjects of a great deal of controversial literature[129] as to whether they are specific or nonspecific neurological problems, the result of social–cultural deprivation, or a psychoneurotic reaction to poor schooling or to early difficulties in the parent-child relationship. In any of these diagnostic assumptions the child would still need some combination of the following treatment programs: (1) early prediction; (2) a form of tutoring adapted to the child's specific learning disability—often a maturational problem in auditory, visual, or proprioceptive sensory function, or a combination of these; (3) compensation for the social-cultural deprivation; (4) (sometimes) psychotherapy, in addition to or instead of tutoring by those who see a learning disability as an ego defect; and (5) pharmacotherapy. It has been well documented that drugs, and especially the stimulants such as the amphetamines and methylphenidate, are markedly effective with many of these children with learning disabilities.[5,36,66,133] It has also been shown that there is apparently no relationship between prepuberty children receiving these drugs, under these conditions, and adolescent addiction.[71]

Neurotic Disorders

It has already been suggested that neuroses are defense responses to more threatening, disorganizing disorders such as brain damage or schizophrenia. Unless the neurotic disorder is disturbing in itself, such as some hysteriform states or severe obsessional compulsive behavior, it should be protected and utilized and perhaps even strengthened.[39] The anxiety and neurotic symptoms, together with other findings, tend to point to the underlying diagnosis. Pseudoneurotic schizophrenia emphasizes this situation well.[92] Psychoanalytic therapy or some modification of it has been widely used in such cases, and frequently with the conviction that it is beneficial. More recently the wide range of psychotropic drugs, together with some form of psychotherapy or counseling to the parents, has been the treatment of choice. Fish[66] emphasizes the importance of careful diagnosis and the careful choice of drugs for different symptoms or syndromes, and objects to the "one drug–one child" practice. Wender,[133] on the other hand, prescribes drugs (starting with the stimulants) as a diagnostic test, without any careful diagnostic interviewing or examinations.

Many child specialists see the majority of children's problems as essentially neurotic, in reaction to an early psychic trauma or other anxiety-producing environmental factors. Consequently psychotherapy is the treatment of choice for them. Sometimes insightful interpretations are given to the child, especially by those trained in the Kleinian school.[103,131] The interpersonal relationship with the therapist and the sense of security provided by the dependable repetition of the time and place where the therapy occurs are considered important. There is also a rich availability of play materials, toys, arts and craft materials, and water. *The Lowenfeld World Technique*[46] is a good example of such routines.

Since, in my experience, the major causes of anxiety in children are brain damage (including minimal brain damage) and beginning schizophrenia, I see these neurotic features as defenses and normal curative processes and believe that interference with them will expose the anxiety and the more disturbing disorganization from the brain damage and possible psychosis. Neurotic features belong to the normal personality of all of us, with whatever degree of potential pathology we may have.

Success in the treatment of some specific syndromes often classified as neurotic, such as school phobias, has had considerable recognition in the literature.[60,75] Treatment usually consists of an immediate return to school, some form of psychotherapy, counseling (at least for the parents), and some form of psychopharmacotherapy. School phobia is usually seen as a separation anxiety. In children at puberty or older, it is known that school phobias often indicate an early onset of schizophrenia; in my experience the same is true of many younger children as well. The above program of treatment, however, may well be effective until the next phase in development —which may lead either to a better remission or a more psychotic phase of the schizophrenic. The syndrome of Gilles de la Tourette[124] is another condition that is often treated as a neurosis, since there are often no gross neurological signs. Later life may show the true neurological condition, or the child may go into a good remission in adolescence— spontaneously, with drugs (haloperidol has been especially recommended), or with one or another form of essentially supportive psychotherapy.

Social-Cultural Deprivation

Severe early social-cultural deprivation in infancy—as in, for example, the institutionalization of babies—has been seen by many as the cause of serious crippling of personality and mentality and even of physical development.[45,11,12,79] It has been variously called the deprivation syndrome, psychopathic behavior disorders of childhood, affect hunger,[105] psychosocial dwarfism,[127] and mental retardation with psychosocial deprivation (recognized by DSM-II).[2]

Typically these children have been deprived of any persistent relationship with a caring adult and of sensory, social, or cultural stimuli. Their personality formation does not mature to the superego level. They are without anxiety or any neurotic defenses. There appears to be something like an imprinting period in children, such as the one Harlow[88] found in monkeys who were deprived of a live maternal relationship in their early infancy. The best and most specific treatment is prevention. Much has been done in this way by not allowing infants to remain in institutions, infant homes, hospitals, or convalescent homes, but instead arranging for a substitute mother in some form if their own mother is not available.

There has been a tendency to confuse the apathy, withdrawal, and interference in development that occurs in severely deprived infants with autism.[131] Unless the child is also vulnerable to schizophrenia by heredity, the two conditions are actually quite different. The differences are: (1) there is a lack of schizophrenia heredity in the deprived child; (2) the nonautistic or nonschizophrenic child will not develop schizophrenia later but more likely will be a sociopathic or inadequate personality; (3) the deprived nonautistic child has none of the cardinal signs of schizophrenia described by Kanner,[99,100] nor the hypersensitivity to perceptual stimuli described by Bergman and Escalona,[43] nor the signs of embryonic plasticity described by myself[27] and Fish;[67] and (4) the autistic child is basically anxious with some kind of defense mechanisms, whereas the deprived child is without anxiety or neurotic mechanisms.

The child seriously deprived in infancy does not appear to respond to any therapeutic efforts but can adjust in a protective institutional environment, especially from adolescence on. He usually does find some supportive person or institution, such as a foster mother, a spouse, the marines, or employment in an institution such as a mental hospital. As an adult he tends to become inconspicuous and does not have a criminal career unless he is also schizophrenic or brain-damaged. Less severe grades of deprivation may develop crippled personalities who are immature and demanding of attention, who may become acting-out sociopaths, and who often find themselves in correctional institutions.

Reactions to Situational Stress

Any child with any other neuropsychiatric or behavioral problem can also react to situational stress. A child made vulnerable because of minor grades of the above-described conditions may frequently be most likely to react to stressful situations, even when not presenting any conspicuous behavior disorder. The child will return to satisfactory behavior if the stress is removed. Too often, however, a stressful situation (if found) is offered as the major problem, while a serious problem that exists in some other area is too willingly overlooked. Diagnosticians are often impressed with a bad social-cultural or family situation and do not want to seek further for the child's real vulnerability or pathology. Siblings behaving and developing normally in the same situations often exist; they should indicate the need to look into the disturbed child for his own problems. Presumably the test should be that the child will recover from the disturbed reaction if the stress is corrected.

⟦ Programs and Activities Called Therapeutic

There are many programs, disciplines, and activities that are referred to as therapies when they are furnished to children who have mental disturbances, developmental problems, and behavior disorders, including delinquencies. They are especially designed for children who are in residential or institutional care, but they are also used in less comprehensive programs in an outpatient and even a private practice setting. Included are milieu therapy, occupational therapy, recreational therapy, and play therapy. More recently, programs of behavior therapy, operant conditioning therapy,[76,134,136] group therapy,[125] and family therapy[1] have been developed. All of the projective techniques and creative arts have also been used as therapies, such as the graphic arts, plastic arts (clay), music (paraverbal therapy[89]), dance, puppets,[15] and drama (called psychodrama by Moreno). Remedial tutoring and any school program are referred to as educational therapy.

There is an enormous literature on these subjects that cannot be reviewed or even referred to here. I myself, in a book, *Child Psychiatric Techniques: Diagnostic and Therapeutic Approach to Normal and Abnormal Development through Patterned, Expressive and Group Behavior,*[15] summarized nearly twenty years of work at Bellevue that was made possible, in part, by the federally-funded New Deal Arts Project (Public Works Project, or PWA). Often these therapeutic techniques are performed by trained medical professionals, psychiatrists, psychologists, social workers, nurses, or trained teachers. Often they are also performed by untrained persons and volunteers. Sometimes the "therapist" is trained in his own skill as an artist, musician, or dramatist. Courses and even special schools of such specialized therapies now exist.

Nevertheless it is doubtful if such activities should be called "therapy" and the persons who perform them "therapists." There is no evidence that they have any specific treatment effect or that they are curative in any medical sense. These activities are usually carried on as a part of a larger program for the care of problem children. Any worker who is a part of a program for problem children is called a "therapist." But the same activities carried on in a program for normal children would be called education, recreation, arts, crafts, and tutoring. For the most part they are educative and recreational. They may initiate or stimulate maturation and development and show the child that he is capable of some new skill. They may facilitate expression and communication with others and thus help or enable the child to promote his own maturation, cope with developmental disturbances or lags, and compensate for deprivations in life experiences. That they may help the child to enter into interpersonal relations and often enrich the maturational and educational experiences of the child is, of course, very important for all children, whether normal or deviant. Many times, however, the activities are most useful for the participating and observing adult, giving him more insight into the child and a better understanding of children's capacity for growth and creativeness and personality expression. Thus they facilitate the adult's capacity to interact with the child to make a diagnosis and prognosis and to contribute to new insights into his own personality problems.

More recent studies of the artwork produced by the children at Bellevue in the 1930s and 1940s led to the conclusion that children with reading disabilities often compensated for their difficulties in language communication with special abilities in graphic and pictorial art.[42] The opportunity to perform such art certainly gave the child more confidence. Those studied responded favorably when they were also offered rather elaborate programs of foster homes and special educational programs with tutoring and recreational programs. It was further observed that series of disturbed boys and girls during puberty, who were productive in art classes and able to express their body-image problems in symbolic graphic art work, tended to have a good prognosis regardless of their diagnosis. The prognosis was confirmed by adult follow-up reports.[29]

The present trend is for far less separation and isolation of the problem child from the community and from normal activities. Public and private schools for normal children have guidance programs and special classes for the emotionally disturbed. State residential programs are more diversified, with day schools and night and weekend programs.[57] Arrangements are made for weekend visits, vacation release, rapid discharge, and easy readmission. Follow-up care (preferably by the same doctors and social workers who know the child) and many community activities are used.[38] There are more private and public facilities available for all through special funds. Mental health for the deviant child has become part of public health.[110]

(Concluding Remarks

Every child is a unique person in a unique cultural-social relationship in the world. All his parts are also unique—his body, his physical appearance, his developmental pattern, his behavior, his personality, his mental functions, his relationship with other unique individuals, his problems, and his own ability to deal with his problems.

There is no perfect model for a child, and therefore every child is deviant to some degree in all his parts and all his functions. This creates the problems.

But every child also has a strong drive for normal development. This is the evolutionary process. Every child has a strong drive for compensating and coping with his deviancies and problems. Therefore most children will not need professional mental hygiene or psychiatric care, even if some professional can pinpoint some sign of deviancy.

The child who is referred may have a more severe defect or pathology of an organic nature (in the brain), a developmental or maturational problem, or a lack in the social-cultural environment or in his coping and compensating mechanisms. Or the combination of disorders in all areas may overwhelm him; it must not be forgotten that there are also problems in the areas not grossly pathological.

The law of parsimony—one diagnosis or one disease for one patient—does not apply to children's behavioral, developmental, or psychiatric problems. Therefore there is no one treatment that can be prescribed for a problem child. The prescription for treatment must be for the child, not for a disease. There are, of course, specific disease processes for which there are specific treatments, and there are specific developmental defects and matura-

tional lags for which more or less specific training and rehabilitation programs can be applied. And there are specific situational stresses that can be corrected. But the child will retain the scar and the memory of the experiences that affect his development, as well as retaining all the other deviancies in his make-up. He will also have the drive for normal development, for compensating and coping with these problems, from which he will profit and be a better person.

The prescription for treatment of every child should be based on full knowledge of the child and his functioning in his environment. It should include a careful history; a knowledge of the social, cultural, familial, and school environment in which he lives (this is usually obtained by a social worker); an interview and observation, in an interpersonal relationship, by a knowledgeable professional; special examinations of psychological, psychometric, and educational functions (usually by a psychologist); and a neurological examination, including an EEG (usually by a neurologist), as indicated. These observations and data must be integrated by an experienced professional or multidisciplinary staff group. A second interview, after trial treatment or a trial period of the child developing on his own or in a changed environment, should be a part of the prescription.

Treatment should be specific for any specific disease process or deprivation. There should be prescribed training and tutoring for motor or educational handicaps; psychotherapy for strengthening self-concepts and identifications and increasing the capacity to interrelate and communicate; appropriate psychopharmacology, because it has proved to be so helpful in many childhood problems; counseling and therapy to the family members, if they are available and need and want it; and a change in environment when indicated.

Finally, every prescription for treatment of behavioral, developmental, or psychiatric problems of childhood should be checked frequently. Children change as they develop. They may improve or get worse from their

own inner resources as they progress from infancy, to early childhood, to mid-childhood, to
puberty, to adolescence, and on to early adulthood.

(Bibliography

1. ACKERMAN, N. W. "Family Therapy," in
S. Arieti, ed., *American Handbook of Psy-
chiatry*, 1st ed., Vol. 3, pp. 201–212. New
York: Basic Books, 1966.

2. AMERICAN PSYCHIATRIC ASSOCIATION. *Diag-
nostic and Statistical Manual of Mental
Disorders* (DSM-II). Washington: Am.
Psychiatric Assoc., 1968.

3. ANNEL, A. L. "Insulin Shock Treatment in
Children with Psychotic Disturbances,"
Acta Psychother. Orthopaed., 3 (1955),
193–205.

4. BANKER, B. Q. and J.-M. LARROCHE. "Periventricular Leukomalacia of Infancy,"
Arch. Neurol., 7 (1962), 386–410.

5. BECK, L., M. MacKAY, and R. TAYLOR.
"Methylphenidate, Results on a Children's
Psychiatric Service," *N.Y. State J. Med.*,
70 (1970), 2897–2902.

6. BENDA, C. E. *Developmental Disorders of
Mentations and the Cerebral Palsies*. New
York: Grune & Stratton, 1951.

7. BENDER, L. *The Visual Motor Gestalt Test
and Its Clinical Use*. New York.: Am.
Orthopsychiatric Assoc., 1938.

8. ———. "The Psychology of Children Suffering from Organic Disturbances of the
Cerebellum," *Am. J. Orthopsychiatry*, 10
(1940), 187–292.

9. ———. "Organic Brain Conditions Producing Behavior Disorders," in N. D. C. Lewis
and B. Pacella, eds., *Modern Trends in
Child Psychiatry*, pp. 155–192. New York:
Grune & Stratton, 1946.

10. ———. "One Hundred Cases of Childhood
Schizophrenia Treated with Electric
Shock," *Trans. Am. Neurol. Assoc.*, 72
(1947), 165–169.

11. ———. "Psychopathic Behavior Disorders
in Children," in R. M. Lindner and R. V.
Seliger, eds., *Handbook of Correctional
Psychology*, pp. 360–377. New York: Philosophical Library, 1947.

12. ———. "Genesis of Hostility in Children,"
Am. J. Psychiatry, 105 (1948), 241–245.

13. ———. "Psychological Problems of Children
with Organic Brain Disease," *Am. J. Orthopsychiatry*, 19 (1949), 404–415.

14. ———. "Anxiety in Disturbed Children,"
in P. Hoch and J. Zubin, eds., *Anxiety*,
pp. 119–139. New York: Grune & Stratton,
1950.

15. ———. *Child Psychiatric Techniques: Diagnostic and Therapeutic Approach to Normal and Abnormal Development through
Patterned Expression and Group Behavior*. Springfield, Ill.: Charles C. Thomas,
1952.

16. ———. "Schizophrenia in Childhood: A
Confirmation of the Diagnosis," *Trans.
Am. Neurol. Assoc.*, 77 (1952), 67–73.

17. ———. *The Psychopathology of Children
with Organic Brain Disease*. Springfield,
Ill.: Charles C. Thomas, 1955.

18. ———. "Schizophrenia in Childhood: Its
Recognition, Description and Treatment,"
Am. J. Orthopsychiatry, 26 (1956), 499–
506.

19. ———. "Specific Reading Disability as a
Maturational Lag," *Bull. Orton Soc.*, 7
(1957), 9–18.

20. ———. "Emerging Patterns in Child Psychiatry," *Bull. N.Y. Acad. Med.*, 34 (1958),
794–810.

21. ———. "Problems in Conceptualization
and Communication in Children with
Developmental Alexia," in P. Hoch and
J. Zubin, eds., *Psychopathology of Com-
munication*, pp. 155–176. New York:
Grune & Stratton, 1958.

22. ———. "Emotional Deprivation in Infancy
and Its Implications in Child Psychiatry,"
A Crianca Portugesa, 19 (1960), 83–107.

23. ———. "Diagnostic and Therapeutic Aspects of Childhood Schizophrenia," in
P. W. Bowman, ed., *Mental Retardation*,
pp. 453–468. New York: Grune & Stratton,
1960.

24. ———. "A Twenty-five Year View of
Therapeutic Results," in P. Hoch and
J. Zubin, eds., *Evaluation of Psychiatric
Treatment*, pp. 129–142. New York:
Grune & Stratton, 1964.

25. ———. "The Treatment of Childhood
Schizophrenia with LSD and UML," in
M. Rinkel, ed., *The Biological Treatment of
Mental Illness*, pp. 463–491. New York:
Page, 1966.

26. ———. "Theory and Treatment of Child-

hood Schizophrenia," *Acta Paedopsychiatr.*, 34 (1967), 298–307.

27. ———. "Childhood Schizophrenia, A Review," *Int. J. Psychiatry*, 5 (1968), 298–307.

28. ———. "Prognosis of Infantile Psychosis and Neurosis," (Discussion) *Excerp. Med. Int. Congr. Series*, 150 (1968), 124–126.

29. ———. "Body Image Problems Expressed in the Art of Emotionally Disturbed Puberty Boys and Girls," in R. Wolmat and C. Wiart, eds., *Art and Psychopathology*, pp. 19–27. Amsterdam: Excerp. Med. Found., 1969.

30. ———. "Children's Reactions to Psychotomimetic Drugs," in D. H. Efron, ed., *Psychotomimetic Drugs*, pp. 265–273. New York: Raven, 1970.

31. ———. "The Life Course of Schizophrenic Children," *Biol. Psychiatry*, 2 (1970), 165–172.

32. ———. "Childhood and Adolescent Remissions and Adult Adjustment in Shock Treated Schizophrenic Children." Paper read at East. Psychiat. Research Assoc., New York, Feb. 1974. In press.

33. ———. "Alpha and Omega of Childhood Schizophrenia," *J. Autism Child. Schizo.*, 1 (1971), 115–118.

34. ———. "The Schizophrenic Spectrum in Childhood Schizophrenia." Paper read at 63rd Ann. Meet. Am. Psychopath. Soc., New York, March 1973. In press.

35. BENDER, L. and K. ANDERMANN. "Brain Damage in Blind Children with Retrolental Fibroplasia," *Arch. Neurol.*, 12 (1965), 644–649.

36. BENDER, L. and F. COTTINGTON. "The Use of Amphetamine Sulphate (Benzedrine) in Child Psychiatry," *Am. J. Psychiatry*, 99 (1942), 116–121.

37. BENDER, L. and G. FARETRA. "Organic Therapy in Pediatric Psychiatry," *Dis. Nerv. Syst.*, Monogr. Suppl., 22 (1961), 110–111.

38. BENDER, L., G. FARETRA, and S. GRUBER. "Early Discharge as a Policy in a New Children's Unit," *A Crianca Portuguesa*, 8 (1958), 461–464.

39. BENDER, L. and S. GUREVITZ. "Results with Psychotherapy with Young Schizophrenic Children," *Am. J. Orthopsychiatry*, 25 (1955), 163–169.

40. BENDER, L. and S. NICHTERN. "Chemotherapy in Child Psychiatry," *N.Y. State J. Med.*, 56 (1956), 2791–2795.

41. BENDER, L. and D. V. S. SANKAR. "Chromosome Damage Not Found in Leukocytes of Children Treated with LSD-25," *Science*, 159 (1968), 749.

42. BENDER, L. and P. SCHILDER. "Graphic Art as a Special Ability in Children with Reading Disability," *J. Clin. Exp. Psychopath.*, 12 (1951), 147–156.

43. BERGMAN, P. and S. ESCALONA. "Unusual Sensitivity in Very Young Children," in *The Psychoanalytic Study of the Child*, Vol. 3/4, pp. 333–343. New York: International Universities Press, 1949.

44. BETTELHEIM, B. *The Empty Fortress.* New York: Free Press, 1967.

45. BOWLBY, J. *Maternal Care and Mental Health.* Monograph No. 3. Geneva: World Health Organization, 1951.

46. BOWYER, L. R. *The Lowenfeld World Technique: Studies in Personality.* Forword by M. Lowenfeld. Oxford: Pergamon, 1970.

47. BRADLEY, C. "Benzedrine and Dexedrine in the Treatment of Children's Behavior Disorders," *Pediatrics*, 5 (1950), 24–37.

48. BRADLEY, C. and M. BOWEN. "Amphetamine (Benzedrine) Therapy of Children's Behavior Disorders," *Am. J. Orthopsychiatry*, 11 (1941), 92–103.

49. BUCK, J. N. *The House-Tree-Person Test.* (Mimeographed manual) Colony, Va.: Lynchburg State Colony, 1947.

50. CAPLAN, H., R. BIBACE, and M. S. RABINOVITCH. "Paranatal Stress, Cognitive Organization and Ego Function: A Controlled Follow-up Study of Children Born Prematurely," *J. Am. Acad. Child Psychiatry*, 2 (1963), 434–450.

51. COTTINGTON, F. "The Treatment of Childhood Schizophrenia by Metrazol Shock Modified by B-Erythroidin," *Am. J. Psychiatry*, 98 (1941), 397–400.

52. ———. "The Treatment of Childhood Schizophrenia," *Nerv. Child*, 1 (1941–42), 172–187.

53. CREAK, E. M. "Schizophrenia Syndrome of Childhood: Progress Report of a Working Party," *Br. Med. J.*, 2 (1961), 889–890.

54. DE HIRSCH, K. and W. S. LANGFORD. *Predicting Reading Failures.* New York: Harper & Row, 1966.

55. DETRE, T. P. and H. G. JARECKI. *Modern Psychiatric Treatment*. Philadelphia; Lippincott, 1971.

56. DOLL, E. A. *Measurement of Social Competence: Vineland Social Maturity Scale*. Minneapolis: Educational Test Bureau, 1947.

57. DRABMAN, R., R. SPITALNIK, M. B. HAGAMEN et al. "The Five-Two Program: An Integrated Program to Treating Severely Disturbed Children," *Hosp. Community Psychiatry*, 24 (1973), 33–36.

58. DUBOS, R. "Individuality, Personality and Collectivity," in *A God Within*, pp. 71–86. New York: Scribners, 1972.

59. DUNHAM, W. "Social Cultural Studies of Schizophrenia," *Arch. Gen. Psychiatry*, 24 (1971), 206–214.

60. EISENBERG, L. "School Phobias: A Study in Communication of Anxiety," *Am. J. Psychiatry*, 114 (1958), 712–718.

61. ———. "Role of Drugs in Child Psychiatry," in S. Fisher, ed., *Child Research in Psychopharmacology*, pp. 26–35. Springfield, Ill.: Charles C. Thomas, 1959.

62. EKSTEIN, R. *The Challenge: Despair and Hope in the Conquest of Innerspace*. New York: Brunner/Mazel, 1971.

63. FARETRA, G. and L. BENDER. "Autonomic Nervous System Responses in Hospitalized Children Treated with LSD and UML," *Recent Adv. Biol. Psychiatry*, 7 (1964), 1–8.

64. FARETRA, G. and A. E. GRUGETT. "A Five Year Follow-up Report on Children Treated with Electric Convulsive Therapy," *A Crianca Portuguesa*, 21 (1962), 461–471.

65. FISH, B. "Convulsive Therapy for Children," in A. M. Freedman and A. Kaplan, eds., *Comprehensive Textbook of American Psychiatry*, pp. 1471–1472. Baltimore: Williams & Wilkins, 1967.

66. ———. "The 'One Child One Drug' Myth of Stimulants in Hyperkinesis: Importance of Diagnostic Categories in Evaluation of Treatment," *Arch. Gen. Psychiatry*, 25 (1971), 193–203.

67. ———. "Contributions of a Developmental Research to a Theory of Schizophrenia," in J. Helmuth, ed., The Exceptional Infant. Vol. 2, *Studies in Abnormality*, pp. 473–482. New York: Brunner/Mazel, 1971.

68. FISH, B. and T. SHAPIRO. "A Descriptive Typology of Children's Psychiatric Disorders: 2. A Behavioral Classification," in *Psychiatric Research Report* no. 18, pp. 75–86. Washington: American Psychiatric Association, 1964.

69. ———. "Typology of Children's Psychiatric Disorders: 1. Its Application to a Controlled Evaluation of Treatment," *J. Am. Acad. Child Psychiatry*, 4 (1965), 32–52.

70. FREEDMAN, A. M., A. EFFRON, and L. BENDER. "Pharmacotherapy in Children with Psychiatric Illness," *J. Nerv. Ment. Dis.*, 122 (1955), 479–486.

71. FREEDMAN, D. X. (chairman) "Report of the Conference on the Use of Stimulant Drugs in the Treatment of Behaviorally Disturbed Young School Children," *Psychopharmacol. Bull.*, 7 (1971), 23–29.

72. FREUD, A. *The Psycho-analytic Treatment of Children*. New York: International Universities Press, 1946.

73. ———. "Assessment of Childhood Disturbances," in *The Psychoanalytic Study of the Child*, Vol. 17, pp. 149–152. New York: International Universities Press, 1962.

74. ———. "The Symptomatology of Childhood: A Preliminary Attempt at Classification," in *The Psychoanalytic Study of the Child*, Vol. 25, pp. 19–29. New York: International Universities Press, 1970.

75. GARVEY, W. and J. R. HEGRENES. "Desensitization Technique in the Treatment of School Phobia," *Am. J. Orthopsychiatry*, 36 (1966), 147–152.

76. GELFAND, D. M. and D. P. HARTMANN. "Behavior Therapy with Children: A Review and Evaluation of Research Methodology," *Psychol. Bull.*, 69 (1968), 204–215.

77. GESELL, A. and C. S. AMATRUDA. *Developmental Diagnosis*. New York: Hoeber, 1949.

78. GOLDBERG, I. "Use of Remedial Reading Tutoring as a Method of Psychotherapy for Schizophrenic Children with Reading Disabilities," *Q. J. Child Behav.*, 4 (1952), 273–280.

79. GOLDFARB, W. "Emotional and Intellectual Consequences of Psychologic Deprivation in Infancy," in P. H. Hoch and J. Zubin, eds., *Psychopathology of Childhood*, pp. 105–119. New York: Grune & Stratton, 1955.

80. ———. *Childhood Schizophrenia*. Cambridge, Mass.: Harvard University Press, 1961.

81. GOODENOUGH, F. *Measurement of Intelligence by Drawings.* Yonkers, N.Y.: World Book, 1926.

82. GREENACRE, P. "The Predisposition to Anxiety," in *Growth and Personality*, pp. 27–82. New York: Norton, 1952.

83. GROUP FOR THE ADVANCEMENT OF PSYCHIATRY: GAP COMMITTEE ON CHILD PSYCHIATRY. *The Diagnostic Process in Child Psychiatry*, GAP Report no. 38. New York: Group for the Advancement of Psychiatry, August 1957.

84. ——. *Psychopathological Disorders in Childhood: Theoretical Considerations and a Prognosed Classification.* GAP Report no. 62. New York: Group for the Advancement of Psychiatry, June 1966.

85. GRUENBERG, E. M. "How Can the New Diagnostic Manual Help?" *Int. J. Psychiatry*, 7 (1969), 368–374.

86. HALLGREN, B. "Specific Dyslexia: A Clinical and Genetic Study," *Acta Psychiatr. Neurolog.*, *Suppl.* 65, (1950).

87. HAMMER, E. F. *The Clinical Application of Projective Drawings.* Springfield, Ill.: Charles C. Thomas, 1957.

88. HARLOW, H. and M. K. HARLOW. "Social Deprivation in Monkeys," *Sci. Am.*, 207 (1962), 136–146.

89. HEIMLICH, E. P. "Paraverbal Techniques in the Therapy of Childhood Communication Disorders," *Int. J. Child Psychiatry*, 1 (1972), 65–83.

90. HESTON, L. L. "The Genetics of Schizophrenia and Schizoid Disease," *Science*, 167 (1970), 249–256.

91. HOCH, P. and P. POLATIN. "Pseudoneurotic Forms of Schizophrenia," *Psychiatr. Q.*, 23 (1949), 428–254.

92. HOCH, P. and J. ZUBIN, eds., *The Evaluation of Psychiatric Treatment.* New York: Grune & Stratton, 1964.

93. IRWIN, S. and J. EGOZCUE. "Chromosome Abnormalities in Leukocytes from LSD-25 Users," *Science*, 157 (1967), 313.

94. JANSKY, J. and K. DEHIRSCH. *Preventing Reading Failures, Prediction, Diagnosis and Prevention.* New York: Harper & Row, 1972.

95. JENKINS, R. L. and J. COLE. *Diagnostic Classification in Child Psychiatry.* American Psychiatric Association Research Report no. 18. Washington: Am. Psychiatr. Assoc., 1964.

96. KALINOWSKY, L. B. "Evaluation of Somatic Therapies," in P. Hoch and J. Zubin, eds., *The Evaluation of Psychiatric Treatment*, pp. 45–57. New York: Grune & Stratton, 1964.

97. KALINOWSKY, L. B. and H. HIPPIUS. *Pharmacological, Convulsive and Other Somatic Treatments in Psychiatry.* New York: Grune & Stratton, 1969.

98. KALLMANN, F. J. "A Genetic Theory of Schizophrenia: An Analysis of 691 Schizophrenic Twin Index Families," *Am. J. Psychiatry*, 103 (1946), 309–322.

99. KANNER, L. "Problems of Nosology and Psychodynamics of Early Infantile Autism," *Am. J. Orthopsychiatry*, 19 (1949), 416–429.

100. ——. "The Conception of Wholes and Parts in Early Infantile Autism," *Am. J. Psychiatry*, 108 (1951), 23–26.

101. KEELER, W. R. and L. BENDER. "A Follow-up Study of the Children with Behavior Disorders and Sydenham's Chorea," *Am. J. Psychiatry*, 109 (1952), 421–428.

102. KENNARD, M. A. "The Electroencephalogram and Disorders of Behavior," *J. Nerv. Ment. Dis.*, 124 (1956), 103–124.

103. KLEIN, M. *The Psycho-analysis of Children.* London: Hogarth, 1937.

104. LAUFER, M. "The Assessment of Adolescent Disturbances: The Application of Anna Freud's Profile," in *The Psychoanalytic Study of the Child*, Vol. 20, pp. 99–1230. New York: International Universities Press, 1965.

105. LEVY, D. "Primary Affect Hunger," *Am. J. Psychiatry*, 94 (1937), 643–652.

106. MAHLER, M. "Benign and Malignant Cases of Childhood Psychosis, (Schizophrenic-like)," *Am. J. Orthopsychiatry*, 19 (1949), 295–305.

107. ——. *On Human Symbiosis and the Vicissitudes of Human Individuation:* Vol. 1, *The Psychosis.* New York: International Universities Press, 1968.

108. MEAD, M. *From the South Seas.* New York: Morrow, 1939.

109. MENNINGER, K. *The Vital Balance in the Process in Mental Health and Illness.* New York: Viking Press, 1963.

110. NEW YORK STATE DEPARTMENT OF MENTAL HYGIENE. "Currents," *Ment. Hygiene News, Suppl.*, 44 (March 2, 1973), 1S–12S.

111. ORTON, S. T. *Reading, Writing and Speech*

Problems in Children. New York: Norton, 1937.

112. PASAMANICK, B. "Anti-convulsive Drug Treatment of Behavior Problem Children with Abnormal Electroencephalograms," *Arch. Neurol. Psychiatry,* 65 (1951), 752–757.

113. PENFIELD, W. and L. ROBERTS. *Speech and Brain Mechanisms.* Princeton, N.J.: Princeton University Press, 1959.

114. RABINOVITCH, R. D., A. L. DREW, R. N. DE JONG et al. "A Research Report on Reading Retardation," *Neurol. Psychiatry Child.,* 34 (1956), 363–399.

115. RANK, B. "Adaptation of the Psychoanalytic Technique for the Treatment of Young Children with Atypical Development," *Am. J. Orthopsychiatry,* 19 (1949), 130–139.

116. RAPOPORT, J. "Therapeutic Process in a Case of Childhood Schizophrenia," *Nerv. Child,* 1 (1942), 188–198.

117. ———. "Phantasy Objects in Children," *Psychoanal. Rev.,* 31 (1944), 316–331.

118. ROSENTHAL, D. and S. S. KETY, eds. *The Transmission of Schizophrenia.* Oxford: Pergamon, 1968.

119. RUTTER, M. "Childhood Schizophrenia Reconsidered," *J. Autism Child. Schizo.,* 2 (1972), 315–337.

120. RUTTER, M., S. LEBOVICI, L. EISENBERG et al. "A Tri-axial Classification of Mental Disorders in Childhood," *J. Child Psychol. Psychiatry,* 10 (1969), 41–61.

121. SCHILDER, P. "The Psychology of Schizophrenia," *Psychoanal. Rev.,* 269 (1936), 380–389.

122. ———. *Contributions to Developmental Neuropsychiatry.* L. Bender, ed. New York: International Universities Press, 1964.

123. SECHEHAYE, M. A. *Symbolic Realization: A New Method of Psychotherapy Applied to a Case of Schizophrenia.* New York: International Universities Press, 1964.

124. SHAPIRO, A. K., E. SHAPIRO, and H. WAYNE. "Treatment of Tourette's Syndrome with Haloperidol: Review of 34 Cases," *Arch. Gen. Psychiatry,* 28 (1973), 92–96.

125. SLAVSON, S. R. *Introduction to Group Psychotherapy.* New York: International Universities Press, 1965.

126. SPITZ, R. A. "Hospitalism: An Enquiry into the Genesis of Psychiatric Conditions in Early Childhood," in *The Psychoanalytic Study of the Child,* Vol. 1, pp. 53–74. New York: International Universities Press, 1945.

127. TALBOT, N. B., and M. C. HOWELL. "Social and Behavioral Causes and Consequences of Disease Among Children," in N. B. Talbot, J. Kagan, and L. Eisenberg, eds., *Behavioral Science in Pediatric Medicine.* Philadelphia: Saunders, 1971.

128. THOMAS, R. "Comments on Some Aspects of Self and Object Representation in a Group of Psychotic Children: An Application of Anna Freud's Diagnostic Profile," in *The Psychoanalytic Study of the Child,* Vol. 21, pp. 527–580. New York: International Universities Press, 1966.

129. THOMPSON, L. J. "Learning Disabilities, An Overview," *Am. J. Psychiatry,* 130 (1973), 393–399.

130. TOWBIN, A. "Organic Causes of Minimal Brain Dysfunction," *JAMA,* 217 (1971), 207–214.

131. TUSTIN, F. *Autism and Childhood Psychosis.* London: Science House, 1972.

132. WECHSLER, D. *Intelligence Scale for Children: Manual.* New York: Psychol. Corp., 1949.

133. WENDER, P. *Minimal Brain Dysfunction in Children,* p. 12ff. New York: Wiley, 1971.

134. WERRY, J. S. and J. P. WOLLERSHEIM. "Behavior Therapy with Children: A Broad Review," *J. Am. Acad. Child Psychiatry,* 6 (1967), 346–370.

135. WINNICOTT, D. W. *Therapeutic Consultation in Child Psychiatry.* London: Hogarth, 1971.

136. YATES, A. J. *Behavior Therapy,* New York: Wiley, 1970.

CHAPTER 5

THE PRESCRIPTION OF TREATMENT FOR ADULTS

Daniel X. Freedman and Jarl E. Dyrud

TODAY, to use the expression "prescription of treatment" in psychiatry is all too apt to sound either quaint or presumptuous. It is both. There was a time, and not too long ago, when we knew so little that there were only a few standard prescriptions for all the emotional ills of man. Now that we know more, we have just begun to think about matching treatments to specific syndromes. We are just beginning to sober up from a thirty-year binge of trying to be all things to all people and remember that ours is a medical specialty.

The psychiatrist—whatever his private interests, aptitudes, aesthetic or socializing ability—is first of all sanctioned as a medically trained practitioner. As a physician, he is expected to fulfill certain responsibilities, including scrutiny of the scientific rationale for his specific therapeutic interventions. A complete scientific rationale does not exist for most drug therapies of even the infectious diseases; but the trained physician is supposed to under-

stand the extent to which such knowledge is available, the research by which such knowledge can possibly be attained, and the risks and gains that pragmatically can be identified for a specific use of therapy in a specific condition, in a specific patient.

Psychiatric training begins in the broad area of human biology and requires experience in the management of a number of human ills and ailments. The training of the medical student begins with anatomy and cell biology and includes medicine, surgery, neurology, pharmacology, and some exposure to the behavioral sciences, to general psychiatry, and to psychoanalysis. The specialist in psychiatry focuses on the latter three, with emphasis on clinical experience guided by a trained psychiatrist.

What does society expect of such training? The psychiatrist should be able to recognize among the patterns of disordered behavior referred to him those that have some identifiable organic cause, such as toxic psychoses and chronic or acute brain syndromes. He, in fact, will have learned about a number of characteristic problems and their characteristic solutions as they are found in hospitals, clinics, and medical-school environments. In order to identify problems and solutions, he should have an accurate sense of what disorganized people or people in trouble experience, how their environment characteristically reacts, and how such events influence the behavior in question. If he is very well trained, he should be able to select from among the array of available options the one that is specific to a particular case.

At the least, his preparation entails firsthand experience with the severe psychoses and a range of disordered behavior, from transient anxiety to severe symptomatic neuroses to character problems, with its manifestations in specific situational conflicts. He should be sensitive to vicissitudes precipitated not only by different social classes and settings but also by the life cycle operating in them—the inherent problems, conflicts, and capacities of age groups such as the adolescent and the aged.

Most of all, he should learn to find, recognize, or elicit the potential for recovery—for organizing and adapting—which to varying degrees is present in all patients. He should appreciate transactional and biobehavioral factors that impede this process. In so doing, he will employ pharmaceuticals (commonly called drugs), direction, manipulation, persuasion—any *tested* procedure that might aid treatment. This program refers to the realistic responses of an expert, trained to be responsive, responsible, and comfortable in his work. Psychiatric prescription of therapy depends on special training, competence, experience, and the ability to be explicit.

What the psychiatrist really gains in training (apart from specific knowledge about practices, theories, and methods) is a preceptor-guided experience in handling a wide variety of crises. In short, he learns the criteria for self-confidence as he tries to achieve an acceptable level of competence. He also learns something quite general about crisis management and, more importantly, something about himself as a party in it. Thus, it is in some self-

mastery in the management of a range of brief or enduring crises affecting personality organization and personal and family life that the psychiatrist has some extensive experience if not expertise. Fully trained, he has acquired accountability and he has learned how to relate these skills in a social system that requires and trusts in responsible conduct.

The physician is trained to act on carefully garnered half-knowledge—and the mode for accomplishing this training has been called the acquisition of wisdom or clinical judgment. He is also trained to take a high degree of personal responsibility for his task, which can be quite demanding—both of him and of the patient. The patient is an essential collaborator of the physician—while yielding autonomy in technical decisions, the patient expects technical competence to be exercised in his behalf. This orientation around personal responsibility is paramount because as physicians we have inherited the implicit social agreements regulating transactions among the community, patients, and doctors. Like other medical specialties, our discipline is not a science in and of itself, but a collection of sciences, methodologies, and techniques to be used in the service of man, around the central identifiable problem of mental illness. By mental illness we mean, the psychobiological malfunctioning of the person as a whole.[16] This definition put forward by Adolph Meyer is a broad mandate reminiscent of Auguste Comte's ironic statement, "the subject matter of each discipline stretches literally to infinity."[1]

Our dual obligation to be committed to both inquiry and service has kept psychiatry singularly prone to excesses of enthusiasm over new discoveries. In our eagerness to meet the tremendous and increasing service demands developed in the thirty years since World War II, we have responded with a striking increase in the number and variety of treatment modalities available to psychiatric practitioners. The last fifteen years has seen an exponential rise in their number. Many of them are old treatments in new disguises, a few represent real advances in knowledge.[8] This proliferation of new techniques has been in part the consequence of the application of basic research findings to the area of clinical practice. In other instances, it has been the product of clinical impatience with the long and arduous course of the prevailing mode of treatment along psychoanalytical lines. This impatience was well understood by Sigmund Freud who said that the psychoanalysis should, in fact, not be tried until all simpler methods have been tried and failed.[3] It was also Freud who said, "Anyone who wants to make a living from treatment of nervous patients must clearly be able to do something to help them."[9]

Internal medicine some twenty years ago was faced with a proliferation of new and effective specialized treatment techniques. The response was to develop subspecialty training programs to the detriment of the field from the consumer's point of view. The wise diagnosticians became an aging group without new recruits. Now family-practice training programs are attempting to meet this need, but the shortage will not be rapidly made up.

Psychiatry has similarly been lured into subspecialization by the temptation to know one system of treatment well. In the past we were fortuitously spared severe fragmentation by the dominance of the field by psychoanalytic teaching. Now that several real alternatives exist, we must protect the training of the clinical diagnostician against the temptations of technical narrowness.

When the physician intervenes, his first task is to define the patient's problem. Diagnosis or recognition of the problem for which subsequent treatment may be designed can in itself be a time consuming and extensive technical procedure. Diagnosis of the dysfunction of both person and situation as well as a careful assessment of both personal and situational resources permits the physician to plan. The categorical diagnosis as well as the diagnosis for treatment must both be tested over time. Having defined the problem, the physician assigns and plans the subsequent treatment, makes an ongoing assessment of the process, and watches out for the patient's welfare. The patient may be referred by the physician to special rehabilitation and educational experts or to social or public-health agencies, whose specialists may or may not be required to have medical training. Such generalities obtain for tuberculosis, cerebral palsy, or poliomyelitis as well as for a wide variety of behavioral disorders. As physicians, psychiatrists have particular problems, notably the extent to which the doctor–patient interaction itself may be emphasized as a therapeutic tool and the reluctance with which patients identify their behavioral as opposed to physiological problems.

The manifest psychoses have historically been the psychiatrist's focus. Yet, paradoxically, during the past thirty years psychiatric talent has been largely deployed to care for a minority of relatively rich people with neurotic and character problems.[6] Currently, the demand is that this care be extended to a wide population of persons with a variety of complaints. If social values were the criteria for extension, arguments could be marshalled for any pattern of service delivery. If proof that therapy works is the criterion, then we have to deal with a number of issues, including the adequacy of research data. Where specific interventions for specific disorders are clearly efficacious—penicillin for syphilis—then the medical imperative clearly is dominant in dictating both social values and the deployment of professional functions. But it is not yet at all clear that specific therapies produce cures of the dramatic variety akin to that produced by penicillin.

Today, the psychiatrist often diagnoses not only the level of organization and capacity for adaptation and response to therapy of a particular patient but also the various systems in which behavior disorder can be enhanced or diminished. He begins to understand families, office organizations, and all the various subcultures—occupational, avocational, and affectional—that bear upon specific instances of misbehavior. He will have seen adolescent children whose acting-up and acting-out behavior somehow serves to keep marital conflict between the parents contained, while they focus, displace, and agitate through their child. Similarly, the military psychiatrist will have learned that the frequency of behavior problems is often related to the practices and behavior of unit commanders. He will understand that what is deviance in the middle class may be a way of life for the upper or lower classes. Deviance does not necessarily mean disorganization of psychobiological functions any more than conformity means organization.[7]

In dealing with such systems, the psychiatrist should maintain an open and candid relationship with his patient, siding with his patient's capacity to adapt and organize. He is a partisan to growth and development in the patient, but not an advocate of various conflicting positions. He elicits, welcomes, and depends upon the patient's capacity and motives to participate and to direct energy and attention to the tasks of therapy. Therapy is a collaboration in which roles are assigned but personal responsibility—to the degree possible —by the patient is also important, if not crucial (whether he is taking medication or engaging in insight therapy). The psychiatrist attempts not to act out his own moral dilemmas, personal needs, ambitions, and political antagonisms. His job is to help the patient assume some effective control over his own destiny.

Whether the unconscious is deep or extensive—whether it has vertical or horizontal coordinates—might well be a matter for debate; such metaphors do not lead to the devising of specific responses adequate for a specific problem. Nor do they substitute for evaluations of therapeutic techniques, processes, and outcomes in specific populations. Such sloganeering in psychiatry has diverted attention from realizable accomplishments. The extension of the term "psychoanalysis" to almost any technique that utilizes a fifty-minute time span several times a week (if not a couch) for almost any disorder has further clouded definition and progress in understanding and advancing psychiatric therapies.

The investigative intent of classical psychoanalysis is often forgotten by practicing psychoanalysts, some of whom treat the theoretically desired outcome as a real and proven achievement. The facts are that profound

therapeutic consequences often can ensue with brief interventions and that profound experiences occur in many therapeutic settings, from groups to hypnosis. The overwhelmingly challenging fact is that we still lack evaluations that give us scientifically sound bases for classifying different therapies. The real hope for highly differentiated and specific therapies lies in identifying different subgroups of patients, in finding distinctive dimensions differentiating apparently similar kinds of behavior.

This goal has been approached during the past hundred years in such advances as differentiating the psychoses from all toxic conditions and CNS syphilis or pellegra from all psychoses. New biochemical definitions are beginning to be more clearly articulated, and attempts at dissecting the different modes of intake, modulation, and processing of sensory input show the possibility of distinguishing subpopulations among the schizophrenic psychoses.[14] The regulation of sleep through certain brain "centers" is under investigation and distinct "phases" in the course of a psychosis may possibly be delineated. Whether or not drugs are useful or harmful for certain of these subgroups is now being tested. This thrust in research points to the new directions from which genuine progress toward therapeutic control can rapidly advance.

Today, we can recognize a common brand of talking therapy known as "dynamic psychotherapy," or psychoanalytically oriented psychotherapy. The dynamic therapist has cognizance of the characteristics of behavior that the classical psychoanalytic investigations described, but no matter how he comprehends the anatomy of psychological forces, he tends to focus on assets and on explicit and soluble problems. He encourages less regression, less free-floating associations, and a more circumscribed program of focusing upon immediate problems as a paradigm of important personality issues. He has thus learned principles— only some of which he applies—from classical procedures.

The psychiatrist, then, should have had the experience of knowing a variety of people— both like himself and dissimilar—who present themselves with severe troubles, with mistrust, with hope or despair; he should have seen some quick and some long-term resolutions of these situations into outcomes useful to the patient; and he should have encountered striking failures in his ability to influence behavior. Having dealt with death and disorder in both medical and psychiatric patients, he should have some appreciation of the possible real outcomes of psychiatric (or *any* well-intentioned) interventions undertaken. He may even have found each individual's unique way of organizing experience (and experiencing those modes of being) an education in psychology—but he will not tax the patient unduly for such education.

Whether he orients his activities around notions of self-actualization, the learning of preferred behavior, intervention in social systems influencing the patient, or the dampening of intensity in behavior by pharmacological agents, the psychiatrist develops a keen appreciation of his own limits, the limits the situation offers, the patient's assets and resources, and the pragmatic outcome useful to the patient. He does not expect to "cure" aggression or instincts or any other given fact of life but rather aims for diminished suffering or new learning that can help the patient to develop or to get around previously aggravating and disorganizing obstacles. He will have learned from the experience of the psychoanalyst that one diagnoses or accesses a situation in an ongoing fashion, just as in medicine, and that in having a sequence of specific goals, an open-ended and expectant view of the unfolding relation is a possible and useful attitude. But he will not prescribe psychoanalysis for every disorder, or mistake it for a really deep therapy striking at true causes (rather than a really broad theory, which it is). After all, the physiology of fever indicates that temperature regulation occurs in the hypothalamus; but physicians do not employ surgery or depth electrodes in treating a fever —mistaking basic anatomy for proximal causes and effects.

Jerome Frank has commented that all therapies must do some good, or they would disappear.[5] In the past decade, there have been serious efforts to establish the appropriate criteria for evaluating therapies.[2] This trend was accentuated with the advent of psychopharmacological agents. Studies of their efficacy employ highly sophisticated methodologies comparing various drugs in specified patient populations or a single drug in an appropriate range of dosage in different therapeutic settings. The development of reliable rating scales for a variety of simple or complex kinds of behavior has advanced.[11] Criteria for outcomes are intrinsically difficult to establish and global ratings still remain useful, but use of discharge rates from the hospital or clinic as end points appears crude because they may be dependent only on social interactions in these settings and assets in the community. Other dimensions center around the actual kind of psychotherapy undertaken, for the actual behavior and interventions of therapists belonging to the same school might differ vastly. Moreover, the therapist's level of experience, accurate empathy, and nonpossessive warmth and genuineness are characteristics recently indicated to be important.[17]

More differentiated criteria have to do with evaluating the status of the patient; these include his self-evaluations and those of others. The patient's comfort, self-awareness, and social effectiveness are important outcome variables. More ambitious research might well provide a description of the neurotic patient, his setting, the phase of his dysfunction, and his specific modes of successful and unsuccessful adaptation and might evaluate, in terms of these, what has happened after the period of therapy.

Psychiatry is thus emerging from the stage of taking either the patient's or the doctor's word for its successes as sufficient data.

For the psychoses, sophisticated studies consistently tend to show pharmacotherapy to be generally more useful than any other approach.[15] Psychotherapy combined with pharmacotherapy has been investigated in such studies; this combination may be useful, but, used alone, psychotherapies do not show superiority for such conditions. The type of psychotherapy shown to be most effective in this combination is work in which old competences are reinstated and new ones developed.[12]

We can look forward to more realistic and sophisticated evaluations, and the search for predictors (what will be the best drug or therapy for a patient) is in the process of objectifying the field. Yet, it must be recognized that the choice of therapy today is frequently dependent upon what the therapist is comfortable in doing. Thus, most therapists see a wide variety of problems in different phases of development and intensity. If the response is that the patient needs therapy, this statement frequently means that the patient needs what the therapist knows how to do. In situations in which a wide range of talent is scarce, it is difficult to argue with this approach, but one need not be satisfied with it.

The patient, on the other hand, must take what he can get, but he tends to bring to any therapy his intrinsic capacity for recovery of function. Any therapist does well if he can quickly recognize the extent to which his approach and capacity can meet the needs of the patient and, at the very least, can be alert not to put obstacles in the patient's way. Every therapist can—if trained and willing—have a clear conception of his realistic limits and resources. When this potentiality is comprehended by both the patient and the doctor, the patient is able to orient toward the realistic resources that are authentically available to him—an auspicious beginning phase of therapy. Patients establish a relationship and invest their sense of security in even the clinic building or the administrative arrangements of the help-giving resource. This relationship is evident although they may be seen only once a month, primarily for medication (as the case must be with many chronic schizophrenics): patients get some orienting anchors and frames of reference in even brief interactions. Thus, the need to be recognized, visible, respected, looked after, or even rescued is basic to bringing doctor and patient together, and some realistic regard *and* limits with respect to these needs are helpful.

Nonrational and rational needs for personal attention and the wish for competence make up the dominating motivational dimensions of the doctor–patient relationship. The patient's willingness to concur with the doctor's regimen or to rebel can be influenced, in both the somatic and the psychosocial therapies, by the physician's attitudes and approach. In successful therapy, many patients have followed the doctor's orders in one sense: they identify their wishes with his wishes to foster some solution to a current or chronic condition or problem. For some patients, the therapy is experienced as a competitive and antagonistic venture, and yet even though full of turmoil, they may well show improvement in spite of— in order to spite—the therapy or therapist.

Just as it is better to be rich than poor, handsome than ugly, so it is better to be a talented healer than one not so gifted if one enters the field of psychiatric practice. This capacity to elicit hope and trust cannot be discounted as an important factor in achieving emotional arousal that leads to favorable change in the patient. Obviously, one of the ways of eliciting this hope and trust is for the therapist to be confident of his potential usefulness, which usually implies having confidence in his theory of what is wrong with the patient and what he proposes to do about it. One of the hazards is that the therapist usually has only one theory and it may or may not be relevant to what the patient needs. This can, upon occasion, lead to a procrustean application of a theory and a technique to a heterogeneous population of patients that comes to his doorstep.

The population of patients that comes to see a psychiatrist is distributed on a normal curve ranging from high-expectant trust to a very low capacity for this readiness to be helped. Where high-expectant trust is present, particularly in situations of acute stress with only a temporary deficit in functioning, almost any technique will work and often the directive techniques are faster. Where low-expectant trust is present, the opening steps of treatment require a diligent cultivation of the patient's nascent capacity to trust before any specific therapeutic work can be done. This cultivation of the relationship per se works so well to relieve the demoralization of patients that it all too commonly is seen as an end in itself and many therapies focus exclusively upon this one ingredient of treatment. The reason it works so well may lie in the fact that in such a benign and nurturing relationship a great deal of inadvertent learning can take place. Modeling one's self on the therapist can encourage modulation of intolerable affects as well as improved cognitive skills in problem solving. Many of the improvements in technique that have been proposed in recent years have been attempts to deal with this problem of inadvertence on the assumption that paying attention to what you are doing can be more efficient and goal oriented than not noticing. Our present diagnostic classifications undoubtedly have to undergo revision in order to be relevant to this type of careful assessment of behavioral deficits that call for specific remedies. Steps are being taken in this direction. It is our understanding that DSM-III will be another step closer to using observable validatable data for diagnoses. It would be fair to say that at this time we have much more information than can be taught and made use of by the average psychiatrist treating a housewife in Peoria for headaches. In addition, commonalities of effectiveness are being dissected out of a welter of apparently different techniques.[4,10,13] We find that hysterics who improve in any of a variety of treatments have, in fact, received what they need. That is, discrimination training. They simply start with too few conceptual categories for affect and experience in order to modulate their responses. Obsessionals, on the other hand, need to be catapulted into action. Schizophrenics who respond well have received unambiguous cuing that permits them to track better. Ambiguous cuing has been clearly demonstrated to increase schizophrenic confusion.[17] Even so, it remains uncommon for a diagnosis to mandate a specific therapy or how possibly it is to be carried out. In this lies the therapeutic art. In our eagerness to transmit all that is new and technically relevant to our residents in training, we must recognize that normative training in the role remains central and that the selection of trainees for talent will always remain the single most important requirement for advancing the field of psychiatry.

Bibliography

1. BECKER, E. "The Tragic Paradox of Albion Small and American Social Science," in *The Lost Science of Man*, p. 27. New York: Braziller, 1971.
2. BERGIN, A. E. "The Evaluation of Therapeutic Outcomes," in A. E. Bergin and S. L. Garfield, eds., *Handbook of Psychotherapy and Behavior Change: An Empirical Analysis*, pp. 217–270. New York: Wiley, 1971.
3. BRELAND, K. and M. BRELAND. *Animal Behavior*. New York: Macmillan, 1966.
4. DYRUD, J. E. and I. GOLDIAMOND. "Some Applications and Implications of Behavioral Analysis for Psychotherapy," in J. M. Schlein, ed., *Research in Psychotherapy*, Vol. 3, pp. 54–89. Washington: American Psychiatric Association, 1968.
5. FRANK, J. D. *Persuasion and Healing: A Comparative Study of Psychotherapy*, rev. ed. Baltimore: The Johns Hopkins Press, 1973.
6. FREEDMAN, D. X. "Psychiatric Therapies," in *Psychology Today: An Introduction*, pp. 557–573. (Commun. Res. Machines, CRM Books.) DelMar, Calif.: David A. Dushkin, 1970.
7. ———. "Introduction: Session 6, Animal Behavior Studies—Sleep: The Relation of Serotonin to Sleep," in J. Barchas and E. Usdin, eds., *Serotonin and Behavior*, pp. 381–383. New York: Academic, 1973.
8. FREEDMAN, D. X. and R. P. GORDON. "Psychiatry Besieged: Attacks from Without (or, Psychiatry Madly Ridden from All Directions at Once," *Psychiatr. Ann.*, 3 (1973), 10–34.
9. FREUD, S. (1905) "On Psychotherapy," in J. Strachey, ed., *Standard Edition*, Vol. 7, p. 259. London: Hogarth, 1957.
10. GOLDIAMOND, I. "Toward a Constructional Approach to Social Problems," *Behaviorism*, 2 (1974), 1–84.
11. GUY, W. and R. R. BONATO. *Manual for the ECDEU Assessment Battery*, 2nd rev. ed. Washington: NIMH, 1970.
12. HOGARTY, G. E., S. C. GOLDBERG et al. "Drug and Sociotherapy in the Aftercare of Schizophrenic Patients: One Year Relapse Rates," *Arch. Gen. Psychiatry*, 28 (1973), 54–64.

13. HUNT, H. "Behavior Therapy for Adults," in S. Arieti, ed., American Handbook of Psychiatry, 2nd ed., Vol. 5, pp. 290–318. New York: Basic Books, 1975.

14. KLEIN, D. F. and J. M. DAVIS. Diagnosis and Drug Treatment of Psychiatric Disorders. Baltimore: Williams & Wilkins, 1969.

15. MAY, P. R. A. Treatment of Schizophrenia: A Comparative Study of Five Treatment Methods. New York: Science House, 1968.

16. MEYER, A. "Dealing with Mental Diseases," in E. Winters, ed., The Collected Papers of Adolf Meyer, Vol. 4, pp. 101–106. Baltimore: The Johns Hopkins Press, 1952.

17. TRUAX, C. B. and K. M. MITCHELL. "Research on Certain Therapist Interpersonal Skills in Relation to Process and Outcome," in A. E. Bergin and S. L. Garfield, eds., Handbook of Psychotherapy and Behavior Change: An Empirical Analysis, pp. 299–344. New York: Wiley, 1971.

CHAPTER 6

ELEMENTS OF THE THERAPEUTIC SITUATION: THE PSYCHOLOGY OF A BEGINNING ENCOUNTER

Lawrence Friedman

THE BEGINNING ENCOUNTER is a good place to look for the basic elements of psychotherapy. That is not because it encompasses all important features. The over-all shape of the relationship is important. The way treatment ends is important. Some psychoanalysts feel that treatment does not even begin until the initial phase is over and a solid relationship with the therapist is established. Nor is the beginning a simpler subject than a total therapy, for in many respects the early phase is more chaotic than anything that follows.

The beginning of treatment is interesting because in it major problems of the thera-

peutic *task* stand out most boldly. Meeting a psychiatrist adds a multitude of layers to the already myriad aspects of life; it supports an endless variety of theories. With so many possible ways of describing a therapeutic relationship, one looks to grasp it by its most insistent and least random protuberance, namely, the problem, task, burden, or work imposed.

This chapter is about the challenge that people accept in undertaking psychotherapy. The challenge exists on several planes of abstraction, the more concrete difficulties mirroring the more general ones. Some repetition is unavoidable as we examine the tasks of coping with a new experience, a new person, a new psychotherapist, and a new type of relationship. For the sake of simplicity, the discussion will be confined to individual therapy.

❲ Encountering Something New

The meeting of a patient and therapist is first of all a new event in their lives. That by itself presents the task of incorporating something new in an old self. Although it has been suggested[35] that people who seek therapy have trouble assimilating new situations, assimilation is by and large a routine, continuous task of life, handled easily and without attention. Nevertheless we do not entirely understand how it is done. Philosophers have pondered this question for centuries. It is noteworthy that two recent philosophers, George Herbert Mead and Alfred North Whitehead, thought that the growth of the mind was the clearest picture of the way a thing can be itself and yet develop. Mead[63] held that something changes when it is in two different perspectives at once, as for instance when I incorporate another's image of myself with my own image, and affect him in different ways than I affect myself. Whitehead[106] believed that nature's fundamental task is to combine stability with change. He wrote that inanimate things do this by "ignoring" most changes, sacrificing richness to endurance, whereas living things, and especially the mind, can respond to changes by incorporating them into pre-existing purposes. This makes our existence rich but vulnerable. Nothing could set the stage for our subject better than Whitehead's paradox:[106]

The world is thus faced by the paradox that, at least in its higher actualities, it craves for novelty and yet is haunted by terror at the loss of the past, with its familiarities and its loved ones . . . Part of the joy of the new years is the hope of the old round of seasons, with their stable facts—of friendship, and love, and old association. Yet conjointly with this terror, the present as mere unrelieved preservation of the past assumes the character of a horror of the past, rejection of it, revolt . . . [p. 516]

Among psychotherapists, the existentialists have been most aware of this very general problem of therapy. May,[61] for instance, appreciates the cost of destroying what one is to become something new—a problem confronting every organism in every encounter with a new event, and therefore confronting patient and therapist in therapy. It is the sort of task that Piaget considers to be the engine of development and the source of cognition. In Piaget's[67] system the need to reverse an impingement, to get back one's balance when surprised by something new, to preserve a constancy whatever comes—in effect, the need to be less affected without being insensitive—is what makes an organism an organism. A similar task has been referred to by others as homeostasis, repetition compulsion, identity needs, the orienting reflex, and so forth.[31,32,56,68]

❲ Meeting a New Person

More particularly, in psychotherapy, the new event is a meeting of two people, and that presents a more particular problem. "The self-system," Sullivan wrote, "views the stranger as an enemy."[95] Existentialists like May have pointed out that the milieu a person creates for himself is part of his identity,[61] and in the face of the stranger people will seek "to preserve their *center*."[62] At the same time, a person's mere identity is scant company, and his potential loneliness drives him toward others though it means destroying what he is in order to become something new.[56,61,62] The strangers in a meeting thus threaten each other as assailants and as tempters.

To ease this risk, society provides formalities that blur the sharp edges between private worlds. There are conventional politenesses and expectations, obligatory recognitions of the other's position. There are standard greetings, gestures of welcome and hospitality, allotments of host and guest status, attentions and avoidances in facial expression. All of these cushion the crunch of strangers on each other.

Yet a cushion also separates. Social niceties allow people to remain strangers to each other.[8] Cushions that are not dictated by social convention are often called "defenses" by psychotherapists, who notice that they distract from the business of therapy—which is, after all, concerned with intimacy. Nevertheless these protocols provide a structure of familiarity as an orienting grid, thus easing therapy's first task, which is to keep stranger anxiety within bounds.[40,95] Even a highly idiosyncratic meeting style serves for that patient the same function (among others) as a simple hello.

(Meeting a Psychotherapist

The Public Role of Patient and Therapist

Psychotherapy is not the type of random conversation that two strangers might strike up on an airplane. Defined social roles both facilitate and complicate the meeting. Roles quickly become conventionalized in our unstable society, where communications are highly developed. Among sophisticated people in metropolitan regions of the United States, established patterns of psychoanalytic procedure affect patients' expectations. And the newer patterns that are developing (encounter groups, T-groups, guru-guidance, and so forth), though they may be hard to describe, are not for that reason unfamiliar or strange even to beginners.

Despite the proliferation of styles, there are features common to most psychotherapeutic roles. The therapist is entitled to make certain demands and his partner certain complementary demands.[71] Usually the therapist is vested with authority, so the entitlements are apt to be obedience on the one hand and caretaking on the other. As an authority, the therapist can represent society as a whole and can demand some token of conformity in return. Frank[21] has shown that this exchange is common to many different techniques of changing people's attitudes.

To the extent that the therapist represents society he may seem to be a superadult and his patient, accordingly, a child. There is general agreement that, for better or worse, this is one of the most significant built-in structures that shape the meeting. It is the occasion of deep shame and high expectations, and of various behaviors designed to disguise them. The patient's subculture may qualify how much the therapist's social-expert role parallels the role of the patient's parent, since we know that patients from different social classes have different attitudes and expectations toward therapists that radically affect the fate of treatment.[47]

The Patient Is Observed

In industrial society, psychotherapy partners usually meet as physician and patient regardless of the therapist's title or intent. A patient will naturally feel the meeting to be an examination. And since he submits for examination not his body but himself as a person, he will feel intensely observed—the more so if he seeks help for what he ordinarily keeps hidden. Defining the meeting as an examination limits its ambiguity, but it does little to soften the stranger's threat to the patient's supportive world. One of the patient's most pressing questions at the beginning of therapy is, "What does the therapist think of me?" The patient silently guesses. He is hyper-alert to hints, and thereby open to subtle suggestion.[21] According to Greenson,[43] the awe-inspiring uncertainty prompts the patient to endow the examiner with attributes of important people in his past. Identifying with the examiner may help in understanding him.[56]

Heider[46] suggested that being observed puts one person in another person's power, because the subject's region of action is integrated with the observer's. (For instance, the therapist can pass judgment.) At the same time, one who is observed exerts power and control over the observer. Thus, being observed can make one feel important, especially with a prestigious observer, and the increased self-esteem may allow the subject to risk greater closeness. Paradoxically, being observed also makes a person more aware of himself as separate. It can lead to self-consciousness, humiliation, concealment, and disguise[55] and make the therapist seem hateful.

Observing someone not only compliments him but also enhances the dignity of the feelings he displays, thereby encouraging him to give those feelings longer tether and a more respectful hearing. Subtly imagining the observer's response, the patient creates an internal dialogue that extends self-inquiry. (We can carry a thought further when explaining it than when thinking alone about it.) If, in addition, the patient senses that the observer reacts accurately and responds concretely to rather vague feelings, the patient is likely to discover additional significance in what he expresses.[35,36] If the patient even wrongly believes that the observer can tie the patient's feelings into "the order of things," he will be more hopeful, introspective, and respectful of those feelings. This force not only affects the patient's attitudes to his feelings generally, but also his attitude to the specific areas in which the therapist shows interest. The impact of *focusing* has been discussed by Coleman[13] and Gendlin.[36]

Thus, exposing and being observed allows the patient to feel his identity more strongly as he extends his influence to another, but at the same time leaves him open to disruption by an alien perspective. The status of the examining therapist gives the patient social support, dangling the lure of individual companionship and society's approval. However, it also subverts the patient's comfortable ability to take himself for granted and makes him feel isolated. The relationship of patient and therapist makes a meeting more defined than a meeting of socially anonymous strangers, but that very definition creates still other uncertainties that are even more uncomfortable and exciting.

The Public and Private Roles of the Therapist

So far we have considered the involuntary aspects of therapy: the roles that cling to participants as members of their society. These roles are not chosen nor indiscriminately reinforced as therapy progresses. The same cannot be said for roles imposed by the therapist's subculture: the world of therapy and thera-

pists. As a result of his habitual activity, a therapist usually acquires a very different picture of himself from the one that prospective patients piece together out of popular culture and imagination.

The patient's view of the therapist is closest to the therapist's own view in folk healing and aboriginal therapies.[21] But even in such thoroughly socially integrated activities there may be the beginning of a split between the doctor's appearance to the patient and how he sees himself, since there is evidence that the "witch doctor" uses tricks unknown to his patient. Certainly the difference between the therapist's role as seen by the patient and by the therapist widens progressively as we approach modern, "dynamic," "expressive," therapies.

❲ Meeting a Prospective Therapy Partner

Although meeting a psychotherapist is an ambiguous social situation, bringing together parties who are far from unanimous about protocol, we have seen that there is some *de facto*, temporary agreement on roles, which fits the meeting into a recognizable pattern and makes it understandable to the patient. In any important meeting we try to find something familiar to help us master its newness, but it is especially urgent in therapy because therapy is more than a chance encounter and more than an encounter with a therapist. It is a meeting that is supposed to lead to a relationship that has duration and direction, and the partners must find ways of getting along with each other. The conventions of meeting are a platform from which some sort of ongoing relationship may be launched. The social structure gradually, though at best only partially, gives way to an individualized one.[8]

Showing and Perceiving Needs

Individualized structures are based on wishes. In order to have an ongoing relationship, patient and therapist must fit their desires together. To do that each must show his needs and look for the needs of the other. Both "probe the other's reaction to alarm."[78] Conventional roles can only help a little in manifesting and scouting needs. Consequently in the beginning of therapy there is urgent activity to pin down these variables. (In this the beginning of therapy is unique,[20] and offers unique opportunities that are sometimes wasted.) The patient looks at the therapist and asks himself, "Can he give me what I want? What does he want from me, and how does that jibe with what I want?" The therapist looks at the patient and asks himself, "What are my chances of success with him? How well does he take to my personality and procedure? How much leeway does he give me?" In other words, both patient and therapist weigh their opportunities, and these deliberations give a clearer shape to stranger anxiety and determine initial moves.

Exhibiting needs and scouting wishes are very complex tasks, because they affect each other. We identify people's attitudes by those signals that have meant the most to us in the attitudes of people who have been important to us. These ubiquitous transferences of previous forms onto a present companion have been called by psychoanalysts "floating transferences"[41] or "pseudo-transferences"[9] (to distinguish them from the specific response to the psychoanalytic atmosphere, known as the transference neurosis).[26] They are a universal kind of recognition. In a sense, they enable man to create his surrounding world, and in the same sense psychotherapy partners "create" each other.[32,53,61]

So Peter paints Paul with Peter's palette. But Peter's palette is not just a collection of colors accumulated at random over the years. He has gathered pigments according to his pressing needs and interests. Needs help to organize the phenomenal world,[32,53,61,103] and especially the human scene. (For instance, needs affect the transference image of the therapist.)[43] So when the patient wonders, "What does the therapist want from me?" he will answer in terms of what he wants for himself.

The therapist does the same thing. He has his own transferences (about which more later). He also has a preexisting theory that makes his new patient's wishes familiar. By means of the memory of people in his past, the patient's transference traces what the therapist can offer to his hopes. Similarly, by means of doctrine and clinical experience, the therapist's theory translates the patient's behavior into therapeutic objectives. (For instance, the theory of psychological "mechanisms" is a biased way of describing the patient according to the therapist's focus.)[80]

Mutual Accommodation and Its Limits

Each party in therapy progressively estimates what his partner wants from him and tries to show his needs in a way relevant to the other. Each finds ways of complementing the other, of putting himself in the other's world. Even therapists who plan no intense personal relationship realize that they have to "attract and keep the patient".[18] A therapist must meet at least some of the patient's expectations.[95] He must perform a real service, plainly intelligible to the patient, in addition to whatever role he allows the patient to imagine for him.[90] In the beginning he must reply to the patient in the patient's mode.[79] But with the best will to accommodate, neither party sees the other the way the other sees himself. The patient addresses his wishes to a tempting therapist who he suspects will scorn, resent, ignore, or—most upsetting of all— respond to them. Since the patient is not aware of all that he wants, he is also not aware of those fears, but he is automatically cautious and indirect.

Although more aware of discordant images, the therapist also tends to see a very different person from the one the patient feels himself to be, and gently refuses to address himself exclusively to the persona that is offered. (Coleman warns against total bypassing.[14])

And after all, neither party in therapy has the best will to accommodate. The patient will not give up what is most important to him in order to "play the therapy game" the way the therapist might wish.[33] And neither will the therapist blend into the patient's world without reservation, because however necessary some accommodation might be, it is not retractable. What helps partners get along smoothly also limits their further possibilities.[97]

Thus a patient who feels like a guest and supplicant may be required to find his own seat and direct conversation. Or a therapist who feels like a stimulating listener may expect a patient to be reflecting while the patient is really waiting to be rewarded by a "treatment" for information already given. The one thinks, "He is rude and withholding." The other thinks, "He is passive and oversensitive."* The reason for the discomfort lies in the nature of the partnership.

❰ Forming a Psychotherapeutic Partnership

Psychotherapy is more than an ongoing relationship between people who recognize each other as patient and therapist. It is supposed to supply something unavailable in other relationships. Therapists picture the "something extra" in various ways. Some say that it is information;[17,80] others, a unique emotional experience;[2] still others, a kind of child re-raising.[40,90] The patient may not be deliberately looking for any kind of relationship. He may simply want to get rid of a disturbance. He may expect a relationship no more exotic than the one he has with his family physician. That relationship is far from simple, but it *is* defined by previous experience. If a patient expects to have such a familiar relationship with his therapist, he will not be able to figure out how it can help his different kind of problem.

The Patient Develops a Theory

Probably all patients wonder, "How can talking help?" This universal bewilderment is often heard by therapists as a demand for a magical cure derived from infantile myths.[65] Someone who spends his life practicing ther-

apy may find it hard to fully appreciate how little a prospective patient may know about therapy.[13] (Therapists themselves understand it far from perfectly.) Beyond reflecting the vagueness of the talking treatment, the wish for a "magical" cure may simply express the helplessness of a person who is offered a promising relationship so novel that it does not fit any image of what he needs. To delineate a partnership in this anomalous relationship is a magnification of the task two strangers have in getting along together. The patient must work harder to make the benevolent apparition materialize in terms of his wishes and understanding than he needs to in ordinary situations.[56]

In other words, the patient has to develop an implicit plan or theory about his therapist's possibilities and the approach that will get results.† The patient has many wishes, not all mutually consistent, and corresponding conflicting fears. His tacit theory has to subordinate some of his wishes to others, and to heed some of his fears more than others. His theory will include accustomed compromises. To the therapist, the patient's theory may represent a deception, a pose, an indirection, a lack of straightforwardness, a game. He will sympathize with it as a manifestation of anxiety or inner conflict. But if the patient's wishes are brought into conflict in dealing with a vaguely defined therapist, the patient has no alternative but to work on some such incompletely fulfilling and partially expressive theory or plan.

The Therapist Develops a Personal Theory

The therapist already has a theory that governs his professional behavior. But, like the

---

* For useful inventories of patients' initial concerns see Coleman,[13,14] Goldstein,[42] Ruesch,[79] Redlich and Freedman,[71] Szasz,[97] and MacKinnon and Michels.[58]

† Sullivan[95] said that both patient and therapist have a theory about the other's behavior. Reik[73] holds that in everything we do we unconsciously picture the other's reaction. Mead[63] says that objects get their meaning from the tacit plans we have for them. Ruesch[78] says that therapy aims to develop the patient's ability to perceive his actions, codify them, and respond to the therapist's reactions, so that he will be better able to derive meaning from his and the other's behavior. This is a way of saying that therapy is a polishing of patient's theorizing abilities.

patient, he also needs a plan to integrate his subtle, nontechnical goals and tastes with the new person in his life. Therapists generally discipline these needs. There has even grown a belief that a proper therapist is self-less in the conduct of his work. The picture is an ideal model, useful for encouraging self-understanding and self-control, but it is not the picture of a living therapist. No treatment or training abolishes the unconscious; sexual responses are not completely governable; a person will always have nonspecific habitual characterological attitudes.[100] All of these parts of the therapist's humanity may foster implicit plans or tacit theories about how to proceed with the patient. A therapist may establish a transference to his patient. (Gitelson[39] warns that an initial over-all attitude toward a patient is a sign of the therapist's transference even when it pretends to be an intuitive recognition of the patient's needs.) And then there are approaches to the patient coaxed out of the therapist by the patient's approaches to him—the counter-transferences of psychoanalysis. They cannot be avoided and are often not even detected.[53,56,85,101]

This means that some inexplicit theories by which the therapist operates, just like the patient's theories, are ways of harmonizing his personality with that of his partner. (Wexler[104] says that not all of the ideas the patient develops about the relationship are unreal and not all of the therapist's ideas are real.)

The therapist may even choose his technical theory to match the kind of relationship he wants to have with patients. The gross difference between types of therapists found by Whitehorn[107] may be matched by subtle differences within each group. Some therapists have static and some dynamic self-images.[80] Some especially respect the discovery of theoretically germane information, others respect more the evocation of dramatic affect. Some pride themselves in helpfulness, some in research. Some fancy themselves midwives, others surgeons. Some hold themselves out as models, others as muses. This is what Rank[70] referred to as the therapist's "vocational psychology." The way the therapist fits his personal needs into the patient's pattern reflects a

nonprofessional and undeliberate theory that highlights certain significant features in the patient and singles out certain approaches to him. It is, again, the counterpart of the plan or theory that the patient is at work on.

The Therapist Has a Prefabricated Theory

Nevertheless, the most distinctive feature of the psychotherapeutic relationship is that one party has some standard, prefabricated, goal-directed theory in addition to whatever personal plans he may develop during the meeting.

Theories of different therapists are not all equally explicit. Some therapists operate with elaborate, abstract theories, others with a cloud of implicit theory supporting a kind of therapeutic reflex.*

Thus while patient and therapist each develops a tacit theory about how the new companion relates to his outlook and ranked goals, the therapist is also busy relating the experience to his (usually more explicit) professional theory. Whereas people in a relationship ordinarily integrate themselves according to their own wishes and wishful perceptions, *the therapist, by adopting a professional theory, adds an artificial set of "wishes" and "wish"-determined structures that stands in the way of both parties finding fast and familiar harmony.* (Lewis[56] says that the therapist has "Plans to change the patient's Plans.")

Therapeutic Conflict

The above statement means that the psychotherapeutic relationship is characterized by a special estrangement between patient and

---

* Rogers[77] holds that the personality of the therapist heals *despite* the obstruction of his theory. But what he means is that only as much theory is needed as is employed by any healthy person in his dealings with everyone. Since the Rogerian qualities of (self) congruence, empathy, and uncriticalness are only a few of the attitudes that people show to others, a special concentration on them for beneficial purposes is part of a theory. Rogers' view of the source of his patient's discomfort, although simpler and less individualized than many popular theories of pathogenesis, is nevertheless another part of his theory.

therapist, which makes their adjustment more difficult than the adjustment of two people who merely seek to get along with each other. It results in a struggle or conflict that may be quite invisible or may be loudly evident, but in some fashion is preserved by the therapist with an artificial stubbornness in honor of a rival allegiance to his professional theory.

The limitless and contradictory hopes that most therapies encourage cannot be satisfied, and even the limited ones that can be are slow of fulfillment. Add to this that a patient who has difficulty in living is presented with a task that in some ways is even more difficult, and the result should be chronic dissatisfaction. Actually, dissatisfaction is not as apparent in therapy as one would expect. Perhaps it is slowly worn down, or waits for the time of termination and flourishes after the end of therapy. But in light of the patient's theory, the therapist's theories, and the struggle between them, the therapist is often an unwilling deceiver and a willing frustrater. One job description of a psychotherapist is that he must bear the obloquy for defaulting on his (apparent) promises without justifying himself or retaliating. In that respect his theory repays him for the trouble it has caused. (Unhappily it must be acknowledged that the theory is also sometimes used to counterattack.[6])

Literature on the Psychotherapeutic Struggle

Haley[45] has specialized in therapeutic struggle. Adler[1] described the therapist's struggle against the patient's wrong direction. Nunberg[65] portrayed the psychoanalyst as forcing the patient to give up infantile demands by an implicit threat of abandonment, a theme that is implicit in Freud's dictum that cures are cures of love. According to Strupp,[93] the therapist forces the patient against his will to trust and depend on him. We shall discuss below the principle of absolute nongratification (e.g. cf., Fenichel[20]); this would surely reflect a struggle or conflict between patient and therapist. Bird[9] says that analysis is not merely an intellectual or emotional exercise,

but a conflict (albeit a conflict projected onto —i.e., attributed to—the relationship from within the patient's own mind). Levenson[53] is eloquent on the struggle of the therapist to keep clear of the roles that the patient desperately tries to make him take. Ruesch[79] says that the therapist does not accept the role the patient offers him, despite considerable pressure. And Berne[8] wrote that when the therapist, properly, does not take up the role that is thrust on him by the patient, it breaks the smoothness of the relationship and leads to trouble.

The psychoanalytic theory of resistance concerns the struggle in therapy.[30] Rank[70] was particularly interested in the therapeutic struggle. He described a "battle of ideologies between therapist and patient," which he saw as a fundamental conflict of wills. "That something is exacted of the patient by the therapist other than what he expects, is one of the oldest fundamental theses of psychoanalysis." Nevertheless, said Rank, "As the therapist can only heal in his own way, the patient also can only become well in *his* own way."[70] Even Greenson,[43] who counts on a great deal of harmony between therapy partners, acknowledges that the patient is primarily interested in what he can get out of the personal relationship (in Greenson's words, the transference), while the therapist's primary investment is in relatively detached observation (in Greenson's words, the working alliance).

Tarachow[98] contrasted the stringent conditions of formal psychoanalysis with ordinary social responses, where, for instance, a plea for help is answered by giving help, or the wish to fight is answered by fighting. The psychoanalyst, according to Tarachow, is required to create a "therapeutic barrier." Szasz[97] also cautions against the ordinary social attempt to create an early harmony. He acknowledges a great deal of struggling and even bullying in most therapy, but feels that it is avoidable if the therapist shows the patient what he is willing to provide and leaves the patient free to do what he wants with it or reject it. Experience is necessary to determine if this avoids or intensifies the struggle. Lewis[56] believes that the therapist's job is to place obstacles in the patient's customary path and thus help him to learn. Klauber[50] feels that one function of psychoanalytic interpretation is to keep the analyst from resonating with the patient's sexual urges. He refers to an "inherent struggle in psychoanalysis—almost a tease." The emphasis placed by Rogers[74-76] and Truax[102]— and also by Szasz,[97] in a different spirit—on the steadfastness with which the therapist maintains his genuineness is an acknowledgment that the therapist's theory makes a mutual accommodation harder, at least early in therapy. Gestalt therapists[54] sometimes forbid patients their habitual style of communication, and Fagan[19] is keenly aware of the need to fight the patient for control. In behavior therapy, patients are forced (however willingly) into situations they seek to avoid. Ruesch[79] refers to an inevitable "stalemate."

We will now consider this strange, frustrated cooperation in terms of the polarity and mutuality of therapist and patient.

⦅ The Therapist's Pole

Therapists tend to think of themselves as educators. They see themselves as revealing either the nature of reality or the true state of affairs within the patient, or the most "real" way to experience feelings, or the most fruitful way to live. A therapist may see himself as dispelling the patient's myths about living,[17] his harmful habit patterns,[15] his illusions about himself and about others.[95] He intends to demonstrate the inefficiency of the patient's patterns[48,100] and the futility of some of his hopes.[30]

Usually the therapist believes that he sees things correctly where the patient errs, and that he can show the patient's view to be insupportable or without value. This belief is not held by all therapists, but it underlies most theories of psychotherapy and almost all practices. In such a perspective the patient appears negativistic,[1,70] resistant,[41] rigid,[35,72,103]

self-indulgent,[30] stubborn,[30] partially lifeless,[35] misled,[17] or badly trained.[15,80] And as an educator, the therapist may correspondingly present to his patient the figure of a taskmaster and critic.

Psychoanalysts have elaborated the therapist's pole in the concept of the therapeutic alliance.[88] The therapeutic alliance is where the therapist wants the patient to be; it therefore represents the therapist's professional wish. It is usually described as a disinterested or drive-independent way of organizing perceptions.[33] (Berne expresses a wish for an adult–adult relationship in therapy.[8]) Some form of the therapeutic alliance is a touchstone for many dynamically-oriented psychotherapists. Correspondingly, a therapist employing Ruesch's outlook[78] will want his patient to be more interested in pure communication than in warfare or diplomacy. Haley's[45] therapist wants his patient to cease trying to control the therapy situation. Influenced by Horney,[48] a therapist will want his patient to give up futile posturing and accept himself for what he is. Therapists of all persuasions basically want their patients to be braver than they are.

⦅ The Patient's Pole

Being a patient is not a profession, so patients organize the shadowy new psychotherapeutic relationship in even more diverse ways than do therapists. But experience shows some common features. The patient wants to maintain his self-esteem, and manages the situation with that in mind.[95] In his heart a patient wants to be loved as he loves himself. He evaluates the situation in terms of the likelihood of such admiring love, and tries to identify the therapist as someone whom he can love for the love, appreciation, admiration, and partisanship he shows for the patient.[65] He may try to recapture in the therapeutic relationship a two-person harmony, or a merging with another person that he wanted in the distant past and never acquired.[5,51] Yet he may sense dangers in that situation (such as feeling himself to be less whole, individual, or capable) that justify animosity to the therapist.[72,81]

The most universal and definitive past pattern for structuring the therapeutic relationship is that of child and parent. Many therapists regard the infant–mother relationship as the central orienting structure of therapy.[39,86,90] According to Nunberg,[65] the patient does not simply want to shed symptoms, he wants to realize all the grandiose fantasies of his infancy, to be all-powerful and to be permitted all indulgences. Fenichel[20] wrote that the patient wants the unrealistic gratifications that his symptoms symbolize.

This is not to say that patients ask to be treated like infants. Adults are usually intensely ashamed of such wishes. We have noted that the patient's pole includes the wish to seem admirable and, especially in the United States, that means to be independent. Therefore the patient's implicit plan usually involves a covert quest for parental care and overt rejection or resentment of it, which in turn may be disguised by a dutiful submission. Some authors feel that "hostile dependence" is a frequent prelude to therapy and an absolutely dependable part of the therapeutic scene.[81] The situation illustrates the dangers of either opposing or cooperating with the patient's theory.

Other patterns can be discerned as well. The patient sees an opportunity to be understood. Understanding may be a token of love[56] or a demonstration of symbiotic closeness. But it may also be a separate need,[79] a foil for the kind of internal dialogue that keeps experience alive.[35] The patient may recognize in therapy a chance to learn and develop. That may be reminiscent of earliest care-taking.[90] Or it may be a formative aim in itself.[60]

Not all investigators, therefore, feel that the patient's orientation is a reenactment of earlier dramas. But many have thought that almost all of the patient's urgent orientations are significant because of their historical meaning. Psychoanalysts in particular feel that one very strong pull by the patient is in a "regressive"

direction,* i.e., is aimed at making a past relationship come to life again with the therapist.[41] The disharmony between patient and therapist is therefore described by psychoanalysts as a struggle between the patient's regressive strivings toward childish satisfaction and the therapist's forward urgings toward adult responsibility. Everyone agrees, however, that most patients also want forward movement, while the therapist often encourages regression to provide information for growth.

⟨ The Overlap

Harmonizing Forces

Pure dysharmony between patient and therapist would be no relationship at all.[101] But after all, the struggle between them is only an exaggeration of the general difficulty of fitting a new partner and a new relationship into familiar terms, and of fitting oneself into another framework. As previously noted, fitting is a reciprocal process. To an extent, the patient gives the therapist what he wants[34,89] while the therapist tries not to disappoint the patient.[95]

Although therapeutic fitting together is more difficult because the therapist's theory intrudes, therapy provides compensating factors that foster harmony. On the patient's side the need for help induces "suggestibility."[21] Some authors believe that the specific kind of frustration that brings patients to treatment also produces a receptive attachment to the

---

* Psychoanalysts disagree among themselves over how much the patient's quest and the analyst's are at odds. Freud,[30] Tarachow,[98] Nunberg,[65] and Fenichel[20] feel that many of the patient's efforts run counter to the analyst's. Some of their writings suggest that the patient's moves toward his analyst are not really directed toward a person, but rather toward himself as imagined in the loving eye of an analyst. In this sense the strivings are said to be not "object-directed" but, rather, "narcissistic," and a retreat from the real world. Other analysts such as Gitelson,[40] Stone,[91] Loewald,[57] and Balint[6] feel that a healthy quest is larval in the patient's primitive wishes, just as the adult is implicit in the child. These writers do not give the impression that strivings toward the analyst are the opposite of what the analyst considers healthy.

therapist,[39] although others say that patients who need therapy most are least suggestible.[93] The patient also initially grants the therapist respect and accepts his authority.[13,21]

Certain qualities of the therapist also facilitate agreement. Most therapists (not all) observe a rule of gradual and gentle introduction of their own perspective. Moreover, therapists develop ways of braking the pull toward the patient's pole. In psychoanalytic terms this means modulating the "regressive" tendency of the patient.[13,50]

Another therapist-inspired aspect of most therapeutic relationships that moderates opposition is tentativeness, which is made possible by the therapist's limited participation in the activities of the patient's life.[56] There is less playing for keeps than in other relationships. Commitment is only partial,[8] games are welcomed,[11] play is encouraged directly[54] or by the therapist joining the patient's progression of thought without really subscribing to his views.[99] The therapist does not stick to any one role.[79] He discourages too much seriousness too soon.[25] Orthodox psychoanalysts select patients who can put on and take off childlike attitudes (reversible regression). The therapist arranges an atmosphere of experimentation[15,21] He engages his patient in a middling rather than passionate or detached fashion.[83]

Certain of the therapist's social skills also help to reduce disharmony. He should handle stranger anxiety with ease[40] and be a good conversationalist,[84] i.e., have a talent for effectively including another in his perspective and vice versa, which does not necessarily employ seduction or persuasion. The therapist should be imaginatively evocative.[4,19]

One of the most significant harmonizing elements in therapy is the therapist's theory— the very theory which we have seen to be an obstacle to easy harmony. The therapist's theory is designed to encompass many human frameworks and relate them to therapeutic goals. Ideally it is elastic enough to translate any attitude of the patient into a familiar and hopeful perspective of the therapist. Labeling patient behavior in terms of the therapist's theory draws the patient into the therapist's orientation.

Gratification

The overlap between the patient's and the therapist's goals is often called "gratification." The therapist's fidelity to his own perspective leads him to be cautious about gratification. Like most authorities, Sullivan[95] warns that the therapist must want nothing from the patient by way of personal response, except respect for his competence; he must not "come on" to his patient. Here the restraint clearly augments the patient's freedom as well as his security, though it may at the same time hurt his pride in himself and his therapist. In a venerable psychoanalytic tradition, gratification is to be totally avoided precisely because it compromises the therapist's stand.[20] And yet some sort of harmony is required for a relationship, and some sort of gratification will be had.[14,101]

The therapist is gratified by progress[20] and the patient can be gratified by pleasing the therapist. Sullivan[95] said that the therapist's expertness reassures the patient; that achievement must gratify the therapist as well. Furthermore, the therapist is mildly excited by the coloring his theory gives to the picture of his patient, and the patient is similarly excited by the drama of his theoretically described situation.[50]

Competitive desires may be visibly or invisibly gratified in the struggle between the patient's pole and the therapist's.[45] Overt sexual behavior, of course, is ethically prohibited. Inability to overcome the prohibition often makes the patient profoundly resentful—hurt in his sexual pride and snubbed in his wish to be special to the therapist or at least accepted by him as an equal. (The Freudians relate this to oedipal ambitions.) In a way, the sexual prohibition echoes the inability to achieve natural harmony with the therapist. The patient has a rival in the therapist's theory. Tarachow[98] thought that masochistic gratification was required for enduring therapy. And yet the patient can seduce the therapist in countless subtle ways: for instance, by playing on his therapeutic ambitions. Indeed it is possible that the patient must *succeed* in seducing the therapist on a subtle emotional plane if he is to make major improvement.[101]

We have seen that therapy offers an echo of early dependency. Many therapists regard this particular indulgence as a healing device, just as many worry that dependency gratification interferes with growth.[9] But even if the therapist wants to moderate it he does not have the unilateral power to do so. The common experience that patients report as, "My therapist doesn't tell me anything," may increase dependency more than a stream of authoritative advice. Since a relationship is whatever it is felt to be,[7,53] and since relationships can in some ways be enforced,[12,45,56] the patient's plans will succeed in some degree.

Obviously too much sexual success deprives the patient of some dependency gratification and blocks other wishes. Too much dependency robs him of self-respect and buries other tendencies. Insofar as any behavior can be camouflage for other behavior, gratification may mean that the therapist agrees with the patient about the wisdom of hiding other stifled wishes. Therefore both patient and therapist have mixed feelings about gratification. Nevertheless, however wary, in the end they gratify each other in many ways.

Literature on Gratification

Even among those who consider gratification the enemy of therapy, some patients have been allowed to compromise the therapist's role in a limited way through what the Freudians call "parameters" of technique, which allow transactions between therapist and patient other than interpretation. Tower,[101] in fact, asserts that no one is cured by interpretation per se. Like French,[24] she feels that some progression of gratifications is the moving force in treatment. Even Tarachow[98] allows that there must be some agreement between therapist and patient. Eysenck,[18] as noted, holds that the therapist must attract and keep the patient before he can expect anything from him, whatever the theory of cure. Stone[90] says that the patient must actually find something of what he seeks in the physician, in other words, some real gratification in the therapeutic relationship. The recent trend in psychoanalysis led by Loewald,[57] Stone,[90] and Gitelson[39] represents a quest for a gratification of the patient that is compatible with analytic aims. These psychoanalysts believe that the overlap on which patient and therapist can agree is gratification of the wish for good parenting, i.e., the wish for a parent who helps to integrate and discipline the child's needs with an eye to his potentialities as an adult,[57] a parent who is able to promise a satisfactory wholeness out of what is expressed by the child, who guarantees continued concern and caring,[39,90] who serves as a loving model, who can accept the wish for attachment and for independence at appropriate intervals, and who can perform the functions of the mother of separation and the mother of nurturance.

Stone[90] believes that these roles are acceptably combined in the vocation of the physician. Saul[81] also feels that the therapist is in a position to gratify the child in the patient without slighting the adult. Greenson[43] says that the combination of "mother" and researcher gratifies the patient without the danger of compromising either role. Giovacchini[38] holds that the analyst can in good conscience be a comforting and gratifying haven for wishes of symbiotic union, while still helping to untie the symbiosis. Balint[6] and Kohut[51] emphasize the passive but willing gratification of certain "regressive" needs (such as idealizing or merging with a parent-figure), which the patient must experience before he can move on from his own pole toward the therapist's. Maslow[60] also suggests that some gratifications (of what he calls deficiency needs) may have to be combined with the teaching of independence (which he calls gratification of growth needs). Berne discusses this as well.[8]

All of these ideas are ways of describing the overlap between patient pole and therapist pole. They are a bridge between what is familiar to the patient and what is new. Although the therapist remains slightly aloof, out of loyalty to his theoretical postulates, in the overlap area he provides the patient something old which is something new, something that connects with the past while it leads forward—as, for example, the mother of nurturance who is also the mother of separation. The therapist makes some of the patient's dream come true.

At the same time we should keep in mind the reservations of Tarachow,[98] Szasz,[97] and Bird,[9] who remind us of the hazards of this double role. They speak about the dangers of infantilizing the patient. The wishes at the core of the patient's pole are mutually contradictory (as are everyone's wishes, including the therapist who wants maximum suggestibility and independence on the part of his patient). That means that *any* gratification is also a frustration. The patient wants something familiar that he can integrate with his experience, but also some movement, improvement, relief, and increased freedom. The struggle in therapy prevents the frustration of some wishes (for growth or change). By the same token, the gratification of overlap may foster that very frustration.

The tradition of Loewald, Gitelson, and Stone tried to find the middle ground that stands for the old and the new at the same time and therefore does not shortchange one wish for another. They found it in the paradigm of the child's relationship with his parents, which should not, ideally, be infantiliz-*ing*. However, there is some doubt whether such a middle ground is still available for an adult patient. Tarachow and Szasz think not. Rank says that you cannot raise a grown person again; he can only be accepted. Many patients distinctly feel that therapy at its best is still infantilizing.

The search for a relationship that represents at once the therapist's new pull and the patient's old orientation is not confined to psychoanalysts. Gratification of any sort seems to have to do with love. Practitioners would like to say that love is the bridge. But love is different things to different people and is usually recognized diversely by patient and therapist. (Such a discrepancy is often what brings patients to therapy.) Moreover, there is no reason to think that therapists have a greater capacity for love than anyone else, and every

reason to think that theirs is limited and makes its own, personal, and not necessarily therapeutic demands. So therapists are tempted to define love as whatever it is they especially have to give. Formulas such as "love equals understanding" naturally abound. But that simply transfers the problem from love to understanding, which is just as ambiguous.

Some of the most systematic efforts to pick out of the therapeutic transaction an element that is universally desirable, unconflicted, and compatible with both patient's and therapist's poles, have been made by theoreticians of evocativeness, such as Rogers and Gendlin who hold that the therapist is not so much a guide as he is a medium or foil who elicits the patient's potential. Avoiding the difficulty of integrating the mother of nurturance and of separation, or of choosing between mothering and an egalitarian relationship, these investigators have, in effect, asked what universal, interpersonal gift the mothering relationship itself exemplifies. Gendlin[35] feels that the very process of living requires a dialectic of feedback. Everyone needs someone's reaction to make concrete the vague possibilities of his body feeling. Such a helper is not a condescending comforter but an interlocutor who crystallizes the patient's meaning by bringing it into a process of new, adaptive experience. For Rogers and Gendlin, the mother of union and the mother of separation are two aspects of every person (therapist or nontherapist), aspects that are essential to any sentient being. One aspect is an otherness that allows a person to see more in his potentialities and thus move his experience in a fluid and living fashion. The other aspect is an empathic togetherness which makes a real response possible. There is some empirical evidence, collected independently of this school, that such factors are crucial.[49]

But the problem is not so neatly solved. Rogers points out that the therapist must not only be empathetic but also be *seen* as empathetic.[77] The patient may insist that empathy be shown in *his* way, and that leads back to the conflict between patient and therapist poles. And Gendlin has admitted that some patients do not use the therapist's feedback profitably, which suggests individual variation even in this basic human need. (Perhaps Witkin's work[108] bears on these individual differences.)

There is, therefore, still much room for further understanding of how patient and therapist get together while keeping apart in a helpful way. A synoptic example is the situation of the therapist as an accepting and tolerant person while being something like a critic.

❨ Polarity and Overlap: Criticism in Psychotherapy

A patient who comes to therapy suffers the realistic danger of an authoritative put-down. But because he is alert to any possible self-affirmation, he may also spy an opportunity within that danger. A judge who can condemn can also exonerate; a critic can praise; and therefore the patient can easily fit the therapist's educative program into his own plan (for self-adulation, for instance). Or he may see an opportunity to become a powerful judge by identifying with the therapist. Furthermore, a judge can accept a confession.[84] Tacit forgiveness in the form of noncriticism is enormously important in the early stages of therapy.[15,43,76]

Exposure to shame is, however, quite different.[55] The need to hold on to self-respect is paramount. Patients welcome the chance to express guilt but stubbornly conceal what would produce shame.[65] Even to enjoy exoneration can feel shameful, as being worthy only of a child. Indeed, shame can and frequently does arise simply from exposing oneself to a therapist without reciprocation.[55]

Therapists are aware that fear of criticism and contempt reinforces the patient's rigidity and his resistance to the therapist's pull. Most therapists therefore make great efforts to be accepting and non-judgmental.[75,84] But once again, the therapist does not decide how he will be seen or indeed what he will actually be to the patient. It may be impossible for the therapist to be non-judgmental, since the therapist moves in a genuinely conflicting direc-

tion from the new patient. Patients sense where their guilty or shameful impulses correspond to the therapist's technical taboos; and that, rather than the therapist's willingness to listen to confessions, is where his acceptingness is tested. What strivings the therapist will or will not allow is told by how he reacts to the patient's conduct in therapy, not by how he reacts to life situations and issues that do not involve him. So the therapist's divergent professional wishes suffice to limit his acceptingness or appreciativeness of, and even possibly respect for, the patient.

A still more vital issue is at stake. The patient's general goals are represented by specific behaviors that the therapist may criticize when they occur in the consulting room. That disapproval is tantamount to condemning the general aims that stand behind them. Unresponsiveness to his therapist's wisdom may be sexually satisfying to a patient; disapproving that "resistance" may be equivalent to a Victorian sexual taboo.[53] This is a problem as long as interpretations are admitted to have overtones of criticism.[98]

Judgment, then, is something that the patient wants and fears. It is difficult for the therapist to avoid judgment, partly because of his educative commitment and partly because the patient, for educative and other reasons, entices him to judge. Yet the therapist knows that judgment is often restrictive and discouraging. The situation shows how tricky the task is that patient and therapist face in maintaining a rich relationship with a permanent built-in estrangement.

❨ Outcome

Psychotherapy exaggerates and prolongs the inherent difficulty of a new relationship, namely, the difficulty two people experience in trying to find an opening for their wishes in the other's wish-system. By exaggerating the difficulty, therapy keeps possibilities open. In all of the conflicts between patient and therapist, an area of hopefulness is enforced. The patient may fight with the therapist for endorsement of his strivings (as currently clothed in his neurosis), but because he does not win the fight he can hope that other, opposite ambitions are also approvable. And because his struggle for approval is not neatly won, he can retain the hope that he is autonomous and does not need an authority's approval. The therapist may find a stubborn enemy in the patient's "unrealistic" attitude toward him, while discovering hope and opportunity in the patient's resulting respect, which lets the therapist "reach" him. Though they are not likely to visualize their conflict or their opportunity in the same way, both patient and therapist find a hopefulness, an openendedness, that would not be there without the conflict.

As long as there is conflict, no hopes are ruled out. As long as there is conflict, no roles are ruled out. As long as there is conflict, no perspectives are ruled out. As long as there is conflict between therapist and patient, no premature, intrapsychic, institutionalized resolution need congeal.

Two people in therapy stretch their usual way of seeing and wanting (on the part of the patient) and seeing and wanting and theorizing (on the part of the therapist) in order to encompass the recalcitrant partner. The stretch leads to hope.

The Literature on Hope

French[24] has shown in detail how hope leads, inch by inch, to the resolution of problems. Frank[21] has pointed out how crucial hope is to a change in attitudes. Stotland[92] has gathered evidence for the strengthening effect of hope, both hope offered from outside oneself and hope from noticing one's success. (This is important, since several authors have pointed out that the sheer magnitude and length of the therapy project cumulatively instill certain feelings in its participants.) Sullivan[95] said that the patient must always be able to see a convincingly likely benefit in order to progress through any interview. Ruesch[79] says that there is always a covert promise in therapy.

We have seen how psychoanalysts try to find some genuine personal but legitimate gift that is immediately hopeful to the patient, even while the therapist plans to demolish other hopes. The balancing of closeness and separateness, gratification and deprivation, is the therapist's way of encouraging hopes without confirming them. Levenson,[53] Lewis,[56] Chessick,[12] Haley,[45] Gestalt therapists, and many others recommend a fluidity in the therapist's attitude that prevents him from being trapped in the stereotype that the patient's pole draws him to. Most writers stress how important it is to break the patient out of his old structures. The shiftings of the therapist's outlook between old and new, between one role and another, preserve the therapy as a convertible situation that is new but also reachable by variations of past themes. Old hopes are encouraged but not allowed to smother other hopes.

Hope leads to courage and discovery and change. Risks are dared and anxiety found to be unrealistic. The encouragement comes not from the therapist's theory but from the flexibility the theory imposes on the relationship, where it constructs a free field for experimentation[15] or an arena of transference.[28]

The dialectic of a personal encounter is enormously complicated and descriptively inexhaustible.[35,53] We need to develop many different conceptualizations of the therapeutic relationship. A concrete event such as a meeting in therapy can only be understood by using many coordinates and locating their intersections.

One such intersection seems to be that the therapist offers structures that tempt the patient because they are familiar to his active wishes but are different enough to arouse dormant ones. Such a new structure might be the comfortable acknowledgment of a frightened impulse; a different moral standard; a new definition of a feeling; a therapist who does and does not act like a parent; a theoretical formulation; a new connection between two thoughts; an imaginary re-positioning of the patient in a remembered encounter; a new attitude; a new way of listening to oneself; an ordered behavior; or a programed confrontation with what has been avoided.

In practice, different therapists aim for different degrees of flexibility. Sometimes the therapist seems to lay down structures for the patient to adopt. But what is common to therapy generally is not a proffered set of structures so much as a *temptation* lurking in therapy's curious welcoming obstacle path—a temptation to risk a difference.

⟦ Bibliography

1. ADLER, A. (1916) "The Concept of Resistance during Treatment," in B. B. Wolman, ed., *Success and Failure in Psychoanalysis and Psychotherapy*, pp. 21–34. New York: Macmillan, 1972.

2. ALEXANDER, F. *Psychoanalysis and Psychotherapy: Developments in Theory, Technique and Training.* New York: Norton, 1956.

3. ALLPORT, F. H. *Theories of Perception and the Concept of Structure.* New York: Wiley, 1955.

4. APPELBAUM, S. A. "Speaking with the Second Voice: Evocativeness," *J. Am. Psychoanal. Assoc.*, 14 (1966), 462–477.

5. BALINT, M. *Primary Love and Psycho-Analytic Technique.* New York: Liveright, 1953.

6. ———. *The Basic Fault: Therapeutic Aspects of Regression.* London: Tavistock, 1968.

7. BATESON, G. *Steps to an Ecology of Mind.* New York: Ballantine Books, 1972.

8. BERNE, E. *Transactional Analysis in Psychotherapy.* New York: Grove Press, 1961.

9. BIRD, B. "Notes on Transference: Universal Phenomenon and the Hardest Part of Analysis," *J. Am. Psychoanal. Assoc.*, 20 (1972), 267–301.

10. BOSS, M. and G. CONDRAU. "Existential Psychoanalysis," in B. B. Wolman, ed., *Psychoanalytic Techniques: A Handbook for the Practicing Psychoanalyst*, pp. 443–467. New York: Basic Books, 1967.

11. BRAATØY, T. *Fundamentals of Psychoanalytic Technique.* New York: Wiley, 1954.

12. CHESSICK, R. *How Psychotherapy Heals: The Process of Intensive Psychotherapy.* New York: Science House, 1969.

13. COLEMAN, J. V. "The Initial Phase of Psychotherapy," *Bull. Menninger Clin.*, 13 (1949), 189–197.

14. ———. "Aims and Conduct of Psychotherapy," *Arch. Gen. Psychiatry*, 18 (1968), 1–6.

15. DOLLARD, J. and N. MILLER. *Personality and Psychotherapy: An Analysis in Terms of Learning, Thinking and Culture.* New York: McGraw-Hill, 1950.

16. DREIKURS, R. "The Adlerian Approach to Therapy," in M. I. Stein, ed., *Contemporary Psychotherapies*, pp. 80–93. New York: Free Press, 1961.

17. ELLIS, A. "Rational Therapy: A Rational Approach to Interpretation," in E. F. Hammer, ed., *Use of Interpretation in Treatment; Technique and Art*, pp. 232–239. New York: Grune & Stratton, 1968.

18. EYSENCK, H. J. "A Mish-Mash of Theories," *Int. J. Psychiatry*, 9 (1970), 140–146.

19. FAGAN, J. "The Tasks of the Therapist," in J. Fagan and I. L. Shepherd, eds., *Gestalt Therapy Now: Theory, Techniques, Applications*, pp. 88–106. Palo Alto, Calif.: Science and Behavior Books, 1970.

20. FENICHEL, O. *Problems of Psychoanalytic Technique.* New York: Psychoanalytic Quarterly, 1941.

21. FRANK, J. *Persuasion and Healing: A Comparative Study of Psychotherapy.* Baltimore: The Johns Hopkins Press, 1961.

22. ———. "The Role of Influence in Psychotherapy," in M. I. Stein, ed., *Contemporary Psychotherapies*, pp. 17–41. New York: Free Press, 1961.

23. ———. "Therapy in a Group Setting," in M. I. Stein, ed., *Contemporary Psychotherapies*, pp. 42–59. New York: Free Press, 1961.

24. FRENCH, T. M. The Integration of Behavior. Vol. 3. *The Reintegrative Process in a Psychoanalytic Treatment.* Chicago: University of Chicago Press, 1958.

25. ———. *Psychoanalytic Interpretations: The Selected Papers of Thomas French.* Chicago: Quadrangle Books, 1970.

26. FREUD, S. (1912) "The Dynamics of Transference," in J. Strachey, ed., *Standard Edition*, Vol. 12, pp. 99–108. London: Hogarth, 1955.

27. ———. (1913) "Further Recommendations in the Technique of Psycho-Analysis: On Beginning the Treatment," in *Collected Papers*, Vol. 2, pp. 342–368. London: Hogarth, 1948.

28. ———. (1914) "Further Recommendations

in the Technique of Psycho-Analysis: Recollection, Repetition and Working Through," in *Collected Papers*, Vol. 2, pp. 366–376. London: Hogarth, 1948.

29. ———. (1915) "Further Recommendations in the Technique of Psycho-Analysis: Observations on Transference Love," in *Collected Papers*, Vol. 2, pp. 377–391. London: Hogarth, 1948.

30. ———. (1937) "Analysis Terminable and Interminable," in *Collected Papers*, Vol. 5, pp. 316–357. London: Hogarth, 1948.

31. FRIEDMAN, L. "The Significance of Determinism and Free Will," *Int. J. Psycho-Anal.*, 46 (1965), 515–520.

32. ———. "Drives and Knowledge: A Speculation," *J. Am. Psychoanal. Assoc.*, 16 (1968), 81–94.

33. ———. "The Therapeutic Alliance," *Int. J. Psycho-Anal.*, 50 (1969), 139–153.

34. FROMM-REICHMANN, F. *Principles of Intensive Psychotherapy*. Chicago: University of Chicago Press, 1950.

35. GENDLIN, E. "A Theory of Personality Change," in P. Worchel and D. Byrne, eds., *Personality Change*, pp. 102–148. New York: Wiley, 1964.

36. ———. "The Experiential Response," in E. F. Hammer, ed., *Use of Interpretation in Treatment: Technique and Art*, pp. 208–227. New York: Grune & Stratton, 1968.

37. GILL, M., R. NEWMAN, and F. REDLICH. *The Psychiatric Interview in Clinical Practice*. New York: International Universities Press, 1954.

38. GIOVACCHINI, P. L. *Tactics and Techniques in Psychoanalytic Therapy*. New York: Science House, 1972.

39. GITELSON, M. "The Emotional Position of the Analyst in the Psycho-Analytic Situation," *Int. J. Psycho-Anal.*, 33 (1952), 1–10.

40. ———. "The Curative Factors in Psycho-Analysis: 1. The First Phase of Psychoanalysis," *Int. J. Psycho-Anal.*, 43 (1962), 194–205.

41. GLOVER, E. *The Technique of Psycho-Analysis*. New York: International Universities Press, 1955.

42. GOLDSTEIN, A. P. *Therapist-Patient Expectancies in Psychotherapy*. New York: Macmillan, 1962.

43. GREENSON, R. *The Technique and Practice of Psychoanalysis*, Vol. 1. New York: International Universities Press, 1967.

44. GREENSON, R. and M. WEXLER. "The Non-Transference Relationship in the Psychoanalytic Situation," *Int. J. Psycho-Anal.*, 50 (1969), 27–39.

45. HALEY, J. *Strategies of Psychotherapy*. New York: Grune & Stratton, 1963.

46. HEIDER, F. *The Psychology of Interpersonal Relations*. New York: Wiley, 1958.

47. HOLLINGSHEAD, A. B., and F. REDLICH. *Social Class and Mental Illness*. New York: Wiley, 1958.

48. HORNEY, K. *Neurosis and Human Growth: The Struggle Toward Self-Realization*. New York: Norton, 1950.

49. KERNBERG, O., E. BURSTEIN, L. COYNE et al. "Psychotherapy and Psychoanalysis: Final Report of the Menninger Foundation's Psychotherapy Research Project," *Bull. Menninger Clin.*, 36 (1972), 1–275.

50. KLAUBER, J. "On the Relationship of Transference and Interpretation in Psychoanalytic Therapy," *Int. J. Psycho-Anal.*, 53 (1972), 385–391.

51. KOHUT, H. *The Analysis of the Self: A Systematic Approach to the Psychoanalytic Treatment of Narcissistic Personality Disorders*. New York: International Universities Press, 1971.

52. KUBIE, L. *Practical and Theoretical Aspects of Psychoanalysis*. New York: Praeger, 1950.

53. LEVENSON, E. A. *The Fallacy of Understanding: An Inquiry into the Changing Structure of Psychoanalysis*. New York: Basic Books, 1972.

54. LEVITSKY, A. and F. S. PERLS. "The Rules and Games of Gestalt Therapy," in J. Fagan and I. L. Shepherd, eds., *Gestalt Therapy Now: Theory, Techniques, Applications*, pp. 140–149. Palo Alto: Science and Behavior Books, 1970.

55. LEWIS, H. B. *Shame and Guilt in Neurosis*. New York: International Universities Press, 1971.

56. LEWIS, W. C. *Why People Change: The Psychology of Influence*. New York: Holt, Rinehart & Winston, 1972.

57. LOEWALD, H. "On the Therapeutic Action of Psychoanalysis," *Int. J. Psycho-Anal.*, 41 (1960), 16–33.

58. MACKINNON, R. A. and R. MICHELS. *The Psychiatric Interview in Clinical Practice*. Philadelphia: Saunders, 1971.

59. MAHLER, M. S. *On Human Symbiosis and the Vicissitudes of Individuation*, Vol. 1.

New York: International Universities Press, 1968.

60. MASLOW, A. *Toward a Psychology of Being.* New York: Van Nostrand Reinhold, 1968.

61. MAY, R. "Contributions of Existential Psychotherapy," in R. May, E. Angel, and H. F. Ellenberger, eds., *Existence: A New Dimension in Psychiatry and Psychology*, pp. 37–91. New York: Basic Books, 1958.

62. ———. "The Context of Psychotherapy," in M. I. Stein, ed., *Contemporary Psychotherapies*, pp. 288–304. New York: Free Press, 1961.

63. MEAD, G. H. *The Philosophy of the Present.* Chicago: Open Court Publ., 1932.

64. MENNINGER, K. *The Vital Balance: The Life Process in Mental Health and Disease.* New York: Viking, 1963.

65. NUNBERG, H. *Practice and Theory of Psychoanalysis*, Vol. 1. New York: International Universities Press, 1948.

66. ———. *Principles of Psychoanalysis and Their Application to the Neuroses.* New York: International Universities Press, 1955.

67. PIAGET, J. *Play, Dreams and Imitation in Childhood.* New York: Norton, 1951.

68. PRIBRAM, K. *Languages of the Brain, Experimental Paradoxes and Principles in Neuropsychology.* Englewood Cliffs, N.J.: Prentice-Hall, 1971.

69. RACKER, H. *Transference and Countertransference.* New York: International Universities Press, 1968.

70. RANK, O. *Will Therapy and Truth and Reality.* New York: Knopf, 1945.

71. REDLICH, F. C. and D. X. FREEDMAN. *The Theory and Practice of Psychiatry.* New York: Basic Books, 1966.

72. REICH, W. *Character Analysis.* New York: Noonday, 1947.

73. REIK, T. *Listening with the Third Ear: The Inner Experience of a Psychoanalyst.* New York: Farrar, Straus, 1948.

74. ROGERS, C. "The Conditions of Change from a Client-Centered Viewpoint," *J. Consult. Psychol.*, 21 (1957), 95–103.

75. ———. "The Characteristics of a Helping Relationship," in Morris I. Stein, ed., *Contemporary Psychotherapies*, pp. 95–112. New York: Free Press, 1961.

76. ———. *On Becoming a Person; A Therapist's View of Psychotherapy.* Boston: Houghton Mifflin, 1961.

77. ROGERS, C. and B. STEVENS. *Person to Person: The Problem of Being Human.* Lafayette, Calif.: Real People Press, 1967.

78. RUESCH, J. "The Therapeutic Process from the Point of View of Communication Theory," *Am. J. Orthopsychiatry*, 22 (1952), 690–700.

79. ———. *Therapeutic Communication.* New York: Norton, 1973.

80. RUESCH, J. and G. BATESON. *Communication: The Social Matrix of Psychiatry.* New York: Norton, 1968.

81. SAUL, L. J. *Technique and Practice of Psychoanalysis.* Philadelphia: Lippincott, 1958.

82. ———. *Psychodynamically Based Psychotherapy.* New York: Science House, 1972.

83. SCHEFLEN, A. E. "Quasi-Courtship Behavior in Psychotherapy," *Psychiatry*, 28 (1965), 245–257.

84. SCHOFIELD, W. "Some General Factors in Counseling and Therapy," in B. Berenson and R. R. Carkhoff, eds., *Sources of Gain in Counseling and Psychotherapy*, pp. 137–147. New York: Holt, Rinehart & Winston, 1967.

85. SHANDS, H. C. "Paradoxes of Consonance: A Structural View," *Ann. N.Y. Acad. Sci.*, 193 (1972), 194–199.

86. SPITZ, R. "Transference: The Analytical Setting and Its Prototype," *Int. J. Psycho-Anal.*, 37 (1956), 380–385.

87. ———. *The First Year of Life: A Psychoanalytic Study of Normal and Deviant Development of Object Relations.* New York: International Universities Press, 1965.

88. STERBA, R. "The Fate of the Ego in Analytic Therapy," *Int. J. Psychoanal.*, 15 (1934), 117–126.

89. STEVENSON, I. "The Psychiatric Interview," in S. Arieti, ed., *American Handbook of Psychiatry*, 1st ed., Vol. 1, pp. 197–214. New York: Basic Books, 1959.

90. STONE, L. *The Psychoanalytic Situation: An Examination of Its Development and Essential Nature.* New York: International Universities Press, 1961.

91. ———. "The Psychoanalytic Situation and Transference: Postscript to an Earlier Communication," *J. Am. Psychoanal. Assoc.*, 15 (1967), 3–58.

92. STOTLAND, E. *The Psychology of Hope.* San Francisco: Jossey-Bass, 1969.

93. STRUPP, H. H. "On the Technology of Psychotherapy," *Arch. Gen. Psychiatry*, 26 (1972), 270–278.

94. STRUPP, H. H., R. Fox, and K. LESSLER. *Patients View Their Psychotherapy*. Baltimore: The Johns Hopkins Press, 1969.

95. SULLIVAN, H. S. *The Psychiatric Interview*. New York: Norton, 1954.

96. SUOMI, S., H. HARLOW, and W. McKINNEY, JR. "Monkey Psychiatrists," *Am. J. Psychiatry*, 128 (1972), 927–932.

97. SZASZ, T. *The Ethics of Psychoanalysis: The Theory and Method of Autonomous Psychotherapy*. New York: Delta, 1965.

98. TARACHOW, S. *An Introduction to Psychotherapy*. New York: International Universities Press, 1963.

99. TARACHOW, S. and A. STEIN. "Psychoanalytic Psychotherapy," in B. B. Wolman, ed., *Psychoanalytic Technique: A Handbook for the Practicing Psychoanalyst*, pp. 471–510. New York: Basic Books, 1967.

100. THOMPSON, C. M. *Interpersonal Psychoanalysis: Papers of Clara M. Thompson*, M. Green, ed. New York: Basic Books, 1964.

101. TOWER, L. E. "Countertransference," *J. Am. Psychoanal. Assoc.*, 4 (1956), 224–255.

102. TRUAX, C. B. "Effective Ingredients in Psychotherapy: An Approach to Unraveling the Patient–Therapist Interaction," *J. Counsel. Psychol.*, 10 (1963), 256–263.

103. WALLEN, R. "Gestalt Therapy and Gestalt Psychology," in J. Fagan and I. L. Shepherd, eds. *Gestalt Therapy Now: Theory, Techniques, Applications*, pp. 8–13. Palo Alto: Science and Behavior, 1970.

104. WEXLER, M. "Concluding Remarks of Milton Wexler," *Int. J. Psycho-Anal.*, 51 (1970), 147–149.

105. WHITAKER, C. A. and T. P. MALONE. *The Roots of Psychotherapy*. New York: McGraw-Hill, 1953.

106. WHITEHEAD, A. N. (1929) *Process and Reality: An Essay on Cosmology*. New York: Social Science Books, 1941.

107. WHITEHORN, J. C. "Studies of the Doctor as a Crucial Factor for the Prognosis of the Schizophrenic Patient," *Int. J. Soc. Psychiatry*, 6 (1960), 71–77.

108. WITKIN, H. A., R. B. DYK, H. F. FATERSON et al. *Psychological Differentiation: Studies of Development*. New York: Wiley, 1962.

109. WOLBERG, L. R. "The Psychodynamic-Behavioral Polemic," *Int. J. Psychiatry*, 9 (1970), 155–162.

110. WOLPE, J., A. SALTER, and C. J. REYNA. *The Conditioning Therapies: The Challenge in Psychotherapy*. New York: Holt, Rinehart & Winston, 1964.

PART TWO

The Psychosocial Therapies

CHAPTER 7

GENERAL PSYCHOTHERAPY: THE RESTORATION OF MORALE

Jerome D. Frank

PSYCHOTHERAPY encompasses all those activities by which one person seeks to relieve the distress and beneficially affect
the behavior of another through psychological
means. At first glance, the variety of psychological healing procedures seems virtually endless. It encompasses all helping activities
based on symbolic communications that are
primarily although not necessarily exclusively
verbal, such as religious healing and a range
of secular activities that aim to modify behavior, expand consciousness, or enhance personal
growth. The target of these efforts is an individual, but he is often treated in a group. Proponents of each method of psychotherapy
enhance the impression of diversity by stressing how their particular approach differs from
and is allegedly superior to all others.

The varieties of distress and disability for
which psychotherapy is offered seem equally

diverse, including psychoses, neuroses, character and personality disorders in children, and
bodily diseases with an emotional component.
The only feature these conditions have in
common is that they involve disturbances in
the person's communicative behavior.

The thesis of this chapter is that the diversity both of psychotherapies and the conditions that respond to them is more apparent
than real, and that in actuality all candidates
for psychotherapy suffer from a single condition that takes protean forms. This condition
may be termed demoralization. Similarly, all
forms of psychotherapy, beneath their superficial differences, share certain features that
combat demoralization and thereby account
for most of their actual effectiveness.

This presentation attempts to define demoralization, to explore some of its causes and
its relation to patients' complaints, and then to

review evidence from various areas for the hypothesis that all psychotherapies essentially endeavor to overcome the demoralized state of mind. This is followed by a brief consideration of the features shared by all psychotherapeutic procedures that promote this outcome. Finally, some implications of the demoralization hypothesis for the selection and preparation of patients for psychotherapy and then for the conduct of psychotherapy are explored.

❰ The Demoralization Hypothesis

Definition of Demoralization

Demoralization is a state of mind that ensues when a person feels unable to cope with a problem that he and those about him expect him to be able to handle. Demoralization can vary widely in duration and severity, but the full-blown form includes the following manifestations, not all of which need be present in any one person. The person suffers a loss of confidence in himself and in his ability to master not only external circumstances but his own feelings and thoughts. The resulting sense of failure typically engenders feelings of guilt and shame. The demoralized person frequently feels alienated or isolated. He may also feel resentful, because others whom he expects to help him seem unable or unwilling to do so; their behavior, in turn, may reflect their own irritation with him, creating a vicious circle. With the weakening of the person's ties often goes a loss of faith in the group's values and beliefs, which had helped to give him a sense of security and significance.[2] The psychological life-space of the demoralized person is constricted in space and time. He becomes self-absorbed, loses sight of his long-term goals, and is preoccupied with avoiding further failure. His dominant moods are usually (1) anxiety, ranging from mild apprehension to panic, and (2) depression, ranging in severity from being mildly dispirited to feeling utterly hopeless.

Most episodes of demoralization are self-limiting. These crisis responses[6,34] can enhance a person's mental health by stimulating him to seek better solutions to his problems, strengthening his emotional ties with others, and demonstrating to himself that he can overcome obstacles. Prolonged states of demoralization, however, are self-perpetuating and self-aggravating, since they lead to increasing discouragement, which impedes recovery. Some evidence will be adduced below that neurotic and psychotic symptoms contribute to demoralization and, in turn, are aggravated by it.

Causes of Demoralization

A person experiences demoralization when his coping capacity is inadequate to meet a stress that he is experiencing. Factors affecting coping capacity—or, in negative terms, vulnerability—may be modifiable or unmodifiable by psychotherapy. Constitutional vulnerabilities (those built into the structure of the organism) may be primarily genetic in origin or may result from damaging experiences, during critical periods of pre- or postnatal development, that leave permanent defects in the growing nervous system. That traumata or deprivations of early life can permanently affect the organism has been amply demonstrated by animal experiments, and it seems to account for some of the personality characteristics of adults who were raised in exceptionally brutal or depriving environments. However, many vulnerabilities created by trouble-making distortions of perception and behavior, or by stress-producing value systems arising from past experience, can be modified by subsequent experience such as that provided by psychotherapy.

The severity of the stress component of demoralization depends on how the person perceives inner and outer events; and this is determined by his own assumptive systems[10] as well as by the objective nature of the events. Some of these assumptions are widespread in a culture. For example, hallucinations in the United States in the twentieth century are viewed as signs of mental illness; hence they are much more stressful to Americans than to members of a culture that does not view them with alarm. The severity of other stresses depends on idiosyncratic assumptive worlds. Examples are promotions, which severely stress some persons, or deaths in the family, which may be experienced by some family members as a relief and by others as a maximal stress. The severity of such stresses may be aggravated or reduced by whether they remind the person of situations in which he has previously failed or succeeded.

Stresses built into the system of society may also create demoralization. American society contains a subtle but pervasive source of stress that seems amenable to psychotherapy—the collapse of traditional value systems and institutions for assuaging the "existential anxiety" that arises from awareness of the apparent transitoriness and insignificance of individual human life. The ways in which more gross and obvious societal stresses summarized by the term "socioeconomic oppression" may contribute to psychiatric illness, and their implications for psychotherapy, raise controversial issues which it would take us too far afield to explore here.[14]

Relation of Demoralization to Psychiatric Symptoms

Persons who seek psychotherapeutic help are usually in the middle range of demoralization. Mild forms are relieved by advice or reassurance from family or friends, or by changes in life situation (such as a change of job) that result in the person regaining his sense of mastery and connectedness with his group. At the other extreme, if demoralization is sufficiently severe, the person believes he is beyond help and simply withdraws into a shell. Such persons do not seek help; and some, such as derelicts, seem unable to use it.

In order to receive psychotherapy, the patient must experience certain symptoms viewed as especially amenable to this remedy. Many of these symptoms, such as anxiety, depression, and feelings of guilt, may be direct expressions of demoralization. Others, such as obsessions, dissociative phenomena, and hallucinations, have a variety of causes, many of which are still not understood. Sometimes they seem to be symbolic ways that the patient has chosen to express or resolve the problems that demoralize him.

That anxiety aggravates symptoms was shown by Lesse.[23] Using a simple anxiety rating scale administered to a wide variety of patients, he concluded that the anxiety level mounts before the appearance of clinical symptoms, and that under treatment "A given symptom or group of symptoms did not seem to completely disappear until the degree of anxiety decreased below a certain threshold which was unique for the individual patient." He concludes: "The greater the stress, the greater the degree of anxiety; the greater the degree of anxiety the more symptoms and signs that are called into play."

A finding of Luborsky and Auerbach[28] suggests that symptoms apparently unrelated to demoralization may, in fact, be symbolic or indirect expressions of this state. Through detailed study of psychoanalytic sessions, they found that patients complained of migraine headaches in an emotional context of feelings of lack of self-control, helplessness, and hopelessness, and of stomach pains in a context of helplessness and anxiety.

Whatever their ultimate etiology, symptoms interact in two ways with the degree of demoralization. First, the more demoralized the person is, the more severe these symptoms tend to be; thus patients troubled with obsessions find them becoming worse when they are depressed. Secondly, by crippling the person to some degree, symptoms reduce his coping capacity and thereby aggravate his demoralization.

Symptoms alone do not bring persons to psychotherapy. Some degree of demoralization must also be present, and relief of this rather than elimination of symptoms is the main criterion of successful treatment. Restoring a person's morale has certain beneficial consequences. It restores his sense of control over that segment of his life experience which he felt he had lost. This reopens his future, increases his options, and diminishes his concern with his symptoms, because he now feels that he can master them instead of their mas-

tering him. Usually his symptoms will diminish, but he may also recover his zest and enjoyment of life despite their continuance. One
is reminded of the old story of the stutterer
who spent several years in psychoanalysis and
then announced that he was cured because
although he still stuttered, he now knew why.

Coping Capacity, Stress, Symptoms, and Demoralization

The demoralization hypothesis may be illustrated by Figure 7–1. Demoralization is a

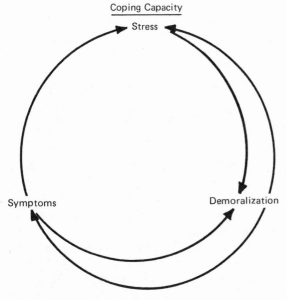

Figure 7–1. Relationship between symptoms, demoralization, and stress.

function of the relationship between stress and
coping cacpacity. If coping capacity is greater
than stress, a person presumably is not demoralized; if stress is greater than coping capacity, a person would be demoralized. Demoralization interacts with both the balance
between stress and coping capacity and the
patient's symptoms. The more demoralized a
person is the less he feels able to cope, the
more stress he experiences, and the more severe are his symptoms. Symptoms, in turn, increase his sense of demoralization by reducing
his coping capacity and increasing his sense of
stress. Psychotherapy functions chiefly to restore morale, thereby increasing the patient's
coping ability and reducing his symptoms.

Evidence for the Demoralization Hypothesis

Before considering the implications of the
demoralization hypothesis for psychotherapy,
it may be well to review some of the data
from surveys and questionnaires and, primarily, from studies of the processes and outcomes of psychotherapy itself that can be interpreted as supporting it.

SURVEYS OF TREATED AND UNTREATED POPULATIONS

Surveys of stratified samples of the population, based on interviews and questionnaires,
consistently reveal that psychopathological
symptoms alone are not sufficient to bring persons to psychotherapy. For example, Srole et
al.[36] found that about 80 percent of a stratified sample of city dwellers had "significant
psychopathology," while Gurin, Veroff, and
Feld,[13] in another survey of a similar sample,
found that only 14 percent had sought professional help at some time in their lives. This
discrepancy is usually attributed to the unavailability of psychiatric resources or lack of
information as to their existence. The latter
survey found, however, that "The presence of
mental health resources made it easier for
people who are already disposed to look for
this help to obtain it, rather than motivating
people to seek assistance;" that is, many persons with "significant psychopathology" presumably do not see themselves as needing
help.

This conclusion is confirmed by comparing
samples of treated and untreated persons, the
former being designated as "patients" or "neurotics." The samples show not only a high
prevalence of so-called psychopathological
symptoms in a nontreated group but also a
much greater prevalence of attributes associated with demoralization in the patient group.
For example, Vaillant,[41] using a questionnaire
survey of male alumni twenty-five years after
their graduation from a liberal-arts college,
compared the 17 percent who had sought psychotherapy (defined as a minimum of ten visits to a psychiatrist) with the 83 percent who

had not. He found that persons who experienced subjective ill health and also had less than four social supports were more than six times as likely to have sought psychotherapy. Since social supports per se were not correlated with physical and mental health, he concluded: "Ready recourse to psychotherapy may reflect social isolation from a variety of causes . . . people who seek psychiatrists have trouble in sustaining relationships." A sense of alienation characterizes demoralization.

Katz[19] asked relatives of a large sample of "normal" persons to fill out a questionnaire concerning them, and compared the findings with those obtained on the same questionnaire from persons in outpatient treatment. Among the normals he singled out a subgroup whose relatives reported them to be as depressed as the mean severity of depression of the patients. The patients, however, were distinguished from the normals by being much more self-accusatory and helpless. Again it appears as if features associated with demoralization, notably guilt feelings and helplessness, rather than a depressed mood in itself, brought the patients to psychotherapy.

Finally, Kellner and Sheffield[20] compared samples of persons not receiving psychiatric treatment (whom they called normal) with those receiving psychiatric treatment (whom they labelled neurotic), in both England and America. The results were consistent in the two samples. Many normals complained of symptoms associated with mild demoralization, such as tension, worry, unhappiness, and nervousness. These were about three times more frequent in the neurotic group, however, accounting for about 90 percent of the patients as compared to about 30 percent of the normals. Two complaints, a sense of failure and unworthiness (65 percent as compared to 13 percent) and "no hope" (60 percent to 6.5 percent), were very much more heavily represented in the treated group. These are similar to the self-accusatory feelings and feelings of helplessness reported in the survey by Katz.[19]

The central point is that psychological symptoms alone do not bring patients to psychotherapy. Whitehorn had distinguished between "compensated" and "decompensated" neuroses.[42] The material here revewed suggests that it is the decompensation and not the neurosis which leads the patient to seek help.

PROGNOSTICATORS OF THERAPEUTIC OUTCOME

Just as demoralization is the main incentive for seeking psychotherapy, so do (1) ability to use this form of help, and (2) general coping capacity seem to be the major prognosticators of therapeutic outcome. That is, most of the factors contributing to improvement lie in the patient's personal qualities rather than in his symptoms or the therapeutic procedure. The universal clinical impression, borne out by the findings of the Menninger Foundation's Psychotherapy Research Project,[21] is that persons with good ego-strength—a concept that includes coping capacity and ability to form rewarding personal relationships—do well. Facility in expressing feelings and problems is also associated with a good prognosis. So is a desire for help, indirectly revealed by emotional tension and self-dissatisfaction. These impressions are firmly supported by Luborsky et al.'s[29] detailed, quantitative analysis of over 100 reported studies of interview psychotherapy. Prognosticators of a good outcome were adequacy of personal functioning, motivation, intelligence, anxiety, and educational and social assets. The researchers conclude: "High affect . . . with high integration or ego strength form a good combination of prognostic conditions for change through psychotherapy." Persons with these attributes probably are able to utilize many other forms of personal help.

The scanty findings on the relation of attributes of therapists to the therapeutic outcome are consistent with the hypothesis that features of the therapists' personality and style that counteract demoralization are more important determinants of their success than are their specific procedures. Truax and Carkhuff[40] found warmth, genuineness, and empathy to characterize the successful therapist. Whitehorn and Betz[44] found that "active personal participation," associated with successful therapy with schizophrenics, would seem to be related to the therapist's ability to inspire the patient's hopes and raise his morale.

The fact that all therapies seem to work

best when first introduced is also consistent with this assumption. Novelty inspires the patient's hopes and the therapist's zeal. In this connection, a major finding of Malan's[30] elaborate study of short-term psychoanalysis involving eleven analysts and fifty analysands was that the best predictor of improvement was the patient's chronological place in the series of patients seen by each analyst. Of the eight patients who received maximum-improvement scores, four were the analyst's first patient and two were his second one. The role of novelty in maintaining the interest and hopes of both therapist and patient suggests that the therapist's flexibility and ingenuity, within the limits imposed by his conceptual scheme, may contribute to his success. Observations of video tapes of well-known therapists confirm this supposition. Perhaps one of the virtues of behavior therapies, seldom mentioned by their advocates, is that their underlying conceptual scheme permits and encourages flexibility. The approach is openly experimental, and whatever the therapist does he can justify and explain by the extremely loose body of concepts known as learning theory.

PATIENTS' IMPROVEMENT AND PSYCHOTHERAPY

A final line of evidence for the concept that the main function of all psychotherapies may be to combat demoralization derives from studies of improvement. With rare exceptions, it has been impossible to show that one form of therapy is more successful than another. The exceptions are that circumscribed phobias and fetishes have apparently responded better to behavior therapies than to interview therapies, but Davison and Taffel[8] have reviewed recent studies that cast doubt on many of these findings. Agras et al.[3] examined thirty phobic patients discovered in an epidemiological survey who received no treatment for five years, and found that their rate of improvement was the same as that from two studies of treated phobics. For both untreated and treated phobics, moreover, the degree of generalization of the phobia and the degree of general fearfulness carried a poor prognosis.

These findings are consistent with the assumption that if phobics are not severely demoralized, they recover, and that what keeps them "ill" may be their degree of demoralization.

In any case, regardless of initial diagnosis (according to Stone et al.),[38] the symptoms of those psychiatric outpatients most likely to show prompt improvement are anxiety and depression—the cardinal manifestations of demoralization. Moreover, most patients show progressive improvement over time, and this overall trend typically washes out the differences in improvement observed immediately at the close of therapy in patients treated by different methods. Whitehorn[43] found this to occur with schizophrenics, and Liberman et al.[24] with neurotics. This suggests that the chief function of psychotherapy, as with most medical treatments, may be to accelerate improvement that would have occurred anyway. Just as the healing power of the body may require time to overcome a bodily illness, so may the patient in psychotherapy take awhile to regain his morale. The process is often aided by his ability gradually to mobilize respect, reassurance, and affection from others, as Stevenson[37] suggests.

That improvement is closely associated with gains in morale is suggested by a study of Lorr et al.'s[27] psychiatric outpatients, in whom improvement in anxiety and other symptoms was accompanied by subjective feelings of increased aggressiveness, personal resourcefulness, and self-reliance, and independence. More recently Gillis and Jessor,[12] Smith,[35] and Liberman et al.[25] have all found that improvement in psychotherapy parallels an increase in the degree to which a person sees himself as controlling his life rather than being controlled by external forces.

One way of raising morale is to provide a person with experiences of success. Loeb et al.'s study[26] showing that depressed persons respond more strikingly to such experiences than do nondepressed persons therefore seems relevant to this discussion. A simple task was given to twenty depressed patients; ten were led to believe that they were succeeding at it, and ten that they were failing. In contrast to a control group of nondepressed patients who worked faster after failure experiences, the depressed patients worked faster after success experiences. They also showed a higher level of aspiration and better actual performance after success, compared to the nondepressed patients.

(Schools of Psychotherapy and Demoralization

In the light of these findings, it seems appropriate to ask why so many different schools of psychotherapy continue to thrive. One reason, of course, is that they all obtain enough favorable results to justify their existence, and proponents of each school can attribute its successes to the features that distinguish it from its rivals. Differences in conceptualization and procedure, however, may primarily represent different views concerning the major sources of the patient's demoralization and the ways of restoring his morale. The following descriptions are greatly simplified in order to make this point.

Proponents of behavior therapies view the *symptom* as the reason the patient seeks treatment, and see it as resulting from faulty environmental reinforcement schedules, present and past. Restoration of morale, if considered at all, is presumed to result from relief of the crippling symptom. That relief of symptoms and improved morale go hand in hand cannot be doubted, but a growing body of data indicates that even behavior therapies may reduce symptoms largely because they have restored the patient's morale by aspects of the therapeutic situation that escape their purview. For example, all behavior therapies provide clear and definite experiences of success, and it is these that may enable the patient to overcome his symptoms, rather than the reverse.

Along the same lines, the effectiveness of implosion therapy may lie in its showing the patient that he can tolerate his fears in their most extreme form. This proves that he is the master of his feelings rather than being controlled by them. Analytically oriented insight therapies see patients' complaints as resulting from unconscious inner conflicts and seek to help him resolve these, thus helping him to regain a sense of control over his thoughts, feelings, and behavior. As Freud put it, "Where Id was, there shall Ego be."

The conceptual schemes of existential therapies are closest to the one advocated here. They view the patient's distress as an expression of his struggle to achieve a sense of identity, purpose and meaning, and their approaches are aimed at combating the sense of isolation, meaninglessness, or despair. The therapist combats these feelings, basically, by entering into the patient's experiences and thereby validating them.[22] Some existential therapists such as Frankl offer the patient an explicit philosophy that helps him to achieve a sense that life has meaning.[11] Therapists who attempt to produce in the patient a "psychedelic" experience through the use of LSD have the same aim.[1]

It should be added that from many standpoints group therapies may be more effective than the individual approach in restoring the patient's morale. Since group methods are described in detail elsewhere in this volume, however, they will not be further considered here.

This short survey of the psychotherapeutic spectrum leads to the conclusion that psychotherapy can be defined only in the broadest terms. It clearly has escaped from the medical model of a form of treatment for a disease. The term "psychotherapy" includes all types of planful interactions by which the therapist, with or without a group, tries to enhance the patient's subjective life by providing new interpersonal experiences that help him to cope with sources of subjective distress and to behave in a more socially desirable way. Characteristically, these objectives reinforce each other. Behavior that yields rewarding rather than stressful interactions with others enhances subjective experience, and persons who feel serene are more able to initiate mutually rewarding interactions with others. Either way, the patient's morale is improved.

⟮ Common Features of Psychotherapies

What are the features shared by all forms of psychotherapy that help the patient to overcome his sense of alienation and regain a sense of control or mastery over his inner feelings and external events? Four can be readily distinguished.

The first feature is a certain type of relationship, often described, between a therapist who offers help and a patient who seeks it. The therapist conveys concern for the patient's welfare and enters into a trusting, confiding, emotional relationship with him. The relationship, however, has definite spatiotemporal boundaries and is structured by the requirements of the therapeutic role. While in one sense this role places constraints on both participants, in another it permits maximal spontaneity within its limits by assuring both patient and therapist that the relationship will remain within bounds. Typically, the relationship is mediated exclusively by words; however, certain therapies permit or even require bodily contact, which can be strongly supportive, between therapist and patient. The therapist's attitude always conveys genuine acceptance of the sufferer, not necessarily for what he is but for what he can become. It also conveys the therapist's belief that the patient can master his problems. The therapist being a representative of the larger society and often of the patient's subculture as well, his acceptance helps to overcome the patient's sense of alienation. Since most patients reach the psychotherapist only after they have failed to gain consideration or help from others, their discovery that someone has enough faith in them to make an effort to help is in itself a powerful boost to morale. In the initial phases of therapy, the patient may be said to borrow hope and confidence from the therapist.

While some demoralized persons may indulge in displays of emotion or even violence, most are timid. Because they are so unsure of themselves, they fear to express their anxiety or resentment lest others take advantage of them or retaliate. This feature of demoralization is counteracted by a second shared feature of psychotherapies, their setting. Psychotherapeutic settings ordinarily are sharply distinguished from the arenas of daily living by possessing features that identify them as sanctuaries and places of healing. In many societies the favored place for healing is a temple; if healing rituals are conducted in the patient's home, it is first sanctified by appropriate rites. In industrialized nations the therapist's office or the hospital has an equivalent aura. In this sanctuary, presided over by a tolerant protector, the patient can safely let himself go, releasing his pent-up emotions and trying out new ways of behaving, secure in the knowledge that he is safe from retaliation.

The third common ingredient of all psychotherapies is a cognitive structure, or conceptual scheme. Such a scheme enables the patient to explain and label his inchoate or bewildering subjective states and behaviors, thereby gaining a sense of control over them.[15,39] To be effective, the scheme must be convincing to the patient; hence it is characteristically validated by being linked to the dominant cosmology of his culture. In the Middle Ages the conceptual scheme underlying what we today call psychotherapy was demonology. In many primitive societies it is witchcraft, while in the United States it is science. At a conference on psychotherapy in which proponents of various schools described their methods, each introduced his procedure by invoking symbols of science. One showed anatomical charts, another used polygraphic tracings, and a third referred to experimental work with animals. Psychotherapists who have been trained as physicians or psychologists automatically carry the mantle of science, and the same is true, to a lesser degree, of social workers. (Reflecting the growing disillusionment with science, however, an increasing number of therapies are appearing that are validated by religious or mystical cosmologies.) From the standpoint of the therapist, an underemphasized function of the conceptual scheme is to maintain and enhance his relationship with the patient by sustaining his own interest and reassuring him as to the validity of his procedure in the face of therapeutic failure. As one young adherent of a rigid therapeutic school remarked, "Even if the patient doesn't get better, you know you are doing the right thing."

Fourthly, every therapy prescribes a procedure (based on the conceptual scheme) that requires the active participation of both patient and therapist and that is believed by both to be the means for restoring the patient's health. This procedure serves as both a vehicle and a justification for the maintenance of the therapeutic relationship.[33] Through repetition it divests anxiety-laden symbols of their anxiety, and it impels the patient to experiment with new behaviors. Interview therapies do this indirectly by offering insights that imply that the patient should be doing something different, whereas behavior therapies convey the message directly. The task enables the patient, through repetition, to practice the new behaviors that are helpful, first in the therapeutic setting and then outside. Since the autonomic nervous system learns slowly, extinction of autonomic symptoms may require much repetition; it is this that may largely account for the need of some patients for long term therapy. And finally, if the procedure is sufficiently impressive, it affords the patient a face-saving device for relinquishing his symptoms after he no longer needs them. Procedures such as hypnosis, relaxation, or emotional flooding, in which the therapist alters the patient's subjective state, are especially convincing demonstrations of the therapist's competence. Any procedure that can alter one's state of consciousness must be powerful indeed. The central point is that the therapeutic efficacy of rationales and techniques may lie not in their specific content but in their morale-building functions. Their contents differ, but their function may be the same.

(Common Effects of Psychotherapies

All forms of psychotherapy have certain similar effects. The first is that they produce some degree of emotional arousal, which seems to be a prerequisite for change in patterns of attitudes and behavior.[16] Many currently popular therapies try to produce intense emotional states, thereby following a tradition that can be traced at least as far back as Mesmer. In all therapies, however, the relationship itself, with its hope-inspiring qualities and its sense of trustful intimacy, is emotionally arousing, especially when the therapist is enthusiastic. Many therapies also stir the patient's anxieties by forcing him to dwell on distasteful feelings, thoughts, or behaviors, and to discover and face previously disowned aspects of himself.

Secondly, all therapies expand the patient's horizons and increase his options by helping him to develop fuller awareness of himself, a more accurate perception of others, and a wider range of behaviors. This comes about through a combination of cognitive and experiential learning. The patient not only learns new ways of formulating his problems and gains new information about himself but also has new experiences and may model himself, wittingly or unwittingly, on certain aspects of the therapist. The lessons he learns in therapy are reinforced and extended by new experiences in daily life resulting from his greater self-awareness and from changes in the responses of others generated by his own changed behavior.

Thirdly, all therapies arouse and maintain the patient's hope for improvement, initially through the optimism of his therapist and later through evidence that he is making progress.[9,10] This evidence typically takes the form of success in gaining new depths of self-understanding and overcoming behavioral blocks, or of other experiences regarded as signs of improvement by the particular therapy in question. These experiences increase the patient's sense of mastery or self-control.

Ideally, then, all successful psychotherapies enhance the patient's sense of personal integration and security and his ability to enter into warm relationships with others. This implies an increased ability to accept his limitations as well as a fuller recognition of his assets. All these changes can be summed up as greater self-acceptance—the healed patient can comfortably say, with the cartoon character Popeye: "I yam what I yam." Concomitantly, the symptoms for which he sought therapy diminish or may even disappear.

❪ Some Implications of the Demoralization Hypothesis

Diagnosis

If the purpose of diagnosis is to determine appropriate therapy, then current diagnostic schemes have been resounding failures. Proponents of every school claim to be able to successfully treat patients who fall into all the conventional diagnostic categories. All agree that some patients in each are inaccessible to their method, but insist that these patients are equally impervious to the approaches of their competitors.

In the light of the demoralization hypothesis, diagnosis has two functions: first, determination of the relative importance of modifiable and unmodifiable sources of demoralization; and, second, identification of personal qualities that would make the patient more accessible to one therapeutic approach than to another. Constitutional aspects of the person that determine the limits of his responsivneess to any form of psychotherapy have been discussed earlier (see p. 118). They are clearly prominent, for example, in cyclical illnesses and in defects of mentation such as overinclusiveness. They probably also prove to play a part in severe neuroses, as well as in such temperamental qualities as the patient's emotional lability and threshold for anxiety.

The treatment of choice for constitutional disabilities is medication that corrects the biochemical defects underlying them. Although psychotherapy cannot directly correct such defects, it can help the person to live within his limitations or to avoid situations to which he is especially vulnerable. For example, although psychotherapy cannot overcome the enzyme deficiencies in some schizophrenics, as May[31] points out, it can help such patients to identify and avoid or cope more effectively with the stresses that overtax their adaptive capacities.

From the standpoint of the environment, the therapist obviously cannot abolish stresses created by poverty, a brutal parent, or a querulous, senile relative in a small apartment. In such circumstances, the primary goal must be to help the patient change his environment or to tide him over until the environmental crisis resolves itself. Psychotherapy can help the patient to endure and cope with unmodifiable environmental pressures, however, by changing his stance toward them.[11] On the other hand, sources of demoralization that *are* modifiable by psychotherapy arise from the reversible results of early life experiences that lead to the acquisition of maladaptive behaviors, distorted perceptions of self or others, and stress-producing value systems. Having been created by symbolic communications, these sources of difficulty are alterable by the same means; hence are ideal targets for psychotherapy.

Adequate diagnosis must include not only the determination of the patient's accessibility to any form of psychotherapy, but also his relative accessibility to the particular kind of help-giver and procedure that would be most likely to gain his confidence and inspire his hopes. Most patients will accept a wide range of therapists, but sometimes a patient is accessible only to one with quite specific qualities. An example is a man in his sixties who had lost his father in infancy and for twenty-five years sought periodic reassurance from a male psychiatrist older than himself, to assuage bouts of freefloating anxiety. After the death of this older man, an attempt to substitute a psychiatrist younger than the patient failed, but an older one was again able to form a therapeutic relationship with him. With respect to the therapist's professional identification, some persons are most accessible to psychiatrists, others to psychologists, others to those who bear the imprimatur of various schools regardless of their academic qualifications, and still others to persons like themselves who have conquered similar difficulties. Thus addicts are often best helped by exaddicts[5] and alcoholics by exalcoholics.[4]

A related diagnostic question is: what conceptual scheme and procedure is most likely to increase the patient's sense of mastery or give him feelings of success? Are these feelings best provided by new insights, by the discovery that he can tolerate emotional states that he had feared, or by the discovery that he can change his behavior in ways that elicit more favorable responses from others? Is he seeking increased self-confidence, resolution of existential anxieties, a greater sense of personal integration, relief of a circumscribed symptom, or merely help in tiding himself over a transient period of strain? The patient mentioned immediately above, for example, controlled his anxiety for years through brief telephone conversations, often months apart, with the older psychiatrist; he definitely did not wish anything more. A patient's expectations and accessibilities depend on qualities such as psychological-mindedness as well as on his previous knowledge of psychotherapy (gained through reading or conversations with friends and acquaintances) and the attitudes of his subculture.[18] Psychotherapists in private practice can assume that many persons who appear before them are familiar with and predisposed to benefit by their concepts and methods. Since the choice of a therapist often involves an element of chance, however, the patient's familiarity with the therapeutic approach cannot always be taken for granted. Clinic patients, in particular, often have either no knowledge of psychotherapy or else gross misconceptions of it.

Preparation of Patients for Therapy

The psychotherapist himself is usually the main determinant of the accessibility of patients to his type of psychotherapy, and preparing them for his ministrations is a major purpose of the initial interview. In it the therapist obtains information needed to plan treatment, establishes his competence and credibility in the patient's eyes, describes the treatment plan, and elicits the patient's cooperation with it. To these ends he sounds out the patient's attitudes and expectations about psychotherapy, sometimes directly but more typically indirectly, by exploring the patient's explanation (or lack of it) for his complaints,

his account of what led him to seek therapy at this particular juncture and the path by which he reached the therapist's office. If the patient has had previous therapy, the therapist seeks to determine in what respects it succeeded or failed, including why the patient did not return to his previous therapist. In addition, although schools of therapy emphasize different aspects of the patient's functioning, all try in the initial interview to elicit information about past and present circumstances related to his complaints. From all this material the therapist arrives at a tentative formulation of the patient's problems and a program of treatment.

As a result of this exploration, the therapist should be prepared to entertain the possibility that a therapy in which he is not skilled might more closely accord with the patient's expectations and therefore have a greater likelihood of success. In such circumstances, the conscientious therapist will accept his limitations and refer the patient to someone he believes can be more helpful.

If, as typically occurs, the therapist accepts the patient, he may find it useful to spend some time and effort to align the patient's expectations with what he has to offer. Depending on the patient's sophistication, this may require discussion of the therapeutic rationale, but in any case it should include a description of the procedure, including frequency of visits, total duration, and hoped-for outcome.[17,32] Since formulations of problems and expectations of outcome may both change in the course of treatment, it is well to re-examine these matters from time to time.

⟨ The Conduct of Therapy

The demoralization hypothesis does not prescribe any particular conceptualization or form of procedure for the conduct of psychotherapy. Rather it implies that a therapist should familiarize himself with a wide variety of approaches, master those that best suit his personal style and, within this range, choose the combinations that best fit the predilections of different patients. Since, as already mentioned, most conceptual schemes have more in common than their proponents recognize, it is not difficult to pick and choose features from different ones and weld them into a loose integration.

Thus, using the conceptual scheme outlined below, I can comfortably use nondirective interviewing, interpretation of dreams, relaxation exercises, covert aversive conditioning,[7] and so on, without feeling confused or intellectually dishonest. According to this conceptualization, the patient's demoralization results from handicaps to successful coping that were created by inadequate awareness of his own motivations, distortions of his self-image, and unawareness or misinterpretation of the effects of his behavior on others. His symbolic communications with himself and others are disturbed. The aim of therapy is to expose and correct these disturbances through interventions that are mainly verbal. The therapeutic conversation aims to alleviate pathogenic emotional states and to offer the patient corrective experiences and information. The therapist is the primary agent for the achievement of these aims, but he can often increase his effectiveness by including relevant others— strangers, in conventional group therapy, and members of the patient's family, in marital or family therapy. Such interaction systems more efficiently expose and correct the disturbances in the patient's communications, especially since these usually dovetail with disturbances in the communications of others.

A few of the implications of this view for the actual conduct of therapy follow.

The Therapist's Behavior

Except when the patient expects the therapist to be a "mirror," the therapist is most effective if he acts as a real person with whom the patient has a genuine encounter. This means, first of all, that he should not try to imitate a style that does not fit his own personality, since the patient will almost surely sense and be constrained by the artificiality. Accordingly, the therapist should not fear being spontaneous within wide limits, expressing pleasure, concern, sorrow, or even anger, admitting when he is sleepy or when he is uncertain as to what is going on, and the like. If humor is within his repertoire, it can be a great help in enabling the patient to achieve some detachment from his troubles, as long as the patient feels that the therapist is laughing with him and not at him.

By being open with the patient, the therapist makes it easier for the patient to be open with him and also to use him as a model. While relying on spontaneity increases the likelihood of making errors, it is my experience that if the therapist has convinced the patient of the sincerity of his effort to be helpful, the patient will forgive and forget almost any stupidity he may commit. As an aspect of his regard for the patient as a person, the therapist should assume that the patient is potentially capable of handling his own problems once he has recognized the blocks to their solution or has been helped to change his behavior by more direct means. Over the long run the therapist therefore discourages the patient's dependency, although he may let it develop initially so that patient can borrow confidence from him. To this end he may offer to let the patient call him at home or to make an extra appointment on request. This tangible demonstration of concern is more convincing than any amount of statements to this effect. In my experience, very few patients avail themselves of the invitation. Those who do rarely repeat the action, since their real purpose was almost always to test if I really meant what I said.

The therapist's assumption that the patient is capable of managing his life is conveyed by being chary with advice. This does not preclude informing the patient about relevant matters on which he is ignorant or misinformed, such as the relationship between psychic and bodily perturbations.

Along the same lines, the therapist should convey the expectation that therapy will be time-limited. Patients who seek therapy while in the throes of a transient crisis may need only one or two interviews to tide them over. The therapist must resist the temptation to turn them into candidates for longer therapy by dwelling on their personal weaknesses rather than their coping capacities and by underestimating the role of the immediate stress in their decompensation. This contributes to the patient's demoralization rather than combating it.

The assumption that therapy will be time-limited is an implicit vote of confidence in the patient and may also speed up the therapeutic process. Accordingly, early in the proceedings, it is well to discuss a possible date for termination, with the understanding that treatment may be extended beyond this date by mutual agreement. As termination approaches, it is sometimes useful to test the effect of reducing the frequency of interviews. Spacing them out, if handled properly, can enhance the patient's self-confidence.

The Facilitation of Communication

It is well for the therapist to keep in mind that the patient may not be able to communicate honestly and freely with him at first. Not only does he bring distorted ways of communicating characteristic of his daily life into the interview, he will also be partly preoccupied with testing the therapist to determine how open he dares to be. The therapist's success in facilitating free communication depends primarily, of course, on his general ability to win the patient's trust and confidence, but attention to certain specific aspects of the situation that can hamper free communication may also sometimes be helpful.

For example, for most patients the face-to-face position is most natural, with the chairs arranged so that the patient or therapist can comfortably look away if either wishes to do so. Some patients, however, are able to communicate more easily when lying on a couch, with the therapist out of the direct line of vision. I have found this useful with patients who seem excessively alert to my facial expressions and guide themselves accordingly. Lying down also seems to ease the flow of thought in some patients by facilitating muscular relaxation.

Along the same lines, some patients at times communicate more easily through reports of dreams than direct accounts of events, perhaps because they have been led to believe that the therapist expects this, or because attributing feeling or attitude to a dream relieves the patient of full responsibility for it. An occasional patient may wish to rely on a diary or journal, to be read by the therapist between visits.

The therapist's skill in picking up and interpreting nonverbal cues accompanying the patient's words can significantly improve communication. These include communicative behaviors such as changes in voice tone, facial expressions, gestures, and bodily postures, as well as evidences of emotional tension that signal the importance of the topic under discussion. If the therapist learns that these evidences have no outward manifestation—for example, stomach pain—it may be useful to ask the patient to report when he experiences such a reaction. Since commenting on nonverbal communications may create considerable anxiety, especially when they are discrepant with verbal ones, the therapist, having noted them, sometimes reserves comment until he feels that the patient's trust is sufficiently strong to enable him to hear and use the information.

The Temporal Focus of the Interviews

Ordinarily therapy should focus on the patient's current life, for several reasons. The patient comes for therapy for help in resolving a present crisis, not past ones. He wants to talk about the here and now, and encouraging him to do so helps to establish rapport. From a theoretical standpoint, moreover, only forces operating in the present can be changed.

In this connection, attention to the patient's reaction to the therapist during the interview can be useful. For one thing, these are the only reactions that the therapist can directly observe instead of having to rely exclusively on the patient's reports, which may be considerably distorted. For another, how the patient handles the interview may be a valid sample of his behavior in important confrontations of daily life, especially when (as is not uncommon) the therapist is a stand-in for other persons significant to the patient. Finally, the therapist can offer immediate feedback on his own reactions. For the patient this may illuminate reactions of other persons that had bewildered or upset him. This is most apt to happen when the patient is unaware of aspects of his communicative behavior that disturb others. In this connection, a useful therapeutic maneuver is to call the patient's attention to any discrepancy between his verbal and nonverbal communications—for example, pointing out that he says he is angry in a sweet tone of voice while smiling. Videotape playbacks, by sharply confronting the patient with the way in which he presents himself to others, can enhance this aspect of therapy.

Exploration of the patient's past history, however, is essential to a full understanding of his present situation. We screen objective events and react to them, not as they exist in the eye of God, but in terms of what they mean to us. As suggested earlier, the same objective event, such as the death of a close relative, may be experienced as a tragedy or a relief, depending on its meaning to the survivor.[10] Since the meanings of present events are largely determined by past experiences, considerable review of the past may be needed to understand the patient's predicament today.

Review of the past can also serve to enhance rapport. A patient may be able to reveal embarrassing or anxiety-provoking features of his history before he can discuss their repercussions in his current life. That is, he may need to test the therapist's reactions to remote material before he can bring up immediate feelings. Finally, although the explanation remains unclear, the therapeutic value of abreaction in different guises cannot be gainsaid. Some patients clearly gain self-confidence and an increased sense of mastery by emotionally reliving traumatic early experiences while in the protective context of therapy.

Other Therapist Interventions

What the therapist actually does or says in the interview varies considerably depending on his conceptual scheme. However, a few observations on certain types of intervention that seem applicable to almost all forms of therapy seem in order.

Simply repeating what a patient has said, especially if the patient was hesitant to say it, indirectly conveys certain messages that facilitate therapeutic interaction. It shows that the therapist has heard the patient, understood him, and accepted his statement. This implicitly gives the patient permission to continue further along the same lines.

Interpretations that link feelings or behaviors not previously connected by the patient may be therapeutic in several ways. The interpretation "You feel to your wife as you did to your mother," for example, may be supportive by demonstrating the therapist's competence and enabling the patient to make sense of feelings (in this case, toward his wife) that had been mysterious, thereby enhancing his sense of mastery. At the same time, since such an interpretation implies that the patient's current reactions are inappropriate, he may feel it as an attack. Inexperienced therapists, not appreciating this, may be thrown off by the patient's defensive or hostile response. Such a reaction, however, is not necessarily bad—in fact, it may create a useful emotional stir and open up new areas for exploration.

If at the end of an interview the therapist can single out a theme linking many of the patient's superficially unrelated comments, this is a powerful way of demonstrating his attentiveness and skill. It also enhances the patient's self-confidence by indicating that his thoughts and feelings were better integrated than he had realized.

Finally, it is well for the therapist always to keep in mind the importance of "accentuating the positive." Given a choice, he should take the optimist's view of the glass as half full rather than half empty. It is very easy to become absorbed in those aspects of the patient's life that are working badly; it is for these that he sought treatment in the first place, after all, and his demoralization leads him to dwell on them. This tendency may be reinforced if the therapist focuses on evidences of illness rather than health. An example of the value of reinterpreting a bit of behavior as a sign of strength rather than weakness is afforded by an anxious, depressed night school student who started and then dropped a day course, on the grounds that it was too hard for her. As she went on to elaborate the reasons for her decision, it became clear that she was actually doing satisfactory work and probably could have continued to do so had she wished to expend the necessary time and effort. However, she found her daytime (as opposed to evening) classmates uncongenial, and the course was interfering with activities that were more rewarding. In short, she had dropped the course not because she had to but because she wanted to. Thus the act became evidence of her ability to make a sensible choice rather than a sign of failure. With this realization she experienced an immediate rise in morale.

Accentuation of the positive by no means implies that the therapist should offer superficial reassurance. This usually makes matters worse, by conveying to the patient that the therapist does not take him seriously or has failed to appreciate the gravity of his predicament. It is reassuring, however, to listen fully to the patient's worst misgivings without sharing them, and to seize every appropriate opportunity to remind the patient of what has been working well, or of his latent abilities that he is not using to full advantage.

In prolonged therapy, the patient's goal often seems to become more ambitious as he improves. Because it keeps receding before him, he may feel he is making no progress. If the therapist senses this, a reminder of the patient's state when he first entered therapy and the gains he has made since then can be powerfully reassuring.

❲ Bibliography

1. ABRAMSON, H. A. *The Use of LSD in Psychotherapy and Alcoholism.* Indianapolis: Bobbs-Merrill, 1967.
2. ADLER, H. M. and V. B. O. HAMMETT. "Crisis, Conversion, and Cult Formation: An Examination of a Common Psycho-

social Sequence." unpublished paper.
3. AGRAS, W. S., H. N. CHAPIN, and D. C. OLIVEAU. "The Natural History of a Phobia," *Arch. Gen. Psychiatry,* 26 (1972), 315–317.
4. ALCOHOLICS ANONYMOUS. *Alcoholics Anonymous: Twelve Steps and Twelve Traditions.* New York: Alcoholics Anonymous, 1953.
5. BORENSTEIN, D. "The Relative Value of the Medical Staff versus Addicts in the Rehabilitation of the Drug Users in a Drug Abuse Program," *Johns Hopkins Med. J.,* 129 (1971), 290–297.
6. CAPLAN, G. "Emotional Crises," in A. Deutsch and H. Fishman, eds., *The Encyclopedia of Mental Health,* Vol. 2, pp. 521–532. New York: Franklin Watts, 1963.
7. CAUTELA, J. R. "Covert Conditioning," in A. Jacobs and L. B. Sachs, eds., *The Psychology of Private Events,* pp. 109–130. New York: Academic, 1971.
8. DAVISON, G. C. and S. J. TAFFEL. "Effects of Behavior Therapy." Paper presented at 80th Ann. Conv. Am. Psychol. Assoc., Honolulu, 1972.
9. FRANK, J. D. "The Influence of Patients' and Therapists' Expectations on the Outcome of Psychotherapy," *Br. J. Med. Psychol.,* 41 (1968), 349–356.
10. ——. *Persuasion and Healing: A Comparative Study of Psychotherapy,* 2nd ed. Baltimore: The Johns Hopkins Press, 1973.
11. FRANKL, V. E. *The Doctor and the Soul: From Psychotherapy to Logotherapy.* New York: Knopf, 1965.
12. GILLIS, J. S. and R. JESSOR. "Effects of Brief Psychotherapy on Belief in Internal Control: An Exploratory Study," *Psychother. Theory Res. Pract.,* 7 (1970), 135–137.
13. GURIN, G., J. VEROFF, and S. FELD. *Americans View Their Mental Health.* New York: Basic Books, 1960.
14. HALLECK, S. L. *The Politics of Therapy.* New York: Science House, 1971.
15. HOBBS, N. "Sources of Gain in Psychotherapy," *Am. Psychol.,* 17 (1962), 741–747.
16. HOEHN-SARIC, R., J. D. FRANK, and B. J. GURLAND. "Focused Attitude Change in Neurotic Patients," *J. Nerv. Ment. Dis.,* 147 (1968), 124–133.
17. HOEHN-SARIC, R., J. D. FRANK, S. D. IMBER et al. "Systematic Preparation of Patients for Psychotherapy: 1. Effects on Therapy

Behavior and Outcome," *J. Psychiatr. Res.*, 2 (1964), 267–281.

18. KADUSHIN, C. *Why People Go To Psychiatrists.* New York: Atherton, 1969.

19. KATZ, M. M. "The Classification of Depression," in R. R. Fieve, ed., *Depression in the 1970's*, pp. 31–40. Amsterdam: Excerpta Medica Foundation, 1971.

20. KELLNER, R. and B. F. SHEFFIELD. "The One-Week Prevalence of Symptoms in Neurotic Patients and Normals," *Am. J. Psychiatry*, 130 (1973), 102–105.

21. KERNBERG, O. F., E. D. BURNSTEIN, L. COYNE et al. "Psychotherapy and Psychoanalysis: Final Report of the Menninger Foundation's Psychotherapy Research Project," *Bull. Menninger Clin.*, 36 (1972), entire issue.

22. LAING, R. D. *The Politics of Experience.* New York: Pantheon, 1967.

23. LESSE, S. "Psychodynamic Relationships between the Degree of Anxiety and Other Clinical Symptoms," *J. Nerv. Ment. Dis.*, 117 (1958), 124–130.

24. LIBERMAN, B. L., J. D. FRANK, R. HOEHN-SARIC et al. "Patterns of Change in Treated Psychoneurotic Patients: A Five-Year Follow-up Investigation of the Systematic Preparation of Patients for Psychotherapy," *J. Consult. Clin. Psychol.*, 38 (1972), 36–41.

25. LIBERMAN, B. L., S. D. IMBER, A. R. STONE et al. "Mastery: Prescriptive Treatment and Continued Change in Psychotherapy," (in preparation.)

26. LOEB, A., A. T. BECK, and J. DIGGORY. "Differential Effects of Success and Failure on Depressed and Nondepressed Patients," *J. Nerv. Ment. Dis.*, 152 (1971), 106–114.

27. LORR, M., D. M. McNAIR, W. W. MICHAUX et al. "Frequency of Treatment and Change in Psychotherapy," *J. Abnorm. Soc. Psychol.*, 64 (1962), 281–292.

28. LUBORSKY, L. and A. A. AUERBACH. "The Symptom-Context Method: Quantitative Studies of Symptom Formation in Psychotherapy," *J. Am. Psychoanal. Assoc.*, 17 (1969), 68–99.

29. LUBORSKY, L., A. H. AUERBACH, M. CHANDLER et al. "Factors Influencing the Outcome of Psychotherapy," *Psychol. Bull.*, 73 (1971), 145–185.

30. MALAN, D. H. *A Study of Brief Psychother-apy.* Springfield, Ill.: Charles C. Thomas, 1963.

31. MAY, P. R. A. "The Hospital Treatment of the Schizophrenic Patient," *Int. J. Psychiatry*, 8 (1969), 699–722.

32. ORNE, M. T. and P. H. WENDER. "Anticipatory Socialization for Psychotherapy: Method and Rationale," *Am. J. Psychiatry*, 124 (1968), 1202–1211.

33. PANDE, S. K. "The Mystique of 'Western' Psychotherapy: An Eastern Interpretation," *J. Nerv. Ment. Dis.*, 146 (1968), 425–432.

34. RUSK, T. N. "Opportunity and Technique in Crisis Psychiatry," *Compr. Psychiatry*, 12 (1971), 249–263.

35. SMITH, R. E. "Changes in Locus of Control as a Function of Life Crisis Resolution," *J. Abnorm. Psychol.*, 75 (1970), 328–332.

36. SROLE, L., T. S. LANGER, S. T. MICHAEL et al. *Mental Health in the Metropolis: The Midtown Manhattan Study.* New York: McGraw-Hill, 1962.

37. STEVENSON, I. "Processes of 'Spontaneous' Recovery from the Psychoneuroses," *Am. J. Psychiatry*, 117 (1961), 1057–1064.

38. STONE, A. R., J. D. FRANK, E. H. NASH et al. "An Intensive Five-Year Follow-up Study of Treated Psychiatric Outpatients," *J. Nerv. Ment. Dis.*, 133 (1961), 410–422.

39. TORREY, E. F. *The Mind Game: Witchdoctors and Psychiatrists.* New York: Emerson Hall, 1972.

40. TRUAX, C. B. and R. R. CARKHUFF. *Toward Effective Counselling and Psychotherapy: Training and Practice.* Chicago: Aldine, 1967.

41. VAILLANT, G. E. "Why Men Seek Psychotherapy: 1. Results of a Survey of College Graduates," *Am. J. Psychiatry*, 129 (1972), 645–651.

42. WHITEHORN, J. C. "Guide to Interviewing and Clinical Personality Study," *Arch. Neurol. Psychiatry*, 52 (1944), 197–216.

43. ———. "Studies of the Doctor as a Crucial Factor in the Prognosis of Schizophrenic Patients," *Int. J. Soc. Psychiatry*, 6 (1960), 71–77.

44. WHITEHORN, J. C. and B. J. BETZ. "A Study of Psychotherapeutic Relationships between Physicians and Schizophrenic Patients," *Am. J. Psychiatry*, 111 (1954), 321–331.

CHAPTER 8

PSYCHOTHERAPY WITH CHILDREN AND ADOLESCENTS

Peter Blos, Jr. and Stuart M. Finch

T HE FIRST PUBLISHED REPORTS of psychotherapeutic work with children—Itard's *The Wild Boy of Aveyron* (1801)[39] and Freud's "Little Hans" (1909)[28] —were separated in time by over a hundred years. Yet the outlines of the field they presaged are clearly discernible in the educational emphasis of the first case and the concern with intrapsychic conflict and its resolution in the second instance.

The so-called "wild boy" was eleven to twelve years old when he was captured. The child had no language, poor use of humanoid mobility, little capacity to relate, and, of course, poor habit training. He was at first diagnosed by Pinel as being hopelessly mentally defective. But Itard differed with this opinion and reasoned that the boy's condition was more likely to have been caused by the absence of social stimulation. (In recent years some have suggested that the boy may in fact have suffered from autism, a still unknown entity in Itard's time.[56]) Be that as it may, the boy was named Victor—a charmingly optimistic gesture—and Itard spent considerable time trying to teach him how to adapt himself to the amenities of civilization. Itard's therapy was based on moral principles and employed techniques such as training, teaching, and the fostering of comfortable human relationships, which today we would identify with education. Through the teaching of proper conduct, language usage, and habit training, Itard attempted to foster what we would now call ego development, and, in this sense at least, his work resembled the efforts of parents on behalf of their own young children. Although success with Victor was minimal, Itard's impact on the teaching and training of the re- tarded was significant. Many of his ideas were brought to America by his student, Sequin.

The case of "Little Hans" was quite differ- ent. One day, out on the street, this five-year- old boy suffered an acute anxiety attack. Thereafter his fright became more and more constricting; he could scarcely leave the house without an intense fear that horses, carts, vans, and the light might injure him or that they might themselves fall down and become hurt or broken. It was the boy's father, himself a student of psychoanalysis, who consulted Freud about the child's phobia.

The assumption of the treatment was that the anxiety and phobia were manifestations of a childhood neurosis resulting from uncon- scious conflict and consequent symptom for- mation. The unusual and rather delightful treatment plan that evolved was for Freud to treat the boy through his father, the two men reviewing the content of what father and son had discussed. Also pertinent to their work was the knowledge that, earlier on, Hans had evidenced a lively interest in his "widdler," and that this curiosity about his own anatomy gradually extended to his parents and to the sister who was born when he was three and a half. To those capable of understanding them, Hans' fantasies revealed his efforts to try to solve the mysteries of his sister's conception and birth and the riddle of the difference be- tween the sexes, as well as to control his own desires. But because Hans still lacked impor- tant information about reality, still lacked mature logic, and—most important—because of the conflicts aroused by his own wishes and fears, the child's private conclusions were problematic and distorted. As treatment pro- ceeded, father and son would talk about the boy's fears and associated fantasies. These di- alogues would be reported to Freud and dis- cussed with him. Returning to Hans, the fa- ther would then further explore the small boy's conflicts. Gradually the misinformed conclusions and the unconscious conflicts they reflected were brought into the open. By pro- viding the child with needed information and missing data and bringing the unconscious conflicts to light without resultant catastrophe,

the phobia was dissolved. (It must be added that in a brief 1922 postscript[29] to the case report we learn of the divorce of Hans' par- ents subsequent to the treatment. We can only speculate that this parental discord must have had some effect on the development and course of the phobic symptomatology.)

It is these dual functions of educational training and psychological insight that have characterized child and adolescent psycho- therapy from Freud's day on. Ever present in the child therapist's work are the roles of edu- cator and psychic enlightener. Indeed, the mental and social immaturity that distinguish children from adults determine how these roles are mixed at any one time in the treat- ment of a case.

The first American textbooks about child psychotherapy were written by Jessie Taft[60] in 1933 and Fredrick Allen[3] in 1942. Both emanated from Philadelphia and had consid- erable impact in this country. Both laid stress on the relationship between therapist and child, with the focus of therapy on the pres- ent. "Interpretation," wrote Taft, "there was none, except the verbalization on my part of what the child seemed to be feeling and doing, a comparatively spontaneous response to her words or actions which did clarify or make more conscious the self of the moment, whatever it might be." In other words, empha- sis was on the here and now and on trying to help the child express his thoughts and emo- tions of the moment. No attempt was made to connect these to the historical past or to un- conscious impulses. Virginia Axline[6] (1947) also stressed the friendly relationship between therapist and child and the importance of ac- cepting where the child was, emotionally, at the moment. But she more strongly under- scored nondirective play and stressed a cli- mate of permissiveness in which the child's thoughts, feelings, and ideas were allowed to unfold with little interference.

Beginning in 1927 in Vienna and continuing in London at the Hampstead Clinic, Anna Freud[24-26] founded another line of child treatment based on the psychoanalytic model developed by her father. Initially she had trained as a kindergarten teacher, but then she became curious about the psychological aspects of child development and child psychopathology. From her work grew child analysis and psychoanalytically oriented psychotherapy as we know them today. The essence of this approach lies in helping to acquaint the child with the connections between his conscious and unconscious processes; current play and past history are woven together through interpretation. The goal is to provide insight and thus to "free up" psychic energy and enhance the capacity for ego development. The relationship between child and therapist is still a "real" one, but today it is thought to contain many important transference aspects.

Melanie Klein, to whom Anna Freud credits the use of play as a medium of communication in work with children,[26] is another important figure in the history of child psychotherapy. Although her ideas have never been particularly influential in this country, in England and South America they play an important role in the field of child treatment.

Adolescence, as a transitional period in life, has interested people for centuries, and many of them have recorded their own memories and observations of the period.[43] But scientific interest in it was relatively late to develop. (In 1907 the American psychologist G. Stanley Hall[33] wrote a massive two-volume encyclopedic work on this subject which today remains only as an interesting curiosity.) During the last thirty years, however, we have seen a burgeoning of concern with all aspects of adolescence, including a strong interest in pathology and treatment. In time it became evident that many of the techniques described in these introductory remarks are difficult or ineffective with many adolescent pathologies. Aichorn[1,2] in Vienna was one of the first and most gifted of those working with adolescents to find in psychoanalytic theory a conceptual framework to explain what he had been doing successfully with delinquent youngsters. Although Blos, Sr.,[12,13] and Erikson,[18,20] both received psychoanalytic training in Vienna, they conducted their researches into adolescent development along divergent lines. Blos' primary interest has been the conceptualization of the adolescent's intrapsychic development, whereas Erikson has emphasized the interrelationship between psyche and society.

For many, these two lines of interest have resulted in a strong tendency to separate the treatment of adolescents from that of children, since they stress the recognition that adolescents present unique problems deserving special study. (We would add that visability, pressure, and the number of adolescents with problems also contribute to this dichotomy.) The emphasis has been on three aspects of adolescence: the strong biological push at puberty;[61,62] the separation–individuation phase of adolescence, marking the entrance of the youngster to adult society;[12] and the interaction between the adolescent and society.[18–20] Some have felt these processes to be so different from those of childhood developmental tasks that the period should be dealt with as a separate specialty.[4] By discussing the psychotherapy of children *and* adolescents in a single chapter, we are not trying to turn back the clock. Rather, we are using this as a way of emphasizing the concept of development as a primary determinant in the practice of psychotherapy with both these age groups.

At the same time, we must acknowledge the conceptual wisdom in not only separating childhood from adolescence but also dividing each into subphases—infancy, toddlerhood, preschool, and the school years; and early, middle, and late adolescence, respectively. Here we may note that the phase-specific developmental problem facing each of these subphases is different, and that each subphase is developmentally related to the one before. Although relatively successful sequential resolution of phase-specific tasks is optimal in normal development, adolescence also offers some opportunity for the spontaneous reworking of earlier unresolved issues. Division into subphases has some validity in the selection of appropriate psychotherapeutic techniques, as well. For example, the younger the teenager, the more effective are some of the techniques that work well with children, whereas older adolescents can often be treated very much like adults. More will be said later concerning this.

With the upsurge of interest in adolescence

have come changes within the psychatric profession. Child psychiatrists have taken a growing number of teenagers into treatment, while adult psychiatrists have become increasingly drawn toward working with late high school or college students. However, while adult psychiatrists have often proved extremely adept in this work, many child psychiatrists feel that their thorough training in child psychiatry has better prepared them for coping with the problems of adolescents, especially the younger ones. In whatever ways these issues of professional competence ultimately evolve, developmental requirements will necessitate the attainment and mastery of special skills to meet the specific needs and problems posed by a patient in a particular age group.

(Theoretical Framework

Although there are many ways of describing the development and workings of the human mind, we as clinicians have found in dynamic psychology the most useful body of theory for conceptualizing the problems with which our patients struggle. With this bias stated, we feel some obligation to the reader to acquaint him with the key concepts forming the basis for our thought and clinical work; beyond that, we must refer him to the working bibliography at the end of this chapter. For purposes of discussion, we will consider in turn the psychological, biological, and sociological systems within which the patient functions, suffers, and causes pain. (The order is not to be construed in a hierarchical sense.)

We begin with those concepts that describe the psychic apparatus: the notion of the unconscious, and the constructs of id, ego, and superego. As detailed by Freud,[27,30,31] Anna Freud,[24,26] Hartmann,[35,36] and others, these concepts enable us to understand the intrapsychic structure. Closely related are the concepts of intrapsychic conflict, the role of anxiety, and the defenses. Together they enable us to understand and assess the psyche in its dynamic aspects—its course of development (or nondevelopment) as well as its weaknesses

and strengths. (It is also necessary to take note of conceptual and cognitive development, as described by Piaget.[23,51] However, attempts to integrate this body of knowledge with intrapsychic structures and clinical child psychiatry have hardly begun.)[65] As a related issue, it should be mentioned that there has been much interest in behavior modification and its roots in learning theory in recent years; but this has not been taken up with enthusiasm in the child psychotherapy literature.[10]

To continue the discussion: the human psyche is housed in a physical organism, the body, which is presided over by a most complicated neuro-endocrine system. Biological factors to be considered include the organism's genetic heritage, rate and sequence of maturational development, physical health and diseases, and temperament (see below). Among the attempts to relate these factors to psychological growth is the work of Gesell and his group[32] in the 1930s and 1940s, with their systematic study and mapping of the psychomotor development of children and the valuable assessment scale that they devised. Valuable data concerning the sequence of pubertal development in the male and female have been collected by Tanner.[61,62] More recently, Chess, Thomas, and Birch[15] (1968) have developed a concept of "temperament," a phenomenological term that refers to behavioral style; although they have not specifically investigated the basis for a particular temperament, we are inclined to place their concept in the biologic area. Others have contributed to the concept of individual differences, as well.[64]

Finally, it is important to keep in mind that this psyche-within-a-physical-organism lives in a world, a social-cultural matrix composed of parents, siblings, peers, and society at large. Together, these three broad, interlocking arenas—intrapsychic, physiological and sociocultural—must form a homeostatic balance. Each individual attempts to achieve, maintain, and regain a balance between agencies of the mind, between mind and body, and between the inner and outer world. To preserve this dynamic equilibrium, the individual creates methods by which he strives with greater or lesser success to do this tripartite balancing act.

Obviously, artificial separations between these arenas must be made by investigators for purposes of study and clarification, but the separation can result in a fragmented picture. For example, the sequential steps in acquiring speech (from the coo and cry, to the pre-verbal babble, to the spoken word) do not come about in a vacuum. They are interdependent with all other areas of development, such as hearing, vision, capacity to discriminate and integrate, memory, motility, attachment to significant persons, verbal stimulation, and so forth. An interesting research example of the more integrative approach is presented by Ritvo et al.[54] (The material comes from a larger, longitudinal study of the Yale Child Development Center.) Observational data provided by the parents are available from the prenatal period and include the baby, "Jerry," from birth onwards. Regularly collected environmental data from the home and later nursery school are presented. Intrapsychic information is obtained from Jerry's two-year psychoanalysis, begun when he was three and a half years of age because of symptom formation. The multidimensional interaction of nature and nurture is convincingly demonstrated (as is a certain continuing thread of high activity level, probably of constitutional origin).

Since the practice of psychotherapy must be grounded in the practical, we also stress that any so-called "normal" is an ideal. The reality is that even though the development of a single capacity does follow a regular sequential pattern, overall development is never an orderly, synchronous sequence for any single youngster. This is especially true for the one who needs psychotherapy; in fact, one way of defining such a need is by the degree to which development has not been synchronous. Distorted development may show up as a lag of certain capacities or a precociousness in others (more commonly both), or a reaction to a traumatic event or inability. The overall task of psychotherapy is to correct the imbalance, help the youngster regain his appropriate place in the bio-psycho-social sequence of maturational processes, and help him develop operational methods to maintain the homeostatic balance suitable for his age and social reality. Of critical importance here is the innate push of such developmental processes, which acts as a silent assistant to the therapist. Or perhaps more correctly, the therapist is the needed assistant to ensure that the patient will indeed "grow out of it."

If psychotherapy is conceptualized as a method of modifying malfunctioning intrapsychic processes, then one can readily see that the request for treatment will come when the malfunctioning brings pain and suffering to the individual or causes problems for those around him, or both. (This approaches the medical model.) The patient's mode of dealing with difficulties may be predominantly autoplastic (acting to modify the self) or alloplastic (acting to modify the outside world). For example, one person may turn his problem inward and feel anxiety as a prominent symptom, which makes him very uncomfortable but does not necessarily disturb those around him; whereas a second person may be chronically provocative, which is troublesome to those about him but not necessarily painful to him. Furthermore, in evaluating a patient for psychotherapy we must differentiate between types of malfunctioning, each with their own defensively-produced symptomatology. Is the malfunctioning caused by current outer stress (such as a parental divorce, a move to a new location, or a death)? Then perhaps brief psychotherapy can bring relief, help master the crisis, and offer a growth-enhancing experience.[8,9,53] Or is the malfunctioning a continued effect of some traumatic event that occurred in the past? Is it a maladaptive defensive maneuver that may have been appropriate at an earlier time but has never been modified by subsequent events? Then perhaps longer-term, more intensive psychotherapy will be necessary. (A more ambitious plan in these instances may be to alter the character distortions that result from the prolonged maladaptation.) Or is the malfunctioning a learning disability based on a perceptual or integrative neurological misfunction, with a resultant psychological defensiveness and sense of inadequacy? Then perhaps special education techniques will have to be added when the psychotherapy has relieved the sense of hopelessness and futility and the youngster can engage in learning. Here psychotherapy may be prolonged to assist with a vulnerable sense of adequacy. But the length or frequency of treatment is not to be equated with effectiveness. Both short-term and long-term treatment, when properly selected, can be of long-standing benefit to the patient.

This chapter focuses on therapy for those youngsters who have neurotic or characterological disorders, and to some extent on those with psychophysiological problems. We do not attempt to deal with the treatment of infantile autism, severe psychosis, childhood or adolescent schizophrenia, or the seriously sociopathic youth, all of which we feel to be highly specialized areas of work. Nevertheless, much of what follows may indeed apply, with some modification, to work with youngsters who suffer from those illnesses.

(Treating Children and Adults: Some Differences

Differences between psychotherapeutic work with adults and work with children and adolescents have been discussed in general terms. We would now like to explore several of them in more detail. One difference is the way in which children perceive or express their problem. As a rule, children are less capable of describing uncomfortable, neurotic symptoms. Rather, anxiety will be manifested by hyperactivity, and depression concealed by aggressive or provocative behavior. Often, too, children will tend to see their problems in terms of the outer world: "The teacher doesn't like me," "They all pick on me," "They make me go to school," and so forth. True, an occasional youngster will be aware of an inner pain, worry, or fear and acknowledge that he wants help with it, but this is not the rule. A corollary to this difference is the observation that children do not seek psychotherapy; it is rather the parents who do. Parents may initiate it because of their own concern about the

child's behavior or because they were pressured to do so by the school, the court, or some other social agency, as a consequence of the child's behavior. From the very start, then, because of the role of parents, the psychotherapy of youngsters is radically different from that of adults.

With regard to adolescent psychotherapy, the role of parents can vary. The adolescent may wish to seek out professional consultation because of his own concern, or he may get "dragged in" and see the problem as being outside himself. Either case may be a reflection of the in-between state of adolescence: a stage at which one is trying to become an adult but has not yet put his dependent childhood behind him; a time when many changes are going on—bodily, energetic, social, familial—concurrent with the demands of integration, separation, and reorganization of the psyche. At this age, dependency needs may be felt only to be cast aside—denied—because they are considered childish. The more disturbed adolescent feels even more concern about his mental and emotional condition. Any suggestion that he get help from a psychiatrist may be met with the anxious question, "Do you think I'm crazy?" Like his younger counterpart, only occasionally does the disturbed adolescent find his symptoms so painful that he accedes readily to the notion of getting help.

A second difference between the psychiatric treatment of youngsters and adults is the make up of the real elements which impinge on him from the actual environment. The assessment of the world in which a child lives must include not only parents but also his siblings and any others who either live in the home or are very active figures in his daily life (relatives, household help, and so forth). It is well known that the person with the overt symptomatology is not always the most disturbed member of a family. A child may be used as a "ticket of admission" to treatment for a parent. A relative may be sexually seducing a child in the family, with the only overt symptoms being presented by the child. If the child's everyday world is one in which he is continually exposed to that which is harmful and destructive to his growth and development, then psychotherapy has little to offer. Neither children nor adolescents can do much to control the immediate environment in which they live. In situations where a noxious environment is unalterable, it may be the first order of business to arrange for nursery school, kindergarten, foster care, boarding school, or other residential placement. The younger the child, the more true this is; conversely, the older the youngster, the greater the possibility that psychotherapy can help in the adjustment to reality.

Obviously, parents hold a paramount place in a child's life and retain a measure of his loyalty no matter how "awful" they may be.[50] Even in adolescence, when teenagers may show considerable rebelliousness towards parents, more often than not there is a deeply hidden but strong measure of attachment. Roles in the process of transition are complex for all concerned. It is also important for the physician to recognize that parents do not just pay the bills, but that they are truly responsible for the youngster; therapist, child, and parents need to know and openly acknowledge this fact. Sometimes parents mistake the therapeutic process to mean that the therapist will take over parental functions with the child, and thereby abdicate their rightful role, maybe with resentment or maybe with pleasure and relief. In either case, the misperception must be clarified very early in the work.

A third difference between therapy for child and adult is the so-called "rescue fantasy." Here we allude to the feeling on the part of the therapist that he must literally "rescue" the child or adolescent from his "bad parents." Such fantasies exist also in adult work; but when one is working with children, the power of this countertransference fantasy is peculiarly strong and ever-present and can be insidious. For one thing, the child's actual parents are always readily available, thus inviting the unwary therapist to project his own disappointment in parents and parent figures. The implication, of course, is that the therapist himself will become the "good parent." Few things could be more damaging to patient or psychotherapy. Thus parents—except in those

unusual cases in which their parental rights have been terminated by court order—need to recognize from the very beginning of treatment that they are extremely important to the whole therapeutic process, and the therapist must respect and mean this when he tells them so. Needless to say, parents need acknowledgement by the therapist of the stresses they too are experiencing and of any past deficits for which they are now struggling to compensate.[34] It may also happen that, during the course of treatment, the child will talk or act at home in a manner that threatens the parents' own feeling of parenthood; this, too, may require help. There are some cases in which a child cannot live at home during the course of treatment—perhaps cannot even be returned to his parents when therapy is over. But these situations are comparatively rare and require special handling.

(The Therapist

No attempt will be made here to define all that makes for a successful child therapist since no two will work exactly alike, nor will any two have identical personalities. Still, any successful child therapist will have a reasonably clear awareness of and psychological acquaintance with his own past. What is required is not a childlikeness on the part of the therapist but, rather, an open line from the adult person to the condition of being a child. It is important to communicate with children and adolescents without losing one's own identity, and to empathize with a patient's worries, feelings, and view of reality without identifying with them. With adolescents in particular, where the pressure so often takes the form "you're either with me or against me," the adult who can experience and express empathy without taking sides may be very helpful indeed. Even where we cannot experientially know life beyond our ken or the genital or bodily sensations of persons of the opposite sex, it is very valuable when the therapist can acknowledge the existence and reality of the youngster's perceptions and assist in the development of verbal description.

In this connection we note that the ensuing comments on the technical aspects of psychotherapy with children and adolescents are intended to apply equally to the work of male and female therapists with patients of both sexes. In a small number of cases, as when a youngster expresses a preference for a man, or woman, as therapist, matching the sex of the patient with that of the therapist may become an issue.

Although little has been written on this particular topic, there does seem to be a professional concensus that the matching of like-sexed patient and therapist has its greatest significance for the pre- and early adolescent when such matching may prove to enhance the initiation and development of a viable therapeutic relationship. Where it is not possible, the alert therapist may, after all, allow this issue to be tactfully turned to therapeutic advantage.

Perhaps we can shed further light on what makes a good child therapist by asking: "What goes on in the mind of a child therapist while engaged in his work?" The process is not only complex, it also differs in certain respects from what happens in adult work. The therapist is engaged in play with the child. He may be actively playing a role, such as the wicked stepsister, the helpless frightened child, the criminal, or the isolated bystander; or, with the early adolescent, there may be an earnest engagement about cars, hobbies, clothes, fashions, fishing, politics, the plot of a movie or a book, or the life of a celebrity or hero. Whatever the role he is cast in or the subject being discussed, the therapist must be genuinely engaged. If the therapist is not sure how a wicked stepmother behaves or what she says, the patient will be glad to write the script, or, if the therapist does not know much about cars or fishing, the patient will be happy to instruct. The therapist must also observe the play or the dialogue, looking for the prevailing theme and the inner, personal (latent) meaning it has for the child, such as anger, depression, fear, misinformation, sexual fantasy. Whenever there is a discontinuity or play disruption, the psychiatrist must try to grasp the

reasons. And while all this is going on, the observing part of the therapist should also be correlating the current theme with earlier themes, with the patient's current life situation, and with his past history. What then follows is probably the most difficult task of all: when and how should the therapist intercede with verbal comment? We use the word "comment" here to denote a verbal communication, which may take the form of (1) clarifying questions, (2) comments on the play content, form, or thematic sequence, or (3) an interpretation that would link feelings discussed earlier, themes played out earlier, current life situations, unconscious impulses, or past traumatic events.

The decision as to what the therapist elects to comment upon and the manner in which he does it will reflect what he wants to accomplish. In short-term treatment or crisis intervention, where the focus is on clearly delineated problems, he will focus only on those aspects of the personality that relate to the current issue. In longer-term psychotherapy, he may decide to pursue more extensively the patient's hidden or disguised affects and those defenses that are constrictive or maladaptive for the personality. The goal will be to make the defenses less harsh and more useful, and to allow the patient more affective awareness, better reality testing, and stronger relationships with others. To use Kessler's[42] example: a six-year-old boy gets into fights because he attacks whenever he fears being attacked, though unaware of the anxiety that began the whole sequence. The psychotherapist will try to help the boy become aware of his fear (anxiety), make the maladaptive defense of counterphobic attack no longer necessary, and clarify some of the misconceptions of reality. The psychoanalyst will want to go further and uncover the instinctual-drive derivative, the boy's unconscious wish to be attacked and (in this particular example) made into a girl, that is, castrated. Stated very briefly, the psychoanalyst believes that the uncovering of the id derivatives, coupled with defense analysis, will render the child less vulnerable to recurrent psychic problems, more able to deal with those that may arise later on, and emotionally stronger and more flexibly able to cope with his own wishes and the outer reality. Whether this formulation is or is not correct and efficacious remains one of the many problems in the field of psychotherapy.

Youngsters in treatment must proceed in their own fashion at their own speed. Like adult patients, some are more intuitive than others and, given the chance, will almost "treat themselves." Some are far more cautious, and if pushed will only grow more and more resistant. Almost anything a child says or does—including body language, fantasy, the form of the play, and even lies—can add to the therapist's understanding of the youngster. Perhaps the most frequent mistake of the neophyte child psychiatrist is the effort to push the child into more adultlike verbalizations. Another frequent mistake is to permit the child unlimited freedom in the sessions, which may lead to either overexcitement or aggressive acting out. This only frightens the child, because it is painful and scary to feel out of control. It also distances the therapist, who may begin to feel irritated and withdraw.

Any discussion of the psychotherapist must include the phenomena of transference and countertransference. These concepts are vital to the treatment process, with children as with adults, but all too often they are ill-defined if not reduced to absurdity—as, for example, when positive transference is equated with the youngster liking the therapist and negative transference with his dislike of the therapist. Transference may be defined as those unrealistic feelings (whether positive or negative) that the patient ascribes to his therapist, by means of displacement, but that more correctly belong to significant others in his life, such as parents, siblings, or teachers. They are thoughts, expectations, and feelings that are unconsciously directed toward another person —in this case the therapist—for whom they are inappropriate. Yet the patient always experiences these feelings as genuine and correctly directed. Transference phenomena occur in all relationships but are usually correctable by reality testing or are irrelevant to the transaction.

Certainly not all feelings about the therapist can be classified as transference. Many are genuine reactions to things the therapist says and does, or does not say or do. Others are projected and externalized feelings of the patient, which are attributed to the therapist. For example, a youngster's ambivalent feelings towards his parents are frequently split, with the negative, critical feelings externalized onto the therapist while the child virtuously defends the good parent. Or the child may feel the therapist does not like him, whereas in fact the child is projecting his own inner, harsh self-criticism. It is part of the therapist's task to initially accept these "slings and arrows" and work with them as though they were correctly directed. Then slowly, when the defensive posture is less necessary, the therapist will help his patient correct the distortion. For example, a girl of sixteen reluctantly acknowledged some mildly sexual fantasies about her male therapist, after having "put down" her father for some time. With her therapist's help, the girl's feelings of guilt, embarrassment, and pleasure about these fantasies were explored. In this case, for a variety of reasons, they were not able to discuss the bodily sensations which probably accompanied these fantasies. When she was more comfortable with some aspects of her sexuality, the therapist attempted to interpret the transference—that is, to show that she also felt toward her father these feelings that they had been talking about, and that she did not see him only as fat, ugly and dumb. She denied it. Later, when the parents were in the process of separation and divorce, she visited her father, who was living alone. Suddenly she became aware of a complexity of feelings toward him, which included feeling sorry for him, wanting to take care of him, and sexual feelings. She was frightened, but she did not have to resort to the kinds of warding-off behavior (such as isolation, withdrawal, and disdain) that heretofore had interfered with many relationships, including the one with her father. In therapy she began to assess her father more realistically, and her view of men in general became less harsh.

The phenomenon of transference neurosis, on the other hand, has been described primarily in adults. It involves the patient literally, unconsciously, and with emotional conviction, displacing many unrealistic feelings, expectations, and attitudes onto the therapist. This temporarily frees the patient of the major part of his neurotic symptomatology, and the "neurosis in situ" becomes the working arena. There has been much debate over the years as to whether such a phenomenon can occur in children or adolescents. Though child psychiatrists and child analysts lack consensus on the question, it seems far less likely that a true transference neurosis occurs in children. After all, the child still has his original love objects, namely his parents, and it would seem more difficult for him to transfer all of these feelings onto a therapist. But there is agreement that forms of transference do occur in the treatment of children and adolescents, and that recognizing their presence and working with the feelings and attitudes related to them may be critical to the success of the psychotherapy.

Countertransference phenomena are those feelings and thoughts that the therapist has about the patient, but do *not* belong to the real situation. Thus if a child patient means to hurt you by kicking or throwing something, and you feel an inner angry response, that is real. It is not countertransference. A seven-year old boy comes to his therapy hour on Valentine's Day, carrying nonchalantly a handmade greeting card for his therapist. In his haste he drops the valentine at the office door and greets the therapist cheerfully with "Hi, Dr. Fucker." If the therapist feels hurt and offended at the bad language and can not respond to the card lying on the floor, that is countertransference. The therapist's own emotions of distaste and social disapproval are aroused by the obscene word and obscure his ability to perceive the underlying message of endearment.

⟨ Play

Children, as mentioned earlier, express themselves most naturally in the form of play; and beginning with the early work of Anna Freud

and Melanie Klein, play has been a *sine qua non* of child therapy. Erikson, who studied play as form, holds that it differs for boys and girls.[16,17] The boys he observed tended to play vigorously, constructing shapes and spaces going upward and outward; the girls created more enclosed areas and dealt with protected spaces. He felt that these differences were not just culturally determined but reflected real body difference. The meaning of play and its unfolding stories and themes can then be variously interpreted. But few would doubt that play reveals the inner life of the child, or that it is by means of play that the child can best communicate his fantasies about life and its processes, his fears, his hopes, and his desires. In addition, within the therapy hour the child will commonly use play as a way to master traumatic events or the fearful content of fantasy, to tell about unspeakable things, and to make gratifying (if temporary) changes in reality. But play can also be used as resistance, in which case the play functions to obscure and hamper communication.

When play therapy is planned, questions invariably arise as to what types of materials should be made available. Obviously the answer will differ with the age of the child. It seems a truism that the longer one has been treating children in play therapy, the more one trusts the children themselves to adapt available materials to their needs. For example, one of us has a plastic washbasket in the office that is used for storing toys. Children three to five years old have used it as a crib to curl up in, as a den for the wicked fox, and (upside down) as a cage to restrain a wild and dangerous bear. An older youngster, age ten, may ignore it as a play object and see it only as a utilitarian storage container. A twelve- or thirteen-year-old may spot it and decide to practice his basketball shots in it while he "has to see his shrink." Checkers, a classical game, also lends itself to multiple uses, depending on the age of the youngster.[45] The young child may use a checker to represent special food for a play animal or, perhaps, to construct a decorative tower for his building. He may try to assert his wish to be older by playing a real game of checkers, but with little concept of moves or rules. The child of latency age may also wish to play checkers, but as a way of concealing his problems and conflicts. Nevertheless he may reveal himself by how he reacts to the possibility of losing; he may cheat, disrupt the game, or try to change the rules.[48] For him the struggle for self-esteem is played out in the game along with issues of power, fighting, and being vanquished, a fear that winning will bring retaliation, or an inability to delay gratification. For the pre- or early adolescent the checker game may be intently focused on to keep his mind off disquieting things, or in a seemingly idle way he may stack the checkers as a wall between himself and the therapist while he talks about an emotionally significant event or situation. Even if a youngster only uses the game in a token way, he may feel more comfortable if there is something to diffuse the contact between self and therapist.

Language is another aspect of play. With toys for his props, the young child may use language to elaborate the fantasy he is busy unfolding. The adolescent will use fewer props or even none at all. Instead the words themselves become a kind of prop as he talks with great enthusiasm about some current interest, some event that occurred, or some intellectual thought. These subjects are indeed current and real, but they also have latent content for which the therapist listens. Such a use of words is typical of early adolescents, who are often conflicted because they are at an inbetween stage—above playing with toys, but not yet able to talk directly with the therapist without an in-between buffer. Another reason for the self-consciousness of early adolescents is that in their play they tend toward large muscle movement, which becomes awkward in an office.

In the practical matter of what kinds of play materials to have, we might offer two generalizations. First, the play materials need not be complicated and should not be highly structured. Second, they should be few in number but carefully chosen for versatility of function. Plain wooden blocks of assorted shapes and sizes are excellent; for the younger

child they should be of a fair size, similar to those used in kindergartens, because at this age the child is not adept with fine motor and eye–hand movement. Cars, trucks, and airplanes provide the element of movement. Dolls, including family figure dolls of various ages and color, provide the *dramatis personae* for significant play. Some children prefer more distance from areas of conflict and tend to keep things in displacement by using animal figures for playing out family scenes. Hand puppets attract some youngsters as a means of telling stories or relating true events. While some therapists find a dollhouse useful, others prefer to use blocks and let the children build their own room-outlines or buildings. Beyond these, a variety of everyday items lend themselves to play, such as paper, cardboard, scissors, crayons, pencils, felt-tip pens, paste, tape, rubber bands, and paper clips. A range of things can be improvised from such materials without the need to buy particular toys. Truly, there are no limitations save the imagination of therapist and child.

Youngsters of all ages will reach for crayons as a medium of expression. The younger adolescent who is uncomfortable and does not know what to do with his hands will often relax visibly when given a pad of paper and a pencil so that he can "sketch" while he talks. If male therapists may sometimes seem more comfortable and adept than women at using toy soldiers and war-like toys it is less important than that professionals of both sexes can readily find the means for enabling youngsters to express aggression. With younger children the chance for water play is, at times, important, but on occasion we have worked quite successfully with imaginary water to produce an imaginary mess. A baby doll with a baby bottle and related equipment may prove inviting. A simple sewing kit or bits of cloth will sometimes tempt a child to make clothes for a doll. And if the therapist proves as, or more, awkward than the patient in making miniature fashions that work, this permits direct discussion of skills and competence. Should sex-linked stereotypes be evoked, a therapist may turn his (or her) ineptitude to advantage by openness to these issues. Finger-paints, clay, play dough, and paper-mâché are other materials that aid the development of fantasy as well as granting the permission to make a mess. Board games such as checkers, Chinese checkers, cards, and commercial games with pieces, dice, or spinners attract older children who often find things like "play dough" too "babyish" and need to avoid the seduction to such regressive play. At times children will bring their own games from home, and these too can be useful. Chess and Monopoly are two popular games that deserve particular mention. Both tend to last a long time and serve all too easily as a form of resistance. Yet one of us recalls a seven-year-old son of a real estate man who delighted in playing Monopoly and once, legitimately and with pleasure, made the therapist bankrupt in a single hour.

When space permits, it is useful to have a private place in the office for a youngster to store a project or favorite toys he may have brought to the office. An older child may elect to bring a copy of *Playboy* or some other reading matter that would not be acceptable at home. It is important that the therapist let the youngster know that while such materials are acceptable in the office because they help the doctor understand the curiosities of the child, they are not necessarily acceptable elsewhere. Many children like to display their art work. This also provokes fantasies of sibling rivalry and concern about "who indeed is fairest (most beloved) of them all." Such youngsters may wish to write their names on their art work, but it is best to discourage the use of last names. When a child asks to leave an unfinished project in plain view, hoping to finish it at the next visit, he should be told that the therapist may not be able to preserve it in the interim. Pictures that the child displays on the wall may also not be as well protected as when tucked away in a folder containing only that child's material.

Many youngsters will want to take home with them something they have made. Often it represents the youngster's desire to keep some kind of contact with the therapist between visits. In general, it is best to have the youngster leave all such materials in the office but to let him know that he can have his own pictures

back when treatment ends. As to taking play materials out of the office, our general rule is that this cannot be done (but this can be mitigated by developmental considerations). There is the practical reason that the toys are there for all to use. More important, the rule is a guard against acting out, and it assures discussion of the wish, its symbolic significance, and the urges that arise when a wish is thwarted. Most youngsters accept this, but some will occasionally pocket a small toy without the therapist's knowledge. Resultant guilt may then come into focus in the form of provocative behavior in the subsequent hour. As for adolescents, one may find them "stealing" an object, however insignificant, from the office. The taking must be dealt with directly as a symptomatic act, with restitution as part of reality. One should be cautioned that not all taking is hostility; it may be concealed love, idealization, or identification. In related but different behavior, the youngster may seek the therapist's approval or sanction. But beware: the words of the therapist may be used as ammunition in a battle with parents or other authority figures. Being supportive of an adolescent's apparently valid complaint without taking sides requires skills worthy of a diplomat or negotiator.

On the question of office space, some therapists recommend a playroom that is well equipped and comfortable but that is furnished in a way that is relatively indestructible. This leaves the "grown-up" office as a place to talk. Such a luxury of space is not always available. Some therapists divide their office so that the "adult" part of it is on one side and a cabinet containing play materials on the other, a plan that has both advantages and disadvantages. For example, many children are fascinated by things like a telephone or a dictating machine. If a youngster happens to be aggressive and to have negative feelings toward the therapist, he can play havoc with these instruments. On the other hand, the same instruments have brought many therapists's important revelations. For instance, a child who can use a dictating machine properly can often be urged to tell a story into it. The same holds true for a telephone if the child agrees to let the therapist hold the button down.

We believe that many questions concerning space and play equipment relate in part at least to temperament. Some children are extremely innovative, clever, and capable of imaginative games and constructions with a minimum of play materials. Others will complain of the lack of certain games or toys, often with the unspoken wish to see if the therapist "loves" them enough to get the missing materials. For ten years, one of us treated children of all ages (in the same office space where he saw adults), and the fact that the desk or book shelf was "off limits" never seemed to inhibit the child's freedom of expression. In fact, curiosity about the desk was invariably a way of indicating curiosity about the therapist himself. Nevertheless, if issues of space and equipment reflect the temperament of the children, the same is true for the therapist too. Some therapists are just not good with puppets, others find board games a bore, and still others find that chess can divert them too much, so that they lose track of what is going on in therapy. Each must choose his own play tools and admit that others just do not catch his interest.

(Parents

Legion are the therapists who have felt, "If only he had other parents, I could really help this child." This is true whether the patient is six or sixteen. Indeed, some physicians have given up the practice of child psychiatry because of parental "interference" that they saw as beyond their control. The feeling is understandable. But periodically it helps for the physician to remind himself that parents do indeed have the last word, and surely no one would contest the fact that the treatment of any minor who is still in the custody of his parents must have their tacit backing. At this point it is important to mention several still-changing aspects of the term "minor." First, the age of majority is now eighteen instead of twenty-one in many states. Second, there is a

growing lack of consensus about the age at which the teenager may demand his own legal counsel (this has to do with the pressuring of a youngster into treatment, as in residential treatment), or the age at which he may enter into a psychotherapeutic relationship without parental knowledge or consent (this pertains to "drop-in clinics" where adolescent clients are seen and may even be encouraged to enter into a longer term therapeutic relationship). While it is to be hoped that some of these confusions can be clarified legally in the next few years, things remain in flux for the present.

To return to the alliance between parents and therapist, a collaborative relationship exists even if they never see each other—as is recommended by some in the treatment of adolescents. It is our feeling that the majority of teenagers will do better if their parents' acceptance of the treatment is direct and openly acknowledged. We believe that a smoother therapeutic course, one less likely to be threatened by disruptive parental actions, is well worth the investment of a few extra hours in the initial work-up in meeting with the parents. The short-run gains are obvious, for it is clearly better to have obtained parental cooperation ahead of time than to begin the work while they are ambivalent or openly resentful. But long-run gains may be more important. For example, if the therapist shares with the parents the prediction that their child may appear to be getting worse as his emotional constriction begins to lift, the parents' unhappiness may be spared and their disappointments kept from being vented on the child.

It is not difficult to be responsive and sympathetic with the parents if one keeps in mind that most parents who come for help with their child are under pressure.[5] Somewhere, somehow, they feel they have failed.[34] Hence, the therapist is initially perceived as a judge of how well they have done their job as parents. Soon they may begin to fear that the child will prefer the therapist to them because he is sympathetic, understanding, and nondemanding. Jealousy may develop, along wth a growing sense that the youngster shares more with the therapist than with his parents. It is at these times, when many parents feel vulnerable because their child has an ally who knows things about the child but will not share his knowledge, that a "rescue fantasy" on the part of the therapist can be especially dangerous. But if parents can come to know that the therapist understands their position and plight and respects them as people—in fact relies on their help and tacit support—they will be much more cooperative. This is true even where there are disagreements between parents and therapist about child-rearing practices.

Specific aspects of the therapist's relationship with the parents will depend on the age of the child. For example, because it tallies with his everyday life, the youngster between the ages of three and six is rarely troubled by the fact that the therapist is in regular communication with his parents. It is often hard for the young child to recount important events of the week, so the therapist relies on obtaining parental information on a regular basis. Again, knowledge of a difficult weekend at home, a fight at school, parental illness, an accident, an absence, or even a particularly successful handling of a difficult situation can often help the therapist make better sense out of events that occur in the sessions. Nor do we hesitate to share such information with a child. This is because he looks on the therapist as a helping person, and the discussion or play that may follow will make the child's anxiety more manageable and lessen his more inappropriate defenses.

Developmental processes in the youngster from ages six to ten move him into the world of his peers and of adults other than his parents. The size of his private world is literally expanding. Stronger assurance can now be given a child, when he needs it, that although the therapist may talk with his parents he will disclose nothing of what goes on between himself and the child. This is usually termed confidentiality.[55] It is unwise to make these assurances absolute and unconditional, since promises of confidentiality may sometimes have to be "bent." Even at these ages youngsters assume that the therapist will have some communication with his parents. Many will

conclude on their own that, despite this communication, they do in fact enjoy confidentiality; if not, then the child's fears and worries about what will happen are well worth exploring. It is common practice to furnish the youngster with an explanation of why the physician talks with his parents from time to time. He can be told, for example, that the doctor needs to know about events that happened so early in his life that he cannot remember them, or perhaps other things that his parents would be more aware of than he is himself. All of this should be explained to the youngster in a way that helps him to understand how it will aid his therapist in understanding his problems. (One can also acknowledge that parents sometimes need help in understanding their children and knowing how best to deal with them.)

The picture changes somewhat for the pre- and early adolescents. At this stage of development there are often sharp differences between parent and child, which provoke arguments, angry outbursts, and even periods of intense withdrawal. Youngsters are now prone to see one as a person who is either for or against him, and alliance by association is quickly seized upon. The therapist must, therefore, ally himself more specifically with the youngster than his parents, but never exclusively so. At no other time in the life cycle does a psychotherapist tread a finer line than with these youngsters, and never are the guideposts more camouflaged. The therapist should be available to parental phone calls that are often about extraordinary events that the patient "forgot" to tell the therapist. Examples would be an explosive fight with his parents, a threat to run away, a suicidal gesture, or even an especially happy time or a good report card. These should be brought up in the treatment situation in a sympathetic manner, because they indicate the youngster's unhappiness or despair or his conflicts about success.

We would like to emphasize that the youngster's therapist, no matter what the age of the child, should strive always to deal with the parent only as parent and not as patient. This means discussing the parental role, behavior management suggestions, and support for maintaining parental function and authority. It does not mean exploring the personality, motivations, or psychopathology of the parents. If these *are* required, as they often are, either psychiatric social casework or psychotherapy for the parents can be a valuable adjunct to the child's treatment process. If circumstances are such that no one else is available, and the parent is in need of psychotherapy, then careful consideration must be given to the possible ramifications and complications of being psychotherapist for two or more members of the same family at the same time. For example, one thirteen-year-old patient threatened that he was no longer coming to treatment because it was useless. "My mother makes me come," he said, "and I won't come unless she does too." (The parents had divorced and the father had subsequently died.) Attempts to explore the reasons behind this challenge were to no avail. As far as the boy was concerned, either both came or no one; faced with such an ultimatum, one could only agree. In this particular case it was fortunate that his mother, although in treatment herself, went along with the plan. There followed six months in which the therapist witnessed a full array of vicious battles and threats, followed quickly by tearful and emotional reunions. This, however, allowed the physician to begin to work out a most tangled relationship so that both people could begin to separate and live as autonomous persons and subsequently return to individual psychotherapeutic work.

What about the other side of confidentiality? This is an area that has been little discussed in the literature of child and adolescent psychotherapy. What stance do we take when we learn from a five-year-old patient that he is heavily but secretly involved in neighborhood sex play, and while he claims it is lots of fun, there is much to indicate it is making him highly anxious? What is our role when a ten-year-old discloses with considerable hesitation that he is involved in a local extortion racket at his school but cannot break free? What is our role when a fifteen-year-old girl confesses to her therapist that she is pregnant and her friends are collecting money so that she can go

to New York for an abortion? All of these, in our opinion, are cries for help—help that, for the most part, only parents are qualified to give. In instances where the parents have unwittingly failed to protect their child as he deserves, or the youngster has not dared to solicit their help, the therapist should provide such moral and emotional support as will enable the child to broach the subject with his parents. With a younger child, after the therapist has talked it over with his patient, it may be best for him to discuss the situation with the parents alone. They can then help the child with his ambivalent wish to get out of an overstimulating situation. For example, one five-year-old very adroitly maneuvered one of her parents into the office and, in the ensuing doll play, proceeded to demonstrate graphically the sexual games she was then engaging in with a male playmate. The parents, who had earlier been skeptical when the therapist had raised the possibility, were now satisfied that the quietness in the basement and outdoor playhouse needed closer monitoring.

With older children it may be best to invite the parents in for a discussion, with the child participating. Correct judgment in such cases may be difficult, but more often than not a frank discussion with the patient will bring the hidden call for help to the fore. A fifteen-year-old boy comes to mind who had been in treatment only briefly when he made a moderately serious suicidal gesture. That evening (after appropriate medical care had been rendered) he was interviewed with his parents, and while the gravity of the situation was noted, the decision was that there was no need for hospitalization. Two days later the youngster announced that he was fine and was discontinuing treatment. At this point, the therapist indicated to the youngster that he was forcing his hand and that if he could no longer come voluntarily to therapy, there was no choice but to hospitalize him. The boy was frightened and angry. It took six more months of treatment, while in the hospital, before he could reveal that several weeks before the suicidal gesture he had told his parents that he felt only hospitalization could help his depression and isolation. When they made light of his plea and tried to reassure him, he interpreted it as the usual parental reaction of not taking him seriously.

(School

The psychiatrist who works with children and adolescents inevitably must have contact with our largest social institution, school.[49,57] In fact, school can be considered the third point of a triangle that confronts the psychiatrist, the other two being the child and the parents. When it functions well the triangle is effective, growth enhancing, and very sturdy (a characteristic shared with all triangular structures). The child psychiatrist needs to be aware of these three points and the interplay between them, although his primary attention, of course, is directed to the individual psychotherapeutic work. If the psychiatrist knows something about the schools in his area and has had contact with key persons in the local school system, his task will be easier.

A youngster's behavior or achievement at school is frequently one of the primary complaints that brings him to us for evaluation. Whether it is poor achievement, disruptive behavior, truancy, or excessive withdrawal, all are symptoms the school recognizes as signs of trouble. As a usual first step, parents are invited by the teacher or counselor to discuss the problem. Then, if things do not improve despite the involvement of school personnel, child, and parents, referral is made to a child guidance clinic or private psychiatrist. In the ideal situation the perceptive teacher would recognize a youngster's need for help, have the backing of her superiors, and discuss the recommendation with the parents, who would readily and comfortably authorize the school to share with the psychiatrist its knowledge of the child and of pertinent aspects of his academic and social behavior. However—the ideal being infrequent—it is worth mentioning some common variations. For example, there is the situation complicated by parents who side with the child to such a degree that they can only regard the school personnel as being at fault or incompetent. Conversely, the teacher may see the parents as overindulgent or unwilling to recognize obvious problems. In either or both of these polarized relationships a psychiatric consultant may find himself being asked, however subtly, to take sides. Here, as in divorce struggles, he should be prompt to make the problem explicit and make clear that his task will be to try and determine what will be best for the youngster.

Once the referral for consultation has been made, the school is usually willing to share its observations and test results with a psychiatrist, given the parents' permission. School data are for the most part observational and have to do with problems and styles of peer relationships and the ability to concentrate, to recall, and to reason. Also described are odd or persistent habits or compulsions, how the youngster relates to adults, and so forth. A good teacher-observer can provide excellent vignettes of a variety of ego functions in action. These are not likely to be couched in psychiatric terminology, but they often prove invaluable in assessing a child's personality. Grades and group IQ test scores are usually less valuable except as they reveal trends or sudden discontinuities. This seems as good a point as any to mention that we usually let a youngster know, if he is eight or older, which people we are asking information from and why.

At the conclusion of the evaluation it is important to give the school some feedback, with the consent of the parents, and after an age-suitable discussion with the child. However, the information furnished should not be in psychiatric jargon but in precise, descriptive English. In general, diagnoses are not as valuable as are suggestions for management in the classroom. One should not release data about family, parents, and patient—however important such data are to understanding the case dynamically—if they will be of no help to school personnel in their daily management. What the school can do to help is, however, a valuable part of the overall treatment plan. It may be a change in classroom, remedial education, or active teacher support for early intervention as the student's behavior spirals. At times the school may provide realistic punishments and restrictions; at other times, a "safety valve" way of getting out of the classroom, or other ways of temporarily restructuring school routines for the child. Of course it should go without saying that *no* sharing of information obtained in circumstances of confidentiality should occur without first having cleared the matter by discussion with the persons involved—that is, parents and child.

There are times when a youngster needs to be confronted with discomfiting realities. Unfortunately, too many schools consider the child in treatment to be very fragile and, as a consequence, avoid revelations of unpleasant truths, thus keeping the child in limbo. It is important, although difficult, for the therapist to make clear to the school that it need no longer protect the youngster, that indeed he has to become aware of the consequences of his actions (or his failure to act), and that usual rules should be followed—which is not to say that the school should be harsh; merely honest and just. Strategically, this task may be quite difficult for the therapist. Great care must be taken, on the one hand, that the school will not misuse the therapist's sanctions, and, on the other hand, that the therapeutic alliance with the child will not be damaged.

Sometimes a child will be brought to treatment when there are no manifest problems at school. Then we feel it quite appropriate to omit contact with the school and to rely instead on reports of parent–teacher conferences. This is a different situation from the one in which the parents are very reluctant to have the psychiatrist contact the school because they fear a social stigma. Occasionally the parents are right in their opinion that the school teacher or principal is actively judgmental against the youngster's need for treatment, or openly prejudiced against psychiatric intervention. More often, however, such an attitude proves to be a parental rationalization that must be dealt with and that represents a projection of the parents' feelings toward, and rejection of, psychiatric care.

Utmost cooperation between therapist, parents, and school is required in the treatment of the symptom complex called "school phobia," or "school refusal."[22,40,47,63] Assuming, of course, that it has been established that the child is not psychotic, the first task is to get the child back into the school. It would not be inappropriate to define the initial phase as an emergency situation requiring extraordinary amounts of attention and attentiveness to child, family, and school. Because all those concerned are feeling anxious and unsure at this time, the therapist must not only supply a rationale for his difficult prescription (the return to school) but also concrete suggestions for case management. The most useful stance is to be kindly and supportive but also firm. The child must enter the school building even if he only sits in the principal's or counselor's office to do some school work; the therapist can acknowledge the anxiety feelings—including preschool nausea and vomiting—of the child, support the parents' understandable fear of hurting the child, but remain steadfast in his insistence that it must be done. A physical examination by the family physician that gives a clean bill of health is helpful in assuaging dire catastrophic fantasies that child, parents, or school officials may harbor. The child can express his rage at the psychiatrist for "not caring" and for causing him such suffering. When things are no longer acute, the therapist may withdraw from his contacts with the school and direct all his efforts to the psychotherapy. Parent therapy may also be necessary after the acute issues have been handled.

One word of caution: under the laws of professional confidentiality, all school contacts require clearance from the parents; in addition, the rights of the adolescent to confidentiality are changing even now. In this connection it is important to keep in mind that, in certain states, parents may see all school records simply upon demand. Written reports must be carefully composed so that they contain only such relevant data as the school needs in its program planning for the youngster. (For instance, data about extramarital affairs of a parent, illegitimacy, adoption, marital discord, and so forth, have no place in such reports. Neither is it relevant to include details of a child's fantasy life, secret sexual experimentation, and so forth.) As a safeguard, we think it is wise to discuss with all parents and older children the recommendations that the school will receive from the psychiatrist.

(Common Technical Problems

Among the technical problems unique to the treatment of a youngster, some are more typical of one age than another. In the following discussion each will be touched on from a developmental point of view.

Limit Setting

At some time in the treatment of almost every child, the endurance of the therapist is put to the test. With a young child this most often takes the form of attacks on the doctor's person or on objects in the room. While motivations vary, such behavior usually stops if correctly defined and interpreted. It often helps to divert the behavior onto dolls, puppets, or other appropriate objects. But there may come a time when none of these methods work and the child must be physically restrained. The therapist may then be surprised to find that the patient struggles *into* his lap instead of away from it. It helps if the restraint comes with a clear, definitive statement from the therapist that he will not let the child hurt him but also that he will not hurt the child. Youngsters who are out of control are often both angry and frightened. They find it reassuring to know that the therapist will control them at the moment and later suggest alternative modes of expression such as words or play. It is essential that the child feel himself being controlled without the therapist's opinion of him changing.

Older children may not lose control as frequently but are more difficult to manage when they do. Because the chances are greater that either the therapist or the child will be accidentally hurt, stringent efforts should be made to avoid this outcome. Shunning direct physical contact, older children will resort to methods such as "snitching" things from the office,

cheating at games, and so forth. At such times, limits are best and most appropriately set in terms that let the youngster know that the therapist is aware of what is going on and that it raises questions in his mind as to the youngster's insecurity and sense of unworthiness. When a ten-year-old cheats in a checker game, the therapist may suggest that since he (the therapist) is older and has played more, he would be willing to take a handicap. Some youngsters can accept this and some cannot. The therapist may then inquire as to whether the youngster would prefer to play by his own rules or the real rules, getting across to the youngster an awareness of the youngster's absolute need to win.

With an adolescent, these problems may take the form of lying or distorting the truth. Here the situation becomes somewhat delicate, because to accuse a child of lying is apt to provoke more open resistance. Instead one may, for example, tell the youngster that apparently he wishes so desperately that certain things were so that he comes to feel they really are so. This lets the youngster know that the therapist is aware of what is going on and understands the psychological motivation, but it avoids direct accusation, which could only be understood as disapproval.

Resistance

To resist, to want not to know, is part of all psychotherapy. It means that the patient is unwilling or unable to learn more about himself through sharing his thoughts and feelings with his therapist. Although at times this may be conscious and deliberate withholding, more often it is unconscious. Also possible is the preconscious existence of a memory of an event, thought, or feeling that may be lost from awareness, only to reappear later. If prodded by the therapist, the patient may easily recall the memory (even if only to dismiss it as unimportant). The only generalization we can make is that any mode that can be used to express oneself can also be used in the service of resistance. Play can become dull, repetitive, and confusing. Drawing can become stereotyped and abstract. Game-playing can become strict, repetitive, and unemotional. Each is a form of resistance. Resistance may also shade into long periods of silence during which the youngster claims he has nothing to say.[11]

We find there are several distinctions that help in dealing with resistance, no matter what the age of the patient is. (1) It may be a defensive maneuver to protect the youngster from fantasied punishment at the hands of the therapist, whether it is based on pure fantasy or on actual experience at the hands of other adults (transference). In such instances it can be valuable to talk about the fantasy and feared dangers before the thought or event the youngster has in mind can be revealed. (2) Resistance may be expressing some conflicted loyalties, often related to a family secret that no one is to tell. Either directly or indirectly, it has been gotten across to the child that a certain fact or event must remain a secret and thus cannot be shared with the therapist. (3) For the latency-age or adolescent youngster there may be conflicts about peer loyalty; in such cases it is useful to discuss the loyalty issue, which is often part and parcel of concerns about confidentiality.[55] With children perhaps six to eight years old, one may need to discuss with parents the child's need for them to allow him to speak of anything in treatment and to let him know that secrecy *vis-à-vis* the therapist is not only unnecessary but contrary to his needs. Younger children—that is, those who are about four to six years of age—have trouble keeping secrets anyway. Often they reveal in speech and play many of the intimate details of what goes on at home. (4) On occasion, resistance is found to be an expression of anger at the therapist, and the withholding is then an effort to blackmail or retaliate. Finally (5), there are situations, most common in early adolescence, in which resistance is a defense against the patient's fears of an emotional outburst or a torrential pouring-out of dammed-up material. Here it is best to deal with the feared danger and to discuss with the youngster what he feels would happen if this material were revealed, rather than trying to get him to talk about the content directly.

It should be emphasized that resistance is not "bad behavior." An essential process in the healthy psyche, it is mobilized by dangers perceived as coming from the outside. Although the therapist offers verbal reassurance that anything may be said in the office, such permission is often insufficient. The youngster in treatment may feel transference threats in the therapeutic situation, and he needs to assess them. In fact, if one sees a child who is ready and willing to tell everything about himself without reservation, it should be cause for concern, for this may well be a sign of an ominous prognosis.

Hours and Frequency of Visits

There is no way to predict the exact number of hours that should be given to any one case of psychotherapy. In general, if one elects to do short-term intervention, one might see the youngster six or seven times on a weekly basis, with perhaps one or two hours spaced farther apart toward the end. One must then have clearly in mind that this is a time-limited task, with the end of the treatment program remaining constantly in focus. At times one may misjudge the child's (or even his immediate environment's) capacity for change, and one may have to revise initial recommendations in favor of longer-term treatment or other types of intervention.

Long-term intensive psychotherapy may vary from one to three hours a week over a period of many months; psychoanalysis requires four to five hours a week for several years. A variety of factors determine the plan, but prescription writing—as in so much of psychiatry—is not possible yet. For instance, one hour a week may not be enough, because continuity is more easily lost and because the infrequency makes it difficult to keep up with events in the child's life. Having twice-a-week sessions, in our experience, seems more than twice as effective as seeing the child once a week, though we have no statistical studies to prove it.

The conventional length of the psychotherapeutic hour is forty-five to fifty minutes. But with certain youngsters, particularly young ones, the closing of the hour may be difficult, and one should allow extra time for this in one's schedule. In other cases a youngster, for one reason or another, may be unable to tolerate more than perhaps twenty-five minutes. Each case has to be judged according to its own particular needs.

Many youngsters, particularly those in latency and adolescence, look upon school vacations as a time to interrupt the psychotherapy and will make a prominent issue of this. Somehow they associate therapy with school attendance and feel that when there are school holidays, therapy should also be interrupted. Often one can deal with this as direct resistance and use it as an opportunity to point out the purpose of psychotherapy. For example, a ten-year-old boy who wants to have all his days free to play baseball in the summer may have to be reminded that his troubles at school (such as not paying attention, forgetting, and in general not doing as well as he wishes and is capable of), which have made him so unhappy and frustrated, have not ended just because school is drawing to a close. His wish "not to know," "to forget," and "to put off" is actually a part of his problem with learning, his difficulty with tension tolerance, and his fear of discovering that he is really "inadequate" or "damaged." As another example, a seven-year-old girl wishes to interrupt treatment over the school's Christmas holiday so that she can play with her friends. She adds quickly that she will come back when school starts. Yet she still has problems with her temper and gets into provocative fights with boys and her father. The threat of temper if she is thwarted hangs in the air; from earlier data her therapist points out her desire to have a "fight" with him, her need to be in control, and her wish to retain her therapist by prolonging therapy. He stresses the importance of continuing their work even though it may upset her, in order that her temper, which causes her so much trouble, can be tamed. She then starts a puppet play that evolves into a modified Cinderella: the rejected, mistreated girl who triumphs by winning the prince's hand—with the help of the fairy godmother (the therapist).

There are times when it may be appropriate to allow an interruption in treatment, but the therapist should then verbalize his reasoning. For instance, a youngster who has had few friends is invited to a birthday party or an overnight visit. It may be more important, therapeutically, to let him socialize than to insist upon his keeping his hour. Another example would be that of an adolescent girl who mentions on Wednesday that on Friday she is going out on her first date and must cancel her Friday appointment, because otherwise she will have too much to do to be ready on time. It would be poor strategy to insist that she keep her hour and perhaps be late for the party. Nevertheless, one might discuss with her why she did not mention the party earlier, or ask for an alternative appointment. In this way the therapist would indicate that he is indeed in favor of her evolving social life, but would also let her know that some resistance may be advisable.

Food and Gifts

Many therapists have candy or snacks on hand in the office because they feel this is important to children, but child psychiatrists differ widely on this point.[38] There are those who feel it is quite possible to do psychotherapy without snacks. Others feel that this type of feeding may be important, particularly with certain children who are especially "hungry." All would agree, of course, that merely to feed the child candy or snacks without meaningful talk or play is incomplete treatment. But beyond that, feeding can create problems. For example, a youngster may gorge himself on sweets and candy to the point where the psychiatrist becomes concerned about the effect on his overall dietary intake as well as the possible result of dental cavities. (Some have tried to solve this problem by using sugarless candy or fruit.) Thus the neophyte child psychiatrist should be wary of using candy or snacks as a means of gaining "friendship" with the child, only to find himself later in a situation that is hard to control. Some child psychiatrists resolve the problem by having a very limited amount of food openly available and keeping the main supply elsewhere, so that even if the youngster eats everything in sight, he will not have consumed an excessive amount.

Gift-giving poses similar problems, and again one finds a divergence of opinion among therapists.[44] Some rarely, if ever, give gifts (except perhaps to very young children), while others feel much more comfortable about the practice. The problem can be looked at developmentally: until they are about seven or eight years old, children have come to expect gifts—no matter how modest—from important adults on birthdays, Christmas, or Chanukah. A child of this age would certainly feel very deprived should a favorite person not respond in some way on such occasions, nor would his ego be of sufficient maturity to profit from the failure. But with older children, one may decide not to give gifts on special occasions, as an indication that the skill and interest the therapist offers make for a special working relationship where love and appreciation are not expressed by gifts.

This brings us to the perennial problem: if one chooses to give gifts, what is the right type of gift? For example, what does one give the youngster of nine or ten who is the offspring of a wealthy family and can have what he wants? If such a child is then confronted with the more puritanical standards of the therapist, this could provoke some realistic frustration that he might respond to, rather than the endless gratifications that have surrounded him at home. (And it might indeed be difficult to find this child a gift that he would not demean.) If, on the other hand, the child comes from a deprived family, then the giving of a gift may have quite other meanings. In this case one must be aware of the impact the gift may have on the child's family. His siblings may be jealous and his parents may feel guilty at not being able to provide the kinds of things that the therapist is saying implicitly their youngster should have. Some child psychiatrists resolve the issue by merely sending a greeting card, especially to youngsters of latency and adolescent age. Our own feeling is that the best and most important gift the therapist can give to a youngster is his interest in the child and his well-being. If the therapist decides to give a present, it should be modest and should fit the therapeutic process itself. For example, one little girl who was approaching her fifth birthday had been discussing at some length her curiosity about procreation, birth, and the question of her own origin. With this in mind her therapist gave her a brightly painted wooden doll, in the Russian style, that had one doll within another doll within another. An older youngster of twelve, who had a reading difficulty but who had made considerable progress after hard work in both remedial reading and in therapy, was given a book that she was quite capable of mastering; it was also a book whose theme and heroine were apt to strike a responsive chord within this child.

One final complexity can be the youngster's giving of gifts to the therapist, with or without the assent of his family, which can easily lead to the parents' and/or child's concern about who gave whom the better gift. This can be a very delicate issue that involves not only aspects of competitiveness but also genuine feelings of gratitude, affection, and love. Whether to accept or not, how to accept without letting the transference aspects get lost, how to refuse the gift without generating feelings of personal rejection—all are difficult strategic problems that require very tactful and empathetic handling.

(Phases of the Therapeutic Process

Initial Phone Call and Evaluation

For the child or adolescent the opening phase of psychotherapy begins when either the parents or the adolescent first begin to think of getting outside help. How this comes about—whether by internal awareness or outside suggestion—and how this is related to and then acted upon, will be important in determining the various states of mind that the psychiatrist will confront at the first meeting.

The decision to ask for help is critically important, and psychic change is apt to take place in the family even as early as the first phone call requesting an appointment. For example, there may be relief and hope because something finally is going to be done, however differently each person may picture the optimum resolution. The youngster may fear punishment or subtle coercion, while parents struggle with a sense of shame at having failed in the tasks of parenthood.[5] The hopes raised may be just as magical and irrational as the fears. In fact, all these emotions may exist side by side or be split among family members. How the psychiatrist handles all these various and contradictory expectations in the early visits will have important repercussions. In fact, we would underscore that the initial consultative visits should be seen as occasions in which parents can raise questions to help them find out whether the problem has been brought to the right place and, if so, what would be the best plan for evaluation.

The purpose of an evaluation is to study and assess the various aspects of the problems presented. The evaluation may need to include psychological testing, educational evaluation, EEG and neurological examinations, school reports and other relevant studies, and medical tests or reports. All of these become part of a psychiatric evaluation—data that will enable one to understand the problem and make a diagnosis, resulting in appropriate recommendations. How long the process takes and what it entails will depend on a variety of factors. Foremost will be the urgency of the need for action (often grossly over- or underestimated in work with the age groups we speak of), the available financial resources, the confusing nature of the problem, or other special aspects. Nevertheless we would agree with McDonald[46] that an evaluation is a finite process that ends when the psychiatrist presents his findings to the parents and discusses his recommendations with them.

There is no question that psychic effects are created—therapeutic or otherwise—by the referral to a psychiatrist and by the consultation and evaluative process. Perhaps we are stressing the obvious when we say this is not psychotherapy proper. But all too often we have found, to our dismay, that a psychotherapist has begun treatment while the parents and the patient have not yet openly contracted for it, with the result that all are working at cross purposes.

What is the role of the youngster in this stage of the process? We would again differentiate in terms of developmental stages. Children in early childhood (up to age eight, let us say) see their parents and other adults as authorities: benign, malevolent, or something in between. Another characteristic of these younger children is that their reasoning powers are such that their thinking is still fairly concrete and is oriented to the here and now. This is not to deny their often excellent capacity to question and articulate the obvious or the sham, their sharp observational powers, and their often refreshing directness. But they are not yet in the habit of being included when their parents consult other adults on their behalf (to set a medical appointment, arrange for a parent–teacher conference, and so forth). A child does not feel offended or threatened when he is not included in these adult exchanges. In the case of the psychiatric evaluation, his parents are interviewed first; this sanctions the child contact that follows. Parents also give important historical data, providing the therapist with a context within which to view the young child. The diagnostic results and the recommendations are discussed with the parents first. Then, depending on what the actual plans will be, the psychiatrist should discuss them with the child in language that he can understand. Treatment recommendations, if accepted by parents, are usually accepted by children of this age group without much difficulty. More specifically, although a child comes with his parents, it is up to the therapist to arouse the youngster's interest and overcome expectations derived from previous poor experiences with adults.

As children grow older, they tend to become more involved in decisions that affect their immediate lives. Whether the issue is a paper route, a summer camp, neighborhood boundary limits, bedtimes, or entry into psychotherapy, their wishes and views have a growing impact on what they will do. Also, youngsters in the age range of eight to twelve may be quite reluctant to involve themselves in the evaluative stage or the actual initiation of treatment, whether for reasons of shyness, of natural reticence, or of outright resentment over and resistance to what is viewed as an intrusion. Adolescents may show reluctance for a different variety of reasons. They may be afraid of potential dependency feelings, expect "exhortative lectures" from the doctor, or fear that the doctor will discover a serious mental illness or that they will be stigmatized by their peers.

Special circumstances—to us, the only ones —that seem to warrant seeing a child younger than fifteen or sixteen prior to the consultative visit with his parents, are represented by the situation in which the youngster's wish has initiated the referral to a psychiatrist. Here we would try to respond to this mature attempt to get help by seeing the youngster first. Indeed, we sometimes try to structure this attitude in the older adolescent; that is, we suggest to the calling parent that his son or daughter should call for a first appointment so that it can be arranged without the parent as intermediary. Our justification for this, or for actually seeing the youngster before the parents, is to indicate our respect for the youngster and his opinions and to lend support to his sense of self and autonomous responsibility. But this should not be an empty gesture, whether in terms of the psychiatrist's attitude, the realities of the situation, or the youngster's capacity to respond to such an overture.

Much has been written in recent years about the need of the psychiatrist to ally himself with his adolescent patient and have as little to do with the parents as possible. We feel this has sometimes been carried to extremes. Parents should be seen at least once or twice in the evaluation phase, and they deserve a summary discussion of the assessment and recommendations. This may take place with or without the designated patient being present. We find also that it prevents a lot of disruption if the parents are seen once or twice in the early weeks of treatment, when someone other than the therapist has done the evaluation. We think they have a right to see the person to whom they have entrusted their youngster's treatment. At the same time these visits give the psychiatrist a chance to form a mental image of the parents, to be placed alongside the image the adolescent is creating for him.

The adolescent who is attending college or is working to support himself, whether away from home or not, is more appropriately dealt with as an autonomous person who is responsible for his own financial and other arrangements. Problems arise when the youngster has not yet reached his majority; in fact the legal questions involved here, as previously noted, have recently been in flux.

Long-Term Psychotherapy: General Considerations

Psychotherapy has often been likened to chess. Certainly one can speak of "opening moves," with their potential problems and strategies, and of the "closing" or termination phase. Things are much less clear when we turn to the phase of the "middle game." Here the possibilities are far more varied and reflect what is unique and idiosyncratic to the particular patient. This chesslike, three-phase division is particularly true of long-term treatment or crisis intervention, even though in reality these boundaries between phases will blur and overlap.

Whatever the age of the child patient, there is one essential to all successful psychotherapy: it must be interesting to the youngster himself. Many children would find it impossible to explain what goes on in treatment to an outsider or even to their parents; they only "know" that something good is happening. If therapy becomes dry and dull, it can become self-defeating. Conversely, one must guard against its becoming overly exciting, stimulating, or seductive, since this too can drive the patient away. As alluded to earlier, resistance can sometimes take the form of making the treatment hours dull and uninteresting. This seems to happen most often with the young adolescent who must defend himself from getting overly involved with an adult. At the same time, if the physician is to keep the youngster's interests and gain his respect, he must be ready to recast some of his thinking about the therapist's role. For example: to be too flat, too quiet, too unemotional, too much the "psychoanalytic screen" can be deadly in work with children or adolescents. (It can, in fact, be just as deadly for adults, but fortunately they are somewhat more tolerant.)

Treatment proper begins after the evaluation of the youngster and his family is completed and the recommendation for treatment has been made and accepted.[14,37,41,59] The acceptance will have different meanings for different family members and will in any case be ambivalent. Some older children may be quite reluctant and will unconsciously test the parents' convictions that change can indeed occur. Others will be resistant for reasons that can often be dealt with during a trial period that is labeled as such. But care must be taken that the patient does not take this "trial" as permission simply to "hold out for the duration" and never let himself be engaged.

There is no doubt that the young adolescent can render all treatment efforts impotent. But it is also surprising how often the angry, blustering youngster continues to show up for his sessions even when no parent has brought him. It is unwise to interpret this attitude too early, because it will threaten the youngster's defense and have the effect of forcing him into leaving. The better course is to acknowledge to the youngster how hard it is for him to do things that others—most of all, perhaps, his parents—demand of him. One can suggest that he may want to make the best of it and find something interesting and useful for himself in the therapeutic process. Here the physician attempts to divert the transference from aligning the therapist with the parents, since for such an adolescent the strong concern may be that the therapist wants mainly to change him into the kind of person his parents would want him to be. As an adult, the therapist has to convince him instead that he is a potential ally and able to help the adolescent achieve his own goals. Often these goals turn out to be quite close to what his parents also would want: doing well in school, planning for college, having friends, being social, holding a job, and so on.

OPENING MOVES

All initial moves in psychotherapy, whether with child or adolescent, are part of the process of getting acquainted. Keeping in mind the youngster's developmental capacities or stage, the therapist tries to create a nonthreatening climate in which two people can try to get to know each other better in a unique situation. By being as open and direct with a given patient as that youngster can tolerate, the therapist is sending a unique and perhaps unusual message: most youngsters have had no experience with doctors except for physical illness, and the concept of a "talking doctor" or "worry doctor" may find them somewhat skeptical. From television they may have come to think of psychiatrists as "mind readers," as working miraculous transformations, or as having other fanciful skills. It is very possible that heretofore most of the adults in the child's life have tended to tell him what he could do and what he could not do, what was good and what was bad, and what things he would be punished for doing. Thus he is initially mystified to find a strange and different type of doctor and adult—one who seems only to want to get to know him better, and on the youngster's own terms. In addition, this adult seems oddly interested in things such as what the child felt when something happened or what he thought about a given event. It is these qualities of thoughtfulness, interest, and insightfulness that the child gets to know in the initial process: a nonjudgmental stance that does not ignore potential consequences of action but lays equal stress on an awareness of feeling states.

In this process of getting acquainted, the child will gradually reveal to the therapist bits and pieces of his life and his interests (or lack of interests). It is a period of experimentation in which the child will be testing his concerns and preoccupations with this unusual adult. Will the therapist after all be like all other adults he has known? Is this adult's interest and attentiveness going to end up badly, as it has with others? Gradually he reveals more of his private world of thoughts and fantasies, his worries, his fears, and other important feelings. In the case of the younger child, who in many ways takes new "goodies" for granted, the provision of play materials may claim his immediate attention. Others are inhibited and may need the physician's encouragement to reach out for them. With the older youngster, one may want to explain that this talk and play is not just for fun alone but also for the clues that it can yield about the patient's worries and behavior. For the young adolescent this may be an awkward time, and the therapist may have to acknowledge this fact. He may also need to be somewhat active and participate more.

The opening phase of treatment allows the child, unconsciously, to chart the course of the treatment. Much can be learned from how he handles these early interviews—what he brings up and what he leaves out. Often the most revealing thing is not the manifest content so much as what is latent within it; a comparable situation is the first dream an adult may report in psychotherapy. Comments from the therapist in these openng hours are mostly inquiries for clarification, expressions of interest or curiosity, and, if necessary, the acknowledgement of some difficulty the youngster is experiencing. The therapist tries to convey his benign, adult interest without intrusiveness. He shows patience without compliance, empathy without identification, and, finally, his belief that he can be helpful without being overwhelming.

After a time a youngster may become aware that this "getting acquainted" is not exactly what he expected, but by then the therapy has entered the middle phase. What has probably struck him is that he knows little of the therapist's private life, and he may come to feel he was slighted or tricked into revealing himself. This is especially true of young and middle adolescents, who may feel "put down" or manipulated by what they perceive as an unjustly unequal relationship. Usually these accusations are signs of the adolescent's sudden, unconscious awareness of vulnerability and constitute a defensive maneuver—that is, "the best defense is an offense." Depending on when this maneuver appears in the course of treatment, and it may appear many times, one

can deal with it factually. It is a technique well-suited to helping people with their troubles. Start to interpret the defense: "Something just happened in your thoughts that made you feel the relationship is unfair;" or explore the transference: "This feeling of being 'tricked' or 'put down' is something you often feel with people." To give a little information is also not harmful and, surprisingly, can be quite helpful, even if nonspecific—as, for example, saying that one is going to Europe this summer, or that one's summer house is in the Upper Peninsula of Michigan.

MIDDLE PHASE

To generalize about the so-called middle phase of treatment is risky at best, because so much depends on the individual therapist who is working with a particular child who presents a certain picture of pathology and strengths. This is the period in which the therapist must rely the most on his own initiative, imagination, and skills. In the literature, this is the period of treatment that is usually condensed in the case presentation and sounds planful and orderly, and in retrospect it may indeed be simple enough to classify the work into periods or stages. But in the heat of the actual process these stages are not always easy to recognize, since this is a fluid period. Themes may occur and appear to be resolved, only to occur again, perhaps with variations. Sometimes one gets the feeling of whittling away at or gradually peeling back the elements of the problem. "Working through," a term hard to define, has been used to describe much of what happens in the middle phase of treatment. On another level, there may also be periods during this middle phase when the therapist is excited by capacities that the child suddenly exhibits for communicating and integrating insights. And there may be periods when he grows discouraged by a plateau the child has reached, and by a resistance that seems impenetrable.

The length of this middle stage may sometimes be dictated by external events or circumstances. There may be a move out of town by the therapist or the patient and his family, some member of the family may develop a chronic illness, and so forth. But whatever the cause, this middle stage is brought to a close when either the parents or the therapist announce the necessity for termination. Of all the physician's reasons for this move, the most desirable, of course, is that the therapeutic goals have been achieved and that the child has improved to the point where therapy can be called successful. In other cases, some gains will have been made while other goals remain to be achieved, and yet further therapeutic work is not possible—perhaps for financial reasons, or because the child has grown so heavily involved in school work or peer activities that it becomes more appropriate to stop treatment even though not all respective goals have been realized. Finally, the therapist may have had only limited goals in mind, and calls for an end to therapy because he feels he has accomplished as much as he could.

TERMINAL PHASE

The last phase of treatment begins when the question of termination has been seriously raised and affirmatively answered. While parents or child may speak of termination themselves, this is technically considered a resistance problem until the therapist himself is convinced. It is then his prerogative and duty to suggest ending psychotherapy. Whether he raises it first with the child or the parents will depend on the age of the child. Each will have feelings about it that must be allowed expression and dealt with. This may also be a very natural time to review with the patient what has been talked about, events that have taken place, what the youngster was like when treatment began, and what he is like at this point. Everyone, parents included, can now look at the overall situation, past, present, and even future. Stimulated by such a review and by the prospect that the era of therapeutic help will be ending, one can expect some resurgence of original symptoms in the child. Often parents and/or child, as well as therapist, are made anxious by this and begin to doubt the correctness of the decision. But usually the recurrence of symptoms is transient and is worked through fairly rapidly. Since much of child psychopathology is rooted in issues of

separation, none of this should be surprising. Indeed, this work can be thought of as a consolidation of gains and a working through of separation anxieties and residual fears about the return of symptoms.

One important aspect of termination that is often overlooked or minimized is the nature of the separation anxieties and discomforts that are stimulated by approaching termination. The therapist who minimizes the difficulty of termination or delays announcing it is expressing, through countertransference, his own emotional difficulty in disengaging himself from patient and family. If the therapist has been reasonably successful, the youngster has had a rich and valuable experience and formed a unique relationship. The therapist, for his part, has had an enriching and gratifying experience and a relationship that has claimed much of his thought and attention. Both will experience some pain at separation. It is an essential, concluding, and integrating experience and must be worked out either in metaphor, in play, or in direct communication, because it is a basic ingredient of the human experience.

With the older child and adolescent, there is great value in stressing that problems are inevitable and will continue to arise in the course of his life. But the therapist must also express confidence in the youngster's ability to cope with them in the future, emphasizing that it is his coping capacity that has grown in the course of therapy and not that he will encounter no further problems.

It takes time to work through what took place and what was accomplished in the course of treatment. It also takes time to work through the painful ending of a mutually valued relationship. How much time, it is difficult to say; but more often than not, one tends to underestimate it. Even young children need time, though they may have no clear time concept as yet. It helps to make them a calendar on which they can keep track of how many appointment hours remain until the last one. Selecting a date that falls right before a well-known holiday or the ending of school is another way of helping them. Older children who can manage time quite well may suddenly have trouble remembering when the last appointment will be, or will proceed as if nothing unusual lies ahead. They will have to be gently confronted with such avoidance of a painful topic, though the child may not directly acknowledge it until the last hour.

Short-Term Treatment

In general, treatment that is three to fifty sessions in duration is regarded in the literature as "short term," and it has been variously defined and recommended.[8,9,52,53] For example, some consider it appropriate therapy only for acute reactive problems, while others see it as being used to make circumscribed contributions to severely troubled youngsters. A third group of writers view time-limited treatment as being focused by the presence of crisis; the therapeutic work is then regarded as growth through crisis resolution. It is our opinion that, for the very young child expressing distress, a short intervention may be very useful in helping mother and child realign their relationship before it has become entrenched. Here the relative plasticity of the child's psychic structure allows rapid change to occur. Similarly, for the adolescent who often experiences intense worries and preoccupations and who tends to view all problems as crises, a short and skillful intervention can be very helpful. Here, too, the psychic agencies, although more complex than the young child's, are less rigidly fixed than the latency-age or adult psyche and therefore more amenable to short interventions.

It would be gratifying to assert that the decision to undertake short- (rather than long-) term therapy is dictated solely or at least primarily by clinical considerations. But in reality, the duration of treatment is more often determined by time availability. Often a clinic must serve many patients, and thus a short, specifically focused bit of therapeutic work is the most that can be offered. Or perhaps a trainee has a relatively short, finite period of time to work with a case. Sometimes a family lives so far from the treatment center that prolonged treatment is impractical. We mention such factors not as criticisms but rather as re-

ality parameters that the therapist must recognize and resolve. If he does not come to terms with them, he runs the risk of attempting more than he can actually hope to achieve. To put it simplistically, when the time is short —for whatever reason—then short-term treatment is in order, and realistic goals must be set for all persons involved.

Effective short-term therapy may well be the most difficult of the psychotherapies, since there is little leeway for error or change in therapeutic direction. The starting phase of treatment must be quickly accomplished and depends on accurate and confident appraisal of the young person's psychopathology, psychic strengths, and actual environment (that is, his home/school situation). The therapist must have a good knowledge of the way the youngster of a particular age perceives, thinks, and fantasizes, and of the modes in which he can communicate his concerns and worries. The therapist must be able to be active without giving wild interpretations, be ego- rather than id-oriented, and be selective in what he comments upon and how. He must feel comfortable with limited goals and see them as valid contributions to a youngster's mental health. Finally, it should go without saying, that the special conditions of short-term treatment also apply to and affect the nature of the work with the parents.

The primary characteristics of short-term psychotherapy, then, are goal-directedness, the defining of an arena of work that serves to focus the therapist's thought and comments, and a finite time limit that is known by all concerned when treatment begins. There are several derivative requirements: (1) The youngster must have the capacity and the willingness to relate rather quickly to the therapist, who in turn must possess the reciprocal capacity. (2) The therapist must be able to determine, from the historical material and his first interview with the youngster, what the focusing should be. (3) Termination must be recognized as a topic with which one must deal. In some cases where object loss has played an important role in the pathology, this may itself prove to be the focus. If, however, self-esteem for example, is the focus, termination may appear as proof of "I'm not worthy," which must then be worked through. (4) Particular care must be taken to direct interpretations to the focal arena. (5) Comments on material should be directed "upward" to ego capacities and affects rather than "downward" to id impulses. One does not want to arouse defenses but rather to increase the capacity to cope, and the courage to use this capacity.

The difference between short- and long-term therapy might best be illustrated by an analogy. The novel and the short story have many charactertistics in common. When skillfully done, different effects are achieved, and it would be incorrect to assert that either one is "better." Only in terms of what is being attempted can one assess the form. The same is true in the choice of therapies. Does the technique match the goal? Does the goal match the needs of the patient?

❪ Concluding Remarks

We have attempted to provide an outline of psychotherapy with children and adolescents that is based primarily on a developmental and psychodynamic understanding of psychopathology. We have discussed qualities that we feel are essential for a child therapist, and delineated at least some of the mental processes that go on while doing such work. The primary arena of play has been explored. The role of parents has been discussed, including the frequent problem of patient confidentiality. Common technical problems have been related to developmental levels, on the one hand, and to the opening, middle, and terminating phases of psychotherapy on the other. Finally, we have attempted to differentiate long-term psychotherapy from short-term treatment on the basis of what the therapist intends to do with material gleaned from the history of the youngster and observation of his play and talk. Our bibliography has been in large measure selected with the intention of making available to the reader further knowledge about the many aspects of psychother-apy with children and adolescents that have been touched upon here, but only briefly.

❪ Bibliography

1. AICHORN, A. Wayward Youth. New York: Viking, 1935.
2. ————. Delinquency and Child Guidance: Selected Papers. New York: International Universities Press, 1964.
3. ALLEN, F. H. Psychotherapy with Children. New York: Norton, 1942.
4. AMERICAN SOCIETY FOR ADOLESCENT PSYCHIATRY. "Position Statement on Training in Adolescent Psychiatry," in S. L. Feinstein, P. L. Giovacchini, and A. A. Miller, eds., Adolescent Psychiatry, Vol. 1, pp. 418–424. New York: Basic Books, 1971.
5. ANTHONY, E. J. and T. BENEDEK, eds. Parenthood: Its Psychology and Pathology. Boston: Little, Brown, 1970.
6. AXLINE, V. M. Play Therapy. Boston: Houghton Mifflin, 1947.
7. BARDWICK, J. M. Psychology of Women. New York: Harper & Row, 1971.
8. BARTON, M. and S. S. BARTEN. Children and Their Parents in Brief Therapy. New York: Behavioral Pubs., 1973.
9. BERLIN, I. N. "Crisis Intervention and Short Term Therapy: An Approach in a Child Psychiatric Clinic," J. Am. Acad. Child Psychiatry, 9 (1970), 595–606.
10. BLOM, G. "A Psychoanalytic Viewpoint of Behavior Modification in Clinical and Educational Settings," J. Am. Acad. Child Psychiatry, 11 (1972), 675–693.
11. BLOS, P., JR. "Silence: A Clinical Exploration," Psychoanal. Q., 41 (1972), 348–363.
12. BLOS, P., SR. On Adolescence: A Psychoanalytic Interpretation. New York: Free Press, 1962.
13. ————. The Young Adolescent: Clinical Studies. New York: Free Press, 1970.
14. BRODY, S. "Aims and Methods in Child Psychotherapy," J. Am. Acad. Child Psychiatry, 3 (1964), 385–412.
15. CHESS, S., A. THOMAS, and H. G. BIRCH. Temperament and Behavior Disorders. New York: Brunner/Mazel, 1968.
16. ERIKSON, E. H. "Studies in the Interpretation of Play: 1. Clinical Observation of Play Construction in Young Children," Genet. Psychol. Monogr., 22 (1940), 557–671.

17. ———. "Sex Differences in the Play Configurations in Pre-Adolescents," *Am. J. Orthopsychiatry*, 21 (1951), 667–692.

18. ———. "Identity and the Life Cycle," in *Psychol. Issues*, Vol. 1, no. 1. New York: International Universities Press, 1959.

19. ———. (1950) *Childhood and Society*, 2nd ed. New York: Norton, 1963.

20. ———. *Identity: Youth and Crisis*. New York: Norton, 1969.

21. FEINSTEIN, S. C., P. L. GIOVACCHINI, and A. A. MILLER, eds. *Adolescent Psychiatry*. Vol. 1, *Developmental and Clinical Studies*. New York: Basic Books, 1971.

22. FINCH, S. and H. BURKS. "Early Psychotherapeutic Management of the School Phobia," *Postgrad. Med.*, 27 (1960), 140–147.

23. FLAVELL, J. H. *The Developmental Psychology of Jean Piaget*. Princeton: Van Nostrand Reinhold, 1963.

24. FREUD, A. (1936–1937) *The Ego and the Mechanisms of Defense*. New York: International Universities Press, 1946.

25. ———. *The Psychoanalytical Treatment of Children*. Translated by N. Procter-Gregg. London: Imago, 1946.

26. ———. *Normality and Pathology in Childhood*. New York: International Universities Press, 1965.

27. FREUD, S. (1905) "Three Essays on the Theory of Sexuality," in J. Strachey, ed., *Standard Edition*, Vol. 7, pp. 123–243. London: Hogarth, 1953.

28. ———. (1909) "Analysis of a Phobia in a Five-Year-Old Boy," in J. Strachey, ed., *Standard Edition*, Vol. 10, pp. 5–147. London: Hogarth, 1955.

29. ———. (1922) "Postscript to the 'Analysis of a Phobia in a Five-Year-Old Boy'," in J. Strachey, ed., *Standard Edition*, Vol. 10, pp. 148–149. London: Hogarth, 1955.

30. ———. (1923) "The Ego and the Id," in J. Strachey, ed., *Standard Edition*, Vol. 19, pp. 1–66. London: Hogarth, 1961.

31. ———. (1926) "Inhibitions, Symptoms and Anxiety," in J. Strachey, ed., *Standard Edition*, Vol. 20, pp. 77–175. London: Hogarth, 1959.

32. GESELL, A. L. and C. S. AMATRUDA. *Developmental Diagnosis: Normal and Abnormal Child Development*. New York: Hoeber, 1941.

33. HALL, G. S. *Adolescence*, Vols. 1–2. New York: Appleton, 1907.

34. HALPERN, H. M. *A Parent's Guide to Child Psychotherapy*. New York: A. S. Barnes, 1963.

35. HARTMANN, H. *Ego Psychology and the Problem of Adaptation*. New York: International Universities Press, 1958.

36. ———. *Essays on Ego Psychology*. New York: International Universities Press, 1964.

37. HAWORTH, M. R., ed. *Child Psychotherapy: Practice and Theory*. New York: Basic Books, 1964.

38. HAWORTH, M. R. and M. J. KELLER. "The Use of Food in the Diagnosis and Therapy of Emotionally Disturbed Children," *J. Am. Acad. Child Psychiatry*, 1 (1962), 548–563.

39. ITARD, J. M. (1801) *The Wild Boy of Aveyron*. Translated by G. Humphrey and M. Humphrey. New York: Appleton-Century-Crofts, 1962.

40. JOHNSON, A. M., E. I. FALSTEIN, S. A. SZUREK et al. "School Phobia," *Am. J. Orthopsychiatry*, 11 (1941), 702–711.

41. KEITH, C. R. "The Therapeutic Alliance in Child Psychotherapy," *J. Am. Acad. of Child Psychiatry*, 7 (1968), 31–43.

42. KESSLER, J. W. *Psychopathology of Childhood*. Englewood Cliffs, N.J.: Prentice-Hall, 1966.

43. KIELL, N. *The Universal Experience of Adolescence*. New York: International Universities Press, 1964.

44. LEVIN, S. and H. WERMER. "The Significance of Giving Gifts to Children in Therapy," *J. Am. Acad. Child Psychiatry*, 5 (1966), 630–652.

45. LOOMIS, E. A., JR. "The Use of Checkers in Handling Certain Resistances in Child Therapy and Child Analysis," *J. Am. Psychoanal. Assoc.*, 5 (1957), 130–135.

46. McDONALD, M. "The Psychiatric Evaluation of Children," *J. Am. Acad. Child Psychiatry*, 4 (1965), 569–612.

47. MALMQUIST, C. "School Phobia: A Problem in Family Neurosis," *J. Am. Acad. Child Psychiatry*, 4 (1965), 293–319.

48. MEEKS, J. E. "Children Who Cheat at Games," *J. Am. Acad. Child Psychiatry*, 9 (1970), 157–170.

49. MILLAR, T. P. "Home–School Communication Concerning Nonadjusting Children," *J. Am. Acad. Child Psychiatry*, 4 (1965), 320–329.

50. NEWMAN, M. B. and M. SAN MARTINO. "The Child and the Seriously Disturbed Parent:

Treatment Issues," *J. Am. Acad. Child Psychiatry*, 12 (1973), 162–181.

51. PIAGET, J. and B. INHELDER. *The Psychology of the Child*. New York: Basic Books, 1969.

52. PROSKAUER, S. "Some Technical Issues in Time-Limited Psychotherapy with Children," *J. Am. Acad. Child Psychiatry*, 8 (1969), 154–169.

53. ———. "Focused Time-Limited Psychotherapy with Children," *J. Am. Acad. Child Psychiatry*, 10 (1971), 619–639.

54. RITVO, S., A. T. McCOLLUM, E. OMWABE et al. "Some Relations of Constitution, Environment, and Personality as Observed in a Longitudinal Study of Child Development: Case Report," in A. Solnit and S. Province, eds., *Modern Perspectives in Child Development*, pp. 107–161. New York: International Universities Press, 1963.

55. ROSS, A. O. "Confidentiality in Child Guidance Treatment," *Ment. Hyg.*, 42 (1958), 60–66.

56. SILBERSTEIN, R. M. and H. IRWIN. "Jean-Marc-Gaspard Itard and The Savage of Aveyron: An Unsolved Diagnostic Problem in Child Psychiatry," *J. Am. Acad. Child Psychiatry*, 1 (1962), 314–322.

57. SKUROW, N. R. and I. M. DIZENHUZ. "Teaching about Teaching: A Program Sensitizing Child Psychiatry Fellows to Schools,"

J. Am. Acad. Child Psychiatry, 12 (1973), 354–365.

58. STONE, L. J. and J. CHURCH. *Childhood and Adolescence*, 2nd ed. New York: Random House, 1968.

59. SYLVESTER, E. and S. COOPER. "Truisms and Slogans in the Practice of Teaching Child Psychotherapy," *J. Am. Acad. Child Psychiatry*, 5 (1966), 617–629.

60. TAFT, J. *The Dynamics of Therapy in a Controlled Relationship*. New York: Macmillan, 1933.

61. TANNER, J. M. *Growth At Adolescence*, 2nd ed. Springfield, Ill.: Charles C. Thomas, 1962.

62. ———. "Sequence, Tempo, and Individual Variation in Growth and Development of Boys and Girls Age 12 to 16," in J. Kagan and R. Coles, eds., *12 to 16: Early Adolescence*, pp. 1–24. New York: Norton, 1972.

63. WALDFUGEL, S., J. C. COOLIDGE, and P. HAHN. "The Development, Meaning and Management of School Phobia," *Am. J. Orthopsychiatry*, 27 (1957), 754–780.

64. WESTMAN, J., ed. *Individual Differences in Children*. New York: Wiley, 1973.

65. WOLFF, P. H. *The Developmental Psychologies of Jean Piaget and Psychoanalysis*. Psychol. Issues Monograph no. 5. New York: International Universities Press, 1960.

CHAPTER 9

CLASSICAL PSYCHOANALYSIS

John C. Nemiah

"THE MAN OF SKILL," wrote Nathaniel Hawthorne in 1850, "the kind and friendly physician strove to go deep into his patient's bosom, delving among his principles, prying into his recollections, and probing everything with a cautious touch, like a treasure seeker in a dark cavern. Few secrets can escape an investigator, who has an opportunity and license to undertake such a quest, and skill to follow it up. A man burdened with a secret should especially avoid the intimacy of his physician. If the latter possesses native sagacity, and a nameless something more—let us call it intuition; if he show no intrusive egotism, nor disagreeably prominent characteristics of his own; if he have the power, which must be born in him, to bring his mind into such affinity with his patient's, that this last shall unawares have spoken what he imagines himself only to have thought; if such revelations be received without tumult, and acknowledged not so often by an uttered sympathy as by silence, an inarticulate breath, and here and there a word, to indicate that all is understood; if to these qualifications of a confidant be joined the advantages afforded by his recognized character as a physician,

then, at some inevitable moment, will the soul of the sufferer be dissolved, and flow forth in a dark, but transparent, stream, bringing all its mysteries into daylight."*

Here, before Freud was born and almost in caricature, Hawthorne portrays for us the very archetype of the popular image of the psychoanalyst: removed but empathic; silent yet alert to nuance; listening with quiet understanding and without moral judgment or prejudice; passive in appearance only, as, midwife to the soul, he awaits the propitious moment to deliver the guilty secret from his patient's breast.

The popular notion of the psychoanalyst is, of course, incomplete. It seizes on the obvious and the visible, with no awareness that the analyst's apparent inactivity is only the first step in a series of technical maneuvers aimed at uncovering and altering the elements of a psychological conflict that produces symptoms and disease. Hawthorne's physician was adept at eliciting information. For the modern analyst, that is only the beginning of the process of therapy—a clinical activity that has evolved

* Hawthorne, N. *The Scarlet Letter*, p. 98. Garden City, N.Y.: Doubleday, 1970.

over the past two centuries into a set of analytic procedures that can be both practiced and taught. Let us approach a discussion of these procedures through a brief historical survey of their development.

❪ The Development of Psychoanalysis

Mesmer

Franz Anton Mesmer (1733–1815) is generally thought of as being the *fons et origo* of modern psychotherapy; and from the early techniques of mesmerism, it is said, have evolved the more elaborate and sophisticated therapeutic measures of the analyst and his colleagues. Although Mesmer was certainly dealing with individuals suffering from a variety of neurotic disorders, and though the clinical successes he achieved were the result of psychological processes that his procedures induced in his patients, Mesmer's theoretical formulations, his understanding of the nature of the treatment he elaborated, and his specific procedures were all totally different from those of the twentieth-century analyst.

Mesmer's basic therapeutic maneuver was the "magnetic pass." Patient and "magnetist" sat opposite one another, and as the latter clasped the knees of the former between his own, he repetitively drew his hand in great, sweeping movements from the patient's face downward over his chest and abdomen and thighs—sometimes actually touching the patient's body, at others holding his hand an inch or two away. In response, the patient would feel a sense of warmth suffuse his body. After a period of time (especially when the treatment was effective) he would lose consciousness in a hysterical seizure (the so-called *mesmeric*, or *magnetic, crisis*), from which he would recover to discover his symptoms markedly improved if not completely gone.

Mesmer saw in this the result of physical, mechanistic forces. Borrowing heavily on the speculations of Paracelsus and on the scientific climate of his day, he attributed the phenomenon to the effect of a subtle, invisible but real

magnetic fluid that, if not similar to the force that held the planets in their regular orbits, was at least related to it and could be controlled and manipulated by the operations of one human being on another. This so-called "animal magnetism" was at the basis of both disease and its cure. In the normal individual the magnetic fluid flowed smoothly and unnoticeably throughout his body. If, however, the flow of the fluid was obstructed for whatever reason, it would be dammed up and accumulate in one organ or another, producing symptoms at the site of its stasis. The mesmeric treatment relieved symptoms because the mesmeriser, with his passes, not only increased the amount of magnetic fluid in his patient's body but also intensified its flow, so that the obstructions were overcome, the pathological accumulation of the fluid was dissipated, and its normal flow and balance restored.[34]

There are several characteristics of Mesmer's approach to his patients that should be noted. In the first place, although he was clearly aware of the importance of the setting as it influenced the individual's response, his theory was mechanistic and based on a physical, materialistic view of the nature of the universe. He conceived of illness as having a physical basis, and his treatment techniques were as much aimed at restoring a physiological balance as were those of the more traditional physicians of the day, with their purgings and cuppings and bleedings and emetics. The concept of psychotherapy was totally alien to his scheme of things. Secondly, despite the fact that Mesmer was aware of the importance of a special rapport between patient and therapist, he was not concerned with the inner mental life or psychological conflicts of the patients he was treating. His aim was solely, through the operations of the magnetist, to restore the balance of the magnetic fluid and overcome its pathological accumulation in bodily organs. Finally, in his therapeutic system, the patient remained entirely passive. The therapist acted upon him with his mesmeric passes, and the patient was merely the recipient of external influences that affected him, without his in any way contributing to the process of treatment (other than by virtue of the fact that he submitted himself to the mesmerist's manipulations).

The Nineteenth Century

Those who followed Mesmer worked within the same frame of reference. De Puységur,[7] it is true, through his interest in the somnambulistic state, focused his attention on the experience of both patient and therapist as this contributed to the relief of symptoms; but he held to the theory of magnetic fluid, and the patient remained a passive recipient of the therapist's operations. There was little significant development in the theory until Braid[5] challenged the notion of the magnetic fluid and explained the clinical phenomena as being the result of internal factors within the patient himself. Hypnotism (as Braid named it) was effective not because of any fluid instilled in the patient by the therapist but because of his idea of what the therapist expected him to experience. This was the basis for the modern concept of suggestion, which over the succeeding decades gradually replaced the fluidic theory, culminating in the triumph of the Nancy School over that of Jean-Martin Charcot and his colleagues at the Salpêtrière in Paris—of psychology over physiology. But despite this fundamental change in theoretical outlook, the patient remained the passive recipient of ideas and suggestions provided him by the hypnotist. He was no more the active participant in his treatment than were his predecessors in the days when magnetism held sway.

Although the Salpêtrière remained closer to biological concepts than did Bernheim[4] at Nancy, whose espousal of suggestion placed the emphasis on the psychological basis of hypnosis, it nonetheless made a number of important psychological observations that helped to explain symptom formation. In particular, it recognized that traumatic events in an individual's life could lead to the dissociation of memories related to these events, and that the form of the individual's symptoms was often determined by these dissociated memories.

Later, the clinical investigations of Pierre Janet led (in his hands) to a highly sophisticated elaboration of the concept of dissociation. But Janet's clinical observations and theoretical formulations were overshadowed by the rising star of Sigmund Freud, and by the excitement over the discoveries and ideas that he began to make public in the 1890's.

Freud's Early Theoretical Formulations

The rich variety of intellectual and scientific forces that influenced Freud's thinking has not yet been fully explored, but certainly his own observations during his visit to the Salpêtrière in 1885–1886, as well as his familiarity with the clinical experiences of his older colleague, Josef Breuer, played an important part in his early practices and formulations. At the Salpêtrière Freud was able to observe patients with major hysteria and to see how the unconscious memories of traumatic events not only determined the form of symptoms but also could be recovered under hypnosis. From Breuer he learned that the recovery of the memories *and* the affect associated with traumatic events could lead to a removal of the symptoms determined by them. These were the clinical experiences that directed Freud's attention to hysteria; they formed the launching pad from which he soared into his own original ideas about the pathogenesis of hysteria. His initial theoretical formulations provided a basis for innovative techniques of exploration, which then evolved into the practices of classical psychoanalysis. Let us look at these each in its turn.

The Salpêtrière investigators developed a theoretical scheme to explain their observations that reached its apogee in the formulations elaborated by Pierre Janet. We have already hinted at the fact that they were aware that unconscious memories of traumatic events could determine the form of symptoms. Janet,[31] for example, describes the origin of a woman's phobia by reference to a painful loss. His patient, Gu, suffered from "a singular horror of the color red" and from time to time had typical attacks of hysterical somnambulism in which she would enter a state of altered consciousness and lose contact with people around her. During her waking state she had absolutely no knowledge of the reason for her terror of the color, which was an entirely ego-alien symptom. One day Janet overheard the patient speaking as follows during one of her hysterical attacks: "Take it away! Take the coffin away! Close it up! I don't want to see his head any more. Oh! That bunch of red flowers—take them away!"

Janet, suspecting that the patient in her somnambulistic state was undergoing a hallucination of the scene relevant to her fear of the color red, by a clever maneuver transferred her spontaneous somnambulism into one over which he had control and during which he could converse with her. His surmise turned out to be correct. While the patient was in a period of somnambulistic altered consciousness her range of memory was wider than in her normal waking state, and she revealed events in her past of which she had no trace of memory while awake. "Gu," wrote Janet, "explained to us very well during her somnambulism how her attacks were provoked by the recurrence of an old emotion dating back many years. She had seen her father's corpse at the moment that they were closing the casket, and with each attack she beheld this cruel sight afresh. She also accounted for her horror of the color red by the memory of the flowers which had been on the coffin."

The basic mechanism involved here was a *dissociation* of the memories of the traumatic events. As the result of the dissociation, certain elements of the psychic contents were rendered unconscious—became unavailable to conscious, voluntary recall—but, though unconscious, nonetheless determined the nature of the surface symptoms. Dissociation was, then, a key process in symptom formation, and the problem lay in trying to understand how dissociation occurred in the first place.

The Charcot school, represented in its most sophisticated form by Janet, proposed a theoretical explanation that was essentially biological in character.[31] Each individual, it postulated, is endowed at birth with a certain quantum of nervous energy, the function of which is to bind the elements of brain and mind into a functioning, coordinating whole;

the acme of this process is the sense of the self as a distinct, real entity. In certain individuals, however, the quantity of energy is pathologically diminished, either because of a hereditary inadequacy or because it is exhausted by excessive emotions. When this occurs, the unity of the personality is compromised. Clusters of associated mental events fall away from the main body of psychic elements that constitute the self and become unavailable to that self. They are now dissociated and unconscious and therefore, by definition, pathological, since in the normal human being mind is coextensive with consciousness.

Freud was, of course, exposed to the observations and ideas that surrounded him during his visit to the Salpêtrière. In his early work[6] with his collaborator, Breuer, he focused on the traumatic nature of hysterical symptoms and the phenomenon of dissociation that formed the basis of symptom formation. To explain the genesis of the dissociation, he somewhat reluctantly adopted Breuer's concept of the "hypnoid" state. This concept, based on the physiological approach of the French school, postulated that the patient was in a pathologically altered state of consciousness when the emotionally traumatic event occurred; when normal consciousness returned, the memories and related affects pertaining to the traumatic event failed to be incorporated into consciousness, but remained behind in a dissociated, unconscious state to provide the pathogenic source of the hysterical symptoms. At the same time, Freud—at first softly and then in an increasingly audible voice[15]—proposed an alternate explanation for the occurrence of dissociation: ideas and affects that were unacceptable to the individual were *forced* out of consciousness; and, thus rendered unconscious, formed the focus of hysterical symptoms. He suggested the term *defense hysteria* (as distinct from Breuer's *hypnoid hysteria*) to designate hysterical symptoms arising on this basis.

The concept of "defense" introduced an entirely new theoretical view of symptom formation. It laid the groundwork for all subsequent psychoanalytic theory and the therapeutic techniques derived from it. Freud's novel view of psychic functioning was entirely different from that of those in the French school. The latter, as we have seen, based their concepts on physiological notions; for them, unconscious mental processes were pathological in nature, and symptoms resulted from a passive falling away of mental elements in a patient predisposed to illness by hereditary factors. Freud (in spite of his physiological predilections and although he was at the time still struggling to construct a physiological model of the neuroses) was a psychologist; in his scheme, symptoms arose from the conflict that resulted from the active operations of the psychic apparatus to push undesirable mental elements out of consciousness. Ultimately, in his *conflict psychology*, repression and unconscious mental processes were viewed as normal attributes of the human personality.

The Development of Psychoanalysis as Therapy

At first Freud's formulation did not lead to any change in his therapy of the patients he saw. Instead he continued to employ the cathartic method which Breuer had discovered in the course of his treatment of "Anna O." The cathartic method, although it employed hypnosis, represented a radical departure from the usual procedures of hypnotic therapy. The aim of the latter was to remove symptoms by direct suggestion—and indeed it was with this goal in mind that Breuer began his treatment of Anna O., a young woman with multiple hysterical symptoms. In the course of therapy, however, the patient began actively to revive and to recount ordinarily unconscious memories while she was under hypnosis or in spontaneous somnambulistic trances. As Breuer listened to her recitation, he recognized that she was describing the past traumatic events related to the onset of her symptoms, and was at the same time giving vent to the emotions that were associated with them. As she raised both the memories and the affects into conscious expression, her symptoms disappeared.

Breuer commented:

When this happened for the first time . . . I was greatly surprised. It was in the summer during a period of extreme heat, and the patient was suffering very badly from thirst; for, without being able to account for it in any way, she suddenly found it impossible to drink. She would take up the glass of water she longed for, but as soon as it touched her lips she would push it away like someone suffering from hydrophobia. As she did this, she was obviously in an *absence* for a couple of seconds. She lived only on fruit, such as melons, etc., so as to lessen her tormenting thirst. This had lasted for some six weeks, when one day during hypnosis she grumbled about her English lady–companion whom she did not care for, and went on to describe, with every sign of disgust, how she had once gone into that lady's room and how her little dog—horrid creature!—had drunk out of a glass there. The patient had said nothing, as she had wanted to be polite. After giving further energetic expression to the anger she had held back, she asked for something to drink, drank a large quantity of water without any difficulty and woke from her hypnosis with the glass at her lips; and thereupon the disturbance vanished, never to return. A number of extremely obstinate whims were similarly removed after she had described the experience which had given rise to them. She took a great step forward when the first of her chronic symptoms disappeared in the same way— the contracture of her right leg, which, it is true, had already diminished a great deal. These findings—that in the case of this patient the hysterical phenomena disappeared as soon as the event which had given rise to them was reproduced in her hypnosis—made it possible to arrive at a therapeutic technical procedure which left nothing to be desired in its logical consistency and systematic application. Each individual symptom in this complicated case was taken separately in hand; all the occasions on which it had appeared were described in reverse order, starting before the time when the patient became bed-ridden and going back to the event which had led to its first appearance. When this had been described the symptom was permanently removed.[6]

Following this discovery, Breuer and Freud made use of hypnosis, not to suppress symptoms by direct suggestion but to uncover the dissociated pathogenic memories and affects. After his formulation of defense hysteria, Freud continued to employ hypnosis as a means of bringing into consciousness the repressed mental contents that produced the surface symptoms. His ultimate abandonment of the cathartic method resulted not from his innovative theoretical concepts but because he had difficulty with the techniques themselves. He soon discovered that many patients were not capable of being brought into a hypnotic trance of sufficient depth to enable them to recover the relevant memories and affects, and he apparently himself felt uncomfortable in the role of hypnotist. Accordingly, the number of patients who could be helped by hypnosis was limited, and Freud experimented with a variety of techniques that would permit the emergence of the pathogenic mental contents in those individuals for whom hypnosis was impossible. He maintained the reclining position of the patient in hypnosis (as have analysts ever since, by "putting the patient on the couch"), but instead of inducing hypnotic trance, he used other methods to deliver the unconscious material. Initially he would press the patient's forehead with his hand and instruct him to report on all the thoughts and images that came into his mind in connection with specific symptoms and other important events. He soon abandoned this technique, however, and moved to the procedure of free association. The nature of this procedure and the rationale for its use will be dealt with in more detail later. Suffice it to say here that it required the patient to report *every* thought, feeling, memory, and image that came into the center of his consciousness as he let his mind wander freely and without voluntarily focusing attention on any specific detail. No matter how painful, shameful, disgusting, or trivial his thought, it was to be revealed to the analyst.

From that point on in its development, free association became the hallmark of psychoanalytic treatment. At the same time it disclosed further technical difficulties and led to the discovery of two phenomena that became central features in the process of psychoanalysis: resistance and transference. As Freud required his patients to free associate in his search for the unconscious origins of symptoms, he soon recognized that free association, so simple in principle, was very difficult for his patients to carry out in practice. Despite themselves, however eager they might be to cooperate in the treatment, they were unable to bring themselves to report every thought that crossed their minds, and with a variety of rationalizations they would withhold much of that which they were conscious of. Furthermore, quite involuntarily, their minds would go blank or they could not maintain a sequence of thoughts, with the result that their train of verbalized associations would be incomplete, fragmented, and often unintelligible to the listener. Freud soon recognized that the repression that had banished the pathogenic material from consciousness in the first place exerted a continuous force against its revival in free associations; it created a *resistance* on the part of the patient to full divulgement of all that his mind contained. At the same time as Freud recognized the force of resistance, he observed that in the course of the analysis he became a person of special and central importance for his patients. They developed a variety of intense feelings for him that recapitulated their ties to earlier important people in their lives and recreated earlier patterns of relationships. This *transference* provided important observations about the patient's conflicts but also led to yet further resistances to the therapeutic processes; these in turn had to be analysed if the patient was to progress toward a resolution of his difficulties.

The Development of Ego Psychology

The clear conceptualization of the phenomena of resistance and transference enabled Freud to develop a variety of technical maneuvers, which he described in a series of papers on technique published between 1911 and 1915.* Although during much of this time Freud was in the process of revising his concepts of the structure of the psyche, these papers are based on his earlier *topographic model* of psychological functioning. In this view, the psyche is conceived of as a system of two opposing dynamic forces: the sexual instincts—their ultimate form and quality deter-

* See references 20 through 25.

mined by their shaping during the crucial early years of childhood sexuality and its development from infancy onward—are countered and controlled by the ego, motivated by the self-preservative instincts. The ego is roughly equatable with consciousness, whereas much of the instinctual life is hidden from conscious awareness through its repression into the unconscious. In this view, then, treatment is aimed at making the unconscious instincts and their derivatives available to the control of the conscious ego through the analysis of resistances and transference, and the emphasis is on delivering from below the repressed sexual conflicts deriving from the oedipal struggle of the early years of childhood.

In his earlier model, Freud's interest and emphasis were on the instinctual components of the psychic apparatus, but his observations of the phenomena of narcissism gradually led him to a more detailed consideration of the nature of the ego. After a decade and more of reconceptualization, this resulted in the *structural model* of psychic functioning. Instead of two major elements in the psyche (the ego and the unconscious), the personality is conceived of as tripartite, consisting of ego, id and superego. Elements of each of these may be unconscious; that is, the unconscious is thought of not as a region but as an attribute of mind. Furthermore, the old duality of ego instincts and sexual instincts is replaced by a *dual instinct theory* of sexuality and aggression, with both instincts deriving from the id, being pitted against one another, and requiring control by the Ego. Finally, anxiety, seen in the earlier model as the physiological derivative of repressed, undischarged sexual libido, is viewed in the structural model as an *ego affect*, serving the function of signaling danger to the ego from the underlying id instincts. Anxiety, in other words, is considered to be the cause rather than the result of ego defenses.

The new model of psychic functioning did not bring about a change in the basic therapeutic goals of psychoanalysis, which remained founded on the analysis of resistance and transference. It did, however, result in a shift of emphasis on what was to be analysed, for it was now seen that unconscious elements of the ego and superego had to be dealt with in the analytic process. Attention was increasingly focused on *ego analysis*: on the unconscious aspects of ego defenses; the intricacies of character structure; and the pathogenic influence of the unconscious pressures of the superego. Concomitantly, further clinical observations—primarily in the realm of ego psychology—were reported not only by Freud but also by many of his co-workers, such as Anna Freud[13] (ego defenses), Alexander[1] (superego functions), and Reich[37] (character analysis), all setting the stage for an elaboration of the theories of ego functions and the development of parameters in the classical psychoanalytic techniques. Despite the more recent introduction of such parameters, however, the procedures described in Freud's publications on technique between 1911 and 1915 remain the method of classical psychoanalysis as it is still practiced today. This will shortly be described in greater detail, but first let us compare and contrast the therapeutic approach invented by Freud with that of his predecessors.

As we have seen, from the distant origins of psychotherapy in Mesmer's magnetic passes to Freud's time, the patient was consistently the passive recipient of the doctor's active interventions. Whether his symptoms have been viewed as stemming from physical or psychological disturbances, he has been subjected to therapeutic maneuvers aimed at restoring his deranged physiology or suppressing unwanted symptoms without his taking any active part in the procedures or assuming any responsibility for his cure, other than allowing the therapist to treat him. With the advent of Freud and the development of the psychoanalytic method there was a radical change in outlook. The patient was now seen as having both autonomy and responsibility in regard to his illness and its cure. Not only were his symptoms viewed as being the result of inner psychological conflicts, those conflicts were also conceived of as stemming from inner, autogenous needs and drives that motivated the individual from within and became a source of difficulty when they ran contrary to the sanctions and codes imposed by his conscience and by society. In therapy it became the task of the patient to "know himself," to join the therapist in an active search for the inner, often irrational drives hidden from consciousness by repression. In that search the patient had to confront himself with courage and to push ahead with his self-exploration despite the pain and anxiety this might cause him. This alteration in the patients' role was reflected in a comparable change in the therapist's stance, for instead of being the active manipulator of an individual passively submitting himself to treatment, he became more the aiding midwife, working together with his patient in the struggle to deliver into the light of conscious awareness the unconscious pathogenic forces that only the patient himself could reveal. In this therapeutic partnership lies both the unique power of psychoanalysis as a curative agent and, as we shall see, its limitations as a treatment for emotional disorders.

(The Strategy of Psychoanalysis

The fundamental aim of psychoanalysis is to bring into conscious awareness the unconscious elements of the psychological conflicts that underlie symptoms and character problems, and to trace these roots to their genesis in the childhood distortions of the normal process of growth and development. The two basic strategical operations employed to achieve this ultimate goal are the analysis of resistances and of transference.

Resistances

We have seen how Freud, when he began to employ the techniques of free association, recognized the phenomenon of resistance in the breaks that occurred in the free flow of those associations. Theoretically, if an individual allows a completely unguided, uncontrolled, unfocused, unwilled play of ideas to pass across the stage of his consciousness, its form, nature, and content will be determined

by and an expression of the underlying drives and emotions pressing for discharge. In fact this rarely happens—even in the dreaming state, when ego-controlling functions are diminished. On the contrary, as undesirable and anxiety-provoking elements begin to surface, ego defenses are automatically brought into play to counteract and contain them. The resistances to free association observed by the analyst are the visible effects of the operation of these ego defenses. Resistance, then, is a function of the ego, its nature being determined by the nature of the defense behind it. Hysterical repression, for example, will be manifested by a sudden drying up of thoughts or by the forgetting of significant links in the chain of associations. Isolation will be manifested as a failure to include references to emotional reactions despite a ready flow of associations describing the more cognitive, perceptual aspects of events or fantasies.

From an analytic and therapeutic point of view it is essential for the analyst to deal with resistances. He must himself be alert to their existence, must help the patient to see them, and must analyze them along with the related defenses in order to penetrate through to the underlying, unconscious, anxiety-provoking drives and affects that constitute the driving force of the pathological psychic conflict. Without this fundamental maneuver analysis cannot proceed.

Transference

Transference is the source of special and often stubborn resistances that need particular attention during the process of analysis. The phenomena named transference are found in a variety of human relationships (student–teacher or employee–employer relationships, for example), but they are particularly encouraged to appear in the patient–analyst relationship by the very nature of the analytic process itself. The individual displaces onto the analyst old patterns of relationships developed with the significant figures in his childhood. As these old patterns are repeated with the analyst, they tend to be viewed by the patient as having a reality and legitimacy of their own in his current relationship with the analyst. This tends to prevent him from remembering the earlier events and the relationships that gave rise to them, a particularly effective form of resistance known as *transference resistance*.

A distinction is generally made between transference and *transference neurosis*. Transference, the more general term, refers to readymade, irrational attitudes toward the analyst that the patient brings to the analysis. As the analysis proceeds, however, and previously unconscious conflicts come closer to the patient's awareness, the transference phenomena are intensified into a neurosis. The patient regresses to earlier forms of relating that he may not initially have manifested, and behavior patterns that stem from his early childhood appear in his relationship with the analyst.

Far from being an unwanted artifact, the transference neurosis becomes a central focus of the analytic process; for here, in a controlled and almost laboratory-like situation, the patient brings into the view of both himself and the analyst attitudes and patterns of behavior intimately related to his neurotic problems. It then becomes possible to define the nature of these patterns, to trace them to their origins in childhood, and to discover their role and function in the patient's psychic economy.

Resistance is related to the transference in two ways. There may be a *resistance to the transference*: that is, the patient resists the development of a transference neurosis and thereby deprives himself and the analyst of a vital avenue to the analysis of his conflicts. In transference resistance, on the other hand, the transference itself is used as a resistance, as has been already noted: rather than remembering the early experiences that lie behind the transference manifestations, the patient stubbornly maintains his transference patterns and tends to insist on the legitimacy of his feelings for the analyst.

As is implied in the references to the childhood roots of transference, it may contain many colorings related to the variety of relationships the patient has had with significant figures in his past (notably mother, father, and siblings), and the analyst may be reacted to as several different people in turn. The transference may be loving, dependent, or hostile, the quality being determined by the nature of the earlier relationship that at the moment is determining the patient's behavior in analysis.

Countertransference

Just as the patient has irrational and inappropriate attitudes toward and feelings for the analyst that are displaced from his relationship to early childhood relationships, so too, and for the same reason, the analyst may have similarly irrational and inappropriate attitudes toward and feelings for his patient. This is called countertransference. As with the patient's transference, the analyst's countertransference is determined by his unconscious conflicts. It may be manifested by unrealistic feelings (anxiety or hostility, for example) or by unnecessary if not outright antitherapeutic behavior (forgetting an hour, for instance, or falling asleep repeatedly). It is, of course, essential that the analyst examine his own behavior and analyze any manifestation of countertransference as it arises.

The Therapeutic Alliance

Not all the attitudes and feelings a patient has for his analyst are necessarily the manifestations of transference. Indeed, in the patient who is a good subject for analysis, it is assumed that his childhood relationships have enabled him to develop basic trust, so that he comes to analysis with a genuine faith in the good will, skill, and reliability of the analyst. Classical psychoanalysis cannot proceed very far unless it rests on this fundamental sense of mutual trust between analyst and patient. The trust, furthermore, is the basis for the *working*, or *therapeutic alliance*,[29] of patient and analyst that is essential for the progress of the analysis. The working alliance is founded not only on this basic trust but also on the capacity of the patient to achieve an inner split between one part of his mind, which relives and expresses his psychic conflicts, and another, which maintains a distance on himself that enables him to observe his own behavior and feelings and to recognize their irrational quality.

❨ The Tactics of Psychoanalysis

If the goals and strategy of psychoanalysis can be simply stated and adequately painted in the sweeping strokes of generalizations, the tactics by which the goals are accomplished are impossible to convey, for they are as richly variegated and complex as the infinite variety of human personalities with which they deal. "Anyone who hopes to learn the noble game of chess from books," wrote Freud,[23] "will soon discover that only the openings and end-games admit of an exhaustive systematic presentation and that the infinite variety of moves which develop after the opening defy any such description. This gap in instruction can only be filled by a diligent study of games fought out by masters. The rules which can be laid down for the practice of psychoanalytic treatment are subject to similar limitations." Freud's discouraging if not despairing comment was subsequently extensively documented by Glover,[28] who in a survey of the practices of English analysts in the late 1930s found a wide diversity in the application of techniques generally thought to be clearly defined and standardized in their usage. And more recently a committee of the American Psychoanalytic Association[36] had to abandon a comparison of the effectiveness of psychoanalysis and psychotherapy when its members could come to no agreement as to an operational definition of either. It would be rash, therefore, in the space allowed here, to make definitive or dogmatic statements about the tactics of psychoanalysis. What follows must be viewed as empirical generalizations describing some of the more common clinical problems with which the analyst must deal and how he attempts to approach them. These will be discussed under four main headings: (1) the selection of the patient; (2) the preparation of the patient; (3) the process of anal-

ysis; and (4) the evaluation of the effects of analysis.

The Selection of the Patient

Psychoanalysis, especially when it is restricted to the classical techniques, has a limited applicability. Quite apart from the fact that it is time-consuming and expensive, it requires of patients a degree of discipline and psychological strength that is lacking in many individuals. Originally developed by Freud in his work with neurotic patients, analysis is still best suited for the treatment of the neuroses and for dealing with individuals with character problems that are compatible with the requisite strength of personality. In addition to the nature of the symptoms, there are a number of criteria that help to determine the suitability of any given patient for analysis.

MOTIVATION

The presence of ego-alien symptoms and character traits that cause the individual person distress and discomfort is a strong motivating force for seeking help and is a sine qua non for the long, rigorous, often painful process of psychoanalysis. The person who lacks such motivation, who undertakes analysis because of external pressures from friends or family or simply out of curiosity, is not liable to stick to it—with the possible exception of the psychiatrist or other therapist who may be strongly motivated to a self-knowledge that will help him in dealing with others.

CAPACITY TO FORM OBJECT RELATIONSHIPS

A degree of narcissism is normal for all people, but when it is so extensive as to compromise the individual's capacity to make genuine object relationships, classical psychoanalysis cannot easily be carried out. The patient must have a sufficient degree of basic trust to make an early working alliance with the analyst and to maintain this intact throughout the stormier periods of the process. He must also be capable of developing a transference neurosis, investing the analyst with love, hate, and other feelings that, though displaced from earlier figures, become attached to a real person external to the patient. It is further helpful if he has at least one good relationship in his real adult life.

PSYCHOLOGICAL-MINDEDNESS

Many patients bring to analysis a curiosity about their inner psychological life and a capacity for introspection that is invaluable to them in carrying out the tasks required of them by analysis. Analysis itself will, of course, help to develop skills in this regard, and one must not expect every patient to come to treatment fully adept in self-examination, but he must have the potential for it if analysis is to be in any degree successful. The ability to achieve a therapeutic splitting of consciousness should be included here—that is, the capacity to set one part of consciousness over against the other so that the former can observe with a reasonable detachment the flow of fantasies and feelings through the latter.

AVAILABILITY OF EMOTIONS

In general, patients should be able to reach, experience, and report on their emotions if analysis is to proceed. A possible exception to this is the individual with an obsessional character structure, who may bring to analysis a well-developed defensive isolation that makes him at first appear to be without strong emotions. This tends to lead to a longer analysis than in an individual whose emotions are more accessible, but unless the isolation is inflexible, the patient's emotions can ultimately be freed from their prison house as the analysis reaches a successful conclusion.

INTELLIGENCE

Although it has not been subjected to experimental testing, it is generally felt that a reasonable degree of intelligence is a prerequisite for analysis. It is required for the ready grasping of connections and nuances and for the capacity to understand the nature and goals of the treatment.

AGE

There have been a few attempts to analyze patients in the later years of life. The results have surprised the investigators with the plasticity and adaptability of some older people. These few analytic experiences, however, do not yet justify discarding the general consensus that younger individuals are fitter candidates for analysis because they are less liable to be set in rigid patterns of thinking and behavior and hence have greater capacity for change.

FREEDOM FROM ENVIRONMENTAL TURMOIL

Anxiety and emotional upset arising from disturbed and chaotic external situations in an individual's life are usually inimical to the successful search within for internal conflicts rooted in the individual's past. A degree of external calm and order is necessary for the orderly progress of an analysis. In general, analysis should not be undertaken with a patient, however suitable he is in other respects, if his life is not free from serious environmental crises. This is not to imply that other forms of therapy involving supportive measures should not be employed. These, indeed, may help a patient through to a more tranquil situation in which analysis may be started.

The Preparation of the Patient

Once the patient has been evaluated and the decision reached to proceed with analysis, certain preliminaries are necessary before the analysis proper begins. In the early days of psychoanalysis an extensive preparation and education of the patient was often carried out, in which he was informed in general terms of the nature, theory, and goals of analysis. This was before the widespread popularization of psychoanalysis, which underlies the current general knowledge about it and makes such detailed instruction unnecessary.

It is wise, however, not to take too much for granted, and to make sure that the patient understands the basic ground rules of operation. One often starts by asking the patient exactly what he knows about analysis and the techniques for carrying it out. One proceeds from there, either correcting the patient's misinformation or supplementing what he does know with the appropriate facts. The patient should understand the use of the couch and the nature and importance of free association and what is to be expected of him in this regard. The time and frequency of hours are arranged and his responsibility for keeping his appointments should be made clear to him. General guidelines about vacations and holidays should be clarified, fees set, and agreement reached as to what lines of communication are to be used when either analyst or patient needs to be in touch with one another about canceling or changing appointments or other similar issues. Finally, if the patient has no physician and has not recently been examined, it is generally considered wise to refer him to an internist with whom the analyst has a comfortable professional working relationship. In the younger population with whom analysis is usually carried out, serious physical illness is not liable to occur; but in those instances when it does, the best care of the patient and the least disruption of the analytic process are ensured if both patient and analyst have a trusted physician who is prepared to assume the responsibility for his intercurrent medical or surgical problem.

The Use of the Couch

Having the patient lie horizontal as the analyst sits out of sight behind him is, it is commonly pointed out, a relic of the position assumed in the early days of hypnosis. While this may be true, the horizontal position has a justification in its own right. It removes from the patient the multiple cues he could obtain about his analyst's responses from watching his face and gestures; and by minimizing this intrusion of reality, it allows a freer play to the patient's fantasies and emotions and the impulses that lie behind them. At the same time it frees the analyst from the need to police his mien and behavior, and it allows him to relax into that frame of mind of *free-floating attention* (discussed below) that is so essential to his task of understanding his patient's associations. The power of the simple maneuver of having the patient lie on his back and stare at the ceiling, with his analyst out of the range of his vision, is attested to by the frequently rapid deterioration of reality testing and

emergence of psychotic productions in those patients with borderline psychotic personality organizations who, through an error in diagnosis, are sometimes mistakenly started in analysis.

Frequency of Hours

In the early days of analysis, patients were generally seen an hour a day, six days a week. When analysis was imported to England, the six-day week, as Glover[28] commented, "did not . . . withstand the impact of the British week-end habit," and five days a week became the usually accepted custom. With the yet farther westward movement of analytic treatment to American shores, analysis has frequently been shorn to four sessions of fifty minutes a week by the American penchant for technical efficiency and assembly-line production. Anything less than this, especially in the initial stages of analysis, is generally thought to be incompatible with effective analysis. If the patient goes too long between hours, there is a tendency (especially in those with obsessional character structures) to "seal over." That is, defenses that may have been loosened in the process of analysis become stronger again, and the momentum gained in reaching the underlying conflictual material is lost. This is often particularly noticeable after a vacation break of several weeks and, in some, even after the two days of the weekend, a phenomenon colloquially termed the "Monday-morning crust."

Abstinence and Prohibitions

In the early days of analysis, stringent restrictions were often imposed on the patient with respect to his bodily (especially sexual) appetites, on the assumption that his motivation for analysis would wane were he to experience too full a gratification of his drives. Such specific prohibitions are not customarily enforced in contemporary analytic practice, but care is exercised by the analyst not to gratify the patient's dependency needs. Requests for medication, questions about the analyst's life or attitudes, and a variety of bids for love and attention are not responded to or gratified by the analyst. He may, furthermore, make specific injunctions about major changes that the patient may be considering in his life, such as marriage or a new career, especially when these moves appear to be significantly motivated by the neurotic conflicts or the forces of the transference neurosis. In such cases the patient is warned of the dangers of a poorly-understood decision and is strongly urged to postpone action until such a time as his contemplated behavior has been thoroughly analyzed.

Trial Analysis

Once the patient has been evaluated in one or more face-to-face interviews as well as through the employment of any adjunctive studies that are indicated, such as psychological testing, the patient is ready to lie down on the couch and begin the analysis proper. In some patients, however, this may not mark the end of the analyst's evaluation of his suitability for analysis. On occasion, despite an extensive initial evaluation, questions may still remain as to the patient's ability to withstand the stresses of analysis, to free associate, to form a working alliance, or even to maintain basic ego functions intact in the analytic position. In such cases the analyst may recommend to the patient a period of trial analysis of limited duration (no more than a few weeks) to determine, from the early responses to the analytic process, whether analysis is the treatment of choice for him, or whether some other therapeutic measure would be more helpful.

Free Association

The requirement that the patient tell the analyst every thought, fantasy, and feeling that enters his consciousness has been termed the "fundamental rule of analysis." We have already seen that completely free association is an ideal, rarely achieved skill. Indeed, it has been said that when the patient does truly associate freely, analysis has been completed. And we have noted that the variety of impediments to the process of free association reveals

resistances that point to the psychological conflicts needing analysis. Most patients coming to analysis at the present time are sophisticated enough to have heard of free association, but the analyst should nonetheless discuss the process with the patient to reinforce what he does know, to correct his misapprehensions, or to fill in any gaps in his knowledge. Free association is still the central tool of analysis; it should not be slighted or passed over lightly by either patient or analyst.

Free-Floating Attention

The counterpart of free association in the patient, free-floating attention forms the basic stance of the sensitive and effective analyst. A state of mind hard to define, it is perhaps easier to describe in negatives than in positives. The analyst avoids an active, voluntary focusing of his attention on specific aspects of his patient's associations. He does not single out a conflict or set of conflicts that appear to him to be significant, and he eschews any attempts (especially during analytic hours) to put the pieces together intellectually, to define a pattern, to determine mechanisms, or to arrive at a rational formulation of the patient's problem. Rather, he focuses his attention on the patient himself and immerses himself in the whole stream of associations, allowing them to flow through his alert, receptive mind without any concentrated effort at intellectual understanding. His is a passive, unguided attention that, in absorbing all of the patient's associations, permits the unconscious, intuitive elements of his mind to sense connections among associational fragments and to see patterns and significant relationships in the seemingly amorphous productions of the patient. In due course these connections and patterns are delivered into the analyst's consciousness seemingly unbidden, without his voluntarily trying to raise them. Like the *donée* of the poet, they are a gift to his conscious awareness. They emerge accompanied by the same sense of insight and discovery that the artist often experiences. The work of the analyst is a truly creative act. This fundamental approach to his patient's associations provides him with the basis for his subsequent therapeutic interventions as well as for his more theoretical, intellectual formulation of the nature of the patient's psychopathology.

The First Hour

Much has been made of the mystique of the first hour and the far-reaching predictions the seasoned analyst can make from his observations of the patient during that initial session. No doubt the patient's conflicts and patterns of behavior are indeed visible then. But the analyst who is unable to unravel all of his patient's mysteries after that single hour need not turn in his couch in despair, for there are many hours of observation to come.

Each patient, of course, approaches analysis in his own unique way, but there are several general categories of initial behavior that may be mentioned. Most patients begin analysis with some degree of anxiety, especially over the idea of lying on the couch. In a few this is sufficiently great to be disorganizing, sometimes to the point of making the patient barely able to talk, if not altogether mute. In such cases, general and quiet support from the analyst—a question or two to get things started, or an open recognition of the patient's anxiety—is sufficient to quiet his nervousness so that he can carry on. Some individuals come with a hitherto unconfessed guilty secret, which they proceed to pour forth, often with considerable apprehension and anxiety. The analyst's simple acceptance of the patient's recital is generally a sufficient response, and the patient usually feels better after his emotional catharsis.

Patients also vary in the form and content of their productions. Some begin with a detailed account of current conflicts and problems, others with an intellectualized analysis of their own characters, and still others with an orderly chronological account of their life histories. The more obsessional patient tends to talk without much affect, and has often rehearsed what he plans to say during his hour long before he arrives. In contrast, those with

hysterical traits may be more openly emotional and effusive in their speech. Certainly, these early observable patterns of behavior give the analyst a clue as to the patient's style and what lies ahead, but it is, after all, only the opening engagement between the two of them. Much remains to come, as the transference neurosis develops and unconscious material begins to appear in consciousness as a result of the analytic process.

The Course and Stages of Analysis

The usual analysis requires from three to five years, if the goal includes an analysis of character traits as well as of symptoms (which often disappear early in the development of the analytic relationship). Many individuals come to analysis without having sharply defined symptoms and seek help, instead, for difficulties in their human relationships.

As Freud suggested in his metaphor of the chess game, each analysis unfolds in a unique way, depending on the infinite combination of variables that go to make up human personality. Thus it is impossible to describe sharply-defined categories of stages in the unfolding of the analytic process. There are, however, certain general phases that characterize the course of analysis in most patients.

1. In the initial phase, the patient often continues very much as he has started in his opening hours, recounting problems, reviewing the history of his life, and revealing his own conscious introspections about himself as a person. The gratification involved in being able to talk freely about oneself to an interested listener, the support provided by the basic trust in his analyst and the positive transference felt for him by the patient, and the relief attendant on confessing guilty secrets or on the early disappearance of painful symptoms—all these carry the patient along without undue disruptions of the analytic process.

2. Although in the initial phase there may have been early minor evidences of resistance, resistances become more prominent and the analysis begins in earnest with the develop-

ment of the transference neurosis and the gradual emergence of unconscious conflicts closer to the surface. A prominent feature of this next phase is the regression of the patient to early forms of relating, and to the expression of drives and emotions—erotic, aggressive, and dependent—that have characterized earlier relationships (especially those in childhood) and are now transferred onto the figure of the analyst.

3. Though not sharply delineated from the previous stage, the phase of working through (discussed below) can be a protracted and tedious process. It may constitute the longest period of the analysis, as the patient repeats over and over his early patterns of relationships, gradually frees himself of neurotic behavior and reactions, and develops new ways of viewing himself and other people.

4. In the terminal phase of analysis, early material relating to losses and separations are often revived that have not emerged beforehand. Dependency issues are dealt with in this context and the transference neurosis is resolved. The patient is finally freed of crippling neurotic patterns so that he can carry on by himself, made more effective in his work and relationships by the self-knowledge he has gained during his analysis.

Specific Techniques

Much of the time, as we have seen, the analyst is quiet during a session. However, he is by no means passive or inactive, for he is following his patient's associations closely, searching for patterns of behavior, for signs of psychological conflict, for resistances, and for evidence of transference. His therapeutic goal is to uncover, through the analysis of these surface manifestations, the unconscious determinants of the patient's neurotic disorder and their genesis in his early childhood experiences. Especially since the pioneering work of Wilhelm Reich[37] on character analysis, it has been a general principle that patient and analyst must begin their work of analysis with the outermost layers of the psychic structure— that is, with the psychological defenses and

the resistances that result from them. Since the defenses serve the function of protecting the patient from the painful ego affects of anxiety and depression by rendering unconscious his undesirable impulses, affects, and fantasies, the patient must be able to tolerate the emergence of both these affects as the defenses are modified by analysis. At the same time he must be helped to discover, to experience, and to integrate into his consciousness the impulses and their derivatives that underlie his painful anxiety and depression and are the ultimate source of his neurotic difficulties. In carrying out this therapeutic task, the analyst's active interventions are generally limited to three basic tools: (1) confrontation; (2) clarification; and (3) interpretation.

CONFRONTATION

Many aspects of the patient's neurotic problems are ego-alien. That is, he recognizes them as being painful, undesirable, and distasteful, or as an impediment to his goals. This is particularly true of symptoms, which are usually felt as phenomena imposing themselves upon the patient from without and against his will. He may also experience certain of his character traits and patterns of relationships with others as being unacceptable to him because of the problems they pose for him. But more often than not, the distortions in his personality and relationships go unrecognized by him. They are the "way he is," and he accepts them without question; they are ego-syntonic. This is especially true of the resistances and transference manifestations that arise in the course of the analysis, and it is a primary task of the analyst to confront the patient with his behavior, his attitudes, and his irrational affects. When successful, this has the effect of making the patient, for the first time, look objectively at an aspect of himself and raise questions about the meaning, origin, and obligatory nature of what he sees.

CLARIFICATION

When, through confrontation, the patient has been made to see himself in a new light, the next step is to pass through the door that has thus been opened and explore the room into which it leads. With the guidance and questions of the analyst, the patient's behavior is examined in depth. The details of his behavior patterns, character traits, and resistances and transference attitudes, as well as the situations in which they occur, the consequences to which they lead, and their beginnings in the past, are all made explicit. Further questions are raised as to their meaning and function and their relations to the neurotic symptoms and conflict.

INTERPRETATION

Confrontation and clarification are only the prelude to interpretation—that is, to making conscious the unconscious roots of the patient's observable surface behavior. Interpretation involves a weakening of habitual defenses. It helps the patient to discover previously unrecognized character traits, long-repressed drives, isolated affects, and connections among significantly related phenomena that had been kept separate in his mind by isolation, until ultimately he finds the childhood roots of his adult neurotic disorder. The proper timing of interpretations—a function of the analyst's experience and skill—is essential, since premature interpretations not only will be rejected by the patient but may even increase his resistances. Interpretations ideally are made only when the unconscious material is on the verge of emerging into the patient's awareness as a result of the analysis, through confrontation and clarification, of his defenses and resistances.

WORKING THROUGH

The technical procedures that have just been described form, as we have said, the analyst's classical *modus operandi*. However, it is important to recognize that the simple application of confrontation, clarification, and interpretation usually has only a temporary effect on the material thus under analysis. Human behavior patterns tend to be stubborn in their persistence; early in the development of analytic procedures, Freud and his colleagues discovered that the repetition of such patterns (the *repetition compulsion*) was a

fundamental characteristic of human psychological functioning.

Practically speaking, therefore, any symptom or other neurotic manifestation must be "worked through" over a period of time. That is, it takes repeated confrontations, clarifications, and interpretations to enable the patient to make a permanent change in his psychic structure and resulting behavior. Patients, of course, vary in their flexibility and in the ease with which they can alter their behavior patterns; but at best, change is a slow and painstaking process. Just as the nature of tissue regeneration limits the speed of wound healing, so does the necessity for working through pose an inherent limitation on the rapidity with which analysis can be completed.

DREAM ANALYSIS

Before concluding with the classical techniques, we must say a word about the role of dream interpretation in analytic treatment. Freud, as we know, considered dreams to be "the royal road to the unconscious," and the momentous discoveries he made about the human psyche from the analysis of his own and others' dreams are presented in his classic *The Interpretation of Dreams*.[16] Perhaps because dreams and dream analysis proved such a powerful tool in unlocking the mysteries of the unconscious, Freud and the early analysts who worked with him placed a great deal of stress and reliance on the extensive analysis of individual dreams. This often took up several analytic sessions in sequence, as analyst and patient followed each element of the dream from the highways to the remotest byways of the territory it revealed. Analysts nowadays are less inclined to be so exhaustive in their analysis of the dreams their patients report. They may pursue the associations to selected dream elements that appear clearly related to problems the patient is currently working on, and occasionally may direct the patient back to his dream in the hour or two following its recital, but often they are content with hearing only the patient's spontaneous associations to his dream, viewing all the productions of the patient as equally important signposts of conflict and resistance.

(Variations in Technique

As the practice of analysis has grown over the years, and as larger numbers of patients have been treated for longer periods of time, analytic methods have been applied to individuals with a wide variety of clinical disorders and character problems. The classical procedures were initially developed in the context of working with patients with neurotic difficulties that derived mainly from oedipal problems, and for many analysts this still remains the main indication for psychoanalysis. The striking effectiveness of analysis in many clinical situations, however, quite understandably led to its experimental application to the more serious conditions (such as the psychoses and narcissistic disorders) for which it was generally felt to be contraindicated. As a result, a number of variations in technique have been proposed that are aimed at overcoming the difficulties that many of these patients pose for the application of classical procedures alone.

Ferenczi was one of the first to advocate modifications when, in the early 1920s, he suggested "active treatment"[11,12] for patients in whom the defense of phobic avoidance or the gratification of erotic impulses precluded the raising into consciousness of important pathogenic affects. Such patients, he recommended, should either be forced to expose themselves to the phobic situation or should be prohibited from erotic gratification in order to make them more accessible to analysis.

It is important to note that Ferenczi's suggestions were concerned only with the activity of the patient. Apart from his injunctions, the analyst restricted himself to the classical methods of analysing resistances and transference in the traditional manner. With the tremendous expansion of interest in analysis in the United States after World War II, further modifications of techniques were suggested that involved activities on the part of the analyst constituting a considerable departure from the more restricted, traditional procedures. Eissler,[8,9] for example, recommended the use of "parameters" with patients with serious ego defects that precluded a response to classical analysis—variations that permitted the analyst to be actively supportive and directive when necessary. Alexander[3] proposed varying the number of analytic sessions to control regressive transference, which was in his view an often harmful artifact of analysis. At the same time he suggested that the analyst should manipulate the transference by purposely assuming specific roles different from those the patient had known in previous relationships, in order to provide the patient with a "corrective emotional experience."[2] In a series of symposia and papers, others[32,39] have made further proposals for modifications in techniques so that analysis might be adapted to serious disorders such as schizophrenia or sexual aberration. These proposals have not gone unchallenged by adherents of the more classical form of analysis; and, lacking adequate data to settle the matter definitively, the debate continues.[14]

(Termination and Follow-up

Termination

Mention has already been made of the fact that as analysis enters its final phase, a date is set for termination. This should not be confused with forced termination, a minor parameter first employed by Freud in his famous case of the "Wolf Man".[26] Freud's aim in this instance was to motivate a patient locked into a comfortable dependent transference to make a renewed effort at analytic self-examination; the setting of the termination date, in other words, was a one-sided decision used by the analyst in the interests of furthering the analytic process. In the usual termination this is not the case. The date for ending is arrived at by mutual agreement between patient and analyst, and it is set far enough ahead in time to allow for the proper resolution of the conflicts that usually arise at the prospect of separation. Some analysts cut down on the number of weekly sessions during the terminal phase, with a view to enhancing the patient's return to complete autonomy, but many maintain a full schedule of hours right up until the last. There is no consensus either as to the indications for or the value of such a modification.

Follow-up

There is no general rule with regard to seeing the patient again after the analysis is terminated. The fact that the more formal, systematic procedure of analysis is completed does not mean that its effect is no longer felt. On the contrary, many patients continue to grow and change, either because of the forces set in motion by the analysis itself, or because they can apply to themselves the process of analysis they have learned in their work with the analyst. Analysis, furthermore, is no certain protection against further emotional difficulties in the future, in the face of environmental stress or the biological changes associated with the continuing phases of life. Freud,[27] in a pessimistic paper written late in his life, came to the conclusion that analysis worked best for those patients whose neurotic problems were primarily traumatic in nature, and he doubted that analysis could activate and preventively influence latent conflicts that might at some future time cause the patient difficulty. Analysts vary in the readiness with which they will see patients again after the analysis is ended. Many will at least be available to a patient who runs into difficulties, to help him evaluate the new situation and to obtain further treatment if it should be necessary.

(Evaluation of Therapeutic Results

When we turn to a consideration of the therapeutic results of analysis, we find ourselves in a morass of methodological complexities. Analysts, when they have focused their attention on this question, have been more concerned to examine the theory of therapeutic results than the actual nature of the therapeutic outcome itself. Critics such as Eysenck,[10] have martialed statistics to show that prolonged psychotherapy, including analysis, is less effective

as a treatment than are simpler measures involving support and suggestion, or than no treatment at all. And yet despite dire predictions about its imminent demise, and despite a recent and probably salutary falling-off of applicants for analytic training, analysis and analysts continue to thrive.

It is perhaps easier to explain than to resolve this paradox. The methodological problems inherent in evaluating the results of psychoanalysis are so complex as to be overwhelming. There is neither agreement nor consistency among analysts as to the criteria for selection of patients, the technical procedures to be included under the term "psychoanalysis," or the criteria for improvement or cure. Some analysts, for example, restrict their patients to those with transference neuroses, whereas others are willing to apply it to psychotic individuals. Some stick strictly to the methods of classical analysis; others are flexible in their introduction of parameters. Some judge improvement by the amelioration of symptoms; others turn more to changes in personality structure and quality of relationships as their indications of improvement. The variables introduced by these differences alone (to say nothing of the difficulty in collecting large series of patients or establishing adequate controls) make the task of evaluating the effectiveness of analysis a Herculean if not impossible one.

Aerodynamics engineers, it has been said, have proven that given the ratio of wing area to body weight, it is impossible for the bumblebee to fly; but the bumblebee, ignorant of their mathematically arrived-at conclusions, continues happily to remain aloft. Certainly, in the intimate relationships between analyst and patient, many things happen that are hard to record or document but that are emotionally and experientially convincing to each—of the power of analytic procedures to induce changes in the patient, to bring him to a wider knowledge of himself, and to enable him to learn new ways of living that make him a richer, more effective person.

The individual patient has no doubt of the value of the knowledge he has gained. But the knowledge is not intellectual alone; it involves a change in perceptions, attitudes, and responsiveness to life. The heart has reasons of which the head knows nothing, as Pascal long ago recognized. For the patient, his immediate knowledge of the effect of analysis is sufficient evidence of its worth, however skeptical the outside observer may be and however lacking the statistics to "prove" its usefulness.

Perhaps its effectiveness can never be shown by scientific methods, and possibly, because of the complexity and nature of the analytic process, it is a mistake even to attempt such a demonstration. Perhaps the experience of analysis is like that of beauty, of mysticism, of love—self-evident and world-shaking to him who knows it, but quite incommunicable to another who does not. This, of course, is entirely unsatisfactory (if not evidence of downright folly) to the uninitiate, and he will and should demand more scientific evidence for the practical value of analysis. Fortunately, so do many analysts, and there is now an increasing interest in the better definition of analytic procedures. These are being investigated, not in the almost impossibly complex situation of psychoanalysis but in the more restricted area of briefer analytically-oriented psychotherapies, where the variables are fewer and more manageable.[38] There is hope that sharper definitions and valid statistical statements will come from these investigations, and that further insight into the nature of analysis will arise from these more limited observations. Meanwhile, let the bumblebee fly.

❲ Bibliography

1. ALEXANDER, F. "A Metapsychological Description of the Process of Cure," *Int. J. Psycho-anal.*, 6 (1925), 13–34.
2. ———. "Analysis of the Therapeutic Factors in Psychoanalytic Treatment," *Psychoanal. Q.*, 19 (1950), 482–500.
3. ———. "Some Quantitative Aspects of Psychoanalytic Technique," *J. Am. Psychoanal. Assoc.*, 2 (1954), 685–701.
4. BERNHEIM, H. *Suggestive Therapeutics.* Translated by C. A. Herter. New York: Putnam, 1897.
5. BRAID, J. *Braid on Hypnotism. The Beginnings of Modern Hypnotism*, A. E. Waite, ed. New York: Julian, 1960.
6. BREUER, J. and S. FREUD. (1895) "Studies on Hysteria," in J. Strachey, ed., *Standard Edition*, Vol. 2, pp. 1–305. London: Hogarth, 1955.
7. DE PUYSÉGUR, A. M. J. C. *Du Magnétisme animal.* Paris: de Callot, 1807.
8. EISSLER, K. R. "The Effect of the Structure of the Ego in Psychoanalytic Technique," *J. Am. Psychoanal. Assoc.*, 1 (1953), 104–143.
9. ———. "Remarks on Some Variations in Psycho-analytical Technique," *Int. J. Psycho-anal.*, 39 (1958), 222–229.
10. EYSENCK, H. E. *The Scientific Study of Personality.* London: Routledge and Kegan Paul, 1952.
11. FERENCZI, S. "Technical Difficulties in the Analysis of a Case of Hysteria," in J. Rickman, ed., *Further Contributions to the Theory and Technique of Psychoanalysis*, Vol. 2, pp. 189–197. New York: Basic Books, 1952.
12. ———. "The Further Development of an Active Therapy in Psycho-analysis," in J. Rickman, ed., *Further Contributions to the Theory and Technique of Psychoanalysis*, Vol. 2, pp. 198–216. New York: Basic Books, 1952.
13. FREUD, A. *The Ego and the Mechanisms of Defense.* London: Hogarth, 1947.
14. ———. "The Widening Scope of Indications for Psychoanalysis: Discussion," *J. Am. Psychoanal. Assoc.*, 2 (1954), 607–620.
15. FREUD, S. (1894) "The Neuropsychoses of Defense," in J. Strachey, ed., *Standard Edition*, Vol. 3, pp. 43–61. London: Hogarth, 1962.
16. ———. (1900) *The Interpretation of Dreams*, in J. Strachey, ed., *Standard Edition*, Vols. 4 and 5. London: Hogarth, 1953.
17. ———. (1904) "On Psychotherapy," in J. Strachey, ed., *Standard Edition*, Vol. 7, pp. 257–268. London: Hogarth, 1953.
18. ———. (1910) "The Future Prospects of Psycho-analytic Therapy," in J. Strachey, ed., *Standard Edition*, Vol. 11, pp. 139–151. London: Hogarth, 1957.
19. ———. (1910) "'Wild' Psycho-analysis," in J. Strachey, ed., *Standard Edition*, Vol. 11, pp. 219–227. London: Hogarth, 1957.
20. ———. (1911) "The Handling of Dream

Interpretation in Psychoanalysis," in J. Strachey, ed., *Standard Edition*, Vol. 12, pp. 91–96. London: Hogarth, 1958.

21. ———. (1912) "The Dynamics of Transference," in J. Strachey, ed., *Standard Edition*, Vol. 12, pp. 97–108. London: Hogarth, 1958.

22. ———. (1912) "Recommendations to Physicians Practising Psycho-analysis," in J. Strachey, ed., *Standard Edition*, Vol. 12, pp. 109–120. London: Hogarth, 1958.

23. ———. (1913) "On Beginning the Treatment," in J. Strachey, ed., *Standard Edition*, Vol. 12, pp. 121–144. London: Hogarth, 1958.

24. ———. (1914) "Recollection, Repetition, and Working Through," in J. Strachey, ed., *Standard Edition*, Vol. 12, pp. 145–156. London: Hogarth, 1958.

25. ———. (1915) "Observations on Transference-Love," in J. Strachey, ed., *Standard Edition*, Vol. 12, pp. 157–171. London: Hogarth, 1958.

26. ———. (1918) "From the History of an Infantile Neurosis," in J. Strachey, ed., *Standard Edition*, Vol. 17, pp. 7–122. London: Hogarth, 1955.

27. ———. (1937) "Analysis Terminable and Interminable," in J. Strachey, ed., *Standard Edition*, Vol. 23, pp. 209–253. London: Hogarth, 1964.

28. GLOVER, E. *The Technique of Psychoanalysis.*

New York: International Universities Press, 1968.

29. GREENSON, R. R. "The Working Alliance and the Transference Neurosis," *Psychoanal. Q.*, 34 (1965), 155–181.

30. ———. *The Technique and Practice of Psychoanalysis.* New York: International Universities Press, 1967.

31. JANET, P. *Névroses et idées fixes.* 2 vols. Paris: Félix Alcan, 1893.

32. LOEWENSTEIN, R. M. "Remarks on Some Variations in Psycho-analytic Technique," *Int. J. Psycho-anal.*, 39 (1958), 202–210.

33. MENNINGER, K. *Theory of Psychoanalytic Technique.* New York: Basic Books, 1958.

34. MESMER, F. A. *Le Magnétisme animal.* Paris: Payot, 1971.

35. NUNBERG, H. *Practice and Theory of Psychoanalysis.* New York: Nervous and Mental Disease Monographs, 1948.

36. RANGELL, L. "Similarities and Differences between Psychoanalysis and Dynamic Psychotherapy," *J. Am. Psychoanal. Assoc.*, 2 (1954), 734–770.

37. REICH, W. *Character Analysis.* New York: Orgone Institute Press, 1949.

38. SIFNEOS, P. E. *Short-Term Psychotherapy and Emotional Crisis.* Cambridge, Mass.: Harvard University Press, 1972.

39. STONE, L. "The Widening Scope of Indications for Psychoanalysis," *J. Am. Psychoanal. Assoc.*, 2 (1954), 567–594.

CHAPTER 10

PSYCHOANALYTIC PSYCHOTHERAPY

William Offenkrantz and Arnold Tobin

I N THIS CHAPTER the term "psychoanalysis" has specific boundaries. It is explicitly referred to as a method of treatment and not as a general psychology, a tool of clinical research, or a social movement.

(Distinguishing Between Psychoanalysis and Psychotherapy

We characterize psychoanalysis as follows: first, it represents a strictly deterministic view of all human behavior; second, this determinism is manifested by the significant effect that early life experiences have upon adult behavior, attitudes, and feelings; third, the fact of unconscious mental activity can be inferred; and fourth, consciousness produces "cure." We believe these characteristics are common denominators for treatment by "classical" analysis and by the other analytic "schools" with which we are familiar, those of Adler, Fromm, Horney, Jung, Rado, Rank, and Sullivan. Nevertheless, it has been our experience that there

are several common misconceptions about classical psychoanalysis *as it is currently practiced* and since we will be describing psychoanalytic psychotherapy as a derivative of classical analysis, we believe it is worthwhile to begin by outlining the classical analytic treatment method as well as some of these misconceptions. Classical analysis is usually characterized, by both its practitioners and its critics, as "a systematic analysis of the transference." Transference is a concept that is not always well understood, even though its use is not restricted to any one analytic school. As defined by Freud,[6] transference is a manifestation of the mind's general tendency to displace the emotions of early life that are still unconsciously involved with important objects* and

* Throughout this chapter we use the word "object" as though it were interchangeable with "person," in the social-psychological sense of a figure in the external world. This is not what we intend. First, we follow the original German usage, in which "object" is distinguished from "subject" and the word therefore has no dehumanizing implications. In classical psychoanalytic usage, "object" refers to feelings and attitudes towards "internal representations in the mind" of

forgotten experiences. These early emotions are displaced onto, among other things, (a) activities of waking life (as when one makes slips and errors); (b) perceptions while asleep (dream images); and (c) symptoms (phobias, conversion phenomena, compulsive rituals, obsessional thoughts, and others). Freud regarded the distorted perceptions of the analyst that may occur under the influence of these unconscious emotions as only special cases of the more general phenomenon.

The classical analytic situation is organized to promote a regression to a "transference neurosis." This is evidenced by a reexperiencing with the analyst of the most affectively intense involvements, from before age six, that are still unconsciously active in the patient's mind. The principal factor that promotes this intentional therapeutic regression to the transference neurosis is the frustrating ambiguity with which the patient is faced in the analysis. He reacts to this frustration by trying to achieve gratification through means he has learned in the past—that is, through regression to reexperienced demands and expectations. At the same time, a therapeutic alliance is developing between the conflict-free "adult portion of the patient's mind" and the analyst. This indispensable alliance is characterized by the patient's ability to experience his regressive transference reactions with full intensity, and then, alternately, to "stand off," observe, and understand them in collaboration with the analyst.

One common misconception of this process is the idea that, as it once was in the 1930's, the classical analyst's goal still is to uncover the original historical "trauma"—the "why" of a behavior—with the implication that this discovery is the curative act. It would be more correct to say that an analysis can be roughly divided into two phases. The therapeutic task of the first phase is to make the "here-and-now" experience between patient and analyst come alive with feeling, in order to discover

the ways in which the past is still active in the patient's current perceptions and behavior. In this process, recovered memories only enhance the patient's sense of the personal reality of the continuity between his past and present.

A second common misconception of this regression to a transference neurosis is that it induces an unnecessary, deleterious dependency relationship. Actually, it is clearly understood by the classical analyst that the experiencing of the therapist as identical with the objects of the patient's memories is indeed to the patient's end of maintaining the transference as a child to a powerful parent. Therefore—and this is crucial—the classical analyst understands that in the second phase the task of treatment is to help the patient grasp the way in which the present is different from the past. This must include the patient's coming to understand how he tries to make present people, especially the analyst, behave in particular ways. If he can do this the patient's conviction of what his parents really were like will be perpetuated or, more often, the way in which he wished to see his parents will be sustained. By preserving this mythology about his past, the patient can maintain his current behavior, using the past as justification for it. It is our impression that this distinction between present and past takes place in any successful psychoanalytic treatment, whether it is called "classical" or some different adjective. But it does not necessarily occur in psychotherapy.

A third misconception is that the classical analyst attempts the impossible task of preserving his relationship with the patient as that of a blank screen for the patient's projections. The facts are that, throughout the analysis, not only are the reactions of the classical analyst used by himself as an orienting guide to the meaning of the material, but also these spontaneous reactions as a "real" person are particularly important in the terminal part of the second phase. They enhance the process of differentiating present from past. For example, a woman patient with no distortion of her reality-testing function comes into a session in the terminal part of the second phase and says, "I noticed you sent your secretary out as

figures (including oneself) in the external world. This is of particular importance later on, when we rely heavily on the explanatory power of "identification" to account for the changes that occur in psychoanalytic psychotherapy.

I was coming down the hall, to see how much better-looking I am now." In the initial phase of treatment the analyst's task is to help the patient understand the way in which this is a transference reaction that recreates the feelings she had toward her father, a man who really was too inhibited to tell her directly when he was pleased at how well she was doing. In the terminal part of the second phase, the analyst might respond, "Why would I be that indirect?" This is a correct use of the analyst's characteristics as a real person —*if* it facilitates the task of helping the patient to become aware that she *wants* to continue seeing the analyst as she saw her father, so that she can continue to believe that her father really did secretly prefer her to her mother. In that case, she would never have to face either her former inadequacies as a child, or her shame at still wanting the preferred position with a currently unavailable object, or her need to assume what for her are painful adult responsibilities.

Having thus described classical psychoanalysis, we can proceed to characterize "classical" psychoanalytic psychotherapy. One difference already noted is that the distinction made between past and present may not occur in psychotherapy. A second difference is that the transference should be handled differently. In psychotherapy there will be equally intense emotional experiences, including transference reactions, and the understanding and interpreting of these transferences may be crucial for the success of the therapy. However, there will not be a systematic effort to create a transference neurosis. The therapist is required to deal with these transferences in a much more flexible way than is generally considered appropriate or necessary in ordinary psychoanalytic technique. Thus we believe that in some ways the psychotherapeutic task is more difficult, and in accord with this belief we will discuss the technique of making transference interpretations in a later section.

Other Relevant Concepts

In addition to transference, several other concepts are relevant in understanding psychotherapy from a variety of seemingly disparate viewpoints—including behavioral analysis and modification, transactional and existential analysis, and the various "neo-Freudian" schools previously listed. These concepts are: self-esteem (including the concept of "narcissism"—see page 201), superego, ego-ideal, and identification. We recognize that these are at different and not necessarily optimal distances from the data of (self) observation, but we find them all indispensable to our understanding.

We will generalize that patients come for treatment because of a loss in self-esteem either when: (1) they have experienced a real or imagined defeat; or (2) they have lost their previous ability to integrate the normal balance of love and hate that characterizes all important human relationships; or (3) they have lost the ability to regulate other aspects of their inner life that are important for the maintenance of self-esteem. This loss of self-esteem is associated either with guilt at having transgressed the prohibitions of unconscious and preconscious conscience (super-ego), or with shame at having failed to live up to unconscious and preconscious goals and ambitions (ego-ideal).[14] But for whichever reasons they come, patients experience shame about their need for help from another person. The way in which they deal with this shame is a crucial element in their readiness (or lack of it) to accept a dependent relationship with the therapist. Usually these tensions set in motion the desire to believe in the benevolent power of another person—in this instance a therapist—who will relieve the patient's guilt, shame, and lowered self-esteem by some means. This belief usually results in the process of identification, a concept discussed in the section on methods of psychotherapy.

◖ Indications for and Goals of Psychotherapy

The following situations, in our experience, indicate the adoption of psychoanalytic psychotherapy.

1. *Patients who show acute symptomatic reactions.* Among such reactions are: acute or free-floating anxiety attacks; acute symptom-formation in the "transference neuroses," including conversion and anxiety hysteria, obsessional thinking, or compulsive rituals (because psychoanalysis cannot be effective during the acute phase of these neuroses); traumatic neuroses; adolescent crises (delinquency or acute inhibition of schoolwork); and acute grief reactions.

2. *Patients who show more chronic, characterological forms of psychopathology.* For such conditions (in contrast with the fourth situation listed below) the desirability of psychoanalysis is outweighed by factors "inside" the patient, and (in contrast with the third situation below) these internal factors are not of the nature that makes analysis a high-risk treatment. These are the patients who may for a variety of reasons not be introspective, whose cultural background is such that a procedure such as analysis is opposed by powerful group norms, or who are afraid of the procedure (without, however, demonstrating excessive rigidity of the high-risk group in (3) below.) Among them are: hysterical characters; obsessive-compulsive characters; depressive characters, including addicts and parent-loss patients; paranoid characters, including schizoid and borderline characters; true hypochondriasis; and narcissistic personality disorders.

3. *Patients who have psychotic disorders.* These include schizophrenic reactions or manic-depressive reactions that are considered unsuitable for psychoanalysis, usually because of excessively rigid attitudes and behavior patterns masking a weak "ego structure." Such persons superficially manifest an insufficient motivation for analysis. However, it is important to understand that this superficial disinterest actually serves to protect the patient against his potential for disintegration under the pressure of a therapeutic regression in analysis.

4. *Psychoanalysis would be desirable but is "externally" unavailable.* Such instances arise either because of geography, time, money, or a crippling external life situation, or because a practitioner or trainee wants the gratification of successful therapy with a patient otherwise well suited for psychoanalysis.

5. *If suitability is uncertain.* Psychoanalytic psychotherapy may be used for exploratory purposes when it is difficult to decide whether psychotherapeutic or psychoanalytic methods are more suitable. The patient's experience during psychotherapy in any of the above categories may also serve as an important preparation for the work of analysis.

What are the goals of psychoanalytic psychotherapy? They are, primarily, the alleviation or elimination of "symptoms," defined by us as whatever distress the patient comes for "help" with. When this goal is reached, it is important for a therapist with integrity to make it easy for the patient to terminate the treatment—to believe that the therapist's door is open for him to return without risking humiliation. Under integrity we include such gross issues as a therapist's capacity to deal with his need of the patient for his income, but we also mean facing up to subtler issues, such as the therapist's need of the patient for personal training goals. And finally, by integrity we mean the capacity to face the problem that we believe is the common denominator for all psychotherapists: determining whether, if he is reluctant to help the patient terminate, it is because he is unwilling to deprive himself of the pleasure or the self-esteem, or both, that he obtains from the patient's progress. If the patient does express a desire to continue, after the original symptomatic relief has been achieved, the therapist should make an explicit agreement with the patient to work toward one or more goals in the areas of intimacy, work, or general interpersonal relations.

(The Methods of Psychoanalytic Psychotherapy

Before listing specific methods of psychotherapy, we will continue our earlier discussion of the distinguishing characteristics of the procedure by describing some of the external configurations of treatment that are methodological expressions of our basic concepts.

Psychotherapy is an asymmetrical[8] two-person relationship with an outpatient, initially occurring once or twice a week. Our experience has been that psychotherapy occurring more than twice a week makes strong transference reactions inevitable, with the concomitant likelihood of strong countertransference reactions. It then follows that transference interpretations as well as systematic self-scrutiny by the therapist must become a regular part of the treatment. Therapists who choose not to do this are urged not to increase the frequency of sessions.

The treatment may go on for an agreed-upon number of sessions or for an indefinite period. In either case, the original agreement to proceed is explicitly related to some consciously formulated distress that the patient experiences. The duration of each session is not as important as the patient's sense that the sessions will recur regularly and that during each one he will have the therapist's attention, free of external distractions. We ignore here the subtleties involved when the therapist takes notes, answers telephones, offers different appointment times each week, sees patients in several different locations, including vacation places, and so forth. Our general position is that within broad limits, any conditions enabling the therapist to function with sufficient freedom to understand the patient cognitively and empathically are their own justification. We include the possibility that some patients cannot accustom themselves to a therapist who, for example, needs to answer the telephone. A therapist free to respond in the ways we have just described will refer that patient elsewhere before the patient interrupts the treatment or a stalemate occurs.

Whenever possible, an appropriate fee should be set. Preferably it should be given by the patient to the therapist, even if a third party either has produced the money or is to receive it. The purpose of this is to increase the likelihood that important positive or negative feelings about the therapy will be brought into awareness and expressed.

All of the foregoing characteristics potentially enhance the patient's self-esteem by identification with a therapist who, at least by "middleclass, contemporary American" criteria, experiences himself as serious in his work and possessed of personal dignity. Such a person appears at least to be getting satisfaction from treating patients. This implies a hope of success with which the patient can identify. It is enhanced by the therapist's sense of assurance, which the patient experiences as encouragement to be hopeful about himself.

Dependency and Identification

A second brief remark about identification is relevant in connection with the referring of patients for psychotherapy. We believe that the patient's learning about himself and about the external world (particularly as seen through the therapist's eyes) are important tools for achieving the goals of psychotherapy. Further, we agree with Piers and Piers[15] that this learning occurs in three modes during treatment: by identification, by conditioning, and by insight. We also agree with their suggestion that our unconscious or preconscious predictions regarding the potential ease with which such identifications will be likely to occur may determine our choice of the therapist to whom we refer a particular patient. Another way of expressing this is that we unconsciously estimate the congruence between the patient's and the potential therapist's ego-ideal and superego. This is generally experienced by the therapist and patient as "liking each other." We will return to this point in the later section on folk-wisdom, where we will explicate certain transactional characteristics of therapy with particular types of patients.

Of the traditional approaches to the methods of psychotherapy, the best one we are familiar with is by Goldman,[8] who lists the following methods: management of dependency needs, evaluation of emotional reactions with positive focus, objective review of stress situations, emotional decompression, reinforcement of ego defenses, educative guidance, effecting of changes in the life situation, modification of patient's goals, use of magical omnipotence, and use of transference. For the student of psychotherapy, Goldman's presentation is a valuable orientation to the field because it helps organize a series of techniques within the adaptational approach to psychodynamics, emphasizing the interaction between the individual and his current environment. Most useful is Goldman's explicit awareness that "the ways in which the therapist gratifies the dependent needs of the patient are infinite." This correctly conveys the idea that the major beneficial effects of all the methods he details result from their occurrence within the context of an ubiquitous, but frequently covert, dependency relationship in which the patient experiences the therapist as a benign, powerful parent. He also realizes that it is crucial not to underestimate the powerful tendency in this direction set in motion by the sincere interest, attention, and reliable presence of the therapist, and the reciprocal tendency of one human being to want to believe in the benevolent power of another.

However, we find that Goldman has not taken the next, necessary step in the understanding of the therapeutic process, although we believe it is implicit in many of his comments. This step is: the inevitable following of the ubiquitous, covert frequent dependency relationship by the tendency, both conscious and unconscious, to want to be like the loved or admired object (the therapist). This tendency refers to the process of *identification*. When it occurs, it increases the likelihood that the patient's self-esteem will be elevated because his subjective sense of self will be enhanced, as Schafer [p. 164][18] says, by "enriching it with the object's good qualities." More precisely, the particular good quality with which the patient will identify in the therapist is that, insofar as the patient perceives him, the therapist either does not have the same conflicts as the patient or does not have guilt or shame, as the patient does, in response to his impulses.

One immediate consequence of understanding the importance of identification in therapy is that it provides a more dynamic view of a traditionally misunderstood concept: abreaction, which is synonymous with Goldman's phrase, "emotional decompression." This is usually taken to mean the reliving, in therapy,

of a forgotten, painful experience, with re-experiencing of the hitherto repressed emotion. The beneficial effect is thought to be the result of the release of tension on a "hydraulic" model, a concept still derived from Freud's original view of the etiology of hysteria.[3] Our own view is that when a hitherto unacceptable feeling is remembered, or is experienced for the first time and expressed verbally, in the presence of a comprehending and accepting authority figure, the patient's self-esteem rises. This occurs because when the patient perceives the therapist's reaction, he can then identify himself with the more realistic prohibitions and ideals of the therapist instead of his own archaic prohibitions and ideals.

However, this rise in self-esteem may be spurious,[14] precisely because the identification is still largely dependent on the reassuring presence of the external object. That is, the object of the identification may be experienced only as an "introject," in Schafer's sense, [p. 164][18] with whom an internal dialogue is being carried on because "relations with introjects are as variable as those between two persons." Thus, the new attitude may not yet be an indication that, within the patient's mind, his actual self-representation coincides with the representation of the therapist. However, if the patient can use the rise in self-esteem he gains in the therapist's office to risk new behaviors in the "real" world, he may then experience approval—or at least the absence of distress—from significant people. When this happens, we believe that the rise in self-esteem, which began with dependent longings toward the "parentified" therapist, becomes a more real expression of an internal shift in self-perception.

Until therapists understand the power of covert dependency gratification and the identification that results from it, they sometimes miss the importance to the patient of the therapist's subtly communicated pleasure when the patient risks these "new behaviors." A corollary to this pleasure is that the therapist also accepts the patient's inevitable failures in a way different from either the patient's view of them or the view held by the patient's original objects.

Interpretation
"From the Side of the Ego"

One important technical consideration is the way in which the therapist communicates his comprehension and acceptance of the patient's hitherto unacceptable impulses. Our shift from our earlier word "feelings" to "impulses" indicates the usefulness to us of the structural point of view provided by classical psychoanalytic metapsychology. The structural metaphor (ego, super-ego, and id) admittedly represents a very high level of abstraction within this theory, in contrast to the data of clinical observation and clinical inference [p. 617].[19] Nevertheless we find it a useful shorthand, because it enables us to conceptualize the therapist's communications as interpretations "from the side of the ego"[4] [p. 57]. A simple example of this is when the therapist might say, "I understand how painful it is to feel so angry at me and yet be so afraid to express it." The appropriateness of such a remark derives from the contact that is thus made with the patient's experiencing ego, which "feels itself caught" between the id impulse (hostile feelings) and the super-ego reaction (feelings of guilt, fear of retaliation, inferiority, or helplessness). The therapist's interpretation promotes an identification by the patient with the therapist's ego, which is better able to tolerate both sides of such a conflict. This process is analogous, on a higher developmental level, to the one by which a child learns to neutralize his own untamed impulses by identification with his parents. For example, when a mother is confronted with her little boy's unneutralized sexuality, she responds with a firm but loving "No"—that is, with her neutralized aggression. The little boy can identify with this attitude in his mother and thus achieve mastery over his own impulses as she has over hers. Thus the therapist is like the optimally frustrating parent when he confronts the patient's excessive emotionality with his words and his calmness, in the face of the patient's anxiety over his powerful feelings.

If the patient has been unable to express directly to the therapist either his impulses or his reaction against them, he may do it in the form of "latent language."[12] The patient can do this unconsciously, for example, by making reference to a situation involving two people outside the therapy. In such an instance, the therapist may do well to respond with a congruent latent reference to the same people outside the treatment, so as to avoid confronting the patient prematurely with his impulses.

In the event that the patient has responded to the permissive atmosphere of the therapy with an upsurge of dependency longings that he does not experience with shame, but only with frustration when they are not gratified, the therapeutic problem is different. Then it is important to acknowledge explicitly the unusual quality of the treatment situation, and the special relationship to the therapist that makes many kinds of intense feelings inevitable (including whatever form the dependency demand has taken). Further, as long as the therapist is privately convinced that the patient *wants* but does not *need* whatever is being asked for, he should explicitly acknowledge the frustration that the patient feels when these demands are not gratified. If the dependent demand for explicit gratification continues, the indication is for the therapist to direct the inquiry toward a different time and place in the patient's life, which is the first step in making a transference interpretation.

The Use of Transference Interpretations

Our experience in the supervision of trainees of varying disciplines as well as in consultation with colleagues has been that, except for psychoanalysts, other psychotherapists usually regard transference interpretations as a subject either for exaltation or depreciation. In the former case, the psychotherapist feels that transference interpretations are not in his province. In the latter, he feels that they are a pejorative invitation to the patient to turn attention away from the "more important issues here and now" in the patient's current life. Our position is that every competent psychotherapist, regardless of discipline, must (a) be able to recognize the occurrence of a transference reaction, (b) define the criteria for deciding when to interpret its presence, and (c) know how to make a transference interpretation. These three tasks are discussed below.

RECOGNITION OF OCCURRENCE

The occurrence of a transference reaction is suggested when the therapist empathically perceives any overly strong emotional reaction during a session. If this becomes repetitive and eventually predictable, the likelihood is high that the patient is experiencing a transference reaction. A simple example is a patient who feels criticized and responds defensively whenever the therapist asks a clarifying question, even when the query does not begin with the infamous blame-seekers, "Why?". Another common example is a patient who believes the therapist is angry or sexually aroused. The first step is for the therapist to investigate himself to determine whether the patient's perception is accurate. Occasionally, when it is, the therapist can infer from his specific countertransference reaction a clue to the nature of what the patient may be denying and projecting from within himself—that is, the nature of the patient's transference. Thus if the therapist feels exasperated, it can indicate that the patient, by behaving as a disobedient, provocative child, may be expressing unconscious feelings in a parental transference. However, if the same qualitative reaction in the therapist reflects a more personal idiosyncratic anxiety, it may reach a maladaptive level. Then it may be experienced as exasperation with *all* patients who unconsciously feel themselves to be helpless and longing in the presence of a powerful parent, and who then react against these longings in provocative ways.

Apart from these common projections, which can be understood as transference expectations or wishes, a host of subtler misperceptions based on transferences frequently pass unnoticed in once-a-week or twice-a-week psychotherapy, because they are lost in the press of current, stressful material. Often these misperceptions are assumptions based on fantasies about the therapist's personal life —his religion, marital relations, children, financial status, cultural interests, professional relations with colleagues, superiors, and so

forth. One "special" category of these subtler transference reactions is that of the fantasies of patients whose therapists are in training situations. These patients may reexperience old feelings of deprivation and injury because they believe the therapist's personal training goals are in conflict with the patient's own needs. What makes this "special" is that therapists in such a situation almost always experience anxiety about helping patients make these transference reactions explicit. This is usually due either to the therapist's shame at feeling less than fully adequate to his patient's needs, or to his guilty feeling that he is exploiting his patients. If the therapist cannot believe that his training needs and the patient's need for help can be met simultaneously, then the therapist will not be able to help the patient deal with these negative feelings. Following this failure, the patient may improve for reasons not previously described in our discussion of identification; he will improve as a result of unconsciously depreciating the consciously idealized therapist. Following this depreciation, the patient again identifies with the therapist, who is now "no better off" than the patient. This new identification relieves the shame that the patient felt at needing to come for help. (Further consideration of the therapist's need for self-scrutiny is on page 204.)

Another special group of transference reactions occurs when the therapist is employed by an agency or institution or is paid by a third party. The therapist's relationship to this third party is frequently experienced by the patient in a primitive way. He may have a sado-masochistic fantasy in which the therapist is subservient and mistreated and then becomes the object of the patient's contempt or pity. Or it may be an exhibitionistic-voyeuristic fantasy in which the therapist is imagined to be exploiting the patient's improvement by showing it off to his institutional supervisors and colleagues, or to a third party payer, all of whom become very excited about the treatment. In all these situations the transference comes from the time in the patient's life when he had similar primitive fantasies about his parents' interactions with each other. He needed to create these fantasies to deal with the pain of being left out of his parents' ordinary interactions with each other. In addition, the fantasies were an expression of the child's primitive ways of experiencing his own sexual and aggressive feelings (both exhibitionistic-voyeuristic and sado-masochistic), which he then projected onto his parents according to the formula, "If I don't understand them, they must be like me." Following this projection, he could more easily unconsciously identify with either one of the parents and consequently participate in their interaction by means of his fantasy, no longer feeling left out.

Definition of Criteria for Interpreting Transference

The second task of a competent therapist is to define when the existence of the transference reaction needs to be interpreted—that is, made known—to the patient. Four criteria are given here.

1. The first criterion is that it should not be interpreted until the peak of the affect is past. A transference interpretation is a method of helping the patient to observe himself and thereby to take distance from an affect that the therapist believes is not useful for the patient's treatment. And this is more difficult to accomplish if the full intensity of feeling is not over. In addition, when he is experiencing the feeling most intensely, the patient may not believe that this interpretation is being offered for his benefit. Instead he is likely to feel either (a) that the therapist is unable or unwilling to accept the reality of the patient's impulses toward the therapist, or (b) that the therapist accepts the reality of the feeling but depreciates its importance by calling it "nothing but" a reexperiencing of the past. This results in a narcissistic blow to the patient, experienced as a loss of self-esteem.

If the patient's impulses have been object-instinctual (loving or hating), the frustration engendered by the premature interpretation will bring about the patient's characteristic life response; this must then be understood in turn. The responses cover the entire gamut from separation anxiety when primitive dependency longings are frustrated, to guilt and expiatory self-punishment when aggressive impulses are turned against the self. If the transference is a narcissistic one (either mirroring or idealizing), then a premature transference interpretation will result in a pathognomonic regression. (See the section on narcissistic personality disorders beginning on page 201.) This is a more total regression than the narcissistic blow described in the preceding paragraph, which may occur with any type of patient.

2. The second criterion for determining when to make a transference interpretation comes from the therapist's sense of "the optimal flow of the material." This is often determined by his judgment regarding the degree of anxiety needed to promote the desired introspection in the service of the eventual relief of symptoms. By contrast, in psychoanalysis, a transference interpretation may be offered not only when a painful affect is too intense, but also at a time when the patient is experiencing only a pleasurable feeling toward the analyst. The analyst will do this if he believes that the pleasure is being used in the service of "resisting" further introspection. He will then offer a transference interpretation as a means of providing optimal frustration. Also, in classical analysis, transference interpretations are made to promote the regression that is vital in helping the patient discover the ways in which his past is still alive in his present (see page 184). In psychotherapy, by contrast, transference reactions should be interpreted only when the intensity of the patient's unpleasant affect and discomfort is such that it is difficult for him to continue the work of introspection. However, this decision can be based on data of varying degrees of subtlety, as well as on observable or verbalizable discomfort.

For example, a thirty-year-old male patient continually referred to his closest female friend as "this girl" in the first several weeks of therapy. When the therapist wondered aloud about this, the patient responded with a memory from seventh grade, when his school suddenly became coeducational and he told his family of his interest in a twelve-year-old girl who had just joined his class. His father had depreciated his interest in her, and the patient spontaneously connected the shame of that experience with the fear that the therapist might react like his father if he used the woman's name in therapy. The question might be raised, whether this example truly indicates a difficulty in carrying on the work of introspection that required the therapist to speak. The answer is that the therapist's first intervention was a tentative observation that gently pointed to an omission in the flow of the material. The observation also served the therapist's conscious goal of using the psychotherapy as an exploration of the patient's suitability for analysis.

In accord with our basic position that psychotherapy in large measure should promote symptom relief through identification, it follows that not all interruptions of introspection will be attended to as potential transferences. When symptom relief is the primary goal, then the flow of the material and the nature of the transference will all be secondary. For example, a patient experiencing a negative transference—that is, behaving as an angry or distrustful or provocative child—may achieve symptom relief in order to *defy* the therapist. It is commonly thought that negative transferences impede symptomatic relief because of the wish to deprive the parentified therapist of the pleasure he will obtain from the patient's improvement. However, a negative transference may also protect a patient against his fear of dependency longings, which he then deals with by a pseudo-independent protest that results in the disappearance of symptoms. The important reminder in this regard is to help the patient leave when the "symptom" has been relieved. The corollary is that the patient must believe he is free to return without risking humiliation for either party. In the case of a positive transference, this means that returning will not be experienced by the therapist as a blow to his own pride. In the case of a negative transference, this means that the therapist will not experience the return as a victory over the patient.

3. A third criterion for the timing of transference interpretations relates to when the interpretation provides a truly psychologically-minded patient with an opportunity to understand the nature of his own inner life. This is particularly likely to occur when a patient experiences regressive reactions during psychotherapy and—while not overwhelmed by the intensity of the unpleasant emotion—seeks an explanation. A common manifestation (of this regression) that occurs at the start of therapy and responds well to transference interpretation is the temporary deterioration of the patient's previous capacity for expending energy on highly integrated vocational or personal activities. The relevant interpretation may be the patient's fear of failure, in making a commitment to this new challenge of therapy; or his pleasureable anticipation that an interested expert will wish to show him what needs to be done to improve his life; and so on. In any event, when the connection is made with the past, the patient may experience relief and be motivated to introspect more deeply.

4. A fourth criterion for the timing of a transference interpretation derives from evidence that the reaction may be close to the patient's awareness. Such evidence would include the following: (a) a dream in which the transference feeling, as well as the original figure toward whom it was directed, can be inferred by the therapist from the manifest content; (b) any of the manifestations of the slips and errors of everyday life, in which the original object is alluded to or named; and (c) sequential, direct references to the original person, following thoughts about a presentday experience. A typical instance of this would be a patient who falls silent every time he complains about his boss, then reports a thought about his father. What is omitted from this sequence is the patient's reaction to the therapist as part of his presentday experience that he needs to bring into full awareness[13] [p. 150].

MAKING THE INTERPRETATION

The third task of a competent therapist is to know how to make a transference interpretation. (1) The first step is to invite the patient's curiosity about what seems to the therapist to be a relatively extreme form of emotional reaction. The importance of this step cannot be overestimated, because the patient's reaction to this invitation will indicate whether or not the crucial split has taken place upon which the therapeutic alliance must be based—that is, whether the patient, having experienced the emotion, can now "stand off alongside the therapist" and observe himself. It would be a hopeful sign if the patient responds to the therapist's invitation by making some generalization about the therapist's example of extreme affect to indicate that it occurs outside the therapy situation as well. (2) The second step is to demonstrate for the patient the repetitive nature of the reaction, after both have agreed that it exists. (3) The third step is to suggest to the patient that what he is feeling, while certainly real "right here and now," is also a reaction to people from a different time and different place in his life. If the therapist is reasonably sure of what he understands about the patient, he may name the person from the patient's past life with whom this reaction was most commonly experienced. (4) The fourth step is to assess what follows the interpretation. We are not particularly concerned with whether or not the patient agrees with it, as a criterion for assessing its correctness. What is of the essence is that which comes to the patient's mind next,[7] which the therapist then evaluates as a potential corroboration, correction, denial, or refutation of the interpretation. A complete transference interpretation must eventually include the naming of the past person and situation that is being reexperienced. This is a process that takes many repetitions before the situation is completely understood, hence the designation "interpretive process"[2] (see pp. 184–185).

What are the advantages and the risks in making transference interpretations? In addition to the pitfall cited earlier (that the patient may feel put off if he believes the therapist will not accept or will depreciate the reality of the patient's experience), there are other dangers. One is that the patient may feel that the therapist is afraid of the emotion the patient is experiencing. Another is the possibility that when the interpretation relieves the anxiety that may be disrupting the optimal flow of material, it may simultaneously dissipate the very tension that is helping the patient to continue the process of self-examination.

(Treatment According to Diagnostic Entities: "Folk Wisdom"

In this section we present an idiosyncratic approach to the psychotherapy of several diagnostic categories. First we discuss several commonly-seen acute symptomatic reactions. We then proceed to the more stable, characterological disorders. We have selected the ones whose frequency in our practices leads us to hope that they are similarly familiar to other psychotherapists and hence merit consideration. Because of our psychoanalytic bias, we will emphasize the limitations as well as the usefulness of symptom-relief-oriented psychotherapy. We will also emphasize the psychotherapist's reactions, as a clue to the presence of a particular diagnostic entity among those discussed below, and as an indication for a desirable form of treatment. The reader is advised to consult other chapters for a systematic approach to each of these entities—their psychopathology, the range of psychodynamic conflicts, the typical life histories, and a balanced view of the most complete forms of treatment. The lack of balance in our own approach will be particularly evident in our omission of the use of medication, either as an alternative to psychotherapy or in conjunction with it.

Acute Symptomatic Reactions

Any discussion of acute reactions might begin with acute symptom-formation in the transference neuroses: anxiety hysteria (phobias); conversion hysteria; obsessional thinking; compulsive rituals; or an acute, endogenous depressive reaction. Our recommended approach for these symptoms of acute onset is to investigate with extreme care the circumstances surrounding the onset of the symptoms. Our experience suggests that by doing this, a prior equilibrium will once more be established for the patient on the basis of an identification with the therapist, regardless of the diagnostic category of the patient.

In approaching patients with *free-floating anxiety* attacks or a *traumatic neurosis*, the therapist should again foster identification with himself. Since he does not have the same problems, he can help the patient with his shame over having "broken down." It is often useful to explain to the patient, in these very terms, what he has been experiencing. In other words, the therapist should couch his explanations in terms of problems of self-esteem and loss of pride, as reactions to adaptive failure. This is more useful than it is to confront the patient experiencing acute anxiety attacks with the underlying issues of his involvement (in libidinal or aggressive ways) with members of the same or the opposite sex, even though it is these issues which are implicated in the onset of the symptoms. In addition, the use of the patient's prior group allegiances—to the extended family, the church, and others—are extremely helpful. In the case of traumatic neuroses, following any of the disasters of modern life, further special problems derive from the guilt of the survivor, his fear of the aggressive impulses that have been stimulated by the violence of the disaster, and his shame over having been helpless at the time of the trauma.

Certain reactions are usually acute and always taxing for the therapist. These reactions occur in adolescents and often present themselves as problems of delinquency or acute inhibition of schoolwork. Many techniques have been devised to accomplish the difficult task of establishing a libidinal bond of friendship between the adolescent delinquent and the therapist. Aichhorn's[1] success with these patients seems to have been achieved by setting aside his middleclass superego and "playing by the patient's rules" in order to bridge the differences in cultural background and social class between himself and his patients. Kohut's[10] understanding of Aichhorn's success seems cogent to us. He suggests that the therapist may initially mirror the adolescent's grandiosity by falling in with his view of life and trying to "beat the delinquent at his own

game"—for example, by cheating at cards. This will then initiate a "veiled mobilization" of the delinquent's need to idealize a strong parental figure, without challenging the patient's grandiosity by confronting him with this need. Thus the initial behavioral improvement may take place on the basis of wanting to impress the therapist with the patient's omnipotence. Later, this can shift to a desire for an identification with the idealized therapist. This may achieve a symptomatic improvement, which will then permit normal tendencies for maturation and development to occur once more.

A more ambitious goal with these patients is to help them understand that their behavior is the acting out of an (unconscious) fantasy. And when the delinquent comes from a middleclass background characterized by a "stable" family, that fantasy is often shared by the entire nuclear family. (This is more difficult to uncover, since the patient's total family group unconsciously discourages revelation and cooperation with the therapeutic process while consciously encouraging it.) The most difficult requirement for a therapist in these situations is that he be able to function in the face of the danger of the patient's further delinquent behavior. His task is to avoid becoming a controlling superego figure, by consistently empathizing with and "interpreting from the side of" the patient's ego. This inevitably involves active interpretive intervention with the persons in the patient's familial or institutional milieu. They must be helped to understand that the delinquent is living out a fantasy that may be unconscious, and that they may be unwitting participants in or perpetrators of the drama, or both.

Another form of adolescent maladaptation may be reflected in an inhibition of schoolwork, in the absence of delinquent behavior. If the patient has previously identified himself with excessive demands made upon him by his parents and is now failing (either to spite them or to avoid the shame of trying to meet their demands and then failing), the therapist should offer his own ego ideal as a source of pleasure and self-esteem in achieving more realistic goals—as, by implication, the therapist has also done. The pitfall here is that the patient will feel depreciated, a hopeless second-rater, unless the therapist genuinely believes in the value of what he is covertly suggesting. The paradox of such treatment is that once the patient is able to lower his goals more realistically by identification with the therapist, he is subsequently frequently able to live up to his full potential.

In the psychotherapy of *acute grief reactions* to death and so forth—in contrast to the traumatic neuroses—it *is* important to help the patient express his guilt or shame about the negative feelings that he has had difficulty facing toward the loved one who has been lost. Another helpful approach for mastering the grief is to encourage the patient to reexperience it in regard to each action, place, or event that reminds him of the loved one. This approach, although requiring the patient to experience the painful grief once more, has the desirable effect of encouraging the reexperiencing of life as the lost person did, thereby decreasing the sense of loss by identification with the departed object.

In all of the foregoing conditions we understand the limited nature of symptom relief based on a transference reaction and a positive identification with the therapist, as we have described it in earlier sections. Thus the therapist needs to be alert, when symptom relief has occurred, to any communication from the patient indicating a desire for a more thorough exploration of his inner life in regard to conflicts that are sensed although they do not produce symptoms. The indication then may be for psychoanalysis rather than continued symptom-relief-oriented psychotherapy. A second possible path for the therapist is the one described earlier (see page 192), which leads to a recommendation for the patient to return if decompensation occurs in the future.

Hysterical Characters

Hysterical patients, particularly when they are of the opposite sex, make their therapists feel important. This is a result of the patient's "pleasurizing" the relationship—superficially in a sexual way while, more deeply, obtaining dependency gratification. How the therapist responds will depend on whether or not he enjoys the stimulation of apparently being thought of as sexually desirable or omnipotently desirable. Many therapists feel a rise in self-esteem at such times. Others feel teased, provoked, and either indignant or anxiously angered by such stimulation.

What should be done about this? If the patient's transference as an obedient or seductive child results in the loss of symptoms, do nothing. Accept the transference cure. Therapists frequently have difficulty in dismissing hysterical patients (particularly those of the opposite sex) when this point has been reached, because the patients are such fun to be with; treatment is often continued past the time when the symptoms have disappeared and therapy is no longer indicated.

If the symptoms do not disappear, what should be done about it? To begin with, we define "the disappearance of symptoms" as the subjective experience of a patient who feels that he has now received relief for whatever it was that moved him to come. However, when frustration occurs, either because of external circumstance or because of a shift in the therapist's previous willingness to be emotionally available, the patient feels pain. This frustration is commonly experienced by hysterics as damage inflicted on them. One occasion for such painful frustration is any discussion of termination of treatment. During the termination phase, hysterical patients want to believe that the therapist's efforts have been to make up to them for the ways in which life has been unfair. They believe that the therapist has wanted to do this because he finds them irresistible. As one patient put it, "If I ever really allow myself to accept the fact that life has been unfair to me, then there will never be a reason to come back to you."

It is not an infrequent occurrence that psychotherapists—who are, on the average, probably more obsessional than they are hysterical—are made uneasy and are perhaps annoyed by the extravagant displays of emotion that characterize the hysteric. An emotional storm, full of feeling and signifying nothing, is characterologically uncomfortable for a therapist heavily invested in cognitive functioning. The psychotherapist's job may be seen as an effort to put content into the emotionality—that is, to help the patient get at the specific fantasies that accompany the affect. Initially these patients usually react with denial. When denial gives way to the therapist's continued pressure, it is replaced by anger as a result of the frustration produced when the fantasy is brought into the open, where it cannot be gratified in an emotional storm.

Obsessive-Compulsive Characters

Obsessive-compulsive characters usually make therapists feel depreciated in a very specific way. In general the therapist finds himself trying to demonstrate to the obsessive the presence of affect, and to help the patient experience that affect from reported experiences and fantasies. Usually the obsessive first treats this effort with doubt and intellectualization, and then with contempt. The therapist frequently feels not only depreciated but also enraged. This is true even if the therapist does not have a problem with competitive strivings, because of the universally appropriate vulnerability of therapists to having their offerings depreciated by the recipient.

Treatment requires the therapist to wait until he has his feelings under control, before trying to help the patient understand what he is doing. This may be accomplished by helping the patient see that it is difficult for either therapist or patient to know whether the therapist's interpretations are correct, because each time the patient finishes talking about them the interpretations have disappeared. Many obsessive-compulsive characters are dimly aware that they are unsuccessful in their relations with other people, because they perceive they are disliked. However, they have no clear sense of why this is. Potentially, the psychotherapist's approach suggested above may offer the patient a sense of relief, at which time he can begin to see what he does to many different people. This is clearly easier for the patient to realize when the therapist is no longer feeling depreciated or angered.

Our understanding of the origin of this kind of behavior is that it derives from the familiar struggle around toilet-training and autonomy. This results in alternating attitudes of defiance and submission in the child, which then continue over into the adult obsessive. What is less well known is the patient's unconscious pleasure in the struggle with the therapist, and in the endless continuation of an alternating defiance and submission. The other side of this coin is the experience by obsessives of their own vulnerability to feeling depreciated by verbal criticism. This vulnerability is stimulated every time the therapist speaks, because he may be about to demonstrate his power to depreciate the patient by his knowledge of the patient. Thus these patients deal with their fear by the use of verbal "magic" to preserve their autonomous self-esteem and to perpetrate onto the therapist what they themselves fear. It may be necessary to make a transference interpretation to help the patient realize the current inappropriateness of what he is doing.

In contrast to hysterical and depressed characters, the obsessive-compulsive character is afraid to wish that the therapist would make up to him for life's unfairness. He fears this because he is already sufficiently frightened that such longings, if expressed, would give the therapist the power to control and manipulate him, usually by criticism.

Depressive Characters

The approach to depressive characters described here is based on our experiences in psychotherapy in which we did not use antidepressant medication. A psychotherapist is quite likely to feel guilty at the unconsciously reproachful behavior of the depressed patient who, consciously, is aware only of self-reproaches. This is true regardless of the psychodynamic issue of whether the depression is a result of guilt, shame, or a loss of emotional sustenance. The indication for psychotherapy is to help the patient face the underlying anger at the important object who is not providing the patient with what he unconsciously feels he needs. However, after this anger is mobilized, it frequently turns against the therapist because of the underlying shame at having needed the therapist's help. If the therapist cannot help the patient face these feelings, the anger may once again become retroflexed and the patient may become suicidally depressed. When self-destructive tendencies become ascendant, the therapist may need to "take over" and make suggestions regarding necessary externally imposed or self-protective behaviors. The best of course is to help identify the true object of the retroflexed rage.

After the patient's guilt-or-shame-induced depression is relieved, an *anaclitic depression* may emerge. That is, the patient comes to feel that there is no hope for emotional gratification sufficient to his needs, even when he knows that his needs cannot possibly be met in the therapeutic situation. His hopelessness may elicit hopelessness in the therapist. Treatment cannot then progress until the latter can accept, without guilt or shame, the disparity of which the patient complains.

A subdivision of the depressive character is the *addict*: the person dependent on alcohol, opiates, or any other drug. We subscribe to the oversimplification that such people are in fact addicted to the achievement of pleasure, or at least the relief of pain without effort, but with inevitable self-destructive consequences. When the therapist points this out, the patient may become abstinent to please the therapist. This leads him to believe that the therapist will then be vulnerable to feeling guilt or shame himself, when the addict once again becomes involved with his drug. Our experience in the psychotherapy of addicts is that the patient has a specific fantasy in which he believes that the therapist needs to make the patient become abstinent in order to alleviate the therapist's own sense of inner emptiness, lack of pleasure, and craving for relief. This fantasy represents a precise projection of the addict's own inner experience. As one supposedly mentally-retarded addict put it succinctly, "You can kill me, but you can't eat me." Both depressives and addicts wish that the therapist were in fact trying to make up to them for what life has perpetrated on them unfairly, because of the therapist's guilt at the patient's suffering. This is in contrast to the hysterical

and obsessive-compulsive characters described above.

A related clinical problem is that of the patient who has suffered a *parent loss* either during or before adolescence. In such a patient there is an arrest of development at the point of the loss.[5] This appears in the form of (a) various forms of denial of the loss, or (b) re-creating, by living out in the transference, some aspect of the relations (real or fantasied) from the time preceding the loss. Frequently the patient's way of life subsequent to the loss has been totally organized around resisting acknowledgment either of the parent's death or its significance. This often is manifested in therapy by the patient's propensity to leave and then return. We understand such behavior as an effort both to flee from the recognition of the painful longings that have been reawakened in the transference and, simultaneously, to master the trauma of the loss by turning passivity into activity through leaving and returning. The therapist needs to exercise flexibility and patience in order not to confront the patient prematurely with the pain he is denying. In this way, the therapist allows himself to be used as a real object for the purpose of helping the patient experience a missing developmental relationship. We regard as an important curative factor in this treatment the patient's recognition that he *is* being treated in a special way; he correctly perceives this as the therapist's effort to make up to him for the blow that life has dealt him.

Paranoid Characters

With paranoid patients, the task is the opposite of the way in which one works with depressives—namely, one helps a paranoid individual realize his passive longings beneath his presenting attitudes of self-sufficiency and arrogance. This is a delicate task, because a paranoid individual, when confronted with such issues, becomes intensely anxious and prefers to hold the position that he needs nothing from anyone. He experiences any awareness of longing with humiliation and fear of annihilation, which may be specifically experienced as castration anxiety. In addition, he frequently has the potential to react to such a frightening possibility with violence. The therapist is frequently puzzled by the fact that such a patient continues to come, since he seems to do so for the sole purpose of using the therapist as an object of contempt. In addition to the therapist's fear of the paranoid's potential for violence (and his aversion to being the object of contempt), there is little gratification in any other aspect of the treatment as well, particularly when the patient cannot admit directly to feeling any relief as a result of coming. Thus, like obsessional patients, the paranoid patient also makes the therapist feel the way the patient does: helpless, vulnerable to humiliation, and afraid of violence.

Frequently the crucial psychotherapeutic method with the paranoid character is to let him maintain his distance from the therapist, who is experienced as an authority figure whom he consciously holds in contempt while denying his strong unconscious attachment. Enormous patience while awaiting the occurrence of very small changes is crucial with such a patient, because he is prone to believe that the therapist will exploit any progress he makes for his own pleasure. The therapist's patience enhances the possibility for identification with the therapist and his self-control.

There is a group of patients in this category whose primary symptomatology we call *true hypochondriasis*. They respond well without medication despite the fact that they are on the spectrum of extremely serious disturbance, between suicidal depression and paranoid schizophrenia. We are excluding from this group those patients who are basically hysterical, with multiple complaints that are usually amenable to suggestion. We are also excluding patients whose narcissistic personality disorder makes them vulnerable to a reversible hypochondriacal regression (see p. 203). Our approach to these patients is to legitimize and dignify their suffering by taking it extremely seriously; however, the price for this is our demand that they continue functioning. They have usually been told either that their pain is imaginary or that it is the result of emotional conflict; both of these comments humiliate

them. We do not take either of these positions. Instead we offer explicit verbal acknowledgment that their suffering is indeed as severe as they say, no matter how grandiose their claim may be. When they believe that we are sincere, we are then able to take the next step of empathizing with their distress when they realize they must nevertheless carry on their daily activities.

When these patients begin to function better, our experience has been that it is an error to reveal any pleasure we might feel at their success, because this often results in an exacerbation of the symptom. In addition, we encourage them to continue therapy past the time when they are less troubled by their complaint.

We have no adequate theoretical understanding of the primary symptom in these patients, although their separation anxiety is prominent if they are confronted with our pleasure at their loss of the symptom. We are able to find evidence to support either of the two hypotheses with which we are familiar. The first is Freud's, that hypochondria represents the patient's effort to theorize about an internal state in which object representations have lost their investment of psychic energy for the patient, and "objectless libido" is instead attaching itself to body organs. The second hypothesis is Rado's, that hypochondria is a symbolic expression of unconscious guilty fear of punishment for a variety of sins. Our own hypothesis is a partial one, based on an overt characteristic behavior of therapists who have treated such patients successfully. When they describe to us the effort involved in convincing the patient that his suffering is comprehended, they often chuckle sarcastically. We infer this to be their sadistic response to a patient with whom they have previously behaved in a way that convinces the patient that the therapist is suffering along with him. In addition, the therapist has listened to the endless recital of the patient's complaint. Thus, we infer that the therapeutic effect comes from a pleasurable discharge of hostility for the patient, and that the effect is maintained when the therapist neither retaliates, nor takes pleasure for himself as the patient improves, nor interferes with the patient's pleasure by interpretation.

Another particular subdivision of the group of paranoid characters is the one we call *schizoid characters*. Such a patient is intensely dependent. He protects himself against these dependency longings—which are an even greater threat to him than they are to the paranoid patient—by maintaining emotional distance, with a sense of isolation and detachment. The therapist frequently reacts to the schizoid individual's unconscious attempts to infect him with the patient's fear of his own longings and consequent fear of disintegration under their impact. The chief difference between such a patient and a paranoid is that the latter is expressing a fear of his own violence and engendering a defensive reaction or counter-fear in the therapist. The schizoid patient is instead afraid of his own intense libidinal demands, which again provokes a defensive reaction in the therapist. As a result, the therapist may feel little gratification from working with such a patient, because of the belief that his importance to the patient is nil. Such a therapist is avoiding the awareness that behind the wall of isolation and detachment, the patient actually is intensely involved with him.

We view *borderline characters* as a decompensated form of a previously stable schizoid state. We believe this decompensation occurs after the patient has been frightened by a close relationship with a potentially gratifying and frustrating object. The result of such closeness is that the patient's ego has been flooded by primitive impulses, both sexual and aggressive. This is a reexperiencing of the traumatic circumstances of the patient's childhood. Formerly the patient had adapted to that state by withdrawal and distancing. Now, however, that earlier adaptation is abandoned and a further regression occurs, accompanied by a specific loss in the function of reality testing. For such patients, the acute episode should be managed in the way described in the following section on schizophrenic reactions. During the interim phase the treatment approach will differ, depending on whether the patient presents a stable schizoid character or whether paranoid, hysterical, or anaclitic depressive features are dominant.

Schizophrenic Reactions

We are in agreement with the current prevailing view, that schizophrenic reactions probably represent a response that is differentially available to many people. We further agree that there is a core group throughout the world for whom the genetic contribution is sufficiently powerful to result in a predisposition toward schizophrenic reactions in the face of stress. The psychotropic drugs, by reducing the disorganizing effects of anxiety on the thought processes, have been extremely useful in resocializing a large number of these coregroup patients. However, we address ourselves here to therapists who are specifically interested in the psychotherapy of schizophrenics beyond the extremely important but limited goal of getting them to function outside a hospital. Our opinions are based on personal successes and failures that are appropriate to this framework of "folk wisdom."

For such patients, the disorganizing effects of acute anxiety may be countered by the therapist's willingness to be available at times outside the regularly scheduled office appointments, rather than by the use of medication. During the acute phases of the illness it is important to help these patients learn that behavior occurs in sequences, and that minor grades of anxiety frequently pass unnoticed because they are immediately followed by characteristic defensive activity. When powerful feelings such as rage, guilt, or fear have been part of the sequence, the patient is better able to regulate these tensions when they are identified with the therapist by the use of words. As a consequence of viewing behavior as occurring in sequences, the patient may begin to substitute psychology for morality as a frame of reference. This substitution again is made possible when the patient identifies with the therapist's value systems, and can move from notions of good and evil into the understanding of anxiety as a prime mover in human relationships. This procedure enhances identification with the therapist and sanctions covert dependence on him.

During the periods between crises, schizophrenics induce feelings of helplessness and inadequacy in the therapist by their fear of their vulnerability to the frustration of emotional involvement. If they are treatable by psychotherapy at all, they make themselves available by trying to live up to what the therapist wants and expects of them. They make such a commitment with great ambivalence, because they greatly fear failure of any kind; its resulting shame devastates them. Thus their commitment to treatment is so inconsistent that it effects their ability to communicate thoughts and feelings in a way that the therapist can readily follow. Unlike the situation with the obsessional, where the therapist frequently has the conviction that the patient will destroy his understanding as soon as it is uttered, despite its correctness, the therapist has an endless sense of groping with the schizophrenic. Our experience over a number of several-year courses of successful outpatient treatment of different schizophrenics has been characterized by the following: (1) no anticipation of termination; (2) complete honesty on the part of the therapist about his own emotional reactions to the patient; and (3) explicit verbalized faith that the patient will eventually function adequately—which is no contradiction to (1) above. Following such a period, a schizophrenic may reveal the secret pleasures of his existence, the foremost among which may have been the pleasure of having frustrated the therapist to the point of helplessness, as he himself had always felt defeated and humiliated.

Manic Depressive Reactions

Our position in regard to the etiology of this illness is the same one we held, above, in regard to schizophrenia, with this difference: lithium carbonate seems more precisely useful in decreasing the sense of internal pressure that ushers in the manic phase than do any of the psychotropic drugs in controlling the disorganizing anxiety of acute schizophrenia. We have a verbal report from one experienced psychotherapist who finds that lithium is useful as an adjunct because it "damps down" the patient's libidinal, aggressive, and narcissistic (grandiose and exhibitionistic) tensions, thus making it easier for the patient to collaborate in serious psychotherapy.

Our own experience in psychotherapy with manic patients provides us with the following tentative formulations. Preceding the onset of a manic episode there was always, in retrospect, a specific instance of adaptive failure, followed by a feeling of emptiness and despair. Then there was a downward spiral in response to unrealistically severe self-punitive tendencies that destroyed the patient's self-esteem still further. The manic episode that followed was characterized by attempts to deny his shame by striving for grandiose achievements. He attempted to accomplish this by various forms of extreme behavior, often of a tremendously provocative nature. The purpose of this provocativeness was to force others, especially the therapist, to become indignantly angry, defensively set limits, and reject the patient, thus behaving in compliance with the patient's projection onto them of the patient's self-punitive superego.

We have no way to decide at present whether or not this exaggerated reaction of our patients, which seems to be the essence of mania, is constitutionally determined. One reason why this question is difficult to answer is that these patients uniformly deny the existence and the significance of any psychologically meaningful events, such as the prior adaptive failure mentioned above. The result of this denial is to increase the puzzlement of the therapist who is trying to treat the patient etiologically by understanding the biological and psychological threads of his behavior. Such patients are empathically in tune with the therapist's ego-ideal. Therefore they are able to exploit his discomfort when he cannot meet his own standards and avoid becoming provoked or confused by the patient's behavior. This is in contrast with the schizophrenics, who take a more detached attitude toward the therapist's ambitions; they have been so thoroughly defeated in the past that they are less willing to attack directly than are the manic patients.

Narcissistic Personality Disorders

These patients are described in several publications by Kohut,[10,11] who emphasizes their suitability for psychoanalytic rather than psychotherapeutic treatment. Although we agree that psychoanalysis is the treatment of choice for them, we have several reasons for including them in this chapter. First, in our experience, every psychotherapist is confronted not only by narcissistic personality disorders as such, but also by identical narcissistic problems within a number of other conditions as well. Second, the diagnostic criteria that simultaneously indicate the presence of the pathognomonic narcissistic transference and guide the therapist in treating it are as evident in psychotherapy as in the "trial analysis" that Kohut recommends[11] [p. 4]. Third, our experience has been that psychotherapy provides these patients with symptomatic relief, which, while it falls short of the results we have seen from the psychoanalysis of similar cases, nevertheless provides many patients with results that satisfy them. It achieves this primarily by providing the patient with an opportunity for a stable, narcissistic transference. The patient's self-esteem is restored by means of this transference, through the use of the therapist either as a "mirror" or an "idealized parental image." The use of the therapist in each of these ways represents a reactivation, in the transference, of a particular developmental phase in the patient's life that had been cut off from normal maturation. If it is a "mirror transference," then an archaic, grandiose self-image has been reactivated. If it is an "idealized parent" transference, then a somewhat later, but still very early, merging relationship with a "perfect" admired parent has been reactivated.

In Kohut's framework, the normal developmental sequence from infantile to adult narcissism is as follows. During the first two years, "the child's original narcissistic balance [i.e., feelings of euphoria and perfection] . . . is disturbed by the unavoidable shortcomings of maternal care, but the child attempts to save the original experience . . . by assigning it, on the one hand, to a grandiose and exhibitionistic self-image: the (cohesive) grandiose self; and, on the other hand, to an admired you: the idealized parent imago." [p. 86][10]

"Under optimum developmental conditions, the exhibitionism and grandiosity of the archaic grandiose self are . . . tamed, and the whole structure ultimately becomes integrated into the adult personality." [p. 87][10] There it is manifested by our healthy ambitions and the self-confidence to achieve them; enjoyment of our activities; humor, characterized by an ability to laugh at our own shortcomings; empathy; and important aspects of our self-esteem. "Under similarly favorable circumstances, the image of the idealized parent also becomes integrated into the [healthy] adult personality." [p. 87][10] It provides the sense of pleasure we derive in obeying the dictates of our conscience as well as in living up to "the guiding leadership of its ideals." Eventually it provides us with the capacity for a mature form of admiration for others, and for enthusiasm about our own achievements.

Kohut describes the developmental sequence of the future candidate for a narcissistic personality disorder as follows. "If the child suffers severe narcissistic traumata, (particularly at the hands of parents who are unempathic, depressed, or self-preoccupied for other reasons), [and thus unable to provide the child with a mirroring, echoing presence], then the grandiose self-image is [unconsciously] retained in its unaltered form [into adult life] and strives for the fulfillment of its archaic aims. Similarly, if the child experiences traumatic disappointments from the admired adult, then the idealized parental image, too, remains in the unconscious [in adult life] as an archaic transitional-object that is sought for, for the maintenance of the patient's homeostasis in regard to tension regulation and self-esteem. When such patients . . . become involved in treatment they form one or the other of a pathognomonic narcissistic transference.

"When the grandiose self is [re]activated in the transference, it is a replica of the way in which the child attempts to retain a part of his original . . . sense of perfection by [experiencing the] power and perfection [of his] grandiose self-image: 'I am perfect,'" [p. 28][11] and assigning all imperfections to the outside. This occurs in three forms, and Kohut's description of its most mature form, the "mirror transference" per se, is instructive. He calls it "the reinstatement of the phase in which the gleam in the mother's eye which mirrors the child's exhibitionistic display and other forms of maternal participation in the child's narcissistic enjoyment, confirm the child's self-esteem and . . . begin to channel it into realistic directions." [p. 96][10]

When the idealized parent is reactivated in the transference, the patient has an experience of the therapist that can be summarized as "You are perfect, and I am a part of you." As Kohut describes it, "Since all bliss and power now reside in the idealized object, the patient (like the child) feels empty and powerless when he is separated from the therapist, and attempts to maintain a continuous union." [p. 37][11] This can be especially noticeable over weekends when the patient is not depressed but feels empty, drained, and powerless.

For the informed therapy of these patients, it is crucial to grasp that narcissism is *not* the antithesis of object relationships. The fact is that narcissistic objects are ones with whom the patient is deeply involved. The differences are in the nature of the relationship with the object. For example, when the therapist is a narcissistic object for a patient, he may feel tyrannized by the patient's expectations and demands, and have the sense of not being in control of his own initiative. As Kohut says, "The [patient's] control over such (self-object) others is . . . closer to . . . the control which a grown-up expects to have over his own body and mind than to . . . the control he expects to have over others." [p. 27][11] Thus, the therapist may feel himself to be the object of admiration or contempt, rather than of the love or hate that are more likely to emanate from a patient with a "well-delimited, cohesive sense of self, and whose impulses are directed toward . . . objects which have . . .

become fully differentiated from the self." [p. 19][11]

The technical implications of this difference between object-instinctual impulses (love or hate) and narcissistic impulses (admiration or contempt) are exemplified by one of Kohut's patients. [p. 252][11] When his comments were couched in terms of "affectionate longing or angry resentment and destructiveness" toward the therapist, they "fell flat." Progress could be made only when the therapist ceased to regard himself as a separate, distinct person, but rather as a mirroring, admiring parent, an alter ego, or a literal extension of the patient. The progress was manifested by spontaneously confirmatory memories, shifts in self-perceptions (for example, dreams in which machines were replaced by people), and evidences of an increase in functioning associated with the increase in the patient's self-esteem.

Kohut suggests that idealization is the more usual transference at the start of therapy and that, as it recedes, the mirroring transference may emerge as the more basic one. These patients are particularly vulnerable to a regression of either the idealizing or the mirror transference when the therapist is physically absent, such as over weekends, or emotionally absent, such as in a failure of empathy. There then occur what Kohut has described [p. 97][11] as "typical regressive swings" to: (a) fragmented and archaic forms of grandiosity (manifested by imperious behavior, affectations of speech, or unrealistic grandiose fantasies); or (b) archaic forms of idealization (manifested by mystical or ecstatic religious feelings such as a merging experience between the true believer and God or some other, more vaguely experienced outside power); or (c) autoerotic tension states (manifested by hypochondria or perverse fantasies and activities).

What many psychotherapists have found and our own experiences have taught us is that these patients respond favorably with amazing rapidity when the therapist explicitly recognizes the effect that his literal absence, or his lack of empathy for the patient's need for either a mirroring or an idealized presence, has had on the patient. Another requirement of therapists treating such patients is the ability to comprehend the primitive developmental nature of (rather than simply reacting to the contempt expressed by) the patient's vengeful rage at small disturbances in his control over the therapist, whom he experiences as an extension of himself. This rage occurs particularly in the form of over-reactions to small slights, which are experienced as enormous insults. The rage's developmental nature is analogous to the experience of helpless anger when a part of one's own body or mind does not function as one wishes it to.

Another way to approach the difficulty in treating these patients is to understand the vicissitudes of the therapist's own narcissism. These are manifested, in the mirror transference, by the vulnerability of his self-esteem to the demands of a patient who uses him without recognition of his characteristics as a real person. As a result, the therapist may feel bored and emotionally distant from the patient. In the instance of an idealizing transference, the therapist may feel embarrassed by the patient's gross admiration of him. Psychotherapists who can recognize the underlying developmental nature of the patient's needs are better able to tolerate these transferences and to help the patient either terminate in narcissistic equilibrium or go on for further psychoanalytic work.

A brief case vignette from the psychotherapy of a narcissistic personality disorder may illustrate some of these issues, with particular reference to the consequences of a psychotherapist's embarrassment at being grossly idealized. At the end of the first month of therapy a patient made out his check to the therapist instead of to the institution, as he had been instructed to do by both the billing form and the therapist. The therapist did not endorse it over to the institution and wait to approach the event the following month, with the understanding of the patient's need to idealize him. Instead, he returned the check to the patient and suggested that perhaps the therapist had not been explicit about the need for the check to be made out to the institution. Within twenty-four hours the patient was convinced that the bright red blood on his toilet paper was evidence of cancer of the rectum,

although he had had adequate previous experience with his own hemorrhoids to be capable of recognizing the true probability. This kind of sequence characteristically follows a therapist's embarrassment and subsequent lack of empathy for a patient's need to idealize him. In this case the patient's need for a merger with the powerful object (the idealized parent imago) had been frustrated, following which there was a disturbance in the transference equilibrium, with a regression to an "autoerotic tension state:" hypochondria. Subsequently the therapist was able to explain the sequence to the patient in terms of the latter's feeling of loss when the therapist had failed to comprehend and accept the check as an expression of admiration and of the sick feeling that followed this loss. As is so often the case, the explanation was followed by relief for the patient and the spontaneous recollection of his admiration for, desire for closeness with, and wish to be like his father, who had returned from serving in World War II when the patient was five.

This ancedote also illustrates the problem of differentiating between a narcissistic problem and one in which object instinctual strivings (love or hate) are at issue, on the basis of a single example. Thus the check could be seen as a gift of love, which, when spurned, caused guilty rage in the patient. The rage was then symbolized by the experience of an internal disease. However, the check could also be seen as a hostile act, intended to discomfort the therapist in his relations with his administrative superiors. In that case its return might have been experienced as retaliation, and a guilty fear of further punishment might again have been symbolized as an internal disease. As in any psychotherapeutic situation, the correct treatment derives from a correct diagnosis; and in this instance, the crucial data were: prior evidence for the idealizing transference, the confirmatory memories, similar fragmentation phenomena that occurred subsequently when this transference was similarly disturbed, and the eventual transformation of the patient's primitive narcissistic impulses into more mature ones.

Thus it may be stated that with these patients, the diagnostic criteria that appear during the treatment process rather than during a diagnostic interview are: (1) the pathognomonic idealizing or mirroring transference; (2) the subjective response of the therapist to feeling himself a narcissistic object; and (3) the characteristic forms of more archaic idealization or grandiosity that occur when the idealizing or mirroring transference is disturbed by a lack of empathy from, or the temporary physical loss of, the narcissistically loved therapist.

(Concluding Remarks on the Patient–Therapist "Fit"

In several places we have referred to the therapist's anxiety, which derives from a variety of sources, and to the particular problems that may arise from his sexual or aggressive feelings (see pp. 190–191) or from the vulnerability of his self-esteem (see p. 202). These are background issues that may present occasional difficulties for a therapist with almost any patient. We wish to conclude by suggesting several other considerations that every competent psychotherapist needs to consider about his relationship with particular patients. First, if a patient reminds him specifically of a significant object from his own past life, he is likely to have trouble establishing the optimal cognitive and emotional distance. Second, he needs to be able to empathize with the patient's experiences. If these are alien to him, this creates a problem similar to the difficulty involved when a patient is unable to identify with the therapist's attitudes. Third, there are predictable consequences that follow from the interactions of certain character types. Hypomanic therapists often do well with depressed patients. Obsessional therapists do well with hysterical patients, if they are not made anxious by the patient's emotional storms; conversely, hysterical therapists often do well with obsessional patients. In these examples, the therapists are all assumed to be operating from the base of their raw character and its stylistic derivatives in their treatment behavior. It is equally true, however, that a therapist

who has faced and integrated the relevant conflicts within himself is in a much better position to empathize freely and correctly with patients who are similar to the way he once was. From such a base he can provide the patient with an object for identification in accord with the basic tenet of this chapter. It has been our experience that the optimal level for this kind of functioning is rarely achieved solely through the educational process, without the help of personal therapy.

(Bibliography

1. AICHHORN, A. *Wayward Youth.* New York: Viking, 1953.
2. BIBRING, E. "Psychoanalysis and the Dynamic Psychotherapies," *J. Am. Psychoanal. Assoc.*, 2 (1954), 745–770.
3. BREUER, J. and S. FREUD. (1895) "Studies on Hysteria," in J. Strachey, ed., *Standard Edition*, Vol. 2, pp. 1–305. London: Hogarth, 1955.
4. FENICHEL, O. *Problems of Psychoanalytic Technique*, p. 57. Albany, N.Y.: Psychiatric Quarterly Press, 1941.
5. FLEMING, J. and S. ALTSCHUL. "Activation of Mourning and Growth by Psychoanalysis," *Int. J. Psycho-anal.*, 44 (1963), 419–431.
6. FREUD, S. (1900) *The Interpretation of Dreams*, in J. Strachey, ed., *Standard Edition*, Vol. 5, London: Hogarth, 1953.
7. ———. (1937) "Constructions in Analysis," in J. Strachey, ed., *Standard Edition*, Vol. 23, pp. 255–271. London: Hogarth, 1964.
8. GOLDMAN, G. "Reparative Psychotherapy," in S. Rado and G. Daniels, eds., *Changing Concepts of Psychoanalytic Medicine*, pp. 101–113. New York: Grune & Stratton, 1956.
9. GROUP FOR THE ADVANCEMENT OF PSYCHIATRY: COMMITTEE ON THERAPY. *Psychotherapy and the Dual Research Tradition.* New York: GAP Publ., 1969.
10. KOHUT, H. "The Psychoanalytic Treatment of Narcissistic Personality Disorders," in *The Psychoanalytic Study of the Child*, Vol. 23, pp. 86–113. New York: International Universities Press, 1968.
11. ———. *The Analysis of the Self.* New York: International Universities Press, 1971.

12. MAZZANTI, V. and H. BESSELL. "Communication through the Latent Language," *Am. J. Psychother.*, 10 (1956), 250–260.

13. MENNINGER, K. *Theory of Psychoanalytic Technique.* New York: Basic Books, 1958.

14. OVESEY, L. and J. JAMESON. "The Adaptational Technique of Psychoanalytic Therapy," in S. Rado and G. Daniels, eds., *Changing Concepts of Psychoanalytic Medicine*, pp. 165–179. New York: Grune & Stratton, 1956.

15. PIERS, G. and M. PIERS. "Modes of Learning and the Analytic Process," in *Selected Lectures of the Sixth International Congress on Psychotherapy*, pp. 104–110. London, 1964.

16. PIERS, G. and M. SINGER. *Shame and Guilt: A Psychoanalytic and Cultural Study.* Springfield, Ill.: Charles C. Thomas, 1953.

17. RADO, S. *Adaptational Psychodynamics*, J. Jameson and H. Klein, eds. New York: Science House, 1969.

18. SCHAFER, R. *Aspects of Internalization.* New York: International Universities Press, 1968.

19. WAELDER, R. "Review of S. Hook, ed., 'Psychoanalysis, Scientific Method, and Philosophy'," *J. Am. Psychoanal. Assoc.*, 10 (1962), 617.

CHAPTER 11

PSYCHOANALYTICALLY BASED CONJOINT THERAPY FOR CHILDREN AND THEIR PARENTS

Justin D. Call

I<small>N THIS</small> <small>CHAPTER</small>, interest centers predominantly on the various modes of psychotherapy that are based on concepts of how the child's mind develops from infancy into adulthood. Before describing and illustrating current approaches to child therapy, however, some historical perspectives will be outlined in order that present trends can be understood in this wider context.

(The Psychohistory of Childhood

The history of civilization is in substance a record of man's thoughts about himself, the universe, and the relationship between the two. However, no attempts were made to understand the mental life and development of man as an infant and a child, with few exceptions, until the work of Charles Darwin, Sigmund Freud, and, more recently, Heinz Werner and Jean Piaget.

Attitudes toward the mental life of children, throughout history, have been determined by assumptions and pre-formed concepts of what a child is. The frescos of ancient Egypt depict infants and children as miniature adults. Indeed, the changing bodily form of infants and children at various ages was not acknowledged in paintings and drawings throughout antiquity. These developmental sequences of infancy and childhood were not recognized until the flowering of civilization in Greece and Rome, when infants and children came to be depicted by sculptors and painters of that era in their true physical proportions. Even so, the dominant social attitude of that time gave children the status of property—an attitude still prevalent in the custody and divorce proceedings of our day. The pregnant and nursing mother did receive special status and attention in ancient Greece, but in other respects both women and children shared the fate of being outside the social, political, and economic power structure of society.

Concepts of Women and Children in the Past

The history of man's thoughts about childhood is, understandably, directly related to the history of his thoughts about the place of women in society. Now, throughout history, man's thoughts about himself—particularly about his origins, his place in the universe, and his ultimate fate—have been dominated by illusions and myths. Such myths have provided a transitional model of thought around which these complex issues can be organized before more certain knowledge is possible. Concerning present matters, one consistent aspect of many myths was the belief that women had closer contacts with evil, supernatural forces—that is, the unknown—than did men. This view of women probably stems from the mystery surrounding the female generative capacity. Before men understood their own role in impregnation, women were looked upon as creators of life; and, according to the ancient Egyptian myth of the Osiris and Isis, women also had power over death. Dominance of social institutions by men, some postulate, arose from man's jealousy of this power of women.

Both the over- and underestimations of women and children by men in a phallocentric culture helped men deny the significance of the mother–infant bond. Extreme views have always dominated men's thoughts about children, women, and minority groups. The infant has been viewed either as innocent, touched by godliness, and full of unlimited potential-

ities—a "tabula rasa"—or tainted by original sin, animallike in disposition, and devoid of meaningful sensitivities or thought. The tragic children's crusade of 1212 A.D., whch sent many thousands of French and German children to their deaths, was organized and supported by adults who believed that children could convert the Moslems to the Christian belief.[11] The thought of the child as a distinctively unique kind of human being, with a growing and changing capacity for feeling, learning, thinking, and acting, instead of simply as a potential adult, was not a consistently held concept until quite recently. Even now, the full implications of the child's own development are barely understood or acknowledged in actual practice. For most adults the child is either a container to be filled with ideas from adulthood or an undifferentiated, amoral being whose basic sinfulness, dirtiness, and ignorance of truth must be replaced by the righteous motives and knowledge of adults. It is often asked: When does the child gain distinctive feelings, thoughts, and reasoning ability? When can a child be accepted as a witness? The assumption behind these questions is that at some point the child becomes adult-like. The issue of distinctive feelings and thoughts characteristic of each developmental phase of infancy and childhood is thus bypassed.

Interestingly, the development of man's thinking about the child parallels the history of thinking about the "insane" adult. Hard-won insights into understanding both "insane" adults and growing children are often washed away by a return to more simplistic notions of organic causation and original sin. Even among students of human behavior and mental health workers, the capacity for sustained empathy with insane adults and with children is evanescent and fragile. It readily undergoes repression and requires continuous relearning. Genetic epistemology (the development of man's thoughts about his capacity for thinking) must be recapitulated in each new generation of mental health workers. Society engages alternately in progressive and regressive attitudes toward children. This is often-times reflected in the liberal-versus-conservative views on funding such social institutions as aid to needy children; foster home care; care of the handicapped; legal and social attitudes toward child abuse; education, particularly the "soft" aspect of education involved in the arts and social science courses; and, last but not least, the extreme ambivalence of society toward the development of adequate child mental health programs. Thus the past is still with us in terms of both the "empathy gap" in adults approaching child care, and the social attitudes toward children and child-care institutions. The extremes dominate now as in the past. (A new journal, *The History of Childhood Quarterly*, is attempting a scholarly review of childhood in history.)

A recent evidence of society's reactionary attitudes toward children was the "Sputnik neurosis." All of this now seems quite remote, in light of repeated landings of man on the moon by the United States from 1969 to 1973, and the new political attitudes of "detente" with the Soviets. But when on October 4, 1957, Soviet scientists launched a small satellite in orbit around the earth by means of a powerful rocket, there was a reaction of amazement and shock in this country. The reaction received a further boost when these same scientists succeeded in orbiting a dog, accompanied by another collection of impressive hardware. In fact, as we in the United States compared ourselves with our chief competitors for world status, our feelings of esteem varied in direct proportion to the number of pounds of thrust produced by our rockets as compared to theirs, or by the weight of our satellites as compared to theirs. Clearly, for many of us it was a case of competition for mother earth, accompanied by phallic envy and its associated feelings of anxiety. We seriously questioned our own functioning and, as is characteristic for our time and culture, declared the schools to be the source of our trouble: we should stop coddling our children and start to get tough with them.

The Modern Era

When the infant, child, or adolescent is brought for "therapy" the child psychiatrist, child analyst, or other child mental health worker by either the parents, the school, or child protective services, the problem, variously stated, is either that the child is not behaving as he should or that the child's intellectual development is impaired. More often, the parents or the school are having difficulty managing the child's behavior. Rarely is there clear concern about how the child himself is feeling or whether his present problem will impair his future potential for personal, affective functioning. Doing well scholastically is often equated with good mental health. Most of the people who refer or bring the child for help rarely appreciate the fact that the child himself may be able to express and clarify the nature of his own distress either in language or in play. Often the child has been quite explicit and even eloquent, but no one has listened. The child's statement of the problem deserves detailed attention.

These attitudes of present adults and social agencies illustrate the fact that the child is still being viewed in "moral" terms. The paramount issue is seen as one of how to make the child behave, how to guide the child into adult mentality, how to control the child, how to eliminate undesirable behavior or promote desirable behavior. These are the issues that bring children to therapy. The ideas of protecting the child so that his own developmental potential might be reached along his own inherent maturational lines, and of understanding how the child is thinking and feeling, are still foreign to most adults dealing with children. Therapy is often seen as a danger that presents a risk of damage to the child. In fact, the parent's fear is that the child's suppressed and repressed sexuality and aggression will run rampant if the child is allowed and, indeed, encouraged to explore his thoughts and feelings. Parents also often resent the privacy between the child and the therapist. Frequently this is because they are concerned about the child's interest in and attachment to the therapist, who is thus seen as a rival by the parent. And finally, a common fear is that the record of the child will become blotted by having had to go to a psychiatrist.

(Problems of Strategy in Case Management

Diagnosis and treatment are not the first issues with which the child psychiatrist or child analyst is confronted. Before them come the initial telephone contact or letter communication and the structuring of expectations in the child and the parent by the referral source. The preconscious expectations and fears of the parents as well as those of the therapist must also be sufficiently understood and resolved before evaluation can proceed. Many drop-outs from therapy could be prevented if these initial strategic issues could be adequately appraised and resolved. Exploration of this often treacherous territory requires a subtle combination of good sense and deep insight into one's self and others, including those who refer child patients for help.

On the practical side, we may cite a few rules:

1. Always respond to telephone or letter inquiries promptly, preferably within twenty-four hours. A well-timed response is more efficient because it is less guilt-burdened. It can be brief and helpful. If the patient cannot be seen because of time limitations or other reasons, the rejection and referral elsewhere will be less traumatic if it is not compounded by delay which is taken as an additional rejection by both child and parent.
2. Determine the referral source as soon as possible, since the patient's expectations are often prestructured by the referral source. If continued contact with the referral source is likely, ask for permission to discuss the problems with the referral source prior to the first visit.
3. Ask who is most concerned or interested in evaluation and determine what expectations this person has for the evaluation and its outcome.
4. Find out what concern the person calling has about bringing the child to see you. He or she could at first be more concerned about you and what you intend to do than about the child.
5. Determine whether the child has any known concerns about himself or his family.
6. Find out what the father and mother think about the problem.
7. Answer questions about fees and time considerations as directly as possible, but keep communication open on these issues.
8. Help parents prepare the child for the first visit by telling the child who you are, what you are going to do, what is expected of him, and when this is going to happen. One or two days' notice is sufficient.
9. Determine what attempts have been made previously to help the child, and their results.
10. Try to outline what can be expected in the way of time and interviews, with whom, and what additional information may be needed.
11. Express an expectation of seeing both parents and other centrally involved adults.

All or some of these considerations may be dealt with in part at the first telephone contact and preferably no later than the first visit with the most involved parent.

When to See the Child

The child's general appearance, initial response to the therapist, reaction to separation from the parent, and other behavior such as play, verbalizations, drawings, and expressed fears and fantasies provide the surest guide to his problems. Not infrequently, they also provide significant clues to problems in the family. Once the therapist has seen the child, he becomes a more creative listener as the parent describes his view of the evolution of the child's problems. The therapist, by virtue of having some primary data from the child, may have some basis for independent judgments that allow him to observe gaps, omissions, and differences in emphasis offered by the parent. Each of these provide clues to the nature of the parent–child relationship. It is therefore highly desirable to see the child as soon as possible. In many situations this can and should be done even before the parent is seen in the first interview. Most parents welcome this approach. Children less than three years old should initially be seen with their parents in the same room. After initial introduction and warming up, the therapist can set the stage for separation and observe the child's reaction to and recovery from this all-important event. Over the age of three, many children can tolerate separation from the parent and enter the interview room containing play materials with very little anxiety. All of this initial structuring is very different, of course, in dealing with an adolescent.

In the case of the child who is likely to be seen in psychoanalytic treatment, on the other hand, it is desirable to delay contact with the child until such time as continuity and intensity of contact can be assured. The child may be seen very briefly, at first, until the arrangements for psychoanalytic treatment are completed with the parents. The reason for this is that the transference relationship with the child in psychoanalytic treatment must be preserved from the beginning. More will be said about these differences in approach later.

Sharing of Information Between Child and Parent by the Therapist

In child psychiatric practice, the younger the child, the more information is to be shared in both directions between therapist and parent as to what the child has said and done. The therapist may gain considerable cognitive and affective leverage on the child's play, fantasy, and dreams by sharing such information with the parents and including parents in the elaboration and understanding of such material. Latency-age and pre-adolescent children, as well as adolescents, can rightfully expect the therapist to keep some private information absolutely confidential—such as, for example, masturbatory fantasies, sexual and aggressive urges and actions, and oedipal wishes. And when the parent shares the same such information about the child with the therapist, the

therapist is to make use of it only to improve his own listening and empathy.

It is sometimes helpful for the therapist to share with the parent certain puzzling play sequences that the child has produced in his visit, for further comparison, associations, and interpretations. This is particularly true of the younger child, when play is the major mode of communication and requires translation. For example, a five-year-old boy engaged in repetitious designs of an airport, with jets frequently crashing into the buildings. The sequences were repetitive and suggested a traumatic origin. On sharing this information with the mother, she stated that the father made frequent airplane trips away from home and that separations took place at the airport. She reported that the child was very frightened of the noise made by the jets. This information was crucial in formulating interpretations of the play taking place in the interview room.

When One Parent Is "Opposed" to the Therapy

Not infrequently the mother will report that the father believes everything is fine and that only she is concerned about the child, and indicates the father's unwillingness to participate in either the evaluation or the therapy. Occasionally this is true, but more often, when direct attempts are made to involve the father in the evaluation, he is quite willing to come and often offers valuable insight and perspective into the problems in the family. Situations of this sort often emerge from an unresolved mother–child symbiosis. The father regards the therapy as just one more example of his being excluded from any libidinal claim on the mother.

Occasionally career-minded mothers suggest that the father should bring the child to therapy or that a maid or other relative should take responsibility for the evaluation. This usually indicates a serious estrangement between the mother and the child that cannot be resolved without contact with the mother. When she is seen, the focus often shifts from the child to the marriage or to the mother's problems.

Extended Evaluation and Goals

Since the child's problems are so often intertwined with those of other family members (as will be described later), it is good practice to proceed with the evaluation over an extended period of time, if necessary, in order to evaluate the inherent pathology and strength of each family member and of the family interaction. This evaluation may require several months. In younger children with developmental disturbance, etiological factors in the child's illness and in the family interaction are particularly difficult to pinpoint early in the contact. Nor is it always easy to determine the future potential for growth in the child without a series of evaluations extending over several months or years. A single determination of speech retardation or autistic behavior, for example, cannot provide the basis for an ongoing prognosis. Parents can be quite understanding of such a need and often welcome the opportunity for a more leisurely and extended contact prior to any clear commitments to therapy. The need to establish a clear-cut diagnosis (including quantitative appraisal of etiological factors) and to outline a course of definitive treatment in one family member is probably a greater need for the therapist than it is for the family.

Goals of evaluation and treatment should be discussed with both the child and the family. This can be done in stages rather than all at once, beginning with what is required during evaluation and then proceeding to additional goals once this is achieved. Near the final phases of therapy, goals should again be reviewed along with the entire course of treatment. Such a process strengthens the healthy ego in building a therapeutic alliance.

Physical Problems

If the parent does not present a concern about physical or neurological difficulties in the child during the initial contact, it is appropriate for the therapist to introduce these topics so that they may be resolved, clearing the way for psychological work. Correct evaluation of the child's physical status includes a detailed medical and neurological history and physical examination as well as a history of psychological development beginning with conception. A record of all illnesses, hospitalizations, and injuries, together with the treatment given and the complications ensuing, should be listed. A detailed neurological evaluation by a competent pediatric neurologist, electroencephalographic evaluation by an electroencephalographer acquainted with normal developmental shifts in the EEG in children, an educational evaluation, and psychological testing for the more subtle kinds of organic brain damage are all procedures that should be utilized with clear indications in each case. All of this information on the child's physical status must be appraised, organized, integrated, and synthesized with the child's history of psychological development, since it pertains very directly to the child's growing self-concept. It should be remembered that the first self to gain mental representation is a bodily self.

❲ Origin and Development of Psychopathological Behavior in Childhood

Child behavior can be analyzed in many different ways. If, indeed, one begins with the assumption that infants and children are unique individuals whose development and behavior are first and foremost to be understood (even when changes are considered desirable for the child and from the parents' viewpoint), one soon realizes that the child's history of psychological development—including any behavior, attitude, symptom, or functional limitation—is highly relevant and in fact indispensable to an understanding of such behavior. This process of understanding has often been bypassed in the past. It is often bypassed at present by symptomatic approaches to therapy that proceed immediately with reactions to the child's behavior or are designed to eliminate or modify behavior on *a priori* moral grounds—those of aduts who deem what is desirable or undesirable for the child. Work however, with infants and children has provided and is continuing to provide new understandings to the developmental processes that underlie all subsequent behavior. Child behavior does not arise *de novo*; it is a product of interactions between inherent tendencies, maturational patterns and environmental influences.

The human infant is born in the state of adaptiveness to the average expectable environment. He begins the process of adaptation to the specifics of this environment soon after birth. Each infant, for example, makes a specific adaptation to his mother's specific feeding style.[7] Many studies have shown significant differences between individual infants and between boy and girl infants.[9] Thus Richard Bell[3] has shown that hyperresponsive male infants at birth have a disproportionately higher incidence of behavior disorder and social isolation in the preschool period.

Developmental Origins

The treatment process in child psychiatry and child psychoanalysis requires an understanding of both normal and psychopathological development. When normal psychological growth is compared with psychopathological development at each age period, the contrasts suggest that the process of adaptation is active and oriented to inner as well as outer events, and that it involves the child's attention, sensorimotor functioning, and, later, his intellectual functions. Given a physically healthy baby at birth, a supportive environment, "good-enough" mothering,[17] and subsequent social and educational experience, the individual emerges with continued capacity to adapt. Plasticity of function is preserved in both the psychological and intellectual areas. Remaining growth potential and the capacity for creative problem-solving and invention continue to be demonstrated. These are all hallmarks of the psychologically healthy individual.

Psychopathological development may arise from organismic limitations or faulty personal, social, or educational experience. But regardless of the relative importance of specific etiological factors, the overall result in psychopathological development is the same: a narrowing of adaptive capacity; a fixation and overspecialization of psychological and intellectual processes; and a serious limitation in possibilities for further growth, creative problem solving, or invention. Any psychologically-based treatment procedure should attempt to assess and resolve issues that have led to psychopathological development and augment factors that would promote normal psychological and intellectual growth.

During infancy and childhood, developmental deviation, symptoms, and psychopathological character development must be distinguished from the following:

1. Normal maturational crises.
2. Transient growth crises.
3. Temporary reactions to interpersonal or environmental stress.
4. Regression in the psychological functions associated with physical illness and injury.
5. Normal plateaus and quiet periods in development.

Such distinctions are not always easy, especially if one is committed to identifying early signs of psychopathological development or to applying early treatment in order to prevent significant later pathology. A listing of the most serious (as contrasted with the least serious) complaints of parents about their children or of symptoms in children has not yet been developed—nor is it likely to be, since any externally observable behavior may emerge from a wide variety of underlying conditions. The significance of a "symptom" must be evaluated in the background of ongoing developmental progress. In clinical situations where the meaning of a given behavior, symptom, or reaction may be in doubt, the best one can often do is to help the parents stay in good communication with the child, become good observers of themselves as they relate to the child, follow further progress, and report back at reasonable intervals.

It is an interesting paradox in the field of infant and child psychiatry to discover that what appears at first as a psychopathological development—that is an overspecialized adaptation to a non-average acceptable situation, to not good-enough mothering, and so on—may emerge over a period of a few months as a useful and more generally applied adaptation to the wider environment. Heinz Hartmann referred to this process as that of a symptom or conflict gaining secondary autonomy. The price paid for such a symptom-oriented adaptation is constriction of ego functioning. The infant or child may make an appropriate adaptation to the mother or to other environmental situations, only later to discover that the adaptation doesn't serve him well in the world at large. This is probably the reason most child psychiatric referrals of even severely disturbed children do not occur until the child is evaluated within his peer group by persons outside the family, such as when he begins attending nursery school or kindergarten. This is an example of how an early, successful adaptation that was originally conflict-free becomes conflict-ridden.

The dynamics of psychopathological development change with time as a child's normal psychological growth proceeds. Among such growth processes are the following:

1. Ego functions become more coherently organized.
2. Object relations proceed from a "boundless" quality to a clear, distinct separation of self from others.
3. The capacity to master the environment increases.
4. The child's capacity to form a mental representation of his own experience with the mother and his capacity to remember the mother as a person even when he is anxious, gradually increases.
5. Superego and ego ideals change.
6. Processes of identification begin in the first years of life with imitative behavior and piecemeal incorporation of the attitudes and feelings of others, with progress to identification with the aggressor and identification with the provider (see below), and finally to the use of the love object as a model around which the child organizes his own character.

Stages of Development

The stages of psychopathological development are discussed briefly below.

BIRTH TO AGE THREE: EARLY ADAPTATIONS AND DEVELOPMENTAL DEVIATIONS

John Benjamin,[4] some years ago, showed that the predisposition toward anxiety that is the basis for symptom formation in later development is established by the age of three months and results primarily from the way in which the infant and mother resolve problems of sensory overload (from within and from without) in the first three months of life. This process depends upon the timing and character of soothing and protection offered by the mother—that is, her style.[8] Study of the earliest deviant behavior in infancy, such as pathological head-nodding, turning away, failure to thrive, projectile vomiting, difficulty in establishing eye contact, and rumination, are at first an adaptation of the infant to his experience and particularly to the mothering he has received. Such adaptations, if continued, may later become the basis of true symptoms.

Some symptoms in early infancy may reflect deficits in underlying neurological organization, such as the inability of an infant to hold its head up, irritable crying, colic, and disturbances in its capacity to maintain a state of quiet sleep or quiet attentiveness. Other symptoms may arise from deviant mothering and still others from specific kinds of disturbance in the mother–child relationship. For example, psychogenic megacolon in the early months of life has been found to arise from a pathological "tilting" of the relationship between the mother and the infant to anal-erotic modes of communication between mother and infant.

AGES THREE TO FIVE: SYMPTOM FORMATION AND FAMILY DYNAMICS

The capacity to form a symptom presupposes a psychological conflict between the expression of an instinctual drive and the defense against it. Instinctual drives become conflicting if they are experienced as dangerous. They become dangerous if the infant is capable of perceiving his abandonment by the love object. The love object does not exist separate from the self until the infant achieves beginning resolutions of the separation-individuation phases of development. Thus, true symptoms turn an external conflict into an internal one and represent an attempt at conflict resolution—that is, a compromise formation.

Examples of such early symptom formation may include the following:

1. Withholding of bowel movements. Here the conflict involved is between the impulse to smear and touch and to aggressively expel bowel content, and the fear that the parent will disapprove. The child's resolution of the conflict is to withhold.
2. Night terrors—that is, images of being bitten, eaten, or chased by wild animals. In this case the child's hostile, angry, destructive biting feelings are displaced onto the animal, which represents both self and disapproving adult.
3. Phobias of early childhood, such as fears of certain places or situations or of persons who are actually associated with threats of abandonment. These phobias are elaborated by the child's fantasies of what would happen in such a situation.
4. Eating disturbances, failure to speak, bizarre play, rocking, head-banging, tics.

At this stage of symptom formation, the symptom is intimately interwoven in the system of communication with family members, particularly parents. The symptom may also be a response of the child to parental communications. Because of the child's own fantasy (to project his own impulses to primary figures in disguised form) and his capacity to internalize an external conflict, he goes beyond the stage of adaptation to the stage of symptom formation proper.

Ages Five to Ten: Internalization and Acting Out of Conflict

At this stage in development, the child's defenses are more firmly organized. Each child shows a more consistent preference for particular defensive operations. The child's object relations have become clear—and also more complex, since the complexities of the oedipal situation present a three- rather than two-party conflict situation for the child to resolve. It is within this context that the "infantile neurosis" was originally conceived by Freud. What has been described in the preceding stages could be referred to as the early infantile neurosis before age five.

There are two major ways for the child to resolve conflicts characteristic of this time. He may either completely internalize the conflict —as observed, for example, in the obsessional neurosis—or he may act out elements of the neurotic conflict in relation to peers and other adults outside the family. Since normal latency is characterized by heightened mobility and action as a normal mode of communication, acting out of neurotic conflict should be considered an age-appropriate mode of expressing neurotic conflict.

Symptom patterns during this time are characterized by the following problems: bowel and urinary problems; lying; persistent fearfulness regarding school, other children, and new situations; finickiness with food; persistent phobias; open masturbation or sexual exploration (which normally would be private and with consenting peer-group members); overdependence; fire setting; pseudomaturity; running away; nonadaptive neatness; persistent thumb-sucking; strange, bizarre, or withdrawn behavior; uncommunicativeness; cruelty to animals; no friends; lack of interest in appearance or development of skills; disturbed sleep and frightening dreams and nightmares; persistently upset by changes; excessive clinging to transitional objects; withdrawal; obsessional behavior; speech problems; and hallucinations.

Ages Ten to Thirteen: Regression

Preadolescence is a confusing time for teachers, parents, and therapists because, as a preadolescent begins contemplating the advent of adolescence (that is, the loss of original love objects and the shift to new ones), he resumes the earlier psychological stance of the preoedipal child. Earlier defensive organizations are weakened. Pregenital behavior emerges. Language function regresses and undergoes reinstinctualization. Anxieties increase. Both boys and girls become preoccupied about the earlier preoedipal attachment to the mother, showing a liberal reorientation toward oral and anal erotic activities.

Symptom patterns reflect this situation. They include characteristic problems, as follows: depression; antisocial behavior; suicidal attempts or rumination; use of dangerous drugs; avoidance of school; school failure; reversal of value systems (rather than testing of value systems); no friends or personal interests; promiscuous sexual behavior; anorexia or obesity; avoidance; persistence of conforming or passive behavior; lack of interest in future; sudden total personality change or deterioration in mental functioning; acute phobia or obsessional behavior: excessive preoccupation with body; persistent somatic complaints without organic disease: and regressive behavior.

AGES THIRTEEN TO FIFTEEN: RECONSTRUCTION

Rapid physical growth and the appearance of secondary sexual characteristics propel the child into adolescence proper. This, incidentally, has been occurring at younger ages (at the rate of four months per ten years) since the onset of the twentieth century, so that the onset of puberty now occurs twenty-eight months earlier than in 1900. No single factor (for example, nutrition, urbanization, mass media, a change in parental expectations, or some racial or climatic influence) has been sufficient to explain this earlier onset of adolescence. A combination of factors seems the most likely explanation.

Puberty refers to bodily changes induced by the secondary sex hormones. Adolescence refers to associated psychological processes, which may precede or follow puberty by a highly variable time interval.

The search for new love objects may at first turn the adolescent toward objects of the same sex or toward group identifications. Such a move may be the best compromise available to the adolescent in dealing with renewed oedipal struggles and as a defense aganst heterosexual object ties. During this phase of adolescence, new capacities for intellectual, social, and physical functions do emerge as a child's greater social perspective increases. Symptoms reflecting this underlying state of affairs do not differ significantly from signs of disturbance found in early adolescence. Increased intellectual growth, self-awareness, and capacity to verbalize provide the mid-adolescent with increased leverage in getting his complaints heard and responded to either by family or social agency.

AGES FIFTEEN TO EIGHTEEN: CONSOLIDATION OF SYMPTOM TRENDS AND CHARACTER TRAITS

As reconsolidation of the personality takes place during this period, both the strengths and the vulnerability of the emerging independent person are revealed. A second opportunity for resolution of the primary oedipal ties and pregenital fixations presents itself during this important phase of adolescence. While the role of parents is less intense in terms of actually monitoring the details of daily experience, the shift toward independence provokes children and their parents into a further loosening of ties. This forces a reorientation on both sides toward one another. A new period of growth can emerge from such reorientation. Some of the characteristic problems in psychopathology for this age group include: schizophrenic reactions, in contrast to adolescent turmoil; delinquency; obsessional neurosis; depression; abuse of drugs; and school failure.

◖ Dynamics of Psychopathology in Parent–Child Relationships

Projection, Identification, and Narcissism

Diagnostic manuals are oriented toward the phenomenology of psychopathology in the individual. Yet much of what the child and family specialist is called upon to "treat" is found in disturbed interrelationships rather than clearly in one or another of the individuals involved. Folie à deux and sadomasochistic relationships are illustrations of similar phenomena from the field of adult psychiatry. The psychopathology of interaction between parent and child is very complex, because it is closely interwoven with the child's prolonged normal relative dependency on the parent. Also, the full complexity of verbal and nonverbal patterns of communication in the family does not make an impact of equal significance on the infant and child at all stages of the child's development. The influences that family interaction will have on the child depend on the child's level of psychological development, intelligence, and special characteristics at specific ages. In addition, family organization is not only complex, it also changes as parents themselves change and as the ages and characteristics of the children in the family change. Thus, no two infants growing up in the "same" family ever actually share a truly similar experience.

Parental caretaking and protection involve matters of body illness, injury, nutrition, and interpretation of the world to the child. The physiological and hormonal changes of pregnancy prepare the way for a psychological reorientation of energies and interests on the part of the mother in the direction of infant feeding and care, together with a willingness and even eagerness to assume such responsibility for the infant. This leads to a state of normal psychological symbiosis during the first year of life. The mother functions as an auxiliary ego for the child, as a protective shield, as a source of narcissistic "supplies," as a source of stimulation for the development of the child's cognitive functioning, and as a libidinal object. On this last depends the infant's capacity for developing loving bonds with other human beings.

From the child's second year of life on, the parent is called upon to facilitate individuation through a series of separation–individuation phases of development. Congenital abnormalities, physical illnesses, hospitalizations, and psychological disturbances in this early period of life call for even more highly specialized adaptations of care by the parent, since such disturbances inevitably distort the normal phases of attachment, symbiosis, and separation for the parent. The capacity to let go or to allow the child to emerge independently after such intense involvement, and yet to continue functioning as a parent in more subtle ways, is a task that many parents find particularly difficult. (Infantile attachment, symbiosis, and separation issues emerge for reconsideration in adolescence.)

One of the requirements of good-enough mothering is the capacity to endure what the infant projects onto the mother. That is, the projection of aggressive, destructive impulses is likely to arouse retaliatory feelings in the mother, who must inhibit or displace these feelings or turn them upon herself. This is the rub of motherhood, and it provides a major root for masochism. However, it is not limited to women who care for infants but is found in all helping relationships. It probably has its origins in man's development as a social animal. Much of the disturbing sadomasochistic relationship that may exist in a marriage is borrowed from infancy.

On the other hand, one of the psychological tasks of infancy and childhood is to endure what the parent projects onto or acts out with the child. It is out of such stuff that confusion and ambivalence in all human relationships grow. Thus, everyone is destined to become somewhat confused and disillusioned with everyone else, no matter how gratifying the relationships otherwise are. *The problem in all human bonds is to find the capacity to endure so that some love is possible.*

Another basic fact of human experience is that the infant is experienced more or less as an extension of the parent. The parent is thus narcissistically identified with the infant, making it possible for many parents to care for an infant when they would not have been able to do so out of a sense of empathy. Many parents were themselves insufficiently cared for as infants and children and do not have within themselves the memories, models, or skills of good-enough parenting. Or else they have gaps and odd points of emphasis, making parenting a series of disjointed communications and responses in relation to the child. For such parents the narcissistic model of child care is the only possible outcome short of abandonment of the child, but narcissistically-oriented child care fails as the child strives to maintain self-esteem during the process of separation and independence. Many parents whose care is predicated on the narcissistic model vascillate in actual practice between deep infantile narcissistic orientation of self-object attachments and abandonment of the child, thus recreating their own life history. (These and similar problems are expanded upon in a recent valuable edition to the literature, *Parenthood: Its Psychology and Psychopathology.*[2]) Certain children also elicit specific underlying sensitivities and vulnerabilities of the parents and rekindle their primitive mental life.

Taking care of others—a task so ubiquitous, so necessary, and so much a part of being human—is humane, high-minded, socially-sanctioned behavior that serves to ensure survival of the species. It is also a means by which each human being attempts to recreate the gaps and traumas from his own past in a belated attempt at mastery. Because of this, taking care of others can at times become confusing and self-defeating. Parents and therapists, particularly those who work with children, share this common maturational struggle. Becoming a parent and taking care of others offer another chance for reorganizing one's primitive psychic life.

The child, narcissistically identified with the parent as self-object, feels himself to be what is projected onto him by the parent. His feelings of self-esteem reflect changing moods and feelings in the parent. Many mothers and fathers will confirm that their own feelings of self-esteem are regulated by the child and his responses to their care and affection.

Example: Mrs. Page, one of our longitudinal case-study mothers, got off to a good start breast-feeding her child. Things were going well despite the fact that the family was looking for a new house during the child's first two and one half months. When some tensions originating from this source erupted openly between the parents, the mother felt angry but could not acknowledge or express such anger to her husband. She carried this anger and its associated depressive feelings with her to the evening nursing of her child. The infant reacted with irritability and crying. The mother's anger then erupted more openly. She became angry with the baby and said in a loud voice, "Stop complaining!" A vicious circle ensued during the next twelve hours, which kept both mother and infant awake through the night. These emotions were finally quieted by exhaustion and apathy.

Comment: This example is presented not because it is unusual but because it is typical. Suppressed and repressed anger and hostility in the mother resulted in depressive affect and displacement of angry feelings toward the child. The physiological letdown of milk was disrupted. The child experienced feelings of helplessness and rage. The mother was again confronted with her own hostility returned to herself, and a vicious circle was set up that finally resulted in apathy and withdrawal. This experience set the stage for further cycles of the same behavior. The parent–child problem was intertwined with marital difficulties, the past family history of each parent, and the social context of the family (looking for and financing a new house). A transient, self-limited feeding and sleeping problem emerged in the infant. Under some conditions the infant might have reacted with respiratory symptoms or with a skin rash or another form of bodily communication. If the cycles of tension had continued, apathy might have become well established, and failure to thrive could have been the result. If the parent had more fully acted out hostile feelings, child battering could have resulted. However, in the example cited above, the house problem was solved by a low-interest, government-insured loan. The marital relationship was not disrupted, and as the child progressed to more independence, the relationship between mother and child eased.

Unresolved Parent–Child Symbiosis

Psychopathology in the parent–child relationship emanating from psychopathological deviations from normal parent–child symbiosis may be seen in the symbiotic psychosis of childhood described by Margaret Mahler,[13] in the gender disturbances described by Stoller,[16] in the prolonged disturbances and distortions of the feeding process that result in anorexia nervosa and obesity,[5] and in the mutually inhibiting parent–child symbiosis often observed in handicapped children.[6] Recently Anthony[1] studied parent–child interactions involving a psychotic parent and found that in 5 to 10 percent of children involved in a close relationship with a psychotic parent, the syndrome of "supernormality" developed. This was characterized by the child's taking care of parenting responsibilities in the home, including care of the psychotic parent. I had observed this pseudomature syndrome in some children with handicapped siblings. The same problem has been observed in children of alcoholic parents. This is probably an exaggeration of the same but more subtle process occurring in normal children. The child identifies with the provider or caretaker and feels responsible for and responds to the needs of parents and other children, just as the parent feels responsible for and responds to the needs of the child. Recently Margaret Mahler[14] reconceptualized the infantile origins of the borderline patient. She believes that the predisposition towards the borderline state may emanate from the failure to resolve later stages of separation–individuation.

Example: In a group discussion, Mrs. S. said, "You know, doctor, I've been thinking about something for a long time. I've wondered if it means I'm crazy or something. I haven't told anyone about this except my husband." She then said with some surprise and embarrassment, "I sometimes feel as if H. (a handicapped child, age two and a half) is part of me. I don't see her as an individual. I see S.

(a younger, normal child) entirely differently. I see his individuality and his special characteristics, but not so with H."

Incorporation of and Acting Out of Marital Conflict by the Child

Children not infrequently incorporate and act out with each other both sides of the marital conflict. They may also simultaneously displace onto siblings unresolved aspects of both pre-oedipal and oedipal struggles. These complex phenomena are generally described under the very descriptive but undynamic term of "sibling rivalry."

Example: Marvin, age ten, depreciated, tormented, and often physically abused his younger, admiring brother. This brother was born when Marvin was three. Until then Marvin had been maintained as an overprotected child, still in psychopathological symbiosis with his mother, whose clinging to him was determined by her own earlier losses and thinly disguised threats of marital disruption by the father. As Marvin's real struggle with his mother was identified, he allowed himself friendship with the brother.

Comment: The issue here was not rivalry with the brother for their mother's affection. It was how Marvin could liberate himself from the infantile ties with his mother and vice versa. Fighting with baby brother was Marvin's way of fighting with baby-self–mother. Terms such as sibling rivalry, maternal rejection, and dependency refer to the epiphenomena of object relations.

The Sick Role and Scapegoatism in the Family

Treatment of children with a severe psychologic disturbance such as schizophrenia, severe psychosomatic disease, anorexia, delinquency, or psychogenic megacolon has repeatedly demonstrated to clinicians that when the seriously ill child threatens to get better, or in fact makes very definite and highly visible progress, the most involved parent frequently attempts to re-establish the illness even when the mechanisms underlying the illness have become clear and are under the conscious control of the parent. An alternative is for the parent to become ill. The identification of a sick child in the family does a great deal to provide the illusion of mental health in other family members. Relieving the child's illness is like opening a Pandora's box containing the rest of the family pathology, or like removing the scapegoat in the school or classroom.

Example: An eleven-year-old girl, Janet, was brought for treatment (once or twice a week for one year) because of a clearly defined phobia that gradually had been getting worse over the past two years. The child could not leave home except when the mother took her to school and returned her home from school, because she was afraid that she would see a cripple, someone with an arm or a leg missing, someone in a wheelchair, or someone old (about to die). As the sources of this phobia were identified in dreams and in fantasies using the squiggle game (referred to below under "Drawings and Use of Plastic Media" [p. 221]), the child responded very favorably to classical interpretive techniques and not only resolved her phobia but liberated herself from a pathological symbiosis with the mother. When this happened, a serious marital difficulty that had existed for years came to a head. The parents separated. The mother was temporarily relieved but remained deeply disturbed herself, showing depression and suicidal tendencies, which she attempted to utilize in setting up a highly eroticized symbiosis with her therapist. Her underlying borderline state was soon clearly revealed.

Identification with the Provider and the Aggressor

Identification with the provider has already been described above in the case of the pseudo-maturity syndrome. Identification with the aggressor is an unconscious defense mechanism described by Anna Freud,[10] referring to how the individual deals psychologically with externally perceived aggressive threats

that elicit anxiety. The individual takes onto himself certain aspects of the threatening external aggression. For example, he may take on the total identity of the aggressive person, or he may take on only one aspect of the threat situation and act this out in other situations. The clearest example would be the child who, in the face of significant castration threats from the father, becomes cruel to a younger sibling.

(How a Child Makes Known His Inner Psychological Life and Ongoing Experience

Play

Play is the universal language of childhood, and it remains more or less available to older children and even to adults. Play sequences can be analyzed just as verbal sequences can be analyzed. Repetitive play and play paralysis are usually indications of underlying neurotic disturbance or ego deficits.

The term "play therapy" is misleading because it suggests that play in itself is therapeutic. Play becomes therapeutic only when it is understood and responded to as a communication about oneself. Melanie Klein[12] was the first to interpret the child's play as a projection of his inner psychological world onto the world of small objects. Play can be interpreted to the child either directly or within the metaphor.

Example: *George:* (Enters office and engages in favorite play activity of recent sessions: that is, filling ashtrays with "will-hold" glue, dropping in paper clips and coins, and placing the ashtray on the window sill to dry.)

Analyst: Glue is a way of holding on to good stuff and making sure it stays there.
George: (Looks at analyst, says nothing. Brings glue-filled ashtray containing paper clips and coins from prior session to desk and chips glue away to remove paper clips from gluey mass.)

Analyst: Those paper clips are like your coin collection.

George: I can clean my coins with glue. It makes them look like new.

Analyst: That "will-hold" glue is really good stuff. We need a good supply of it.

George: (Spreads glue on hands, waves hands to speed drying of glue, and peels off glue.) Look how clean my hands are when I peel it off.

Analyst: Yes, and you always leave a nice neat pile of it for me to take care of, so I'll be sure and remember you and have some of you left here even after you're gone.

George: (Looks up and smiles while continuing to peel the dried glue from his hands.)

Analyst: Did you think I'd forget, like when your daddy went away, if I didn't have something special from you to remind me of you?

Comment: The choice of these remarks by the analyst was determined by the analyst's empathy with the boy's shame and anxiety in connection with his problem of fecal withholding and soiling, and his current attempt to bring these problems under his own control. The bowel problem had resulted from, among other things, "separation fears" that could be more precisely stated as his fear of being forgotten; toilet fears that, more precisely, are related to fantasies he had that a hand inside the toilet could reach up and pull him down into the pipes; and his mother's willingness and unwitting collaboration in continuing to involve herself in all aspects of his toileting activity, including wiping his bottom so it wouldn't get sore. This had evolved into one of the methods he utilized in controlling his mother.

An effective interpretation is like the day residue of a dream: lodged in a preconscious state, eventually establishing connections with contents of the id that are striving for conscious representation. Well-phrased and well-timed interpretations thus lead to new material in the therapeutic process, just as the mother's empathic holding of the infant (without limiting the infant's capacity to contribute to reciprocity with her) leads to psy-chological growth. Use of the metaphor in the above example (the neat pile of glue on desk referring to a fecal mass inside and outside) and casual openness in speaking of the anxious situation as revealed in the transference (being forgotten by the father, displaced onto the mother, and then onto the analyst) aid the ego in recovering control and resolving conflict.

Words, Action, and Stories

Even before the child can express himself in coherent verbal language, an illusory verbal dialogue can take place between the child and the therapist relating to the activities, reactions, and play of the child. When verbal language does become available to the child, it is highly egocentric and is often at first utilized in a highly condensed fashion organized around the child's internal thought processes. A common and almost universally successful method for encouraging verbal productivity in therapy with a child is to have the therapist dovetail words with play and offer a parallel verbal comment to play sequences or other physical activity.

Example: I asked Mark if he had any dreams, "scary" or otherwise. He said "No." Later, while engaged in tossing a ball back and forth, I asked him the same question in the same words. He replied "Oh, yes," and went on to describe what he said was a "funny" dream but turned out to be a dream of getting lost on the freeways in Los Angeles and not being able to get home. Associations were to the many losses and changes of living situations he had experienced.

Comment: Action is a primary mode of communication. Tossing the ball back and forth is an action metaphor for verbal exchange. I've found such action a useful method in facilitating conversation. In my experience, playful activities of this type, with reciprocity of affect between the patient and the therapist, often overcome both suppression and repression, thus facilitating therapeutic communication with a child. A skillful therapist will not confine himself to asking questions. He will encourage running commentary, story telling, and dramatic play action as a means of facilitating verbal dialogue with the child.

Drawings and Use of Plastic Media

When the child has been able to make reference to some event within his life, either in the outside world or in connection with his fantasies, wishes, or dreams, the therapist may choose to respond by inviting the patient to make a drawing or diagram of what has been described in words; or else the therapist may respond to some aspect of what has been described by making a drawing himself. Frequently the full impact of the event then becomes clear to the therapist. Clay and paint can be utilized as well as pencil, paper, and crayolas. David Reiser[15] has made effective use of drawings to help the child express conflict situations.

Examples: John, a fire-setter age eight years old, had quite matter-of-factly told the therapist that he slept in the same bed with his mother. The therapist responded by drawing a room with a bed, and a mother and a boy in the bed. The therapist showed the picture to John, asking him if he meant "like that." John then became anxious and held his penis. He told his therapist that the boy and his mother were not so close in the bed, to which the therapist replied, "Getting too close to the mother in bed could make a boy excited and then scared of what could happen to his penis if the father found out. Hot feelings are like fires."

Tim, age four, was being seen in the same visit with his two-year-old sister, Marie, and an eight-month-old brother, Peter, who was held during the visit on his mother's lap. I drew a diagrammatic representation of a face and gave it to Tim without comment, along with a pencil and another piece of blank paper. Tim drew a face and looked up at me. I asked him who it was. He said "Peewee." His mother laughed and said that the baby brother, Peter, was called "Peewee." Tim had

only recently given up his position on the mother's lap. Tim then spontaneously drew another, more primitively organized figure identified as a "monster." Following this, both he and his sister pranced about the room pretending to be giant monsters. The mother commented that they often played monster like this at home. I asked if she had any idea why, and she replied that they had seen monsters on television.

Comment: My drawing and accompanying question were designed to elicit relevant data in a spontaneous way, such that it might be relied on in providing Tim with the chance to tell his own story without distorting points of emphasis by using leading questions. Tim's drawing of a face (including hair, eyes, nose, mouth, and ears, all in the proper location) not only revealed his good intelligence and perceptual capacity but also identified the main character and theme in his stream of thought. The spontaneous behavior that followed—first the drawing of the monster and then the dramatic acting-out of monster play with his sister—confirms that the drawing had in itself been an effective means of opening up access to Tim's inner life experience and communicating it to other people. The mother's participation with me in attempting to translate the meaning of his behavior, in all probability, had a liberating influence upon her son. The entire sequence could be translated into any one of the following: "Peewee is a monster," "Peter is a little Peewee baby and I am all grown up like a monster," "Peewee has a tiny peewee and I have a big one," and "When I feed Peewee, I feel like a monster." Any one or all of these statements might be acceptable translations. At this point, however, the important issue was not the precise translation of this sequence but, rather, the use of the drawing in opening up the possibility of Tim telling his own story.

Donald W. Winnicott[18] devoted a book to the use of the squiggle game in understanding and interpreting the child's mental world. This game is played by one person making a line, series of lines, or marks on a piece of paper, and the other person adding additional marks or lines to complete a specific representation. I have combined the squiggle game with a story-making technique.

Example: Janet, a phobic girl of eleven, and I took turns in completing squiggle sequences until five were completed. The five squiggle objects in sequence were: (1) a nose; (2) a smiling face; (3) a snake; (4) a horse; and (5) flowers. She was then told it might help "in our work together" to arrange these in any order and tell a story about them. The story she told went as follows. "There was this girl who liked to put her nose into things. She always smiled except when she met a snake. One day her horse won a race and they gave him a ring of flowers over his neck." To which the therapist replied, "Horses love flowers and hate snakes, and have you ever noticed that the nose is prettiest on a smiling face?" Janet loved to play this game and insisted on playing it in subsequent visits in which the stories were utilized as a basis for self-reference. This eventually evolved into a method to deal with anxiety-ridden situations.

Affectomotor Patterns

The child may reveal more about himself in his postural and motoric activities than he does in words, drawings, or play.

Example: Gerald often became restless if he was not seen immediately on his arrival. On one occasion, instead of waiting for the analyst he immediately left the waiting area, went back to check on his mother, and then subsequently entered the analyst's office in a very excited manner, asking where the analyst had been and why it took him so long to meet him. By this time, the analyst had become aware of an unconscious anxiety situation which gave rise to this behavior, so he replied, "When a boy is afraid of being forgotten he has to keep track of where everybody is and it makes him angry if people aren't there waiting for him. The boy always feels angry if he has to wait for somebody else." Gerald's reply was, "Are you talking about me again?"

Displacement onto Others

Children often refer to others, including adults, pets, siblings, and teachers, as a way of making reference to themselves. It is common for children who have few friends, for example, to claim that others are unfriendly with them or don't like them. Such children often provoke negative responses from others.

Example: George, age eight, began the hour rather excitedly, going to the toy closet and selecting a puppet whom he immediately named E. Howard Hunt. He began beating on the puppet saying, "E. Howard Hunt is a criminal. He broke into Daniel Ellsberg's psychiatrist's office. He took pictures of the records. He broke into the National Democratic Headquarters at the Watergate Hotel, bugged the telephones, and stole records." At this point, George filled the puppet with paper money and continued beating until the money was squashed out of the puppet and scattered on the floor. The analyst knew that George had been watching the Watergate investigation on television and was aware that Hunt's personal life had been discussed, namely, the tragic loss of his wife in a plane accident six months after the bugging incident. It was also known that George's behavior toward many of the objects in the therapist's office was as if they were his own, and he made a special point of collecting valuable objects. This was, in part, an identification with his father. In addition, he had engaged in childhood extortion tactics in controlling his mother. The analyst's response was as follows:

Analyst: Do you think, George, that E. Howard Hunt had a problem?
George: I'll say he had a problem. He was a criminal, and now he's getting punished. Bang, bang.
Analyst: Yes, he certainly has gotten a lot of beatings. He was even beat up and robbed when he was in jail.
George: It serves him right. He was a robber himself.

Analyst: But what do you think was his problem?

George: He liked to tell tall stories and he wrote books. I have some of his books.

Analyst: So you've become an expert on E. Howard Hunt, and now he's getting what's coming to him because he was a criminal?

George: Yes.

Analyst: Are we forgetting something about E. Howard Hunt?

George: You mean because his wife died in the plane crash?

Analyst: Something scary like that could make a person feel real bad.

George: But this money makes him feel better, and that's why he's a thief.

Analyst: It's too bad he didn't have anyone to talk to about his problem. Maybe he wouldn't have got into so much trouble.

George: You psychiatrists have everything figured out, don't you?

Comment: The analyst is focusing more here on the therapeutic process than interpretation of this material. An effort is being made to help the patient see how he himself can move the analysis forward. Experience with George has shown that he often responds to interpretations as castration and ceases supplying more material. It is sometimes more important that the therapist understand the therapeutic process than that he interpret the unconscious meaning of the material.

Dreams

Dreams may play as important a role in child therapy as they do in adult therapy, particularly if they have been frightening dreams or nightmares that reveal the underlying sources of anxiety and conflict in the child. Young children often present clear wish-fulfillment or anxiety dreams. Older children, beyond the age of five or six, often present dreams as highly elaborate and disguised as those that adults present. The use of dreams in psychoanalytically based child therapy is deserving of a detailed chapter or book.

(Choice of Therapy

The choice of therapy offered in a situation in which the child's problems are presented by the parents is determined by many factors besides the nature of the child's problem in itself. Such factors include the following:

1. The training and experience of the therapist.
2. The limitations of time available to both the therapist and the parents at the time of consultation.
3. The financial resources of the family.
4. Transportation arrangements to and from the therapist's office.
5. The level of understanding and psychological-mindedness of the parents.
6. The nature and intensity of unconscious resistance both in the child and in the parents.
7. The stage very often having been set ahead of time by the referral source, in determining the expectations of the parents.

The range of possibilities and the interaction of the variables that determine the choice and nature of the therapy and its outcome can best be understood by reviewing a series of briefly presented case studies. Long-term follow-up information is available on these cases, which constitute the remainder of the article.

Marvin, a Nine-Year-Old: Psychoanalysis

Marvin was brought for evaluation by his father on referral from the father's former analyst, because of Marvin's poor grades in school, lack of friends, withdrawn and sullen behavior, and sadistic attacks on his brother (two and one half years younger), whom he said he wished to kill with a knife. Marvin also suffered from asthma since the age of four, with attacks occurring three or four times a week during six months of the year in the fall and spring. Other reasons included withholding of bowel movements, bed wetting, "hateful" attitudes toward all women and girls, and pervasive, general misery. The father had had two years of psychoanalytic treatment because he himself was uncomfortable with his periodic, overt, homosexual interests, in which a sado-masochistic relationship with a partner was acted out. His wife was unaware of his homo-sexual activity. Psychoanalysis had helped him stabilize his work and his family role, and had reduced but not completely eliminated his homosexual interests. The father had been openly suicidal when the patient was about four years old. The mother was a schizoid, withdrawn, mechanistic person without psychological insight, but she was quite conscientious and wanted to help. Both parents were frightened of Marvin's behavior toward the younger brother and did not expect him to be able to continue living at home. They suggested the possibility of admitting him to a hospital. A school report confirmed what the parents had said.

In the first visit Marvin presented himself in a highly provocative way, acting the part of an anxious dictator with the analyst. I pointed out to him that he must have been pretty scared coming here, thinking that I would be the one to decide what to do about him. I told him that I could see he wanted to be the boss of this situation and tell me what to do, rather than have me tell him what to do. He calmed down considerably in response to these brief comments and then went on to play with his favorite objects, airplanes. I agreed with the parents on the serious nature of his difficulty, but I told them that I thought Marvin was extremely anxious, knew that he was in trouble, and had responded to me as a person who might be able to help him. I told them that in order to do so, it would be necessary for me to see Marvin four or five times a week, and that his treatment would probably extend at least two years. I also indicated that it would be necessary and important for me to meet with them from time to time, and that I would welcome any information from the school. The parents agreed to this as the best alternative open to them, both from the financial viewpoint and from the viewpoint of Marvin's future. They were confident that analysis could help Marvin as it had helped his father.

Marvin had been considered a relatively quiet baby, was bottle-fed, was left in his crib a good deal as an infant, and had experienced separations from his parents for several weeks at a time at the ages of eight months and thirteen months. At the age of two and a half years his brother was born. Two months later the two boys were left with their maternal grandmother, who hired a nurse to care for the new baby while she and a grown but unmarried son cared for Marvin. Toilet training was achieved during this time by the maternal grandmother and the uncle, who gave him model airplanes when he produced on the pot. His attachment to his father was always more significant than that to his mother. When the father became depressed and suicidal when Marvin was four, the child had his first brief asthmatic attack. This was repeated at age six and had worsened since then. Marvin continued to suck his thumb and pull his ear simultaneously until the age of six, when he gave this up suddenly after a brief trip to a distant city with his father. The difficulties that led to treatment had been increasing over the past three years. The main methods of dealing with Marvin's difficult behavior at home included making him sit on a chair for several hours at a time, and spankings administered by the father. The parents had also attempted a variety of pacifying and manipulating maneuvers that resulted in two-way bribery and extortion between the parents and the patient.

During the initial phases of the analysis the patient developed a positive attachment to the analyst, and he began to experience increased feelings of confidence in himself as a working alliance developed. In his omnipotent attitude with the analyst he pretended to be the frightening monster who controlled, sadistically attacked, and castrated the analyst. This was interpreted as his fear of being controlled, castrated, and attacked by others in the environment and being destroyed by the monster within himself. His behavior at home and school improved considerably. Marvin reserved the most primitive aspects of his functioning for the analysis. Gradually the analyst came to be identified as a cruel, bad person from whom he felt he must defend himself. Thus he projected his attacking superego to the analyst, externalizing an internal conflict in the transference neurosis. The major modes of communication included dramatic play actions, provocative behavior with the analyst, many drawings in which he depicted the violent struggles between good and bad (wars), and other drawings, writings, and puzzles in which his dual sadistic impulses and defenses against these impulses were illustrated. His disappointment with the cool, relatively ungiving mother was illustrated by his expectation that the analyst could not give him what he needed. Each hostile attack toward an outside object—including the analyst, the brother, girls, and his own prized belongings—occurred in the context of a threatened deprivation.

When it was possible to interpret the earlier origins of such feelings in relation to the brother and parents, the attack would subside and actions could be replaced by words. For example, Marvin literally wanted to exhibit his "piss and butt" to the analyst repeatedly. He would often back up, behind first, onto the therapist's lap. These behaviors were determined by several causes. They represented his concerns about castration, his fixation on anal matters, and his anxiety concerning wetting and soiling, which he did periodically. These elements were interpreted to him and resulted in a temporary lessening of anxiety. In one session he gave an important clue to the analyst when he recalled scenes from the age of two of his brother's nurse holding and feeding the brother and changing his diapers. The attentive care this brother received was considered more desirable to Marvin than being bribed with small model airplanes to produce bm's on the toilet. The interpretation was then made to him that he had wished to be taken care of like he saw his brother being taken care of, receiving all of the attention to his "piss and butt," and that he wished I could do the same for him now—and was angry because I didn't. It was suggested that he must have been very angry then, too, when his parents weren't around to take care of him while his brother did get taken care of by a nurse.

The exhibiting, provocative behavior had another derivative too: namely, the sadomaso-

chistic relationship with the father, who had engaged in a good deal of spanking, after which father and son would engage in a mutually satisfying make-up. Marvin wished something similar with the analyst. The model airplanes offered as rewards for the deposit of bowel movements in the toilet became transitional objects for him, a way he had of dealing with separation anxiety. He also did a number of things that were calculated to make sure I didn't forget him between visits. He liked to leave his mark in my office. Sometimes this consisted of a pencil mark on the wall, his phone number written down for me, a drawing on my blackboard, or a pile of toys in the middle of the floor. All of these leavings-behind were interpreted as having their origin in his fear of being forgotten. A reunion following a separation was most difficult for him to deal with, and on each return he became provocative. Eventually he learned to express his concern and resentment before the separation and then to reconstruct the events after the separation.

Comment: It is easy in retrospect to agree that psychoanalysis was the treatment of choice in this case, since many such children are hospitalized or placed away from home in a highly structured and controlled environment. "Bad" behavior often stems from anxiety. It was clearly recognized in the beginning that Marvin's acting-out behavior was a reflection of an underlying neurosis. Also, Marvin's response to my initial interpretation assured me that an all-out attempt to deal with the problem, utilizing in-depth psychological understanding, might be successful. Follow-up information confirmed that the effort was indeed worthwhile and perhaps the most economically feasible of alternatives available.

Byron, Age Eighteen Months: Parental Guidance Based upon Psychoanalytic Understanding

Byron was a bright, precocious boy brought for consultation at the age of eighteen months because of biting behavior. He was his mother's first and only child. At the time of referral he bit everybody, showing no remorse when he was reprimanded. When attempts were made to control him, he would bite even more aggressively. The mother was an intelligent young woman; even though she was concerned about his behavior, she also was puzzled by it and wanted to understand it. Her main idea was that Byron was not getting enough love. She felt guilty about working and gave him extra attention. I told her that in order to understand him, we would reconstruct how his thinking and feeling had developed from birth.

I met with the mother and stepfather twice before seeing Byron. In those two visits it was possible to formulate a hypothesis about Byron's biting. The mother was at first not consciously aware of the importance of the continuity of a good maternal relationship with Byron. She herself had experienced many separations and discontinuities with her parents, and by a superhuman effort she had lifted herself from an uneducated status to that of a successful, semiprofessional person, still very much interested in her own education. The pregnancy with Byron was unexpected, although wanted. She liked Byron as an infant but went to work when he was six weeks of age, leaving him in the care of a motherly person with three children of her own. At three months his care was shifted to a loving, easy-going, child-oriented woman who had animals in the house and who provided a great deal of affection both for Byron and his mother, a young woman who thrived on affection. At age one year and four months this woman was no longer available, and Byron was given over to the care of a younger woman who was very perfectionistic, rigid, and enforced many strict rules. It was within a few days of this transfer that Byron's biting behavior began. It did not cease, however, when Byron was transferred to the care of another, more loving person two months later.

Byron had learned to talk at eleven months, and his speech continued to develop in a precocious manner. He was very attentive and precocious and listened well to everything said. (Both Spanish and English were spoken at home.) He told me when I saw him that "biting is good because it makes me feel good." When not biting, he was a delightful, cheerful companion who was very attentive to adults and who showed a good sense of humor. He would pretend to be afraid of dogs, and he preferred to have the light on at night. He was somewhat afraid of loud noises made by trucks. Two sides to Byron emerged in the history and in direct interviews with him. On the one hand he showed many precocious and independent attitudes (pseudo-precocity). On the other hand there was a clear wish—although not easily identified—to recapture some of his position of being a favored and loved baby, which had been disrupted at one year and four months of age.

Byron listened very attentively to me when I told him that I understood that biting made him feel good, because it was his way of getting hold of things that he loved and wanted to have for himself so that he could be a big baby boss. I told him he needed to be a baby for a long time before he grew up. This eighteen-month-old child repeated these statements to his mother at home, and for the next week he often mentioned his visit with me: the toys and play at my office, and the things we had talked about. Subsequent visits with the mother and stepfather revealed that Byron often sought his mother's lap, insisted on being held, returned to the bottle briefly, enjoyed affection by his mother, and stopped biting. This dramatic change in Byron's behavior was sufficient to force the mother to reorient her value systems and attitudes. She delayed her plans to go to school and work and developed a strong attachment to Byron, to some extent living out her own earlier deprivation through narcissistic identification with her son. A follow-up two years later revealed Byron to be asymptomatic and progressing smoothly in his development.

Comment: It is often said that if problems could be identified early, they would be more easily and successfully treated. This, in fact, seems to be borne out in Byron's case. The child's biting behavior served as a catalyst in the mother's own development. The treatment approach involved an interpretation to the mother through the child, which the mother then responded to by providing maternal care to the child and vicariously, to herself.

Norman, an Eight-Year-Old with Tics and Talent: An Eighteen-Year Follow-Up

Norman was the firstborn child of intelligent, accomplished parents. He was planned for, but he was born early in the father's career while the parents were living in the East. He was a full-term baby, healthy in every respect, and was described as being happy, alert, and active. His mother felt that she did not have enough milk to breast-feed him, so he was bottle-fed. He had colic until the age of three months, for which a darkened room was prescribed. In the first few months of life he seemed especially sensitive to the noise of the piano and would stop crying if he heard such a noise. His mother was tense, frightened, and somewhat depressed with her first child and felt as though she didn't quite know how to satisfy him.

Norman remained an active, wiry, and somewhat tense child. He smiled but often also stared at his mother. At about the age of two he became afraid to go to sleep at night without the light on. This fear persisted throughout his early years. There were several moves by the family when the child was between the ages of eight months and five years, due to the unsettled nature of the father's occupation.

Norman's development was quite rapid. He sat at four months and walked with minimal holding-on at eight months. He was able to speak in brief sentences at fourteen months. He was quite outgoing and, as the mother said, "into everything." The mother continued being quite perplexed as to how to manage him. A sibling was born at age three and another at age five. Intense rivalry developed shortly after the birth of the first sibling.

Norman was referred for psychiatric consultation at the age of eight because of eye-blinking and head-shaking movements, unusual voice sounds, grimacing, and unusual hand movements. Bed-wetting had been present from the age of four until the age of eight, occurring once or twice each night, and Norman was beginning to say such things as, "I wish I were dead." All of this had become worse since the family's recent move at the age of five, at which time Norman felt uprooted from friends that he had in the neighborhood. The first eye-blinking and head-shaking movements—the beginning of the "tics" —occurred one afternoon when his mother told him not to go outside without a hat on. He defied her, went to a baseball game, and shook his head to see whether he were getting a headache. It became a pleasurable activity for him, and he later said that he needed to have his "habits" because they were a source of pleasure to him. Also, it was learned that the father's method of discipline had consisted of spanking whenever he lost his temper. Norman had become somewhat defiant and obstructionistic, although he had done well in school. He was preoccupied with television shows of violence, read the newspaper about accidents, and had himself been subjected to the bullying of older boys in a new and unfamiliar neighborhood following the move. He preferred girls to his male peers. His speech difficulty (consisting of unusual voice-cracking sounds) accompanied the tics, along with grotesque facial expressions. Meanwhile Norman began to teach himself the piano. His mother had played the piano and he seemed to be learning very rapidly by himself.

Comment: It was apparent, in the extended evaluation of this family, that the mother displaced some of her resentment from the father onto Norman. She concealed this by oversolicitous attentiveness to Norman's health needs. Norman sensed the tensions between the parents and, particularly, his mother's dissatisfactions with himself, and he acted this out in his rivalry with the younger brother. Initial contact with Norman convinced me that the visits were useful to him and, also, that I could not work extensively with the parents. I referred the mother to another psychiatrist for her depressive symptoms and saw the father occasionally, while continuing once-a-week visits with Norman from the ages of eight through twelve and once-a-month visits from the ages of thirteen through seventeen. The tics diminished considerably by the age of ten and dropped out almost completely at the age of fourteen. In pre-adolescence Norman began to express many of his pregenital anal and oral concerns, using the primitive "gutter talk" characteristic of the era. He revealed to me his "unclean" fantasies about the dignified adults in positions of authority around him. This was associated with transient episodes of paranoia.

More interesting than the disappearance of Norman's symptoms was the emergence of an obvious musical talent. By the time he had finished high school he had not only mastered the piano, including the most difficult Chopin and Beethoven, but had begun composing on his own and had taken up the organ because he felt it offered greater variability in depth of musical expression than the piano. A fascinating sidelight was how Norman "practiced" the piano. Practicing consisted of hearing the music in his head, including all the intonations and variations in style. Once he had been able to do this in his head, the playing of music (including the difficult fingering) came relatively easily, with an actual minimal amount of time spent at the piano—on the order of one half hour every two or three days. I was reminded by this of what Norman had told me about becoming an expert Little League pitcher in baseball at the age of eight, when his tics were still very obvious. While occupying the pitcher's mound, Norman went through the entire repertoire of his facial, head, and bodily movements and voice-cracking sounds. Then he would suddenly throw a finely-executed curve ball over the plate. His tics were, in part, a rehearsal for action. I have wondered about his listening to his mother's piano music as a child. Was listening to and then recreating his own mental music a transitional phenomena for him, and—as Winnicott suggested—a basic source of creativity?

Norman completed one year of college, after which he volunteered for a period of two years of community work in a poor country among the underprivileged. There he met a woman four years his senior, with two young children. He appreciated her sensitivity and understanding of him. She mothered, loved, and charmed him and supported him in his pursuit of music as a career. His parents objected to his announcement of his intentions of marriage, but he returned to the United States with her and her children. He eventually married her, completed college, and continued his musical career as composer and teacher with good success, both artistically and financially. His speech is fluent, his affect is free, and he has received no further psychiatric care. In retrospect, this eighteen-year case study seems to justify the choice of therapy that was originally made: namely, to see the child individually, even though problems of significant proportions were present in the family. This decision was based primarily upon the fact that the child himself felt estranged from the symptom and was interested in tracing its origins and resolving it.

Steve, a Seventeen-Year-Old Football Player: No Consultation with Parents

Steve, age seventeen, had made the first string on his high school football team. He managed a successful window-washing business on off hours and showed himself to be of excellent intelligence on psychological testing. But he felt extremely uneasy with girls, was failing in all his school subjects, and was extremely testy with boys. He himself requested psychiatric help. The choice was made to see him alone without seeing his parents, unless he requested that they be seen. His initial history showed that he had had an extensive medical evaluation two years previously because of "elevated blood pressure." He feared that he might have irreparable kidney damage and would not live very long. Much of his time was spent in angry, depressed brooding over this problem (which he dared not reveal, since he had passed the physical to join the football team). Other boys spoke of masturbation in usual terms and described sexual exploits with girls. He equated masturbation with homosexuality and any kind of sexual interest in a girl, or any girl's sexual interest in him, as dirty and degrading.

After a full medical evaluation, including a review of previous investigations of hypertension and "kidney difficulty," it was found that there was no physical basis for his fears about hypertension and a short life with kidney damage. He had misrepresented some bedside doctor talk during the discussion "on rounds." None of the tests showed any significant organic pathology. Occasional blood pressures of 130/70 was noticed when he was anxious. He could hardly believe that this was the case when the details were presented to him. However, his anxiety diminished in all areas, his grades improved, he got a girlfriend, he masturbated freely with heterosexual fantasies, and on his own he decided to discontinue therapy after three months of once-a-week visits. A follow-up a year and a half later showed Steve doing well in a college business course. He continued in competitive sports and had a steady girlfriend.

Comment: Steve was against having his parents involved in the treatment process, and his wishes were respected. He himself decided on the frequency of visits. When the medical information turned out negative, he was overjoyed but unbelieving. Nevertheless it had a significant impact upon his outlook, and his anxious brooding ceased. It was as if he no longer had to behave as if he were castrated or about to be castrated. It was helpful for him to have someone with whom he could discuss his sexual development.

Judy, a Beautiful, Bright, Autistic Girl of Two and One Half: Treatment Strategy and Outcome

At two and one half, Judy could be described as a delicate, beautiful, neat little wind-up doll. Her first response to me and my office with her parents was to touch her own and her mother's feet and knees and look at the overhead lights. Everything else between was seemingly ignored or looked through. Her mouth was set in a semiclosed position. She quickly put the pieces of a puzzle together and demonstrated a repertoire of three nouns on cues structured by her mother: "elbow," "toy-toy," and "knee." She previously had been able to say "money" (mommy?) and could play pat-a-cake and wave bye-bye, but these achievements had disappeared during the past month. She fingered her shoes and socks and touched her colorful dress with her fingertips, and she repeatedly touched her own knees and ankles in a ritualistic fashion. She had passed the sequin formboard at age four. Her health had been good. Pediatric examination including neurological evaluation, and amino-acid screening of the urine, was normal. Her height was at the 50th percentile level and weight at the 20th percentile. Her diet had become restricted to milk, crackers, and hamburger. She awakened at 4:00 a.m.

This pregnancy was the first for the twenty-three-year-old mother and twenty-seven-year-old father, and it occurred as the mother was finishing college. The father had had labile hypertension since age sixteen. He became very anxious when he married; this worsened, with exacerbation of high blood pressure, when he discovered his wife was pregnant. His pretty young wife responded to the situation with a thirty-five-pound weight gain and a quiet, cautious attitude toward him. Judy weighed six pounds nine ounces at birth and was described as a beautiful, shiny child with a big nose. "She was real pretty." However, she seemed "independent" from the age of two weeks on. She awakened at least once a night through the first two years of life and spit up a lot during the first year. She was cared for intermittently by the maternal grandmother because the parents were often away, including a trip for four weeks when Judy was six months of age. Judy's response to her mother on their return from this absence was to finger the buttons on her mother's dress. Relatives observed that "she seemed to want to be alone" at age ten months. Her first words, "elbow" and "banana," appeared at fifteen months. Placement in normal nursery school at age two years was recommended by the pediatrician. She failed to respond favorably. Further regression in social behavior and speech developed.

Thus by any standard it was clear that Judy's developmental level in social and speech areas was seriously impaired and that a full swing to regressive functioning was in progress. The parents were discouraged and expected continued regression in Judy's behavior. The father compared Judy to his sister, now in her twenties, who did not talk until age five and was diagnosed as "schizophrenic." The father had shared responsibility for the upbringing of this child (five years younger than himself) until he was in his teens, and he had intermittently been seeing the same psychiatrist who treated her (with ECT and medication) for several years. The father also had an aunt in a hospital for the retarded. He spoke readily of his hypertension, his anxiety at work, and his phobic and counterphobic attitudes in social settings, together with the worsening of these symptoms with his marriage and the mother's pregnancy.

Paradoxically, Judy reacted more playfully with the father than with the mother. The father had become increasingly less interested in sex with his wife since the marriage and had expressed no romantic interest at all in her since the pregnancy. The mother was more worried and cautious about the father than about the child. She was only vaguely aware of her depression and withdrawal, as she had become increasingly apathetic and discouraged. She was aware of and clearly expressed the concerns she had about her husband's inability to accept the responsibility of marriage and family life. She had attempted to shield him from burdens of this kind by leaning on her parents.

The father was seen individually and soon revealed some of the deeper origins of his own anxiety hysteria. As he began separating his own problems and prior family problems from those of his current family, the mother (who had unconsciously blamed herself for her husband's distress) became less depressed and withdrawn and became increasingly interested and affectively available to her child. Child and mother were seen in joint interviews, utilizing a psychoanalytically-oriented educational approach. For example, Judy's avoidance of the face and attention to the extremities (including the tail of their cat and an avoidance of the cat's face) was traced historically by the mother. Judy's attention to the buttons on her mother's dress and avoidance of her face at the age of six months was recognized as the first identifiable beginning of Judy's social isolation. Judy's lack of concern about separation from the mother and her "independence" were soon replaced by the development of a strong attachment to a now more responsive and affectively available mother. When the mother's depression was linked up with her low feelings of self-esteem due to her husband's lack of interest in her, the guilt she had in relating to Judy's deviant development diminished considerably. The mother added that another factor in her depression had been her disappointment in not having a man like her father in the household.

Judy's improvement during the early months of this therapeutic program was phenomenal. Within four months she was up to her age level in vocabulary, had good eye contact, and showed only faint reminders of her earlier autistic behavior in the form of transient echolalia. By the age of four she could write her own name, was playing well with other children in a nursery school, and had completely dropped any affectations in her speech or behavior. Her adjustment to kindergarten public school was excellent. She is now in the second grade and is considered by her teacher a "gifted child." There are no social difficulties. Another child was born when Judy was five and a half, to which development she has adjusted very well. On the other hand, the father's problems have not been resolved, since he could not commit himself to intensive psychotherapy or psychoanalysis once Judy's problem was resolved. He did gain sufficient relief to permit another pregnancy without regressive behavior.

Comment: Because the problem of autistic behavior in children is of such considerable interest, and because the diagnosis of autism often carries such a pessimistic prognosis, Judy's case deserves detailed attention because of the success of the treatment strategy applied at an early stage of the child's development. On the surface, the history of Judy's "independence," beginning at age two weeks, *could* all be interpreted as stemming from an inherent developmental deviation in the child. The histories of delayed speech and subsequent schizophrenia in the father's sister and serious mental illness in the father's aunt were factors that might suggest transmission of genetic vulnerability to schizophrenia in Judy. The father's obvious fear of marriage and of pregnancy, supported by the exclusively biological orientation of his psychiatrist (who also treated his sister), all prepared the way for a frighteningly pessimistic attitude toward Judy's future. Judy was, in the father's mind, identified with his sister. He considered himself the bearer of bad genes transmitted to Judy, and he behaved toward Judy as he had earlier to his sister, when he had shared responsibility for her care.

The psychodynamics of the father's anxiety attacks had not previously been explored. While his genetic identification with the sister had been recognized, his psychological identification with the sister and the psychological meaning of his daughter as "another sister" had not been recognized by the father. In this case, the father's psychopathology was a major point of psychological vulnerability in the family. The significance to and impact of this problem on the mother and, through her, on the child had not previously been assessed by two excellent pediatricians or by the father's psychiatrist, who had in fact foreclosed the necessity of a psychodynamic investigation in favor of his own biological orientation.

It is important to note that the mother was not herself aware of depressive feelings. Only as she began to observe the significant impact that she could have upon the child in the context of our joint, psychoanalytically-oriented, educational approach to both child and mother could she realize that she had been depressed. This is not infrequently the case with mothers who have children with significant developmental deviation. In the mother's case, depression had been masked by apathy and cautiousness. In fact she *could* not allow herself depressive affect, in view of the dominating influence of the husband's anxieties and phobias. Like many such mothers, she was psychologically strong and felt the need to support her husband and child rather than experience her own feelings.

On first observing her, it would appear that Judy had a more healthy interest in her father than her mother. In retrospect, however, Judy's greater playfulness with the father could have reflected a deeper underlying attachment to the mother, against which she defended. In other words, she responded to father as a way of avoiding mother. The same mechanism was illustrated in her attention to the buttons on her mother's blouse rather than her face. Her interest in feet and knees—the lower end of the spectrum—when faced with a stranger (myself) in the playroom also suggested Judy's "autistic rituals" as a clear manifestation of defense against the strong affects aroused in making social contact.

Nursery school is often recommended for an unsocialized child. However, such recommendations can induce further regressive autistic behavior in children already showing autistic behavior as a defense against social contact. Nursery-school experience can apparently be of great help to the child who has experienced social deprivation and understimulation, but it cannot help the child who is in the stage of defensive autistic withdrawal. Judy did benefit from nursery school experience *after* she had broken through the autistic barrier separating herself from her mother, and also during the later phases of separation and individuation that followed her establishment of a meaningful symbiosis with her mother. Thus, nursery-school experience must be utilized with sensitivity and care in the treatment of children showing autistic behavior. This point has been emphasized by Margaret Mahler.[13]

John, a Nine-Year-Old Boy with Asthma: A Brief Transference Cure

John, age nine, was referred for psychiatric care by a pediatric allergist who had been unsuccessful in bringing frequent asthmatic attacks under control, either by medication or by desensitization. John's asthma had started at age three and had become worse during the year following the separation of his parents. Since then the maternal grandmother had moved into the home, burdening John's mother with her impending death due to metastatic carcinoma. One aspect of John's problem was that he wouldn't take his pills. It was soon discovered that taking pills had become a serious issue of control between John, his mother, and his grandmother, and that John's father didn't believe in pills. During the first session with the medical student involved, the elements of this struggle were identified. John was helped to express his resentment against the three-way struggle between him, his mother, and his grandmother. He quickly developed a very positive attachment to the student. He demonstrated to the student how he could start an asthmatic attack by coughing. His asthma quickly cleared, and for the next three weeks of contact with the medical student he had no attacks (his longest free period in several years). His fantasy play and drawing activities in the sessions with the student patently revealed his concern about the death of the grandmother and mother and the loss of the father. This is shown by the following, when John spent the first part of the visit making a paper airplane.

Medical Student: Can you tell me who is going to fly the plane?

John: My mom. She used to take flying lessons, you know, but she had to quit.

Medical Student: Where do you think she is going to go?

John: To the Devil's Triangle (at this point, a large smile grew across his face). Do you know where that is? (There had been a recent television show about this area off the coast of Miami, where many airplanes and ships have mysteriously disappeared.)

Medical Student: I have a vague idea. Why don't you tell me about it?

John: (Still smiling.) Well, that's where you go when you disappear.

Medical Student: Where else might your mother go?

John: To the rocks.

Medical Student: Rocks?

John: Yeah, you know (as he simulates the nose-dive of the airplane, crashing it into the ground).

Medical Student: What about your dad, where might he go?

John: He'd go to work.

John then drew a picture of himself and the medical student in the lead car of a train, pulling in sequence "my mom, my new dog, my grandma, my daddy." He placed his sister on top of the train (not inside it). The last car was a dining table with seats for all family members.

Follow-up six months later revealed that the mother had died as a result of an auto accident caused by her drinking. John and his sister were seen at this time by another therapist. Both children expressed foreknowledge of the mother's self-destructive behavior, and they were relieved when what they considered inevitable actually occurred. They have thus far made a good adjustment to life with the stepmother and father. John's asthma has not been a problem since it disappeared following the first visit with the medical student. The stepmother finds John an acceptable child with no problems. His sister's rivalry remains a problem.

Comment: The disappearance of significant asthmatic symptoms in John, and his improvement in overall functioning, can be understood as an immediate response to catharsis and to an attachment to the student as a substitute for the missing father. A response to this, together with the fact that John demonstrated at least some conscious control of his asthmatic attacks, indicated that his problems were not solely determined by internalized neurotic conflict. The treatment choice should be one offering an open resolution of family conflicts and a restoration of contact with the father, and/or a reassurance that the father remains interested in and committed to John's future development despite the divorce and the acrimony between the parents. The issue of the grandmother's death was openly broached by the medical student for the first time in the evaluation study of this family. John's "rivalry" with his sister was a displacement and acting out of these complex problems. This was a source of considerable tension in the family. Many children with somatic symptoms, hypochondriasis, and so forth gain such symptoms through identification with others when they are faced with death and separation fears. Transference "cures" such as that shown in John's case should be regarded with suspicion and should involve detailed follow-up study. The mother's death appears to have been anticipated and represented in John's airplane play regarding the "Devil's Triangle."

(Concluding Remarks

While psychoanalytic developmental psychology is far from having achieved a fully articulate theory, it now provides a sufficiently broad base of empirically decisive propositions about human infancy, childhood, and family life to provide the rationale for a wide variety of treatment approaches to many kinds of childhood and family emotional disturbances.

Any treatment approach to the child based upon psychoanalytic understanding should facilitate the child's statement (in words, action, play, drawing affect, or dreams) about what ails him. The therapeutic task is first to help the child make his own statement in his own way, and then to help the child discover the meaning of what he has been able to say.

The psychology of parenting, particularly the father's psychology, is not very well understood. Parents and surrogate parents need to be included in the treatment programming for the child.

As the progressive and regressive processes, so well understood in symptom formation, become the focus of attention in normal development, it can be proved that new advances in treatment will be made in other areas offering exciting future prospects for new treatment approaches in the better integration of

studies of normal narcissism with the main body of psychoanalytic developmental psychology.

(Bibliography

1. ANTHONY, E. J. "Clinical Evaluation of Children with Psychotic Parents," *Am. J. Psychiatry*, 126 (1969), 177–184.
2. ANTHONY, E. J. and T. BENEDEK, eds. *Parenthood, Its Psychology and Psychopathology*. Boston: Little, Brown, 1970.
3. BELL, R. Q., G. M. WELLER, and M. F. WALDROP. *Newborn and Preschooler: Organization of Behavior and Relations between Periods*. Monogr. Soc. Res. Child Dev., 36, nos. 1–2. Chicago: University of Chicago Press, 1971.
4. BENJAMIN, J. "Some Developmental Observations Relating to the Theory of Anxiety," *J. Am. Psychoanal. Assoc.*, 9 (1961), 652–658.
5. BRUCH, H. *Eating Disorders*. New York: Basic Books, 1973.
6. CALL, J. D. "Psychological Problems of the Cerebral Palsied Child, His Parents and Siblings as Revealed by Dynamically Oriented Small Group Discussions with Parents," *Cer. Palsy Rev.*, 19 (1958).
7. ———. "Newborn Approach Behavior and Early Ego Development," *Int. J. Psychoanal.*, 45 (1964), 286–294.
8. ———. "Styles and Games in Infancy," *J. Am. Acad. Child Psychiatry*, 5 (1966), 193–210.
9. ———. " 'Emotional-Social Factors,' Proceedings of a Conference: 'Early Identification of Children with Learning Problems,' " *J. Spec. Educ.*, 4 (1971), 349–359.
10. FREUD, A. *Ego and Mechanisms of Defense*. New York: International Universities Press, 1946.
11. GRAY, G. Z. *The Children's Crusade*, New York: Morrow, 1970.
12. KLEIN, M. "An Obsessional Neurosis in a Six-Year-Old Girl," in *The Psychoanalysis of Children*, pp. 65–93. London: Hogarth, 1932.
13. MAHLER, M. "On Child Psychosis and Schizophrenia: Autistic and Symbiotic Infantile Psychosis," in *The Psychoanalytic Study*

of the Child, Vol. 7, pp. 286–305. New York: International Universities Press, 1952.

14. ———. "Rapprochement Subphase of Separation–Individuation Process," *Psychoanal. Q.*, 41 (1972), 487–505.

15. REISER, D. "The Use of Visual Media in the Service of Ego Growth." Paper presented Div. Child Psychiatry, Dept. Psychiatry Human Behavior, Coll. Medicine, U. Calif., Irvine, November 1972.

16. STOLLER, R. J. *Sex and Gender.* New York: Science House, 1968.

17. WINNICOTT, D. W. *The Family and Individual Development.* London: Tavistock, 1965.

18. ———. *Therapeutic Consultations in Child Psychiatry.* New York: Basic Books, 1971.

CHAPTER 12

HYPNOTHERAPY

Lewis R. Wolberg

I N RECENT YEARS, hypnosis has gained an increasing acceptance among the psychiatric profession, both as a therapeutic implement and as a research vehicle for the investigation of many complex aspects of human behavior. Instrumental in lending some scientific credibility to hypnosis have been the two leading organizations in the field: the Society for Clinical and Experimental Hypnosis, and the American Society for Clinical Hypnosis. The former publishes *The Journal of Clinical and Experimental Hypnosis*, the latter *The American Journal of Clinical Hypnosis*. Both magazines contain informative articles on hypnosis of contemporary interest. Moreover, a number of serious researchers and clinicians have made contributions that have given an atmosphere of respectability to the practice of hypnotherapy.

Nevertheless, hypnosis continues to be blighted with misconceptions promulgated mostly by uninformed persons or those whose personal needs lead them to link hypnosis with magic and the paranormal. It has been difficult to dislodge this association with the occult not only from the minds of the public but also from some professional groups. Levitt

and Chapman,[26] discussing the problems of research in hypnosis, have pointed out the reasons why hypnosis is not employed more frequently in research: it requires much time and effort; it involves an unusually high probability of sampling bias; and, most importantly, it currently lacks "respectability" in the community of scientists. They state: "Until the mystical aura of the centuries has finally been dispelled, hypnosis will not be afforded a full, fair opportunity to demonstrate its value as a hypnosis and research method."

❨ Hypnosis and Research

In spite of these deterrents, hypnosis has been employed as a research tool in the study of emotions, psychopathological phenomena, dreams, defense mechanisms, physiological processes, and test validation. The available evidence is that it is at least as powerful as other laboratory techniques.

One problem in hypnotic research is that, in an effort to maintain impartial experimental objectivity, the researcher may eliminate or distort the hypnotic phenomena being studied.[47] That is, a hypnotist must approach his subject confidently and optimistically in order to produce the proper expectancies on which much of the trance is based. An attitude of neutral uninvolvement—the preferred stance of the researcher—will tend to act against the hypnotic process itself. It is difficult or impossible for a researcher who fully commits himself to the role of hypnotist not to attempt to validate his personal expectations and thus defeat his desire, as a researcher, to maintain objectivity.

Another problem is how to differentiate the phenomena under investigation that are due to hypnosis from those due to the subject's expectations. Individuals under hypnosis may attempt to please the operator by divining what is required of them and then living up to anticipated demands. Or on the other hand, subjects may try to frustrate or defy the hypnotist because of hostile feelings toward him, or fear of being controlled, or transferential projections. Moreover, the residual prejudices of subjects will tend to contaminate their reports.

An ongoing difficulty in research on the trance state is that of distilling reliable and conceptually meaningful data out of the multiple phenomena encountered. Similar ambiguities, of course, are met in research in psychotherapy and other interpersonal processes. An experimental design often employed in hypnosis to meet this problem is the "subject-as-own-control." For example, physiological measurements are first made during the waking state. After the induction of hypnosis, the same tests are repeated without any direct or indirect suggestions being made. Differences between the two sets of measurements are then attributed to interposition of the trance state. Another design is that of "independent groups," in which two classes of subjects are designated. One receives hypnotic induction, the other gets simple instructions to use their imaginations strongly. The problem of adequate controls continues to plague the experimenter here, but some progress has been made; Orne[39,40] and London and Fuhrer[28] have indicated ways in which control techniques may be employed in hypnosis.

⟮ The Nature of Hypnosis

Speculation about the nature of hypnosis dates back to the earliest writings on the subject in French, German, Italian, and Spanish, which have recently been translated by Tinterow.[50] An appreciation of how hypnosis may help in psychotherapy would seem to presuppose an understanding of its structure, but at the outset we must admit that although hypnosis was identified as a phenomenon two centuries ago, we still know little about its nature. This is not altogether surprising, since consciousness and sleep, the states between which hypnosis is suspended, also remain a mystery. Many of the blind spots in our knowledge of the trance are compounded by our present limited understanding of neurophysiological and psychodynamic processes in general. Future research will undoubtedly shed light on the true nature of the hypnotic state, but until that time arrives we are limited to theoretical assumptions.

Unfortunately, no theory to date is sufficiently comprehensive to explain all of the complex manifestations of hypnosis. This judgment includes the physiological theories that postulate changes within areas of the cerebral cortex such as those of inhibition and excitation; analogical linkages to animal hypnosis; and considerations of dissociation, conditioning, role-playing, regression, or anachronistic revival of the child–parent relationship as the prime process present in hypnosis. What we are probably dealing with in many of these theories is a delineation of phenomena liberated by the trance, rather than a description of the hypnotic state itself.

Attempts have been made in recent years to identify physiological parameters that are distinctive for hypnosis. To date, however, measurements have failed to reveal any specific differences in biochemical and neurophysiological areas. A few features observed thus far may be mentioned. Electroencephalographic patterns during hypnosis differ from those of sleep stages 2, 3, and 4. There seem to be some similarities between hypnosis and the descending stage-1 transitional sleep,[7,49] but the findings are not conclusive. A number of studies are currently taking place, employing sophisticated computer techniques, that may establish a differentiation of brain wave patterns (particularly alpha activity) in waking and in hypnosis.[29,51,52] Evans[16] however, reviewing the available data, concludes that alpha activity does not appear to change during hypnosis and that we cannot predict hypnotizability from alpha activity. At this stage of our knowledge, all that we know is that the trance state lacks the electrophysiological characteristics of sleep; indeed, it subserves a different function.

Barber[3] insists that recent research has produced data incongruous with the prevalent trance paradigm. Among the anomalous findings are the following: (1) unselected subjects given suggestions in the waking state (such as that they experience body immobility, analgesia, hallucinations, age regression, amnesia, and so forth) are just as responsive as are unselected subjects exposed to "trance induction;" and (2) no special physiological changes distinctive for the "trance" state have ever been discovered that would establish that state as a unique entity. Barber offers an alternative paradigm: in order to produce the phenomena considered characteristic of hypnosis, it is essential to give instructions, in any state of subject awareness, that will elicit positive attitudes, motivations, and expectancies toward the test situation. A capacity for vividly imagining things suggested to him increases the subject's responsiveness, as does a covert verbalizing of suggestions to himself, along with an inhibition of contrary thoughts. Thus, according to Barber, the subject's positive reaction in hypnosis is not due to the "trance" but instead is related to psychological and social influence processes such as conformity, attitude change, and persuasion. Abilities believed by some to be characteristic of hypnosis are actually within the normal human repertoire—such as analgesia, hallucinations, age regression, age progression, amnesia, and so forth. In disagreement, authorities convinced of the existence of an identifiable entity in the trance say that what Barber seems to be doing is equating the phenomena produced during hypnosis with the hypnotic state itself. The fact that one can produce practically any phenomenon in the waking state that one can in the trance, in a subject who possesses the proper attitude, motivations, and expectancies, does not nullify the existence of a special condition that we call hypnosis.

For example, by means of sensory deprivation or the use of psychotomimetic drugs like LSD and psilocybin, we can produce some of the same symptoms in a nonschizophrenic person that we find in schizophrenics. These phenomena may therefore be presumed to fall within the normal human repertoire. Moreover, no special physiological findings of a consistent nature have been found in schizophrenia to establish it as a separate state. These facts do not prove that schizophrenia does not exist as an entity. We may employ a second example: the techniques of psychotherapy. The fact that psychotherapeutic effects may be secured spontaneously without benefit of any professional services does not mean that psychotherapy does not exist as a body of procedures that can score significant gains.

From a clinical point of view, arguments as to how genuine a state hypnosis is are more or less arbitrary. What we are interested in discerning is whether the maneuvers we implement in producing what is called a "trance" in a subject will also increase his suggestibility, since this will serve us during treatment. That such is the case has experimentally been demonstrated by Hilgard and Tart.[22] Therapists who employ hypnosis are almost universally convinced of the fact. Whether it is because of the special routines of induction or because the therapist, persuaded by the powers of hypnosis, communicates suggestions more convincingly—hence increasing expectation, motivation, and positive attitudes—does not truly matter from a pragmatic standpoint.

In speculating on the dynamics of hypnosis, it is essential to remember that the experience of being hypnotized is filtered by each patient through a gauze of his own special emotional demands and needs. What we may be seeing in phenomena mobilized by the trance are aspects of the subject's unique psychological problems rather than manifestations of the hypnotic state *per se*.

❲ Characteristics of the Trance

The fact that practically all of the features of hypnosis may also be observed in other states of awareness has tended to obscure the issue of specificity. In addition, we may be confused by the fact that the responses we encounter merge into normal behavioral manifestations on the one hand, and into neurotic and even psychotic symptomatology on the other.

In every trance we may witness a dynamic configuration of many different kinds of phenomena, constantly fluctuating in response to psychophysiological changes within the individual and changes in the meaning of the hypnotic relationship to him. Some of the elements elicited in the trance may lend themselves to therapeutic use. First, largely because the subject equates hypnosis with sleep and because of the therapist's instructions, there is a remarkable easing of tension as muscles relax progressively. Second, the individual becomes extraordinarily suggestible to pronouncements from the operator that are not too anxiety-provoking. Third, he experiences a shift in attention from the outside world to the inner self; there is greater self-awareness, a deeper contact with his emotional life, a lifting of repressions, and an exposure of repudiated aspects of his psyche. Fourth, a relationship develops with the operator that assuages the subject's sense of helplessness and satisfies some of his inner wishes and demands. Any of these effects may be diminished by anxiety in the subject or be neutralized by suggestions from the hypnotist.

Relaxing Effects

Continued stress may have a damaging effect on bodily functions, both physiological and psychological. It can create somatic imbalance, interfere with the healing process in physical disorders, exaggerate the symptoms of psychological ailments, and bring into play various defensive instrumentalities, some of which may be maladaptive in nature. Any device that eases tension may neutralize these ravages and create the most fertile conditions for spontaneous and applied curative forces to work effectively. Even chronic and progressive organic ailments may be benefited greatly thereby.

How hypnosis aids relaxation is illustrated by the studies of Moody,[35] Mason,[33] and Kirkner.[23] Moody divided twenty patients, each of whom had an uncomplicated peptic ulcer of at least six years' duration, into two groups. Medication was discontinued for the experimental group; instead, thirteen one-hour hypnotic sessions were given, oriented around simple suggestions to relax and to concern oneself less and less with stomach pains. Medication was continued for the control group, but no hypnosis was employed. After a period of several months, X-ray and clinical examinations showed a significantly greater number of patients improved in the experimental than in the control group. Mason[34] reported hypnotherapy of 135 cases of chronic skin diseases. The cases, with an average duration of ten years, had not yielded to regular dermatological treatments. Of these, a remarkable total of sixty-six were cured with no return of symptoms, even after a three-year period of observation. Kirkner described sixty individuals with assorted physical disorders who were treated in a general-hospital setting by hypnorelaxation; forty-three cases markedly benefited from this regimen.

A wide variety of medical, orthopedic, and neurological ailments in which stress plays a part have been successfully treated by hypnosis. Describing these is beyond the scope of this paper, but brief mention will be made of the syndromes that have responded. These include hypertension, Raynaud's disease, coronary disorders, paroxysmal tachycardia, cerebral accidents, asthma, speech disorders, enuresis, impotence, chronic gastritis, dyspepsia, spastic colitis, ulcerative colitis, dysmenorrhea, amenorrhea, and menorrhagia. In such diseases of the central nervous system as tabes, Parkinson's disease, syringomyelia, muscular dystrophy, multiple sclerosis, and the post-traumatic syndrome, residual incoordination, muscle weakness, and paresthesias are reduced by decreasing tension through hypnosis. Since peripheral chronaxy may be heightened and lowered by suggestion, nerve function may be improved in conditions where reversible neuropathological changes exist, as in Sydenham's chorea. Thus hypnosis may be effective in both organic and psychogenic somatic disorders, because of its ameliorative influence on provocative and coincident stress factors.

Where the patient is suffering from disabling tension and anxiety, the mere institution of a trance may exert a tranquilizing influence on his symptoms and increase his ability to cope with his immediate difficulties. Once tension is reduced and a sense of mastery restored, it is remarkable how the patient's latent strengths come to the surface and facilitate adaptation. Where the goal in therapy is to restore the individual to the level prior to his immediate upset, no further psychotherapeutic measures may be required. Obviously there will be no great changes wrought in the patient's personality, and under overwhelming stress he may again break down. But if stress contingencies can be reduced or eliminated, a proper adjustment may be indefinitely maintained.

Some therapists, pleased with the outcome of hypnotic relaxation, do nothing more than buttress these effects by teaching the patient self-hypnosis. The results of such techniques are little different from those that the patient may achieve for himself through yoga exercises and transcendental meditation—purely palliative, and only rarely satisfactory in themselves.

Enhanced Trance Suggestibility

In Shakespeare's great drama, Hamlet approaches Polonius and points out ". . . yonder cloud that's almost in shape of a camel." Polonius agrees that it is like a camel indeed. But, says Hamlet, "methinks it is like a weasel." To which Polonius replies, "It is backed like a weasel." Hamlet counters: "Or like a whale?" Says Polonius: "Very like a whale." This kind of interchange, pointing to the power of suggestion, may be repeated in many contexts and especially in the context of hypnosis. Hypnosis wields its effects largely through the influence of suggestion. The degree of suggestibility in a particular subject is of greater importance than is the depth of trance. In extremely suggestible subjects one may obtain phenomena in waking life that are produced in most persons only in hypnosis, such as analgesia and even hallucinations. The virtue of hypnosis is that it reinforces suggestibility, rendering susceptible many of those who would not be responsive to suggestions in the waking state.

How powerful suggestion can be is illustrated by the phenomenon of the voodoo curse among primitive or semiprimitive groups. A member of such a group may suffer illness and even death upon being convinced of a sorcerer's evil magic. Valid cases have been documented of voodoo deaths that were produced solely by the breaking of a taboo, the penalty for which is traditionally accepted as death. The accursed native becomes listless, refuses to eat, and then wastes away. Medical intervention is futile. However, if a friendly witch doctor exorcises the offended spirits and presumedly restores the sinner to their good graces, the latter often recovers immediately—to the consternation of the sorcerer who originally cast the spell.

Suggestion, which influences the individual profoundly in a positive way, is the rationale behind most uses of the trance. Hammer[19] has shown (at statistically significant levels of confidence) that hypnotic and posthypnotic suggestions may produce the following effects: (1) an increase in psychomotor speed and endurance, and a decrease in physical fatigue; (2) an increase in the span and duration of attention; (3) an increase in the speed of learning; (4) an increase in the speed of association, mental alertness, concentration, and general mental efficiency; (5) an improvement in the application of abstract abilities in relation to number content; (6) an improvement in the speed of reading comprehension;

and (7) a heightened sense of enjoyment in performance. The influence on learning is especially interesting, since hypnosis may potentially be able to modify learning processes, breaking long-established modes of action and even conditioned reflexes and thereby altering set habits.[12] In an interesting experiment, Barrios[4] has shown that hypnosis can greatly augment higher-order conditioning.

The patient's exaggerated suggestibility will vitalize the placebo effect of hypnosis, since a great deal of the benefit that an individual derives from therapy is due to his expectancies.[18] Persons who evince sufficient faith in hypnosis to ask for it, are apt to endow hypnosis with healing powers that can have a constructive effect. For example, twenty clients treated by Lazarus were divided into two groups: those whose request for hypnosis was granted, and those in whom it was refused. The relaxation techniques employed with both were identical, except for the avoidance of the word "hypnosis" in the latter group and the inclusion of the words "hypnotic relaxation" instead of "relaxation" in the former group. This resulted in a significantly greater response to behavior modification methods in the former group. On the other hand, we might expect that where expectations are unreasonable, the patient will respond with great disappointment and even hostility when he discovers that his complaints are not immediately dispersed by the magic of hypnosis. This constitutes a problem in starting therapy with a person whose expectations in relation to hypnosis are obviously unreasonable. Should the therapist let the patient ride on his wagon of hope, or should he deflate this exaggerated confidence? Most hypnotherapists do not interfere with their patients' optimistic fantasies until the first signs of lack of progress develop, at which time a correct picture of the therapeutic situation is firmly drawn. [p. 594]

Hypnotic suggestion facilitates many behavioral techniques, such as systematic desensitization, role-playing, behavior rehearsal, time projection, emotive imagery, anxiety relief, Ellis' Rational Therapy, Lazarus' Emotive Therapy, Salter's Assertion Training, modeling, logical problem solving, labeling and expressing the affect, and so forth. I have found in my own work that some patients who have not responded to behavior therapy techniques as I practice them in the waking state, respond easily to the same techniques when hypnosis is employed as a catalyst.

During hypnosis one may take advantage of the patient's enhanced impressionability by proffering persuasive suggestions, or suggestions toward the yielding of noxious symptoms. These exhortations are usually absorbed with greater facility than in the waking state. If accepted, they may be helpful in neutralizing anxiety, promoting a more optimistic outlook, reducing symptomatic suffering, and enhancing adjustment. Whether they can alter the intrapsychic structure and produce any reconstructive character change is dubious. However, they may divert the individual from tormenting himself with his hopelessness and nudge him into more constructive attitudes toward himself and more healthy modes of relating to people. One may, for example, employ John Hartland's "ego-strengthening technique" of altering the suggestions in accordance with the specific problems of the patient. Hartland[20] believes that irrespective of the kind of psychotherapy one employs, preliminary administration of hypnotic "ego-strengthening" suggestions will enhance the effects of therapy, whether these are aimed at supportive or reconstructive goals. The patient becomes more confident and self-reliant, and he finds it easier to adjust to his environment. Hartland points out that the *manner* in which suggestions are given is as important as the content; such elements as rhythm, repetition, interpolation of appropriate "pauses" and the stressing of certain words and phrases are all vital. In my own experience, I have found ego-strengthening suggestions (coupled with the making of a hypnotic tape) valuable in short-term therapy where my goals were not too extensive. They have not added a great deal to working with patients in depth over a long-term period, during which I use traditional analytic methods; but I would not hesitate to employ ego-building where the patient's defenses were shattered, as a preliminary to more elaborate procedures.

SYMPTOM REMOVAL OR ALLEVIATION

Patients whose lives are being tormented by symptoms often possess no further motivation for therapy than to eliminate their complaints. The average psychiatrist, however, would like to pursue more extensive goals than pure symptom relief: namely, betterment of the patient's general adjustment and possibly, where serious characterologic problems exist, a reconstruction of the personality structure. Realism, however, dictates that we may have to abbreviate our goals and simply do as much for our patients as time, finances, and other practical factors allow. It is here that hypnosis can play a significant role, catalyzing the impact of practically any short-term method.

Direct symptom control is often practiced in emergency situations, as when hysterical symptoms cripple adjustment. In such a case, hypnotherapy may be the treatment of choice.[44] The symptoms that respond best to suggestive hypnosis are hysterical amnesia, stupor, coma, twilight and dream states, dramatic posturing and acting, panic reactions, clouding of consciousness, hallucinations, delirium, and dissociated reactions such as somnambulism and fugues. In conditions of exhaustion due to persistent and uncontrollable hiccuping, and in severe undernutrition caused by functional vomiting and anorexia nervosa, hypnosis may be a life-saving measure.

The possibility that another symptom will be substituted upon elimination of the symptomatic complaint factor is not a great one, but it should be kept in mind. According to a controlled study by Browning and Houseworth,[6] of thirty ulcer patients postoperatively examined following a vagotomy, a significant number developed new symptoms after losing their ulcer complaints. These findings were similar to those reported in an independent study by Szasz[48] of other vagotomized patients. Seitz[46] described the case of a man in whom symptom removal by hypnotic suggestion produced symptom substitution. And Crisp[10] published a paper detailing the treatment, by behavior therapy, of nine patients in whom elimination of symptoms resulted in the development of other complaints. Wolpe[60] has suggested that where "neurotic anxiety" is associated with a symptom, failure to eliminate the anxiety may result in symptom substitution.

Against these claims there is a host of evidence that the removal of symptoms is rarely followed by the development of new problems. Indeed, there is evidence that the resulting improvement spreads into other aspects of the individual's adaptation. If the therapist utilizes a permissive suggestive approach, offering the patient an opportunity to overcome his symptoms if he so desires, there is little to fear. On the other hand, if the therapist comes at the patient like a bull in a china shop, his blunt behavior may have a traumatic effect. But this can occur with any therapy, and not only hypnosis. In fact, in cases where symptoms do serve an important purpose in maintaining the patient's psychological equilibrium, some therapists deliberately employ symptom substitution in order to avoid the possibility of reactions. The theory behind this is that the patient's subversive needs for a symptom may be propitiated with a less noxious token. Erickson[15] believes that suggestions are best limited to symptom substitution, transformation, and amelioration. For instance, in two patients with disabling arm paralysis, Erickson substituted, with satisfactory results, wrist stiffness and fatigue in one case, and stiffness of the little finger in the other.

A number of observers have challenged the traditional caution in the hypnotic removal of symptoms. If the therapist is dynamically oriented, watches the reactions of the patient, and restores symptoms by hypnotic command in instances of ego collapse, there is little or no danger in symptom removal by authoritative suggestion. The way in which a suggestion is phrased is also extremely important. When the patient understands that he may retain those symptoms that are important to him, in their entirety or in part, and when his cooperation is obtained for the procedures utilized, there is little hazard involved.

In some patients, a "chain reaction" may be started as the result of the successful hypnotic handling of one aspect of the total problem, with benefit to the individual's general adjustment. For example, a patient applied for therapy with the request that he be taught self-hypnosis to help him retain and recall material for an important examination that was to be held six weeks in the future. As a civil service employee, it was urgent that he pass the examination to fill the vacancy at the head of his department for which he was eligible by virtue of seniority. His fear of failure was compounded by the specter of losing face with his fellow employees in the event he was unable to achieve a passing grade. It was apparent that his faulty concentration and memory were by-products of an extensive personality disorder associated with fear of and resentment toward authority, as well as a greatly devaluated self-esteem. During his childhood he had been repeatedly reminded by a successful and authoritarian father that he was expected to bring credit to the family through his career accomplishments. One of the important operative dynamics in the case was a fear of success coupled with a terror of competing, achieving parity with, and perhaps even vanquishing his father. There was also a hostile defiance of his male parent, since success also symbolized submitting to and being destroyed by the latter. Since the patient lived in the South, refused referral to local psychiatric sources, and saw no need for working on any problem other than his faulty concentration, short-term therapy was considered expedient. In hypnosis he was given suggestions to the effect that his mind would gradually clear, his attention sharpen, and his desire to study improve. Furthermore, he would understand more and more clearly why he was blocked in his memory and recall. A tentative explanation of the dynamics was offered him, and he was asked to consider, think about, and decide for himself which aspects were false or true. He was instructed to explore his reactions and to try to discover reasons for them. In the waking state he was encouraged to talk about his relationship with his parents and to make connections with patterns that were operating in his present life situation. He was additionally taught the process of self-hypnorelaxation for the purpose of reinforcing suggestions.

Therapy consisted of a total of five sessions. Not only was the patient able to pass his examination successfully, but a follow-up visit one year later showed conclusively that his behavior patterns had been beneficially influenced. He had become capable of standing up to authority when necessary, and he felt degrees of independence and assertiveness in himself that he had never believed were within his potential.

HABIT CORRECTION AND REHABILITATION

Hypnosis has been employed for the correction of certain habit disturbances. It is generally satisfactory for this purpose unless the disorder is linked intimately with deep-seated personality problems and needs. Thus obesity that dates back to childhood rarely responds to hypnotherapy. On the other hand, where excessive food intake does not serve an important psychological function such as gratifying frustrated early oral demands or deprivations, dietary control may be materially helped through hypnotic suggestions. Insomnia similarly may respond better to hypnosis and self-hypnosis than to almost any other measure. However, where the patient has become seriously habituated to hypnotic drugs, there may be little reaction to suggestions other than frustration. A gratifying number of patients who wish to give up smoking tobacco, but who cannot do so, find that hypnosis relaxes their tensions sufficiently to keep their suffering from being extreme when they abstain. Some sexual difficulties such as impotence or mild frigidities yield rapidly to reassuring suggestions, made during hypnosis, that are geared toward helping the patients regard sexuality as a pleasure function rather than as a performance. Satisfactory results also have been reported when employing hypnosis in enuresis. I have used hypnosis (coupled with aversive stimulation) in intractable hair-pulling and nail-biting cases and have found it a tactic to which some of these patients will respond. Alcoholic abuse and drug addiction are difficult to treat, but certain dedicated therapists seem to be able to effectuate some constructive impact on these severe habit disorders when motivation is present.

Indeed, through appropriate suggestions, hypnosis may serve as a powerful motivational determinant. For example, it may be possible to motivate a patient to cease resisting medical dietary orders, in obesity; to restore appetite, in anorexia and undernutrition; to avoid excessive stress and overactivity, in cardiac conditions; to facilitate speech retraining, in aphasic disorders; to exercise a limb that has been immobilized by a cast or by arthritis; to obtain essential rest and sleep, in insomnia; and to give up smoking, where nicotine and coal tar exert a dangerous influence. Hypnosis may help divert the patient's mind from unhealthy and self-destructive fantasies, encouraging him toward more productive thoughts and actions. In chronic ailments where the patient has lost the will to live, hypnotic suggestion may inspire him to keep up the fight; it may promote a shift in his attitude that spells the difference between survival and death.

We have only begun to investigate the rehabilitative uses of hypnotic suggestion. It may play a most important role, particularly in individuals who are more disabled by their fears and attitudes than by their physical disorders. In emotional ailments where there is a lack of incentive for psychotherapy, hypnosis may promote an acceptance of the treatment situation by offering active and immediate help, by developing constructive rapport with the therapist, and by demonstrating that the patient's problems are not visited on him by an evil providence but are instead related to conflicts within himself that need treatment.[57]

ALLEVIATION OF PAIN

Proper hypnotic suggestion may lower or eliminate overt and subjective responses to painful stimuli. This is accomplished by the reduction of tension and anxiety, promotion of muscle relaxation, and diversion of attention from the pain stimulus. The resultant is an analgesia that may be advantageously employed in minor surgical procedures, in diagnostic exploration such as sigmoidoscopy, in dental operations, and in obstetrics. Relaxing and analgesic suggestions are particularly valuable as an aid to chemical anesthesia, helping

to reduce the amount of anesthetic required. Indeed, hypnosis may eliminate the need for preoperative analgesics, which, as Beecher[5] has indicated, depress respiration and lower the blood-oxygen level. Smaller quantities of chemical anesthetic may be lifesaving in toxic conditions, as well as in serious operations such as lung and heart surgery. Hypnosis minimizes neurogenic shock and reduces postoperative pain and discomfort. Excellent accounts of the adjunctive uses of hypnosis in anesthesia may be found in papers by Mason,[33] Marmer,[32] Raginsky,[42] Owen-Flood,[41] and Crasilneck et al.[8]

The induction of hypnotic anesthesia sufficiently deep to permit major surgical operations has been reported. Its use here is limited to the 5 to 10 percent of patients who are able to achieve the profound somnambulistic trance required for such employment. As an anesthetic by itself, hypnosis has a limited utility, chemical anesthesia being more universally applicable. The chief advantage of hypnosis is an adjunctive one. It is sometimes employed in dentistry (hypnodontics) (see Marcus,[31] Moss,[36,37] and West et al.[54]). It is used to (1) quiet a terrified and tense patient so that he will permit exploratory and corrective dental measures; (2) reinforce local anesthesia by lowering the required dosage and helping to overcome gagging, coughing, and excessive salivation; (3) foster better cooperation in using dental appliances; and (4) correct habits that interfere with mental health, such as nail-biting and bruxism.

One of the most effective areas for the use of hypnoanalgesia is childbirth.[*] A chief problem in obstetrics is the prolonged period during which pain-relieving measures are necessary. Since difficult labor may go on for hours and even days, chemical anesthetics have a toxic potential for both mother and fetus. They are hazardous in toxemia of pregnancy and in cardiac failure. They may also, when administered during the second stage of labor, tend to depress uterine contractions as well as impair the respirations of the infant. Hypnosis may serve as a competent analgesic

[*] See references 11, 21, 24, 25, and 38.

in itself; the so-called "natural childbirth" method, which consists of conditioning the patient in proper breathing and relaxation during childbirth, is probably a form of hypnosis. Or as said, as an adjunct to chemical anesthesia it may greatly reduce the amount of anesthetic required. Moreover, by improving morale and lessening apprehension, it tends to shorten labor. Patients prepared by hypnosis have had a shorter and less variable labor period, have complained less about pain and discomfort, and have needed fewer analgesic drugs.[1] Owing to the time factor in training preparturient patients, the handling of prospective mothers in groups in prenatal clinics has been advocated.[2]

Hypnoanalgesia may also be valuable in controlling both functional and organic pain.[43] Dolorous hysterical conditions may yield readily to properly phrased suggestions. Organic pain may be relieved by helping the patient to detach from his suffering. The pain stimulus is not eliminated here, as it may be in functional disorders, but by focusing the patient's interest away from himself, hypnosis may ameliorate some of his distress. This is, perhaps, akin to what happens when attention is diverted during pain in the waking state. Beecher,[5] for instance, cites observations of soldiers with severe wounds who, in the heat of battle, have felt no pain; of athletes who were so bent on winning that they were oblivious to extensive physical injuries; and of religious martyrs who have endured unbelievable tortures during ecstatic reveries. Hypnosis, reinforced by self-hypnosis, may be employed for pain associated with such conditions as causalgia, postherapeutic neuralgia, trigeminal neuralgia, cervical discogenic disease, and spinal-cord injuries.[14,27] In advanced cancer, where pain cannot be controlled by other means, hypnosis may reduce suffering and help the patient face the present and the future with greater courage. If the patient is capable of entering a very deep trance state, he may be able to experience almost total relief from pain.

Certain surgical conditions may be helped by hypnosuggestion. Crasilneck et al.[8] have reported excellent results in the hypnotic treatment of patients with very severe burns. Loss of fluids, toxemia, and pain encourage shock reactions, with curtailed appetite, mobilization of tension, and shattering of morale. Hypnosis may be used to advantage as an analgesic for the changing of dressings, debridement, and skin grafting. Because of the toxemia, hypnoanesthesia is better for the burned patient than chemical anesthesia. Direct hypnotic suggestions may also help the intake of food and fluids. Often the effect of hypnosis is dramatic—a listless, depressed, nauseated patient who has resisted feeding and drinking suddenly showing an interest in his meals. Posthypnotic suggestions reduce post-dressing pain and enable the patient to get out of bed and to move about, thereby avoiding becoming bedridden.

DIAGNOSTIC USES

The diagnostic uses of hypnosis are founded on heightened suggestibility. Occasionally it is necessary to distinguish certain functional disorders from organic disorders—for instance, where disposition is dependent upon diagnosis. Thus certain cases of abdominal pain severe enough to simulate surgical emergencies may be hysterically determined; although the patient may clamor for surgical interference, he will need to be treated by psychiatric means. Inconsistencies in signs and symptoms will encourage the cautious surgeon to seek psychiatric consultation, and hypnosis may aid in determining the functional nature of the complaint by temporarily removing it through suggestion. Other symptoms that may call for diagnostic differentiation where signs of organic involvement are not clear are anesthesia, paresthesia, hyperesthesia, headaches, paralysis, spasms, tics, choreiform movements, gait disturbances, convulsive seizures, vomiting, hiccuping, urinary retention, and disorders of vision and hearing. In post-traumatic cases, residual pain may require diagnosis to determine if the pain is related to the original accident or whether it has been elaborated as a psychoneurotic symptom. Hypnosis has been used to differentiate anorexia nervosa from hypophysial cachexia, to distinguish an articulation disorder from stuttering[30] and to detect malingering in cases of feigned color blindness and paraplegia.[13] Hypnosis is also sometimes of diagnostic value in determining the dynamic meaning of symptoms. For instance, Rosen and Erickson[45] (1955) have used suggestion to precipitate attacks in patients with convulsive and asthmatic symptoms. They then blocked the attacks; the effect was to mobilize anxiety, which in turn was repressed by direct verbal suggestion in order to allow the underlying fantasies to erupt into awareness.

During the early stages of psychotherapy, hypnosis may help to demonstrate to a non-motivated patient (or to one who is unable or unwilling to accept dynamic formulations) the workings of his unconscious. For example, a patient suffering from severe and crippling back pains of psychic origin—the basis of which he credited to an undetected arthritic spinal condition—was inducted into a trance, and the pain was transferred from his back to his right shoulder. He was conditioned to experience this transfer of pain to his shoulder whenever I tapped three times on the side of my desk; upon emerging from the trance he expressed surprise that his back pain had vanished, but he complained bitterly of discomfort in his shoulder. After fifteen minutes had passed he again experienced his habitual back agony, with relief in his shoulder, but my tapping reversed his complaint once more. From this he realized that his mind was so susceptible to suggest that it could create and shift pain. He was then able to accept the fact that his mind could also be responding to self-imposed painful suggestions. This helped to remove his resistance to the acceptance of psychotherapeutic help. For patients who stubbornly deny having conflicts, the process of repression may be demonstrated by suggesting that a hypnotically-inspired dream disappear in the waking state and then reappear at a given signal. This may suggest to the patient that he is keeping certain thoughts and feelings from his own awareness. The creation of experimental conflicts is also a most dramatic means of demonstrating psychopathological mental operations to the patient.[58]

Lifting of Repressive Controls

As the trance deepens, there is a relative withdrawal of attention from the outside world and a refocusing on the inner self and its processes. The individual becomes aware of certain aspects of his unconscious life that had eluded him in the waking state. There follows an easing of repressive controls, with release of charged emotional components, a flourishing of fantasy, and an activation of primitive mental operations with more vivid symbolization. These tendencies potentially lend themselves for use in psychoanalytic therapy by encouraging emotional catharsis, by bringing the individual into closer contact with repressed needs and conflicts, and by facilitating a search for significant memories with the aim of exploration of genetic determinants. It does not follow from this that hypnosis is necessary or useful in all patients. If there is no extraordinary resistance, the analytic process proceeds quite satisfactorily without recourse to hypnosis. However, in cases where resistance blocks exploration of unconscious elements, hypnosis may prove to be of help. For example, where the patient is unable to verbalize freely because of overwhelming anxiety, hypnosis may encourage a discharge of obstructive emotions or may relax speech operations sufficiently so that articulation is possible.

A patient was referred for therapy with a severe speech disorder that had defied every physical, rehabilitative, and psychiatric measure that could be applied. When he married at the age of thirty-five, his speech problem (periodic up to this time and appearing only under extraordinary stress circumstances) rapidly became so exaggerated that he could hardly make himself understood. He was able to retain his job because of the influence of his family and because he was considered a gentle and lovable member of his organization. His wife confided that he never displayed anger, being the most reserved and reasonable person she had ever met. This observation conflicted sharply with his productions in the Rorschach test, which were replete with figures moving against each other, tearing things apart, and creating explosions in impact. The patient insisted that his past psychotherapeutic efforts were a rank failure because he was unable to talk. He was willing to expose himself to hypnosis, but he could not guarantee that he would respond. During trance induction, the patient could be observed fighting off succumbing to a trance. He confided that for some reason he was unable to concentrate. He was promised that no "secrets" would be extracted from him; indeed, it was not even essential that he talk. With this reassurance the patient entered into a trance, whereupon he suddenly began to wail and beat the sides of the chair with his fists. A series of bloodcurdling shrieks preceded a torrent of invective directed against his wife and boss. It is difficult to describe graphically the verbal violence that was released. As the patient recounted instances of abuse and exploitation with great passion, his utterances became progressively clearer. In successive sessions we were able to explore the many resentments that he harbored within himself, the fantasies associated with rage, and the origins of the defensive mechanisms, such as his stammering, that he had developed to conceal hostility from himself and others.

In this case the mere induction of a trance lowered repression sufficiently to bring painful thoughts, emotions, and memories to the surface. In most patients, however, probing operations are necessary before a release is possible. With pointed questions the patient may be helped to engage in more productive free associations, to activate fantasies, and to liberate some important memories. Where the patient continues to be resistive, the techniques of regression and revivification may sometimes prove successful.[58]

A patient with strong anxieties and depressions was referred for therapy following hospitalization for an attempt at wrist slashing. Her two years of analytic therapy previous to her referral had helped her greatly, but they had not prevented periodic acting-out tendencies. These took the form of seeking hospitalization compulsively, faking various ailments to ensure her admission, or threatening suicide by cutting the skin of her wrists. The latter act

was always arranged so that she could be apprehended and hospitalized before she had seriously injured herself. A bright, sociable, and intelligent woman, she professed dismay at activities that had brought great embarrassment to her and to her friends. She claimed being possessed by an impulse so powerful that it forced her to execute these bizarre actions, even though she realized that they were against her best interests. Free association in the waking and hypnotic states revealed no clues as to the meaning of her behavior, but whenever she spoke of retreating to a hospital she did so with a none-too-well-concealed excitement that left no doubt that her destructive acts yielded deep and significant gratifications. In a trance she was given the suggestion to return in time to that period of her life when she had first had an impulse similar to the one that now repeatedly forced her to seek hospitalization. Responding to this suggestion, the patient saw herself as a child of nine escaping from her house after a quarrel with her mother, filled with rage after unsuccessfully seeking solace and support from a detached and passive father. In her turmoil she slipped and fell against a barbed-wire fence. She then slowly and deliberately cut her wrists with the barbs of the fence until she drew blood. In part her purpose was to convince herself she could stand pain, which was a way of living up to her mother's ideal of acting like a Spartan; in part it was to bring to her side the family physician who had comforted her far beyond the call of duty in her times of need, acting like a substitute father. As a result of recall of this memory, she was able to realize that her wrist slashing and insistence on hospitalization were revived impulses for seeking help from a doctor who represented to her a giving father figure. She recognized that her episodes developed whenever she experienced severe rejection. This insight enabled her to work through her acting-out and eventually to eliminate from her life her destructive behavioral tendencies.

The bringing to awareness of important past events and experiences may be helpful in a variety of emotional disorders, particularly where there has been a sealing off of powerful emotions associated with a significant past event. Some symptoms are protective defensive devices, elaborated to shield the patient from the return of painful repressed feelings and fantasies. Hypnosis offers the patient a milieu of relaxed relatedness with a trusted person, the hypnotist—an atmosphere that helps the patient to tolerate the implications of the repressed material. Perhaps this accounts for the success of hypnosis in hysterical amnesias, since once the patient feels capable of facing the dangers within, he may be able to drop protective symptoms that have been disorganizing to his total adjustment. It goes without saying that the working-through process, which must be carried on in the waking state, will require many months of laborious effort. Often the release of significant material in the trance may be seemingly forgotten. However, a chain reaction will have been started that reverberates through the individual, eating away at his resistances to waking recall. In this reference, one may witness a change in the character of the dreams as they reflect increasingly less distorted symbols of the repressed material. Finally a breakthrough of important memories may occur in full consciousness. This indicates that the ego has strengthened to a point of tolerating inner conflicts and fears.

It is essential not to take memories and experiences recounted in the trance at face value. The productions elaborated by a person during hypnosis generally are a fusion of real experiences and fantasies. However, the fantasies are significant in themselves, perhaps even more significant than the actual happenings with which they are blended. Asking a patient to recall only real events, or to verify aspects of the material as true or false, reduces but does not remove the element of fantasy.

Hypnosis is a valuable aid in the stimulation of dreams in patients who are unable to remember them or who have "dried up" productively, operating on a plateau in their analysis from which they cannot seem to progress. Often a simple posthypnotic suggestion to remember dreams stimulates the analytic process. For example, a woman in analysis had achieved improvement but continued to de-

tach herself from men, complaining that her contacts were limited by her reality situation. She claimed it was impossible for her to meet the right male companion, because of the restrictions imposed on her by a maiden aunt with whom she lived and by the inroads of her work on her leisure time. Although these excuses were obvious rationalizations, the patient refused to accept them as such, and she obstinately denied that any anxiety promoted her refusal to accept dates. She had no dreams to report, and her free associations assumed a controlled, repetitive quality. Hypnosis was finally employed, and the patient was given a posthypnotic suggestion that she would have dreams that would help her understand better her relationship with men. At the next session she reported a dream that apparently had been provoked by my suggestion. In the dream the patient saw herself inside a house looking out of a window. "I was situated at an enormous distance from an event that was going on that fascinated me. I was afraid to look, but I had to. I needed a telescope to see what was going on. I saw two people in a fight. One man was hitting another man. Blood was drooling from his mouth. I knew if he keeled over and played dead, the man would drop him and leave. I tried to tell him to play dead and not gurgle, so that he would not be killed." In the trance the patient was asked to redream the same dream she had had, but to add any parts she had forgotten. She recalled one element in the dream that she had overlooked, which was that the victim was wearing high heels. Her associations were that the high heels were similar to those on the shoes worn by the men in the third card of the Rorschach test. At the time of her test, she had wondered why men were wearing women's shoes. She then related experiencing a feeling of inconsistency to the effect that she too wore high heels, even though she considered herself to be as efficient as a man. She confided with bitterness that the sexual role she had to play as a woman had bloody connotations for her. To sleep with a man signified being victimized, humiliated, virtually killed. The meaning of the dream became apparent to her after this revelation. Her looking through a telescope was a viewing of her relationships with men from a distance, since she did not want to expose herself to the hurt of a close contact. What she saw in the dream frightened her. A man, an aspect of herself, was being attacked. She could easily be the victim of a bloody assault in a sexual embrace with a man. In the waking state she continued her associations, and soon she confessed having had sexual feelings toward me, which had frightened her so that she could not divulge them. She had responded with defensive detachment and with resistance, which had obstructed her progress. The recounting of this dream enabled us to proceed satisfactorily with her analysis.

Mobilization of Transference

Hypnosis may have a remarkable influence by virtue of the unique relationship that develops between the participants during the trance. For instance, some patients may feel singularly protected, as if they are under the aegis of a powerful and supporting agency who can minister to their needs and defend them from hurt. They may experience warmth in closeness to another human being, which vitalizes them. These attitudes can be extremely meaningful, particularly to persons who are consumed by anxiety and paralyzed with a sense of helplessness, to individuals who are characterologically detached and fearful of human contacts, and to those who lack motivation for therapy. The fact that the patient derives something important from the trance experience often helps him to relate in a more constructive way to the therapeutic situation. Schizoid persons may be enabled to develop a relationship with the therapist in a few sessions that would require many weeks or months of tedious working-through of resistance in the process of ordinary psychotherapy. Fisher[17] has shown that the effect of even a single hypnotic induction may carry over long after the trance has ended. Therapeutically beneficial influences may be stimulated that persist after hypnosis is no longer employed as a technique.

Some patients neurotically interpret the hypnotic relationship as one in which they must yield to every utterance and command of the hypnotist. This makes them peculiarly responsive to suggestions that (if not too anxiety-provoking or too depleting of important defenses) will remove, modify, or control the patient's symptoms. The personality dynamics of such individuals usually require the constant operation of dependency as a security maneuver, and they often compulsively seek to put themselves under the protective custody of some idealized parental agency. The hypnotist easily is identified as such a force and is credited with great power and intelligence. The higher the amount of tension and anxiety, the more the patient will be motivated to establish this kind of relationship. It must not be assumed from this that hypnosis precipitates dependency; the dependent patient will eventually play the same role with a therapist who does not employ hypnosis. The person with no excessive dependency problem will become no more dependent on hypnosis than on any other kind of therapy.

Hypnosis may rapidly mobilize other transference manifestations. Thus patients who are unable to develop strong transferences may be stimulated to do so by the induction of hypnosis. In the trance, the patient may misidentify the hypnotist as a parental or sibling figure, or he may respond posthypnotically with transference dreams. A man with severe gastrointestinal symptoms was referred by an internist for psychotherapy, which he vehemently resisted. Hypnorelaxation produced an abatement of symptoms, fostered a feeling of trust and closeness, and helped motivate him to accept therapy on a level deeper than a supportive one. His resistance, however, was strong, and his progress lagged. Hypnosis was resumed with the goal of helping the patient break through his block. Free associations were accelerated in the trance, and it was possible to stimulate dreams and fantasies that were related to some of his basic conflicts. During one of our sessions, I suggested that the patient think about his feelings toward me. After a silence of five minutes, he opened his eyes with a start. He had a fantasy, he revealed, of me moving toward him with an erect, exposed penis with the intent of forcing it into his mouth. He complained of tension and discomfort, which continued the remainder of the hour. At the next session he reported this dream: "I see my wife downstairs in her panties and bra. I am repelled and furious with her. Then I am outside looking at my car. It isn't as powerful as my brother Jack's car. Then I am at a funeral. A young woman of twenty is crying. I put my arms around her to console her and she responds. But as I look at her she turns older and older and is around fifty. Then I am in a basement, a prisoner of the Communists, and they are sticking rods in my mouth. I am repelled and nauseated and feel that they are out to kill me. I awoke and found that I had had a wet dream." His associations appeared to indicate impulses toward his wife that would have her as a mother figure who attracted, infuriated, and revolted him; and a fear of his older brother and father, toward whom he felt inferior and who, he believed, could render him helpless. On a more unconscious level, the patient apparently sought castration and homosexual affiliation. His relationship with me reflected his fear of homosexual attack. The content of later sessions concerned themselves with working with oedipal and homosexual material that had been stimulated by his hypnotic transference reactions.

⟪ Induction of Hypnosis

Concerning the tremendous diversity of techniques used for the induction of hypnosis, there is no evidence of the superiority of any one method of induction over any other. Actually, all methods are efficacious if the hypnotist adapts them to his personality, applies them confidently, persists in making suggestions in the face of the patient's seeming inability to respond, and avoids haste by allowing enough time to elapse for the patient to adjust himself to the demands that are being made on him in the trance. Successes are most common where the therapist is able to per-

ceive, to recognize, and to deal with the immediate emotional needs of the patient as well as his resistances to trance suggestions. This necessitates flexibility in the employment of techniques, in accordance with the developing reactions of the patient.

Factors in the patient that correlate positively with hypnotizability are a desire for hypnosis, faith in the hypnotist, and confidence in the specific method of hypnosis that is currently being applied. An inner sense of helplessness, intense anxiety, and a loss of feelings of mastery may facilitate entry into a trance state. Thus, as a rule, soldiers in battle fatigue are more easily hypnotizable and enter into deeper trances than after their recovery from the shock of combat. Factors that correlate negatively with hypnosis are distrust of, fear of, and resentment toward the hypnotist; absent motivation; doubts regarding the efficacy of hypnosis as a treatment process; resistance toward the method of induction that is being employed; fear of revealing frightening or shameful secrets in the trance; terror over yielding one's independence or of losing one's will in hypnosis; fear of failure; and the need to dominate and vanquish the hypnotist. The skill of the hypnotist in recognizing and circumventing these resistances will determine whether his results are good or bad.

The actual induction of hypnosis may readily be learned. Involved in practically all induction methods is a gradual narrowing of consciousness by limiting sensory impressions. This is accomplished by fixing attention on a "fixation object" such as a pencil, coin, finger, or spot on the ceiling, or by focusing on a limited group of ideas presented by the hypnotist, such as a restful scene or one's inner sensations. Sensory restriction is reinforced by a rhythmic, monotonous repetition of suggestions to the effect that the subject will feel sensations of tiredness and drowsiness until his lids close and he approaches a state that approximates sleep. Once the eyes are shut, further graduated suggestions are given the subject until he responds satisfactorily to verbal commands. Detailed elsewhere are the various induction methods and induction procedures.[53,55] Experience will best teach the therapist which conditions the trance is most useful for, as well as which specific kinds of techniques are valuable to achieve set goals.

❲ Dangers of Hypnosis

The dangers residual in hypnotherapy are minimal or absent if it is employed by a responsible and well-trained therapist who knows how to handle the patient's general reactions and resistances to psychotherapy. An unskilled and unsophisticated hypnotist, however, may sometimes provoke inimical reactions. Instances have been reported of individuals plunged into anxiety as a result of unwise suggestions given them by stage and amateur hypnotists. Spontaneous hysterical phenomena may be precipitated in some patients during a trance, perhaps as a defense against conflicts mobilized by a return of the repressed material. These will usually disappear after hypnosis is terminated. Sometimes a patient may not be awakened properly, and for some hours he may walk around in a daze. Occasionally, a hysterical patient may develop spontaneous trance states between sessions. These may be eliminated by proper suggestions during hypnosis. The forceful ordering away of symptoms may, in somnambulistic subjects, occasionally release a very intense anxiety that had been bound by the symptoms. The authoritarian use of hypnosis should therefore be avoided except in certain emergencies. Hypnosis-inspired instances of uncontrolled sexual acting-out and of dependency and infantilization were rarely or never encountered in a survey covering a sizable number of psychiatrists who employed hypnosis regularly in their practices.[56]

It is theoretically possible to release criminal tendencies in persons who have latent impulses in this direction that are repressed and controlled in ordinary life. How this may happen is suggested by what occurs in fugue states and in dissociated personality disorders, in which an aspect of the patient's personality takes over and displays unusual or antisocial behavior for which there is amnesia later on. By carefully worded suggestions, one may (in certain individuals) activate parts of the self that have been dissociated from the personality mainstream and that respond to criminal incitement. However, attempts to implant criminal impulses in people who are not latently psychopathic are fruitless, no matter how deep the trance may be, and whether or not antisocial behavior is possible in the trance, one assumes that the therapist who employs hypnosis is not himself criminally inclined and would no more attempt to influence a hypnotized patient toward criminal or self-destructive behavior than he would prescribe a lethal dose of a toxic substance under the guise of its being a medicament, or cut a patient's heart out during surgery after rendering the patient helpless with anesthesia.

❲ Hypnosis in a Comprehensive Psychotherapy

A great deal of the disillusionment in psychotherapy stems from the fact that patients are reluctant to give up their distorted values and maladoptive drives even when they see clearly that these bring unhappy "rewards." The peculiar tenacity of human nature in clinging to self-defeating behavior has confronted philosophers and healers from time immemorial. The fact that we have not yet devised universally successful modes of rectifying this blemish in the human condition need not deter us from working toward this end. Success and failure in therapy will ultimately depend on whether or not we can reeducate our patients toward behaving in life with a new logic. The crucial question is how best can we do this.

Perhaps one of the reasons we are either blessed or burdened with so many different kinds of therapeutic stratagems is that people come to have unique patterns through the processes of learning and change. What works for one patient may have no effect whatsoever for another. One group of individuals will respond rapidly, almost miraculously, to simple suggestions proffered by a respected authority figure, or to philosophical formulations, persuasive injunctions, or recipes for correct behavior. Others, balking at these expediencies, will react gratifyingly to various modes of behavior modification, to systematic desensitization, aversive conditioning, assertive training, role playing, and the like. Still others find challenge and change in a cognitive approach, in searching out sources of conflicts, in tracing behaviors to genetic origins, in employing the resulting insights toward corrective adaptations.

The variables in psychotherapy are great and still beyond our complete understanding. It is fortunate indeed if a therapist happens to employ a method and to have a personality that coordinates with a special patient's needs. The fact that a patient does not happen to respond or responds negatively to our stratagems, does not necessarily mean that the technique is worthless. It may merely signify that the patient is not a suitable subject for the technique, or that a temporarily existing combination of factors does not enable the patient to utilize that technique at the time.

In the light of these circumstances, one can understand why a comprehensive psychotherapy employing flexible procedures offers the therapist the best opportunity to fashion his approach to the realities of the moment. Within the past two decades a host of methodologies have invaded psychotherapy. Some of these use accepted scientific precepts. Others proceed pragmatically. If the therapist is able to experiment with a number of methods, he will eventually evolve modes of operations for himself that are singularly suited to his personality and skills. It is in this manner that hypnosis offers itself as an approach that can potentially enhance the effects of a broad spectrum of treatment approaches ranging from simple relaxation, to symptom-relieving suggestions, to behavior modification, to psychoanalytically oriented psychotherapy.

Hypnosis serves as a unique interpersonal process that can catalyze therapeutic effects and rapidly bring out latent needs and defenses. [pp. 182–200][59] It is helpful in creating incentives when the patient lacks motivation for treatment. It is particularly useful for the patient who refuses to begin therapy unless he is assured of immediate relief of his symptoms. It is valuable as an expedient in

helping to develop a warm working relationship between patient and therapist. It may restore communication when the patient is unable to verbalize freely, and by lifting repressions it can expose pathological zones of conflict. It may enable a patient to remember dreams and fantasies in psychoanalytic therapy. By facilitating transference it can expose the harmful imprints of past relationships. It is sometimes useful in bringing repressed and repudiated memories to the surface, when these are deemed essential to the therapeutic process. It may permit more rapid progress in behavior modification than the many different behavioral techniques.

These are only brief indications of how hypnosis can be effective in psychotherapy, whether the therapist fashions his methods around the theory that unconscious memories or conflicts are the basis for emotional ailments, or whether he adheres to the hypothesis that neuroses are exclusive products of faulty learning and conditioning. Not all therapists are able to employ hypnosis, either for personality reasons or because of unresolvable prejudices. But the therapist capable of transcending his fears and prejudices will find that the practice of hypnosis adds an important dimension to his technical skills.

Bibliography

1. ABRAMSON, M. "Hypnosis in Obstetrics and Its Relation to Personality," *Personality*, 1 (1951), 355.
2. ABRAMSON, M. and W. T. HERON. "An Objective Evaluation of Hypnosis in Obstetrics," *Am. J. Obstet. Gynecol.*, 59 (1950), 1069.
3. BARBER, T. X. "An Alternative Paradigm," in E. Fromm and R. E. Shor, eds., *Hypnosis: Research Development and Perspectives*, pp. 115–182. Chicago: Aldine-Atherton, 1972.
4. BARRIOS, A. A. "Posthypnotic Suggestion as Higher Ordered Conditioning: A Methodological and Experimental Analysis," *Int. J. Clin. Exp. Hypn.*, 21 (1973), 32–50.
5. BEECHER, H. K. "Pain and Some Factors that

Modify It," *Anaesthesiol.*, 12 (1951), 633.

6. BROWNING, J. S. and S. H. HOUSEWORTH. "Development of New Symptoms following Medical and Surgical Treatment for Duodenal Ulcer," *Psychosom. Med.*, 15 (1953), 328–336.

7. CHERTOK, L. and P. KRAMARZ. "Hypnosis, Sleep, and Electroencephalography," *J. Nerv. Ment. Dis.*, 128 (1959), 227–238.

8. CRASILNECK, H. B., E. J. McCRANIE, and M. T. JENKINS. "Special Indications for Hypnosis as a Method in Anaesthesia," *JAMA*, 162 (1956), 1606.

9. CRASILNECK, H. B., J. A. STIRMAN, B. J. WILSON et al. "The Use of Hypnosis in the Management of the Patient with Burns," *JAMA*, 158 (1955), 103.

10. CRISP, A. H. "'Transference,' 'Symptom Emergency' and 'Social Repercussion' in Behavior Therapy. A Study of Fifty-four Treated Patients," *Br. J. Med. Psychol.*, 39 (1966), 179–196.

11. DELEE, S. T. "Hypnotism in Pregnancy and Labor," *JAMA*, 159 (1955), 750.

12. DORCUS, R. M. "Influence of Hypnosis on Learning and Habit Modifying," in R. M. Dorcus, ed., *Hypnosis and Its Therapeutic Applications*, pp. 5–12. New York: McGraw-Hill, 1956.

13. ———. "The Use of Hypnosis as a Diagnostic Tool," in R. M. Dorcus, ed., *Hypnosis and Its Therapeutic Applications*, pp. 17–18. New York: McGraw-Hill, 1956.

14. DORCUS, R. M. and F. J. KIRKNER. "The Use of Hypnosis in the Suppression of Intractable Pain," *J. Abnorm. Soc. Psychol.*, 43 (1948), 237.

15. ERICKSON, M. H. "Special Techniques of Brief Hypnotherapy," *J. Clin. Exp. Hypn.*, 2 (1954), 109.

16. EVANS, F. J. "Hypnosis and Sleep," in E. Fromm and R. E. Shor, eds., *Hypnosis: Research Developments and Perspectives*, pp. 43–83. Chicago: Aldine-Atherton, 1972.

17. FISHER, S. "The Role of Expectancy in the Performance of Posthypnotic Behavior," *J. Abnorm. Soc. Psychol.*, 49 (1954), 503.

18. GOLDSTEIN, A. P., K. HELLER, and L. B. SECHREST. *Psychotherapy and the Psychology of Behavior Change*. New York: Wiley, 1966.

19. HAMMER, E. F. "Post-hypnotic Suggestion and Test Performance," *J. Clin. Exp. Hyp.*, 2 (1954), 178.

20. HARTLAND, J. "Ego Building Suggestions," *Am. J. Clin. Hypn.*, 3 (1965), 89–93.

21. HERON, W. T. and M. ABRAMSON. "Hypnosis in Obstetrics," in L. M. Lecron, ed., *Experimental Hypnosis*, pp. 284–298. New York: Macmillan, 1952.

22. HILGARD, E. R. and C. T. TART. "Responsiveness to Suggestions following Waking and Imagination Instructions and following Induction of Hypnosis," *J. Abnorm. Psychol.*, 71 (1966), 196–208.

23. KIRKNER, F. J. "Hypnosis in a General Hospital Service," in R. M. Dorcus, ed., *Hypnosis and Its Therapeutic Applications*. New York: McGraw-Hill, 1956.

24. KLINE, M. V. and H. GUZE. "Self-hypnosis in Childbirth: A Clinical Evaluation of a Patient's Conditioning Program," *J. Clin. Exp. Hypnosis*, 3 (1955), 142.

25. KROGER, W. S. "Hypnotherapy in Obstetrics and Gynecology," *J. Clin. Exp. Hypnosis*, 1 (1953), 61.

26. LEVITT, E. E. and R. H. CHAPMAN. "Hypnosis as a Research Method," in E. Fromm and R. E. Shor, eds., *Hypnosis: Research Developments and Perspectives*, pp. 85–113. Chicago: Aldine-Atherton, 1972.

27. LIVINGSTON, W. K. *Pain Mechanisms*. New York: Macmillan, 1944.

28. LONDON, P. and M. FUHRER. "Hypnosis, Motivation and Performance," *J. Pers.*, 29 (1961), 321–333.

29. LONDON, P., J. J. HART, and M. P. LEIBOVITZ. "EEG Alpha Rhythms and Susceptibility to Hypnosis," *Nature*, 219 (1968), 71–72.

30. MADISON, L. "The Use of Hypnosis in the Differential Diagnosis of a Speech Disorder," *J. Clin. Exp. Hypn.*, 2 (1954), 140.

31. MARCUS, H. W. "The Use of Hypnosis in Dentistry," *J. Dent. Med.*, 12 (1957), 59.

32. MARMER, M. J. "The Role of Hypnosis in Anesthesiology," *JAMA*, 162 (1956), 441.

33. MASON, A. A. "Hypnosis for the Relief of Pain," *Proc. R. Soc. Med.*, 49 (1956), 481.

34. ———. "Report of Annual Meeting of the Royal Medico-Psychological Association," *Int. J. Soc. Psychiatry*, 2 (1956), 151.

35. MOODY, M. M. "An Evaluation of Hypnotically Induced Relaxation for the Reduction of Peptic Ulcer Symptoms," *Brit. J. Med. Hypn.*, 2 (1953), 1.

36. MOSS, A. A. *Hypnodontics*. Brooklyn: Dental Items of Interest, 1952.

37. ———. "Hypnodontics," in L. M. Lecron,

ed., *Experimental Hypnosis*, pp. 303–319. New York: Macmillan, 1954.

38. NEWBOLD, G. "Hypnosis and Suggestion in Obstetrics," *Br. J. Med. Hypn.*, 1 (1949), 36–37.

39. ORNE, M. T. "The Nature of Hypnosis: Artifact and Essence," *J. Abnorm. Soc. Psychol.*, 58 (1959), 277–299.

40. ———. "Demand Characteristics and the Concept of Quasi-Controls," in R. Rosenthal and R. L. Rosnow, eds., *Artifact in Behavioral Research*, pp. 143–179. New York: Academic, 1969.

41. OWEN-FLOOD, A. "Hypnosis in Anaesthesiology," in J. M. Schneck, ed., *Hypnosis in Modern Medicine*, pp. 89–100. Springfield, Ill.: Charles C. Thomas, 1953.

42. RAGINSKY, B. B. "The Use of Hypnosis in Anesthesiology: Symposia on Topical Issues," *Personality*, 1 (1951), 340.

43. ROSEN, H. "The Hypnotic and Hypnotherapeutic Control of Severe Pain," *Am. J. Psychiatry*, 107 (1951), 917.

44. ———. "Radical Hypnotherapy of Apparent Medical and Surgical Emergencies: Symposia on Topical Issues," *Personality*, 1 (1951), 326.

45. ROSEN, H. and M. H. ERICKSON. "The Hypnotic and Hypnotherapeutic Investigation and Determination of Symptom Function," *J. Clin. Exp. Hypn.*, 2 (1954), 201.

46. SEITZ, P. F. D. "Experiments in the Substitution of Symptoms by Hypnosis," *Psychosom. Med.*, 15 (1953), 405–422.

47. SHOR, R. E. "The Fundamental Problem Viewed from Historic Perspectives," in E. Fromm and R. E. Shor, eds., *Hypnosis: Research Developments and Perspectives*, pp. 15–40. Chicago: Aldine-Atherton, 1972.

48. SZASZ, T. S. "Psychiatric Aspects of Vagotomy II. A Psychiatric Study of Vagotomized Ulcer Patients with Comments on Prognosis," *Psychosom. Med.*, 11 (1949), 187–199.

49. TART, C. T. "The Hypnotic Dream," *Psychol. Bull.*, 63 (1965), 87–99.

50. TINTEROW, M. M. *Foundations of Hypnosis: From Mesmer to Freud.* Springfield, Ill.: Charles C. Thomas, 1970.

51. ULETT, G. A., S. AKPINAR, and M. I. TURAN. "Quantitative EEG Analysis during Hypnosis," *Electroencephalogr. Clin. Neurophysiol.*, 33 (1972), 361–368.

52. ———. "Hypnosis: Physiological, Pharmacological, Reality," *Am. J. Psychiatry*, 128 (1972), 799–805.

53. WEITZENHOFFER, A. M. *General Techniques of Hypnosis.* New York: Grune & Stratton, 1957.

54. WEST, L. J., K. C. NIELL, and J. D. HARDY. "Effects of Hypnotic Suggestion on Pain Perception and Galvanic Skin Response," *AMA Arch. Neurol. Psychiatry*, 68 (1952), 549.

55. WOLBERG, L. R. *Medical Hypnosis.* New York: Grune & Stratton, 1948.

56. ———. "Current Practices in Hypnosis," in F. Fromm-Reichmann and J. Moreno, eds., *Progress in Psychotherapy*, Vol. 1, pp. 217–233. New York: Grune & Stratton, 1956.

57. ———. "Hypnosis in Psychoanalytically Oriented Psychotherapy," in J. Masserman and J. Moreno, eds., *Progress in Psychotherapy*, Vol. 2, pp. 177–187. New York: Grune & Stratton, 1957.

58. ———. *Hypnoanalysis.* New York: Grune & Stratton, 1964.

59. ———. *Hypnosis: Is It for You?* New York: Harcourt, Brace, Jovanovich, 1972.

60. WOLPE, J. *The Practice of Behavior Therapy.* New York: Pergamon, 1969.

CHAPTER 13

BRIEF PSYCHOTHERAPY

Pietro Castelnuovo-Tedesco

O F ALL THE PSYCHOTHERAPY that is practiced, most of it belongs under the general rubric of "brief psychotherapy." It is, therefore, of signal importance to define what is encompassed by this term: the scope it covers; the theory on which it is based; the techniques it uses; and, finally, its particular indications, limitations, and results.

The special significance of brief psychotherapy is social as well as medical. Not only is it the most commonly employed psychological modality for the treatment of a host of emotional difficulties, but also—increasingly—it has been seen as a vehicle for making psychotherapeutic help available to broad segments of the population. The great concern that has emerged during the past two decades over the distribution of medical services, both in this country and abroad, has further increased the practical as well as the scientific interest in this form of treatment.

⟦ History of Brief Psychotherapy

Brief psychotherapy is not a new discovery. This deserves emphasis, because in the recent climate of great social interest in this form of treatment, it often has been looked upon as a special creation of the last few years. As a matter of fact, all psychotherapy is a relatively new development. If we exclude the ancient world, when psychotherapy was practiced among the Greeks by priests in the Aesculapian temples and was an integral part of organized religion, we can say that psychotherapy as a secular undertaking did not exist until the end of the eighteenth century, when Mesmer first practiced hypnosis in Paris. But in this form of treatment the physician still acted upon the patient, through injunctions and suggestions, much as in traditional organic therapy. Modern psychotherapy really began in Vienna in the early 1880s. Here, for the first time, the hypnotic state was employed not to "order away" symptoms (as Mesmer and others had done) but to create a special climate in which the patient was listened to. In the now famous case of Anna O.,[6] we find that Josef Breuer, her physician, visited her daily and listened to her recite her symptoms. He observed that as she recalled, with feeling, the events associated with the onset of her symptoms, these subsided and disappeared. This was the cathartic method, discovered by Breuer[6] and later developed by Freud into a complex instrument that he called psycho-analysis.

The earliest forms of psychotherapy, there-fore, were in fact instances of brief psycho-therapy. The longer forms of psychotherapeutic treatment, preeminently psychoanalysis, were developed later. Thus psychoanalysis and brief psychotherapy share their early history.[24,43] For example, in the case of Elizabeth Von R.,[6] Freud demonstrated the therapeutic value of the device of confrontation, which is extensively used in current brief psychotherapy. He pointed out to Miss Von R. that she was in love with her brother-in-law and that this longing, which she had repressed, was the basis for the leg pains that had begun after a long walk she had taken with him. Dora,[16] the patient from whom Freud learned so much about transference, was in treatment only three months. In the case of the Wolf-Man,[17] Freud first introduced a time limit. This technical device, which Rank later emphasized in his system of treatment, has become an important part of the armory of brief psychotherapy. Even after becoming established as a psychoanalyst, Freud continued to use brief psychotherapy, when indicated, as in the cases of Gustav Mahler,[27] the composer, and Bruno Walter,[49] the conductor.

Later, as psychoanalysis increasingly concerned itself with the resolution of longstanding personality malformations, treatment became more lengthy and required several years rather than just a few months. Concurrently as analytic treatment grew in length, a number of workers, impelled by practical considerations, felt the need to try to shorten treatment. At this point psychoanalysis and brief psychotherapy began to diverge with regard to their aims and methods. Thus, the contributions of some of the early "deviationists" from psychoanalysis (particularly Adler, Stekel, and Rank and later, to some extent, Ferenczi and Horney), with their emphasis on current adaptation and on therapeutic activity, bear directly on brief psychotherapy. In the 1940s Franz Alexander[2] and his colleagues at the Chicago Institute for Psychoanalysis made a systematic study of the application of analytic principles to brief treatment. Their now-classic book, *Psychoanalytic Therapy*, is a milestone in the development of this subject. At about the same time, from a nonanalytic viewpoint (although strongly influenced by the work of Otto Rank), Carl Rogers,[40] a clinical psychologist, addressed himself to the role of nondirective techniques in his "client-centered psychotherapy," a form of brief treatment. During the 1950s a considerable effort was made to separate more sharply classical psychoanalysis from all other forms of psychotherapy, and a number of important papers[19,22,39,50] appeared that were aimed at resolving this issue.

Most recently, during the 1960s, there has been a great resurgence of interest in brief psychotherapy. This interest developed not only from a renewed scientific impetus to understand its basic principles, but also from an intensified awareness of its social significance and of its potential for broadened delivery of psychiatric care. Outstanding among recent writings is Malan's *A Study of Brief Psychotherapy*,[32] a detailed and sophisticated clinical and research effort. Wolberg's[53] *Short-Term Psychotherapy* offers a practical and comprehensive review of the topic. Many other books and papers have appeared as an outcome of this interest. A good number have centered on the application of psychoanalytic concepts to brief psychotherapy,[*] but significant contributions have also derived from the crisis model[1,4,8–10] and that of behavior therapy.[37,54,55]

([What Is Brief Psychotherapy?

The term "brief psychotherapy" attempts to define the process of treatment purely in terms of its overall length, but it is not possible to do justice to its complexities solely in terms of its duration. Actually, brief psychotherapy is often used to refer to one or more of the following somewhat overlapping variables: (1) the *length* of the treatment, from inception to termination; (2) the *frequency* of the therapeutic sessions and the *duration* of each ses-

* See references 2, 4, 12, 30–32, 46, and 51.

sion; (3) the *intensity* of the treatment, which depends on item 2 as well as on the particular techniques employed; and (4) the *goal* of treatment, which is often expressed in terms of polarities, even though, in reality, various blendings of the following alternatives are the common occurrence: "supportive" or "suppressive" as contrasted with "insight-oriented," "expressive," or "exploratory."[29]

In reviewing the literature, one soon discovers that the term "brief psychotherapy" is quite elastic in its meaning. Generally it is used synonymously with "short-term" psychotherapy, whereas the term "crisis therapy" is reserved for the briefest forms of intervention. Gill[19] has pointed out, appropriately, that one should recognize not only "brief" and "long-term" psychotherapies but also those of intermediate duration. It is important to emphasize that there is a wide range of time alternatives, and that the dividing line between the various forms is not a sharp one. Most writers in the field consider "brief" any treatment extending from ten to twenty-five sessions and spread out over a period of three to four months, whereas others allow forty or fifty sessions and sometimes more, or permit the span of treatment to range up to six months or even a year if the sessions are sparse and the climate remains nonintensive.[2,32,38] Sometimes, when indicated, treatment may be limited to five sessions or less.* Treatment then often falls under the general heading of "crisis therapy,"† especially when the difficulty is associated with a fairly clearcut external predicament. The reason that brief treatment generally is not allowed to extend beyond the limits just stated is that, otherwise, the focus inevitably broadens beyond the current predicament to include a study of the patient's fundamental and longstanding ways of reacting, i.e., a study of his personality and character.

The frequency of the visits generally is once or twice a week. More frequent and even daily sessions may be needed occasionally, if the patient is at first highly distressed and symptomatic or if he has difficulty maintaining adequate continuity. However, as soon as he becomes more comfortable, the frequency of visits would be decreased to once or at most twice per week. The reason why great frequency of visits is to be avoided is that (as will be discussed in more detail later) it intensifies the transference, an occurrence that is not considered desirable in brief psychotherapy.

The duration of each visit generally is the standard fifty-minute hour, but shorter treatment periods also have been tried and are satisfactory under certain circumstances.[11,12,33] An example of a briefer time period is the *Twenty-Minute Hour,*[11,12] which was introduced as a model for supportive work by the general physician. Optimally, the length of the psychotherapeutic session should be geared to the goals and the methods of the treatment. Periods of fifty minutes are desirable when the treatment is insight-oriented and aimed at the interpretive analysis and working through of conflicts. Shorter periods usually are adequate when the treatment is primarily supportive and based mainly on catharsis, clarification, and simple reassurance. However, psychiatrists are inclined to arrange their schedules in forty-five to fifty minute units and tend to adhere to this format even in situations where shorter visits would accomplish the purpose just as well. By the same token, the ability of patients to work in treatment varies considerably. Some are able to function in an insight-oriented way and achieve considerable self-understanding, even in the context of short time periods.

To return to matters mentioned earlier: brief psychotherapy may or may not be intensive, may be primarily supportive or insight-oriented, may stay on the surface, or may, in some cases, deal with surprisingly "deep" issues. This varies not only with the characteristics of patients whose needs and capacities differ considerably, but also with the characteristics of therapists, whose skill and clinical boldness similarly cover a wide range. These variables all contribute to defining the nature of the process and the final result.

---

* See references 2, 13, 25, 26, 28, 42, and 47.
† See references 1, 4, 8–10, and 46.

(Fundamental Issues of Brief Psychotherapy

Although brief psychotherapy cannot be defined solely in terms of its duration, time, nonetheless, has a distinct influence on the treatment. Of necessity, the brevity of the treatment affects its scope, helps to select its goals and methods, and serves to establish its priorities.

Inevitably, the emphasis is practical and pragmatic and centers on taking care of first things first. The treatment, therefore, is anchored in the present, and its main thrust is to relieve the patient's suffering—in particular, his most pressing symptoms—as promptly and expeditiously as possible. It tends to be predominantly symptom- and/or situation-oriented,[38] and it makes no attempt to modify or reorganize the patient's basic personality or to disturb well-established defensive patterns. Sometimes treatment goes well beyond symptomatic relief: under certain circumstances (depending on the presenting symptoms, the vigor and effectiveness of the patient's personality, the favorableness of his social circumstances, and the skill of the therapist), modification of some sectors of the personality can take place. When this occurs, however, it is an unexpected plus rather than something specifically anticipated or deliberately planned. The principal task of brief psychotherapy is to bring about symptomatic relief and/or the resolution of a situational predicament. When character change is specifically looked for, the therapist should consider one of the longer and more intensive forms of treatment.

Brief treatment is indicated especially where the patient's distress is not so much the expression of a long-standing neurotic struggle as of particular circumstances that have impaired his endurance and rekindled an internal conflict that was previously dormant or at least adequately managed. The goal of the treatment is not so much to bring about a new level of organization, i.e., to "change" the patient—as to restore the one that existed before his acute difficulties began. It is fundamentally restitutive in its intent.[28] Nonetheless, from the recent literature on crisis invention comes the reminder that a crisis regularly presents the individual not only with an inescapable demand or burden but also with a new opportunity. As Caplan[10] says, "During this period of tension, the person grapples with the problem and develops novel resources, both by calling upon internal reserves and by making use of the help of others."

Again, although there are important differences between what various patients accomplish during brief treatment, time ultimately defines the limits for the working through of conflicts and the boundaries of the treatment process—in sum, it defines just how far one can go. Much of the working through, in fact, is left for the patient to accomplish on his own after treatment has stopped, whereas in long-term psychotherapy (and particularly in psychoanalysis) termination is deemed possible only after substantial working through has been achieved.

Another fundamental characteristic of brief psychotherapy is that the focus is on the present but also on interpersonal issues,[38,44,46] i.e., on key relationships that the patient is not negotiating to advantage at that particular time, so that the relationships have become a source of difficulty. The interpersonal focus is readily understandable to the patient because that, typically, is where he feels his distress and centers his complaints. It is also consistent with the therapist's plan to avoid restructuring the patient's personality and to confine his efforts to a sector that is manageable in the limited time available.

Finally, there is the matter of the therapist's attitude toward brief psychotherapy. To be effective, he must be able to free himself of therapeutic overambition[18] and to regard this modality as the best treatment for some cases rather than as the second best. Often enough, as Coleman[15] observes, "the patient contents himself readily with limited treatment objectives when the therapist can allow him to do so."

❰ Techniques of Brief Psychotherapy

Every psychotherapeutic modality inevitably develops a range of techniques designed more or less consciously to serve its ends. In the case of brief psychotherapy, there is fairly general agreement that considerable flexibility is a prime requisite for this type of treatment. For many therapists, indeed, it has been part of the appeal of brief psychotherapy that it permits and even encourages versatility and individuality of style and gives the therapist the opportunity to take a very active part in the treatment process. Semrad[44] observes, "Styles vary so much that sometimes they may almost appear to be different techniques." However, while there is a wide variety of approach, so that one cannot speak of a "standard technique" (as in the case of psychoanalysis), over the years a number of principles have nonetheless accrued to its practice, to which most writers on the subject appear to subscribe.

The Strategies of Brief Psychotherapy

The principal goal of brief treatment is to achieve maximal effectiveness in the context of brevity and economy of time. Time, within limits, decides what is feasible and what is not. Several fundamental and interrelated processes are involved.

1. Emphasis is deliberately on the present and on the interactions that are shaping it, because these are the most fluid and readily accessible. Attention is focused on the patient's major current conflict(s) and the main object relationship(s) involved in the current upset. Although the contributions of the past are not totally neglected, the focus primarily is on the present ("What ails him now?") rather than on the past ("How did he become what he is?") or the future ("Where is he going?" and, "Is his life fulfilling its basic goals?").

2. Transference reactions (the tendency of the patient to reexperience feelings and attitudes toward the therapist that were once part of the patient's relationship to the key figures of his childhood, such as parents, siblings, and so forth) are discouraged. In particular, a full transference neurosis is not considered desirable and does not develop, in part because time is insufficient and in part because of specific steps taken to prevent it. These include avoidance of fantasy material, emphasis on reality and the 'here and now,' and, at times, the deflection of particular feelings toward the therapist onto an important current figure.[38] The regressive state, which is part and parcel of a full-fledged transference, not only does not serve the aim of promoting a rapid recompensation but is actually detrimental to it.

Despite the therapist's efforts to discourage the development of transference reactions, they do, of course, occur. They are then recognized and dealt with, especially if they are negative but fairly superficial (as, for example, expressions of doubt, disappointment, and mild resentment). On the other hand, negative responses that appear related to deep-seated paranoid and depressive anxieties usually are left untouched, for fear of stirring up issues that cannot be settled in the time available. Also untouched and deliberately unresolved are the positive transference reactions, i.e., feelings of special liking—inasmuch as these support the goals of treatment and promote an atmosphere in which the patient is especially responsive to the therapist's influence. Some authors,[23,31,32] in particular, stress that they work quite actively with the transference. They regard it as a critical therapeutic factor in brief psychotherapy nearly as much as in the longer forms of treatment, to be exploited to the fullest within the time available rather than bypassed.

3. During treatment the patient typically demonstrates a range of defenses, i.e., characteristic responses, that serve to contain various anxieties, both deep and superficial. The therapist addresses himself mainly to the more superficial ones, which are readily accessible and closely related to the current material. On the other hand, defenses of long standing, especially those frozen into the character, cannot be usefully approached and should be circumvented. Brief psychotherapy and char-

acter analysis are a different order of business, not to be confused with one another.

The Tactics of Brief Psychotherapy

It is proverbial that all is fair in love and war, and—one might also add—in brief psychotherapy. Typically, brief psychotherapy has been recognized as an unabashedly expedient affair. Thus every device has been used that might help achieve the desired results quickly.[43,53] The tendency generally has been to regard the situation in brief treatment as highly idiosyncratic and as favoring (at times even requiring) boldness, enthusiasm, and an individualistic style. In fact, enough instances have been recorded in the literature to establish the appeal of an approach that encourages decisive and dramatic interventions. Here, perhaps, the all-time classic story is the one about the late N. Lionel Blitzsten[35] who, quickly guessing the meaning of a singer's acute aphonia, thrust a wiener at her mouth and made her scream, thus freeing her voice and enabling her to proceed with the next performance. Stekel's[48] writings also contain a number of examples that attest to the value, in particular instances, of a dramatic brief interaction.

Other authors,[14,19] on the other hand, have pointed out that the flair for the dramatic and, more generally, the usefulness of manipulative interventions have perhaps been overemphasized, and that there is also much room in brief psychotherapy for quiet and detailed interpretive work. This is especially true in situations that do not require the resolution of an acute crisis. Thus, Gill[19] says, "I believe we have failed to carry over into our psychotherapy enough of the non-directive spirit of our analyses. I do not refer to the emergency situations where active interventions seem unavoidable and where the essential goal is supportive but to the less urgent problems seen over longer periods of time with more ambitious goals."

Now let us look more closely at the technical aspects of brief psychotherapy and the way in which the element of time influences the initial evaluation and onset of treatment as well as goal setting and termination.

Initial evaluation and onset of treatment are less sharply differentiated from one another than in the longer forms of psychotherapy.[32,38,44] Brief therapy truly begins right off, with the first contact; history-taking is generally more limited and tends to confine itself predominantly to the current predicament. Although the therapist will seek some general background information to help place the presenting complaint in an understandable historical context, he will not pursue anamnestic material in great detail, especially that which pertains to childhood development. History-taking, like treatment itself, remains centered largely on the present. This is made possible, in part, by the fact that the typical candidate for brief psychotherapy generally presents himself as having a specific "problem" clearly in the present and quite directly interpersonal in nature. Moreover, the therapist from the very beginning helps to circumscribe the task by coming to grips interpretively with the material the patient brings him.[43] This kind of participation begins right away, during the first hour. An initial "wait-and-see" attitude is not consonant with the pace and the goals of this form of therapy. The experienced therapist generally has an immediate intuitive conviction, based on a very early perception of "movement" on the part of the patient, that the case is "right" for brief treatment. If he does not quickly achieve this spontaneous conviction, it usually means that the case is not suitable for brief treatment and that the patient is likely to require more time. The patient's responsiveness to the therapist's first interventions will confirm the correctness of the initial impression.[38] Relevant here, of course, is Semrad's[44] dictum that "one must really understand the patient before he will believe that he is understood." Another positive prognostic clue is whether the patient initially presents his difficulty as an interpersonal problem rather than, primarily, as a concern over symptoms.[38]

Even when the therapist does not announce a specific time limit, he conveys that the treatment will be brief by addressing himself to a circumscribed problem that is generally the particular interpersonal predicament that the patient has brought in. Thus from the very beginning, and quite spontaneously, brief treatment is likely to assume a tone of "problem solving"[38,44] that is absent in cases where the difficulty is more diffuse, more centered in the personality's inner workings, and likely to require more time. A specific time limit may be employed in some cases where the presenting problem is highly circumscribed and where the patient is strongly motivated to find a resolution to that problem, yet is unlikely to wish to involve himself in a more far-reaching exploration. The time limit tends, then, to stimulate the patient's motivation and helps him make the most of the time available. An unconscious resistance to entering into a more binding treatment relationship is bypassed when the patient is, in effect, reassured that treatment will last just so long and no longer.

The time limit is employed primarily in situations where the treatment can be expected to be quite short (five to ten sessions). Once a specific time limit has been announced, one adheres to it, and both patient and doctor use it as a goal to work toward. This also means that termination of treatment can be considered as soon as the presenting problem has been favorably modified to some extent. Frequently one does not wait for its resolution but will be satisfied if the patient, in response to its clarification, appears to be working in the right direction and is showing increasing mastery of the initially troublesome situation. Malan[32] emphasizes the importance of the patient experiencing some grief over termination. This is clear proof that the treatment has touched him in a significant way.

As mentioned earlier, the technical devices used in practice (and advocated in the literature) as applicable to brief psychotherapy, cover the widest range.[51,53] To be more specific, one might list the following:

1. Rapidly establishing (and then maintaining) a warmly positive relationship.[43] A number of devices are known to affect the quality of the relationship, for example, a time limit,

the frequency and duration of sessions, the "role" adopted by the therapist, his degree of activity, and focusing on the healthy aspects of the patient[3,38] and on the positive features of his current reality while bypassing old issues left over from the past. In short, the time-honored Meyerian principle of emphasizing assets and deemphasizing liabilities has an important place here.

2. Ventilation and emotional catharsis. It is generally recognized that much of the benefit that the patient obtains in psychotherapy (especially the brief forms) derives from the opportunity to unburden himself of painful emotions (mainly over situations that have evoked resentment, guilt, or shame) in a setting of benevolent acceptance.

3. Reassurance, suggestion, and (occasionally) hypnosis.[41,53] These represent a spectrum of devices that use the therapist's "authority" to allay the patient's anxiety and persuade him. According to Ferenczi (as quoted by Oberndorf),[34] suggestion "consists of influence on a person through and by means of the transference manifestations of which he is capable." Thus the effectiveness of these approaches is limited by the patient's need and willingness (at any given time) to be persuaded, reassured, and so forth.

4. Exhortation, counseling, advice, and environmental manipulation. All these devices have a place in helping the patient cope more effectively with his external reality.

5. Explanations and pedagogic remarks. These devices also promote greater mastery, by informing the patient where he is handicapped by misinformation. They help to "spell out" the nature of the difficulty and the aspects of it that he should try to accept or modify.

6. Drugs. Sedative, tranquilizing, and antidepressant drugs have a place in controlling and altering distressing emotions that impair the patient's effectiveness. Their role is that of auxiliary aids to psychotherapy. Their use is described in detail elsewhere in this *Handbook*. It will suffice to say that drugs are of value particularly in helping to control the more acute and emergent manifestations of distress.

7. Desensitization by counter-conditioning techniques.[37,54,55] These techniques can prove helpful especially for phobias and other focal anxiety responses. It is an axiom of behavior therapy that symptomatic behavior is not the outcome of emotional conflict but the result of conditioning which, in turn, makes it amenable to treatment by deconditioning techniques. The symptom is seen as a circumscribed phenomenon, essentially unrelated to the patient's character structure. Therefore, the treatment that is applied can be quite brief. During the past fifteen years a considerable literature has developed in this area. The reader is referred to it for a more detailed account of its contribution.

8. Interpretive techniques.* These techniques originally derived from psychoanalysis, are the standard armory of what is generally referred to as "dynamically oriented psychotherapy." They include clarifications (of feelings, thoughts, and attitudes), confrontations, and interpretations proper. Clarifications summarize and sharpen the meaning of what the patient has just said without, however, going beyond the largely conscious aspects of the particular material. Interpretations, instead, try to capture meanings beyond the patient's immediate awareness and beyond the material that he has just discussed. Confrontations serve to remind the patient of some aspect of reality that he appears to be neglecting at the moment.

Interpretations tend to be used somewhat differently in short-term than in long-term treatment. They are ". . . couched in more general terms . . . not related . . . necessarily [to] specific historical conflicts and difficulties in the patient."[38] Their goal often is to bring material into harmony with the ego, as for example when "interpreting to the patient the underlying motivation for an act or thought which has hitherto appeared to him senseless."[38] Moreover, interpretations are addressed primarily to preconscious rather than to unconscious material and are stated mainly in terms of object relations rather than of drives and impulses.[38]

* See references 2, 23, 32, 38, 41, 44, and 46.

9. Dream Analysis. This is not one of the usual tools of brief psychotherapy, both because emphasis is placed chiefly on reality and because many therapists are not trained in the techniques of dream analysis. However, in the hands of the skilled therapist, a dream occasionally may prove a very useful starting point for the analysis of a crucial current conflict.[23]

The factors that influence the choice of techniques include the preference of the individual therapist and his level of training, as well as the requirements of the particular case. Some brief psychotherapy can be carried out by relatively untrained therapists who depend on simple methods and a rudimentary theoretical orientation, since time is short and it is possible to stay close to the surface. Thus, one purpose of the *Twenty-Minute Hour*[11,12] was to offer a simple technique that could be managed safely and effectively by the occasional psychotherapist. On the other hand, situations do often arise in brief treatment that are unexpectedly complex and demanding of skills, and this makes the task variable and highly uneven. The two basic mainstays for much of the brief psychotherapy that is carried out are a positive relationship and adequate catharsis. Many therapists add (in varying proportions) such manipulative devices as suggestion, exhortation, advice, environmental manipulation, drug-giving, and, occasionally, desensitization. Still others—especially those who are analytically trained—rely on interpretive techniques that can be used, with appropriate modifications, as in the more intensive forms of long-term treatment. Such therapists emphasize insight and self-understanding and try to go as far in this direction as time and the opportunity for working through of conflicts will allow. The outcome depends, among other things, on the accessibility of the conflict, on the patient's ability to work collaboratively with the therapist and identify with the latter's efforts, and on the time available for working through.

An important question for the therapist is whether to use predominantly interpretive or predominantly manipulative techniques. Over the years, brief psychotherapy has acquired a reputation as a form of treatment where, in the interest of economy and expediency, manipulative techniques naturally reign supreme. On the other hand, a number of analytic therapists[14,19] have pointed out that one should distinguish the extent to which manipulative devices may actually be needed at a given time to stabilize an otherwise uncertain treatment situation, from the extent to which they mainly represent the therapist's predilection. Waelder[52] has summarized the issue quite simply: "The therapeutic method of making conscious unconscious material . . . is most effective in cases where the ego is really mature. The less the ego has grown to the maturity it might be expected to attain, the more deficient the ego system is, the more it will be necessary to try to influence the ego . . . [by applying] a certain amount of direct *educational* influence."

❰ Indications and Limitations of Brief Psychotherapy

When we try to state the "indications" of brief psychotherapy, we are in effect attempting to define its scope. It soon becomes apparent, even if it is not apparent already, that its boundaries are fluid and variable rather than subject to sharp definition, and that the decision as to the appropriateness of brief psychotherapy in any given case rests on a whole range of factors that we will try to canvass step by step.

Right at the start it should be made clear that brief psychotherapy has much to offer a variety of patients and that, for some, it is specifically the treatment of choice. At the same time it should also be underlined that it is not suitable for all patients and all conditions, and that there are some for whom it is distinctly unsuitable. Moreover, decisions about the appropriateness of brief psychotherapy often cannot be made on clinical grounds alone, i.e., on the specific features of the patient's disturbance. Extraneous factors inevitably play a role as well. In private practice the patient's

finances must be considered, as must be in public clinics the wish to spread the therapist's limited time among many patients. Finally, there is the therapist's personal preference, which definitely tips the scales for one or another mode of treatment. Some therapists tend to steer patients toward intensive long-term treatment because that is their *métier*, while others are inclined to make short shrift of every problem. Thus some patients may be "undertreated" while others are "overtreated." Ultimately one would agree with Gillman[20] that "Selection [for brief psychotherapy] must not be based merely on the absence of some criterion for psychoanalysis, or because a particular therapist needs to feel the power of directive therapy and quick cure, or because the predilection is for more limited goals rather than getting to the bottom of things."

The question of the indications for brief psychotherapy is a complicated one, because it cannot be divorced from the issue of treatment goals or from the therapist's orientation toward these goals. In speaking of the indications for brief psychotherapy, we are referring to those conditions and situations where this mode of treatment can be expected to provide reasonably stable and predictably positive results. It seems preferable to speak here of the limitations rather than of the contraindications to brief psychotherapy. One cannot define contraindications that are absolute; rather, one describes a number of emotional states where success by these methods is increasingly less likely. On the other hand, the range of indications can be broadened considerably beyond what will be discussed below. In practice, a wide spectrum of patients are treated with brief psychotherapy, including many patients that would be declared unsuitable by more stringent criteria. Therefore it would be unrealistic and arbitrary to attempt a list of "treatable" and "untreatable" conditions. Instead we will consider the principles that determine how accessible patients are to brief treatment and that form the basis for the clinical decisions that are made in each case.

In keeping with what has been said above—namely, that standards and criteria for case selection vary among different therapists and that sharp categorizations are not possible—we will first try to account for the group of patients who are most likely to profit from brief psychotherapy, later adding in those with whom results tend to be more doubtful. We are dealing with relative indications or, put otherwise, with a gradient of probabilities.

Suitability of Patients

Brief psychotherapy probably is best limited to patients of reasonably mature personality and adequate motivation whose emotional disturbance is focal, acute (rather than chronic), of less than extreme intensity, and associated with fairly apparent situational factors.

It seems desirable to break down this definition into its component parts, so as to be able to expand on each clause. (1) What is meant by "patients of reasonably mature personality" is that such patients, although troubled, show at least fair ego strength and are not involved in a major regression. (2) "Adequate motivation" is important because brief treatment is successful only when the patient is well motivated to resolve his difficulties.[32] Inadequate motivation may exist when the presenting problem is trivial or too overwhelming or when particular transference attitudes (see below) hinder the development of a therapeutic alliance. (3) Our description of the emotional disturbance as "focal, acute, of less than extreme intensity, and associated with fairly apparent situational factors" means that the difficulty is circumscribed and affects a segment rather than most of the ego's functions. Moreover, it is of relatively recent onset and, although painfully severe in some instances, is not of such extreme intensity as to have overwhelmed the patient's adaptive capacities. Finally, the struggle is not primarily limited to the intrapsychic domain but has instead been externalized and tied to a specific and identifiable external situation. In other words, when the patient comes for treatment he has already chosen some key person in his environment (often a spouse, a boss or a co-worker) to serve as the "transference"[*] object onto whom he tries to displace some aspects of his infantile struggles.[14] In these cases, not only is the neurotic conflict already full-blown, but a "transference" has developed and is being elaborated toward a key figure in the person's current environment. Thus, typically, the patient complains that he is in a quandary and seeks professional help to try to resolve it. The doctor, then, provides this help by interpreting the patient's conflict in the context of the displacement that the patient has created. This situation differs from the typical one in intensive analytic psychotherapy (and particularly psychoanalysis) where the transference develops gradually as the treatment unfolds and is kept centered on the person of the therapist as much as possible. Not infrequently the patient in analysis also tries to "externalize" the problem through acting-out, while the analyst, by consistent interpretation, seeks to bring the focus back onto the doctor–patient relationship.

The suitability of patients for brief psychotherapy can be considered further in terms of the following factors:

Ego Strength

It is desirable that the patient's ego still be reasonably competent and, in particular, that there be no serious impairment of its synthetic, integrative, and adaptive capacities. The most direct evidence for this is to be found in the patient's continued capacity to function in his accustomed social role[14] and to sustain meaningful relations with people.[38] Although when first seen the patient may be under considerable stress, as evidenced by anxiety, depression, and other symptomatic manifestations, he still retains good adaptive resilience and is not in the throes of a major and incapacitating decompensation. In the typical case, according to Pumpian-Mindlin,[38] ego

---

[*] The term "transference" is enclosed in quotation marks because, traditionally, it has served to describe the displacement of feelings, originally experienced with significant figures of one's childhood, to the therapist in the course of psychoanalytic treatment. Similar displacements, however, can occur spontaneously also onto other current, extratherapeutic figures.

functions might be described as "crystallized" rather than as "amorphous," at one extreme, or "calcified," at the other. We have already indicated that brief psychotherapy depends for its effectiveness on the patient's capacity to ally himself with the therapist, to marshal his own adaptive resources, and to bring them quickly to bear upon the presenting problem. Therefore, the more serious the patient's regression and the greater the impairment of his adaptive capacities, the less is the likelihood that he will be able to profit from brief psychotherapy.

In this category of persons who are not grossly incapacitated and who respond well to brief treatment we include, primarily, *psychoneurotic* patients. Some are trying to cope with particular crises (for example, grief following a loss, illness, hospitalization, or surgery) or with periods of maturational transition (for example, leaving home for the first time, marriage, pregnancy, changes in occupational status, or aging).[44] Generally, they see their previous functioning as fairly satisfactory, or at least not so uncomfortable as to require a prolonged therapeutic commitment. Not infrequently, however, brief treatment is also employed as a first-stage procedure for sicker patients in an acute turmoil, to be followed later by a more prolonged psychotherapeutic intervention with broader goals.

SYMPTOMATOLOGY

The presenting symptoms bear some relationship to the patient's suitability for brief treatment, but not an overly close one. The simpler symptomatic manifestations—anxiety, depression, or minor hysterical conversions—usually respond quite well,[13,18,23,44] but there is evidence also that mild obsessive symptoms can show a good response as well.[45] In contrast, more complicated symptoms such as phobias or deep-seated hypochondriacal preoccupations are less likely to be significantly affected by a brief course of treatment. However, more important than the symptomatology or the diagnosis is the patient's accessibility and his capacity for rapid involvement with the therapist.[32] This depends on the depth and character of the patient's psycho-

pathology, as well as on his motivation and typical transference attitude.

TYPICAL TRANSFERENCE ATTITUDE

Patients also vary in terms of what might be called their typical transference attitude—the basic "stance" that they characteristically present toward human relationships and that they bring to the treatment situation, where it inevitably influences the course of treatment. Thus, Stekel[48] emphasizes the importance of noting, early on, whether the patient shows a "willingness to be cured."

Patients who generally respond very favorably to brief psychotherapy and are able to make the most of the opportunity are those who demonstrate a "latency type transference", i.e., who readily take a posture as "father's (or mother's) helpers." They identify strongly with the therapist's efforts and get to work tidying up the neurotic predicament.[14] Seeking a therapist often is an expression of the patient's readiness to arrive at certain solutions, as one observes with some couples who consult a marriage counselor when they already have decided to "save" their marriage. On the other hand, some patients bring with them transference attitudes that are quite maladaptive and in conflict with the goals of brief treatment. For example, some would rather oppose the therapist than assist him, while others need to feel coerced or oppressed and wish to prove that the treatment is really for the benefit of the therapist and at his request. Some, who are full of feelings of entitlement, sit back and wait for the therapist to perform the therapeutic miracle. Still others, inhibited by mistrust and fears of being hurt, remain protectively aloof. It should be made clear that these attitudes do not necessarily mean that these patients are sicker or more incapacitated than those who present with more adaptive attitudes, but simply that they are less suited (occasionally quite unsuited) for brief psychotherapy. Long-term treatment often is required in these cases precisely because the patient is unable, for a variety of reasons, to become engaged quickly in the therapeutic task. Relevant here is Berliner's[5] statement that "the quick removal of a symptom . . . is best achieved under a state of positive mother transference to which persons with an oral disposition are particularly inclined . . . They absorb friendly transference influences readily . . . They are easy to guide, in contradistinction to people of anal disposition. However, the result of this guidance remains superficial. The old ambivalence is always ready to get the upper hand . . . Symptoms of oral disposition . . . require great caution and their quick disappearance must be judged with reservation."

Limitations of Brief Psychotherapy

The limitations of brief psychotherapy are most readily observed with the following categories of patients who share a distinct impairment of the ego's synthetic and integrative functions and whose responsiveness is typically, though variously, diminished. They are likely to respond unimpressively to brief treatment, and some soon prove distinctly unsuited. Here we specifically include *psychotic* patients, those with *major character disorders* of long standing (especially those with poor impulse control, such as alcoholics, drug addicts, and the severely unstable and self-destructive), and those with chronic, severe, and *disabling psychosomatic illnesses* (such as ulcerative colitis, rheumatoid arthritis and the like). With psychosomatic patients, sharply focused psychotherapy may be very helpful in alleviating the distress associated with hospitalization and in clarifying the issues surrounding a particular exacerbation of the illness; yet such efforts often also serve to underscore the need for more definitive long-term treatment, which then must be arranged.

Brief psychotherapy also tends to be inappropriate or of limited value in the special categories that follow. Deeply depressed patients with persistent or recurrent suicidal urges generally do not find, in brief treatment, either enough protection or enough time to resolve their difficulties. Schizoid patients, typically bland and detached, simply do not make sufficient contact with the therapist to achieve much benefit when time is short. Neurotic patients with difficult or negativistic transference

attitudes have already been discussed. However, one might also include here those patients who are markedly dependent and need the continuing support of an extended relationship, as well as those who derive strong secondary gain and neurotic satisfaction from their symptoms and therefore are unlikely to part with them easily.[53] In conclusion, long-term treatment is called for whenever a focal time-limited approach will not suffice or whenever there is a clear and patent need for personality reconstruction.

Not all authors would concur with the foregoing statement of indications, which they might regard as too stringent. Wolberg,[53] for example, says, "The best strategy, in my opinion, is to assume that every patient, irrespective of diagnosis, will respond to short-term treatment unless he proves himself refractory to it." But then he too allows that certain conditions—for example, pronounced dependency and immaturity, major character disorders with persistent acting out, and near-psychotic states with massive anxiety—sharply prejudice the outcome. Similarly, Burdon[7] believes that ". . . almost all patients can profit from brief psychotherapy . . . [and that] a therapeutic trial . . . [is] indicated in most cases . . . ," although he later acknowledges that the optimal indications for brief psychotherapy are in the range of those given above. Wolberg[53] reports that he has also used short-term methods to advantage in treating patients with serious chronic disorders, including obsessive compulsive neurosis and borderline schizophrenia. Other authors[21,30] likewise report a favorable response in some severe cases—including, again, instances of borderline schizophrenia. Malan[32] is of the opinion that patients with disturbances of moderate severity actually may do better than mildly ill patients, especially if they are highly motivated and work well in interpretive therapy. Nonetheless, his evidence would suggest that the poorest therapeutic results were obtained with the sickest patients. Relevant here is Berliner's[5] observation that "the feasibility of short treatment does not depend on the duration of the illness but on the depth of the neurotic disposition."

A case certainly can be made for offering each patient an initial therapeutic trial of brief psychotherapy, inasmuch as our ability to predict therapeutic outcome is imperfect; at times one is pleasantly surprised by a patient's unanticipated responsiveness. Jacobson,[26] for example, estimates that of 3000 patients who presented themselves at a major crisis center, "approximately two thirds . . . were considered improved" after a course of up to six visits. Thus it is common policy in public clinics, which have an obligation to provide some service to all comers, to introduce each new patient to a course of brief treatment (either individually or in a group setting) in the hope that such a course will suffice in most cases. Nonetheless, it must be kept in mind that as the criteria for patient selection are broadened, the likelihood of a definitive therapeutic result inevitably decreases.

Because a good prognosis in brief psychotherapy has been linked to the presence of substantial ego integrity, the question sometimes is asked whether patients who are ideal candidates for brief treatment are not the very same who generally are considered best suited for intensive analytic psychotherapy or psychoanalysis. And if so, the question continues, is it not just a matter of the therapist's personal predilection whether in some cases he recommends short-term or long-term intensive treatment? While it is true that this characteristic, i.e., substantial ego integrity, enhances the prognosis with any form of psychotherapy, these two groups of patients in fact still differ in some important ways. Primarily, brief-psychotherapy patients tend to have disturbances that are more focal and easily circumscribed, and their suffering is not so deep, persistent, or pervasive as to sustain or justify a therapeutic effort of several years' duration.

The question also arises as to what one can do when an adequate response to short-term treatment is not obtained. The principal alternatives are either long-term treatment or the repetition of one or more courses of brief psychotherapy. Long-term treatment, in turn, may either be intensive and aimed at significantly modifying chronic character pathology, or primarily supportive and non-intensive (either individual or group) and aimed at "carrying" the patient at a tolerable equilibrium so as to prevent critical decompensations. The decision here rests, of course, on the clinical characteristics of the individual case and, not infrequently, also on external factors that determine the availability of professional time. The choice between repeated courses of short-term treatment and some form of long-term treatment should include some judgment of how the patient will manage the regressive trends that, in varying degrees, accompany long-term treatment. The choice also reflects the therapist's preference. Repeated courses of brief treatment are often the approach of choice for many poorly-compensated patients, who should not be exposed to a prolonged dependent transference with its attendant risks of a serious regression. On the other hand, such repeated courses also find favor with therapists who are basically skeptical of the accomplishments of long-term treatment and who believe that the main contribution of psychotherapy is to provide support when the patient is in a crisis.

❲ Brief Psychotherapy: Some Conclusions

As noted at the outset, brief psychotherapy is not new. It has actually been with us from the very beginnings of psychotherapy proper. But it is true that in the last one or two decades its place in the therapeutic armory has been consolidated and its importance, both social and medical, realized as never before. There has been an increased appreciation of its scope, capabilities, and its essential techniques, thanks to our greater understanding of transference, crisis, and ego mechanisms, and of the multiple internal and external forces that facilitate or hinder adaptation. The scope and significance of brief psychotherapy can be gathered by considering not only the range of patients to whom it is applicable, but the range of therapists by whom it is practiced. Paradoxically, it is a form of treatment that at times presumes the most complex psychotherapeutic skills, slowly garnered through intensive work with patients; yet at the same time it also is practiced, usually quite safely and with substantial effectiveness, by the relative beginner. Brief treatment also stands, Janus-faced, at the center of a very controversial question not yet resolved to everyone's satisfaction: whether psychotherapy truly heals (by altering and reversing fundamental psychopathology) or mainly palliates (by providing, predominantly, consolation and support). At any rate, despite uncertainties and controversies, there is no question about the vitality and importance of this complex field. It represents the treatment of choice for many patients and, frequently, the only available treatment for many more. Technically, it has come a long way in almost a century since Anna O. became the first beneficiary of this new method and appreciatively named it "the talking cure."[6]

(Bibliography

1. AGUILERA, D., J. M. MESSICK, and M. S. FARRELL. *Crisis Intervention: Theory and Methodology*. St. Louis: Mosby, 1970.

2. ALEXANDER, F. and T. M. FRENCH. *Psychoanalytic Therapy*. New York: Ronald, 1946.

3. BANDLER, B. "Health Oriented Psychotherapy," *Psychosom. Med.*, 21 (1959), 177–181.

4. BELLAK, L. and L. SMALL. *Emergency Psychotherapy and Brief Psychotherapy*. New York: Grune & Stratton, 1965.

5. BERLINER, B. "Short Psychoanalytic Psychotherapy: Its Possibilities and Its Limitations," *Bull. Menninger Clin.*, 5 (1941), 204–213.

6. BREUER, J. and S. FREUD. (1895) "Studies on Hysteria," in J. Strachey, ed., *Standard Edition*, Vol. 2., pp. 1–305. London: Hogarth, 1955.

7. BURDON, A. P. "Principles of Brief Psychotherapy," *J. Louisiana Med. Soc.*, 115 (1963), 374–378.

8. CAPLAN, G. *Principles of Preventive Psychiatry*. New York: Basic Books, 1964.

9. ———. *The Theory and Practice of Mental Health Consultation*. New York: Basic Books, 1970.

10. CAPLAN, G., E. A. MASON, and D. M. KAP-

LAN. "Four Studies of Crisis in Parents of Prematures," *Community Ment. Health J.*, 1 (1965), 149–161.

11. CASTELNUOVO-TEDESCO, P. "The Twenty-Minute 'Hour:' An Experiment in Medical Education," *N. Engl. J. Med.*, 266 (1962), 283–289.

12. ———. *The Twenty-Minute Hour: A Guide to Brief Psychotherapy for the Physician*. Boston: Little, Brown, 1965.

13. ———. "Brief Psychotherapeutic Treatment of the Depressive Reactions," *Int. Psychiatry Clin.*, 3 (1966), 197–210.

14. ———. "Decreasing the Length of Psychotherapy: Theoretical and Practical Aspects of the Problem," in S. Arieti, ed., *The World Biennial of Psychiatry and Psychotherapy*, Vol. 1, pp. 55–71. New York: Basic Books, 1970.

15. COLEMAN, J. V. "The Initial Phase of Psychotherapy," *Bull. Menninger Clin.*, 13 (1949), 189–197.

16. FREUD, S. (1901) "Fragment of an Analysis of a Case of Hysteria," in J. Strachey, ed., *Standard Edition*, Vol. 7, pp. 7–122. London: Hogarth, 1953.

17. ———. (1918) "From the History of an Infantile Neurosis," in J. Strachey, ed., *Standard Edition*, Vol. 17, pp. 7–122. London: Hogarth, 1955.

18. FUERST, R. A. "Problems of Short Time Psychotherapy," *Am. J. Orthopsychiatry*, 8 (1938), 260–264.

19. GILL, M. "Psychoanalysis and Exploratory Psychotherapy," *J. Am. Psychoanal. Assoc.*, 2 (1954), 771–797.

20. GILLMAN, R. D. "Brief Psychotherapy: A Psychoanalytic View," *Am. J. Psychiatry*, 122 (1965), 601–611.

21. GITELSON, M. "The Critical Moment in Psychotherapy," *Bull. Menninger Clin.*, 6 (1942), 183–189.

22. ———. "Psychoanalysis and Dynamic Psychiatry," *Arch. Neurol. Psychiatry*, 66 (1951), 280–288.

23. GUTHEIL, E. A. "Psychoanalysis and Brief Psychotherapy," *Clin. Psychopathol.*, 6 (1944), 207–229.

24. HUNTER, R. A. and I. MACALPINE. "Follow-up Study of A Case Treated in 1910 by 'The Freud Psychoanalytic Method,'" *Br. J. Med. Psychol.*, 26 (1953), 64–67.

25. JACOBSON, G. "The Briefest Psychiatric Encounter," *Arch. Gen. Psychiatry*, 18 (1968), 718–724.

26. JACOBSON, G. F. "Some Psychoanalytic Considerations Regarding Crisis Therapy," *Psychoanal. Rev.*, 54 (1967), 649–54.

27. JONES, E. *The Life and Work of Sigmund Freud*, 2 Vols. New York: Basic Books, 1955.

28. KNIGHT, R. P. "Application of Psychoanalytic Concepts in Psychotherapy: Report of Clinical Trials in a Mental Hygiene Service," *Bull. Menninger Clin.*, 1 (1937), 99–109.

29. ———. "An Evaluation of Psychotherapeutic Techniques," *Bull. Menninger Clin.*, 16 (1952), 113–124.

30. KOEGLER, R. R. and N. Q. BRILL. *Treatment of Psychiatric Outpatients*. New York: Appleton-Century-Crofts, 1967.

31. LEWIN, K. K. *Brief Encounters: Brief Psychotherapy*. St. Louis: Warren H. Green, 1970.

32. MALAN, D. H. *A Study of Brief Psychotherapy*. London: Tavistock, 1963.

33. MANDELL, A. G. "The Fifteen-Minute Hour," *Dis. Nerv. Syst.*, 22 (1961), 1–4.

34. OBERNDORF, C. P. "Constant Elements in Psychotherapy," *Psychoanal. Q.*, 15 (1946), 435–449.

35. ORR, D. W. "Lionel Blitzsten, the Teacher," in *N. Lionel Blitzsten, M.D., Psychoanalyst, Teacher, Friend, 1893–1952*, pp. 21–69. New York: International Universities Press, 1961.

36. PARAD, H. G., ed. *Crisis Intervention: Selected Readings*. New York: Family Service Assoc. Am., 1965.

37. PHILLIPS, E. L. and D. N. WIENER. *Short-term Psychotherapy and Structured Behavior Change*. New York: McGraw-Hill, 1966.

38. PUMPIAN-MINDLIN, E. "Considerations in the Selection of Patients for Short-term Psychotherapy," *Am. J. Psychother.*, 7 (1953), 641–652.

39. RANGELL, L. "Similarities and Differences between Psychoanalysis and Dynamic Psychotherapy," *J. Am. Psychoanal. Assoc.*, 2 (1954), 734–744.

40. ROGERS, C. *Client-Centered Therapy*. Boston, Houghton Mifflin, 1951.

41. ROTHENBERG, S. "Brief Psychodynamically Oriented Therapy," *Psychosom. Med.*, 17 (1955), 455–457.

42. SAUL, L. "On the Value of One or Two Interviews," *Psychoanal. Q.*, 20 (1951), 613–615.

43. SCHMIDEBERG, M. "Short-Analytic Therapy," *Nerv. Child*, 8 (1949), 281–290.

44. SEMRAD, E. V., W. A. BINSTOCK, and B. WHITE. "Brief Psychotherapy," *Am. J. Psychother.*, 20 (1966), 576–599.

45. SIFNEOS, P. E. "Psychoanalytically Oriented Short-Term Dynamic or Anxiety-Provoking Psychotherapy for Mild Obsessional Neuroses," *Psychiatr. Q.*, 40 (1966), 271–282.

46. ———. *Short-Term Psychotherapy and Emotional Crisis*. Cambridge: Harvard University Press, 1972.

47. SOCARIDES, C. W. "On the Usefulness of Extremely Brief Psychoanalytic Contacts," *Psychoanal. Rev.*, 4 (1954), 340–346.

48. STEKEL, W. *Conditions of Nervous Anxiety*. New York: Liveright, 1950.

49. STERBA, R. "A Case of Brief Psychotherapy by Sigmund Freud," *Psychoanal. Rev.*, 38 (1951), 75–80.

50. STONE, L. "Psychoanalysis and Brief Psychotherapy," *Psychoanal. Q.*, 20 (1951), 215–236.

51. STRUPP, H. H. *Psychotherapists in Action*. New York: Grune & Stratton, 1960.

52. WAELDER, R. "The Goal of Psychotherapy," *Am. J. Orthopsychiatry*, 10 (1940), 704–706.

53. WOLBERG, L. R. *Short-Term Psychotherapy*. New York: Grune & Stratton, 1965.

54. WOLPE, J. *The Practice of Behavior Therapy*. New York: Pergamon, 1969.

55. WOLPE, J. and A. A. LAZARUS. *Behavior Therapy Techniques*. Oxford: Pergamon, 1966.

CHAPTER 14

THE NEWER THERAPIES

Eugene T. Gendlin

❨ Introduction

Iᴎ ᴀᴅᴅɪᴛɪᴏɴ to psychoanalysis and behavior
therapy, a third type of psychotherapy
has most recently developed and is widespread. Sometimes called "the third force," or
the "humanistic'" or "existential" or "experiential" therapies, or simply the "newer therapies," they consist of many different methods
with different names and procedures. A number of these will be discussed in detail. Although they have a great deal in common,
there is not a universally accepted body of
common principles. However, certain things
are clearly stressed by most of them.

❨ Attributes of the Newer Therapies

Direct Experience

Something happens during interviews that
is other than words. These therapies emphasize one or more of the following: emotions,
feelings, images, role playing, body tensions,
choices and taking responsibility, hugging and
touching, autonomously arising sentences and
body-movement expressions. One or another
of these kinds of direct experience is concretely worked with, and cognitive analyzing
is explicitly downgraded. Something more
than words and thoughts and externalized
descriptions must occur. However, these therapies, and the individual practitioners, vary in
regard to this emphasis. Some of the newer
methods are not so very different from psychoanalysis, although they use a different vocabulary; other therapies consist, very centrally, of quite concrete bodily, imaginative, or
felt events so that a person can be in no doubt
whatever that something more than thinking
or just talking is occurring.

This emphasis during the interview on
something other than words is in sharp contrast to psychoanalysis and operant-behavior
therapy in which the interviews center on
cognitively defining one's experience, or on
analyzing one's external behavior and situations.

In psychoanalysis, the person's difficulties
and experiences are translated into conceptual
categories of dynamics and diagnostics. The
therapy process is then guided by, and carried

on in terms of, these conceptual definitions. The analyst moves from the patient's experience to conceptually understood categories, and then works with these. The person's experience is defined by them. The analysis is guided by them. In operant-behavior therapy the analysis of external behavior and situational circumstances has the guiding role. The person's experiences are related to externals, and these latter are then worked with. In contrast, most of the newer therapies work directly with concrete, experienced events during the interviews.

Change Now

Among other related principles held in common is the conviction that *concrete personality change can happen now*. There is a great rebellion against the psychoanalytic emphasis on the patient's past, and the psychoanalytic way of postponing change to a future that is thought to come only after years of talking sessions. Cognitive analyzing does not bring change or it brings very little, and only slowly. Instead, the emphasis is on what the person feels right now. The question is, how can we work with and move further with what the person feels right now? The content of the feelings may well concern events of infancy and childhood, but feeling them and crying is now, and the fresh release and new movement from these feelings into new experience can happen now.

Something more than words and ideas must happen right now, and this is always the main aim.

These methods have various procedures for moving off the level of mere talk and directly into concrete feelings. As will be seen, these procedures range all the way from simply condemning "head trips" (useless intellectualizing) to subtle methods for aiding a person to get directly in touch with a feeling process and having movement in it right now.

Responsibility

Concurrent with the emphasis on bringing about something more than ideas right now is an emphasis on the person's own responsibility. These therapies imply a *denial of determinism*. The past may have made one what one is, but changing now is possible now and it is one's own responsibility to choose and make a change. There is a flat denial of the psychoanalytic belief that natural-science forces keep one as one is.

Trust Your Own Body

Another emphasis held in common is *a reliance on the trustworthy and adaptive nature of the organism*. This emphasis opposes Freud who considered mental health a balance of forces that were in themselves pathological. He held that repression was essential for civilized society, and viewed the body without socialization as a seething cauldron of savage, separate id drives. In the newer methods, the body is viewed as an adaptive self-balancing system. Integration and balance are not due to conscious ego control, as in Freud, but are natural in the body. Therefore, the solutions are already inherent in the organism, and must be allowed to emerge. Feelings can be trusted—their good reason will emerge. If any aspect of humans is mistrusted in some of these therapies, it is precisely the rationality and control in which Freud placed his faith. This mistrust of reason and thinking gives some of these newer methods a certain imbalance—as though reason and thinking were not also a proper part of the human organism. But this mistrust is meant to counteract the widespread overemphasis on reason and control in our culture. For many people, therapy is a process of loosening overdeveloped controls and tensions so that a more natural process can be liberated.

Interaction

There is also an emphasis on *interaction*. Denying the psychoanalytic view of humans as intrapsychic mechanisms, most of these therapies imply that a person *is* an interaction with others and the environment. Instead of internal entities, drives, complexes, unconscious fantasies, and so on, the emphasis is on modes of living and relating to other people, the therapist, one's sexual partner, parents, friends, authorities, work, culture, and society.

Instead of internal psychic entities what one actually finds when one enters into one's feelings are interactions with others. For example, one finds no fear or hostility, one finds a fear of . . . something that might happen or might have happened or might have been done to one . . . by certain people. One finds one's anger *at* . . . the people who did certain things and forced one to be in certain ways. What one finds are aspects of living done and left undone, not intrapsychic entities.

Therefore, those therapies that deal with directly had feeling, also emphasize interpersonal interaction. That is because when feelings are *directly* explored, they turn out to involve interactional aspects. Only with theoretical concepts can one make purely internal entities, intrapsychic contents. An experiential approach leads to an understanding of human nature as interactional.

Arrested Growth, Arrested Living

The nature of psychosis and neurosis is arrested growth, or arrested living, not pathological contents. Therapists are not so interested in elaborating and understanding strange ways of being as in moving beyond them. From this new viewpoint the most interesting thing about a delusional system would not be its content or symbolic meaning but the living and relating, the absence of which it marks. The effort would not be to interpret it but to contact the person deeply and simply in spite of it. In the newer therapies there is, therefore, much less fear of seemingly pathological entities. Growth and inward richness are the heritage of any human being, and nothing that arises in a person is viewed as inherently sick or wrong or to be feared. The aim is not somehow to do away with seemingly insane content but to enable people to live and interact more fully and to get feelingly in touch with themselves. Therapy is personal growth, not a cure.

Not Adjustment

It follows also that these therapies, at least avowedly, are *not trying to adjust anyone to society as it is*. Rather, they are trying to overcome the stultifying and retarding effects of socialization. In these newer views, it is the dehumanizing, threatening, conventionalizing effects of society that are pathological, not inward contents of a person.

No Authorities

Along with these emphases it follows that *the therapist is not usually viewed as an authority* who knows what is sick or well. There is a revolt against what is called the "medical model," the view that the doctor's authoritative knowledge cures the patient. (The appropriate model would resemble a more ancient concept of medicine as ministering to a self-healing body, and as working with a knowing and self-directed patient whom one advises.) The therapist knows procedures that help get in touch with something and how to feel it through. The therapist is not an authority and cannot tell the person anything substantive, or do anything useful to the person that the person isn't doing.

Training Through Self-examination and Consultation

Accordingly, *the type of training* being advocated is not so much a university education or knowledge of concepts and experimental methods, as it is one's own personal therapy and growth and the opportunity *to explore oneself with someone while one is doing therapy.* Supervision does not consist of an older therapist telling the trainee about the patient (consider—the supervisor hasn't even seen the patient, while the trainee has lived deep hours with the patient.) Rather, supervision resembles therapy except that the trainee's process takes its rise from the relationships with people being seen in therapy.

The more experienced therapist might sit in with the trainee in the session. Similarly, the experienced therapist might let a trainee participate as a cotherapist. The experienced therapist would be more likely to discuss difficult situations, would be more open about failures than perhaps the trainee at first dares to be. The traditional pattern is reversed, according to which the supervisor, almost in military fashion, could never be seen having difficulty.

Bringing Others into the Interview

The therapist–patient relationship *is more open to include others into the hour*, such as both partners of a marriage, all the members of a family, or someone to help the therapist express feelings or difficulties, or to move beyond a stuck situation. Because of the diminution of the authority structure, and because of the emphasis on real interaction and feeling what is happening now, a therapist finds it much easier in these newer methods to own up to errors and conflicts (and to resolve them or process them right there) than used to be the case in the older methods. The therapist's consultant is, therefore, best made part of the ongoing interview, where more can be seen and processed, than in a later separate session consisting only of "talking-about." This emphasis on ongoing interaction makes it similarly desirable that the person and the important people in the person's life are here in ongoing interaction, instead of a lone person merely talking about these interactions.

Choices To Live

There is a strong *emphasis on choice*. Psychoanalytic determinism is viewed as a mere ploy to avoid feeling through what one can change. Behavioral methods of controlling others, as currently being used by jail administrators in many jails, seem patently designed to hide from people, or defeat in them, their own inherent capacity for choice and for assuming the direction of their lives. (On the other hand, behavioral methods for extending one's own control of one's own behavior are welcomed. Behaviorists are often unconcerned about the difference between these two kinds

of uses of their work, a difference which seems so major.) Choice in these newer methods isn't viewed as arbitrary selection from among alternatives. Rather, it is taking on one's living, it is moving to a different mode of being alive, harder perhaps than being controlled, but more exhilarating, more aware, and also safer. People can be controlled into doing almost anything. In contrast, becoming more sensitive and self-directed doesn't lead one to want to oppress others, or to need to hurt them. Rather, one wants others, to live with and interact with, who are also more broadly self-aware and in control of their lives.

Neither control by others, as in some behavior therapy, nor rational secondary process self-control as in psychoanalysis can achieve this manner of living. It makes use of a more holistic instinctual and more globally sensitive totalling in the body than habit or reason alone.

(The Major New Methods

A number of therapies in this group will be discussed separately here. There are quite a lot of supposedly different therapies that are not sharply differentiated from each other. Even the chief ones overlap considerably. Therapists freely borrow procedures from each other. Many therapists hyphenate more than one orientation, calling themselves Client-centered-Existential for instance, or some other combination. In a chapter of this kind, only a few of the major and most representative methods can be discussed.

Most of the newer methods are identified with a specific procedure.

The variety of procedures can best be understood if one bears in mind that something other than mere words or external actions is being worked with. What, other than words and actions, may be worked with? One may work with images or emotions, with directly sensed but unclear feelings, with body tensions, muscles, actual personal interaction, role playing, hugging and touching, music and painting, important words or sentences repeated or screamed, with body postures and expressive motions that come autonomously and can release powerful experiences in a person.

The following gives some notion of the variety, and, running through it, the constant aim for an impactful change or bit of experiential movement now, rather than staying with nothing but endless verbalizations.

Client-Centered Therapy

Carl Rogers,[37] who founded *Client-Centered Therapy*, eliminated all interpretation. Instead, *every* therapist response attempts to state exactly what the client is just now trying to communicate. Nothing is merely inferred. Only what is there for the client is said. Only what the clients themselves bring up is ever talked about by the therapist. However, the therapist responds to the personal edge of what the client says, or implies. If the client tells about an incident, the therapist will respond to what the incident seems to mean to the client, how it makes the client feel. The therapist attempts to stay within the exact limits of what the client is trying to communicate. Any attempts to twist this, to add something, to reinterpret it, are viewed as getting in the way of the client's inward movement.

This method sounds simple, but it is quite demanding. One does not usually grasp another person's meaning and personal sense, because it is with one's own organism that one takes in what others say. Client-Centered Therapy requires that the therapist sense the client's concerns and personal ways of viewing and struggling with whatever is being said, just exactly as it is felt by the client. The therapist must respond to each bit the client expresses. Frequently, the therapist's response is such that the client has to "correct" it, "No, it isn't quite like that, it feels more like . . ." whereupon the therapist will restate it more correctly, until—perhaps after two or three corrections—the therapist grasps exactly how whatever is being worked on feels to the client. At this point, it is crucial that the therapist now keep quiet. The client will continue.

The client senses that what was just talked about has got across. There is now room in the client for some next thing to come up.

The interpersonal space and interaction with the therapist becomes an extension of the client's inner space, and there is a powerful uncramping and moving forward of feelings and perceptions, emotions, and implicitly sensed inward experience. Rogers discovered that a very powerful and self-propelled process takes its rise and continues without being controlled or guided by either therapist or client. Once the process gets going, it is felt powerfully, and is frequently well ahead of what the client can rationally understand. During the week, between interviews as well as in the therapy hours, the client can feel much more going on, more feelings and unclear but important stirrings, than can possibly be kept track of. There is no doubt that a very large change is taking place.

Compared to tense, intellectual talking, and compared to the constant stops and starts of therapist–patient arguments and interpretations that get the patient off the felt track, client-centered therapy feels like being on an express train. It is nothing like "just letting someone talk." When people are not responded to, they tend to talk in circles and remain stuck in the same feeling sets. The Client-Centered therapist responds to each few sentences of the client. Another person sensing exactly where one is and "saying back each step" makes for movement. There is a relief that someone understands, but at the next moment something new arises within that would never have come up had one not been responded to. Therefore, quite often between therapy hours, clients think and talk to themselves, circling round and round their problems, and then find themselves moving swiftly again as soon as where they were stuck for several days has been expressed, heard, and responded to.

Rational Emotive Therapy

This therapy, devised by Albert Ellis,[11] may be viewed as the mirror opposite of Client-

Centered Therapy. The emphasis is on beliefs rather than feelings. The therapist insistently moves the patient's attention away from any sentence that begins with "I feel," and focuses instead on "beliefs" and "ideas." The central notion is that people torment themselves internally on the basis of irrational beliefs. Examples of such beliefs are that one "should" do or feel something, or that one "must" feel bad if certain things have happened. Ellis distinguishes between "It would be nice if . . ." (for example, if I had someone to love) which he considers rational, and "Therefore I *should* feel bad" which he considers insane. The "RT" therapist exhorts the client to make that distinction, and to eschew all "shoulds." Similarly, the client is urged to distinguish between "It is too bad, that . . ." (for example, that he rejected me) and "It's *awful*, that . . ." or "I *must* feel bad, that . . ." The method assumes that bad feelings come from insane beliefs, mostly along the above lines. Many people experience considerable relief when they cut what seems like a logical tie between what is the case, on the one hand, and what they do to themselves inside about it on the other hand.

In a typical Rational-Emotive-Therapy interview, in contrast to Client-Centered Therapy, it is the therapist who does most of the talking. In a transcript, the long paragraphs begin with a "T." The client frequently says only "Yes" or begins sentences with "You mean . . ." trying to understand the therapist's argument. The strongest possible words and forms of persuasion are used by the therapist who is not stopped by a client's tears or rage. On the other hand, the therapist has confidence in the client's capacity to improve.

As in the other therapies in this group, the emphasis is on the present and on stopping maladjustive patterns in the present. The past is no excuse for present behavior. It is in the present that the client is still maintaining and reinforcing his irrational beliefs, still "catastrophizing," still creating inward disturbance.

Even if the client vows to get rid of these beliefs, they are "underlying," and their removal requires practice. The beliefs are implicit and to root them out takes inward work

that is not really as different from the other methods as the rational emphasis makes it sound.

Transactional Analysis

Eric Berne's transactional analysis[5] might at first seem a simplified psychoanalysis. Its basic concepts are three: "PAC," which stands for parent, adult, child. Each person's behavior, both outward and inward, can be classified as being from one of these three sources. One may recognize a simplified superego-ego-id trio here, but all three are viewed as ego states. The therapist points out, and the patient soon learns, that it is "the parent" in the patient's head who does all blaming, reprimanding, finger waving, both when patients blame themselves and when they blame others. Much progress can be made in a marriage, for example, if both people recognize when it is "the parent" in one of them who is berating or infantilizing the other. "The adult" is the rational realistic aspect. The child is both the needy aspect of a person, and the enjoying, consuming, and celebrating aspect. But the child can also be whiny, mischievous, or nasty and intent on getting even.

There is considerable power in the recognitions that one of these parts is originating a type of behavior, an attitude, or a repetitious pattern. The recognition can, in effect, cut the tie between the patient and the pattern or emotion. Recognizing that this way of acting or feeling is "that lousy, blaming parent of mine," removes the emotion and behavior sufficiently from the patient so that there comes to be some freedom of action against it.

Transactional Analysis shares the "now" aspect of the newer therapies. There is a downgrading of dynamics and understanding one's past. One is told that "You can stop behaving like that now, just by stopping." Exploring causes is discouraged.

Aside from "PAC" there are also humorous names for certain patterns people engage in, such as "brown-stamp collecting" (grievance collecting) and "Pay and don't go" (self-defeating patterns), "cop-out" (passive–

aggressive "I couldn't help it"). Again, these patterns are to be stopped by simple exhortation to stop on the part of the therapist, and a discovery that one can stop now by the patient.

Transactional Analysis is often conducted in small groups. In the group the therapist works with one person at a time. People do not relate much to each other.

Transactional analysts typically employ many procedures from Gestalt therapy and encounter groups, which will be discussed under the more proper headings. For example, "the empty-chair" technique (see Gestalt, page 276) is often used so that the patient confronts some particular aspect of the parent or the child.

The chief characteristic of Transactional Analysis is that it is interpretative and insight-based. In this sense it is old-fashioned. Once the insight is had, that a certain pattern obtains, or that a particular behavior is attributable to, for instance, the parent part, it is left to the patient to overcome it. Techniques borrowed from other methods do aid in making change occur. The method shares with other recent methods its emphasis on one's ability to change now.

Imagery Therapies

These therapies begin with Jung. They include Systematic Desensitization (despite its behavioristic vocabulary), and are currently mushrooming. Jung's "active-daydream" technique is, of course, not the whole of Jungian therapy. He emphasized that the images must be allowed to come autonomously (not made deliberately) and *then* the patient must react to the images actively. The patient must behave just as if the images were real. Seeing such and such a frightening figure, for instance, the patient might choose to hide or imagine having a weapon or feed the figure something to propitiate it, or the patient might talk to it, ask it what it has to say. Jungian imagery methods involve a rhythm of letting autonomous images come (a kind of regression) and of reacting quite actively in an alert and assertive way (not at all a regression).

Jung emphasizes that little is achieved if one just lets the images run on and watches them passively. Jung did not think that the images of themselves were therapeutic, but that they were a way by which a conscious person could interact with unconscious material and process it.

Current methods of imagery vary greatly. Some European methods (Autogenic Training)[29] use very systematic steps to train a person to have vivid imagery, and then to use it in various ways. Sometimes these highly systematized methods seem more like research tools than therapies. Many current uses of imagery, in contrast, are rather like parlor games without any systematic effort to pursue and work through what the images arouse. Between these extremes are effective methods.

One can easily engender imagery in a person simply by beginning with one of a number of common formulae: "Imagine the entrance to a cave. Enter it and go a long way." "Imagine a house. Go inside. See what happens." Strong emotions are often aroused and can be worked through in a therapeutic way. Again, this is a method for getting deeply into something quickly, rather than spending years with words only.

A dream the patient remembers can be continued. The patient is asked to recall and once more visualize the end. What would the patient now like to do in this visualization? After doing that, the patient is asked to see what autonomous reaction there now is in the image of the dream scene.

In Systematic Desensitization the person is first helped to relax (a feature also of Autogenic Training and some other imagery methods). Images come more vividly and easily when one is relaxed. The person is then asked to imagine scenes or situations that cause difficulty. The aim is to remain relaxed despite the (imagined) presence of something disturbing. Again therapy consists of not just having images but acting on them. In this instance there is the added aim of remaining relaxed.

Images can also be allowed to form *from* a troubled feeling that is not clear to the person. They often provide a means by which the feeling can become distinct and change. It is important not to get so fascinated by images as to remain with them but to move from them to what is directly felt. What is the felt effect of the image? The *felt* impacts of imagery require pursuing so that therapeutic movement arises.

Gestalt Therapy

This therapy,[34,33] devised by Fritz Perls, features many "exercises." The basic aim is to integrate alienated parts of a person that are projected or in some way function separately. The person may have feelings about such an alienated aspect, or know about it, but it has not been integrated. To integrate that aspect or part, it is necessary that the person engage in a "dialogue" with it. Dialogue is an alternation in which a person spends some time having feelings and reactions toward that part, but also spends some time *being that part* (and feeling what that part says and feels).

One may find such an alienated "part" from talking about anything that causes difficulty, or in dreams—all of which are viewed as projections from alienated parts—or in some other way. The favored way is to sense one's body and find any place in it that is now tense, then to have a dialogue with that body part, beginning by being that part and feeling and saying what it feels and says.

The empty-chair exercise is one way of having a dialogue. One imagines that some aspect is sitting in a chair opposite. The patient then addresses this part. It might be the patient's father or mother, or a feeling or a part of the self that was talked about a moment before. It may be a feeling that criticizes and makes the patient feel bad. The patient then addresses this aspect. Done rightly, the patient waits until words and feelings well up toward what is in the opposite chair. After a few minutes the patient changes chairs and now *is* this aspect. What does the aspect feel and have to say to the patient? Again, quite powerful and surprising feelings and words well up of their own accord.

Similarly, a person can be asked to *be* any part or thing in a dream or fantasy (projections from alienated aspects of the person).

For example, if the person dreamed or imaged being crouched into a corner, the instruction might be, "Now *be* the corner." The person would first be asked to get up, describe the scene, and reenact the actual crouching. Then the person would be asked to step backward just a little and *be* the wall. What does the wall say? What does it feel? What would it like to do? Something will spontaneously come in answer.

Amazingly enough, in the above example, the person found himself kicking with his foot, kicking the imagined himself crouching before him. There was a flood of feeling along with the kicking. Yes, there was a lot of anger at himself, here, suddenly. Then, on reversing and being himself again, he found a tearful, "Yes, I hide from out there, but it's furious at me in here, and there's no place to go."

The Gestalt therapist interacts rather uniquely, sometimes getting quite angry and insulting, and blatantly refusing to take responsibility for the patient. ("That's what I feel like saying. You don't like it, that's your problem. I don't feel like saying anything else.") Great value is placed on people standing on their own two feet, maximally able to bear it that the other person's feelings are other than one's own, and may be negative or critical of oneself. Of course patients may express their feelings toward the therapist whatever they may be, but must learn to do this without encouragement and approval for it. To have and express one's feelings regardless of others' reactions is to "own" them. In the Gestalt view each person stands alone and any togetherness is a fortunate accident on which one does not count.

Primal Therapy

This form of therapy, introduced by Arthur Janov,[25] stems from something like the same phenomenon that is basic to Gestalt therapy, namely the autonomous coming of something the person would not ever deliberately produce. However, Janov concentrates entirely on what seem to be early infantile experiences. He reports that he began from the observation (also had by many other therapists) that some patients have an urge to let themselves go into crying and shouting certain sentences that are powerfully emotional for them. The patient might cry or say, "No, no, no" or cry, "Mama, Mama . . . come here," "Please don't hurt me," "Get away," nonverbal baby sobbing or other less typical things. Janov considered this a working through of infantile traumas and made a method of enabling every patient to experience these "primals." In his method the patient is encouraged to regress: Before therapy begins the patient may spend some days and nights alone, must not smoke or drink, and may be asked to go without sleep. As a result therapy begins with the condition most likely to engender infantile experiences.

The emphasis on regression is atypical for the newer therapies, which have rejected even the psychoanalytic couch. For the most part, these therapies emphasize that the person must now experience a *more* optimal living process and certainly not a more regressed one. The faith in the therapy process rests, in fact, on making the maximally best present process happen. Only because the patient is now living in a fuller and more open, more awake and more interactional manner can we expect that the bad experiences and emotions that arise will turn out for the best—if they are experienced within the present living. Primal therapy eliminates this advantage. Even in regard to the interpersonal relationship, the primal therapist is authoritarian and not very personal, preferring to invest everything into getting the primals and their living through.

The chief assumption of this method is that living through primals *releases* the traumas. But, what if people continue to run through these patterns, perhaps very many of them, again and again? Hart,[22] explaining his offshoot from Primal Therapy, says, "There is no emptying out of all that." The emphasis in this newer therapy is on "being able to feel what happened to you" and on "being able to integrate what you feel."

The integrating process that may be needed would be done in terms of procedures that can be common to other methods as well as this one.

Again here, no primal patient doubts that something more than just words and ideas is happening. In this sense Primal Therapy is very much part of the new trend. As much as any therapy in this group, Primal Therapy emphasizes the uselessness of the old-fashioned "just talking." A primal experience is an unmistakable event of considerable impact and power. One rolls on the floor, screams sentences that move with a will of their own, and certainly knows that one has gone through something.

Reevaluation Counseling

The approach of Harvey Jackins[23] also employs the phenomenon of autonomous emergence (as I term it) common also to Gestalt and Primal Therapy. "RC" is a method capable of being practiced by ordinary people with a minimum of training, and by reference to a handbook by Jackins. The training consists of several months of courses and practice together, with opportunities for further learning. Whereas Primal Therapy is a closely guarded secret, and costs between six and nine thousand dollars per patient, "RC" is given away nearly free. Therapy is mutual "cocounseling", each person is counselor in one hour and client in the other hour. Whereas the safeguards in Primal Therapy, if any, are not known, the safeguards in RC are taught and practiced with great care. The person now doing the counseling holds the person being counseled by both hands. They sit close, just far enough away so one's eye can focus. Throughout, the person is looked straight in the eye, and there isn't a moment when the interpersonal contact is not as strong as possible. Both regression and full awareness are practiced. That is to say, the person is encouraged to sense what unrealistic emotions are being "restimulated" now, and also to sense the difference between the present and the past. The counselor begins, perhaps, by saying, "Whom do I remind you of?" Having one's hands held is in itself likely to be "restimulating," one is likely to sense instantly "my mother" (or some important person). "How am I *like* your mother?" the counselor asks. Whatever comes now, will perhaps surprise the person. At any rate, within three minutes a powerful process has begun. But quite soon the counselor will ask: "How am I different from your mother?" Having got the person into childhood experiences, the person now differentiates that time from the present and fully returns to the present. (For these questions the counselor insists on getting some answer, always.) There are other routine steps. "Tell me two or three new and good things that have happened to you in the last few days." Later: "Tell me two or three minor upsets that happened in the last few days."

The brief account of these things invariably gets the person into deep water. Either the counselor asks the person to repeat some sentence that seemed to have emotion in it or the counselor invents such a sentence and asks the person to repeat it. (For example, "I didn't like it." "I didn't like it." "I didn't *like* it.") Perhaps the person will be asked to scream the sentence. If this fails, another sentence will be tried. If it succeeds, a very powerful emotional process is engendered. The shouting of the sentence begins to happen as if of its own accord. There is usually also a lot of crying. This unmistakably powerful process is termed "discharge."

The purpose is genuine working through, as in most therapy, not only deep feeling as such. Thus, soon, the counselor will ask the person to say the very opposite of what was being shouted. ("It doesn't bother me at all. It makes me feel fine. It doesn't bother me *at all*. It makes me feel *just* fine, *just* fine. I'm not *at all* upset by it.") Both people might laugh, the person might be laughing and crying together, as these obviously false yet also powerful sentences are being said. Returning from the opposite to the original side, the person may again be asked to say the sentence "I didn't like it . . ."

Quite often, in working with emotional material in this way, further sentences come. There is an effect of gradual building. The counselor asks the person to repeat what seems to be the most powerfully *felt* sentence. If new and stronger ones come, these are concentrated on. For example: "I hated it." "Say

that some more." "I hated it. I hated it. I didn't *like* it." The person begins to cry. "Say again I didn't *like* it." "I didn't *like* it. I didn't *like* it. It made me feel small, it made me feel small." The person may now be puckering his lower lip out like a small child and sounding like one. "Go away, stop that. *Stop* that. *Stop* that."

Very powerful, or not so powerful, experiences can be had with this method. Care is taken not to push anything against the person's will. "The client is in charge." After an hour the two people reverse roles. One or both may be experienced or novice, but in any one meeting each will be in each role half the time. Counseling and training are never separate.

Body Therapies

There are a large group of different therapies, as well as a great many individual practitioners with their own approaches.[41] The best-known, current method is *Bio-Energetics*, in a direct line from Wilhelm Reich.[36] This method begins by making the body enormously tense. The person is put through contortions, of which only some people are fully capable, until the body actually vibrates. People are pushed into distinctly painful physical experiences, postures, and exercises (stress positions). This can probably be interpreted as a kind of forceable regression (analogous to Primal Therapy.) One is on the verge of tears, and feels deeply invaded and imposed upon. Naturally enough, this enables infantile experiences of that sort to emerge. One is then encouraged to scream, "NO, NO" or "Leave me alone" or whatever words seem to come with great feeling.

Other body therapies employ opposite methods, many of them much more gentle and sensitive to the individual person. Brown,[9] by touching with his hands, senses tension, but encourages the very opposite of Bio-Energetics. Rather than *peripheral* muscle tension, Brown encourages *inward* body sensing. He holds that people have already abnormally high peripheral muscle tensions as it is, and need to focus on greater inward body awareness. The purpose is to relax peripherally and discover an inward center.

Most body therapies, including the two just mentioned, work with breathing. Some movements, perhaps hopping about, generate heavier breathing, the quality of which is indicative of quite a lot about the person. Most methods also work with specific places on an individual's body, for example, where there is pain in response to moderate pushing of the sort that doesn't generate pain elsewhere.

People's postures, ways of walking, standing, and sitting are also good starting points for therapeutic work. A person sitting tensely or with limbs close together or with legs wrapped around each other, tells a lot about that person. One becomes aware of many personal themes being manifested by how people stand and sit. The person can be asked to exaggerate such body positions and to sense what feelings they express.

Body therapists can see a great deal by looking at an individual's posture. *Rolfing*[38] is a rather more violent body method than any other. It involves rearranging the person's body parts as they ought to be. However, this is no mere correction of posture. The pathological ways in which many years of poor posture has arranged one's body parts has become cemented in by cartilage. To put the parts of the body back into proper relationship involves breaking cartilage, and is extremely painful. Rolfing is undertaken by people who are willing to endure great pain for a few days, and then be, as it were, new people. The reports of those who have gone through this treatment continue to be so positive, however, that others are drawn to it.

The basic view held in common is that a person's body embodies the person's basic personality and ways of living. This is not a theoretical assumption, but something one can see on a person's body. To work directly with that seems much more powerful than merely talking about change while the person sits before one in the solid, vividly expressive posture embodying the difficulty. One is therefore inclined to work directly with the body, and, indeed, a powerful process can begin almost immediately if one does so. Intense emotions are keyed off and lived through in sensing just what is involved, for instance, in the person's chronically raised shoulders. "Exaggerate that a little, pull the shoulders up even higher, sense what that is for you." The person may have an impulse to curve the shoulders forward altogether in an arching, closing gesture around the chest, as if to protect against some attack. Along with this there may be a very real sense of fear or a wish to withdraw. Conversely, when at last the person can let the shoulders drop to a new normal position, what is felt?

There may be some tension on one's face. Exaggerating it, it becomes a grimace. What emotion does it express? The emotion will come along with an acting out, perhaps with words and other gestures involving the whole body. Then, if that chronic tension can at last be relaxed—what feelings occur?

In these therapies, release experiences almost universally give the person at least some days of feeling freer, more open, and eager to live. The concensus is, also, that people's personalities, looks, and postures change, although as yet no research bears this out.

Body therapies often include massage, which is a serious and deep experience. Massage enables the therapist to sense where there is tension in the body. Also, massage reveals what part of the person's body is alive and soft and full of energy, and what part is "dead," stiff, and closed. These metaphoric words describe quite palpable differences in how the various parts of the body feel to the massager's touch. It cannot fail to have a psychological meaning, for example, when the breasts and chest of a woman feel soft and responsive and have a kind of glow to the massage oil, and the lower part of her body feels to the touch like cement. (Roberta Miller,[32]). Equally significant, a stiff, tense upper part of the body is often combined with a tense, hunched posture and raised shoulders. Or more specific parts of a person may be tense, legs, feet only, jaw muscles, etc.

Body therapists differ in how much importance they attach to their psychological working through and personal integrating of the emotions and effects of body work. For some the entire aim is such working through, and the body work is only the take-off point, the most concrete and significant way to start and to make progress. Others believe that in working with muscles alone everything else is indirectly worked through.[1]

By beginning with the body, many of the procedures discussed up to now can be employed in a rather different and sometimes more impactful way.

YOGA

In this context, *yoga* has spread widely among people interested in therapy methods using the body. There is a very distinct effect on one's living generally from doing an hour of yoga stretching exercises every day. While the exercises look outlandish, at least the beginning ones are easy to do. Their purpose is not muscle building but muscle stretching and a general softening that makes the body supple. Tension is lowered, smoking and other nervous habits decrease of themselves. When yoga has been practiced for some time, there is a bodily longing for it when it is omitted.

MEDITATION

The relation between yoga and *meditation* is not accidental. Both are methods that lower tension. Many methods of meditation exist, some drawn from oriental sources, some developed here. They differ as to whether they are a deepening or a scattering of attention, but, at any rate, the person moves away from usual concerns, stops—or tries to stop—talking inwardly, and the body relaxes. Some meditation is religious or cosmic. There is a sense of a vast, positive universe within which one lives and breathes.

The relation of physical yoga and meditation is somewhat analogous to the relation of therapeutic body work, and psychological working through. Many people engage only in the physical side and are sure that the psychological effects, while indirect, are nevertheless there. Others emphasize the need not only to engage in the physical exercises but also to quiet oneself inwardly and psychologically. They feel that the two aid each other. Similarly, the body therapies give rise to psycho-

logical experiences, so that psychotherapy processes arise from and are aided by body work.

Existential Psychotherapy

This therapy[31,12,6,7] does not involve most of the procedures discussed so far. It is usually exclusively verbal. The emphases discussed at the outset are shared by Existential Psychotherapy. Many of them were first articulated by existential writers including Rollo May,[24] Viktor Frankl[31] and Ludwig Binswanger.[6,7] The therapy centers on choice, responsibility, and genuine encounters between the two persons.

Anxiety is viewed as potentially helpful. Anxiety is indicative of unlived life, of opportunities for growth, encounter, and expansion of the person that are being missed. The person is encouraged to meet the challenges of living, the possibilities of radical change in living situations. People make themselves what they are and must continue to do so to stay as they are. There is an emphasis on the waste of life, that is, the avoidance of challenges.

Values and life meanings are focused upon, rather than following the traditional view that in therapy they are ways of avoiding therapeutic material. Values and meanings are considered real, not epiphenomena of infantile conflicts. Social responsibility and an expanded life that expresses itself in social and cultural meanings is considered more truly being human than life without these. Most current neuroses are viewed as unlike those that Freud catalogued. Their etiology is thought to be not from natural-science forces in the person but from meaninglessness and atrophied living. Such narrowing of meaning results from avoiding challenges in life and from avoiding authenticity. A loss of meaning is also inherent in current social pressures to conform and in the downgrading of values.

Frankl, who says much of the above, has also devised the specific therapeutic technique called "paradoxical intention." People who struggle inwardly against certain impulses, or struggle to control them in some way, are asked to reverse this struggle. Instead of fighting against a particular impulse, these people are asked to tell themselves to do it more. From this some therapists have derived "symptom scheduling" and other related ways. The person is taken out of the circular struggle in which the very mode of trying only strengthens the difficulty. A more natural desire to stop the particular kind of behavior then emerges.

Existential psychotherapy varies from being quite like psychoanalysis with different words and concepts to being a genuine encounter in which both persons are changed.

Experiential Psychotherapy

This therapy[14,15,18] consists of working with the concretely felt events to which the person can directly refer, and of living *further* from these felt events during the interview.

The interactional living in the relationship, and inward bodily sensing, are the chief sources of such concretely felt events. One or all of the already mentioned exercises may also be used, but these would be considered only as starting points for an experiential process of many steps in which what is aroused would be pursued, would shift and change, and would be lived further. Therapy is not only emotions and cathartic discharge.

Neither is therapy merely verbal behavior and response. Frequently, the person is asked to stop talking, (out loud and inside) and to sense inwardly. One must get into concrete touch with the bodily felt sense of what is being talked about. This might take only a minute of silence, or it might require a lot of work over many sessions. The person might then talk further, but soon again be asked to sense inwardly.

From a bodily felt sense of some difficulty, steps arise. When one gets in touch with a felt sense, and expresses it, there is a felt effect. The felt sense becomes sharper, or shifts, or further felt aspects emerge. When one first gets the bodily felt sense of a difficulty, there is one global cognitively unclear feeling. From this, quite soon, a specific feeling emerges. As this is "focused" upon, it shifts or releases and gives rise to another step.

Experiential Therapy is possible because people have not only emotions, such as fear, anger, or guilt, but also always a mass of feeling that is implicitly rich and generates movement steps. This level of visceral sensing is, so to speak, "under" emotions. It is a sensing of the whole complexity that gives rise to the emotion. While an emotion as such tends to remain itself, a felt sense can move into a series of quite different emotions and felt aspects. By returning always to the bodily felt sense of each moment, a movement of steps results.

Anyone can have strong emotions, but many people cannot, at first, get in touch with a bodily felt *sense of* the difficulties and life problems they speak about. Their attention, so to speak, floats far above the concrete existence inside them of that of which they speak. When people lack this level of feeling, they are sometimes asked to choose the most meaningful sentence they can form and then to repeat it many times to themselves while trying to feel what felt sense is involved in these words. What feeling does the sentence arise from?

Getting the person in touch with the felt-sense level (under emotions) is the first order of business, if this is lacking. People are asked to note what they *do now feel*. Often they don't feel what they are talking about, but do feel, for example, confusion, or a sense of urgency, or a fear of being empty inside, or annoyance at the therapist's pushing, or a desire to do what is asked for. There may be feelings of unwillingness, restlessness, or trying terribly hard, running scared, doubt that anything in oneself can be of any use. What *is* there now, in the present living, constitutes good concretely felt starting points for experiential process.

There is also a specific procedure—"Focusing"[17]—consisting of instructions to be carried out in silent periods. The first instruction is to let oneself feel the whole of a problem as one global sense of it all, as if all of it together were newly coming home to one. A more specific feeling usually arises from this global feel of the problem. One is then asked to pursue that feeling, allowing attention simply to follow it. After another minute one asks oneself an open-ended question such as, "What is this feeling?" or "What is in the way of it's being all right?" But one doesn't answer the question oneself. Instead, one waits. The answer must come *from* the feeling. The person should let words go by. The only words the person is instructed to hold onto are words that have a distinctly felt effect in the feeling, either a sharpening of the feeling or a shift in it, an opening up, a release.

In some of the other newer therapies, strong emotions and autonomous discharges are viewed as therapy. People are often left with disconnected impactful events. Experiential therapy centers on the experiential working through process. The basic viewpoint of Experiential Psychotherapy is that real change takes place only through *a process* of bodily felt *steps*.

Procedures are not enough. People must be engaged as persons, by the therapist as a person—and this must occur in terms of the richness that is implicit in the ongoing experiencing of both of them.

An Experiential therapist may interpret or do many other things. The widest repertoire is available to the Experiential therapist. On the other hand, anything just done or said would be immediately discarded in favor of following whatever it roused in the patient or whatever the patient concretely feels and finds within. Words or actions or interactions are sought that will make touch with and will shift what the patient just now concretely feels.

The therapist's very honest interacting is a major avenue of getting people in touch with their feelings, and more importantly, an avenue of living them further and enabling them to shift. Most personal difficulties and stuck places also close off really personal interaction. If personal interaction can be carried further in spite of these difficulties, the difficulties resolve themselves. Most difficulties and repetitive patterns are quite general in the sense of being always the same and leaving no room for the richness and specificity of this moment's actual experience. When what the Experiential therapist feels just now is ex-

plored, differentiated, and some of it is expressed in its unique detail, the patient's reaction tends to move beyond the usual pattern. The differentiated texture of actually feeling an interactional moment, is never exactly the same or exactly the opposite of a repetitive pattern. It is always different and much richer than the general repetitive pattern was.

The Experiential therapist welcomes the inevitable moments of interactional difficulties that occur during the interview because they afford opportunities to carry interaction beyond the stoppages by differentiating and expressing what both people just now feel.

The personalities of both people are likely to be involved simultaneously in any one difficulty. Both persons are likely to find themselves broadened if the interaction is carried further, with many steps of more differentiated feeling—expression beyond the point where it traditionally stops due to old patterns, defensiveness, politeness, or the role model of the imperturbable therapist.

On the other hand, the therapist's self-expression is not indiscriminate, but an attempt to open up and live more deeply *what is already happening between* the two people. Therapist expression also depends upon how far the relationship has advanced.

Therapist self-expressions are self-owned and about oneself, they are steps into one's own inwardness. The form, "I feel that you . . ." is not a *self*-expression. When statements of that form are made, they are questions or invitations to the other person to look within. Self-expression does not mean attacks, or expressions the main point of which is something in the other person. In Experiential Therapy one works on a level of bodily visceral sensing that is neither just words nor just game-played routines and also *not just emotions*. There is a texture of specificities in each person that is *felt*. It can be gotten into only by *letting* a felt sense come and by *letting* it express itself. In such a process of steps, what is "next" is not a matter of choice. One may want something to be next, but one's direct inward sensing will meet exactly what it does meet, what is actually there, next. And that is not a matter of choice. The experiential process is not guided by the concepts or decisions of either person. The freeing and expansion of the person is a process that gives rise to *its own* next steps.

Other methods exist, which are certainly worthy of discussion.

Reality Therapy

This therapy[20] combines an explicit emphasis on a caring and involved therapist with a focus on behavior. Planned steps of change in behavior and situation are the stuff of therapy interviews. Decision, will power, commitment, responsibility, maturity, identity, confrontation are some of the concepts used. They mark the struggle to get past "excuses" and avoid explanations of failure. *Confrontation* is extensively used, "You said you would do it. When will you do it?". Confrontation is used when the therapist senses something irresponsible on the part of the patient.

Psychosynthesis

Under this name Assagioli[2] draws together a great many elements that are found separately elsewhere, most of them discussed in this chapter. It is difficult to decide what the central notions or procedures are. Psychosynthesis emphasizes working with the will, and decision making. Self-awareness is considered as a distinct experience in its own right, a sense of self. Spiritual dimensions, music, specific training of intuitive sensing, are included.

Sex Therapy

Masters and Johnson[9,30] provide a step by step program lasting some months, and is undertaken by a married couple. For example, one step in the program requires husband and wife not to have intercourse for a period of time during which the focus is on touching, foreplay, enjoying each other's bodies. With the anxiety about performance thus removed, this step in the program often frees sexual desires and feelings in the participants.

Fight Training

This therapy[3] emphasizes the helpful role in a relationship of being able to express anger, and accept its expression by the other person. Bach[3] teaches joyous attacking by both partners in a marriage, which can reenliven long-frozen relationships.

Parent-effectiveness Training

Client-centered ways of responding are used in a carefully thought-out system of responding to one's children. Detailed practice examples and regular classes are provided.[21] One seeks to grasp and verbalize the sense that the child's behavior and expressions make *to the child*, but, equally, one also expresses one's own parental and personal feelings and needs.

❮ Changing the Dyadic Pattern

The methods to be discussed in this section center not on procedures of therapy but rather on changes in the one-to-one office pattern of therapy.

Groups

Groups,[39,40] while not new in themselves, have become a widespread social movement far exceeding the professional context. Encounter groups, Sensitivity groups, Growth groups, and many other names enable people who do not know each other to be almost immediately more intimate with each other than they can be with the people closest to them in their lives. Some think of this as an artificial and unreal intimacy. Certainly it seems easier to be intimate, self-revealing, and appreciative of another human being's inwardness when the other person isn't one's husband, wife, parent, daughter, or work associate. One can be appreciative of the other person's inward fears, angers, and peculiarities because one does not live in the situations where these feelings or traits of character are making things difficult. One can also risk being looked down upon, since one need never see these people again. But to emphasize this aspect is to understand only half. The other half of the phenomenon of encounter groups is the powerful way they aid one to come alive with others, to sense one's inward reactions and inward richness. Of course, many people have this already, but it seems that the mass of people do not. Encounter groups have, therefore, made a vast and growing subculture of people who have become aware of the richness of their inwardness, and that of others.

Coming, let us say, from a rather cold and defensive family, working in some proper setting, a person may never have experienced interactions that went beyond the everyday routines of stereotyped relating. Even such a person's closest friends are not really close, but only partners in rounds of routine activities, drinking, socializing, small talk, sharing subjects such as baseball, the race question, sex, and TV. With one's marriage partner one is likely to maintain certain well-defended stances and engage in certain routinized ways of relating. These may be vital to a person, but that makes it all the more threatening to risk being more open.

In contrast to this, what happens in the first hours of a good encounter group can be deeper and more enlivening than anything that has happened in the person's life for many years. The person may never have known that people can talk on such a level, that people can differentiate unique reactions within themselves, reactions that have no routine names. No wonder the impact can be quite great.

For the ordinary person an encounter group can mark an utterly new world. If such a world exists, why be alone and stay silent and dumb inside? If people can talk and interact in this way, why stay in the empty routines? "How could I have so long been locked in, unformed and unheard, without even knowing it?"

The professional therapist has long known that therapy is not only a cure for ills, but also a highly exciting and enriching process—after

all, the professional spends his life that way, usually from choice. Can professionals wonder that others, too, experience the process that way? One need not be "sick" to want this process. In encounter groups the focus is less on therapy and more on growth.

Like all types of individual psychotherapy, groups are only successful sometimes. Perhaps half to two-thirds of groups are dull. They begin with haggling and a general unwillingness to open up. They involve a lot of complaining ("Why aren't we doing anything?") or mutual insulting ("You are phony. You aren't really feeling anything."). The wise participant leaves groups of this sort long before they are over. Increasingly, however, groups are not started in this way. Instead, they move directly into something more than words, in one or another of the ways already described. Many of the techniques outlined can occur in groups. The leader institutes them. In addition, groups provide a field of personal *interaction*. People develop strong feelings about each other. (Sometimes, of course, they only wish they did, and make much of small annoyances and a little warmth.) People can dare to try out ways of being more open, more spontaneous, more direct, expressive, courageous, self-revealing. Often they can take the first step toward some needed change.

Many patterns of groups exist. Some meet once a week for many months, most meet one or two successive days (a weekend, for instance.) In *Marathon Groups*, the group continues throughout two days and nights with individuals sleeping when they want to. Intensity is said to be heightened.

Groups of various types are conducted at "Growth Centers" or "Human Potential Centers," which exist in every city.

Family Therapy

Family Therapy,[42] *Couples Therapy, Marriage Counseling*, all are based on the widely shared view that "Not the individual but the relationship is sick." Therefore, the therapist seeks to work not with the individual woman or man but with the marriage. Wife and husband attend therapy together. The therapist may listen and interact, first with one for a while, then with the other. In this way, each is enabled to experience the other being very different, in the relation to the therapist, than at home. Or, the interaction between the two can be worked with.

Family therapy includes the children and the grandparents if they are living in the home. A family is considered a single "system" in which each individual has a certain role. A whole range of phenomena is revealed by family therapy that the individual therapist never sees. It is striking how some members of a family actively resist change in other members. The individual therapist does not see what happens to the patient at home when some change is first tried out—and how quickly the patient is brought back into line by the pressures exerted on him or her by other members of the family. When all are in the office together, the moves each makes in regard to the others are apparent.

In a family or marriage the ways an individual is forced back into old patterns can vary from relatively subtle interaction modes to gross tantrums, goading, or threats. Behavior occurs that an observer would consider obvious, but that may be done without awareness. Even very well-intentioned family members are likely to anticipate the individual's disturbances, react as if the individual were upset again. They are likely to oppose new patterns, and may even become very disturbed and clinically ill themselves if the erstwhile patient remains outside of old patterns and continues strong and growing.

Furthermore, a good deal of psychological disturbance is really "at" someone. Suicide is often "at" someone (both someone past and someone present). Depression may be clinically diagnosed as defended-against anger, but it may be anger "at" the other person in the marriage, (and not, or at least not only, at a parent of long ago). Long-stuck interactions need to move before that changes. An individual patient can struggle alone in a therapist's office for years and be unable to change something because it is really *inter*active— geared in with the responses or lack of them in the other close person. But, then, why does that close person respond this way? That, in turn, is partly due to how the first individual acts—and so it goes round and round. If the therapist can intervene to make a different process happen between them, this changes not only the relationship but also the personality of the individual. Many therapists have now observed this so often and constantly that they refuse to see one person singly—if the person is married or living with a parent.

If one member of a marriage is in traditional one-to-one psychotherapy and the other member isn't, divorce is very often the result, regardless of the original aims and wishes of the patient and the therapist. The patient develops and grows in therapy, the other marriage partner is left out of all this. What happens between them is less and less meaningful and relevant in comparison to what the patient is experiencing in the therapy. The marriage relation is not worked with and does not change. The patient develops new strengths alone without any new developments in the interaction patterns with the other marriage partner.

But the same lack exists if both members of a marriage are in therapy but with different therapists: they grow away from each other and leave their interaction patterns undeveloped.

To make clear how one-to-one therapy for marriage partners omits the work on their own interactions, let us consider the case of two traditional analysts, one of whom is separately seeing the husband, the other the wife. The two analysts then consult with each other, but without husband and wife being present. Instead of husband and wife moving beyond their stuck-interaction patterns, it is the two analysts who are interacting! One analyst tells the other: "If *your* patient acted less castrating, my patient would be more assertive." The other analyst says: "If your patient were less whiny and grievance collecting, my patient would *love* to be more feminine." Looked at from the interactional perspective of the newer therapies, this means that the two analysts are getting all the personality growth inherent in working out interactions. The two patients never get past their stuck interactions and will eventually be divorced.

Family therapy is especially dramatic when an individual is in a psychotic state. Family therapists call the ostensive patient "the person in whom the illness manifests itself." The illness is an attribute of the family system, of the relationships, not of the person who has symptoms. Because this is so contrary to the obvious, it is quite dramatic when observed. Seeing the whole family, one realizes, for example, how psychotic withdrawal is the role enforced on one person by all the others. A psychosis can also remit as a result of one family interaction.[4]

Children especially—it is widely known—should not be treated in psychotherapy separately from their parents. To load the entire difficulty on the child is an error that can have grievous consequences. It can turn the child into a psychological case. Neither should all the blame be placed on the parents. The basic idea of family therapy is that the interaction is sick, not any of the individuals. The patterns of interaction people get into with each other are only indirectly related to their individual dynamics. Also, the causal order may be in either direction. Instead of explaining interaction from individual personality, one can just as well argue that a certain type of interactional pattern rouses one of a great many possible, individual dynamics potentially in any person.

Therapeutic Communities

Many different kinds exist. Their principle is bringing people's real lives into interaction instead of merely the symbolic few hours of psychotherapy. Traditional psychotherapy assumes that psychological factors can change and be resolved, as it were, symbolically, in the therapy relationship. Then it will be possible for people to resolve their difficulties in their real lives. As the foregoing sections show, the newer therapies tend to question this. The therapy process itself should be "real life." The relation with the therapist tends toward perfect realism, honesty, and mutual involvement. Actual life relations (with others in

groups or with family members) are physically brought into the therapy context, as in family therapy. It is a further step of this trend, to establish some form of living together.

A community may meet once a week, daily, or room and cook together. If meetings are only periodic, people see each other outside of such meetings. The basis of the community may be a closed group that wants to be together, or everyone from a given neighborhood may be invited, or everyone with a common problem, or it may be totally open to all. Its principles may be therapeutic in any of the many meanings of that word.

Examples of therapeutic communities are: Laing's community,[24] Changes,[19] Synanon (ex-addicts), A. A. Low's group of ex-patients of "mental hospitals," and many others.

In these communities people help each other to live. They help each other take the needed next steps of living rather than doing only symbolic therapy with each other, as in encounter groups. These communities are usually permanent, whereas encounter groups break up after a weekend. Communities are thus perfectly real, unlike groups where one becomes personally close to people who are not, and will not be, part of one's life. Groups that continue come to be a real life reference point and a place of belonging for each member.

Some few therapeutic communities are old and famous, but most are new and can be found most easily through the networks and connections of young people.

Community Psychology and Social Psychiatry

These therapies[16] work with a neighborhood or an inner city or rural community. Government-supported programs for mental-health centers, storefront clinics, and street workers attempt to bring psychological services to a population that cannot usually obtain such services.

Sometimes Community Psychology efforts are no more than new referral channels, sending to the usual services certain populations omitted until now.

More developed community efforts can include training local people to provide some of services usually done only by professionals. An increasing number of facilities and activities are largely staffed by "subprofessionals." Large numbers of such people can function well under the supervision of a few professionals who run periodic group meetings for them.

A therapist or other professional can take selected local persons in as cotherapists so that some of them can actually learn the skills required. Thus the community is helped to develop resources of its own.

Community Psychology includes efforts to restructure the basic conception of what a school, a hospital, a church, or a welfare agency is. There are experimental "schools without walls" in which the students go to many places in the city for each of their "courses," and the "teachers" actually work at what they teach. For example one course may be in the zoo, another at the art museum, another in a factory. The zoo attendants, painters, and draftsmen are the teachers of these courses about animals, art, and drafting. Hospitals (or at least experimental wards) are being tried in which patients spend most of their time in foster homes or special workshops or jobs. Neighborhood organizations are also being tried that will enable people in a geographical neighborhood to become a community.

Social Structure

Concern with *social structure* further extends the trend of moving beyond one-to-one, individual therapy to groups, family, and community. Part of the trend is the belief that psychological difficulties are not separable from the structure of our society and its roles. The incidence of schizophrenia is much higher in poor communities than among the middle class. Changes in social structure have also changed the typical neurotic patterns. Hysteria, for example, is hardly ever encountered any more, yet it was very prevalent in Freud's

time. Where can one still find hysteria today? In rural communities where the social structure hasn't changed as much. This means that the patterns and roles of society must be taken into account—and one may call *these* "sick" rather than the individual who cannot fit into them.

The most striking instance of this new outlook concerns women. For three generations women were told (usually by male analysts) that a dynamically based lack of femininity prevented them from finding fulfillment in the activities of marriage and child raising. Currently women en masse are rebelling against this structure, and claiming that they too (like men) need not only a family structure but also a work life in the world. It appears to have been an error to assume that a person necessarily should fit into an extant social pattern. Perhaps the pattern, not the person, needs changing.

Taking this line most broadly is *Radical Therapy*.[35] Along with many others it seeks to change the entire social structure or, at least, to free individuals from being blamed and blaming themselves for their difficulties in living in the social structure as it is.

Szasz[36] launched a famous critique in which he held that psychosis is really only a failure to "play the game." Patients called psychotic are simply not responding on cue in the "proper," social ways. That alone is the crime for which they are incarcerated. Cure would consist in teaching the proper responses—and teaching them for what they really are, not health, not morality but simply proper game moves.

Similarly, homosexuals are considered a subgroup of society that is oppressed or suppressed. Blacks, women, gay people, are forced into social patterns that make it difficult to develop and assert one's own needs and nature. Increasingly, they see their struggle as one with social roles rather than with their own natures.

The therapist's reaction to these trends varies. Therapists may sense both pathology and social suppression. They may remain neutral, allowing whatever direction seems right to each individual. Or the therapist may propound the views mentioned above and encourage people to discover the freeing effect of these views. Once people see that they are up against a social pattern, they stop blaming themselves, they feel less inadequate and more able to act, and they come out from behind the false fronts instead of having to live a hidden existence. Individuals who felt personally too inadequate ever to speak up can assert themselves forcefully when they are conscious of belonging to a socially moving segment of the population. Much energy is released not only for social action but also for changing one's own life and going to new places and doing new things.

Women's Rap Groups[8] and other women's activities early adopted therapylike ways (at a time when the radical movement considered therapy as nothing but a way to support the status quo). A personal and therapeutic process occurs when a woman grasps that she is not alone to blame for her inadequacies, that her lack of preparation in worldly things is a social pattern, that her lack of fulfillment from being locked in a little house with a child is shared by millions of other women, that her lack of full sexuality in the current male–female routines is also shared by many. These topics are the same as the topics of therapy, but the social role context differs from the old purely intrapsychic context, and shifts the focus.

The Human Being in the Universe

Religious, spiritual, or cosmic sensitivity is the next logical extension of the movement branching out from the individual to groups, the family, and society. There is a dimension even greater than society—the universe or cosmos. In the current trends this is not a matter of belief. Rather, it is the bodily experience of sensing oneself in a vast cosmic context. It is an experience of breathing more deeply, of having a sense of vastness.

The third-force therapies are not, as a whole, religious. Nevertheless, sufficient numbers of people in them are concerned with meditation and spiritual attitudes toward growth so that these dimensions are generally

accepted. If one says today that therapeutic growth and spiritual growth are the same thing, most people nod. This assertion enlarges what therapeutic growth used to mean. There is little tendency to reduce the religious to the therapeutic. In the newer therapies, it is currently much more likely that people who are not religious will soon acquire some such sense, than that those who have that dimension would lose it. Some current religious-therapeutic methods were discussed in the section on body therapies (see page 280). The religious dimension is most often found together with these, but is frequent throughout.

In addition, the current revival of interest in Jungian therapy must be mentioned. Jung is almost the only one of the therapists of the first half of our century who spoke of the spiritual dimension and its complexity, richness, and power in human nature. Psychosynthesis also emphasizes it. Many of the other newer therapies are at least open to this dimension in people.

⟮ Bibliography

1. ALEXANDER, F. M. *Resurrection of the Body.* E. Maisel, ed. New York: University Books, 1969.
2. ASSAGIOLI, R. *Psychosynthesis.* New York: Viking, 1971.
3. BACH, G. and P. WYDEN. *Intimate Enemy.* New York: Avon Books, 1968.
4. BEEBE, J. E. III. "Allowing the Patient to Call Home: A Therapy of Acute Schizophrenia," *Psychother.: Theory, Res. Pract.,* 5 (1968), 18.
5. BERNE, E. *Transactional Analysis in Psychotherapy.* New York: Grove, 1961.
6. BINSWANGER, L. "The Case of Ellen West," in R. May, E. Angel and H. F. Ellenberger, eds., *Existence,* pp. 237–364. New York: Basic Books, 1958.
7. ———. *Grundformen und Erkenntnis Menschlichen Daseins.* Munich: Rinehardt, 1962.
8. BRODSKY, A. M. "The Consciousness-Raising Group as a Model for Therapy with Women," *Psychother.: Theory, Res. Pract.,* 10 (1973), 24.
9. BROWN, M. A. "The New Body Psychothera-

pies," *Psychother.: Theory, Res. Pract.*, 10 (1973), 98.

10. DA LIU. *T'ai Chi Ch'uan and I Ching.* New York: Harper & Row, 1972.

11. ELLIS, A. *Reason and Emotion in Psychotherapy.* New York: Lyle Stuart, 1962.

12. FRANKL, V. *The Doctor and the Soul.* New York: Knopf, 1965.

13. FREUDENBERGER, H. J. "The Psychologist in a Free Clinic Setting—An Alternative Model in Health Care," *Psychother.: Theory, Res. Pract.*, 10 (1973), 52.

14. GENDLIN, E. T. *Experiencing and the Creation of Meaning.* New York: Free Press, 1962.

15. ———. "A Theory of Personality Change," in P. Warchel and D. Byrne, eds., *Personality Change*, pp. 100–148. New York: Wiley, 1964.

16. ———. "Psychotherapy and Community Psychology," *Psychother.: Theory, Res. Pract.*, 5 (1968), 67.

17. ———. "Focusing," *Psychother.: Theory, Res. Pract.*, 6 (1969), 4.

18. ———. "Experiential Psychotherapy," in R. Corsni, ed., *Current Psychotherapies*, pp. 317–352. Itasca, Ill.: F. E. Peacock, 1973.

19. GENDLIN, E. T. and K. GLASER. "Main Themes in *Changes*, A Therapeutic Community" (abridged and revised from January 1973 *Communities*). *Rough Times* (formerly The Radical Therapist), 3, No. 6 (June–July, 1973), 2–4.

20. GLASSER, W. *Reality Therapy.* New York: Harper & Row, 1965.

21. GORDON, T. *Parent-Effectiveness Training.* New York: P. H. Wyden, 1970.

22. HART, J. T., M. S. CIRINCIONE, and M. S. CORRIERE. *Esalen Seminar on Feeling Therapy*, 1972.

23. JACKINS, H. *Fundamentals of Co-Counseling Manual (Elementary Counselors Manual: Beginning Classes in Re-evaluation Counseling).* Seattle: Ratl. Is. Press, 1962.

24. JAFFE, D. T. "The Floodgates of My Soul are Open," *Psychother.: Theory, Res. Pract.*, 8 (1971), 216.

25. JANOV, A. *The Primal Scream.* New York: Putnam, 1970.

26. JOURARD, S. M. *The Transparent Self.* New York: Van Nostrand, 1971.

27. JUNG, C. G. *Two Essays on Analytical Psychology.* New York: Meridian Books, 1956.

28. KARON, B. P. "The Consequences of Psychotherapy for Schizophrenic Patients," *Psychother.: Theory, Res. Pract.*, 9 (1972), 111.

29. LUTHE, W., ed. *Autogenic Training.* New York: Grune & Stratton, 1969.

30. MCCARTHY, B. W. "A Modification of Masters and Johnson Sex Therapy Model in a Clinical Setting," *Psychother.: Theory, Res. Pract.*, 10 (1973), 290.

31. MAY, R., E. ANGEL, and H. F. ELLENBERGER, eds. *Existence.* New York: Basic Books, 1958.

32. MILLER, R. *Psychic Massage.* New York: Harper & Row, 1975.

33. PERLS, F. S. *Gestalt Therapy Verbatim.* Lafayette, Calif.: Real People Press, 1969.

34. PERLS, F. S., R. F. HEFFERLINE, and P. GOODMAN. *Gestalt Therapy.* New York: Julian Press, 1958.

35. RADICAL THERAPIST COLLECTIVE. *The Radical Therapist.* New York: Ballantine, 1971. *Rough Times.* New York: Ballantine, 1973. See also *The Journal of Radical Therapy.*

36. REICH, W. *Character Analysis.* New York: Orgone Press, 1949.

37. ROGERS, C. R. *On Becoming A Person.* Boston: Houghton Mifflin, 1961.

38. ROLF, I. *Structural Integration.* New York: Viking, 1972.

39. SAX, S. and S. HOLLANDER. *Reality Games.* New York: Popular Library, 1972.

40. SCHUTZ, W. C. *Joy.* New York: Grove, 1967.

41. SELVER, C. "Sensory Awareness and Total Functioning," *Gen. Semant. Bull.*, 20 and 21, 1957.

42. SORRELLS, J. M. and F. R. FORD. "Toward an Integrated Theory of Families and Family Therapy," *Psychother.: Theory, Res. Pract.*, 6 (1969), 150.

43. SZASZ, T. S. *The Myth of Mental Illness.* New York: Hoeber-Harper, 1961.

CHAPTER 15

BEHAVIOR THERAPY
FOR ADULTS

Howard F. Hunt

(Behavioral Therapy Defined

ACCORDING TO most behavioral therapists, the method of choice for eliminating "maladaptive behavior" stresses identifying it, in vivo, and then labeling it, punishing or extinguishing it, and, at the same time, systematically rewarding alternative and more adaptive modes of behavior in replacement. Idealized, behavioral therapy applies the laws of learning and conditioning, as developed in the laboratory, to the alleviation of human maladjustment.[84,100,175] Yates,[188] however, has pointed out that this view is much too narrow and that behavioral therapists call on a wide range of concepts and techniques developed in experimental psychology. Indeed, contemporary reviews (e.g.,[58,102]) reveal a diversity of procedure and an inventive flexibility in adapting psychological technology extending far beyond the traditional limits of animal experimentation, particularly into cognitive manipulation, use of fantasy, and instructional control.

Psychotherapy of whatever stamp must consider matters of cognition, expectation, subjectively perceived affect, personal commitment or intention, and other similarly "mentalistic" phenomena, but behavioral therapists generally nod, at least, in the direction of behavioristic orthodoxy when they do. Behavioral therapy remains behavioral in its conceptualizations and metaphors.

Distinctive Features of the Behavioral Approach

The affiliation with experimental psychology has produced distinctive features that mental-health practitioners from other traditions sometimes find strained, rigid, and even alien. Objective and operational definitions are attempted for all important elements in treatment, even though the referents for some of the terms and procedures may be internal and subjective (e.g., images and fantasies the patient is instructed to produce for himself).

The goals, details of procedure, and the formulation of the "case" are supposed to be spelled out as explicitly as possible in behavioral terms. Therapeutic effect is gauged in terms of overt behavior—by what the patient actually does. If the goal sought or end achieved is something as elusive and subjective (but important) as "happiness," a criterion of improvement might be the patient's self-rating, easily made overt and numerical. Preferably, criteria consist of such things as changes in the frequency of reliably identifiable overt behaviors, recorded mechanically, counted, or rated by observers uninformed ("blind") as to what treatment the patient had. The behaviors to be changed ("target behavior")* are carefully defined and specified, both to facilitate assessment of effect and to permit comparisons among patients and among procedures. Formal control groups, treated differently, or control segments in the treatment sequence for individual cases, are included to demonstrate that the specified experimental (therapeutic) manipulations have been responsible for the benefits obtained. Furthermore, workers in this field make every effort to find some rational connection between the procedures employed and the effects produced, all within the framework of an articulated learning or behavior theory. Characteristically, the "case formulation" or behavioral analysis that identifies the factors responsible for the patient's problems (and often even the definition of the problems) is stated in terms of such a theory, which also illuminates and guides specific therapeutic activities and the evaluation of results. Finally, reports of behavioral therapy tend to be written in scientific terminology and format, often closely resembling reports of regular laboratory experiments.

Behavioral therapists are enthusiastic, optimistic, and indefatigable protagonists, trying to make what they do, and why, public and explicit. They are active and inventive in adapting techniques or creating new ones to deal with symptomatic behavior that has proven relatively intractable to more conventional psychotherapeutic intervention. This openness, this eagerness to strip the veil from the mysterious interpersonal exchanges called psychotherapy, this technological ferment and promise of "something new" have attracted widespread attention. The explicitness of theory and procedure implies that training for therapy can be both concrete and finite. Because of their flexibility, behavioral methods promise effective application across a broad range of situations that remain closed to methods that depend on dyadic verbal interchange in a therapist's office—the school, at home, in organizations, and elsewhere in the field.[67] Finally, behavioral therapy, with its emphasis on rational justification and pragmatic verification, offers the possibility of "doing good" and "being scientific" simultaneously, an attractive prospect to those who have been discouraged by the reported marginal effectiveness of most traditional psychotherapy.†

Of these promises, only the first—the promise of something new—can be considered reasonably fulfilled. The others remain bright possibilities. Truly scientific validation, on a broad scale, has lagged, for understandable reasons of technical difficulty.[22,55] As convincing validation data remain scattered, no one can specify the minimal training required for effective application, though teachers, parents, nurses, and attendants have been trained to carry out behavioral treatment satisfactorily. Nor can the situational or clinical limits for effective application be marked clearly. Furthermore, though the design of behavioral therapy intends to be scientific and rational, substantial contributions from charisma and artistry are still required, however well concealed by the behavioristic rhetoric. A sophisticated clinician, viewing an example of effective behavioral therapy from the outside, may often suspect, justifiably, that the actual selections of what behavior to modify, and the procedure for doing so, reflect inspired implemen-

---

* Target behavior all too often refers to symptomatic and unwanted behavior to be eliminated. The more important referent should be the new, constructive behavioral repertoire that treatment aims to produce, as a goal.

† See references 21, 22, 44, 57, 119, and 158.

tation by a perceptive therapist, guided but not rigidly determined by explicit deductions from learning theory. Furthermore, the enthusiasm and optimism of behavioral therapists, plus the structure they introduce into the clinical setting, no doubt make substantial nonspecific contributions to therapeutic success.[57,85] Finally, critics have noted that behavioral therapists tend to be self-righteous and do not really achieve the scientific rigor they pretend, that laboratory procedures and definitions lose considerable precision when transposed to the clinical setting, and that behavior therapists may well be using the wrong models anyway when they rely on those derived from animal experimentation.[29,85,103,115] In fact, Locke[109] has seriously questioned the behavioristic status of behavioral therapy.

Even so, such valiant efforts to be explicit, such willingness to take on seemingly intractable clinical problems, and such emphasis on evaluation qualify behavioral therapy for the most serious consideration.

A Tale of Two (or More) Models

The polemics of the nineteen fifties and early nineteen sixties placed behavioral therapy (and learning theory) in almost diametric opposition to dynamic personality theory and traditional psychotherapeutic practice (e.g.,[44,183]). The protagonists of behavioral treatment saw adjustment problems and psychopathology as undesirable habits or responses, acquired through some sort of "faulty learning." These behaviors could be eliminated in the most straightforward way by appropriate conditioning or extinction procedures derived from the laboratory, with "improvement" or "cure" defined in terms of attenuation of the undesired behaviors. In contrast, the more traditional view of psychopathology saw the undesired behaviors as symptoms reflecting underlying pathology—some state within the person—and as the best compromise the unaided individual had been able to make with the impossible dilemmas into which the vicissitudes of his developmental history and current situation had thrust him. While symptoms could be manipulated to some extent by reward and punishment, by sympathetic understanding and support and suggestion, relief would be temporary. Little permanent benefit could ensue unless the underlying state were somehow changed through new insights and perceptions, motivational maturation, and so on. Otherwise, the old symptoms would return or new ones take their place in symptom substitution.

Given this polarization, and the unavoidable oversimplifications accompanying it, the two approaches hardly seemed to be seeing the same problem or seeking the same goal: they differed sharply in their definitions of both illness and cure. In the years since, however, clinical experience and interchange between the opposing camps have reduced the conflict.[74,164] For example, symptom substitution in behavior therapy has not turned out to be as inevitable, probable, or even as important a problem as originally supposed. On the other hand, as noted above, the behavioral approach in practice appears to be less rigorously scientific than originally claimed, with procedures sometimes more illustrated by, than derived from, laboratory procedures. Furthermore, effective behavioral methods have been hard to find for some disorders, and linear extrapolations from laboratory procedures have sometimes been weak or transient in their effects.[87,170] Finally, facilitating the transfer of therapeutic gains from the treatment setting to life itself remains a problem for all psychotherapists, regardless of persuasion.

Behavioral and psychodynamic approaches actually were not as far apart as the polemics made them seem. For many years, psychoanalysis (the most influential of the personality theories) has worked from a two-factor learning theory. Behavior could be changed by its rewarding or punishing consequences (as in operant or instrumental conditioning). Also, stimuli could acquire new functional properties, new capacities to evoke and to reward or punish behavior, by virtue of having been associated (paired) with salient life events and private experiences (as in Pavlovian, respondent, or type S conditioning). Through combinations of these two operations, stimuli also could acquire discriminative control over instrumental behavior, as signals indicating it would be rewarded or punished if it occurred.[160]

Many of the stimuli, behaviors, and events or consequences were exotic by laboratory standards, and little of the fine detail had been worked out, but the major outlines were clear.[49] The epigenetic theory of psychosexual development and its implications for the causes of pathology further pinpointed the importance of learning by emphasizing that what actually was learned depended upon the child's developmental status when the learning occurred. The behaviors that the child actually had in its repertoire at the time were the ones strengthened or weakened by reward or punishment. Rewards and punishments were expected to focus on the characteristic problems and behaviors of the developmental stage the child was in at the time. The nature of the sanctions, including their force and character, were determined by the ways in which the child perceived the world at that stage, and so on. As the metaphor of psychoanalysis held that the various stages of early life differed considerably in these regards, instrumental learning and conditioning were critical elements in explaining how early experiences could be projected upon and distort perception and adaptation in later life, a cornerstone of psychoanalytic theory.

Many years ago, the pioneering work of Dollard and Miller[42] and of Mowrer[132] showed how psychodynamic formulations could be translated into the language of learning theory, and how conventional therapeutic strategies could be interpreted within the behavioral framework. Such translations have been helpful in testifying to a unity of purpose, and encouraging in that they implied a focus on common problems of human existence. The two traditions, behavioral and psychodynamic, grew from very different roots, however, and implied points of view and courses of action that differed materially.

The broad domain of psychodynamic theories is largely about mental events—impulses, affects, inter- and intrapersonal perceptions, ideas, convictions, cognitions—and what produces them, as well as what they produce. Mental events produce behavior, basically guide and energize it from inside the organism, so that behavior reflects what is going on there. In some instances, behavior seems a quite remote consequence, almost a by-product, of essential intrapsychic transactions. In the psychodynamic model, what is going on internally is substantially influenced by events in the early life of the individual, though it need not (and usually does not) veridically represent either the objective historical past or immediate present. Indeed, distorted mental representations of the present that recapitulate projectively misunderstood interpersonal and other object relations in the more remote past figure centrally in dynamic formulations of psychopathology. The major preoccupation of psychodynamics is with the transformations and mechanisms of defense and compromise, largely unconscious, that impede gratification in the present. Treatment, then, while it recognizes that a patient's problems arise against the backdrop of a contemporary, average, expectable environment, looks largely to the past and to efforts to undo and rectify the distortions and fixations of an earlier time in the person's life.

The behavioristic approach, on the other hand, is concerned with what the person is doing by way of overt behavior that can be recorded or inferred with confidence from recordable responses, and how similarly objectifiable past and concurrent events shape and control this output. Actually, there has been a shift away from the remote conditioning history of the patient, and how it produced the unwanted behavior, to the contemporary factors that maintain it. Thus, an account of the genesis of some bit of behavior—how it was acquired and by what reinforced—is seen as less useful for therapy than an account of the rewarding consequences that maintain it here and now, and the stimulus contexts that are the occasion for its occurrence. Though the conditioning history is important for understanding behavior in toto, the events that produced the problem behavior are important for therapy only insofar as they currently operate to sustain the behavior or prevent its replacement by new, more desirable behaviors. Though historical factors do sometimes impinge significantly on the present control of behavior, very often they do not or are so easily circumvented that they may be largely irrelevant.

This contrasts sharply with a dynamic view of symptoms as recapitulations of past conflicts in modified form, and deemphasizes the importance of somehow undoing or reworking a patient's past as a necessary part of therapy. It even contrasts with those earlier behavioral approaches in which treatment procedures were thought to produce their results by extinguishing through nonreinforcement, or otherwise reversing, "faulty learning" that took place long before and produced symptoms as enduring monuments to Pavlovian traumatic conditioning. Many competing, distinctly different learning or behavior theories have been developed.[76] Behavior therapists and theories are not "all alike," as erroneously implied in the early literature.

Behavioral therapy is increasingly Skinnerian in its special concern with the manipulation and control of stabilized asymptotic behavior (i.e., behavior that is well established and "overlearned"). The operant-conditioning approach resembles other behavioral views of learning in stressing that behavior arises out of a conditioning history in which stimuli acquire reinforcing and discriminative powers and in which responses are preferentially selected and strengthened by their consequences.[100,146,160,162] Most competing learning theories and much of the experimental literature, however, have focused on the acquisition and loss of conditioned behavior in acute situations over the short term. Operant conditioning, on the other hand, has been more attentive to the possibilities and special analytic problems that arise in dealing with well-established behavior that has gone far beyond the acquisition stage in chronic behavioral situations. Such asymptotic behavior often floats quite free of the conditions that led to its acquisition, passing under the control of (i.e., is "captured" by) new, quite differ-

ent contingencies, given the proper experimental manipulations. The operant-conditioning approach has developed a logic and technology adapted to dealing with asymptotic behavior.[*] This technology also takes account of and even capitalizes on irregular, intermittent schedules of reinforcement. Rewards or punishments may control behavior strongly and precisely, even though they occur only infrequently or irregularly as in real life. Inasmuch as most behavioral pathology probably consists of asymptotic, stabilized, and well-established habits, usually sustained by inconsistent and somewhat irregular patterns of reinforcement, such behavior should be more amenable to operant analysis than to any other.

Operant conditioning is more a pragmatic method for studying behavior than a theory.[146] Much of the important content is essentially definitional and descriptive. It sees two different *procedures* for changing behavior: In conditioning of type S (Pavlovian) the reinforcing unconditioned stimulus (UCS) is paired with some signal (the conditioned stimulus or CS) thereby changing the power of the CS to evoke behavior. The fear that becomes attached to a situation in which a person has been severely threatened or hurt, as well as conditioned salivation in the dog are examples of this type of control. Conditioning of *type R* (operant or instrumental) in which behavior is controlled by its consequences (*reinforcers*) receives more emphasis.

Reinforcers are identified and defined empirically in terms of their effects on the preceding behavior: the onset of primary positive (*appetitive*) reinforcers (e.g., food, water) increases its strength, and the onset of primary negative (*aversive*) reinforcers (e.g., shock, loud noise) has the opposite effect. Termination of or escape from a negative reinforcer, however, strengthens the preceding response (in aversive control or avoidance-escape learning). Most voluntary or self-initiated behaviors are operants. In both procedures, experimental *extinction* occurs if the reinforcing stimulus is omitted—if the CS is repeatedly

---

* See references 66, 83, 126, 146, and 159.

presented without reinforcement in type S, and if the reward or punishment ceases to be a consequence of the responding in Type R. Stimuli associated with the reinforcement in operant conditioning can become *conditioned* (secondary) *reinforcers* (probably through type S conditioning) and reward (or punish) behavior as in the appetitive or aversive modes above.

Discriminative stimuli signal that behavior emitted during their presentation will be reinforced. Their discriminative control is established by reinforcing behavior in their presence and extinguishing it in their absence (*differential reinforcement*). Discriminative stimuli are the occasion for discriminated operant behavior, but do not evoke it, and they also have conditioned reinforcing power. In a *chained* operant, several operant responses are trained to roll off in a fixed sequence, the whole maintained by primary reinforcement of the terminal response. Each element is linked to its successor by stimuli that function as conditioned reinforcers for the immediately preceding response and as discriminative stimuli for the next.

Behaviors very different in appearance (topography) are members of the same *functional-response class* if they are controlled by the same reinforcer. Similarly, stimuli are members of the same *functional-stimulus class*, even though they differ considerably, provided they have the same effect on a particular response. The functional definition of response and stimulus classes, as opposed to an a priori definition with its presuppositions, favors the empirical identification of relevant units of behavior and their controlling conditions in behavioral analysis, both in the laboratory and in the field.

A reinforcer, then, is identified and defined by the effects it *does* produce, not by the therapist's presuppositions as to the effects it *should* produce. That a supposed reward does not function as one, for example, does not mean that conditioning theory does not work. Rather, such an outcome simply indicates that the reward selected was not a functionally effective, positive reinforcer for that person in that context.

An operant must be emitted in order to be reinforced. If an animal does not have the response in his repertoire at the beginning of training, that behavior may have to be "*shaped*" by selective reinforcement of successively closer approximations to the desired response. Control of a particular response by one kind of reinforcement or one kind of discriminative stimulus may be shifted to other, different stimuli by "*fading*." The new stimuli are "mixed" with the old, with the new progressively "faded in" and the old "faded out" (if the former control is to be terminated) by increases and decreases, respectively, in the relative frequency (in reinforcement) or intensity (in discrimination) of the old and new stimuli. "Shaping" and "fading" permit moving stimuli and responses from one class to another, even the creation of new functional classes, as well as the "capture" of behavior by new contingencies that supervene after original learning.

Contrary to popular belief, reinforcement need not be consistent to be effective. Indeed, *schedules* that provide only for intermittent (*partial*) reinforcement influence behavior strongly and characteristically. Reinforcement may be made available for the next response only at *intervals* of time after the last reinforced response; these intervals may be *fixed* and constant (FI) or *variable* (VI). Or the next reinforcement may become available for a response only when a predetermined number of responses has been made since the last reinforced response. For such *ratio* schedules, the work requirement may be *fixed* (FR) or *variable* (VR). Generally, partial reinforcement produces greater resistance to extinction than reinforcement for each response (*CRF*). Also, ratio schedules, like piecework, produce higher outputs than interval schedules, which are more like payment by the hour. In fact, the VR schedule (in which rewards may be scheduled in a manner much like the payoff for three bells in a slot machine) is one of the most powerful known, producing high rates of work and great resistance to extinction. FI and FR schedules produce characteristic distributions of responding in relation to the last previous reinforcement, while the output is more even in variable schedules. In avoidance schedules (*Sidman avoidance*) responses postpone aversive events such as shocks. In another, *DRL* or *differential reinforcement of low rate*, a "stretch-out" contingency requires the animal to wait and not respond for some predetermined interval after the last reinforced response in order to qualify for reinforcement of the next response (responses during the interval only postpone the availability of reward). These schedules, too, generate temporal patterning in responding. (For combinations and variations in schedules and their effects, see[53,146].) Familiarity with reinforcement schedules and their effects is essential for clinical behavioral analysis. In clinical situations, where the control that maintains the target behavior is usually unknown, temporal patterns may suggest what kind of schedule is operating and, consequently, hint at what events may be serving as reinforcers and discriminative stimuli.

Drive and motivation, within the orthodox operant lexicon, have a peculiarly peripheral status. Loose use of motivational constructs to explain a particular behavior, especially in clinical contexts with man, often turns out to be redundant and circular, merely providing a new name for the response pattern, rather than explaining it, i.e., describing the conditions that control it.[162] The operant emphasis, instead, is on reinforcement. Deprivation of such regularly needed inputs as food and water (a specifiable operation) is seen, descriptively, as enhancing or *potentiating* the effectiveness of these primary reinforcers (and their conditioned derivatives) to control behavior. This stringency forces an empirical analysis of clinical behavioral situations in which the behavior of interest may be maintained by social and generalized reinforcers (e.g., attention, praise) or by reinforcement that is idiosyncratic (e.g., "escape" from success). Many of the most powerful reinforcers for social and individual human behavior are social, generalized, and/or idiosyncratic. Deprivation or "setting" procedures sure to potentiate such reinforcers are obscure, particularly in the behavioral disorders where so much of the observed behavior appears cryptic or paradoxical as to the variables that control it.

Identification of the effective reinforcers for a particular person and his particular behavior can be quite difficult, requiring shrewd guesses based on personal experience and empathy, clinical knowledge and dynamic theory, plus a good green thumb for behavior —in context. These guesses are only that, however, and ultimately require support from firm evidence that the reinforcers identified do, in fact, work as expected. Observation and inquiry to determine what a person likes to do or, better, actually spends a lot of time doing when possible, generally is a practical place to start. Then, in accordance with the "Premack principle," access to high-probability behaviors (preferred by the patient) can be used to reward low-probability behaviors (the constructive, adaptive behaviors that are expected to replace maladaptive behaviors in treatment).[143] An everyday equivalent to this use of access to high-probability behavior as a reinforcement is letting a child go out to play (high-probability and presumably preferred behavior) if and when he finishes his homework or piano practice (low-probability behavior to be increased). Of course, preferential access to—i.e., permission for pathological or undesired behavior which usually will be of high probability—should not be used as a reinforcement for desired but low-probability behavior. (No one ever stopped smoking by rewarding himself with a cigarette for "not smoking"!). Furthermore, free access to the high-probability behavior must be blocked for it to become contingent on the low-probability behavior. If the reward remains freely available, or remains as available as it always has been, only the existing behavioral repertoire will be maintained. No changes should be expected. There is no *incentive* to *motivate* change.

Readers who prefer to think within a motivational framework, as an alternative to the operant treatment, will find Logan's concept of *incentive motivation* useful.[111-113] Incentive motivation is, in effect, a learned drive or motive evoked by an incentive acting as a conditioned stimulus. Depending upon the subject's conditioning, it can be either appetitive or aversive in effect. The concept plays a central role in Logan's analysis of self-control.

The behavioral therapist, then, is supposed to direct his attention to a behavioral analysis of the individual case and its context that reveals the present consequences (reinforcements) maintaining the undesirable target behavior.[64-66,97,100] These consequences are to be altered and the patient's circumstances manipulated to make more desirable alternative behaviors possible and more probable by arranging so that a desirable behavioral repertoire is developed and effectively supported by rewards, either tangible or social. Thus, the therapist attends to the details of the patient's behavior, plans concretely, and participates actively in treatment. As behavior is largely controlled by the contexts it occurs in, the therapist must be prepared to deal with the circumstances of the patient's life. He further should arrange things and teach the patient to arrange things so that the desired behavior can continue to be supported by the normal contingencies of life that support the social behavior of all of us, to provide for carry-over or transfer to the extratherapeutic, real-life situation to which the patient will go. All of this is easier said than done, of course.

The reasons are complex and beyond the healing power of simple terminological adjustments and acquiescent intellectual generosity. Three related weaknesses, worthy of comment here, embarrass even the best of the behavioral models if they are extrapolated literally and directly to psychopathology and therapeutic behavior change: *First*, schedules of reinforcement may have important and systematic effects on behavior not being reinforced directly by that schedule. The possibility that target behavior may be affected by some reinforcement schedule aimed toward other behavior altogether, unbeknown to the analyst, makes clinical behavioral analysis somewhat indeterminate. *Second*, the current paradigmatic behavioral models have little capacity to deal with species-specific ethological complications that arise in application at the human level. *Third*, the models are incomplete with respect to accounting rigorously for self-control or self-regulation of behavior (the goal of all psychotherapy, behavioral or otherwise). To make these points is less to jape at imperfections than to encourage new lines of emphasis and elaboration. The clinical application of behavioral models, if taken seriously without glossing over the difficulties, could have a most beneficial impact on future directions in the scientific study of behavior.

The broad spectrum of schedule effects is widely investigated, but still poorly understood.[41] Some are dramatic and well-known, such as the aggressive side effects of aversive control.[88,176,177] Some, such as behavioral contrast in which a change in reinforcement schedule in one segment of a session changes the behavior in another, though the schedule there remains unchanged, are more subtle.[146] Others, such as the more recent discovery of "autoshaping," raise serious questions about how behavior is acquired and maintained. Here, pigeons acquire an operant-pecking response without direct reinforcement of it, as a function of Pavlovian pairings of a signal and reinforcement.[32,91,131,182] As a further example, in the rat FI schedules of food reinforcement that are too "lean" or "stingy" can generate adjunctive, displacement, or interim behavior, such as excessive drinking, licking at an air tube, or eating shavings (pica).[45,187] Thus, the source of behavior or a behavior change may be indirect and obscure. Indeed, the effect of *noncontingent* reinforcers on behavior occupies an increasingly important place in behavioral analysis.[60] More important, once behavior has been generated by these and other indirect or complex effects, it can be captured by direct reinforcement from the reacting environment, to be under more than one kind of control and ambiguous to simple observation.[38,41,85] A diagnostic behavioral analysis that rests content with noting only the most obvious, apparently controlling conditions, may be sadly incomplete.

The ethological problem rests on more than man's supposed complexity in comparison with the infrahuman subjects used in most learning and behavioral research. Basic experiments and theorizing have looked at isolated, arbitrary behavior (e.g., salivation, lever pressing, key pecking) as it covaries with similarly isolated environmental events, usually assuming all of these to be exemplary and representative for analysis and theory construction. Such simplification and isolation are essential steps in scientific understanding, but the model cannot be taken as the complete picture unless applications in the field show it to be accurate and exhaustive. Considerable data already indicate the classical models, simplistically applied, fail to take sufficient account of how a species' behavior is organized (i.e., the interrelations among its "elements") with respect to environmental inputs (i.e., reinforcers, discriminative stimuli, etc.). Breland and Breland's *The Misbehavior of Organisms*, is a humorous but classic account of difficulties encountered, largely because of ethological factors, in training animal species not ordinarily used as experimental subjects.[30] (For broader, more recent accounts, see references 31 and 77.)

Man's capacity for symbolization and his active use of it for controlling his own and the behavior of others, plus his capacity for profiting from essentially vicarious experience, compounds the problems of extending "animal" theories to human behavior. The compounding represents a quantitative increase in complexity, but the increase may be so great that it can be handled best by a qualitatively new behavioral model. Animals that engage only sparingly in identifiable symbolization and learn largely through their own direct experiences may prove to have been of limited value in "analogue" experiments directed toward these important aspects of human behavior. The particular significance of self-referent symbolic behavior, the interesting changes that occur in the capacity of symbolic behavior (including plans and intentions) to control other behaviors, especially as it becomes conscious and subject to the rules of secondary process (as in insight), highlight the problem.[86] The classical behavior theories are generally silent about these matters. Perhaps we need new theoretical inventions as revolutionary and provocative as Skinner's reanalysis

of the concept of the reflex, the concept of functional classes of stimuli and responses, and the powerful pragmatic technology they generated.[160]

The problem of self-control is a most difficult subject to deal with rigorously within the framework of orthodox behaviorism. Doubtless, self-control follows whatever natural laws exist with respect to human behavior in general, but even creative behavioral analysis derived from theory based on animal experimentation suggests only partial solutions. Skinner,[162,163] Goldiamond,[64] and Goldiamond and Dyrud,[66] have been articulate and persuasive about how one can manipulate environmental circumstances to change one's own behavior toward desired goals. This involves arranging discriminative stimuli to make the desired behavior more likely (or the undesired behavior less likely) and scheduling differential rewards for oneself on completion of performance requirements, all in the framework of straightforward (though somewhat "relaxed") operant formulations. The psychology of the "controlled self" is fairly well developed and effective, but the "controlling self" that determines what to control, and for what ends, remains a largely unanalyzed presence shrouded in mystery.

More recent approaches to a theory of human behavior[26,130,142,166] have jumped over the ethological chasm by making assumptions about human cognitive functioning. Though largely begging an important philosophical question, this maneuver opens the door to pragmatic application of some of the most powerful analytic features of orthodox behavioristic theories to complex human behavior (e.g., positive and negative reinforcement, schedule effects, discriminative control). The new developments draw heavily on the thinking of Miller, Galanter, and Pribram[127] in their theoretical proposal for an essentially cognitive psychology. This formulation started from a not unreasonable set of assumptions about the basic roles of imagery, knowledge of outcome, and effects of motivation on planning and organizing behavior with respect to outcomes. Mischel,[130] in his theory of cognitive social learning, describes five fundamental "person variables" (dimensions on which individuals may differ and that, alone and in interaction, exercise determinative influences on behavioral output in context): (1) ability to generate cognitions and behaviors; (2) possession of strategies and constructs for categorizing events and for self-description; (3) expectancies with respect to behavioral and stimulus outcomes in particular situations; (4) subjective stimulus values, including incentives, aversions, and motivating stimuli; and (5) self-regulatory systems or plans, with rules for evaluation of performance and for organization of complex sequences.

Kanfer and Phillips,[96] Kanfer and Karoly,[95] Meichenbaum,[125] Mahoney,[118] Ferraro,[50] Logan,[113] Premack and Anglin,[144] and Franks and Wilson,[58] among others, present thoughtful and cogent analyses of self-control. Effective self-control, generally, depends on knowledge of contingent outcomes, is based on discriminative instructional control (including the human subject's instructions to himself), and a kind of internal evaluative template or image as to how any particular series of actions ought to go. Such cognitive templates determine goals for the person and standards for defining success or failure— whether the person qualifies for or "deserves" self-reinforcement. Given sufficient commitment to standards and goals, the system works within the cognitive-motivational framework. The problem is how to achieve and maintain that commitment; once again, the problem of the "controlling self."

These new approaches may furnish the study of personality with a much needed new lease on life.[54] Certainly, they constitute the beginnings, at least, of a third model to illuminate and guide new developments in behavioral therapy. In this connection, the development of a theory of self-control in no way abandons deterministic assumptions in favor of free will. Rather, the enterprise assumes that choices, commitments, expectations, and the like that direct human behavior obey deterministic principles, and seeks only to find out what these might be.

⟮ The State of the Art

So far, most behavioral therapy has indulged only sparingly in the more detailed considerations in theory and experiment discussed above. In practice, and confronted by major problems in the field, behavioral therapists develop pragmatically oriented, rule-of-thumb solutions to alleviate glaring "defects" in behavior as supported by substantial biases in the environment. The literature tends to emphasize matters of procedure along with testimonials to easily discriminated, clear-cut favorable results.

Opinions differ as to how the various methods should be classified and as to what constitute the "active principles" in each. For purposes of this overview, however, the methods fall into two archetypical categories:

1. Procedures directed toward reducing the power of stimuli (including environmental situations and social contexts) to evoke unwanted symptomatic reactions (usually emotional reactions of the fear or anxiety type). The procedures developed, and are generally discussed within, the metaphor of type S (Pavlovian) conditioning and extinction, and are variously called "desensitization," "deconditioning," "conditioning therapy," or "counter-conditioning."

2. Procedures directed toward replacing unwanted, symptomatic behavior with more constructive, adaptive behavior by manipulating reinforcing consequences. The procedures developed and usually are discussed within the metaphor of operant (type R) conditioning and extinction. "Behavior modification" is a popular generic term for this group, though "self-control" and "feedback" usually refer to it, too.

As indicated earlier, Pavlovian and operant conditioning are two different procedures for influencing behavior, not necessarily two different kinds of behavior. Pavlovian pairing of stimuli and reinforcers occurs as an integral part of operant conditioning, playing a substantial role in establishing conditioned reinforcers and discriminative stimuli. Similarly, operant control develops over responses conditioned in the Pavlovian mode.[91,131] Clinically, a Pavlovian conditioned response (e.g., tantrum) can come under the control of (be captured by) favorable consequences (in terms of attention, etc.) if these are rewarding (secondary gain).[85] And Miller and his colleagues have showed that physiological responses once thought to be under exclusive Pavlovian control can be conditioned operantly.[128] Within the psychodynamic metaphor, defenses against anxiety are operant avoidance-escape behaviors, reinforced by termination of Pavlovian conditioned anxiety. Symptoms, target behaviors that are combinations of defenses, are operantly reinforced by instinctual gratification (however attenuated) as primary gain, plus any secondary gain that accrues. The interpenetration of processes, if not of procedures, seems virtually complete.

Desensitization and Related Procedures

SYSTEMATIC DESENSITIZATION

The best-known and probably the most widely used behavioral technique, it aims to alleviate neurotic fears, anxieties, and inhibitions by reducing the sensitivity of the patient to the stimuli that produce these reactions. Essentially, the procedure rests on and extends the pioneering studies of Watson and Raynor,[179] and Jones.[92] As described by Wolpe,[183, 184-186] its progenitor and energetic advocate, fears and anxieties ("phobic responses") are the product of earlier Pavlovian conditioning in which the "phobic" object was paired with subjectively experienced, traumatic emotional arousal. Such conditioning can be reversed by extinction, in which some representation of the phobic object is experienced repeatedly in the absence of reinforcing traumatic excitation.

Wolpe argued that this required the patient to be confronted only with versions of the stimulus that do not produce fear or anxiety at the time. To achieve this goal, the therapist first, in discussion with the patient, constructs a highly personalized "anxiety hierarchy" consisting of a graded series of partial representations of the phobic object, ranging progressively from minimal and benign versions up to

as full and direct a reproduction as feasible in the therapy situation. (For example, the hierarchy for someone with a snake phobia might start with the word, "snake," go through a range of pictures of snakes of increasing vividness and presence, ending with an item in which the patient might even have physical contact with a snake.) As a preliminary step, the therapist also trains the patient to engage in some activity incompatible with anxiety or fear, usually progressive relaxation,[90] but sometimes a light hypnotic trance, assertive behavior, or sexual fantasy (depending on the patient's problem). Wolpe believed the incompatible behavior "reciprocally inhibited" the neurotic reaction, speeding its extinction, and that the reciprocally inhibiting response came under the control of the phobic stimulus. As a result of the pairing, relaxation, or any other reaction, would be elicited as a Pavlovian-conditioned response, replacing the fear or anxiety through "counter-conditioning."

For treatment proper, the patient is told to relax and then to imagine or experience, remaining relaxed, the weakest version of the phobic stimulus in the hierarchy until the item no longer evokes any discernible emotional response. Then, the patient moves to the next higher item, repeating the procedure and signaling the therapist if that item produces a disturbance that breaks through the relaxation. If it does, they go back to the earlier item, but if not, the second item is repeatedly presented to the patient (or evoked in his fantasy) until it no longer disrupts relaxation. This routine is repeated for all of the items in the hierarchy, progressing eventually to the strongest representation of the phobic object, which the patient repeatedly experiences under relaxation until it no longer evokes an emotional response.

With appropriate modifications, desensitization can be conducted in vivo (in actual, real-life field situations such as a fire escape for a patient who fears heights) or with only pictorial or even covertly fantasied representations of the phobic object in the consulting room. Data on the matter conflict to some extent, but in vivo applications seem likely, on balance, to be more effective, at some cost in convenience.[157] Though Wolpe himself has reported generally great success for his procedure,[184] others have found it less effective for agoraphobic, panphobic, or complex neurotic cases than for focal phobias.[120]

Actually, the heart of the desensitization technique—Pavlovian extinction of responses to conditioned fear stimuli—is applicable to a wide range of problems in a variety of settings, including groups. The use of fantasy and cognitive rehearsal in behavioral therapy extends well beyond this extinction model. In addition to its use in aversive "covert sensitization," positive fantasy manipulation plays a major role in treatment of sexual deviations, to be considered later in connection with mixed strategies (see p. 306).

FLOODING OR IMPLOSION THERAPY

In this procedure,[78–80,167] the patient is exposed for whole sessions, either in fantasy or in vivo, to the most anxiety provoking object or fear in his phobic syndrome. This contrasts diametrically with Wolpe's use of a progressively graded hierarchy that protects the patient from sudden flooding with emotion. The sessions are reported as stormy; yet preliminary comparative data imply that flooding works at least as well as conventional systematic desensitization for focal fears, and better for nonspecific generalized phobias.[121]

Though Wolpe emphasized the reciprocal inhibition or counterconditioning components in systematic desensitization, recent views consider the Pavlovian extinction to be more important.[58] Operant reinforcement may contribute, too.[86] Desensitization procedures provide liberally for reinforcement of counterphobic or counteranxiety behavior. Each step up the fear hierarchy (and demonstrated capacity to endure the stresses of flooding, too) represents progress toward a goal. This behavior qualifies for and usually receives social reinforcement, plus intrinsic reinforcement from increments in the patient's satisfaction and confidence. Achievement of the final counterphobic goal response receives even more substantial positive reinforcement—from the patient to himself, from the therapist, and from those who know of and have been in-

convenienced by the patient's difficulties. The proportional contributions to recovery by Pavlovian extinction and operant reinforcement probably vary from case to case, or, as Murray and Jacobson suggest,[135] both desensitization and flooding may be effective because they change the patient's cognitive belief in his capacity to cope with emotional disturbance.

Operant Procedures and Behavior Modification

TOKEN ECONOMY

The token economy grew out of promising earlier applications of operant procedures to psychiatric patients and their problems.* These and other studies indicated that the symptomatic behaviors of deeply regressed psychotic patients (as well as such limited symptoms as stuttering) were amenable to operant analysis and control by response-contingent consequences. The studies also stimulated the widespread use of individualized treatment programs, largely based on procedures that are widely used in clinical and other settings for symptomatic problems that have been unresponsive to other approaches.†

In a token economy, a set of arrangements provides for systematically reinforcing constructive behavior as and when it occurs in group or ward settings. Idealized, it represents a most ambitious application of operant principles to the functional design of entire therapeutic environments,[36,37] with overtones reminiscent of Bellamy's *Looking Backward*[19] and Skinner's *Walden Two*.[161] Reinforcements are usually in the form of points, physical tokens or chips, or even money that the patient earns by his behavior. These can be exchanged for real amenities not readily available noncontingently in the milieu, plus attention, praise, and encouragement for constructive behavior.[8,11,140,152]

Even such difficult to control symptoms as incontinence in chronic, deteriorated psychotic patients may be controlled by operant procedures,[7] and perhaps more effectively

---

* See references 9, 10, 12, 13, 28, 51, 56, 89, 105–108.

† See references 58, 100, 153, 174, 175, and 178.

than with the Mowrers' bell-and-pad technique,[134] which is a Pavlovian approach more suitable for children.[116,183]

As Krasner describes it:

A token economy has three specific characteristics: first, the designation of certain *behaviors* as good or desirable and hence to be reinforced; second, a *medium of exchange*, an object—the token —that "stands for" something else; and third, a way of utilizing the tokens, in other words the back-up reinforcers or the good things in life. These may include food or being allowed to sit peacefully in a chair, and cover a wide range . . .

The goals of a token program are to develop behaviors which will lead to social reinforcement from other people, and to enhance the skills the individual needs to take a responsible social role in the institution and, eventually, to live successfully outside the hospital. Basically, the individual learns that he can control his own environment. [p. 155][101]

In principle, a token economy creates a ward environment that is preferentially responsive to (i.e., differentially reinforces) constructive, prosocial behavior. This requires more than just enrichment; both rich and deprived environments can be functionally unresponsive. If patients get a lot or just a little, but all on a noncontingent basis, no special support exists for prosocial behavior, even though the patients' troublesome, symptomatic behavior amply demonstrates the need for it. Ironically, many supposedly therapeutic environments that give freely and noncontingently of what they have actually turn out, on closer scrutiny, to be biased in the direction of supporting pathological behavior. The reinforcement may be little more than sympathetic concern from the staff and other patients, or irritated reprisals, but either way the patient gets attention, a sense of "something happening," and a sense that he caused same effect.[62,85]

In practice, the design and operation of a token economy requires effort and skill. Behaviors to be eliminated and constructive behaviors to supplant them must be specific and clearly defined. Systematic observations and ratings, instituted prior to the start of the program (to detect base rates of the behavior of interest) and continued through it (to monitor effectiveness and document change) should emphasize concrete, easily discernible actions and/or criteria to avoid errors that so easily creep into broad, impressionistic judgments.* Finally, an ecologically suitable reward system must be devised. This will ordinarily include not only points or tokens convenient to administer without delay, contingent on desirable behavior to concretize the program (particularly in its inceptional stages and for regressed patients), but also real amenities for which those symbolic rewards can be exchanged. Without the latter, unless prosocial behavior really makes a difference, the whole enterprise will be a sham!

Obviously, sophistication about organizational problems, patience, and skill in bureaucratic expediting also are necessary. If anything can go wrong, it usually does!

Responsive and appreciative attention, supervisory support, and realistic understanding of practical problems faced by both staff and patients are required to get the program started and to keep it viable.[110] Quite correctly, the staff will anticipate added burdens. Eventually, a properly designed program compensates by making the overall workload easier and more pleasant, but at first the attention to detail and other procedural aspects may seem a lot to ask. The staff may feel left alone with problems easy to solve in theory, but difficult in practice. Further, not only will the program have defects that have to be rectified but it must be open-ended and subject to change as patient behavior improves in order to avoid trapping patients in an infantilizing, routinized living situation. It is best to "start small," with modest initial goals that can be achieved quickly through a simple, robust (i.e., relatively foolproof) program, using powerful reinforcers to provide "success experiences" for staff and patients early on. Without staff support, no program—individual or group—can possibly succeed. Undercutting is all too easy. Without patient interest, or at

---

* Observation, as such, may be highly "reactive," producing at least temporary behavior change by itself.[75,180]

least acquiescence, the enterprise degenerates into a power struggle.

Behavior influence is a two-way street! Though staff can control reinforcement for the patients, the patients have substantial control over reinforcement for the staff, and exercise it (by succeeding or failing, by behaving well or acting out, etc.). The same relation holds between the staff and the administration: staff behavior reflects the administration's policy and practice, and vice versa. As in all other behavioral analysis, when acting out, noncooperation, and other behavioral problems occur at any level, one looks first to what those in control of the major reinforcing contingencies in the situation are doing. The behavior of the "controlled" population accurately reflects the contingencies, or lack of them, imposed by the "controllers." The goal, of course, is not to assign blame, but to determine what changes need to be made in the system, and where. The same rules apply in individual treatment, of course.

The reward system, and how it exchanges amenities for constructive behavioral growth, can pose problems of great subtlety. Especially for deeply regressed patients, both the specified performances and their consequences (extrinsic rewards) need to be concrete at the beginning. Except for those patients so impaired that they can achieve only the most elementary socialization and who require indefinitely extended custodial care, the program must aim toward moving into broader realms of constructive socialized behavior. Such behavior eventually has to come under the operant control of the intermittent social rewards that sustain all of us (e.g., real appreciation for a hard job well done; the development of interests and standards that make some achievements intrinsically reinforcing). Otherwise, the goal of restoring the capacity for constructive choice and for self-control will not be achieved.[*]

Several methods, usually in combination, favor the achievement of this goal. Quite simply, the program of concrete rewards for simple performance (e.g., a few points that can be awarded in the canteen for dressing and bed making) can be "faded out" (progressively withdrawn) to be replaced by bigger, better, more adult and normal rewards for more complex self-management and other prosocial behavior. Or the patient may qualify categorically for a new status that confers access to higher density and freer choice among a wider range of rewards, with continued adequate performance at some minimum level required to retain that status (e.g., from "ward" to "building" to "full privileges," move to a more nicely furnished ward, get a private room, go home for visits). Reinforcement by access to preferred activities ("Premack principle," see page 296) is particularly useful.[†]

INDIVIDUALIZED PROGRAMS

These may be used for patients proving unresponsive to conventional treatment and ward milieus. Where token-economy procedures are used, individuals who can do so improve enough to leave the basic ward-wide economy behind, meeting its standards of behavior as a matter of course (and going back to the token economy if these conditions are not fulfilled). In moving to individualized programs, patients should have as much responsibility as they can manage for choosing what behaviors to change and for monitoring their progress. They will differ considerably in their capacities here, and the actual program arrived at requires the exercise of good clinical judgment.

Sometimes desensitization is an essential preliminary step in behavioral modification programs. It can help to reduce fear and anxiety enough for a patient to stop avoiding prosocial target behaviors. Only when the patient can start performing them can he make contact with the reinforcements they produce. Details can be worked out, as far as possible, in discussions between patient and therapist, leading to a specific agreement as to what is expected, what is to be done, and how it is to be judged and rewarded. The agreement can be as formalized as a "contingency contract,"[2,65,171,172] but it must be specific and

---

[*] See references 36, 37, 64–66, and 85.

[†] See references 2, 36, 37, 143, 152, and 170.

push the patient into contact with reality issues. The agreement provides a basis for commitment, but it should not be rewarded as such. To do so may short-circuit the therapeutic process by rewarding promises, however empty.[95] Rather, reinforcement should be for realistic action toward fulfilling the agreement. The patient should play as major a role as he can in record keeping, so he may be rewarded not only for performance but also for accuracy, perceptiveness, faithfulness, and other prosocial aspects of his performance. (Back-up monitoring by staff can provide necessary checks on corner cutting.) Some features should be left out of the program, as discretionary matters up to the patient or as performances that are to be expected of ordinary functioning people.

After all, the activities of half or more of the twenty-four-hour day are discretionary to some degree for most of us. Contingent access to these options powerfully reinforces our prosocial behavior on the job. It is important not to make the patient feel totally hemmed in, helpless, and segregated from the rest of humanity (the patient role does too much of that as it is). Further, maximum use of metaphors implying trust, autonomy, and self-control helps to avoid infantilizing the patient and blocking his growing capacity to exercise these virtues, as long as the metaphors contain a substantial element of realism and truthfulness.

Some form of patient diary to be discussed with the therapist in connection with awarding points and back-up amenities often provides the basis for differentially reinforcing progress to more subtle, self-regulating social functioning, including fantasy. Within this flexible format, and with this abundance of material, a sensitive therapist (in consultation with the patient) usually can discern easily what behaviors are causing difficulty, when and in what regard escalation of the social level of the program is advisable, and even when all or part of the program as such can be discontinued. In effect, the therapist not only differentially reinforces overt behavior, but also what the patient says (writes) to himself about his own behavior, in effect producing a

kind of behavioral control over intrapsychic events.

Interestingly enough, patients reaching and going beyond these advanced stages often continue to keep diaries and use the language of points and rewards long after transactions with the therapist have become largely cognitive and verbal. The concrete rhetoric, based on shared experience between the two people, seems to furnish a vocabulary for referring to things the patient finds it hard to verbalize abstractly. Similarly, through instruction by the therapist and firsthand experience, the patient often develops what might be thought of as a theory about his own behavior and its control by this time. Indeed, workable approaches to self-control often emerge from these experiences, with the "theories reinforced because they worked." Such cognitive formulations may be idiosyncratic, but more commonly are conventionally behavioristic, incorporating some of the conceptual schema used by the therapist. They can be of immense value in active mastery and self-control, if only through essentially obsessive-compulsive ritualization, provided regressive distortions can be avoided, and the patients have reasonably intact basic ego functions.[4]

Even thinking, a covert operant response, or "coverant" as Homme calls it,[81,82] comes to be manipulated by the patient and to be useful as a means of controlling his own behavior.[149,166] More overtly, the patient can arrange to maximize his time in situations that are discriminative for constructive behavior and to minimize or eliminate altogether his time in situations likely to be the occasion for the unwanted behavior. Better yet, the patient can even work toward rediscriminating the stimulus control over unwanted behavior by progressively restricting the range of situations that he permits to be the occasion for it and increasing the range of situations that are not.[52,64,66]

For example, a subject of our acquaintance controlled and finally eliminated cigarette smoking by, first, never smoking while standing up and working, then only smoking while seated in a particular chair, and then moving that chair to an out-of-the-way room where she rarely had time to go. Because she was a busy housewife, the numerous situations that formerly had been the occasion for smoking lost their discriminative control over this behavior and became the discriminative stimuli for competing family-oriented behaviors that were strongly reinforced for themselves.

Manipulation of external discriminative control is critical to management of eating in obesity. Schacter[151] showed that the eating habits of obese subjects are controlled to an unusual degree by external cues, as compared with normal control of eating through internal cues related to need and repletion. Obese people must rediscriminate eating to fixed times and places (meal times), and not combine it with other recreational activities such as reading or watching television, and regularize it as to amount and kind of food eaten.[52,170] Stuart and Davis[169] have described in detail a program for this purpose, extending it to include control of exercise, dietary regimes, and record keeping. The patient is given a theory of behavior control, a set of specific instructions as to what to do (rituals?) with record keeping and explicit standards to provide evaluative feedback for differential reinforcement of performance in rediscrimination. The program is well designed, and probably has been successful because of its completeness. Followed long and carefully, it should restore sound habits of eating and exercise. Indeed, the only aspect not covered fully is the problem of achieving commitment, though a few practical suggestions are made to that end. Measures to control fantasy about food and eating should aid materially.[141]

The emphasis upon producing a repertoire of prosocial behavior, rather than eliminating unwanted symptoms directly by extinction or punishment, attempts to avoid complications likely to develop if the flux of the ordinary amenities of life for the patient drops too low, or if he feels coerced. Extinction generally blocks whatever gratification the patient is receiving, and the point is to help the patient establish more effective ways of obtaining it, and more of it. Extinction is somewhat aversive, besides.[39] Punishment and extinction, if used without reward, generate side effects and by-products that lead to power struggles and other counterproductive events. Punishment that "really hurts" (e.g., even loss of points, restrictions) should be reserved for quickly stopping behavior that actually endangers the patient and others (e.g., fighting). Even then extinction and punishment should be in the context of a fundamentally appetitive program in which constructive behavior can earn rewards to replace what punishment takes away. Furthermore, appetitive control is associated with the subjective feeling of freedom, and aversive control with feeling coerced.[163] Such effects on subjective state and self-perception are important if fostering autonomy is a goal, and if, as often happens, the patient's transferential distortions center around control and rebellion. Prisons and other situations in which the control is preponderantly aversive, however tightly organized, have not produced remarkable therapeutic effects. Rather, they appear generally to produce sullen compliance while the contingencies are in effect, punctuated by episodes of serious symptomatic behavior, escalating power struggles, and skillful evasion.

Mixed Procedures

This section considers procedures that probably involve so much interpenetration of Pavlovian, operant, and cognitive control, regardless of the intent of their developers, that they should be considered as mixed strategies. Practice of behavioral therapy increasingly utilizes hybrid procedures. While many have been described, discussion here can cover only major varieties of special interest.

Modeling, or observational learning, as developed by Bandura,[14,15] capitalizes on the human capacity to profit from other people's experiences as observed. In therapeutic applications, a patient with fears observes either live or filmed situations in which other people (serving as models) approach and manipulate the object of the patient's particular fear, happily and without incident. The modeling situations may follow an hierarchical script in which the model comes into increasingly close contact with the feared object in successive scenes, or may simply depict extended contact. Some clinical work, plus a good deal of laboratory experimentation, particularly with children, indicates that the observational learning provided by this technique not only can significantly attenuate common fears (e.g., of snakes, dogs) but also influence subsequent behavioral output, as the observer learns from seeing what behavior produces rewards and punishments for the model.[16]

Observational learning plays a critical role in socialization. Important aspects of personal style, personal values, and standards are acquired, in identification, empathically and imitatively (and, perhaps, quite obliquely) through interpersonal observations and the fantasies and other responses these generate. Laboratory studies on modeling contribute to extending our behavioral theories into the realm of imitation–identification that is so characteristically human and so critical for self-control.[6,117]

Current interpretations recognize that observational learning or modeling, among its other effects, provides opportunities for Pavlovian and operant conditioning and extinction to change the functional significance of stimuli—their evocative, reinforcing, and discriminative powers—for the observer. With respect to behavioral therapy, these changes reflect systematically what the model is perceived to do and is presumed to experience, providing the basis for learning by imitation and for vicarious desensitization.*

The positive *manipulation of fantasies* plays a growing role in the behavioral treatment of sexual and other deviations. For example, sexual deviants tend to show substantial concordance between their behavior and their sexual fantasies, with successful treatment producing parallel changes in both.[48] Sexual fantasies appear to become particularly acute during the preorgasmic crescendo; orgasm probably serves as a potent reinforcer, both conditioning the fantasy as a stimulus for excitation and supporting the voluntary resort to specific fantasies, as covert operants,[81] to produce or enhance arousal. From this perspective, changes in sexual fantasy could lead to and support changes in overt behavior. In treatment, sexual fantasies are altered by shaping and fading techniques; initial arousal is produced by deviant fantasies (or pictorial representations of them), followed by having the patient masturbate, with the deviant fantasy or stimulus replaced by more conventional heterosexual representations just prior to orgasm. With repeated (self-administered) treatment, the normal fantasies or stimuli are shifted to progressively earlier points in the sequence to support the development of normal patterns of arousal, e.g., Marquis' "orgasmic reconditioning."[123] Davison[40] used a variant of this technique in a partially successful attempt to eliminate sadistic fantasies and augment limited sexual capability. (See Abel and Blanchard[1] for an extended discussion of this general approach.)

The role of fantasy as a factor in behavioral therapy is only beginning to receive the attention it deserves. Hunt and Matarazzo mention the possible contribution of recurrent fantasies of smoking as possibly interfering with treatment of that habit;[87] dieters frequently comment on the arousing effects of frequently recurring thoughts of food. Not only can fantasies arouse powerful incentive motivation[113] but they are also embedded in the totality of a person's existential life and are tied associatively to many internal representations of other incentives, consequences, and values. Patient diaries, as suggested in the discussion of individualized behavior modification programs, maximize access to such material, of course.

Aversive techniques, both Pavlovian and operant, employ noxious stimuli to eliminate behavior. Pavlovian conditioning ("aversion") aims toward eliminating unwanted behavior by pairing it, or the stimuli that evoke it, with electric shock or some other similarly unpleasant stimulus. In the operant mode, shock (or another aversive consequence) punishes the behavior when it occurs, or is used in connec-

---

* For more rigorous behavioral analyses of these and other aspects of imitation–identification, see Gewirtz and Stingle.[59]

tion with anticipatory avoidance training in which the patient can avoid aversive consequences altogether by refraining from the undesired response in the face of temptation.

Stimulus satiation, in which the unwanted behavior is "punished" with an over-supply of the apparent reinforcer, is a "paradoxical" aversive technique. For example, Ayllon and Houghton[12] stopped a psychotic woman from hoarding towels by giving her all she asked for, plus additional towels as often as the staff could, until her room was so full that she asked for the towels to be taken away. Having a patient smoke a number of cigarettes simultaneously and continuously, far beyond his interest in or capacity to enjoy them, has been used to curb smoking. Feather and Rhoads[47] instructed a patient with a compulsion to pick up paper to pick up all the scraps he could find. Yates[188] gave a patient with tics massed practice in performing them deliberately. These approaches, sometimes also called "negative practice," "paradoxical intention," or "beta learning," may be interpreted in various ways: as producing stimulus satiation to the point of aversion, as building up conditioned inhibition against performance, as containing an element of ridicule, as giving "permission" for the behavior, or—in the case of behavior the patient is unaware of or repeated errors— as aiding in regaining control through improved discrimination of the response.

In both modes, Pavlovian and operant, stimuli that evoke the behavior, that are the occasion for it, or that arise from it become conditioned aversive reinforcers through pairing with primary aversive stimuli. "Other behavior," including "not responding" is reinforced when it gets the tempting stimulus turned off or gets the patient out of the situation. While early work emphasized elimination of behavior alone, recent, more sophisticated efforts systematically reward and support alternative behaviors, usually incompatible with the target symptom, by direct reinforcement in addition to reward by escape-avoidance ("counterconditioning").[58,145] In practice, the Pavlovian-operant distinction here is more in metaphor than in process.

Typically, aversion treatment pairs shock, or nausea from drugs or drinking salt water (or in one case, terror, arising from transient paralysis produced by intravenous infusion of succinylcholine[150]) with smelling and/or tasting alcoholic beverages, with looking at male nude pictures, with cross-dressing, or whatever. Antabuse treatment for alcoholism is a prototype, but the delay in reinforcement— the irreducible interval between the thoughts, sights, tastes, and smells of beginning to drink and the inevitable onset of somatic distress— reduce the effectiveness of conditioning. Electric shock, which is easily controllable, has been found at least as effective, temporarily, in intensities not harmful to the patient. In the "aversion–relief" variation, the patient initiates and then reverses the unwanted behavior on instructions from the therapist. When the behavior starts, shocks are given repeatedly; when it stops or reverses, the shocks stop. Supposedly, the shocks produce conditioned aversion to the behavior (and the stimulus that arouses it) and cessation of shock a relief that rewards refraining.

Cautela[34,35] has proposed that the aversion procedure be carried out entirely within the patient's imagination. This "covert sensitization," in reversal of Wolpe's desensitization, has the patient relax, then imagine initiating the unwanted activity (e.g., drinking, eating) and then imagine the development of severe nausea (in graphic detail!). After a number of repetitions, some patients have been able to stop drinking, lose weight, etc. The procedure really is a simplified, one-sided version of Homme's[81] use of "coverants" in self-control, and indicates the potential contribution of cognitive factors and operant control to results supposedly obtained through Pavlovian conditioning (see also[18,133,149,166]).

Birk et al.[25] have reported by far the most sophisticated therapeutic avoidance experiment so far. Carefully selected male homosexuals, in the middle of long-term group therapy, were subjected to a behaviorally powerful operant-avoidance contingency. The task required repeated key pressing to forestall shocks that otherwise would occur every two to fifteen seconds as long as an erotic male picture was presented. The avoidance responses not only forestalled shock, but also changed the picture to one of a female during which no shock ever was given. Escape responses, made during a shock, terminated the shock and changed the picture, too. In the female picture, though a "safe" signal, the patient had to press the key at least once every one-half second or the male picture and its shock contingency would return. The patients furnished their own male "erotic" pictures and pictures of female acquaintances to ensure appropriate stimulus characteristics. In effect, the patients (1) had shocks paired with their individualized homosexual erotica; (2) had to get rid of that stimulus to avoid shock; (3) had freedom from shock ("safety") only in the presence of the female stimulus; and (4) had to work hard to keep from slipping back into the "dangerous" male erotic stimulus and its shock contingency. The experimental patients not only learned avoidance, which was incompatible with viewing the male picture, and to keep the safe female signal on (they reported that that stimulus produced a feeling of "relief") but also in four out of five cases showed dramatic temporary decreases in homosexual behavior, as compared with a control group. Subsequent clinical follow-up after several years, however, revealed that only two of the four patients had achieved any enduring or deep change toward heterosexuality. The authors remarked presciently on the difference between suppressing homosexual behavior and helping a patient to develop appropriate heterosexuality. The latter requires real relationships with females and other supports for heterosexual behavior. They also questioned how "successful" a treatment can be if it leaves the patient without a sexual outlet.

Whether aversive therapy works primarily through Pavlovian aversive conditioning may be questioned. The study by Birk et al.[25] demonstrated aversive control, but within an operant-conditioning framework that hypothesizes no mediating fear or anxiety as necessary for this kind of avoidance. Much of the work with aversive therapy, however, has been within a framework that hypothesizes the conditioning of fear or anxiety reactions as a mediating and intermediate step.[58,104] A recent report by Hallam, Rachman, and Falkowski[68] indicates that, contrary to expectation, patients given shock-aversion therapy reported the development of repulsion or indifference, not anxiety, and that no evidence of conditioned cardiac or skin resistance changes appeared after treatment. Perhaps, then, and in view of the moderate rather than excruciating shock levels usually employed (else the patients might terminate, rebel, or sue) the aversive shocks may convey information rather than condition in the classical Pavlovian sense, and functionally reward the subject for displaying appropriate behavior or preference. Or the patient's persistence in continuing with an admittedly unpleasant treatment may reflect an all-important commitment that serves as the major ingredient in producing change.

Information as "reinforcement" plays a conspicuous role in "biofeedback" training for human subjects. Here visceral, skeletal motor, or other physiological reactions usually inaccessible to detection by the responder are converted into audible or visible signals by suitable transducing instrumentation. On instructions, the motivated subject attempts to maximize the signal indicating he is making the desired response (e.g., a sound or light signal) and to keep on doing it, whatever it is. Auditory signals generated by myographic recorders have been used in feedback to facilitate learning Jacobson's progressive relaxation.[168] Feedback-trained relaxation has been applied to treatment of tension headaches.[181] Miller[129] has applied biofeedback training to lowering blood pressure in hypertensive patients. Kamiya[93] and others have been able to increase EEG alpha time by biofeedback, but therapeutic values of this effect, and of most other therapeutic applications of biofeedback, remain to be verified. Biofeedback procedures applied to visceral, central-nervous-system, and skeletal-muscle responses offer possibilities for new approaches to psychosomatic disorders[129] and to otherwise inaccessible aspects of self-control.[71] They also raise basic problems as to how behavior is organized and controlled.[69,70,72,73] (For more extended accounts, see references[17,94,129,155].)

Information also plays a major role in *social feedback* and *behavioral rehearsal* using videotape playback of patient behavior. Here, the patient can see a sample of his behavior, judge it, reperform it, observe improvement, and so on.* The self-monitoring effect is similar to that in the use of audiotape feedback in music training. Albert et al.[3] have used video playback as an adjunct to aid patients in acquisition of social skills and perceptions. These workers also attempted to foster autonomy (through patient selection of goals), feelings of equality (by role reversals with the therapists), desensitization and learning of coping methods for special problems. The treatment team and the patient role-played selected passages from dramatic works covering sensitive problem areas, with content somewhat removed from the patient because the words used were the author's not the patient's. These methods are in their infancy, and their scope and effectiveness are uncertain. They may provide a behavioral approach, however, to objectifying and influencing subtleties of complex social interaction. (For an integration of videotape playback with a behaviorally oriented, group-treatment program, see reference 98.)

In J. P. Brady's use of metronome pacing of speech for stuttering, sophisticated behavioral and clinical modifications turned a powerful but practically limited technique into an effective therapeutic tool.[27] Brady made the metronome portable and cosmetically satisfactory by using a hearing-aid design, placed control of rate and loudness with the patient, and added desensitization and fading procedures to improve fluency and provide for eventual fluency without the attachment. In desensitization, the patient started in situations of low-stuttering potential, using slow metronome pacing. As fluency was attained, metronome rates increased, and the patient graduated to progressively more challenging situations, in vivo. Care was taken not to push escalation of

* See references 5, 20, 137, 154, 156, and 165.

either rate or challenge too fast, and the patient was always free to retreat to slower rates for more practice and desensitization if trouble developed. In fading, which began after reasonable fluency had begun to be attained, the use of the metronome progressively decreased, first in the easier and then in the more difficult situations. At any time, the patient could resort to the metronome if speech difficulties threatened; such brief "retraining" often aborted what could have become serious attacks of stuttering. Patients also used in vitro imaginal desensitization at times, and had conventional speech therapy for grimaces and other anomalies that sometimes occur in stutterers. As Brady indicated, many factors— Pavlovian and operant conditioning, desensitization, and cognitive and expectational changes—probably contributed to the total effect. That some specific learning was involved, however, is suggested by the small, temporary performance decrement that occurred when the patients switched from a desk metronome to the hearing-aid form early in treatment.

A. A. Lazarus' *Behavior Therapy and Beyond* probably represents the most free-swinging, mixed strategy of all.[103] He departs radically from the stimulus-response-reinforcement rhetoric of behaviorism in essentially clinical analyses of complex psychotherapeutic interchanges. The guiding framework remains in the behavioral tradition (cognitive social learning variety) but some behaviorists decry his deviationism. The presentation leans heavily on case material and transcribed interviews oriented to specific clinical problems, and its major points are clear. Working, eclectic psychotherapists will appreciate his practical sophistication. D'Zurilla and Goldfried[43] treat behavioral therapy as problem solving, within a cognitive social learning framework. The presentation parallels Lazarus in many ways, but is more academic and rationalistic in tone. Lazarus' title is descriptively accurate and also may be prophetic. If and when cognitive social learning and self-control theory really develop, however, he may find himself closer to the central focus of behavioral therapy than he is now.

Psychodynamic Behavioral Therapy

Behavioral therapists tend to shy away from explicit use of psychodynamic concepts and methods. Continued experience and further maturation, however, may demonstrate that undue adherence to a parochial isolation leads to overlooking much that is important. Marmor[122] has noted how complex dynamic aspects of the treatment situation may contribute to or hinder behavioral therapy. His most telling example calls attention to the way Masters and Johnson[124] integrate desensitization into a complex treatment strategy for relief of sexual inadequacy. Here, the marital dyad and the family, viewed dynamically, are dealt with as a unit, with desensitization representing only part of the therapy. Proper management of the total situation probably enhances the effectiveness of the behavioral desensitization. The Birks[24] similarly see an opportunity for "synergistic cooperation" between dynamic and behavioral approaches. They have developed an explicit schema showing how and in what ways behavioral and insight-interpretive methods can be used as complements, for maximal effect.

Feather and Rhoads[46,47,148] have presented a rationale and illustrative case material showing how psychodynamic inferences can be used to identify appropriate response classes and effective stimuli for reinforcement–extinction, and help in determining the sequencing of treatment in an unmistakably behavioral format. In "psychodynamic behavior therapy," the diagnostic analysis extends beyond symptoms to inferences as to underlying conflicts so that dynamic theory can suggest what to deal with in treatment. Then, a behavioral perspective suggests how these problems should be dealt with, e.g., desensitization, manipulation of fantasy in paradoxical intention, rediscrimination. Psychodynamic theory contributes specifics as to content, while procedures are drawn from current behavioral methods. See also Birk.[23]

The matter of content is an important consideration in behavioral therapy because behavior theories tend to be so abstract and paradigmatic in dealing with stimuli, responses, reinforcers, and the like. In clinical application, specifics of content can make all the difference in the world, however, and selections must be made on some basis. In the usual behavioral approach, common sense (or, often, cryptically employed clinical or dynamic sophistication) determines the selection. Feather and Rhoads simply suggest the systematic and explicit use of dynamic theory in this process and in determining the specifics of behavioral treatment.

Nothing here should be taken to imply that research seeking to determine the effective ingredients in psychotherapy may casually mix behavioral and dynamic concepts without regard to assumptions or consequences, just to be "eclectic." Rather, in the absence of competing personality theories of equal stature and completeness, sophisticated awareness and explicit use of dynamic formulations may be turned to advantage in behavioral therapy.

Dynamic knowledge can help therapists make shrewd guesses as to what is controlling problem behavior, and how, i.e., what the patient is working to get, what circumstances he sees as favorable for getting it, and what constructive substitute behaviors and rewards he might be able to settle for.[86] Such knowledge can also help in selecting the most appropriate target behaviors, which may not be the most flagrant symptoms. Patients can trap a therapist by luring him into a power struggle that is most difficult to win, if indeed one ever would want to or need to. From dynamic theory, we can guess that some anorexic patients, for example, literally are willing to die in behalf of rebellion against control, and respond much better to an indirect behavioral approach than to a frontal attack on food intake. Stunkard's[170] successful use of access to activity as a Premack type of reinforcement for weight gain illustrates such an indirect approach.

Further, dynamic theory highlights the importance of the personal relationship between patient and therapist and touches on how it may be manipulated. This is not often considered explicitly in the behavioral literature, but it should be. Without an effective relationship, the therapist cannot be an effective source of social reinforcement for the patient. (These probably represent just two different ways of saying the same thing!) The behavioral literature rarely even touches on transference, yet many failures may arise from the distortions and resistances it introduces. Rhoads and Feather have observed it and suggest ways in which it may be used therapeutically.[147]

Finally, countertransferential reactions of the therapist are never mentioned, though such reactions on the part of other staff are noted in terms of undercutting, "rescue fantasies," disliking certain patients, and the like. These reactions in the therapist, if he is unaware of their very real possibility, can seriously distort planning and decisions and their execution in treatment. Supervisory experience with therapists learning behavioral techniques shows countertransferential problems to be not only important when they occur but also surprisingly ubiquitous even in the supervisor. The risk is always present in this as in any other psychotherapy. Behavioral therapists can help minimize it by always placing the patient's welfare first, being attentive and responsive to the detailed course of events in treatment (never leaving powerful contingencies solely in the hands of unsupervised, untrained staff), always remaining aware of the imminent possibility of countertransferential distortions, and taking frequent counsel with a trusted and competent colleague when things are going badly, when they are going well, or "just because."

In addition, the most sparing use of aversive controls, leaving the patient with large areas of discretionary control and realistic choice (including the choice not to participate), and an emphasis upon positive reinforcement to promote development of a prosocial repertoire and behavioral skills will go far to ward off dangerous consequences of countertransference. Problems of ethics in relation to psychotherapeutic and behavioral treatment deserve more detailed consideration than possible in this chapter. London[114] and Goldiamond[65] should be consulted for recent general reviews of this complex topic, and James Burnham's *The Machiavellians: Defenders of Freedom*[33]

for background as to the necessity for unremitting vigilance in these matters. More particularly, it is important to remember that behavioral therapy, as any other, aims (or should aim) to restore to the patient the possibility of choice among viable, alternative ways of coping, rather than coerce adoption of a particular pattern.[100] Actually, the possibility of seduction is greater than the risk of outright coercion!

◖ Final Comment

Whether behavioral therapy works for the reasons it is supposed to work is far from settled despite favorable presumptive evidence. Behavioral therapy is really a set of techniques with a set of metaphors for behavioral processes tacked on. Most if not all behavioral phenomena can be "explained" by alternative metaphors. Which set points to the "better way" is equally unsettled. In addition, nonspecific factors such as attention, expectancy, placebo effects, structure, and factors as existential as self-esteem, perceived autonomy, and the glimpsed possibility of escaping from hopeless dilemmas all contribute, and no doubt more in some cases than in others. In some cases, it is more than possible that the ritual and the rationalizing metaphor of behavioral treatment allow the patient to relinquish unwanted symptoms without relinquishing dignity and self-respect.

If behavior disorders are really nothing more than problems in living, as some think,[173] then behavioral and other psychotherapies have taken on nothing less than the task of producing the good life! If the job is incomplete, no one should be surprised, but neither can one fault the behavioral therapists for not trying.

◖ Bibliography

1. ABEL, G. G. and E. B. BLANCHARD. "The Role of Fantasy in the Treatment of Sexual Deviation," *Arch. Gen. Psychiatry*, 30 (1974), 467–475.

2. AGRAS, A. S., D. H. BARLOW, H. N. CHAPIN et al. "Behavior Modification of Anorexia Nervosa," *Arch. Gen. Psychiatry*, 30 (1974), 279–286.

3. ALBERT, H. D., R. L. BLUMENTHAL, B. SILVERMAN et al. "Self-observation, Self-correction, and Re-socialization Using Videotape Replay." Submitted for publication.

4. ALBERT, H. D. and H. F. HUNT. "Therapeutic Behavioral Control of Intrapsychic Events," Paper given at Columbia University Psychiatry Seminar, New York, 1974.

5. ALGER, I. "Therapeutic Use of Videotape Feedback," *J. Nerv. Ment. Dis.*, 148 (1969), 430–436.

6. ARONFREED, J. *Conduct and Conscience.* New York: Academic, 1968.

7. ATTHOWE, J. M., JR. "Controlling Nocturnal Enuresis in Severely Disabled and Chronic Patients," *Behav. Ther.*, 3 (1972), 232–239.

8. ATTHOWE, J. M., JR. and L. KRASNER. "Preliminary Report on the Application of Contingent Reinforcement Procedures (Token Economy) on a 'Chronic' Psychiatric Ward," *J. Abnorm. Psychol.*, 73 (1968), 37–43.

9. AYLLON, T. "Intensive Treatment of Psychotic Behavior by Stimulus Satiation and Food Reinforcement," *Behav. Res. Ther.*, 1 (1963), 53–61.

10. AYLLON, T. and N. H. AZRIN. "Reinforcement and Instructions with Mental Patients," *J. Exp. Anal. Behav.*, 7 (1964), 327–331.

11. ———. *The Token Economy.* New York: Appleton-Century-Crofts, 1968.

12. AYLLON, T. and E. HOUGHTON. "Control of the Behavior of Schizophrenic Patients by Food," *J. Exp. Anal. Behav.*, 5 (1962), 343–352.

13. AYLLON, T. and J. MICHAEL. "The Psychiatric Nurse as a Behavioral Engineer," *J. Exp. Anal. Behav.*, 2 (1959), 323–334.

14. BANDURA, A. "Modelling Approaches to the Modification of Phobic Disorders," in R. Porter, ed., *The Role of Learning in Psychotherapy*, pp. 201–217. London: Churchill, 1968.

15. ———. *Principles of Behavior Modification.* New York: Holt, Rinehart & Winston, 1969.

16. BANDURA, A. and R. H. WALTERS. *Social Learning and Personality Development.* New York: Holt, Rinehart & Winston, 1963.

17. BARBER, T. X., J. KAMIYA, and D. SHAPIRO, eds. *Biofeedback and Self-control.* Chicago: Aldine, 1971.

18. BARLOW, D. H., H. LEITENBERG, and W. S. AGRAS. "Experimental Control of Sexual Deviation through Manipulation of the Noxious Scene in Covert Sensitization," *J. Abnorm. Psychol.*, 74 (1969), 596–601.

19. BELLAMY, E. *Looking Backward: 2000–1887.* Boston: Ticknor, 1888.

20. BERGER, M. M. "A Preliminary Report on Multi-image Immediate Impact Video Self-confrontation," *Am. J. Psychiatry*, 130 (1973), 304–306.

21. BERGIN, A. E. and S. L. GARFIELD, eds. *Handbook of Psychotherapy and Behavior Change.* New York: Wiley, 1971.

22. BERGIN, A. E. and H. H. STRUPP. *Changing Frontiers in the Science of Psychotherapy.* Chicago: Aldine, 1972.

23. BIRK, L. "Intensive Group Therapy: An Effective Behavioral-Psychoanalytic Method," *Am. J. Psychiatry*, 131 (1974), 11–16.

24. BIRK, L. and A. W. BRINKLEY-BIRK. "Psychoanalysis and Behavior Therapy," *Am. J. Psychiatry*, 131 (1974), 499–510.

25. BIRK, L., W. HUDDLESTON, E. MILLER et al. "Avoidance Conditioning for Homosexuality," *Arch. Gen. Psychiatry*, 25 (1971), 314–325.

26. BONEAU, C. A. "Paradigm Regained? Cognitive Behaviorism Restated," *Am. Psychol.*, 29 (1974), 297–309.

27. BRADY, J. P. "Metronome-Conditioned Speech Retraining for Stuttering," *Behav. Ther.*, 2 (1971), 129–150.

28. BRADY, J. P. and D. L. LIND. "Experimental Analysis of Hysterical Blindness," *Arch. Gen. Psychiatry*, 4 (1961), 331–339.

29. BREGER, L. and J. L. McGAUGH. "Critique and Reformulation of 'Learning Theory' Approaches to Psychotherapy and Neurosis," *Psychol. Bull.*, 63 (1965), 338–358.

30. BRELAND, K. B. and M. BRELAND. "The Misbehavior of Organisms," *Am. Psychol.*, 16 (1961), 681–684.

31. ———. *Animal Behavior.* New York: Macmillan, 1966.

32. BROWN, P. L. and H. M. JENKINS. "Auto-

shaping of the Pigeon's Key-peck," *J. Exp. Anal. Behav.*, 11 (1968), 1–8.

33. BURNHAM, J. *The Machiavellians: Defenders of Freedom.* New York: Day, 1943.

34. CAUTELA, J. R. "Treatment of Compulsive Behavior by Covert Sensitization," *Psychol. Rec.*, 16 (1966), 33–41.

35. ———. "Covert Sensitization," *Psychol. Rep.*, 20 (1967), 459–468.

36. COHEN, H. "Educational Therapy," in J. M. Shlien, H. F. Hunt, J. Matarazzo et al., eds. *Research in Psychotherapy*, Vol. 3, pp. 21–53. Washington: American Psychological Association, 1968.

37. COHEN, H. and J. FILIPCZAK. *A New Learning Environment.* San Francisco: Jossey-Bass, 1971.

38. COHEN, M., I. A. LIEBSON, L. A. FAILLACE et al. "Moderate Drinking by Chronic Alcoholics: A Schedule-Dependent Phenomenon," *J. Nerv. Ment. Dis.*, 53 (1971), 434–444.

39. COUGHLIN, R. C., JR. "The Aversive Properties of Withdrawing Positive Reinforcement: A Review of the Recent Literature," *Psychol. Rec.*, 22 (1972), 333–354.

40. DAVISON, G. C. "Elimination of a Sadistic Fantasy by Client-controlled Counterconditioning Technique," *J. Abnorm. Psychol.*, 73 (1968), 84–90.

41. DEWS, P. B. "The Behavioral Context of Addiction," in L. Goldberg and F. Hoffmeister, eds., *Bayer Symposium, IV: Psychic Dependence*, pp. 36–46. New York: Springer, 1973.

42. DOLLARD, J. and N. E. MILLER. *Personality and Psychotherapy.* New York: McGraw-Hill, 1950.

43. D'ZURILLA, T. J. and M. R. GOLDFRIED. "Problem Solving and Behavior Modification," *J. Abnorm. Psychol.*, 78 (1971), 107–126.

44. EYSENCK, H. J. *Behavior Therapy and the Neuroses.* New York: Pergamon, 1960.

45. FALK, J. L. "The Nature and Determinants of Adjunctive Behavior," *Physiol. Behav.*, 6 (1971), 577–588.

46. FEATHER, B. W., and J. M. RHOADS. "Psychodynamic Behavior Therapy: 1. Theory and Rationale," *Arch. Gen. Psychiatry*, 26 (1972), 496–502.

47. ———. "Psychodynamic Behavior Therapy: 2. Clinical Aspects," *Arch. Gen. Psychiatry*, 26 (1972), 503–511.

48. FELDMAN, M. P. and M. MACCULLOCH. *Homosexual Behavior: Therapy and Assessment.* Oxford: Pergamon, 1971.

49. FENICHEL, O. *Psychoanalytic Theory of Neurosis.* New York: Norton, 1945.

50. FERRARO, D. "Self-control of Smoking: The Amotivational Syndrome," *J. Abnorm. Psychol.*, 81 (1973), 152–157.

51. FERSTER, C. B. "Reinforcement and Punishment in the Control of Human Behavior by Social Agencies," *Psychiatr. Res. Rep.*, 10 (1958), 101–118.

52. FERSTER, C. B., J. I. NURNBERGER, and E. B. LEVITT. "The Control of Eating," *J. Mathet.*, 1 (1962), 87–109.

53. FERSTER, C. B. and B. F. SKINNER. *Schedules of Reinforcement.* New York: Appleton-Century-Crofts, 1957.

54. FISKE, D. W. "The Limits for the Conventional Science of Personality," *J. Pers.*, 42 (1974), 1–11.

55. FISKE, D. W., H. F. HUNT, L. LUBORSKY et al. "Planning of Research on Effectiveness of Psychotherapy," *Am. Psychol.*, 25 (1970), 727–737.

56. FLANAGAN, B., I. GOLDIAMOND, and N. H. AZRIN. "Operant Stuttering: The Control of Stuttering Behavior Through Response-contingent Consequences," *J. Exp. Anal. Behav.*, 1 (1958), 173–177.

57. FRANK, J. D. *Persuasion and Healing.* Baltimore: The Johns Hopkins Press, 1961.

58. FRANKS, C. M. and G. T. WILSON, eds. *Annual Review of Behavior Therapy, Theory, and Practice, 1973.* New York: Brunner/Mazel, 1973.

59. GEWIRTZ, J. L. and K. G. STINGLE. "Learning of Generalized Imitation as the Basis for Identification," *Psychol. Rev.*, 75 (1968), 374–397.

60. GIBBON, J., R. BERRYMAN, and R. L. THOMPSON. "Contingency Spaces and Measures in Classical and Instrumental Conditioning," *J. Exp. Anal. Behav.*, 21 (1974), 585–605.

61. GILBERT, R. M. and J. D. KEEHN, eds. *Schedule Effects: Drugs, Drinking, and Aggression.* Toronto: University of Toronto Press, 1972.

62. GOFFMAN, E. *Asylums.* Chicago: Aldine, 1962.

63. GOLDFRIED, M. R. and R. N. KENT. "Traditional versus Behavioral Personality Assessment: A Comparison of Methodological

and Theoretical Assumptions," *Psychol. Bull.*, 77 (1972), 409–420.

64. GOLDIAMOND, I. "Self-control Procedures in Personal Behavior Problems," *Psychol. Rep.*, 17 (1965), 851–868.

65. ———. "Toward a Constructional Approach to Social Problems: Ethical and Constitutional Issues Raised by Applied Behavior Analysis," *Behaviorism*, 2 (1974), 1–84.

66. GOLDIAMOND, I. and J. E. DYRUD. "Some Applications and Implications of Behavior Analysis for Psychotherapy," in J. M. Shlien, H. F. Hunt, J. Matarazzo et al., eds., *Research in Psychotherapy*, Vol. 3, pp. 54–89. Washington: American Psychological Association, 1968.

67. GUERNEY, B. G., JR., ed. *Psychotherapeutic Agents: New Roles for Nonprofessionals, Parents, and Teachers.* New York: Holt, Rinehart & Winston, 1969.

68. HALLAM, R., S. RACHMAN, and W. FALKOWSKI. "Subjective, Attitudinal, and Physiological Effects of Electrical Aversion Therapy," *Behav. Res. Ther.*, 10 (1972), 1–13.

69. HEFFERLINE, R. F. and L. J. J. BRUNO. "The Psychophysiology of Private Events," in A. Jacobs and L. B. Sachs, eds., *Psychology of Private Events*, pp. 163–192. New York: Academic, 1971.

70. HEFFERLINE, R. F., L. J. J. BRUNO, and J. A. CAMP. "Hallucinations: An Experimental Approach," in F. J. McGuigan and R. A. Schoonover, eds., *The Psychophysiology of Thinking*, pp. 299–342. New York: Academic, 1973.

71. HEFFERLINE, R. F., L. J. J. BRUNO, and J. E. DAVIDOWITZ. "Feedback Control of Covert Behavior," in K. J. Connolly, ed., *Mechanisms of Motor Skill Development*, pp. 245–278. New York: Academic, 1971.

72. HEFFERLINE, R. F., B. KEENAN, and R. B. HARFORD. "Escape and Avoidance Conditioning in Human Subjects without Their Observation of the Response," *Science*, 130 (1959), 1338–1339.

73. HEFFERLINE, R. F. and T. B. PERERA. "Proprioceptive Discrimination of a Covert Operant without Its Observation by the Subject," *Science*, 139 (1963), 834–835.

74. HERSEN, M. "The Complementary Use of Behavior Therapy and Psychotherapy: Some Comments," *Psychol. Rec.*, 20 (1970), 395–402.

75. HIGGS, W. J. "Effects of Gross Environmental Change upon Behavior of Schizophrenics," *J. Abnorm. Psychol.*, 76 (1970), 421–422.

76. HILGARD, E. R. and G. H. BOWER. *Theories of Learning*, 3rd ed. New York: Appleton-Century-Crofts, 1966.

77. HINDE, R. A. and J. STEVENSON-HINDE, eds. *Constraints on Learning.* New York: Academic, 1973.

78. HOGAN, R. A. "Implosve Therapy in the Short-term Treatment of Psychotics," *Psychotherapy*, 3 (1966), 25–32.

79. HOGAN, R. A. and J. H. KIRCHNER. "Preliminary Report of the Extinction of Learned Fears via Short-term Implosive Therapy," *J. Abnorm. Psychol.*, 72 (1967), 106–109.

80. ———. "Implosive Eclectic Verbal and Bibliotherapy in the Treatment of Fears of Snakes," *Behav. Res. Ther.*, 6 (1968), 167–171.

81. HOMME, L. E. "Perspectives in Psychology: XXIV. Control of Coverants, the Operants of the Mind," *Psychol. Rec.*, 15 (1965), 501–512.

82. ———. "Contiguity Theory and Contingency Management," *Psychol. Rec.*, 16 (1966), 233–241.

83. HONIG, W. K., ed. *Operant Behavior: Areas of Research and Application.* New York: Appleton-Century-Crofts, 1966.

84. HUNT, H. F. "Prospects and Possibilities in the Development of Behaviour Therapy," in R. Porter, ed., *The Role of Learning in Psychotherapy*, pp. 246–261. London: Churchill, 1968.

85. ———. "Behavioral Considerations in Psychiatric Treatment," in J. Masserman, ed., *Science and Psychoanalysis*, Vol. 18, pp. 36–50. New York: Grune & Stratton, 1971.

86. HUNT, H. F. and J. E. DYRUD. "Commentary: Perspective in Behavior Therapy," in J. M. Shlien, H. F. Hunt, J. Matarazzo et al., eds., *Research in Psychotherapy*, Vol. 3, pp. 140–152. Washington: American Psychological Association, 1968.

87. HUNT, W. A. and J. D. MATARAZZO. "Three Years Later: Recent Developments in the Experimental Modification of Smoking Behavior," *J. Abnorm. Psychol.*, 81 (1973), 107–114.

88. HUTCHINSON, R. R. and G. S. EMLEY. "Schedule-Independent Factors Contributing to Schedule-Induced Phenomena," in R. M. Gilbert and J. D. Keehn, eds.,

Schedule Effects. Toronto: University of Toronto Press, 1972.

89. ISAACS, W., J. THOMAS, and I. GOLDIAMOND. "Application of Operant Conditioning to Reinstate Verbal Behavior in Psychotics," *J. Speech Hear. Disord.*, 25 (1960), 8–12.

90. JACOBSON, E. *Progressive Relaxation.* Chicago: University of Chicago Press, 1938.

91. JENKINS, H. M. "Effects of the Stimulus-Reinforcer Relation on Selected and Unselected Responses," in R. A. Hinde and J. Stevenson-Hinde, eds., *Constraints on Learning*, pp. 189–206. New York: Academic, 1973.

92. JONES, M. C. "The Elimination of Children's Fears," *J. Exp. Psychol.*, 7 (1924), 383–390.

93. KAMIYA, J. "Operant Control of the EEG Alpha Rhythm and Some of Its Reported Effects on Consciousness," in C. Tart, ed., *Altered States of Consciousness*, pp. 507–517. New York: Wiley, 1969.

94. KAMIYA, J., T. X. BARBER, and D. SHAPIRO, eds. *Biofeedback and Self-control: A Reader.* Chicago: Aldine, 1971.

95. KANFER, F. H. and P. KAROLY. "Self-control: A Behavioristic Excursion into the Lion's Den," *Behav. Ther.*, 3 (1972), 398–416.

96. KANFER, F. H. and J. S. PHILLIPS. *Learning Foundations of Behavior Therapy.* New York: Wiley, 1970.

97. KANFER, F. H. and G. SASLOW. "Behavioral Analysis," *Arch. Gen. Psychiatry*, 12 (1965), 529–538.

98. KASS, D. J., F. M. SILVERS, and G. M. ABROMS. "Behavioral Group Treatment of Hysteria," *Arch. Gen. Psychiatry*, 26 (1972), 42–50.

99. KAZDIN, A. E. "Covert Modelling and the Reduction of Avoidance Behavior," *J. Abnorm. Psychol.*, 81 (1973), 87–95.

100. ———. *Behavioral Modification in Applied Settings.* Homewood, Ill.: Dorsey, 1974.

101. KRASNER, L. "Assessment of Token Economy Programs in Psychiatric Hospitals," in R. Porter, ed., *The Role of Learning in Psychotherapy*, pp. 155–174. London: Churchill, 1968.

102. ———. "Behavior Therapy," in *Annu. Rev. Psychol.*, 22 (1971), 483–532.

103. LAZARUS, A. A. *Behavior Therapy and Beyond.* New York: McGraw-Hill, 1971.

104. LEITENBERG, H., S. AGRAS, R. BUTZ et al. "Relationship between Heart Rate and Behavioral Change during the Treatment of Phobias," *J. Abnorm. Psychol.*, 78 (1971), 59–68.

105. LINDSLEY, O. R. "Operant Conditioning Methods Applied to Research in Chronic Schizophrenia," *Psychiatr. Res. Rep.*, 5 (1956), 118–139.

106. ———. "Reduction in Rate of Vocal Psychotic Symptoms by Differential Positive Reinforcement," *J. Exp. Anal. Behav.*, 2 (1959), 269.

107. ———. "Characteristics of the Behavior of Chronic Psychotics as Revealed by Operant Conditioning Methods," *Dis. Nerv. Syst.*, 21 (1960), 66–78.

108. ———. "Geriatric Behavioral Prosthetics," in R. Kastenbaum, ed., *New Thoughts on Old Age*, pp. 41–60. New York: Springer, 1964.

109. LOCKE, E. A. "Is 'Behavior Therapy' Behavioristic?" *Psychol. Bull.*, 76 (1971), 318–327.

110. LOEBER, R. "Engineering the Behavioral Engineer," *J. Appl. Behav. Anal.*, 4 (1971), 321–326.

111. LOGAN, F. A. *Incentive.* New Haven: Yale University Press, 1960.

112. ———. *Fundamentals of Learning and Motivation.* Dubuque, Iowa: William C. Brown, 1970.

113. ———. "Self-control as Habit, Drive, and Incentive," *J. Abnorm. Psychol.*, 81 (1973), 127–136.

114. LONDON, P. *Behavior Control.* New York: Harper & Row, 1969.

115. ———. "The End of Ideology in Behavior Modification," *Am. Psychol.*, 27 (1972), 913–920.

116. LOVIBOND, S. H. *Conditioning and Enuresis.* Oxford: Pergamon, 1964.

117. MACCOBY, E. and J. C. MASTERS. "Attachment and Dependency," in P. H. Mussen, ed., *Carmichael's Manual of Child Psychology*, 3rd ed., Vol. 2, pp. 73–157. New York: Wiley, 1970.

118. MAHONEY, M. J. "Research Issues in Self-management," *Behav. Ther.*, 3 (1972), 45–63.

119. MALAN, D. H. "The Outcome Problem in Psychotherapy Research," *Arch. Gen. Psychiatry*, 29 (1973), 719–729.

120. MARKS, I. M. *Fears and Phobias.* New York: Academic, 1969.

121. MARKS, I. M., J. BOULOUGOURIS, and P. MARSET. "Flooding versus Desensitization in

the Treatment of Phobic Patients," *Br. J. Psychiatry*, 119 (1971), 353–375.

122. MARMOR, J. "Dynamic Psychotherapy and Behavior Therapy: Are They Irreconcilable?" *Arch. Gen. Psychiatry*, 24 (1971), 22–28.

123. MARQUIS, J. N. "Orgasmic Reconditioning: Changing Sexual Object Choice through Controlling Masturbatory Fantasies," *J. Behav. Ther. Exp. Psychiatry*, 1 (1970), 263–271.

124. MASTERS, W. H. and V. E. JOHNSON. *Human Sexual Inadequacy*. Boston: Little, Brown, 1970.

125. MEICHENBAUM, D. M. "Cognitive Factors in Behavior Modification: Modifying What Clients Say to Themselves," in C. M. Franks and C. T. Wilson, eds., *Annual Review of Behavior Therapy and Practice, 1973*, pp. 416–431. New York: Brunner/Mazel, 1973.

126. MILLENSON, J. R. *Principles of Behavioral Analysis*. New York: Macmillan, 1967.

127. MILLER, G. A., E. GALANTER, and K. H. PRIBRAM. *Plans and the Structure of Behavior*. New York: Holt, Rinehart & Winston, 1960.

128. MILLER, N. E. "Learning of Visceral and Glandular Responses," *Science*, 163 (1969), 434–445.

129. ———. "Application of Learning and Biofeedback to Psychiatry and Medicine," in A. M. Freedman, H. I. Kaplan, and B. J. Sadock, eds., *Comprehensive Textbook of Psychiatry*, 2nd ed. Baltimore: Williams & Wilkins, forthcoming.

130. MISCHEL, W. "Toward a Cognitive Social Learning Reconceptualization of Personality," *Psychol. Rev.*, 80 (1973), 252–283.

131. MOORE, B. R. "The Role of Directed Pavlovian Reactions in Simple Instrumental Learning in the Pigeon," in R. A. Hinde and J. Stevenson-Hinde, eds., *Constraints on Learning*, pp. 159–186. New York: Academic, 1973.

132. MOWRER, O. H. *Learning Theory and Personality Dynamics*. New York: Ronald, 1950.

133. ———. *Learning Theory and Behavior*. New York: Wiley, 1960.

134. MOWRER, O. H. and W. H. MOWRER. "Enuresis: A Method for Its Study and Treatment," *Am. J. Orthopsychiatry*, 8 (1938), 436–459.

135. MURRAY, E. J. and L. I. JACOBSON. "The Nature of Learning in Traditional and Behavioral Psychotherapy," in A. E. Bergin and S. L. Garfield, eds., *Handbook of Psychotherapy and Behavior Change*, pp. 709–747. New York: Wiley, 1971.

136. NATHAN, P. I., M. S. GOLDMAN, S. A. LISMAN et al. "Alcohol and Alcoholics: A Behavioral Approach," *Trans. N.Y. Acad. Sci.*, 34 (1972), 602–627.

137. PAREDES, A., K. D. LUDWIG, I. N. HASSENFELD et al. "A Clinical Study of Alcoholics Using Audio-visual Self-image Feedback," *J. Nerv. Ment. Dis.*, 148 (1969), 449–456.

138. PAUL, G. L. "Two-year Follow-up of Systematic Desensitization in Therapy Groups," *J. Abnorm. Psychol.*, 73 (1968), 119–130.

139. ———. "Outcome of Systematic Desensitization. 2: Controlled Investigations of Individual Treatment, Technique Variations, and Current Status," in C. M. Franks, ed., *Behavior Therapy: Appraisal and Status*, pp. 105–159. New York: McGraw-Hill, 1969.

140. PETERSON, D. R. *The Clinical Study of Social Behavior*. New York: Appleton-Century-Crofts, 1968.

141. PLINER, P. L. "Effect of External Cues on the Thinking Behavior of Obese and Normal Subjects," *J. Abnorm. Psychol.*, 82 (1973), 233–238.

142. POWERS, W. T. "Feedback: Beyond Behaviorism," *Science*, 179 (1973), 351–356.

143. PREMACK, D. "Reinforcement Theory," *Nebr. Symp. Motiv.*, 14 (1965), 123–180.

144. PREMACK, D. and B. ANGLIN. "On the Possibilities of Self-control in Man and Animals," *J. Abnorm. Psychol.*, 81 (1973), 137–151.

145. RACHMAN, S. and J. TEASDALE. *Aversion Therapy and Behavior*. Miami: University of Miami Press, 1969.

146. REYNOLDS, G. *A Primer of Operant Conditioning*. Glenview, Ill.: Scott, Foresman, 1968.

147. RHOADS, J. M. and B. W. FEATHER. "Transference and Resistance Observed in Behavior Therapy," *Br. J. Med. Psychol.*, 45 (1972), 99–103.

148. ———. "The Application of Psychodynamics to Behavior Therapy," *Am. J. Psychiatry*, 131 (1974), 17–20.

149. SALZINGER, K. "On the Operant Conditioning of Complex Behavior," in J. M. Shlien, H. F. Hunt, J. Matarazzo et al., eds., *Research in Psychotherapy*, Vol. 3, pp. 122–129. Washington: American Psychological Association, 1968.

150. SANDERSON, R. E., D. CAMPBELL, and S. G. LAVERTY. "An Investigation of a New Aversive Conditioning Treatment for Alcoholism," *Q. J. Stud. Alcohol.*, 24 (1963), 261–275.

151. SCHACTER, S. "Some Extraordinary Facts about Obese Humans and Rats," *Am. Psychol.*, 26 (1971), 129–144.

152. SCHAEFER, H. H. and P. L. MARTIN. *Behavior Therapy*. New York: McGraw-Hill, 1969.

153. SCHWITZGEBEL, R. K. and D. A. KOLB. *Changing Human Behavior: Principles of Planned Intervention*. New York: McGraw-Hill, 1974.

154. SERBER, M. "Teaching the Non-verbal Components of Assertive Training," *J. Behav. Ther. Exp. Psychiatry*, 3 (1972), 179–183.

155. SHAPIRO, D., T. X. BARBER, and J. KAMIYA, eds. *Biofeedback and Self-control*, 1972. Chicago: Aldine, 1973.

156. SHEAN, G. and E. Y. WILLIAMS. "The Effects of Videotape Feedback on the Behavior of Chronic Psychotic Patients," *Psychother. Theory, Res. Prac.*, 10 (1972), 163–166.

157. SHERMAN, A. R. "Real-life Exposure as a Primary Therapeutic Factor in the Desensitization Treatment of Fear," *J. Abnorm. Psychol.*, 79 (1972), 19–28.

158. SHLIEN, J. M., H. F. HUNT, J. MATARAZZO et al., eds. *Research in Psychotherapy*, Vol. 3. Washington: American Psychological Association, 1968.

159. SIDMAN, M. *Tactics of Scientific Research*. New York: Basic Books, 1960.

160. SKINNER, B. F. *The Behavior of Organisms*. New York: Appleton-Century-Crofts, 1938.

161. ———. *Walden Two*. New York: Macmillan, 1948.

162. ———. *Science and Human Behavior*. New York: Macmillan, 1953.

163. ———. *Beyond Freedom and Dignity*. New York: Knopf, 1971.

164. SLOANE, R. B. "The Converging Paths of Behavior Therapy and Psychotherapy," *Am. J. Psychiatry*, 125 (1969), 877–888.

165. SMITH, K. V. and T. J. SMITH. "Systems Theory of Therapeutic and Rehabilitative Learning with Television," *J. Nerv. Ment. Dis.*, 148 (1969), 386–429.

166. STAATS, A. W. and C. K. STAATS. *Complex Human Behavior: A Systematic Extension of Learning Principles*. New York: Holt, Rinehart & Winston, 1963.

167. STAMPFL, T. G. and D. J. LEVIS. "Essentials of Implosive Therapy: A Learning Theory-Based Psychodynamic Behavioral Therapy," *J. Abnorm. Psychol.*, 72 (1967), 496–503.

168. STOYVA, J. and T. BUDZYNSKI. "Cultivated Low Arousal: An Anti-stress Response?," in L. Di Cara, ed., *Recent Advances in Limbic and Autonomic Nervous System Research*. New York: Plenum, 1973.

169. STUART, R. B. and B. DAVIS. *Slim Chance in a Fat World: Behavioral Control of Obesity*. Champaign, Ill.: Research Press, 1972.

170. STUNKARD, A. "New Therapies for the Eating Disorders," *Arch. Gen. Psychiatry*, 26 (1972), 391–398.

171. SULZER, E. S. "Reinforcement and the Therapeutic Contract," *J. Couns. Psychol.*, 9 (1962), 271–276.

172. ———. "Behavior Modification in Adult Psychiatric Patients," in L. P. Ullman and L. Krasner, eds., *Case Studies in Behavior Modifications*, pp. 196–200. New York: Holt, Rinehart and Winston, 1965.

173. SZASZ, T. S. *The Myth of Mental Illness*. New York: Harper & Row, 1961.

174. THARP, R. G. and F. J. WETZEL. *Behavior Modification in the Natural Environment*. New York: Academic, 1969.

175. ULLMAN, L. P. and L. KRASNER, eds. *Case Studies in Behavior Modification*. New York: Holt, Rinehart & Winston, 1965.

176. ULRICH, R. E. and N. H. AZRIN. "Reflexive Fighting in Response to Aversive Stimulation," *J. Exp. Anal. Behav.*, 5 (1962), 511–520.

177. ULRICH, R. E., S. DULANEY, T. KUCERA et al. "Side Effects of Aversive Control," in R. M. Gilbert and J. D. Keehn, eds., *Schedule Effects*. Toronto: University of Toronto Press, 1972.

178. ULRICH, R., T. STACHNIK, and J. MABRY, eds. *Control of Human Behavior*. Glenview, Ill.: Scott, Foresman, 1966.

179. WATSON, J. B. and R. RAYNOR. "Conditioned

Emotional Reactions," *J. Exp. Psychol.*, 3 (1920), 1–14.

180. WEBB, E. J., D. T. CAMPBELL, R. D. SCHWARTZ et al. *Unobtrusive Measures: Non-reactive Research in the Social Sciences.* Chicago: Rand-McNally, 1966.

181. WICKRAMASEKERA, I. "Electromyographic Feedback Training and Tension Headache," *Am. J. Clin. Hypn.*, 15 (1972), 83–85.

182. WILLIAMS, D. R. and H. WILLIAMS. "Auto-maintenance in the Pigeon: Sustained Pecking Despite Contingent Non-reinforcement," *J. Exp. Anal. Behav.*, 12 (1969), 511–520.

183. WOLPE, J. *Psychotherapy by Reciprocal Inhibition.* Stanford, Calif.: Stanford University Press, 1958.

184. ———. "Behavior Therapy in Complex Neurotic States," in J. M. Shlien, H. F. Hunt, J. Matarazzo et al., eds., *Research in Psychotherapy*, Vol. 3, pp. 130–139. Washington: American Psychological Association, 1968.

185. ———. *The Practice of Behavior Therapy.* New York: Pergamon, 1969.

186. WOLPE, J. and A. A. LAZARUS. *Behavior Therapy Techniques.* New York: Pergamon, 1968.

187. WUTTKE, W. and N. K. INNIS. "Drug Effects upon Behavior Induced by Second-order Schedules of Reinforcement: The Relevance of Ethological Analysis," in R. M. Gilbert and J. D. Keehn, eds., *Schedule Effects.* Toronto: University of Toronto Press, 1972.

188. YATES, A. J. *Behavior Therapy.* New York: Wiley, 1970.

CHAPTER 16

BEHAVIOR THERAPY
FOR CHILDREN

Sidney W. Bijou and William H. Redd

I N THE past decade psychotherapists have been turning in increasing numbers to behavioral techniques in the treatment of children. Almost twenty years ago, in 1954, a review of the child therapies[10] showed that practically all the techniques then in use could be subsumed under these major categories: child psychoanalysis, the briefer psychoanalytic therapies, and client-centered play therapy. In 1966, a similar review[16] showed the same three categories together with two approaches to behavior therapy. Now there are four approaches to behavior therapy, with a literature of well over a thousand titles.

The rapid acceptance of child-behavior therapy may be attributable to many conditions, some rather obscure, others patently obvious. Among the latter, four stand out. There is, first, the changing paradigms of scientific thought.[53] Psychology viewed as the branch of philosophy concerned with the understanding of the mind has been gradually rejected in favor of a more scientific approach. The current focus of psychology is the control and prediction of behavior rather than the further explanation of mental processes and states. Perhaps more than any other approach to the treatment of psychological disorders, behavior therapy resonates with psychology as a natural science. Thus, behavior therapy appears to bridge the gap between the main stream of academic psychology and clinical practice.

A second factor contributing to the current popularity of behavior therapy is its effectiveness in individual cases. Behavior therapy has been successfully employed across a variety of kinds of behavior, disorders, ages, populations, and settings. If one were to read textbooks published fifteen years ago on the treatment of deviant child behavior, he would find for each problem listed a variety of presumed etiologies and treatment recommendations couched in very general terms. In contrast, current books on the subject[117] suggest definite procedures for assessing a single child's relevant repertoires and programming the treatment sequences.

Third, the explicitness of behavior therapy

has led to its adoption by practitioners in the fields of medicine, education, and speech and hearing, and by counselors, social workers, parents, peers, and siblings. Interestingly enough, research and observation have shown that those individuals who interact with the child and most control powerful contingencies are, with training, very effective therapists. And inasmuch as they also have closer and more frequent contacts with the child than does the therapist, they can carry on the therapy program more regularly and over longer time spans.

The fourth factor is that the behavioral approach is applicable to children with a wide range of problems and deficiencies, i.e., they need not have the minimum prerequisite abilities (language, motor skills, etc.) required by most traditional psychotherapeutic approaches. In other words, behavior therapy assumes that all behavior is governed by the same principles and, therefore, its use is not restricted to populations with particular problems or with minimal behavioral equipment. So adaptable is the method that to be a candidate for treatment a child need be neither verbal nor attentive nor even cooperative. This applicability of the behavioral approach to a broad band of problems has undoubtedly contributed to its rapid acceptance.

Before describing the nature and present status of child-behavior therapy, it may be well to clarify the meaning of two critical and sometimes confusing terms—behavior modification and behavior therapy—and to point out their common elements. Behavior modification refers to the application of behavior principles *or* learning principles to child rearing, education, psychotherapy, vocational preparation, and social movements. A synonym for behavior modification is applied behavior analysis. Behavior therapy, on the other hand, is the application of behavior principles *or* learning principles mainly to psychotherapy—the treatment of behavior problems, disturbances, and disorders in children and adults. The reason for saying that both behavior modification and behavior therapy deal with the application of behavior principles *or* learning principles is that some behavior therapists maintain that they are applying behavior principles (which includes learning principles) in their treatment programs while others claim they are applying learning principles. Other theoretical differences among behavior therapists will be discussed later.

Perhaps the outstanding characteristic of child-behavior therapy is that it deals with inappropriate, maladaptive, or deviant behavior and its determining conditions. In contrast, dynamic and client-centered child therapies focus on intrapsychic problems and consider deviant behavior as symptoms of those problems.

Secondly, child-behavior therapy devotes its total effort to altering the environmental conditions that maintain the disorder. Therapy is concerned with the here and now of the problem behavior: the presenting problem or problems, the precise behavior that requires modification or augmentation, and the specific strategy for expediting changes. The strategy selected for altering behavior constitutes the treatment program, and the goals of treatment are the explicit kinds of behavior that the child is to acquire. Obviously, this approach has little in common with others that seek to "determine the origins and dynamics of inner causes" and to "resolve the underlying psychological conflicts," "help the client achieve insight," etc.

Since child-behavior therapy is, in fact, environmental modification, an understanding of the behavioral-science meaning of environment is essential. Environment does not mean "something out there" that a person can enter or leave at will. It refers to the stimuli that are in *actual* contact with a person. From this point of view, then, a person is *always* in contact with the environment, which is described both in terms of its *physical properties* (a city park may be described according to its size, grassy meadows, majestic trees, play equipment, and picnic facilities) and in terms of its *functional properties* (for one child the same park may be an aversive stimulus, one that produces strong escape and avoidance reactions because during an excursion there he fell off a swing, was injured, and taken to a hospital; for another, it is a discriminative stimulus, a place where he can have freedom, fun, and frankfurters cooked on a barbeque; for a parent, it may elicit fond memories of family outings). Although a stimulus may be assumed to have fixed physical properties (at least for practical purposes) its functional properties vary across children and across time, depending on their past interactions with it and the circumstances at the time of analysis. In principle, the only way to determine what an object, a person, or a situation "means" to a child is to observe and analyze his behavior in relation to it. For practical purposes, however, we assume, at least as a tentative hypothesis, that many things have the same functional properties for most children because of the similarity of experiences with them and because of the similarity in child-rearing practices of the culture. For example, most children respond favorably to some form of social recognition such as praise, a pat on the head, etc. for their accomplishments. For those who do not, the therapist must find, through systematic analysis, the kinds of contingencies that are effective for each one of them. In other words, from a behavioral-science point of view, people, objects, and events in a child's environment are analyzed according to their functions (meanings) for him rather than for some other person, such as his father, mother, or teacher. By knowing the personal meaning of stimuli for a child, the therapist can arrange conditions that will, in fact, help him to modify his own behavior, i.e., to learn.

A third feature of child-behavior therapy pertains to the way in which rapport—the positive emotional relationship between therapist and child—is used. In contrast to more traditional approaches, rapport is not considered to be of therapeutic value in and of itself or as a prerequisite for all therapeutic change. It is only essential if the therapist or person who serves as the change agent (professional or layman) plans to use praise, approval, and attention as reinforcers. This conception of the importance of the therapeutic relationship does not imply that the therapist considers it unimportant when a child is not reasonably responsive to him or to other adults. In such cases, he will include in his treatment plan the development of a positive relationship between himself (or change agent) and the child. Thus, according to behavior therapy, rapport is important as a means of increasing the therapist's value as an agent of social reinforcement, not as a therapeutic catalyst.

Finally, child-behavior therapy has its built-in correctional procedure. With observable behavior as his subject matter, the therapist generally records (usually by a systematic counting procedure) the frequency of the occurrence of the problem with which he is concerned (i.e., base line) as well as the changes in the kinds of target behavior that take place during therapy. Such a monitoring system provides information that is necessary for altering the program when indicated, and for evidence of achievement of the therapeutic goals.

This chapter presents an overview of contemporary child-behavior therapy. It is divided into six sections: (1) historical background; (2) theoretical models; (3) behavioral diagnosis, classification, and initial assessment; (4) treatment procedures; (5) evaluation of child-behavior therapy; and (6) implications and future trends.

❰ Historical Background

Child-behavior therapy has its origins in reflexology and behaviorism, movements that began at the turn of the century. One especially important contributor to reflexology was, of course, Pavlov, the Russian physiologist. Pavlov[75] claimed that the physiology of the highest parts of the central nervous system of higher animals could be successfully studied in the laboratory by the conditioned-response method, i.e., by systematically pairing a neutral stimulus with an unconditioned stimulus and observing the formation of a conditioned response. He asserted, furthermore, according to Boring that this method could be used to solve "problems that had hitherto been thought to be psychological, and that had not been brought to a successive solution, upon animals at least, by the psychological methods" [pp. 581–582].[17]

After he was well along in his research, Pavlov reported that some of his dogs showed "pathological disturbance of the cortex." He described this condition as loss of previously learned responses, restlessness, and excitement in the situation, and resistance to the experimental procedures. Pavlov attributed this disturbed behavior to the susceptibility of the animal's nervous system and to the kinds of stresses he had introduced in the laboratory. Some of these conditions included presentation of conditioned stimuli requiring mutually antagonistic responses, rapid transition between positive and negative stimuli, and reinforcement of a conditioned stimulus that had previously had an inhibitory effect. His findings on disturbed behavior convinced Pavlov[76] that he had opened the way for the laboratory study of neurosis in humans. "The neurosis in man," he wrote in a letter to the American Medical Association, "must be interpreted or understood, that is, analyzed with the help of studies of neurosis in animals, which are naturally more simple . . ." [p. 1012].

John B. Watson,[108,109] an American comparative psychologist and founder of behaviorism, extended Pavlov's theory and laboratory method to all behavior, contending that the subject matter of psychology is behavior, its methods are objective, and its central problem, like that of the natural sciences, is prediction and control. He claimed that human behavior, from the simplest to the most complex, can be accounted for in terms of the original behavioral equipment of an infant (innate behavior) and his interactional history with stimuli (defined physical terms) analyzed according to the principles of Pavlovian conditioning. Guided by this view, Watson and his associates collected experimental and longitudinal data on the behavior of infants, children, adolescents, adults, and senescents. Because of his particular interest in the influence of heredity and environment in determining a class of behavior (e.g., intelligence) he focused his attention on the innate behavior of infants. Watson theorized that innate behav-

ior consisted of unlearned behavior (reflexes) and three basic emotions: fear, rage, and love, but subsequent research failed to substantiate his contention that each innate emotion consists of a fixed stimulus–response relationship (e.g., the stimulus for rage is the hampering of bodily movement and the response is the stiffening of the whole body, the free slashing movements of hands, arms, and legs, and the holding of the breath). However, Watson's studies with Rayner[110] on "fear" behavior were true landmarks,[66] not because of their contribution to the nature of innate behavior but because they demonstrated the process of conditioning and generalization in the human infant. These studies were replicated and extended by a host of investigators (e.g., Bregman;[18] English;[28] Holmes;[39] H. E. Jones;[42] and M. C. Jones[43,44]). Watson's insistence that psychology is the study of the interaction of behavior and environmental events, his pioneering work on conditioning in the infant, and his vigorous interest in applied problems, especially in child-rearing practices, have had, as we shall see, an impact on the development of child-behavior therapy.

In the 1930s, psychologists began treating disorders in children as problems in learning or, stated differently, as replacing undesirable habits with desirable habits. There were, for example, reports on the treatment of tics and stuttering[25,68] and on enuresis.[69,70] This trend was short-lived because in the next 20 years child therapists turned to psychoanalytic theory for guidelines in the treatment of children. During this same time, a few investigators, notably Axline,[2] sought a new orientation in the approach of Carl Rogers.

The late 1950s and early 1960s saw a resurgence of the application of learning principles to child treatment. This time, however, much of the research and practice was tied in with the reinforcement theories of Hull[41] and Skinner.[93] Hull drastically modified Watson's general behavior theory and then attempted to integrate it with the findings of Thorndike[101] that demonstrated that many kinds of behavior are strengthened not by the antecedent pairing of stimuli as in Pavlovian conditioning but by the *stimuli that follow the behavior*—the law-of-effect learning. Hull postulated that both classes of behavior, Pavlovian and Thorndikian, are strengthened (conditioned) by Pavlovian conditioning principles. Furthermore, he theorized that past interactions influence present behavior through the operation of a network of hypothetical variables (e.g., habit strength, drive, inhibitory potential). These internal variables alter a stimulus input in various ways to produce a response output that is a function of both the current situation and the individual's related past experiences. Since all of Hull's hypothetical terms were related to observable stimulus-and-response conditions, they were, in fact, empirical concepts, i.e., they could be used independently of his network of hypothetical variables. Hull's formulation influenced the field of child behavior and human development in many ways but particularly through the writings of Sears[90] and Bandura and Walters.[5] The work of Sears and his colleagues led to generalizations about child-rearing practices,[91] and the work of Bandura and Walters to a comprehensive technology of child treatment.[4] Hull's theory also had an impact on the treatment of adults.[23,30,114] Wolpe's approach is particularly cogent here because of its extension to children, particularly those with fears and phobias.[55]

Skinner[93] systemized the data based on Pavlovian conditioning theory and on Thorndikian law-of-effect learning (sometimes erroneously called trial-and-error learning) in another way. Instead of trying to account for law-of-effect learning in terms of Pavlovian conditioning, he postulated two separate functional processes, one controlled by the pairing of antecedent stimulation (Pavlovian or respondent conditioning) and one by consequent stimulation (operant conditioning). Although the two processes may be separated for analytical purposes, it should be clear that in many everyday activities they interact with each other. Skinner carefully and deliberately restricted all of his analyses to the observable interactions between individuals and environmental events, i.e., hypothetical variables were excluded and generalized statements based on group data were eschewed.

Initial applications of Skinner's theory, known variously as radical behaviorism, descriptive behaviorism, or behavior analysis, were directed to learning by young normal children,[107] grossly retarded children,[32] psychotic adults,[60] and young severely disturbed (autistic) children.[31] These vanguard studies which took place in laboratory-clinical settings concentrated for the most part on exploring the power of reinforcement contingencies to change behavior. A few years later, studies appeared that aimed at developing techniques that would enable teachers, parents, and child-care workers to carry out behavior-modification procedures in the school, home, and hospital. Some examples of such studies are the amelioration of everyday problems in a normal nursery school,[35] of a serious "acting-out" problem in the home,[37] and of severe emotional-problem behavior (autism) in a psychiatric hospital.[113]

Research during the early renaissance period, which emphasized the application of learning principles, set the stage for present-day practice and research in child-behavior therapy. Most present-day investigatory effort is devoted to extending, revising, and refining treatment techniques for simple one-to-one clinical settings and for complex natural situations. The variations in approaches to problems and in the interpretation of findings emphasize the fact that there is no such thing as *a* child-behavior therapy. Child-behavior therapies are tied together by the basic behavioral postulate that the subject for study is behavior in relation to environmental events, but each moves in a somewhat different direction in research and practice on the basis of its own theoretical model, the topic to which we shall now turn.

❲ Theoretical Models

The theoretical models for child-behavior therapies may be grouped variously and may consist of few or many categories, depending upon the purpose of the classification. Essentially there are four major groups: (1) behavior analysis, (2) learning (conditioning) theory, (3) social-learning theory, and (4) eclectic behaviorism.

Behavior Analysis

The behavior-analysis model originated in the laboratory research on the experimental analysis of behavior. This model is founded on the assumptions, empirical formulations, and research methodology of Skinner[93–95] and the developmental theory of Bijou and Baer.[11,12] One basic assumption is that the subject matter of psychology is the *observable* interaction between a total-functioning, biological individual and environmental events, defined in physical and functional terms. Environmental events consist of stimuli from the physical environment, other organisms, and the physiological structure and functioning of the individual. Another basic assumption is that some responses are conditioned by antecedent stimuli (respondent or Pavlovian conditioning) and some by consequent stimuli (operant conditioning). Respondent behavior is strengthened by the pairing of a neutral stimulus and weakened by discontinuing the pairing or by counterconditioning. Respondent behavior plays a part in many kinds of everyday behavior, and particularly in emotional behavior. A fear reaction, for example, usually has a respondent component consisting of marked changes in physiological functioning (the activation syndrome). On the other hand, operant behavior is brought under the control of an antecedent stimulus (as in stopping a car when the traffic light turned red) or modified in form (as in the shaping of a manual skill) by consequent stimuli or reinforcers in the context of some condition, such as deprivation of reinforcing stimuli. Operant behavior is weakened by nonreinforcement (extinction) and by aversive consequences. Verbal (linguistic), motor, and social behavior have operant properties. Complex kinds of operant behavior, such as decision making, thinking, problem solving, and self-control involve large components of verbal behavior

and are viewed as functionally interrelated sequences (interbehavioral structures).

The behavior-analysis model is concerned solely with the behavior of an individual child. Hence, interest is always focused on the conditions that produce change relative to the child's ongoing performance (base line). The treatment technology that has evolved from this model centers on developing abilities, skills, and knowledge repertoires, and on replacing undesirable behavior with desirable ones.

Learning (Conditioning) Theory

The learning (conditioning) theory of child therapy is associated with Wolpe's approach to the treatment of neurosis in adults[114] and its extension to the treatment of children by Lazarus[55] and others. This theory is built around the concept of habit, which may be defined as a consistent way of responding to a defined stimulus condition. Ordinarily, a habit weakens and disappears when its consequences are no longer adaptive. However, Wolpe[115] says that some habits show resistance to extinction despite their unadaptiveness and that such recalcitrant reactions have a large component of anxiety. Since anxiety involves "a primitive (subcortical) level of neural organization, its weakening and unlearning can come about only through processes that involve direction action, i.e., purely intellectual action will not suffice."

According to the learning (conditioning) model, behavior therapy requires the application of experimentally established principles of learning in order to help a client overcome his neurotic habits and to establish new nonneurotic habits. These principles are derived from *one* kind of learning with variations that depend upon "the identity of interconnected neural sequences." The distinction between Pavlovian (respondent) and instrumental (instrumental in producing rewards) conditioning is not in the nature of conditioning but in the fact that in the former nonvoluntary (autonomic nervous system) behavior is involved;

whereas in the latter, voluntary (central and peripheral nervous system) behavior is the main ingredient. In this reductionistic theory, neurotic behavior is primarily a matter of autonomic conditioning, hence treatment techniques are based primarily on the Pavlovian paradigm. Behavior deficiencies, on the other hand, require procedures involving response contingencies or "rewards."

According to Wolpe,[115] treatment is accomplished on the basis of one or more of three conditioning operations: (1) counterconditioning, (2) experimental extinction, and (3) positive reconditioning. Counterconditioning, or the development of reciprocal inhibition, is therapeutic because: "If a response inhibitory of anxiety can be made to occur in the presence of anxiety-evoking stimuli, it will weaken the bond between these stimuli and the anxiety" [p. 15].[115] A response that inhibits anxiety may be established in several ways, including training in assertive behavior or in progressive relaxation. The "positive" feelings generated in assertive training produce conditioned inhibition of anxiety and the motor actions involved inhibit and consequently displace the previous motor habit. By the same token, relaxation responses when properly managed can effectively counteract and replace anxiety responses. Counterconditioning procedures can also be employed to overcome responses other than anxiety reactions. For example, it may be the basis for establishing conditioned inhibition of obsessional and compulsive habits by aversion therapy in which a painful faradic stimulus, or some similar stimulus, inhibits the undesired behavior.

The second conditioning operation—extinction—is the progressive weakening of a habit through repeated nonreinforcement. This holds for responses dependent on positive reinforcers and for avoidance behavior dependent on aversive contingencies. The third conditioning operation, positive reconditioning, is used as a technique to overcome unadaptive autonomic responses, as well as to develop new habits of action or of thought in nonanxiety disturbances, such as in the treatment of enuresis. Wolpe states the principle of

positive reconditioning as follows: "In order to establish a new behavior pattern in a particular situation, the desired response has to be elicited and each time rewarded, while the undesired behavior is consistently not rewarded" [p. 16].[115]

Social-Learning Theory

The social-learning approach to the treatment of children with problems, which stems from the child-development theory of Sears[90] and Bandura and Walters,[5] is best presented in a recent volume by Bandura.[4] According to Bandura, all behavior, from the simplest to the most complex, is acquired and maintained by three regulatory systems. The first pertains to external stimulus control, or the process by which behavior becomes closely related to environmental stimuli. Autonomic responses and emotional behavior can be brought under the control of environmental events through their contiguous association (as in Pavlovian conditioning) either by direct or by vicarious affective experiences. Instrumental behavior is likewise regulated by environmental stimuli that, by virtue of their association with different conditions of reinforcement, signify the consequences likely to accompany certain courses of action. Deviant behavior, based on defective or inappropriate stimulus control, is accounted for primarily in terms of this principle. The second regulatory system relates to reinforcing or feedback processes, such as the conditioning of operant behavior. Both normal and deviant behavior can be eliminated and reinstated by varying their immediate stimulus consequences. The third regulatory mechanism operates through central mediating processes. "At this higher level stimulus inputs are coded and organized; tentative hypotheses about the principles governing the occurrence of rewards and punishments are developed and tested on the basis of differential consequences accompanying the corresponding activities; and, once established, implicit rules and strategies serve to guide appropriate performances in specified situations. Symbolically generated affective arousal and covert self-reinforcing operations may also figure prominently in the regulation of overt responsiveness" [p. 63].[4]

Modeling processes, in which new responses are acquired and existing behavior modified through the observation of other people's behavior, are prominent features in the treatment techniques of this approach. In all observational learning, the modeled-stimulus event is said to be transformed and retained in image and verbal memory codes. "Later, reinstatement of these representation mediators, in conjunction with appropriate environmental cues, guide behavioral reproduction of matching responses. Performance of observationally learned responses is largely regulated by reinforcing outcomes that may be externally applied, self-administered, or vicariously experienced" [p. 202].[4]

Eclectic Behaviorism

Without a doubt the largest group of child-behavior therapists does not adhere to only one theoretical model. These therapists subscribe to the basic behavioral postulate and, depending on the problem at hand, they accept and apply the principles of classical conditioning, instrumental conditioning, operant conditioning, modeling (as a separate process), self-management or self-control mechanisms, correlational and psychometric theories of personality and abilities, psychodynamic concepts of personality and development, central-mediating processes, and cognitive restructuring. This position is admirably expressed and defended by Lazarus[56] who, it will be recalled, espoused techniques based on Wolpian learning (conditioning) theory in his early work with children. Lazarus and other eclectic behaviorists believe that in this early period of its development, child-behavior therapy would probably advance more rapidly if it remained free from the restrictions of any one theoretical model.

As one might expect, eclectic child-behavior therapists also tend to range extensively in their research and service methods. Their research may be designed along either experimental or correlational lines and the former may involve a single individual or several comparable groups, the latter simple normative relationships or complex factor-analytic procedures. Their clinical techniques may include nonnormative assessment procedures such as interviews and informal surveys of behavioral repertoires as well as standardized tests of intelligence, school achievement, preferences, and personality that measure assertiveness, fears, introversion–extroversion, emotional stability, etc.

⟦ Behavior Diagnosis, Classification, and Initial Assessment

The diagnosis and the classification of children's behavior disorders have always been serious problems.[120] Aside from the difficulties inherent in trying to relate symptoms (patterns of behavior) to underlying psychopathic states or processes, there is the ever-present possibility that a diagnosis made at one stage of a child's development will not apply at the succeeding stage, with or without treatment. There is, in addition, a danger of applying to a child diagnostic terms that were developed primarily for adults (e.g., psychoneurosis). It is widely recognized that although a disorder in an adult and in a child may have features in common, each problem probably has a different history, requires different treatment, and is expected to have a different outcome. Furthermore, diagnostic labels probably stigmatize and handicap those who receive them.[86,99] For example, the child who is diagnosed as mentally retarded is often cut off from educational environments, social interactions, and contingencies that promote learning and placed in a sterile, "retarded" environment that may magnify any handicaps that he might have. Finally, these diagnostic categories have not been found to subsume a consistent set of different kinds of behavior[61,119] or to indicate specific therapeutic tactics.[47] At best, the diagnostic category indicates modal characteristics that, in an individual case, may have little resemblance to the child's behavior problems or to his repertoire of positive kinds of behaviors. For these reasons and others the diagnostic categories for the disorders of children in the Standard Nomenclature of Psychiatric Disorders and Reactions of the American Medical Association have not been widely accepted as is indicated by the fact that over the years some forty alternate diagnostic schemes have been offered.

Recently the Group for the Advancement of Psychiatry[34] proposed a juvenile classification scheme consisting of ten major diagnostic divisions, each with several subtypes. The diagnosis of anxious personality is as follows:

These children are chronically tense and apprehensive over new situations, often related to their extraordinarily vivid fantasies. They usually perceive the environment as threatening, however, and are not aware of and do not exhibit crippling anxieties, as do those with anxiety neurosis. Marked inhibitions or serious constriction of the total personality are not present, and they are often able to deal adequately with new situations after initial anxiety, in contrast to children with developmental deviations, who do not have stage-appropriate social capacities available [p. 241].[34]

This approach to the diagnosis of children's disorders is based on the assumption that patterns of behavior are symptoms of psychopathology in the structure and functioning of psychic entities. Furthermore, this classification proposal consists of generalized statements that may or may not refer to actual child-environment interactions. At best, it may have a kind of internal consistency, i.e., an acceptable level of agreement among those trained in psychoanalytic theory. Since the system does not focus on the specific interactions involved, it does not provide the therapist with the kinds of information that would help him determine treatment goals, treatment strategy, program initiation (base line), etc.

Behavioral Diagnosis and Classification

Among child-behavior therapists, there are two schools of thought on the problem of diagnosis and classification. One, represented by Quay,[78] regards it as a group-analysis problem that is handled best by psychometric procedures, e.g., multivariate-statistical analyses of test results. The contention is that such an approach will eventually reveal a relatively independent set of diagnostic categories for juveniles, e.g., conduct disorder, personality disorder, immaturity, socialized delinquency, etc., and when this is accomplished the stage will be set for research on the etiological and predictive correlates for each diagnostic category.

The other view conceives of diagnosis and classification as a problem in individual analysis and in relation to treatment strategy. Here the diagnostic problem is treated like a clinical-intake evaluation (like Kanner's Complaint Factor[49]), the main purpose of which is to provide information that will help the therapist or staff decide whether he or the agency is adequately equipped to handle the problem. Through reports, and sometimes direct observations, the therapist or caseworker categorizes a child in behavorial terms and decides on the basis of the agency's facilities, staff, and case load, whether to accept him or to refer him elsewhere. If the agency's treatment program is carried out primarily through group interactions (e.g., a special class or an activity group) the initial classification of a child helps the staff to determine whether the group can accommodate him. In their comprehensive review of the status of psychotherapy, Strupp and Bergin[98] comment on the behavioral diagnostic approach:

A new philosophy and methodology of diagnosis is developing within the behavioral school. It is being complemented by the work of an increasing number of eclectically-oriented psychiatrists who tend to focus upon pragmatic, behavioral criteria such as being in or out of school, maintaining marriage or becoming divorced, frequency of arrest, being in or out of the hospital, etc. While still in its infancy, this approach is having an increasing impact upon clinical assessment and upon the specification of outcome criteria for research purposes [p. 60].[98]

In the individual-analysis approach, the number of categories and their designations vary. Here we shall adhere to a fourfold classification scheme. The first category consists of problems described as *behavioral excesses.** Behavioral excesses are normatively judged in terms of frequency, intensity, or both. Children considered to have such problems include those described as conduct problems, such as extremely aggressive, hyperactive, disobedient children, etc. The second consists of problems involved in *shy, withdrawn, and fearful kinds of behavior*. It includes children with specific or generalized phobias, children described as adjustment problems[88] or personality problems[78] in which timidity is an overriding feature. The third consists of problems related to *behavior deficits*, or weak behavior,[14,81,87,92] which includes children underdeveloped in self-care, language, social skills, academic abilities, and basic knowledge. The fourth group consists of problems centering on *defective stimulus control*.[14] Children in this category have many serviceable behaviors, but, from the point of view of society, they occur under inappropriate circumstances. Illustrative of this group are children who talk, but do not direct it to people; children who react to people as objects; children who have acquired the proper social behavior, but do not apply it under the proper circumstance (often referred to as psychopathic or inept); and children who do not always differentiate appropriately between imaginary and real interactions.

Can this descriptive classification scheme help the psychotherapist determine the etiology of a behavior problem? Before attempting to answer this question, several points should be made explicit. First, in the science of human behavior, the concept of etiology and the concept of cause are one and the same. Hence, the two terms are used here interchangeably. Second, a pattern of behavior, normal or deviant, is caused by, or is a function of, a child's genetic and personal history (ontology) and the interactional situation in which the behavior is observed. Child psychotherapists seldom investigate the genetic history of a child in seeking the cause of a prob-

* See references 14, 46, 48, 81, 87, 88, and 92.

lem; most often they accept it as a set of conditions that determine, in part, his unique biological structure and physiological functioning, which in themselves contribute some of the conditions that influence the child's behavior. Those psychotherapists who are interested in exploring a child's personal history for clues to the cause of his problem must carefully analyze the entire sequence of interactions between the child's biological make-up and the actual environmental events. In other words, to know why a child behaves the way he does is to know the sequence of interactions that have led to and have produced that particular behavior. Information of this sort is neither easily nor readily obtained. The usual secondary sources, such as retrospective accounts by child and parent and psychological tests, have proven to be useless.[116] Even if it were possible to obtain accurate and detailed accounts of actual interactions, this information would not be particularly helpful since his objective is not to undo or redo a child's history but to deal therapeutically with his problem as it exists. To do so he must analyze the conditions that maintain the problem behavior and rearrange them in ways that will help the child learn new behavior. We therefore conclude that although it is potentially possible to determine the etiology of a child's behavior disorder, it is unnecessary to do so because that knowledge does not contribute to planning and executing an effective treatment program.

To contend that a child psychotherapist need not explore the actual history of a behavior problem does not mean that he ignores information about a child's background and current situation. On the contrary, he usually seeks such data in his initial assessment procedures because they serve other purposes, as we shall see.

Initial Assessment

It was stated earlier that the purpose of the initial assessment is to provide the therapist with the details of the problem and the setting conditions to enable him to prepare a treatment program that meets the child where he is. Initial assessment is accomplished by (1) interview, (2) inventories of the child's behavioral equipment and of his reactions to people and objects (their meaning to him), and (3) standardized tests. The interview not only provides background and current information but also serves to develop a language system that allows the interviewee to communicate with the interviewer, to pinpoint the exact problem that requires treatment,[56] and, in cases with multiple problems, to provide considerations for establishing treatment priorities.[113] Check lists and questionnaires are sometimes included in the interview.[56,105]

The exact behavior categories inventoried in the initial assessment depend on the problem presented but, in general, cover answers to such questions as: (1) What behavior assets does the child have that can be used to build a treatment program? (2) What stimuli have acquired strong conditioned aversive properties for the child and what levels of representation are tolerable for him? (3) What stimuli have strong reinforcing properties for the child? (4) What conditions maintain the problem behavior? This last question is particularly relevant when therapy is conducted *in vivo*, as Wahler and Cormier[105] point out:

> If social contingencies are to be therapeutically rearranged for the deviant child, one must know who provides these contingencies, in what behavior form they are provided, for what child behaviors they are provided, and in what specific settings or sub-setting they are provided. Given this information, the clinician is in position to intervene—to train the significant "contingency dispensers" (e.g., parents and teachers) to modify their interactions with the child [p. 279].[105]

Standardized tests of intelligence, school achievement, and personality are used in different ways and in different degrees by child-behavior therapists. Some use them as an aid for diagnostic determination, therapeutic planning, base-line criteria, and terminal evaluation. Others use them to provide information requested by principals, school psychologists, teachers, and caseworkers. Still others do not use them at all.

(Therapeutic Procedures

The systematic strategies of child-behavior therapy, as we have seen, consist of (1) setting one or more behavioral goals, (2) following therapeutic procedures based primarily on learning or behavior principles, (3) initiating the treatment program at the child's current level of performance (base line), and (4) determining monitoring procedures. This section will deal with the second step, following therapeutic procedures. Steps one and three were discussed in the section on initial assessment. With regard to step four, we need only to add that systematic monitoring procedures are an indispensable approach that aims to bring about changed behavior through environmental modification. When the data from running accounts indicate little or no progress, the therapist is cued to modify his procedures (and sometimes his materials) until there is evidence of change in the direction of the therapeutic object. Typically, procedural alterations mean adjustments of some portions and not abandonment of the entire program for a new one. Monitoring data also supply information relative to the terminal criterion.

The particular set of procedures a therapist uses for a given child depends upon the problem behavior, the conditions that maintain it, and his theoretical orientation. We pointed out in the section on theoretical models (see page 323) that although the various therapeutic approaches subscribe to the basic behavioral assumption, the principles followed by each are somewhat different, hence the techniques employed by each are also somewhat different. Each behavior therapist will tend to view a child's problem within his own theoretical framework, but the indisputable criteria of therapeutic effectiveness are the observable changes in specific aspects of a child's behavior. Thus, it might be said that the behavior therapist's procedures are guided largely by his theoretical orientation, and at the same time controlled by the behavioral outcome.

The main processes of treatment involve

(1) weakening aversive behavior and strengthening prosocial (appropriate or desirable) behavior; (2) replacing shy, withdrawn, and phobic behavior with prosocial behavior; (3) developing new behavior repertoires; and (4) bringing behavior under prosocial stimulus control.

Weakening Aversive Behavior and Strengthening Prosocial Behavior

Extinction or nonreinforcement is sometimes used to reduce aversive behavior (behavior aversive to someone else) in conjunction with positive reinforcement to strengthen desirable behavior that is incompatible with the undesirable behavior. This approach was utilized in a classroom with an eight-year-old, hyperactive, underachieving, second-grade boy.[73] Base-line observation showed that pushing, hitting, squirming, and tapping constituted most of his aversive behavior. The treatment objective was to weaken and eliminate this behavior by reinforcing with candy and by praise for working productively at his desk. A small light and counter, mounted on the child's desk, registered (flashed and counted) after he had remained quietly seated for ten seconds. At the beginning of the program, the teacher came over and reinforced him as soon as the light flashed. After he had become familiar with this contingency, the teacher explained that the counter would keep score of the candy he had earned and that she would come back after a while to give him the pieces he earned. The intervals between teacher reinforcement were gradually increased, and, correspondingly, the child's productive work time increased (up to two hours). In order to enlist the cooperation of his classmates, the teacher instructed them not to talk to the youngster while he was working. To reinforce their efforts, they were given pennies according to the target child's tally at the end of each period. A similar procedure was used with six hyperactive, mentally retarded children.[24] In this study, tokens exchangeable for candy were given, contingent upon quiet, constructive behavior. In all cases, the level of hyperactive behavior was reduced.

Aversive contingencies (rather than extinction) for aversive behavior are often used together with positive reinforcement of incompatible prosocial behavior. One aversive procedure, known as time-out, involves removing for a brief period opportunities for positive reinforcement immediately following the occurrence of some form of unacceptable behavior. In the treatment of a four-and-one-half-year-old boy's aggressive biting, hitting, and kicking, the teacher reinforced cooperative behavior with praise and attention while, at the same time, removing the child from the classroom immediately following aggressive behavior.[96] Time-out consisted of placing the child in an adjacent room free of toys and objects that could provide a source of reinforcement. The teacher who observed his behavior from behind a one-way vision screen returned him to the classroom after he had remained quiet for two minutes. As the frequency of his aversive behavior decreased, the teacher instructed him in cooperative play and provided him with opportunities to generalize his newly learned social behavior. Similar procedures have also been used with older, mentally retarded children with good success.[102]

Another procedure for reducing aversive behavior involves a combination of response costs—taking away reinforcers after undesirable behavior—and providing positive reinforcement of incompatible prosocial behavior. In this approach, the child either receives or loses reinforcers depending upon his behavior. The contingent loss of reinforcers is a variation of an aversive operation. In token economies in which participants in a prescribed group earn money for good behavior, response-cost procedures usually call for fines for inappropriate behavior, i.e., the child loses tokens or points each time he engages in the prohibited behavior.[20,21] Response cost in combination with positive reinforcement has been successful in a comprehensive community program retraining young boys who have been described as delinquent or in danger of becoming delinquent.[112]

Response cost, on a contingency contracting basis,[40] has been applied in individual-therapy programs. For example, all visitation privileges were taken away from a ten-year-old, retarded resident of a treatment center when he was repeatedly found with someone else's possessions.[111] If at the end of a day he had not stolen anything, he was allowed to visit a close friend; if he had taken something he was told why he could not visit and was restricted to the center for the evening. Within twelve weeks the child's stealing ceased and did not reoccur during a five-month, follow-up period.

Contingent physical aversive stimulation, another technique, is used to weaken aversive behavior (usually in cases in which the behavior is aversive to the child) and also coupled with positive reinforcement for incompatible prosocial behavior. The critical behavior usually involves the child's hitting his head or body on hard surfaces, slapping his face, scratching, or biting himself. If extinction, time-out, or response-cost procedures were employed in these cases, the child might seriously injure himself before the behavior diminished to any appreciable degree. The usual institutional treatment procedure of restraining the child, either by physical or chemical means, prevents the child from hurting himself, but severely limits his opportunity to acquire new behavior.

Contingent physical punishment is rarely considered preferred treatment and is generally resorted to when other techniques have proven ineffective. An example is the case of a nine-year-old, blind, mentally retarded boy who persisted in slapping his face, banging his head, and hitting his shoulder.[100] After baseline observations, a treatment program was instituted of presenting and withdrawing positive reinforcers for prosocial and self-destructive behavior, respectively. During daily walks, two attendants talked to the boy and allowed him to hold their hands as long as he did not attempt to injure himself. Whenever he hit or abused himself in any way, the attendants immediately jerked their hands free, moved away, and stopped talking to him. This procedure (time-out from attention) continued until he had stopped hitting himself for three seconds, whereupon the attendants again held hands with him and continued

their walk. Although this procedure resulted in a marked decrease in self-injurious behavior (6.6 responses a minute during base line versus 0.1 response during treatment) the severity of the self-damage even from infrequent occurrences necessitated a modification of the program. In order to more effectively suppress the face slapping, a physical aversive contingency was introduced. Each time the child slapped himself, a brief electric shock was delivered that resulted in an immediate reduction in self-injurious behavior. No side effects were observed. To maintain this improved behavior, adults praised and gave attention to social behavior that was incompatible with the child's self-injurious behavior. The self-injurious behavior was eliminated and it was now possible for the child to go unrestrained during the day. Similar results with other forms of self-injurious behavior have been reported.[64, 65,83] In all instances, physical aversive contingencies were used in conjunction with positive reinforcement of incompatible, appropriate behavior. Elimination of self-destructive behavior enabled the children to participate in social and educational programs.

Replacing Shy, Withdrawn, and Phobic Behavior with Prosocial Behavior

The treatment of isolate behavior in preschool children generally requires changing the contingent social behavior of adults. Children's prosocial behaviors are as a rule followed by adult praise and attention; isolate and withdrawn behavior is associated with contingent withdrawal of adult praise and attention. After observation of a four-and-one-half-year-old girl's social behavior for baseline data, the teacher was instructed to pay attention and give her appropriate praise *only* when she was interacting with other children and to ignore (extinction) her in a natural way when she was by herself.[1] Initially, any approximation of social interaction, such as sitting near another child, was reinforced by the teacher. As the child began to interact more readily with other children, the teacher increased the requirements for reinforcement and attended to the child only when she was engaging in cooperative play. Gradually, she reduced the frequency of her reinforcement. With this procedure, peer interaction during a school day increased from 15 to 60 percent.

Another technique that has been used to increase social interaction is to reinforce behavior that requires social interaction, as in the case of a nursery-school child who received teacher attention when she used play equipment that she had earlier avoided.[19] Once again, as outlined in the previous case, the teacher first reinforced approximations of the target behavior and then gradually increased the requirements for reinforcement until the child was vigorously using the play equipment. Since peer interaction was a corollary of the reinforced-play behavior, there was a concomitant increase in social interaction. In a similar case study, the teacher reinforced a five-year-old, isolate boy with nickels and praise for distributing candy and treats to other children in the class in order to strengthen his social interaction.[52] Following this training there was a marked increase in the child's peer interaction in other school settings as well.

Modeling or imitation techniques have also been employed to reduce isolate, solitary behavior. The child first has the opportunity to observe another person engaging in the behavior he himself fears, with no aversive consequences. (In fact, the model is usualy reinforced for this behavior.) After observing the model, the child is encouraged to do approximately what the model did and is reinforced. This procedure is repeated until the child is able to engage without hesitation in the once-feared behavior. An example is a six-year-old boy whose extreme social withdrawal from his peers was eliminated following such a treatment program.[89] In order to establish generalized imitative behavior, the therapist associated himself with various positive reinforcers, was warm and demonstrative, and reinforced the child for imitating simple motor responses. After the child readily imitated him, the therapist began to model positive social interaction and discuss the positive aspects of peer interaction. During subsequent play periods

the child was reinforced by the therapist for approximations of the desirable social behavior. Treatment continued through a graduated series of social-interaction phases until the child's social behavior resembled that of his peers. After the seven-week program, and in a two-month, follow-up evaluation, there was an appreciable reduction in the child's social-avoidance behavior.

Another technique for weakening or eliminating troublesome fears and phobias is systematic desensitization, which involves gradually weakening the power of a stimulus to evoke a neurotic-anxiety reaction.[114] Although this procedure was initially developed for use with adults, it has also been applied successfully to children. An example is a nine-year-old girl's anxiety reaction to her mother.[97] In her mother's presence she was very quiet and showed little or no spontaneity. During weekly sessions the child played with a therapist while the mother observed from behind a one-way vision screen, receiving instructions from a second therapist on ways to respond to her child so as to help her allay her anxiety. When the child became relaxed and showed a variety of spontaneous expressions in her play with the therapist, the mother was brought into the room. In subsequent sessions, the mother spent more and more time playing with the child until the child was able to play with her in a relaxed spontaneous manner. After only five treatment sessions, the mother reported that there were decided changes in her child's behavior with her at home. An eight-month, follow-up evaluation showed continued improvement in the relationship.

"Emotive imagery," a variation of systematic desensitization, has also been used to reduce phobic behavior.[57] Basically, it involves stimulating reactions to positive stimuli in the context of aversive or feared objects or events to reduce their strength or intensity. After listing the child's fears in order of their severity (constructing the hierarchy) and his most enjoyed storybook characters and events, the therapist creates and tells a story that presents the least fearful on the list in the context of the child's most favored storybook characters.

He is told that if he feels frightened as the story progresses up the fear hierarchy, he is to inform the therapist and he will return to a less fearful part of the story. Cases successfully treated by this technique included an eight-year-old boy who was afraid of going to the dentist, a fourteen-year-old girl who feared dogs, and an eight-year-old girl who was afraid to go to school. With the dentist-phobic boy, the therapist developed a sequence of stories about fictional characters, Batman and Robin, on a variety of adventures all of which eventually lead to the dentist's office. During the sessions the boy was asked to imagine himself on these adventures and then to picture himself sitting in the chair as Batman and Robin watched. Following therapy, the mother reported that the boy visited the dentist for a checkup without any resistance. No relapses or symptom substitutions were found in any of these cases in twelve-month, follow-up inquiries.

School phobias, including feigning illness, tantrums when taken to school, and simply refusing to go to school, have been treated by what may be called in vivo desensitization. One variation is exemplified by the therapist who took a nine-year-old boy for Sunday walks and discussed the enjoyable things and events related to school.[58] In later sessions, scheduled on regular school days, the therapist encouraged him to enter the school yard, then the school building, and finally the classroom. The length of time the boy spent in the classroom was increased little by little until he stayed the entire school day. Simultaneously, school attendance was reinforced with teacher and parental praise as well as with candy, comic books, etc. Gradually, the contrived contingencies were eliminated and the child was able to attend school on the basis of contingencies ordinarily associated with school attendance, namely, parent interest, teacher recognition for achievement, progress in school work, and positive social relationships with peers. In another variation, a mother served as change agent for her school-phobic, eight-year-old daughter, giving her prizes and candy for going to school and withholding treats and nonessential social interactions for staying at home.[59] In order to encourage the mother to carry out the details of the program, the therapist included mildly aversive consequences for her when her daughter resisted going to school. If, for example, the child failed to leave for school at the right time, the mother had to walk three miles to school with her. Within one month, the child was attending school regularly. A one-year follow-up showed no decrease in the child's school attendance or any indication of symptom substitution.

Sometimes the treatment of school-phobic children begins in the therapist's office and ends in the situation that is the problem. In one case, initial sessions with a first-grade boy consisted of doll play that was gradually changed to resemble his school setting.[73] Nonphobic responses to representations of his school setting were reinforced with candy. After he readily played school in the therapist's office, he was escorted to the school by the therapist and was reinforced for doing so. Here, too, the period at school was progressively lengthened, the contrived reinforcers were gradually removed (faded) and the child attended school in typical fashion.

Developing New Behavior Repertoires

Psychotherapy is frequently designed to develop new behavior, behavior as primitive as paying attention to relevant stimuli. Since such attending behavior is a prerequisite for learning social and academic skills, the establishment of eye contact with the therapist is often the first order of business. Although eye contact can be established by contingent adult attention, approval, and praise,[67] edibles are most commonly used. The therapist holds an edible object like a piece of sweet cereal near his eyes and says, "Look at me." As soon as the child looks toward the object, and by necessity at the therapist, he gives the "goody" to him. When the response is immediate and stable, the goody is gradually eliminated as a prompt, and the child responds to the simple request, "Look at me."

A program for strengthening attending behavior is often the initial step in language training.[62] After attending behavior has been established, other prerequisite behavior for language is introduced. For example, many language programs include extensive training in imitation. A five-and-a-half-year-old autistic child was taught to imitate various simple sounds by being reinforced with food, music, and activities for successive approximations of the sounds.[38] Using this shaping procedure, the therapist increased the response requirements for reinforcement until the child was saying recognizable words. The number of words he learned accelerated over sessions. In order to make the child's speech more functional, the therapist's verbalizations, which served as prompts, were gradually replaced with objects and printed words to which responses were required.

A child's ability to attend to another person and to imitate simple kinds of motor behavior is also important in the acquisition of other kinds of complex behavior. If a child can imitate words and actions, training is simpler. Instead of having to shape each new behavior through a series of successive approximations to the final response, the therapist can simply model (i.e., demonstrate) the new behavior and reinforce the child's imitative behavior. The new behavior is usually presented along with behavior already in the child's imitative repertoire. An example of this procedure is the research on developing, in autistic children, complex social and intellectual behavior, such as personal hygiene, nonverbal communication, writing, and playing games.[63] Since social imitation was lacking in these children's behavior repertoire, they were trained with the aid of prompts to imitate sixty simple kinds of motor behavior and were reinforced for their imitations. Once a child learned to imitate without prompts, new kinds of behavior were readily acquired.

The effectiveness of behavior therapy has been clearly apparent in the teaching of self-help skills to children who can attend and imitate. Bensberg, Colewell, and Cassell[8] prepared and evaluated individualized training programs for retarded children in feeding, grooming, toileting as well as following instructions. Typically, each program begins by building upon behavior the child already has, as determined in the initial assessment. If the assessment indicates that certain prerequisites for acquiring a particular skill are absent, training is instituted to develop the required prerequisites. By prompting and then reinforcing, usually with edibles, successive approximations of the desired behavior, the self-help skills are gradually acquired. This procedure ensures that all children associate learning with positive objects and events since the reinforcement contingencies are specified in terms of successive approximations of the desired behavior. In order to prevent dependence on edible reinforcers, the therapist systematically replaces the goodies with social reinforcers. At the beginning of the program, the therapist praises the child as she gives him each edible. After the target behavior has been acquired, the edible reinforcers are gradually discontinued and only social reinforcers are used. With each successive step in the program, longer and more complex behavior is required before a reinforcer is given. If a child fails at any point in the program, the therapist returns him to the preceding step. Monthly ratings on Doll's Vineland Social Maturity Scale[22] showed that the children trained by these programs made substantial improvements as compared to children who had not received this training.

Similar success was achieved with children who had even greater deficits in self-help skills: they were profoundly retarded and unable to feed themselves or use eating utensils.[9] In the initial step of the program, the therapist guided a spoonful of food into the child's mouth. As the child learned to coordinate his hand and arm movements, the therapist's assistance was gradually withdrawn. Negative contingencies were invoked for eating with the hands. For example, if a child failed to use his spoon, he was removed from the table for a period or was not permitted to complete the meal. These training programs, coupled with contingencies aimed at maintaining the newly acquired skills, resulted in marked improvement in mealtime behavior.

Bringing Behavior under Prosocial Stimulus Control

Many children come to the attention of therapists because they engage in certain normal behavior at the wrong time or in the wrong place. They fail to make certain kinds of discriminations that are important to them or to society. For example, an echolalic child's verbal behavior may be adequate, but it is not directed to people and hence cannot be reinforced in the usual way. In such a case, the therapeutic task is to help the child relate his behavior to appropriate circumstances. This is accomplished by discrimination training in which particular kinds of behavior are reinforced in the presence of certain stimuli and ignored or punished in the presence of other stimuli.

The classical features of an autistic child are his inappropriate use of speech and his lack of social responsiveness. These attributes pose serious problems for the therapist because in any treatment plan the child must be able to attend to instructions and demonstrations. The first task for the behavior therapist, working with children who do not relate appropriately to people, is, therefore, to establish the necessary prerequisite behavior. In some instances, he must begin by establishing eye contact and reducing incompatible, disruptive behavior. In others, he may proceed directly to training in stimulus control of verbal behavior. A therapeutic program designed to develop functional speech in echolalic children is an example of the latter approach.[84] In order to prevent the child's repeating what he heard, the therapist immediately prompted and reinforced the first word in the reply. If the child began repeating the word, the therapist quickly turned away (time-out) and removed the box of candy reinforcers. After imitative control was obtained, the therapist shifted from verbal prompts alone to prompts with objects and pictures, and the question, "What

is this?" Incorrect imitation of the question or echolalic speech resulted in the therapist's withdrawing the object or picture and turning away; correct responses were, of course, reinforced. After the child had learned to respond to the therapist's question by naming objects without prompts, he quickly acquired an extended vocabulary. The single words were then expanded to phrases and sentences. Using new skills in appropriate social situations was effected through initial prompting and immediate reinforcement. By gradually increasing the situations in which the child was required to use appropriate speech, the therapist increased the generalization of the acquired behavior. To extend generalization further, speech training was carried on in the home, with the parents serving as therapists.

Incontinence is another example of inappropriate stimulus control. Ellis[27] suggested that appropriate toileting behavior requires making a series of discriminations. The physiological cues generated by a full bladder or rectum, for example, evoke alerting responses that, in turn, stimulate (after training) approach responses toward a lavatory and elimination.

One technique for treating enuresis in the home involved training the child to retain liquids.[51,72] The child was instructed to let his parents know when he felt pressure and had to go to the bathroom. The parent told him to hold for five minutes and, after this period, gave him a cookie or favorite treat and then allowed him to go to the bathroom. The waiting period was gradually increased until the child could wait for thirty minutes before going to the bathroom. As the child learned to retain his urine during the day, there was a corresponding decrease in bed wetting. Of the thirty-one enuretic children who were treated, twenty-three showed significant improvement within twenty days. A nine-month, follow-up study showed no relapses or new forms of problem behavior.

The most comprehensive program for toilet training institutionalized, retarded children is based on precise programming of differential contingencies for voiding and elimination.[3]

Two monitoring devices were developed, one incorporated into training pants, the other installed in a toilet bowl. If a child wet or soiled his pants, a tone was sounded and the attendant immediately initiated a series of mildly aversive consequences. The child was told to shower and change his clothes, then to wash his soiled clothes, and to mop the area in which the "accident" had occurred. A one-hour time-out following each "accident" deprived him of drinks and candy and of the right to sit in his favorite chair. To increase the number of opportunities for the attendant to reinforce elimination into the commode, each child was given quantities of liquids during each hour and was taken to the toilet every thirty minutes. If elimination occurred, the sensing device turned on a signal and the child was reinforced with a big piece of candy and praise for his accomplishment. He was also reinforced once every five minutes he sat on the toilet and tried to eliminate. In this program, modeling procedures were also employed. Groups of children were trained simultaneously so that they could observe each other being reinforced for correct toileting. The outcome of the program was impressive: the frequency of accidents was reduced by 80 percent within seven days. For some individuals, training required only a few days.

Encopresis or involuntary defecation has not received as much attention as enuresis. Programs for such training generally consist of ignoring (nonreinforcing) "accidents" and positively reinforcing each occurrence of the desired behavior.[50,71,77] A variation involving contingency contracting, substituting aversive (instead of nonreinforcing) contingencies for "accidents," was carried out with a seventeen-year-old girl.[26] If daily checks revealed that she had soiled during the day, she was confined to her room for thirty minutes (contingency contracting involving time-out). If there were no signs of soiling, she was excused from the evening dishwashing chores (contingency contracting involving negative reinforcement). After fourteen weeks of this regime, soiling was no longer a problem. A three-month, follow-up evaluation revealed no relapses.

(Evaluation of Child-Behavior Therapy

We shall consider here the evaluation of child-behavior therapy as an issue separate from the references to the outcomes of treatment mentioned in the section on therapeutic procedures. If the frequency of achieving therapeutic goals in individual cases is taken as the criterion of effectiveness, child-behavior therapy, in its present stage of development, deserves a highly favorable rating. The same inference can probably be drawn on the basis of statistical findings, for it is likely that the number of unpublished negative outcomes is at least counterbalanced by the number of unpublished replications of positive outcomes. (It is well-known that editors are loathe to accept research reports that simply replicate findings.) This positive view of behavior therapy is not too surprising when one considers that the approach is anchored to empirical concepts and principles, and that the information derived from monitoring systems is used to correct technological inadequacies and deficiencies. But the true test of a therapeutic program is success in maintaining the desirable behavior. The usual way of evaluating the treatment effects of a brand of psychotherapy is to compare the number of "cures" it yields with the number of "cures" from an untreated control group and/or a group treated by another technique. When child-behavior therapy is evaluated by this type of experimental design, the findings have been inconclusive[38,88] and the result attributable to deficiencies in the conduct of the research.[74] Some studies are considered to have flaws in the way the groups were selected, others have defined "cure" in an ambiguous manner, etc.

The need for a more adequate procedure is clearly indicated[36] not only because the traditional group-design evaluation approach is cumbersome but also because it fails to take into account the effect of the post-treatment environment. Such an omission in an evaluation procedure may be acceptable for assessing the treatment of phenomena occurring in a relatively constant environment such as the human body. For example, the outcome of the medical treatment of a disease is usually evaluated in the context of a fairly stable organismic environment—the physiological functioning of anatomical structures and body systems. Even so, social and physical components of the environment are almost always taken into account, for it is well-known that under certain conditions, they can alter the physiological functioning of an individual. Ulcer and heart patients are notable instances. A disregard of the post-treatment environment may also be acceptable for evaluating the treatment of disorders resulting from Pavlovian conditioning because the exact recurrence of the behavior and environmental conditions or events that generated the problem is highly improbable (for example, a traumatic fall from a dock and a consequent water phobia). However, omission of an assessment of the post-treatment environment in a follow-up study is definitely not acceptable for evaluating the treatment of disorders involving operant (or instrumental) conditioning because the outcome effects depend upon *both* the behavior at the end of treatment *and* what happens (the sequence of response contingencies) in the post-treatment period. Available data suggest that if a child is returned to the environment that originally generated his problem behavior, without any change in that environment, his problem behavior soon reappears.[106] Evaluation of therapy dealing primarily with operant behavior, therefore, should be a two-stage procedure: (1) a comparison of a child's behavior at the beginning (base-line behavior) and end (terminal behavior) of therapy, and (2) a follow-up check that compares the child's behavior at the end of treatment (terminal behavior) with his behavior at the time of the check—*in light of* the child's reinforcement history since treatment. Failure to separate these two kinds of evaluations may lead to erroneous impressions about the adequacy or inadequacy of a treatment program involving operant or instrumental behavior.[13]

The two-stage evaluation design emphasizes the need for using therapeutic procedures that enhance the maintenance of outcome effects, such as conducting the therapy in vivo and incorporating maintenance techniques in programs carried out in office-type clinical settings. With regard to the latter, it has been observed that the effects of treatment in clinics are often specific to the therapist[79,80] or to the therapeutic setting.[29,103] The child may exhibit his newly acquired behavior when he is with the therapist and not in the presence of his parents, or in his classroom and not in his home. One way of broadening or extending treatment effects is to have a succession of therapists, a procedure used by Reiss and Redd[82] who reported that after a therapist had eliminated a nine-year-old girl's self-injurious behavior through time-out and positive reinforcement of incompatible behavior, a new therapist replaced him. At once, the girl resumed her self-injurious behavior and the new therapist reinstated the treatment contingencies used earlier. Upon successfully eliminating the self-injurious behavior, the second therapist was replaced by a third. Again the self-injurious behavior reappeared and again the therapist reinstated the treatment program with good results. A fourth and fifth therapist were introduced without any reappearances of the undesirable behavior. A similar technique used with retarded children[6] indicated that children who had experience with a number of tutors performed more satisfactorily and showed less disruptive behavior in the classroom than children who had only one tutor.

Treatment effects can be extended beyond the confines of the clinical situation in another way: by including in the treatment program techniques of self-management, self-control, or self-regulation. Basically, the training consists of training a child in behavioral techniques that can help him modify his own behavior. Typically, he is instructed to pinpoint the problem, to set realistic goals, to provide himself with a variety of contingencies that are likely to establish and maintain the newly acquired behavior, and to monitor his own progress. Thus far these techniques have been used mainly with preadolescents and adolescents. "The therapeutic methods of self-control have been used most frequently in attempts to reduce excessive eating, smoking, aggressive outbursts, or similar 'impulsive' behavior. However, application of self-reinforcement techniques for study habits, reduction of hyperactive behavior in children, increased social effectiveness, and reduction of masturbation and other sexual excesses have also been reported" [p. 25].[45]

With respect to extending treatment effects by conducting therapy *in vivo*, a study by Wahler[104] is pertinent. He treated two boys, five and eight years of age, who were disruptive and uncooperative at home and at school. His program consisting of differential application of time-out and positive social reinforcement was carried out only in the home. The results showed a dramatic improvement in the cooperative behavior of both boys at home, but not at school. Only after the same treatment was instituted in the school setting as well was there any change in the boys' school behavior. Similar results were obtained in a study in which a preschool child's generally aggressive behavior was reduced to a manageable level in the classroom, but not in the home until an intervention program that included the mother was carried out there.[118]

The two-stage evaluation procedure not only has implications for the development of therapeutic techniques but also for the method of assessing the post-treatment environment. The literature shows that there is a diversity of tools used for assessment purposes: interviews, paper-and-pencil personality tests, self-concept measures, projective techniques, patient check lists and self-ratings, therapists' rating scales, factor-analytic batteries, mood scales, personal-orientation inventories, self-regulation measures, and peer-rating scales. These evaluative procedures may be carried out by a professional worker (e.g., therapist, teacher, or social worker) by the child himself, and by members of the child's family. None of these techniques are adequate for assessing the post-treatment environment because they do not describe the environment in terms of its functional meaning to the child. Describing the environment in functional terms, it will be recalled, is simi-

lar to but not quite the same as describing it phenomenologically, that is, in the way a child "perceives" or "sees" things.[54] Knowing what the environment means to a child is essential in an approach that focuses on the functional or dynamic relationships between the behavior of a child and his environment, especially his social environment. Such information, which can be obtained only from observing the child in his home, school, and other settings, enables the evaluator to determine which conditions are supportive, neutral, or aversive for the child.[15] Research on development of assessment techniques of this sort is just getting under way.[85]

(Implications and Future Trends

The implications and future trends of child-behavior therapy are inextricably related. For that reason they are considered together.

With the continuation of basic behavioral research on both animals and children, and applied research on the treatment of children, the therapeutic techniques described here will inevitably undergo further refinements and extensions. This trend will lead not to a cookbook-type compilation of recipes, with problems indexed and standard treatment procedures set forth for each, but to a set of recommended procedures that can readily be altered to deal with the behavior of a particular child. Guidelines for modifying the recommended procedures (e.g., breaking down the program into smaller units, selecting more effective consequences, shifting from contingency application to contingency contracting, etc.) will, of course, be based primarily on the therapist's knowledge of applied behavior or learning principles.

Further improvement in therapeutic techniques is bound to affect the way in which initial assessment and monitoring procedures are conducted. It is likely that there will be progressively less dependence on standardized, norm-referenced, psychological tests in the initial assessment and progressively more dependence on informal, nonnormative measures (interviews, behavior inventories, direct observation of behavior, etc.) because the latter relate directly to pinpointing the problem and to identifying the environmental conditions that maintain it—essential information for planning an effective therapeutic program. Standardized tests will no doubt continue to serve the purposes for which they were intended; namely, selecting and classifying children for educational placement and making statistical predictions about their performance. The trend in monitoring assessment may well be in the direction of tracking multiple responses in order to keep abreast of some of the concomitant changes in nontreated behavior. For example, in monitoring a child's oppositional behavior to his mother, systematic measures might also be taken on his behavior toward his siblings. Such information would be helpful in planning the sequence of steps that constitute the complete therapeutic program.

Related to the changes in assessment procedures is the real possibility of a change in diagnostic categories. More and more child-behavior therapists are losing interest in conducting extensive evaluations to arrive at a formal diagnosis just for the "record." When they do resort to the use of traditional diagnostic terms, they do so as a means of communicating with others in a common, convenient shorthand. In the future, formal categories may well be replaced with precise behavioral descriptions of a child's problem and the environmental conditions supporting it.

Although often cumbersome, treatment *in vivo*, with a therapist as change agent or as consultant to a change agent, will probably be used with increasing frequency for several reasons: (1) it drastically reduces the transfer or maintenance problem; (2) it helps those involved in treatment to become more effective in dealing with the child on other occasions and in dealing with other children; and (3) it is consistent with the *Zeitgeist* of the psychological community. Accompanying this trend will be the development of effective training programs and techniques for parents, siblings, professionals, and paraprofessionals —all those who will be involved in treatment. Training of such groups in behavior-modification workshops presently follow the same format as that frequently used with child-behavior therapists. Lectures and reading assignments have been replaced by demonstrations of the procedures and supervised practice sessions with a child. In such real therapeutic situations, the trainee's skills can be assessed more carefully and accurately, and, consequently, training can be more sensitively tailored to each individual's learning characteristics. In addition to teaching specific techniques, these programs provide the trainee with an understanding of the basic principles underlying the procedures so that he can apply them to new problems.

As the treatment of children's behavior problems in vivo becomes more common, there will be, in all probability, an increasing concern about maintaining therapeutic change. Therapists and change agents will be more involved in arranging conditions to continue the program after the desirable behavior is established or to apply similar procedures to other behavior of the child. Thus, the teacher would have learned during training or consultation to persist in praising a child for his cooperative work long after his hostile-aggressive behaviors have been eliminated, and would recommend that other teachers do the same. Similarly, the mother would continue attending to her child's requests and ignoring his tantrum-like behavior.

Finally, the further development of child-behavior therapy should contribute to preventing the development of serious problems. This trend is expected to evolve from the fact that when parents, siblings, teachers, child-care workers, and others serve as change agents, they not only derive personal benefits but also acquire skills and knowledge that can be applied to other children. Thus, the teacher can apply behavior principles to manage her class to promote prosocial behavior, reduce aversive behavior, and encourage academic learning,[7] and the parent can help her child or children acquire self-help skills and initial moral behavior in ways that are mutually satisfying.

(Bibliography

1. ALLEN, K. E., B. M. HART, J. S. BUELL et al. "Effects of Social Reinforcement on Isolate Behavior of a Nursery School Child," *Child Dev.*, 35 (1964), 511–518.
2. AXLINE, V. M. *Play Therapy.* New York: Houghton Mifflin, 1947.
3. AZRIN, N. H. and R. M. FOXX. "A Rapid Method of Training the Institutionalized Retarded," *J. Appl. Behav. Anal.*, 4 (1971), 89–99.
4. BANDURA, A. *Principles of Behavior Modification.* New York: Holt, Rinehart and Winston, 1969.
5. BANDURA, A. and R. H. WALTERS. *Social Learning and Personality Development.* New York: Holt, Rinehart and Winston, 1965.
6. BARRETT, B. H. and J. E. McCORMACK. "Varied-Teacher Tutorials: A Tactic for Generating Credible Skills in Severely Retarded People," *Ment. Retard.*, 11 (1973), 14–19.
7. BECKER, W. C., S. ENGLEMAN, and D. R. THOMAS. *Teaching: A Course in Applied Psychology.* Chicago: Science Research Associates, 1971.
8. BENSBERG, G. J., C. N. COLWELL, and R. H. CASSELL. "Teaching the Profoundly Retarded Self-Help Activities by Behavior Shaping Techniques," *Am. J. Ment. Defic.*, 69 (1965), 674–679.
9. BERKOWITZ, S., P. J. SHERRY, and B. A. DAVIS. "Teaching Self-Feeding Skills to Profound Retardates Using Reinforcement and Fading Procedures," *Behav. Ther.*, 2 (1971), 62–67.
10. BIJOU, S. W. "Therapeutic Techniques with Children," in L. A. Pennington and I. A. Berg, eds., *An Introduction to Clinical Psychology*, 2nd ed., pp. 608–631. New York: Ronald, 1954.
11. BIJOU, S. W. and D. M. BAER. *Child Development: A Systematic and Empirical Theory*, Vol. 1. New York: Appleton-Century-Crofts, 1961.
12. ———. *Child Development: The Universal Stage of Infancy*, Vol. 2. New York: Appleton-Century-Crofts, 1965.
13. BIJOU, S. W. and J. A. GRIMM. "Behavioral Diagnosis and Assessment in Teaching Young Handicapped Children," in T. Thompson and W. S. Dockens, 3rd, eds., *Proceedings of the International Symposium on Behavior Modification.* New York: Academic, forthcoming.
14. BIJOU, S. W. and R. F. PETERSON. "The Psychological Assessment of Children: A Functional Analysis," in P. McReynolds, ed., *Advances in Psychological Assessment*, Vol. 2, pp. 63–78. Palo Alto: Science and Behavior Books, 1971.
15. BIJOU, S. W., R. F. PETERSON, F. R. HARRIS et al. "Methodology for Experimental Studies of Young Children in Natural Settings," *Psychol. Rec.*, 19 (1969), 177–210.
16. BIJOU, S. W. and H. N. SLOANE. "Therapeutic Techniques with Children," in L. A. Pennington and I. A. Berg, eds., *An Introduction to Clinical Psychology*, 3rd ed., pp. 652–684. New York: Ronald, 1966.
17. BORING, E. G. *A History of Experimental Psychology.* New York: Appleton-Century-Crofts, 1929.
18. BREGMAN, E. O. "An Attempt to Modify the Emotional Attitudes of Infants by the Conditioned Response Technique," *J. Genet. Psychol.*, 45 (1934), 169–198.
19. BUELL, J., P. STODDARD, R. HARRIS et al. "Collateral Social Development Accompanying Reinforcement of Outdoor Play in a Preschool Child," *J. Appl. Behav. Anal.*, 1 (1968), 167–173.
20. BURCHARD, J. D. "Systematic Socialization: A Programmed Environment for the Habilitation of Antisocial Retardates," *Psychol. Rec.*, 17 (1967), 461–467.
21. BURCHARD, J. D. and F. BARRERA. "An Analysis of Time-out and Response Cost in a Programmed Environment," *J. Appl. Behav. Anal.*, 5 (1972), 271–282.
22. DOLL, E. A. *The Measurement of Social Competence.* New York: Educational Publ., 1948.
23. DOLLARD, J. and N. E. MILLER. *Personality and Psychotherapy.* New York: McGraw-Hill, 1950.
24. DOUBROS, S. G. and G. J. DANIELS. "An Experimental Approach to the Reduction of Overactive Behavior," *Behav. Res. Ther.*, 4 (1966), 251–258.

25. DUNLAP, K. *Habits: Their Making and Unmaking*. New York: Liveright, 1932.

26. EDELMAN, R. I. "Operant Conditioning Treatment of Encopresis," *J. Behav. Ther. Exp. Psychiatry*, 2 (1971), 71–73.

27. ELLIS, N. R. "Toilet Training the Severely Defective Patient: An S-R Reinforcement Analysis," *Am. J. Ment. Defic.*, 68 (1963), 98–103.

28. ENGLISH, H. B. "Three Cases of the 'Conditioned Fear Response'," *J. Abnorm. Social Psychol.*, 24 (1929), 221–225.

29. ETZEL, B. C. and J. L. GEWIRTZ. "Experimental Modification of Caretaker-Maintained High-Rate Operant Crying in a 6- and a 20-Week-Old Infant: Extinction of Crying with Reinforcement of Eye Contact and Smiling," *J. Exp. Child Psychol.*, 5 (1967), 303–317.

30. EYSENCK, H. J. *Behavior Therapy and the Neuroses*. Oxford: Pergamon, 1960.

31. FERSTER, C. B. and M. K. DEMYER. "The Development of Performances in Autistic Children in an Automatically Controlled Environment," *J. Chronic Dis.*, 13 (1961), 312–345.

32. FULLER, P. R. "Operant Conditioning of a Vegetative Human Organism," *Am. J. Psychol.*, 62 (1949), 587–590.

33. GELFAND, D. M. and D. P. HARTMANN. "Behavior Therapy With Children: A Review of Research Methodology," *Psychol. Bull.*, 69 (1968), 204–215.

34. GROUP FOR THE ADVANCEMENT OF PSYCHIATRY. *Psychopathological Disorders in Childhood: Theoretical Considerations and a Proposed Classification*. New York: Group for the Advancement of Psychiatry.

35. HARRIS, F. R., M. K. JOHNSTON, C. S. KELLEY et al. "Effects of Positive Social Reinforcement on Regressed Crawling of a Nursery School Child," *J. Educ. Psychol.*, 55 (1964), 35–41.

36. HARTMANN, D. P. "Some Neglected Issues in Behavior Modification with Children." Paper presented at 6th Annu. Meet. Am. Assoc. Behav. Ther., New York, Oct., 1972.

37. HAWKINS, R. P., R. F. PETERSON, E. SCHWEID et al. "Behavior Therapy in the Home: Amelioration of Problem-Parent Child Relations with the Parent in a Therapeutic Role," *J. Exp. Child Psychol.*, 4 (1966), 99–107.

38. HEWETT, F. M. "Teaching Speech to an Autistic Child through Conditioning," *Am. J. Orthopsychiatry*, 35 (1965), 927–936.

39. HOLMES, F. B. "An Experimental Investigation of a Method of Overcoming Children's Fears," *Child Dev.*, 7 (1936), 6–30.

40. HOMME, L., A. P. CSANYI, M. A. GONZALES et al. *How to Use Contingency Contracting in the Classroom*. Champaign, Ill.: Research Press, 1969.

41. HULL, C. L. *Principles of Behavior: An Introduction of Behavior Theory*. New York: Appleton-Century-Crofts, 1943.

42. JONES, H. E. "The Conditioning of Overt Emotional Responses," *J. Educ. Psychol.*, 22 (1931), 127–130.

43. JONES, M. C. "The Elimination of Children's Fears," *J. Exp. Psychol.*, 7 (1924), 382–390.

44. ———. "A Laboratory Study of Fear: The Case of Peter," *Pedigog. Semin.*, 31 (1924), 308–315.

45. KANFER, F. H. "Behavior Modification—An Overview," in C. E. Thoresen, ed., *Behavior Modification in Education*, pp. 3–40. The 72nd Yearbook of the National Society for the Study of Education. Chicago: University of Chicago Press, 1973.

46. KANFER, F. H. and J. S. PHILLIPS. "A Survey of Current Behavior Therapies and a Proposed Classification," in C. M. Franks, ed., *Behavior Therapy: Appraisal and Status*, pp. 445–475. New York: McGraw-Hill, 1969.

47. ———. *Learning Foundations of Behavior Therapy*. New York: Wiley, 1970.

48. KANFER, F. H. and G. SASLOW. "Behavioral Diagnosis," in C. M. Franks, ed., *Behavior Therapy: Appraisal and Status*, pp. 417–444. New York: McGraw-Hill, 1969.

49. KANNER, L. *Child Psychiatry*, 2nd ed. Springfield, Ill.: Charles C. Thomas, 1948.

50. KEEHN, J. D. "Brief Case-Report: Reinforcement Therapy of Incontinence," *Behav. Res. Ther.*, 2 (1965), 239.

51. KIMMEL, H. D. and E. KIMMEL. "An Instrumental Conditioning Method for the Treatment of Enuresis," *J. Behav. Ther. Exp. Psychiatry*, 1 (1970), 121–124.

52. KIRBY, F. D. and H. C. TOLER. "Modification of Preschool Isolate Behavior: A Case Study," *J. Appl. Behav. Anal.*, 3 (1970), 309–314.

53. KUHN, T. S. *The Structure of Scientific*

Revolutions. Chicago: University of Chicago Press, 1962.

54. LAING, R. D. *The Politics of Experience*. New York: Ballantine, 1967.

55. LAZARUS, A. A. "The Elimination of Children's Phobias by Deconditioning," *Med. Proc.* (S. Africa), 5 (1959), 261–265.

56. ———. *Behavior Therapy and Beyond*. New York: McGraw-Hill, 1971.

57. LAZARUS, A. A. and A. ABRAMOVITZ. "The Use of 'Emotive Imagery' in the Treatment of Children's Phobias," *J. Ment. Sci.*, 108 (1962), 191–195.

58. LAZARUS, A. A., G. C. DAVISON and D. A. POLEFKA. "Classical and Operant Factors in the Treatment of a School Phobia," *J. Abnor. Psychol.*, 70 (1965), 225–229.

59. LEVENTHAL, T., G. WEINBERGER, R. J. STANDER et al. "Therapeutic Strategies with School Phobics," *Am. J. Orthopsychiatry*, 37 (1967), 64–70.

60. LINDSLEY, O. R. "Operant Conditioning Methods Applied to Research in Chronic Schizophrenia," *Psychiatr. Res. Rep.*, 5 (1956), 118–139.

61. LORR, M., C. J. KLETT, and D. M. McNAIR. *Syndromes of Psychosis*. New York: Macmillan, 1963.

62. LOVAAS, O. I., J. P. BERKERICH, B. F. PERLOFF et al. "Acquisition of Imitative Speech by Schizophrenic Children," *Science*, 151 (1966), 705–706.

63. LOVAAS, O. I., L. FRITAS, K. NELSON et al. "The Establishment of Imitation and Its Use for the Development of Complex Behavior in Schizophrenic Children," *Behav. Res. Ther.*, 5 (1967), 171–181.

64. LOVAAS, O. I., B. SCHAEFFER, and J. Q. SIMMONS. "Building Social Behavior in Autistic Children by Use of Electric Shock," *J. Exp. Res. Pers.*, 2 (1965), 99–109.

65. LOVAAS, O. I. and J. Q. SIMMONS. "Manipulation of Self-Destruction in Three Retarded Children," *J. Appl. Behav. Anal.*, 2 (1969), 143–157.

66. McCOLLOM, I. N. "Psychological Classics: Older Journal Articles frequently Cited Today," *Am. Psychol.*, 28 (1973), 363–365.

67. McCONNEL, O. L. "Control of Eye Contact in an Autistic Child," *J. Child Psychol. Psychiatry*, 8 (1967), 249–255.

68. MOORE, W. E. "A Conditioned Reflex Study of Stuttering," *J. Speech Disord.*, 3 (1938), 163–183.

69. MORGAN, J. J. B. and F. J. WITMER. "The Treatment of Enuresis by the Conditioned Reaction Technique," *J. Genet. Psychol.*, 55 (1939), 59–65.

70. MOWRER, O. H. and W. M. MOWRER. "Enuresis: A Method for Its Study and Treatment," *Am. J. Orthopsychiatry*, 8 (1938), 436–459.

71. NEALE, P. H. "Behavior Therapy and Encopresis in Children," *Behav. Res. Ther.*, 1 (1963), 139–149.

72. PASCHALIS, A. P., H. D. KIMMEL, and E. KIMMEL. "Further Study of Diurnal Instrumental Conditioning in the Treatment of Enuresis Nocturna," *J. Behav. Ther. Exp. Psychiatry*, 3 (1972), 253–256.

73. PATTERSON, G. R. "A Learning Theory Approach to the Treatment of the School Phobic Child," in L. Ullman and L. Krasner, eds., *Case Studies in Behavior Modification*, pp. 279–284. New York: Holt, Rinehart & Winston, 1965.

74. PAUL, G. L. "Behavior Modification Research: Design and Tactics," in C. M. Franks, ed., *Behavior Therapy: Appraisal and Status*, pp. 29–62. New York: McGraw-Hill, 1969.

75. PAVLOV, I. P. *Conditioned Reflexes*. London: Oxford University Press, 1927.

76. ———. "Neurosis in Man and Animals," *JAMA*, 99 (1932), 1012–1013.

77. PETERSON, D. R. and P. LONDON. "Neobehavioristic Psychotherapy; Quasi Hypnotic Suggestion and Multiple Reinforcement in the Treatment of a Case of Post-infantile Dyscopresis," *Psychol. Rec.*, 14 (1964), 469–474.

78. QUAY, H. C. "Patterns of Aggression, Withdrawal, and Immaturity," in H. C. Quay and J. S. Werry, eds., *Psychopathological Disorders of Childhood*, pp. 1–29. New York: Wiley, 1972.

79. REDD, W. H. "Generalization of Adults' Stimulus Control of Children's Behavior," *J. Exp. Child Psychol.*, 9 (1970), 286–296.

80. REDD, W. H. and J. S. BIRNBRAUER. "Adults as Discriminative Stimulative for Different Reinforcement Contingencies with Retarded Children," *J. Exp. Psychol.*, 7 (1969), 440–447.

81. REESE, H. W. and L. P. LIPSITT. *Experimental Child Psychology*. New York: Academic, 1970.

82. REISS, S. and W. H. REDD. "Suppression of

Screaming Behavior in an Emotionally Disturbed, Retarded Child," Paper Presented at the Am. Psychol. Conv., Miami, 1970.

83. RISLEY, T. R. "The Effects and Side Effects of Punishing the Autistic Behaviors of a Deviant Child," *J. Appl. Behav. Anal.*, 1 (1968), 21–34.

84. RISLEY, T. and M. WOLF. "Establishing Functional Speech in Echolalic Children," *Behav. Res. Ther.*, 5 (1967), 73–88.

85. ROBINS, L. M. "Follow-up Studies of Behavior Disorders in Children," in H. C. Quay and J. S. Werry, eds., *Psychopathological Disorders of Childhood*, pp. 414–450. New York: Wiley, 1972.

86. ROSENHAN, D. L. "On Being Sane in Insane Places," *Science*, 179 (1973), 250–258.

87. Ross, A. O. *Behavior Disorders in Children.* New York: General Learning, 1971.

88. ———. "Behavior Therapy," in H. C. Quay and J. S. Werry, eds., *Psychopathological Disorders in Childhood*, pp. 273–315. New York: Wiley, 1972.

89. Ross, D. M., S. A. Ross, and T. EVANS. "The Modification of Extreme Social Withdrawal by Modeling and Guided Participation," *J. Behav. Ther. Exp. Psychiatry*, 2 (1971), 273–279.

90. SEARS, R. R. "Child Psychology," in W. Dennis, ed., *Current Trends in Psychology*, pp. 50–74. Pittsburgh: University of Pittsburgh Press, 1947.

91. SEARS, R. R., E. E. MACCOBY, and H. LEVIN. *Patterns of Child Rearing.* Evanston, Ill.: Row Peterson, 1957.

92. SHERMAN, J. A. and D. M. BAER. "Appraisal of Operant Therapy Techniques with Children and Adults," in C. M. Franks, ed., *Behavior Therapy: Appraisal and Status*, pp. 192–219. New York: McGraw-Hill, 1969.

93. SKINNER, B. F. *The Behavior of Organisms.* New York: Appleton-Century-Crofts, 1938.

94. ———. *Science and Human Behavior.* New York: Macmillan, 1953.

95. ———. *Contingencies of Reinforcement: A Theoretical Analysis.* New York: Appleton-Century-Crofts, 1969.

96. SLOANE, H. N., M. K. JOHNSTON, and S. W. BIJOU. "Successive Modification of Aggressive Behavior and Aggressive Fantasy Play by Management of Contingencies," *J. Child Psychol. Psychiatry*, 8 (1967), 217–226.

97. STRAUGHAN, J. H. "Treatment with Child and Mother in the Playroom," *Behav. Res. Ther.*, 2 (1964), 37–41.

98. STRUPP, H. H. and A. E. BERGIN. "Some Empirical and Conceptual Bases for Coordinated Research in Psychotherapy: A Critical Review of Issues, Trends, and Evidence," *Int. J. Psychiatry*, 7 (1969), 18–90.

99. SZASZ, T. S. "The Myth of Mental Illness," *Am. Psychol.*, 15 (1960), 113–118.

100. TATE, B. F. and G. S. BAROFF. "Aversive Control of Self-Injurious Behavior in a Psychotic Boy," *Behav. Res. Ther.*, 4 (1966), 281–287.

101. THORNDIKE, E. L. *The Fundamentals of Learning.* New York: Teachers College, Columbia University, 1932.

102. VUEKLICH, R. and D. F. HAKE. "Reduction of Dangerously Aggressive Behavior in a Severely Retarded Resident through a Combination of Positive Reinforcement Procedures," *J. Appl. Behav. Anal.*, 4 (1971), 215–225.

103. WAHLER, R. G. "Setting Generality: Some Specific and General Effects of Child Behavior Therapy," *J. Appl. Behav. Anal.*, 2 (1969), 239–246.

104. ———. "Oppositional Children: A Quest for Parental Reinforcement Control," *J. Appl. Behav. Anal.*, 2 (1969), 159–170.

105. WAHLER, R. G. and W. H. CORMIER. "The Ecological Interview: A First Step in Out-Patient Child Behavior Therapy," *J. Behav. Ther. Exp. Psychiatry*, 1 (1970), 279–289.

106. WALKER, H. M. and N. K. BUCKLEY. "Programming Generalization and Maintenance Treatment Effects Across Time and Across Settings," *J. Appl. Behav. Anal.*, 5 (1972), 209–224.

107. WARREN, A. B. and R. H. BROWN. "Conditioned Operant Response Phenomena in Children," *J. Gen. Psychol.*, 28 (1943), 181–207.

108. WATSON, J. B. *Behavior: An Introduction to Comparative Psychology.* New York: Holt, 1914.

109. ———. *Behaviorism*, rev. ed. Chicago: University of Chicago Press, 1930.

110. WATSON, J. B. and R. A. RAYNER. "Conditioned Emotional Reactions," *J. Exp. Psychol.*, 3 (1920), 1–4.

111. WETZEL, R. "Use of Behavioral Techniques in a Case of Compulsive Stealing," *J. Con-*

sult. Psychol., 30 (1966), 367–374.

112. WOLF, M. M., E. L. PHILLIPS, and D. L. FIXEN. "The Teaching Family: A New Model for the Treatment of Deviant Child Behavior in the Community," in S. W. Bijou and E. Ribes-Inesta, eds., *Behavior Modification: Issues and Extensions*, pp. 51–62. New York: Academic, 1972.

113. WOLF, M. N., T. RISLEY, and H. MEES. "Application of Operant Conditioning Procedures to the Behavior Problems of an Autistic Child," *Behav. Res. Ther.*, 1 (1964), 305–312.

114. WOLPE, J. *Psychotherapy by Reciprocal Inhibition*. Stanford: Stanford University Press, 1958.

115. ———. *The Practice of Behavior Therapy.* New York: Pergamon, 1969.

116. YARROW, M. R., J. D. CAMPBELL, and R. V. BURTON. *Child Rearing*. San Francisco: Jossey-Bass, 1968.

117. YATES, A. J. *Behavior Therapy.* New York: Wiley, 1970.

118. ZEILBERGER, J., S. E. SAMPEN, and H. N. SLOANE, JR. "Modification of a Child's Problem Behaviors in the Home with the Mother as Therapist," *J. Appl. Behav. Anal.*, 1 (1968), 47–53.

119. ZIGLER, E. and L. PHILLIPS. "Psychiatric Diagnosis: A Critique," *J. Abnorm. Psychol.*, 63 (1961), 607–618.

120. ZUBIN, J. "Classification of the Behavior Disorders," *Annu. Rev. Psychol.*, 18 (1967), 373–406.

CHAPTER 17

GROUPS FOR PERSONAL CHANGE: NEW AND NOT-SO-NEW FORMS

Morton A. Lieberman

THE CURRENTLY fashionable practices in the use of groups for changing people present a real dilemma for traditional mental-health practitioners. The constant appearance of new ideas, the burgeoning variety of settings in which people-changing programs occur, and the articulation of goals that resemble but do not completely overlap those espoused in traditional mental-health settings have made it difficult for most to place the newer forms in a proper perspective in relation to the older ones. The litany of new labels— Bioenergetics, Gestalt, Transactional Analysis, Confrontation Therapy, Marathon, Encounter, Sensory Awareness, T-Groups, and so forth— do not constitute a reasonable road map to diminish confusion. The leadership behavior of the proponents of the various positions suggests that some are primarily analytic and interpretive; others see the management of

group forces as their distinctive function; still others almost exclusively see their role to be to offer instructional (often nonverbal) exercises. Some among the new breed of people changers believe passionately in the healing qualities of group-generated love; others believe just as passionately in the curative powers of hate, seeing the basic stuff of change as stemming from the experience of primary rage. Some depend solely on talk therapy; others use music, lights, and clench of human bodies.

An attempt to reduce the confusion by organizing the array of forms and techniques according to the background, education, or professional disciplines of those who purvey group, people-changing services would be of little help. Those who have made themselves available to lead such groups may have been prepared by long years of training in prestigious professional institutions, by participation in a two-week institute, or purely by personal commitment.

Nor would a sense of order stem from examining the location of such activities. Many personal change-oriented groups are to be found in traditional help-giving institutions, such as mental hospitals, schools, or social agencies; some take place in the offices of mental-health practitioners in private practice. Many are found in growth centers—a new institution specifically formed for conducting such groups. Church basements, dormitories, and living rooms have also become the scene of people-changing groups.

But what of the goals of the groups? Do they not suggest principles of organization into varying types? They may vary all the way from attempts to reduce juvenile delinquency to attempts at reducing weight. Occasionally they may seek only to entertain, to "turn-on," to give experiences in joy. More frequently they involve instrumental goals of personal change—goals at times couched in language familiar to the mental-health profession, but more often described in terms that appear to go beyond the traditional goals of mental-health professionals.

Albeit there have been some important exceptions, by and large the mental-health profession has responded to these new developments, and to its own attendant confusion, with what can best be described in defense-mechanism language. One fairly typical response has been to deny the relevance of the new forms of group therapeutics for the mental-health field; another, to use verbal aggression when their presence could no longer be ignored. On the other hand, some traditionally trained mental-health practitioners have sought to identify with the aggressor and to internalize, at least partially, the rhetoric and techniques cast forth by the newer apostles.

The present chapter is designed to examine the variety in types of people-changing groups, both new and old. We shall look first at what differences characterize the more extreme examples of new and old forms, then, at some historical and contemporary forces that may explain why, despite the vigorous growth in

group technologies, group treatment remains a field beclouded by considerable conceptual fuzziness. Finally, we shall attempt to examine what are the critical practical and theoretical issues that need solution before a truly integrated view of the entire enterprise of people-changing groups can be achieved.

(The "Old" and the "New"

The incredible difficulty and complexity inherent in providing help to one's fellow humans has always produced a multitude of ideas about how best to accomplish this task. Determining the means to help humans overcome their sufferings and frailties can never be solely a scientifically derived decision, for it not only involves questions of technique or efficiency but also confronts us with the ultimate metaphysical questions regarding what is man's disease and what the end point of his quest. What man needs or ought to become are primarily issues of value rather than science. Yet, the practice of psychotherapy must proceed on assumptions regarding the answers to such questions about the ends of life for man. Now, in this arena of choosing among ultimate human values there have been as many answers offered as there have been philosophers to pose the questions. No wonder then that innovation has been rampant in psychotherapy, that the burgeoning of forms has been the rule rather than the exception; no wonder that the push to create distinctive responses to man's complaints has predominated over the effort to build integrative theories of personal change.

Does the variety of activities surrounding the use of groups for people-changing represent useful distinctions, or are they labels much like different brands of soap that encase the same ingredients? To examine this question more minutely, it may be helpful to visualize an example or two of what superficially appear to be extremely different forms of conducting the people-changing enterprise. To observe the initial session of a traditional group therapy session, for example, would be to experience something like this:

About nine people file into a room slowly, tentatively. Each has seen only one other person in the room before—the therapist, a week earlier in a diagnostic interview. Some appear reluctant, some enthusiastic, but all have come to this first meeting with at least the willingness to go along with the therapist's belief that the group can be useful to them. They sit in a circle, quiet and expectant. Their posture seems anxious. What will go on here? What can go on here? What will the therapist do? Several in the group have had previous psychotherapy. One woman begins the interaction by describing the disappointments she has experienced in previous treatments. A note of desperation and near panic is discernible in the responses of others to her wail of self-negation and helplessness. Sympathetic offerings of similar tales of woe are heard from various people in the room. From time to time the therapist comments, pointing out the fearful expectations of the various group members.

Underneath the "stories" and histories offered by various members, the therapist "hears" the patients asking each other a set of questions only hinted at in what they are saying. And underneath these questions about others in the room lies still another set having to do with the person himself. Why did you come? What are your hopes? What forms does your "illness" take? Do you feel that this may do me any good at all? Are you as sick as I? Am I as sick as you? How strange, perhaps even insane, is the arrangement whereby I come to a group of neurotics to get better. Above all what is the "doctor" over there planning to do for me? I don't like people—why must I be here? Who are these others and what have I to do with them?

Thus, group therapy begins. The patients begin an experience in treatment that they may understandably feel violates expectations they bring from their experience in other doctor–patient relationships. Often group-therapy patients cannot see what good it will do an unhappy neurotic person to share his "problems" with other neurotic sufferers. Is it enough to reassure him, as some therapists indeed believe, that a "problem shared is a problem helped" or to provide a context founded on the assumption that misery not only loves but is relieved by company? What of the therapist? Will he, by virtue of some rare professional training and intuitive attributes, be able to understand, diagnose, and change the troublesome personality patterns of a lifetime? And, at that, of a roomful of people simultaneously? The therapist obviously expects something useful to come from the interactions of these people, but how does he see the members to be of use to each other when he remains silent and passive so long? What does he expect will happen?

At the other end of the group-treatment continuum we can imagine another group of people temporarily migrating to a growth center. Their arrival is noisier, more buoyant, more playful; they are robed in vacation garb, their talk is free and more reminiscent of the first evening of summer camp than the still, anxious scene of the group-therapy session. They are likely to have a speaking knowledge of Abraham Maslow, C. Rogers, Eric Berne, and F. S. Perls, and of the latest people-changing procedures. They express their desire for change freely and seem eager to get to know one another. They seem hardly able to await the morning's beginning; if some appear a bit anxious, others are enthusiastic about the drama that will unfold. All know in general what they can expect to happen but seem restless to generate the specific emotions and events that will form the content of their shared experience.

What will the leader, whom they have never met, be like? What will he do or expect of them? In the back of their minds is an accumulation of images based on what they have heard from friends and the popular press —images that are mixed with desires to become changed people. Will it work for me? What about the others? Will they really get to know me? Can I trust them? Will they help me?

They do not have long to wait: the leader begins with an explosion of his inner feelings. He may be sleepy this morning, he may not have wanted to come, he may look around and find the group full of "unattractive people" and "tell it like it is" without pausing. On the other hand, he may express his total positive regard for all and quickly exhibit a readiness to accept any behavior expressed. He may then launch into a set of instructions, perhaps suggesting that "all of you look so 'up tight' that we ought to loosen up and begin by playing a childhood game."

The images evoked by these two settings certainly suggest that the people-changing business in our society today has diverse assumptions, allegiances, and expectations to the point that it might appear sheer folly to consider them under the same rubric.

Let us examine the underlying philosophy, technology, goals, and client types of both forms, and determine points of similarity as well as difference that may have become confused and indistinct in much of the current conversation over the relative merits of the "old" versus the "new."

Although the advent of the "newer therapies" has served to magnify the conceptual confusion surrounding the use of groups for people-changing, the origins of the current dilemmas have their roots in the historical development of the field of group psychotherapy. The use of groups for systematically helping individuals in distress is of relatively recent origin in modern mental-health practice. It is perhaps helpful to recall, however, that small groups have always served as important healing agents; from the beginning of recorded history, group forces have been used to inspire hope, increase morale, offer strong emotional support, induce a sense of serenity and confidence in the benevolence of the universe, thus counteracting many psychic and bodily ills. Religious healers have always relied heavily on group forces, but when healing passed from the priestly to the medical profession, the conscious use of group forces fell into a decline concomitant with the increasing sanctity of the doctor–patient relationship.

The strangeness experienced by many seekers of psychiatric help, when confronted with the help-giving conditions of groups, is the resultant of a complex process affecting both those who seek the help as well as those who give it. The development of psychiatry as an entrenched part of modern medicine was in part predicated on the idea that "scientific medicine" must at all costs distinguish itself from healing that stemmed from nonscientific traditions. Modern Western psychiatry was even more plagued than other branches of medicine with the need to become "scientific." In its beginnings, the medical treatment of psychological problems required, for its legitimization as a branch of medical science, a clear differentiation between its methods and those that preceded it in non-Western societies, where highly developed group-based techniques were used for curing psychological illness within the framework of the family, groups of similar sufferers, the village, or the religious community. This association of "prescientific" therapies with group forms perhaps influenced psychiatry away from utilization of group techniques.

In Western culture, until the recent advent of the new group therapies, it has been expected that personal help will be given by one person—it may be the corner bartender, a personal friend, or a professional such as a lawyer, doctor, or a clergyman—but what is important is the expectation that the context in which it will be rendered will be private, intimate, and exclusive. Even in such congregate bodies as the family or the church, it is generally assumed that personal help will be offered and received in a private, one-to-one relationship, not through the congregate as a whole. The historical roots of modern psychiatry and the general Western cultural context in the first half of the twentieth century in which these roots were dug did not, in other words, create conditions suitable for the flourishing growth of group-based healing technologies.

In the early 1900s, Joseph Pratt, a Boston internist, organized classes for tubercular patients: "The class meeting is a pleasant social hour for members . . . made up as a membership of widely different races and different sexes, they have a common bond in a common disease. A fine spirit of camaraderie has developed. They never discuss their symptoms and are almost invariably in good spirits . . ." Pratt's therapy had many similarities to current-day inspirational group psychotherapy: he hoped to overcome the pessimism of the patients, to discourage neurotic secondary gains from illness, and to encourage self-confidence.

Isolated individuals in the early 1900s reported similar sets of experiences to those of Pratt. In Europe, Alfred Adler established guidance centers that used group concepts in treating working-class patients. An early and important influence in the development of group psychotherapy was the use of the healing group by Jacob L. Moreno, who is best known for his development of psychodrama. The analogies of Moreno's approach to the healing groups described in anthropological literature are impressive. The patient is provided the opportunity to express himself freely through drama, trying the role of himself or others he feels significantly related to his present problems. In this technique, scenes from the patient's past are often enacted, employing other persons as auxiliary egos who articulate feelings, moods, responses, and so on that may not be evident to the patient himself—a kind of Greek chorus orchestrated by the therapist. The work of Trigant L. Burrows was an important, but unfortunately unrecognized, influence in the use of groups. A psychoanalyst himself, Burrows became dissatisfied with the emphasis psychoanalysis placed on the individual, an emphasis that he felt excluded examination of social forces. In the early twenties, he initiated the use of the group context for the analysis of behavioral disorders in relation to social forces and coined the term "group analysis" to describe the treatment setting.

Thus, the techniques characteristic of current group-treatment practices were clearly evident in the first quarter of the century. The inspirational character of Pratt's groups has many modern counterparts in the self-help movement, such as Alcoholics Anonymous; Recovery, Inc.; and Weight Watchers. The employment of the expressive part of the person through dramatization as part of the curative process forms a major component of many current group methodologies. Finally, the use of the social context provided by the group for analysis via a psychoanalytic framework is still very visible as a major direction in current practice. By and large, however, the efforts of men such as these were isolated efforts: their predominantly pragmatic concerns did not lead them or others to explore the conceptual grounds underlying the use of groups to provide therapeutic benefits.

Rather, the often competing concepts of individual psychotherapy have, oddly enough, been the main source of theory underlying various forms of group treatment in current use, a fact that goes far to explain why the degree of conceptual morass in contemporary theorizing about group-treatment practice is as broad as the degree of disagreement regarding principles of individual psychotherapy. All major schools of psychotherapy (with the exception of the Jungian whose philosophical individualism is antithetical to the use of groups) have generated their counterpart in group psychotherapy. More often than not the counterparts of dyadically generated theories of psychotherapy have had a haphazard growth pattern, developed more out of necessity and accident than out of systematic theoretical explanation. Individuals trained in the particular school of therapy conduct groups using their fundamental orientation from individual therapy. Often techniques and concepts have been adapted to the multiperson situation with little formal thought given to the consequences that may be generated by the addition of multiperson social forces to the treatment context. The so-called "new therapies" share a similar history. Although some of the newer ideas were generated out of a movement away from a psychoanalytic view of pathology toward more humanistic or existential theories of personality, both the old and the new are similar in that they stem from theories of individual psychotherapy, not from concepts regarding the influence of the group on processes of individual change. Thus, despite a richness of technique and a tenuous commitment to their pragmatic beginnings, both new and old group-treatment forms share a common ailment—an inappropriate, and consequently barren and confusing, conceptual base. The dyadically oriented intellectual legacy of group treatment has produced a macabre scene. The intellectual battles over the competing ideas offered up by various systems of individual psychotherapy are reenacted in the new group arenas without even a pause to ask whether the concepts being questioned even have relevance to groups.

Some Distinctive Aspects of the "New Forms"

A major theme of many of the new forms of personal-growth groups has been a decided move away from defining individuals who need help as patients who are psychologically ill. The boundary lines between what have for nearly a century been defined as the separate provinces of psychiatry, as opposed to educational endeavors, have become so blurred that the newer forms of people-changing groups are not viewed as simply endeavors to aid those who would classically be described as having psychiatric problems. Certainly the ancient stigmas attached to psychiatric problems have been reduced in importance and the old barriers to seeking out help have been considerably lowered. Clinics or psychiatric consultation rooms no longer are the exclusive settings addressed to changing individuals through group participation. Churches, living rooms, and growth centers specially developed to offer people changing have become major settings for people-changing groups. It seems reasonable to suppose that the diversity of groups and the diversity of settings would bring forth many consumers who heretofore had not sought out psychiatric aid. It also seems quite reasonable to assume that such settings would elicit distinctive expectations and individuals entering these newer people-changing settings might hope to achieve goals different from the traditional psychotherapy patients.

Unfortunately, few data are available even to begin to describe the differences produced in people entering a system for help in which one does not define himself as a patient. Some recently developed information, however,[14] suggests that perhaps the newer therapies that emphasize growth and the development of human potential may not be attracting a different population from that engaged in psychotherapy. In a survey of 500 users of human potential growth centers, eight out of ten reported they had previous or simultaneous psychotherapy. It appears, in other words, to be the same group of middle-class individuals making up the bulk of private practice psychotherapy in this country who are also the participants in human-potential growth centers. Life-stress scores[16] of the growth-center participants were significantly higher than Uhlenhuth obtained in a study of a random sample of normal adults,[22] and resembled the levels of high stress characteristic of psychiatric patients. A similar finding was obtained from symptom scales (Symptom Distress Check List);[12] those who were about to go to growth centers again resembled patients and had significantly more symptoms than Uhlenhuth's population. Finally, self-stated goals for attending growth centers emphasized instrumental, help-seeking issues ("to solve some long-term, personal hang-ups, to deal with current life problems," and so forth) rather than the sort of hedonistic or existential goals frequently expressed as the purposes of membership in the newer types of humanistic groups. Thus, although the symbols of growth, of expanding awareness, and so on, surrounding many of the "new" groups for "normals" sound different, it is difficult to evaluate how closely these symbols are incorporated into the actual, operating functions of the groups. The findings do not support a belief that the newer humanistically oriented groups constitute an alternative pathway for people who would not seek out mental-health settings.

But if the clientele overlap between the new and the old, may they still perhaps be distinguished by the way they go about the business of changing people? What are the unique characteristics of the new forms and what are their contributions to the therapeutic change process? Perhaps the most important technological change characterizing the newer forms is reflected in techniques for *lessening the psychological distance* between the leader and the participant. A variety of methods serve this function. The transparency of the therapist (personal revelations and so forth), the use of warm, informal settings, the emphasis on assuming the stance of a participant, the emphasis that characterizes some of the new forms on diminishing the importance of the expertise of the leader and defining him more nearly as a peer and, finally, the use of physical contact-touching are all devices that seem to be calculated to reduce the psychological distance between the changer and the changing.

Few guides exist to assess the importance of such a change from the traditional patient–therapist relationships. Perhaps all that can be said for sure is that such changes reflect current changes in social mores, which have increasingly moved away from emphasis on the priestly status of healing professionals and other experts. The new forms, having developed more recently, could be expected to be more sensitive than the old to current cultural expectations.

A third major difference is the use of *highly structured techniques* wherein leaders instruct participants to engage in certain kinds of prescribed behavior or relationships for learning purposes. These prescriptive techniques have been variously labeled games, structured exercises, learning arrangements, mini-experiments, and so forth. They represent highly specific leader-arranged situations that include a set of specific directions for "experimenting" with new or rarely used kinds of behavior. These orders limit the participant's opportunity to choose behavioral alternatives. Some illustrations of these techniques are:

"Form small groups of four people. Take turns introducing yourself nonverbally. Take five minutes to decide how you want to do this. Try to come up with a name for your group."

"Each person think of the most joyous moment of your life and then think of the way to describe it . . . first verbally and then by action."

"Get into contact with your inner self of violence. Have a fantasy fight between your weak self and your strong self. See yourself in a fight. Describe it. Get up and be the weak person."

"Fantasy yourself being shrunk to the size of a pin and enter a trip inside your body. Try to imagine what you smell, feel like. Try to imagine what you find. Travel to any part of your body that you are having a problem with. Try to examine the problem. Now imagine yourself exiting from your body at any point. Okay, open your eyes. Who wants to share a trip?"

Although the use of leader-created learning situations is not unique with the advent of these new technologies (Moreno's psychodrama, for example, clearly antedates them) the wide and extensive application, the diversity, and the prominence of such instructional techniques is, in this sense, a major technological innovation. Some[1] have been highly critical of this form of leadership and believe it leads to an unproductive learning climate and to unstable gains. Others have claimed that such structured exercises are effective in producing change and are better than letting the group members spend many sessions groping aimlessly and uncertainly for some understanding of the ways in which they habitually behave.[10]

What are the effects of this innovation on learning? A study of eighteen encounter groups that represented ten encounter technologies[15] indicated that the use of such exercises was neither the royal road to existential bliss nor a robust means of inducing change in individuals. The evidence suggested that structural exercises are, at best, irrelevant in that they do not yield markedly different results whether they are used or not; it can be inferred that they are generally less effective than other aspects of leadership in producing positive outcomes. These instructional techniques, however, are highly effective in increasing the esteem of participants for the leader; a leader who uses many exercises is perceived by the members as being more competent and they are more enthusiastic about him and how much they have learned. The use of exercises increases group cohesiveness. These effects of the use of exercises, namely to make leaders feel that they are doing well and members feel close to one another, may account for their widespread popularity, despite the evidence that suggests that they are not powerful tools for inducing learning, growth, or change in individuals.

A fourth distinguishing characteristic of these newer technologies centers around the emphasis on expressivity and emotional experiencing. There has been a decided shift away from the use of the observing ego and the development of cognitive mastery, which is epitomized in more traditional forms of therapy, in favor of experiencing. Many of the techniques described under the headings "the decreasing of psychological distance between the patient and the therapist and the use of prescriptive learning situations" function to inculcate unique and perhaps previously unrecognized interpersonal, interpsychic, and bodily experiences. Their intention is to generate high levels of intense emotional expression. The newer forms of group treatment appear to be more intense, more active, less silent; much more appears to be going on.

A uniform reaction particularly of those who practice more traditional forms of group therapy is to compare the intensity and the involvement of participants in the newer forms with the often slower paced, less uniformly intense experiences they have as group therapists. There is no question that the current technologies are potent in the sense that they are capable of generating intense involvement and commitment and often become an emotionally moving experience for the participants.

In the previously cited study of encounter groups, the dominant learning mechanisms associated with the newer technologies (some of which are frequently used in traditional group psychotherapy) were examined in relationship to outcome. The findings with regard to expressivity were quite dramatic and unexpected —neither the total amount of expressivity, the importance of it to the participant, nor the context in which expressivity took place was associated with positive outcome. In fact, those who suffered negative outcomes as a consequence of their participation in an encounter group showed significantly more expressivity of a hostile, aggressive kind than

those who benefited from participation in the groups. It is important to stress that, in contrast to levels or amount or kind of expressivity, other mechanisms were able to show significant relationships to outcome. Though people may feel good about getting out their feelings and may believe that it is instrumental in their learning, no evidence yet supports the belief that expressivity per se is specifically associated with differences in individual growth. It should be stressed, however, that the data did not permit a test of the converse hypothesis, nonexpressivity. All groups had relatively high levels of expressivity and most participants perceived these experiences as important. There were individual as well as group differences in the amount of expressivity, but the range in the groups studied should be seen as from moderate to very high degrees of expressivity rather than from very low to very high amounts.

Self-disclosure, a mechanism closely related to expressivity and seen by some[13] as a sine qua non of personal growth, was similarly tested. The findings indicated that the amount or kind of self-disclosure in and of itself did not relate to benefit. Those who benefited from the encounter groups were those who could utilize self-disclosure for cognitive mastery (the ability to place their experience of self-disclosure within some cognitive frame) as well as those who were able to disclose in contexts that proved safe. In other words, self-disclosure itself was not the mechanism that induced learning: how it is related to the participant's intellectual understanding of himself and the conditions under which it takes place appear to make an important difference in its effects on positive change.

The inability of modern man to experience intense emotions may be seen as a primary diagnosis underlying many of the new techniques in group treatment. The mutilation of this ability has been described by many as at the very core of what is responsible for human problems and the essence of what needs correction—hence, the emphasis on increasing sensory awareness and on the stimulation of physical feelings and emotion-provoking experiences. Analyses of intense emotional experiences of individuals indicated that significant differences in outcome were not related to amount of experience with intense emotions. Indeed, those who benefited from the groups *less frequently* cited intense emotional experiences of a positive (love) type. The findings also indicated that participants who were unchanged by the group experience or who had negative outcomes were significantly more often involved in intense negative emotional experiences than those who benefited. Clearly, the three events that are emphasized by many of the new people-changing endeavors are not mechanisms that appear to have great effectiveness in changing people. This does not mean that they are unimportant. Can one, for example, build an environment for personal learning without a modicum of emotionality and disclosure? Although there is no empirical evidence to answer such a question, it seems reasonable to think not. But such a conjecture is not to be confused with the assumption that the new emphases constitute crucial mechanisms for changing individuals per se.

Although not unique to the newer therapies, the rationale underlying the emphasis on the "here and now" is distinctive in the new technologies. The theories of Perls and Rogers, as well as of Kurt Lewin, all point to the essentiality of a here-and-now focus as opposed to focus on the personal past or on current interpersonal problems outside the group itself. The position grows out of the view that the group is a social microcosm wherein the behavior of the patients is an accurate representation of their overall interpersonal behavior. In addition, the here and now possesses a sense of immediacy and is an experience shared by all, against which reality checks can readily be applied. What is unique in the newer technologies is the degree of emphasis on this principle: it is used as an "eligibility requirement" against which to test and ban content that does not meet the here-and-now criterion. Yet findings of the encounter-group study suggested that groups obsessed with here-and-now interaction were poorer learn-

ing environments, not because the need for historical or genetic material could be established per se, but perhaps because of the anxiety created by such a constraint on the range of interaction.

This is a good illustration of the problems plaguing the newer group forms. Within limits their techniques make sense. Their exuberant militancy, however, has pushed the use of certain techniques to extremes. Structured exercises, for example, can be used successfully to create high levels of cohesiveness in the group, but excessive use of such exercises minimizes group-learning potential.

Finally, the *revamping of time intervals for the enactment of the process* has been an important characteristic of the newer therapies. The traditional group in which strangers met for an hour once or twice a week has been greatly altered. Current practices range from the extremes of forty-eight-hours or more continuous therapeutic marathons to weekend or two-week workshops in which the participants spend eight or so hours a day in their groups. This innovation has called into question the arrangement of time as well as how much time it takes to help people deal with their problems and develop themselves. There is no reason to assume that the traditionally expected long-term participation in a treatment group is a necessary condition for meaningful and stable change to take place. Participants in the encounter group spent a total of thirty hours in the groups. Of the 208 participants, 34 percent made significant alterations in a positive direction; of these 75 percent maintained the originally observed changes when assessed a year later. The fact of the matter is that significant change in a person's life style, his coping strategies, his feelings about self and about others and so forth can be brought about within a limited amount of time.

The creative energy associated with technological innovation is unquestionably impressive. The effectiveness for producing beneficial outcomes of many of these innovations, however, is unfortunately limited. The techniques characteristic of the newer therapies appear to be superbly engineered to provide intense, meaningful, transitory relationships with others. They probably satisfy a deep hunger in the individual who experiences a sense of social isolation, chronic boredom, or any other symptoms usually associated with the term alienation. Properly used, the new techniques provide an intense, personal experience with others in a responsible manner. They can induce excitement, increase cohesion, and create openness. Such characteristics cannot, however, be claimed to be causally related to personal change. In this sense, the primary effect of the newer technologies rests in their ability to offer involvement and communion. What is of interest even with respect to these outcomes, however, is that they appear to be severely limited in time and space. The feelings of relatedness engendered in the group were found in the encounter study to ebb quickly upon the termination of the experience. The groups are essentially happenings that are salient and significant and meaningful for most of the participants *at the time they take place*, and perhaps accepted by all as being sufficient as such. Unlike many other institutions or settings to which people have turned for communion—most notably the family and church—the new encounter groups exact no pledge to the future as the price of belonging: no permanent commitment to a set of ideas or a set of individuals is required to experience the joy of membership.

In this sense, the technological innovations are unquestionably successful as transitory and temporary, but meaningful, experience with regard to providing people elements of satisfaction sorely missed in many natural groupings in contemporary social life, but they do not appear to be especially powerful as mechanisms for effecting personal change. Their major import lies not in that they have offered new and powerful means of enhancing therapeutic change but in that they have challenged the assumptions of the traditional forms to which most of us have been accustomed. They contain the potential of an intellectual catalyst for those who would chart out new directions for developing a reasonable science and empirically grounded technology in the people-changing area.

Comparative Effectiveness of Old and New Methodologies

Are there differences between the newer and the older groups in the amount or type of outcomes they are likely to produce? Are the newer forms more effective? Are they likely to change people in ways that are different from changes in the more traditional group therapies? Philosophical distinctions are suggested between the reparative, survival-oriented emphases of the more traditional forms of psychotherapy and the growth or actualization emphases of the newer forms. The image of what man is and what he can become clearly distinguish the two. The need to maximize human potential, as expressed by Maslow, has been a crucial formative influence in the development of the newer therapies, whereas the Freudian image of the far more psychologically limited man has been of more influence in countless clinics that conduct traditional group therapy. Despite these clear philosophical differences, we have suggested that the clientele of newer forms come as much for reparative reasons as do the clientele of traditional therapeutic endeavors. This, of course, does not directly speak to the issue of outcome.

The question of comparative effectiveness is easier to pose than to answer from empirical data. Lieberman, Yalom, and Miles[15] compared the overall effectiveness of encounter groups and individual psychotherapy. Sufficient data from group-psychotherapy research were not available in the literature. All of the outcome studies listed by Bergin and Garfield[3] were used that matched the methodological criteria comparable to the encounter-group study (outcome criteria beyond therapists' ratings and patients' self-perceptions, relatively rigorous methodological design, studies that reported percentage of improvement based upon a complex set of outcome criteria on nonpsychotic patient populations). Percentage of improvement in studies of individual psychotherapy ranged from a low of 33 percent to a high of 87 percent, with a mean of 67 percent and a median of 71 percent. Success rates for the encounter groups ranged from zero to 80 percent with a mean of 33 percent and a median of 33 percent. Although such comparisons are obviously risky because of problems of comparable outcome data, different expectational sets in clients, and so forth, they are instructive in that no evidence exists that suggests that the newer techniques produce results indicative of a breakthrough relative to effectiveness.

The difficulties encountered in attempting to assess relative effectiveness are magnified a hundredfold when trying to determine whether changes that do occur in the newer modalities are distinct from those in the more traditional forms of group therapy. There is no reasonable procedure for assessing the findings from the literature—they are too diverse and do not provide means of comparing types of change. In the encounter groups studied, people were most affected in the areas of values, attitudes, and in the ways they perceived themselves. Value changes were most noticeable: participants emphasized an existential orientation, stressing the values of growth and change and the importance of interpersonal relationships. Those who changed their view of self tended to downgrade agentic motivations and idealize themselves as softer, more lenient persons. Of interest is that no generalized changes were found in how participants perceived the world around them or in their conceptions of significant others. Nor were there generalized changes in participants' life styles or their relationships with people outside the group. Such data suggest that there may be some particular perspectives that could be directly associated with the newer forms of personal change groups. It is likely that comparable data on the more traditional forms of group therapy would yield somewhat different changes in value perspectives or in self-view because the philosophical underpinnings of the older forms are different.

It is not surprising that values and attitudes should show the most uniform changes: group settings are particularly potent contexts for affecting values and attitudes. It seems reasonable to speculate that changes in such areas would not be as strong in individual psycho-

therapy when compared to group settings of any kind. There is scant evidence, however, to suggest even the beginning of a framework for understanding the particular effects of the newer techniques compared to the older group techniques, or to examine the question of the particular influence of groups compared to dyads for purposes of individual change. We should be alert to these questions, but the current state of the art offers no empirical data to help answer them.

([Responses to the Confusion

Although argument abounds over whether particular group methods lead to destructive chaos or productive growth, it seems unnecessary to document the observation that groups are increasingly being used to heal an ever-larger list of human problems. Whether this expansion expresses some deep need for communion or simply represents the restless quest of unhappy adults for "something different" is a less important question than that of how we can improve the group context as a mechanism for people changing. The simple fact that large numbers of people enter groups for personal change demands work on the question of how to meet their needs in a humane and meaningful way.

The responses of mental-health professionals to the many confusing issues generated by the new forms have followed the general pattern of extremes so characteristic of the reaction pattern of the public at large to people-changing groups. Professionals, like laymen, have run the gamut of responses from "keep them out at any cost, all they do is destructive" to totally "incorporative" behavior. The critical extreme is well documented, but it may be useful to explore the characteristics of "incorporation."

The frequency with which mental-health professionals attend the various and diverse workshops offered to train people in the new treatment forms smacks less of a growth-oriented profession seeking to upgrade its level of operation than of a desperate response to a felt sense of inadequacy. The high degree of personal commitment and emotional intensity generated in clients who have been involved with these newer techniques may also motivate some professionals. At any rate, it is not uncommon for experienced therapists to spend several weeks each year in quest of new answers regarding how to provide more adequate professional service. (This year in Gestalt, next year in Transactional Analysis or some other new form.) "Have you heard about the techniques that X has worked out? I would like to go there next time" are remarks reminiscent of conversations frequently held among mental-health professionals. Although it is difficult to determine, it is likely that such responses are more characteristic of group than individual therapists.

Limitation of Eligibility— A Traditional Response

The problems surrounding eligibility for leadership of personal-change groups appear even more complex than those relating to the practice of individual psychotherapy. The traditional avenues of professional training have been shown to be unlikely to provide answers to the problems of training group leaders, either of the highly professional or almost totally lay variety. In the study of encounter groups, it was found that many highly experienced psychiatrists and clinical psychologists proved to be ineffective; some were frankly destructive, an outcome shown to be related to the particular techniques they employed. General professional training in and of itself is not an antidote for poor group practice. Although there are no systematic data on poor practice in nonprofessional people changers, the "horror stories" told by professionals and participants about casualties incurred by non-professionals do little to quiet fears.

Much of the confusion about eligibility for conducting personal-change groups may stem from failure to distinguish between groups and dyads as contexts for therapy. There is no empirical evidence or theoretical reason to assume that the skills acquired through training and practice of dyadic change are trans-

ferable to use in group situations. Some therapists are probably better suited for the group context, others for the dyad. Some therapists, for example, in order to develop sensitivity to another human being, need to know the other person through his history, while other therapists appear more comfortable in being able to achieve a similar understanding simply through seeing how the person behaves. This sort of difference in the personal style of the therapist probably makes for a large difference in effectiveness in a dyad (which emphasizes the former) or a group (which emphasizes the latter in many instances). The assumption of identity of dyadic and group skills is as mythic as the "every man can be a therapist" theme.

Nor are the stresses and strains of the group the same as the stresses and strains of a dyad. The social forces at work in the two modes are different. To assume that one type of training or character unconditionally fits both modes is sloppy thinking.

Thus, to create distinctions between traditional forms of group therapy and the newer treatment group types, based on leader differences in training, serves more to obfuscate than to clarify. The wisdom that has been distilled out of training thousands of therapists for individual psychotherapy has no parallel in the group area. This is, in part, because of the relative newness of the field, but perhaps even more because no one has thought about the issues of eligibility for group leaders with the same intensity as has characterized discussion about eligibility requirements for individual psychotherapists. While the issue of appropriate safeguards for the consumer is not to be dismissed lightly, there is little evidence that traditional eligibility criteria can predict effective group leaders.

The question of who should lead people-changing groups and how they should be prepared obviously involves many problems. Some derive from basically differing value orientations on how nonprofessionals or paraprofessionals can make their best contribution to the mental-health enterprise; others may be more purely technological considerations relating to maintenance of control over entry into the business of personal change. Such issues, however, would seem to follow the question of what the leader contributes to the process of change in groups.

Theories of personal change in groups usually give great emphasis to concepts addressed to the relationship of the leader to the collectivity of people to be changed (patients, members, participants). Similar to theories of individual therapy, they emphasize the central importance of the leader or therapist. It is through his actions or abstinence from action that change processes are initiated, set in the right (or wrong) direction. Theorists are often maximally distinguishable by the particular dimensions of the leader–client relationship they emphasize. For some, the core concepts relate to the interpersonal conditions the leader creates between himself and each participant—positive regard, genuineness, and so forth.[18] Others stress the leader's symbolic properties, such as the specific transference relationships between each individual patient and the leader (or leader surrogate)[24] while others stress the symbolic relationship of the leader to the *group as a whole*.[9,5] Still others, although also stressing the unique relationship of each patient to the leader, emphasize negative rather than positive interaction between and through such devices as the "hot seat"[17] in which the group acts as Greek chorus or background to this primary relationship.

Despite fundamentally different conclusions about what the crucial leader "inputs" are, all these theories agree on the centrality of the leader to the change process. It is he who sets up the learning experience, who makes the interpretations or analyses resistance, who sets the norms, who is the "model," and so on. The specific content of the leader's actions and responsibilities may differ, but the underlying assumption is that the central factor in what changes people is what the leader does or how he expresses himself.

It is quite possible, however, that the leader's behavior, personality, and skill level have taken on mythic proportions as basic causal forces explaining successful personal change in groups. Some obvious factors in the history and development of the use of groups for people changing may have contributed to this view. Theories of group change of individuals naturally have given great prominence to the role of the leader—after all, most of them have been developed by especially artful practitioners who have often also been highly charismatic individuals. It is understandable that the clinicians who have contributed what little theory there is on changing people through groups might be somewhat myopic and could be easily pardoned if they have overestimated the contribution of the leader (i.e., themselves) to the curative process. No theories of group personal change have been advanced that have developed out of the thinking of patients or experimental psychology (perhaps with the exception of some applications of behavioral modification theory that are used in group contexts). Thus, the assumption of leader centrality found in all theories of group personal change may represent an understandable overestimation on the part of the theorist based on his unique perspective upon the process about which he attempts to theorize.

But what about transference? Could anyone who has ever worked with a people-changing group realistically ignore the magical expectations, distortions, overestimations that are directed toward the person of the leader? No matter what one labels the feelings and thoughts of members toward their leader, it is hard to ignore transference as a central phenomenon common to all people-changing groups. I see no reason to question that the complex, convoluted, supercharged feelings that focus on the person of the therapist do exist. Many would agree that the leader need not do anything more than be there to become enhanced with the aura of a professional—a person capable of giving help, of performing a priestly function. Some have, however, questioned the generality of the transference concept under other cultural conditions or situations where the social distance or psychological distance between the one who is helped and the helper is lowered. Whether or not transference is a universal product of psychotherapeutic contact, the fact of transference reactions, where indeed they do occur, does not, in and of itself, *demonstrate* that the leader is central to the *curative process*. That supercharged feelings toward the leader are usually generated in a group therapeutic context does not permit one to jump to the conclusion that transference is intrinsically a curative factor in the group context. In other words, no unquestionable cause–effect relationship relative to outcome is demonstrated merely by the evidence that leaders usually become objects of transference.

As a mode that followed the development of dyadic treatment, it is natural that theories of group personal change should have been influenced by images of the obvious control that the therapist exercises in dyadic relationships. Professionalization, the length of time invested in training, the sharp boundaries surrounding the help-giving professions, the distinctive terminologies, the fee structures, and so forth are also conditions that support unexamined adherence to the view that the leader is central, prominent, critical in the curative process. It seems reasonable to think that to the degree that an activity in our society becomes professionalized, so will the role of the professional who conducts that activity become enhanced in the minds both of the professional and the layman. Consider for a moment the full implications of discovering that most of what helps patients in groups stems from the relationships members have to one another and to processes that are only tangentially related to the behavior and person of the leader. Such a view would in all certainty present difficulties for continued dismissal of questions regarding whether or how much professionalization is necessary.

Thus, many forces exist for creating a mythology surrounding the person of the leader. Journals and professional meetings endlessly encourage debates that support the "prominence" of the therapist or leader through discussions of such issues as what he does, how he does it, when he does it, how he feels, what are his hang-ups, how aware he is, what is his theory, whether he works alone or with a cotherapist, whether "he" is he or she, black or white, kindly or hostile, and so forth.

The empirical findings available in the literature offer little evidence for a reasoned position on the question of how much the therapist or leader contributes to outcome in groups. Some perspective on the question is offered via the analogy from individual psychotherapy relative to the nonspecific treatment or placebo effects. For groups, the analogues to placebo effects are certain events that frequently occur in small face-to-face, intensive groups that can provide experiences that *in themselves* are curative. Because these events occur in concurrence with the presence of a leader, their curative power is attributed to the leader. (The analogy to "placebo effects" and the special properties of small face-to-face groups should not be taken to imply that the curative mechanisms involved in dyadic and group healing processes are necessarily similar.)

The data available only serve to legitimize raising this question; they are insufficient to answer it. Studies reporting no differences in the effectiveness of naive therapists compared to experienced professionals could be interpreted to mean that the group situation within rather broad limits is useful regardless of the specific behavior of the therapist. Studies in which large outcome differences were found among experienced therapists might, on the other hand, suggest that the behavior of the therapist is critical. If we look closely at these studies, however, an alternate explanation could be offered. Suppose for a moment we make the assumption that the major impact of therapists or leaders is to make people worse. Let us also play with the assumption that there are two major factors operating in therapeutic groups: the intrinsic, beneficial effects of the group itself and the inputs of the leader, most of which are not beneficial. The notion behind these assumptions is to establish an appropriate zero point for assessing the leader's contribution.

In the encounter-group study, leaders who had ten or more years of experience conducting groups were compared to leaderless groups that were "led" by the peer-tape program.[4] A large variety of outcome measures (including judgments by leaders, data from social network, a large range of instruments to assess coping changes, changes in self-esteem, decision making, and so forth) were developed and composite outcome scores were assigned to each study participant. The sum of these individual scores yielded a weighted score reflecting the overall effects of each group studied. Of the sixteen leaders studied, only four obtained outcome scores that exceeded the mean score of the two tape groups; of the other twelve leaders, some yielded considerably lower outcomes than the tape groups.

While the tape groups, of course, were not leaderless groups in the strictest sense, only a minimal structure was offered to the participants in the tape situation. It seems reasonable to assume that the tape group created conditions reflecting the curative power of the group under minimal leader input. Thus, the finding suggests that groups may have constructive potential without the intervention of a professional leader. It should be easy to see why this interpretation finds little acceptance among professionals. Like the finding that naive therapists did as well as experts, it could be taken to suggest that most therapists are relatively incompetent. This has, in fact, been the usual response of professionals to such "disturbing" findings when they have appeared in the literature. The prestigious backgrounds and professional esteem of the sixteen therapists studied, however, make it hard to argue for the latter interpretation. These men were clearly competent in executing practices appropriate to their theories of change. They were uneven, however, in the amount of attention they paid or use they made of group forces. Indeed, as already suggested, they may have intervened in ways that obstructed inherent beneficial attributes of the group context.

The study of encounter groups yields further evidence of positive effects of intensive small group experiences that were not attributable to the behavior of the leader. The normative characteristics of the group—the informal, often unarticulated and undiscerned social agreements that regulate behavior of members—were demonstrated in the encounter study to be equal or greater influences on overall outcome scores than leader behavior.

The findings further suggested that leaders contributed a smaller share to establishing the normative structure than would be expected. The ability of participants to identify with the experience of another even without participating in it directly, or to experience similarity between themselves and others in the group, was demonstrated to be a powerful mechanism for inducing individual change. This and other mechanisms of change are stimulated more by the intrinsic characteristics of intensive peer-group experience than by the behavior of the leader. Whether the participant was a deviant in the group or an esteemed, influential member was also demonstrated to account for positive change more than almost any other elements of the change process.

Findings such as these point to the necessity of initiating debate on the importance of the leader to the group, an assumption that may have thus far served more to confuse than to enlighten. They suggest that documentation of personal improvement through group experience is not sufficient evidence from which to conclude what the therapist or leader contributes to such changes. They suggest, further, that control of leadership "quality" through efforts to upgrade skill levels of leaders will not necessarily lead to more effective utilization of groups. Even highly skilled, effective therapists have not been able to transmit their skills in any orderly way. The models presented by such skilled practitioners frequently emphasize meaningless epiphenomena. They tend to offer generalized suggestions on how to "be like me," rather than to identify specific kinds of behavior that are effective. Perhaps an equal or even more significant implication of such findings is that there may be processes, unique to the group context, that *in and of themselves* induce helpful or growth-producing changes. For all these reasons, the current concern with eligibility requirements or with increasing leadership skill levels via frameworks that explicitly or implicitly derive from dyadic psychotherapy and clinical wisdom seems to circumvent three prior and more crucial questions: (1) What are the proper components of effective training for those who **would conduct groups geared toward individ-**

ual change? (2) Can these components be identified via systematic empirical processes rather than through less rigorous attempts to distill wisdom from uncontrolled clinical observations? (3) What distinctive properties do groups possess that must be taken into account in *whatever* methods or training designs are developed?

Group Forces as Healing Sources—
A Social-Psychological Response

Five properties of groups are particularly important in their influence on the therapeutic experience of the participant: the capacity of the group to develop cohesiveness or a sense of belonging; the capacity of the group to control, reward, and punish behavior; the capacity to define reality for the individual; the capacity to induce and release powerful feelings; and the capacity to provide a contrast for social comparison and feedback. What are the implications of these properties of the group for the induction of productive, psychotherapeutic experiences in the group context?

The capacity of groups to develop cohesiveness reflects the phenomenological experience of communion or belongingness that is usually operationally defined as the attractiveness of the group to its participants. Cohesiveness performs roughly the same function in change groups that positive transference performs in dyadic therapy. Studies of individual psychotherapy in recent years have marshaled evidence that points to the importance of the transference relationship. Truax and Carkhuff[21] have shown that patients are more likely to improve with the qualities of positive transference, such as high levels of empathy, nonpossessive warmth and genuineness, or feeling liked by the therapist. The group context does not as readily offer the establishment of such relationships between the larger number of members and a single leader. The group property of cohesiveness, however, elicits analogous feelings. A sense of belongingness motivates the participant to stay in the group and to work with it, which mitigates the pains associated with therapeutic exploration. Cohesive groups are ones that offer members

almost unconditional acceptance no matter what their history and behavior have been outside of the microcosm that is the group. They offer the support and warmth that encourage risk taking; they provide the psychological glue that permits members to reveal themselves; they provide the bases for public esteem, which has the consequential effect of increasing self-esteem.[25]

Closely associated with and dependent on the level of cohesiveness, is the group's *capacity to control behavior and to provide a system of rewards and punishments*. Groups are microcosms of a larger society; they develop their own cultures and, in large part, their existence depends on special rules and standards they establish as they extend their life. How much one talks, what one talks about, what one doesn't talk about, even "the way" one talks about certain things are all aspects of individual behavior that are subject to the social influences of the group. Such control over individual behavior is a central property of a group, including a therapy or growth group. The group member is almost inevitably confronted with pressure from others to change his behavior or his views. The need to be in step, to abide by the rules is a powerful factor, inducing conformity in the group. Disregard for the rules brings the possibility of punishment. The ultimate punishment available to a group is the power of exclusion—either psychological or physical. In dyadic therapy, the patient does not fear exclusion if he does not go along with the therapist; he fears loss of the therapist's respect or love. These two very different psychological experiences lead to similar behavior—conformity.

A strong additional force pulling members toward conformity is the group's most prized reward—its *power to offer the authenticating affirmation of one's peers*. The experience of consensual validation appears to be the most salient experience in group therapy, more powerful than the affirmation of the therapist. The power of groups to exact conformity also frequently induces fear in people; there is much evidence that group members fear punishment for nonconformity or departure from the group norms. It is important to remember that the norms that determine what behavior the group will reward or punish are *shared* agreements developed by the group as it establishes its own culture. The member's belief that he has some power to influence the development of norms and standards in a group mitigates, to some extent, his fear of the power of the group to induce conformity.

Groups also have *the capacity to redefine reality for their members*. In dyadic psychotherapy, one of the major roles of the therapist is to attribute meaning to the patient's behavior—to provide *labels* that offer a new view regarding past and present thoughts, feelings, fantasies, transactions with others. Most schools of verbal psychotherapy view insight or *understanding* as a prime effect to be sought for through psychotherapy; developing understanding or insight is, of course, not simply a matter of the therapist labeling or lending meaning, but the labeling process is indispensable to the production of this sought-after state.

Groups exert strong influence on how each member views himself, the group as a whole, and others in the group. Thus, in a group situation, it is not only the leader who has a salient role in providing insight, understanding, or attributing meaning; the social system, the collection of participants also adds to that meaning collectively. The group's capacity to define reality can be found in a dramatic illustration from a group therapy course in which psychiatry residents observed two classmates working as therapists with an ongoing group:

The observers watched from a darkened observation room and discussed the proceedings afterwards with the two therapists. Before the eighth session began, the window blinds were removed for cleaning, so that the patients could see the observers through the one-way mirror. The two student therapists felt that since all the patients knew they were being observed there was no need to call off the observation. As the patients arrived one by one each looked particularly closely at the large observation mirror and then took his seat. The meeting began with members talking about how difficult it was to communicate with people, "particularly when you couldn't see them—in telephone conversations, etc." They referred to the observers (which they had not done in previous

sessions) with statements like "It's uncomfortable. I don't like being observed because it's one-sided. The observers can see the patients but the patients cannot see the observers." The meeting went on in this vein for about a half hour and then shifted to other topics. After the session, when the two therapists joined the other residents to discuss the session, the observers asked the therapists why they had not intervened and brought some sense of "reality" to the group by pointing out that the observers could be seen for the first time. They answered that the light had shifted and the observers couldn't really be seen. Their belief was so strong that several of us had to accompany them into the therapy room to demonstrate that obviously the group could see the observers—perhaps not every facial gesture, but clearly at least their outlines.

In short, the two therapists, who had entered the session knowing the observers could be seen, and the patients, who collectively upheld as "reality" the illusion that the observers could not be seen, had redefined reality to meet their own needs.

Another important characteristic of groups is *their capacity to induce powerful feelings*. Emotional contagion was the first phenomenon to interest investigators of groups. G. LeBon, W. McDougall, and Freud pointed out that powerful, primitive affects can be released in groups. Individuals may get carried away and act on feelings without displaying their typical controls. This potential of groups can have either positive or negative effects on personal change. An individual may experience previously denied feelings, not with enduring terror but with acceptance; he may undergo, in other words, the "corrective emotional experience" of finding that the feelings are not overwhelming or that the feared consequences do not occur. Negative effects may occur when an individual is overwhelmed by affect and must defend himself against a group by literal or psychological withdrawal or by the invocation of undesirable psychological defenses. The potential to stimulate emotionality although, again, not peculiar to therapeutic groups, is an important quality of groups that bears directly on the sorts of personal learning or changes that take place in group, people-changing contexts.

The fifth characteristic of groups that is an important influence in therapeutic contexts is the *capacity of the group to provide a context for social comparison.* Group-therapy patients frequently compare their attitudes toward their parents, husbands, wives, children; their feelings about things that are happening in the group; what makes them sad, happy, guilty, angry; the ways that each typically deals with and expresses anger and affection; and so on. Such comparisons occur naturally and facilitate revision of the patient's identity by suggesting to him new possibilities for feeling, perceiving, and behaving. In a group, members can compare a number of perspectives because different individuals present new vantage points. This inherent property of the group situation perhaps occurs most powerfully in therapeutic social systems where it is expected, often demanded, that members talk about their behavior. Social comparison occurs as an outgrowth.

What do these properties of groups imply for theories of group personal change? As indicated, all too often theoretical developments in this area have stemmed from the translation, with some technical alterations, of principles of dyadic therapy. The existence of group properties implies the need for a theoretical perspective that takes these properties into account. Although some theorists have initiated their explorations of group therapeutic processes on the premise that groups have special properties, most examples of this orientation are confined to discussions of traditional treatment groups and do not reflect recent developments in the group, people-changing enterprise. A number of theorists[*] have attempted to take both group properties and individual dynamics into account in developing a unified theory of group therapy. The role attributed to the therapist in these frameworks is of particular interest. The English school has used the word "conductor" to explain the function of the therapist in the group; American systems-oriented theorists have often labeled the group therapist or

[*] See references 2, 8, 5, 9, 11, 20, and 23.

leader a social engineer. Both these terms are meant to suggest that the leader's most important function is to help the social system make maximal use of group properties that will induce psychotherapeutic benefits.

A useful way of describing systems-oriented conceptions of group psychotherapy is to distinguish between what have been called therapeutic conditions and therapeutic mechanisms. The former implies the context for change or learning—in the dyad it is the characteristics of the relationship, in the group it is the characteristics of the social system. In both situations the role of the therapist is considered to be to enhance the positive aspects of the condition so that change can occur. This is not the same as saying that the therapeutic relationship is, in itself, therapeutic. It *is* to say that certain events that facilitate growth must happen to the person in treatment. These events are of the sort that were earlier labeled therapeutic mechanisms or mechanisms of change.

Group Change Contexts and Therapeutic Outcomes

These group properties create conditions that engage the group member in a number of activities and concerns that differ from those of the patient in dyadic treatment. In comparison with the latter, the group member gets little practice in reflecting about himself and his interactions with others, in associating about his own feelings, in analyzing dreams, in linking present and past experiences or penetrating covert meanings: he is too busy actively interacting and finding a viable place for himself in the group. However, he gets greater practice than the patient in dyadic treatment in expressing his feelings to peers, in noting the consequences of such expressions, in attempting to understand and empathize with others, in hearing from others about his impact on them, and in comparing himself with others.

Do these differing balances in experience lead to differences in outcome? It is commonly assumed that the group member should end up getting help of much the same order as he would have obtained in a dyadic relationship. It is perhaps helpful to test this assumption against, first, the end state of the person at the close of the change process (symptoms, conflicts, defenses, interpersonal patterns, and the like) and, second, the meta-learning achieved (learning how to approach problems, how to confront and resolve conflicts, and how to cope with anxiety).

Three aspects of the individual's end state are relevant: (1) the symptoms or presenting complaint; (2) the revision of maladaptive patterns, the relinquishment of neurotic defenses or the resolution of neurotic conflict; and (3) the unsought, ancillary gains. Symptom relief, for example, may be achieved at different rates. (The placebo effect, critical in many instances of rapid symptom relief, seems to us unique to the dyad.) Particular behavior changes or conflict resolutions may be accomplished better by one or the other of the two settings, depending on the nature of the problem, the composition (if a group) and so on. For example, a therapy group whose composition encouraged a patient to maintain an established neurotic pattern might be less effective for the patient than individual therapy. On the other hand, a group that, say, through emotional contagion, led a patient to experience positively a previously feared affect might be more effective than individual therapy.

Finally, the two treatment contexts may be conducive to different ancillary benefits. For example, difficulty in giving to others may be only peripherally related to the person's presenting complaint or core conflicts but, nevertheless, an issue. Since giving to others is often a focal concern in a group, many opportunities appear for each member to note the nature of his anxieties about giving and to try out giving behavior. Thus, changes in giving behavior may occur sooner, or more directly, than in individual therapy. The two contexts may also call attention to different aspects of humanness. In group contexts, members are likely to be struck by the common needs for basic kinship, for sharing with others, among persons who on the surface appear quite different. They may be impressed both by the difficulties in communicating meaningfully to others and by the profound rewards experienced when such communication proves possible. The dyad, in contrast, does not directly facilitate such experiences.

The differences for meta-learning may be even greater than the differences in end-state outcomes. In any form of treatment the person often adopts a style for approaching problems that reflects the treatment orientation to which he has been exposed. It is not unusual for a patient to emerge from psychoanalysis with an increased tendency to pay attention to his dreams, to deduce emotional meaning from forgetting, to search out unrecognized feelings when he notes inconsistencies in his behavior. A person who has undergone group treatment may be more likely to seek out feedback from others, to make social comparisons, to test out behavior interpersonally.

An appreciation of the intensive positive and negative forces inherent in the face-to-face, social microcosm that is the group-treatment context is perhaps the single most helpful guide toward developing a realistic picture of both the problems and potentials inherent in using groups for people changing. A systems-oriented perspective to people-changing groups must include consideration of some real problems about groups, problems that need solution before the potential of groups can be realized. The three most critical issues facing the use of groups today have to do with range or applicability, transfer or generalization of ingroup learning to the real world the member lives in, and the emotional potency of groups.

RANGE OF APPLICABILITY

This refers to the degree of fit between specific procedures and member characteristics. The group people-changing enterprise is strewn with illustrations of extending procedures far beyond their range of applicability. This has been particularly characteristic of the newer group forms that usually begin with a simple set of principles stemming from an overall "diagnosis" that contemporary humans suffer from alienation, lack of integration between body and feelings, inability to express emotions, problems of guilt, and that they have unrealized potential because of these problems. Techniques are then developed, which are considered universally applicable, to relieve those sorts of problems. The proposition that, obviously, not all humans suffer the same upsets would find ready agreement; yet, the increasing appearance of techniques that imply that everyone needs the same kinds of simple corrective experiences has caused the new technologies to be judged inappropriate by those focused on the nuances of personality.

Realistic consideration is gravely needed regarding how various approaches to personal change fit the varied client populations to whom they are addressed. To assume, for example, that "freeing up," or encouraging expressivity, is a basic need of the constricted white, middle-class client and also the black, ghetto-dwelling client and to conclude, therefore, that the same techniques are operable for both, borders on being an unregulated, omnipotent fantasy. It is also a gross error to assume that the techniques of confrontation, the "leveling" so characteristic of the Synanon model, will have equivalent effects when used with addicts who live in a tightly bounded, residential treatment community and addicts who live "on the street" and experience confrontation techniques only in a once-a-week session. In a similar vein, is it sensible to apply such techniques with equal vigor in suburbia and Synanon, in California and Cornland, Illinois? These are not new problems; they have been mentioned frequently in questioning the universal applicability of traditional treatment modes developed from exclusive experience with middle-class, cognitively oriented populations. Unfortunately, what was learned from attempts to take traditional treatment to the masses has not been remembered in structuring theoretical premises of current people-changing-group ideologies. The various approaches need desperately to consider for whom they are appropriate and for whom

they are not and to match techniques to the problems and populations they serve.

TRANSFER OF LEARNING

The persuasiveness of groups has been so amply demonstrated in sociological and psychological literature that it needs no amplification here. Because the persuasive power of groups is so great, an illusion that individuals have changed is often created, whereas their alterations of behavior within the group context are simply temporary accommodations to a new referent group, to a different set of norms. The "change," therefore, is often ephemeral because it is more or less a response to the specific group conditions and is dependent on the treatment group for maintenance.

A major, unsolved conceptual requirement in group people changing is to develop not only the techniques but the constructs that will account for how the changes that occur in a group can lead to changes in the member's life outside the group. That lasting change does occur with some frequency is not as important as that it does not occur as frequently as we would like. Yet, no reasonable conceptual system exists to explain the specific relationships between person and group that account for these observed differences in maintenance of change or transfer of learning. How does generalization from the specific context of the treatment group take place? (After all, if the treatment group were identical with normal life little change would probably occur.) Does the inherent persuasiveness of the group situation mean that more attention should be given to providing situations that teach strategies of change and maintenance in the therapy itself? Too often, after participation in the group, the individual faces the external world little prepared to use what he has learned, to try out in the real life the behavior that he has tried out in the group. Or, just as sad, some individuals emerge from the group ready to try their "new learning," directly and overtly in situations where the response is direct and swift ridicule, exclusion, or similar forms of punishment for nonconformity to the norms of the "outside" group.

Treatment groups may be more like "real life" than dyadic relationships with one therapist, but they are certainly not identical with the world outside.

GROUP POTENCY

A dilemma inherent in the task of changing people through groups is that of how to capitalize on the potency of the group (its capacity to involve, to commit, and to move people emotionally) in such a way that this capacity will not be accepted as in itself a sufficient end product, a product that, in all likelihood, has been all that has been gained by many of the millions who have tasted the new group roads to growth. How can we employ the power of groups to involve people, to generate their enthusiasm, to exact their commitment, to move them to deep levels of emotionality so that treatment groups or growth groups or whatever they are called will also serve the purpose of helping to resolve the particular brands of human misery that are driving millions to try them out. Encounter-group participants clearly indicate that they come not simply for entertainment; nor are they existentialists searching for greater meaning to life. They are the same people who come knocking at the doors of mental-health clinics and offices of individual and group therapists. They are people in trouble who come for goal-oriented therapeutic reasons, although the rhetoric of the new forms suggests otherwise. The newer technologies have excelled in adopting old and developing new procedures for creating potent, involving groups. To lead such groups one need not be charismatic (a trait closely associated with group potency); one can effect charisma in himself through use of simple techniques, readily learned from innumerable how-to-do-it manuals. Unfortunately, group potency alone has not been shown to be related to positive outcome.

(Conclusion

The question then becomes, how can one relate the potency of groups—which provides a basis for other processes to occur that do effect change and which forms the basis of attraction of the group, so that people will stay and participate and get involved—to the creation of a viable learning environment? It is not enough simply to suggest that the potency of a group is not itself an effective change mechanism and thereby allow oneself to ignore it. In fact, one cannot ignore it. The way that people package their troubles today, the way they see themselves in a change-inducing situation does not permit dependence on the mores of traditional therapy, in which forbearance, patience, inner motivation are stressed. Such expectations of the client do not match "where it's at." It is perhaps an overly generalized view, but I think one that will become increasingly accurate: group-treatment forms cannot succeed in today's world without approximating the expectations of the members for a potent, moving, emotionally involving experience.

Many dangers lurk in this domain. If therapists and group leaders read potency to mean success, they will err grievously. If they believe they should direct most of their attention to behavior that stimulates group potency, they will have exciting groups, which reward them in a personal sense, but they will not fulfill their function—to provide a setting for growth or change.

(Bibliography

1. ARGYRIS, C. "On the Future of Laboratory Education," *J. Appl. Behav. Sci.*, 3 (1967), 153–183.
2. BACH, G. *Intensive Group Psychotherapy*. New York: Ronald, 1954.
3. BERGIN, A. E. and S. L. GARFIELD. *Handbook of Psychotherapy and Behavior Change: An Empirical Analysis*. New York: Wiley, 1971.
4. BERZON, B., L. SOLOMON, and J. REISEL. "Audio-Tape Program for Self-Directed Groups," in L. Solomon and B. Berzon, eds., *New Perspectives on Encounter Groups*, Ch. 12. San Francisco: Jossey-Bass, 1972.
5. BION, W. R. *Experiences in Groups*. New York: Basic Books, 1959.

6. BURROWS, T. "The Group Method of Analysis," *Psychoanal. Rev.*, 19 (1927), 268–280.

7. CALMAN, W. H., L. MISBACK, and D. V. BROWN. "An Assessment of Round-Table Psychotherapy," *Psychol. Monogr.*, 68 (13) (1954), 1–49.

8. DURKIN, H. *The Group in Depth.* New York: International Universities Press, 1964.

9. EZRIEL, H. "Psychoanalytic Approaches to Group Treatment," *Br. J. Med. Psychol.*, 23 (1950), 59–74.

10. FAGAN, J. "The Task of the Therapist," in J. Fagan and I. L. Shepherd, eds., *Gestalt Therapy Now: Theory, Techniques, and Applications*, p. 96. Palo Alto: Sci. Behav. Books, Stanford University Press, 1970.

11. FOULKES, S. H. and E. H. ANTHONY. *Group Psychotherapy: The Psychoanalytic Approach.* Baltimore: Penguin, 1965.

12. FRANK, J. "Why Patients Leave Psychotherapy," *Arch. Neurol. Psychiatry*, 77 (1957), 283–299.

13. JOURARD, S. *The Transparent Self.* Princeton: Van Nostrand, 1964.

14. LIEBERMAN, M. A. and J. GARDNER. "The Human Potential Movement." Committee on Human Development. University of Chicago, 1973. Unpublished.

15. LIEBERMAN, M. A., I. YALOM, and M. MILES. *Encounter Groups: First Facts.* New York: Basic Books, 1973.

16. PAYKEL, E., B. PRUSOFF, and E. H. UHLENHUTH. "Scaling of Life Events," *Arch. Gen. Psychiatry*, 25 (1971), 340–347.

17. PERLS, F. S., R. F. HEFFERLINE, and P. GOODMAN. *Gestalt Therapy.* New York: Dell, 1965.

18. ROGERS, C. *Encounter Groups.* New York: Harper & Row, 1970.

19. ROTHAUS, P., D. L. JOHNSON, P. G. HANSON et al. "Participation and Sociometry in Autonomous and Trainer-Led Patient Groups," *J. Couns. Psychol.*, 13 (1966), 68–76.

20. SCHEIDLINGER, S. "Group Process in Group Psychotherapy," *Am. J. Psychother.*, 14 (1960), 104–120; 346–363.

21. TRUAX, C. B. and R. R. CARKHUFF. *Towards Effective Counseling and Psychotherapy: Training and Practice.* Chicago: Aldine, 1967.

22. UHLENHUTH, E. H., M. B. BALTER, R. S. LIPMAN et al. "Demography of Life Stress." Paper presented Meet. Am. Coll. Neuropsychopharmacol., Dec. 1972.

23. WHITAKER, D. S. and M. A. LIEBERMAN. *Psychotherapy through the Group Process.* Chicago: Aldine-Atherton, 1964.

24. WOLF, A. "The Psychoanalysis of Groups," *Am. J. Psychother.*, 3 (1949), 529–557.

25. YALOM, I. *The Theory and Practice of Group Psychotherapy*, 1st ed. New York: Basic Books, 1970.

CHAPTER 18

FAMILY THERAPY AFTER TWENTY YEARS

Murray Bowen

FAMILY THERAPY came on the psychiatric scene in the mid-1950s. It had been developing in the private work of a few investigators for some years prior to that. The growth and development of family therapy has paralleled the ferment and change in psychiatry during the same period. There are psychiatrists who consider family therapy to be a superficial counseling method. A majority think of family therapy as a treatment method based on conventional psychiatric theory. A small percentage of family therapists think of family research as providing new dimensions for thinking about human adaptation and family therapy as pointing the way toward more effective ways of dealing with human problems. All three views are probably accurate, depending on the way the person thinks about the nature and origin of human maladaptation. In this chapter the author will present his view of how the family movement began, how it has developed during its first two decades of existence, and how this has been related to the changing psychiatric scene. There are many differences in method and technique in family therapy, based on a variety of theoretical premises. Each therapist is emotionally invested in his own approach and therefore has some degree of bias in the way he views the total field. With awareness of the differences, the author will present one version of the way the field has evolved in the past two decades. The author was one of the originators of the family movement and has continued to be active in the field. He began his family explorations in the late 1940s from a psychoanalytic orientation. He has moved from psychoanalytic thinking toward a systems theory and systems therapy.

❲ History of the Family Movement

The family movement in psychiatry began in the late 1940s and early 1950s with several widely separated investigators who worked privately without knowledge of each other. The movement suddenly erupted into the open in the 1955–56 period when the investigators began to hear about each other, and they began to communicate and to meet together. Growth and development was rapid after the family idea had come to the surface. After family therapy was well known, there were those who said it was not new and that it had developed from what child psychiatrists, or social workers, or marriage counselors had been doing for several decades. There is some evidence to support the thesis that the family focus evolved slowly as early psychoanalytic theory was put into practice. Freud's treatment of Little Hans in 1909,[11] through work with the father, was consistent with methods later developed from family therapy. Flügel's 1921 book, *The Psycho-Analytic Study of the Family*,[9] conveyed an awareness of the family, but the focus was on the psychopathology of each family member. The child-guidance movement passed close to some current family concepts without seeing them. The focus on pathology in the child prevented a view of the family. Psychiatric social workers came on the scene in the 1930s and 1940s, but their work with families was oriented around the illness in the patient. Sociologists and anthropologists were studying families and contributing to the literature, but their work had no direct application to psychiatry. Marriage counseling began its growth in the 1930s, but the dynamic formulations came from conventional psychiatry. Also, general-systems theory had its beginning in the 1930s before there was a recognizable connection between it and psychiatric theory. There is little evidence that these forces played more than an indirect role in ushering in the family movement.

Most of the evidence favors the thesis that the family movement developed within psychiatry, that it was an outgrowth of psychoanalytic theory, and that it was part of the sequence of events after World War II. Psychoanalysis had finally become the most accepted of the psychological theories. It had theoretical postulations about the full range of emotional problems, but psychoanalytic treatment was not clearly defined for the more severe emotional problems. After World War II, psychiatry suddenly became popular as a medical specialty and hundreds of young psychiatrists began experimenting in an effort to extend psychoanalytic treatment to the full range of emotional problems. This includes those who began experimenting with families. A psychoanalytic principle may have accounted for the family movement remaining underground for some years. There were rules to safeguard the personal privacy of the patient–therapist relationship and to prevent contamination of the transference by contact with the patient's relatives. Some hospitals had a therapist to deal with the carefully protected intrapsychic process, another psychiatrist to handle reality matters and administrative procedures, and a social worker to talk to relatives. In those years this principle was a cornerstone of good psychotherapy. Failure to observe the principle was considered inept psychotherapy. Finally, it became acceptable to see families together in the context of "research."

The investigators who started family research with schizophrenia were prominent in starting the family movement. This included Lidz in Baltimore and New Haven,[16] Jackson in Palo Alto,[13] and Bowen in Topeka and Bethesda.[5] Family therapy was so associated with schizophrenia in the early years that some did not think of it as separate from schizophrenia until the early 1960s. Ackerman[1] developed his early family ideas from work with psychiatric social workers. Satir,[20] a psychiatric social worker, had developed her family thinking through work with psychiatrists in a state hospital. Bell[3] and Midelfort[18] were examples of people who started their work very early and who did not write about it until the family movement was well under way. The pattern suggests there were others who never reported their work and who were not identified with the family movement. The formation of the Committee on the Family, Group for the Advancement of Psychiatry, provides other evidence about the early years of the family movement. The committee was formed in 1950 at the suggestion of William C. Menninger who considered the family to be important for psychiatric study. The committee was not able to find psychiatrists working in the field until the family investigators began to hear about each other in the 1955–1956 period.[22]

Spiegel, Chairman of the Committee on the Family, helped organize the first national meeting for psychiatrists doing family research. It was a section meeting at the annual meeting of the American Orthopsychiatric Association in March 1957. It was a quiet meeting. All the papers were on family research, but the notion of "family therapy" or "family psychotherapy" was discussed. Some investigators had been working toward methods of family therapy for several years, but I believe this was the first time it was discussed as a definite method at a national meeting. That was the beginning of *family therapy* on a national level. Dozens of new people, attracted by the promise of *therapy*, and with little knowledge of the family research that had led to the development of family therapy, rushed into the field and began their own versions of family therapy. Another section meeting for family papers at the American Psychiatric Association annual meeting in May 1957 helped amplify the process set in motion two months before. All the papers were on research, but the meeting was crowded and there was more audience urgency to talk about family therapy. The national meetings in the spring of 1958 were dominated by new therapists eager to report experiences with family therapy. Family research and theoretical thinking that had given birth to family therapy was lost in the new rush to do therapy. New therapists entered the field in numbers. Many dropped out after initial therapeutic failure, but there was a rapid net gain in the total field. The 1957–58 period was important in determining the future course of the family movement. In that year family research became known nationally, and in the same year the new family therapists began what the author has called the "healthy unstructured state of chaos." It was considered healthy on the premise that clinical experience would bring an awareness of the theoretical dilemma implicit in family therapy, and awareness would result in efforts to clarify the dilemma. This has not evolved to the degree it was predicted. Some of the newer generations of family therapists have worked toward establishing some theoretical order and structure to the field. A majority of family therapists see family therapy as a method based on conventional, individual theory or as an intuitive, experiential method conducted by therapists who are guided by their own feelings and subjective awareness toward the "use of self" in therapy. Others fall between the two extremes. The range of clinical methods and techniques will be discussed later.

There is suggestive evidence that family therapists come largely from childhood situations in which they had more than average awareness of discord among relatives, some ability to see both sides of an issue, and some motivation to modify the situation. The author uses the term "family movement" in psychiatry to include the theoretical thinking, the family research, and family therapy as they have evolved together and as continue to grow in psychiatric thinking and practice. This is in contrast to the more popular use of the term "family therapy" as it is used to connote a treatment method.

⟮ Common Differences Between Individual and Family Theory and Therapy

The one main difference between an individual and a family approach is a shift of focus from the individual to the family. The nuances of difference between the two approaches are more subtle and far reaching than is evident on the surface. The total fabric of society, as it pertains to human illness, dysfunction, and misbehavior, is organized around the concept of man as an autonomous individual who controls his own destiny. When the observing lens is opened to include the entire family field, there is increasing evidence that man is not as separate from his family, from those about him, and from his multigenerational past as he has fancied himself to be. This in no way changes what man is or has always been. He is as autonomous as he has always been, and he is as "locked in" to those about him as he has always been. The family focus merely points to ways that his life is governed by those about him. It is simple enough to say that the family therapist considers the illness in the patient to be a product of a total family problem, but when this simple concept is extended to its ultimate, then all mankind becomes responsible for the ills of all mankind. It is easy to say this in a philosophical, detached kind of way, but man becomes anxious about the notion of changing himself to help modify the ills of mankind. It is easier for man to fight his wars, inflation, social ills, and pay his money for noneffective corrective action, than to contemplate changing himself. From family therapy, we know it is relatively easy for family members to modify their part in the creation of emotional illness once they clearly see what has to be done, but this does not decrease initial anxiety and evasive action at the mere contemplation of it. This section of the chapter is not designed as a theoretical treatise on the ultimate implications of family theory, but it is to indicate that the deeper implications are there, and they are more far reaching than is easily realized. The following differences between individual and family theory point up a few of the more obvious examples of the differences.

The Medical Model

This cornerstone of sound medical practice requires the physician to examine, diagnose, and treat the pathology in the patient. The medical model also applies to conventional psychiatry and the social institutions that deal with human dysfunction, including the courts, social agencies, and insurance companies. There is an emotional process in the family through which the family helps to create and maintain the "illness" in the "patient." The process is more intense when anxiety is high. The process also operates in the family-therapy sessions. The family members point to the sickness in the patient and try to confirm this by getting the therapist to label the patient the sick one. The therapist tries to avoid diagnosing the patient, and to focus on the family emotional process that creates the patient. The family problem is intensified when the medical records and insurance companies require a diagnosis to comply with the medical model. Each therapist has to find his own way to oppose, neutralize, or deflect the intensity of the family emotional process. The situation is usually less dramatic than presented here, but this illustrates the counterforces as the therapist tries to change the family process and also meet the minimal requirements of the institutions. Some therapists explain the situation to the family that medical-model principles are necessary for records, but a different orientation is used for the therapy. Also, the institutions are a bit less strict in requiring adherence to the medical model. Therapists have come to use the terms "designated patient" or "identified patient" to refer to the symptomatic family member. The mere use of the term implies an awareness of the basic process in the family, in the therapy, and in society. The issues that go around the medical model have ramifications that involve the lives of all the people connected with the problem.

Clinical Responsibility

Members of the mental-health professions have second-nature awareness of the nuances of clinical responsibility for a single "patient." The welfare of the patient comes first and the welfare of the family is outside the realm of direct responsibility. The principles of medical responsibility are changed when the focus is on the entire family instead of the patient. There are situations in which an improvement in the former patient is followed by serious symptoms in another family member. A conventional therapist might send the second family member to another therapist. A family therapist would operate with the premise that the best interests of the family would be served with a single therapist who could deal with the total family problem. There are other similar situations. A conventional therapist could more easily conclude that the patient should be separated from the family, which he considers inately pathogenic to the patient. A family therapist would believe the total family situation would be advanced if the patient were kept at home while he attempted to deal with the overall family anxiety. Family therapists are less likely to consider family members hurtful to each other. They have experience to support the premise that family members want to be responsible and helpful to each other and that it often requires very little help to shift the family climate from a hurtful to a helpful one. The general direction of family therapy is toward helping the family to be responsible for its own, including the "sick" one. It is far more difficult for the impaired family member to begin to assume responsibility than it is for healthier family members. In an effort to more quickly work toward family responsibility, the author developed an approach to work with the "healthiest family member" and to exclude the "sick" family member from the therapy. It has been possible to do an entire course of family therapy with the focus on family health without ever seeing the "sick" family member.

Confidentiality and Secrets

A basic principle of medicine and individual psychotherapy requires that the physician and psychotherapist not divulge confidential information. Family therapists are forced to reevaluate this principle. There are situations in which keeping the confidence of one family member can be detrimental to the total family. From family research we have learned that the higher the level of anxiety and symptoms in a family, the more the family members are emotionally isolated from each other. The greater the isolation, the lower the level of responsible communication between family members, and the higher the level of irresponsible underground gossip about each other in the family and the confiding of secrets to those outside the family. Through pledging a confidence, a person becomes part of the emotional network around the family problem. The basic problem is the relationship pattern in the family rather than the subject matter of the secrets and confidences. A goal in family therapy is to reduce the level of anxiety, to

improve the level of responsible, open communication within the family, and to reduce the irresponsible, underground communication of secrets and gossip to others. When a family therapist becomes entangled in the secrets and confidences, he becomes part of the emotional webwork and his effectiveness as a therapist is lost. Each family therapist has to find his own way of dealing with confidences within the family without becoming part of the emotional entanglements. Most family therapists employ some kind of working rule about not keeping secrets, and they find ways to communicate secrets in the family sessions, rather than err on the side of becoming a part of the family intrigue. From family-therapy experience, we know it can be as detrimental on one side to blindly keep individual secrets as it is detrimental on the other side for the therapist to gossip to outsiders about private matters in a family. The goal of a family therapist is to be a responsible person who knows the difference between underground secrets and valid, responsible, private communication and who respects the difference.

From family therapy we have learned much about the function of secret communication in situations that range from the avowed privacy of the individual psychotherapy hour to the function of secrets and gossip in society. The higher the avowed intent of secrecy in individual psychotherapy, the greater the chance the patient will gossip to others about the therapist, or the therapist will gossip to others about the patient, all done in strictest confidence. In larger social systems, a gossip is one who came from an anxious, gossipy family. The higher the level of anxiety in a social system, the lower the level of responsible communication, and the higher the level of irresponsible gossip and the keeping of irresponsible secret files about individual members. Family-therapy research, with its emphasis on open communication within the family, has been the most observed, audiotaped, filmed, and videotaped of all the psychotherapies. The research points up the emotional problems that result from rigid adherence to conventional rules about confidentiality.

❲ The Spectrum of Methods and Techniques in Family Therapy

The best survey of the family field thus far is *The Field of Family Therapy*, a report by the Committee on the Family, Group for the Advancement of Psychiatry, published in March 1970.[12] It was based on the analysis of a detailed questionnaire completed by some 300 family therapists from all the professional disciplines and all levels of experience. Experience since 1970 indicates that the basic pattern of theory and practice is still very much as it was then. The questionnaire responses represented such wide diversity in theory and practice that it was difficult to find a format to report the results. Finally, a scheme was devised to characterize therapists on a scale from A to Z.

Therapists toward the A end of the scale are those whose theory and practice is the same as individual psychotherapists. They use family therapy as a technique to supplement individual psychotherapy or as the main technique for a few families. The A therapists are usually young or they have just started experimenting with family techniques. The overwhelming majority of family therapists are toward the A end of the scale. The A therapist thinks in terms of individual psychopathology, and he views the therapeutic relationship between the therapist and patient as the modality for emotional growth. He sees family therapy as a technique to facilitate his psychotherapy with the patient, and he speaks of indications and contraindications for family therapy. It is impossible to know how many individual therapists now do occasional family interviews. They characteristically do not make formal reports about their work.

Therapists toward the Z end of the scale use theory and techniques that are quite different. They think in terms of systems, relationships, emotional fields, and breakdown in communication. They tend to "think family" for all emotional problems, and they usually end up seeing a number of family members even if the initial problem in the patient is one for which others would clearly recommend individual psychotherapy. The therapy of a Z-scale therapist is directed toward restoring communication, improving relationships in the family, and toward helping family members toward higher levels of differentiation. There are few therapists toward the Z end of the scale. They are the ones more oriented to research and theory or who have been in practice a long time.

Between the two extremes are therapists with theoretical orientations made up of a mixture of individual and family concepts, and with a wide variety of techniques. The place of therapists on the scale seems to be determined by the therapist's motivation for theory and research, and the professional environment in which he works. The research-oriented therapist is guided more by theory than approval from the professional environment. He usually moves steadily toward the Z end of the scale. The therapy-oriented therapist is more sensitive to the approval of colleagues. He is guided toward a philosophy of treatment that includes a mix of individual and family concepts. When he finds the best "fit" between himself and the professional environment, and between himself and the clinical problem, there is little movement on the scale. The therapy-oriented therapist tends more to try to "sell" his viewpoint and to be critical of others with another viewpoint.

Popular terminology in the field is determined by the usage of terms by a majority of therapists. Most therapists are toward the A end of the scale. They tend to think of family therapy as a method and technique for the application of individual theory. Designations of the type of therapy are determined more by the configuration of family members who attend the sessions than by the theory. The term "family therapy" popularly refers to any psychotherapy session attended by multiple family members. The terms "couples therapy" or "marital therapy" are used when most sessions are attended by both spouses. The term "individual therapy" is used to designate sessions with only one family member. Some use the term "conjoint family therapy" for psychotherapy sessions attended by family members from two or more generations. It often refers to parents and child together. From this orientation it would be possible for a single family to have individual therapy for the patient, couples therapy for the two parents, and conjoint therapy for parents and patient. The author is at the extreme Z end of the scale. For him the terminology is based on the theory. The term "family therapy" is used for the effort to modify the family-relationship system, whether that effort is with one or with multiple family members. Since 1960 he has spoken of "family therapy with one family member," which is consistent with his orientation but can be considered inaccurate by most family therapists. The author objected to the title *The Field of Family Therapy*, for the 1970 survey of the family field on the grounds that it did not recognize the thinking and research that helped create the field. A majority of the committee members insisted on this title on the grounds that it best represented the field as it exists.

❲ Specific Methods and Techniques of Family Therapy

The following is a brief summary of some of the most prominent, different methods of family therapy. The list is designed to communicate the author's view of the overall pattern to the growth and development of family therapy. It is not designed to present the work of any one therapist or any group of therapists. Most therapists tend to use a combination of the methods.

Family Group Therapy

A high percentage of family therapy should more accurately be called family-group therapy since many of the basic principles were adapted from group psychotherapy. It is noteworthy that specialists in group psychotherapy have had no more than a secondary interest in family therapy. There were no group psychotherapists among the originators of the family movement. Some group therapists became interested in developing family therapy a few

years after family therapy was introduced. That group has grown gradually, but it has been relatively separated from the main body of family therapists. The group therapists doing family therapy attend the group-therapy meetings and they publish in group-therapy journals with relatively little overlap between the groups. If one can consider this as a fact without value judgment about why it came to be, it can say something about the nature of the family movement.

Most of the influence of group psychotherapy on family therapy has come from people who had some early professional training in group psychotherapy, but who did not consider themselves to be group therapists. In 1957 when new therapists began developing their own version of family therapy, without much knowledge of family research, the already defined methods of group psychotherapy offered more guidelines than any of the other existing methods. In addition, the psychodynamic formulations of group psychotherapy were reasonably consistent with training in individual psychotherapy. I believe this may account for the strong influence of group psychotherapy on family therapy.

Methods of family-group therapy vary from therapist to therapist, but there are some common denominators. The basic theory, the psychodynamic formulations, and the interpretations are reasonably consistent with individual therapy and also with group therapy. The therapeutic method and encouraging family members to talk to each other come from principles of group therapy. Family-group therapy comes closer to the popular stereotype of family therapy than any other. This involves all the family meeting together to discuss problems. Family-group therapy is one of the easiest of the methods for the relatively inexperienced therapist. It requires that the therapist develop some facility for relating to people in a group without taking sides and without becoming too entangled in the family emotional system. Beyond this, most professional people can operate with skills learned in training. As a method it yields very high initial results with comparatively little effort by the therapist. Most families with symptoms are out of emotional contact and are not aware of what each is thinking and feeling. The higher the level of anxiety, the more family members are isolated from each other. With a family therapist acting as chairman of the group and the facilitator of calm communication, much can be accomplished in a short time. Parents can profit from hearing the thoughts and feelings of each other. Children can be fascinated at hearing the parental side of issues and learning that parents are human, too. Parents can be amazed at the astute observations of their children about the family, and the child is grateful for an opportunity to say what he thinks and for the forum that values his ideas. The family can eagerly look forward to such sessions, which they cannot manage at home because of emotions and communication blocks. The process can reach a point of pleasant exhilaration, with parents increasingly aware of each other and the children increasingly able to accept the foibles in the parents. When communication improves, family symptoms subside and the family can report much more fun and togetherness. Of course, there are situations where the process is not as smooth as described here. These are the very impaired, chaotic families and those in which it is difficult to bring family members together without emotional explosions. However, if the therapist is able to keep the communication calm for the volatile family and if he is able to stimulate communication for the more silent family, the net result is on the favorable side.

The main advantage in family-group therapy is the striking, short-term result. The main disadvantage develops when the family-group therapy becomes a longer-term process. At this point, the family begins to act out the same problems they had at home. The parents begin to expect the children to assume more responsibility in the family. The more adequate children become bored by the repetition of issues and they look for reasons not to attend. If forced to attend, the formerly talkative children can become silent. The maximum results with short-term family-group therapy come within about ten to twenty sessions, depending on the intensity of the problem and the skill of the therapist.

A fair percentage of families tend to terminate at the point of feeling good about the family. If they terminate before they reach the impasse of underlying problems, the family feels confident it has learned to solve its own problems, the family praises the magic of family therapy, and the therapist is positive about his accomplishment. This may account for the use of family-group therapy as a short-term method. Some therapists terminate at this point and arrange follow-up visits for the future. If the family goes into the emotional impasse of longer-term therapy, they may terminate feeling that little was accomplished. It is usually not possible for parents and children to continue together beyond a certain point. It often results in the parents and one child or the two parents continuing without the others.

Family-group therapy is not as effective for long-term family therapy as some of the other methods. The continuation of it as a long-term method, to a reasonable resolution of the underlying problem, depends on the intensity of the problem and the skill of the therapist. Very impaired families may continue for a long time, using the therapy much as an individual psychotherapy patient uses therapy, for support. Therapists tend to develop other methods and techniques if the goal is to get through the emotional impasses.

Couples Therapy—Marital Therapy

These terms help to point up the ambiguity in the field and specifically imply that the spouses are in some kind of therapy in which the focus is on two people and their relationship. The terms convey nothing about the problem for which the therapy is used, or the theory or method of therapy. Some therapists restrict use of the terms to problems in the marital relationship, such as marital conflict or marital disharmony. A high percentage of marriages have some degree of conflict or disharmony. Other therapists have a broader view of marital problems and use marital therapy for an additional range of problems, such as impotence and frigidity. From experience, the focus on the relationship aspects of such problems can more quickly resolve the problems than focusing on the individual aspects of the problems. Others use marital therapy for problems outside the marital relationship, such as problems in a child. Such considerations say nothing about the theory, the method, or the technique of therapy. In general, theory is determined by the way the therapist thinks about the nature of the family problem; method is determined by broad principles for implementing the theory into a therapeutic approach; and techniques are the specific ways or strategies for implementing the method. Therapists trained in individual theory, and who accept the assumptions of individual theory as fact, are usually not much aware of theory. Terms such as theory, hypothesis, assumption, formulation, and concept are used loosely and inaccurately. It is not uncommon to hear someone say, "I have a theory," when it would be more accurate to say, "I have an idea." It would be improbable that anyone could have a theory about marital relationships that is not part of a larger theory. Marital therapy might accurately apply to a method if it is based on a theory about the nature of the problem to be modified. The general use of the terms, couples therapy or marital therapy, implies merely that both spouses attend the sessions together. The use of the terms is a good example of the wide divergence of practice in the family field.

Psychoanalytic Marital Therapy

This term has not been used widely. If it were generally used, it would be one of the more specific terms in the family field. The theory would be consistent with psychoanalytic theory, the method would be reasonably consistent with the theory, and therapy techniques would have a reasonable resemblance to psychoanalytic techniques. This is a method used frequently by family therapists who formerly practiced psychoanalysis. One of the main differences in techniques would be the analysis of the relationship between the spouses rather than the transference relationship with the therapist. This method involves the process of learning more about the intrapsychic process in each spouse, in the presence of the other spouse, with access to the emotional reactiveness of each spouse to the other. The approach provides access to the unconscious through the use of dreams. A new dimension is added when spouses can analyze the dreams of each other. Readings on the intrapsychic process in each are obtained through simultaneous dreams. This is one of the most effective long-term methods of family therapy. It works best when the initial problem was in one spouse or the marital relationship. The author used it a number of years before moving to a systems approach to the entire family-relationship system.

Child-Focused Family

This term refers to a well-defined family problem rather than a therapy approach, but it is used frequently enough to warrant discussion here. The child-focused family is one in which sufficient family anxiety is focused on one or more children to result in serious impairment in a child. The child-focused energy is deeply imbedded, and it includes the full range of emotional involvements from the most positive to the most negative. The higher the anxiety in the parents, the more intense the process. For instance, a mother in her calmer periods can *know* that nagging makes the child's problem worse. She may resolve to stop the nagging, only to have it recur automatically when anxiety rises. The usual approach in family therapy is to soften the intensity of the focus on the child and to gradually shift the emotional focus to the parents, or between parents and families of origin. This might be relatively easy if the problem is not intense, or it can be so intense that little is accomplished beyond symptomatic relief and easing the pressure for the child. There are differences about what to do with the child. Child psychiatrists tend to focus major attention on the child and supportive attention on the parents. Family therapists tend to focus on the emotional process in the family with parents and child together. This approach may bring good initial results, but there are difficulties when it becomes a long-term process. Some family therapists will see the child separately or have someone else see the child. This can result in parents becoming complacent, expecting the problem to be solved in the child's "therapy." There is no single highroad to success in these families. Finding a way through the problem depends on the therapist's concept of the problem and his skill in keeping the family motivated. My own approach is to remove the focus from the child as quickly as possible, remove the child from the therapy sessions as early as possible, and give technical priority to getting the focus on the relationship between the parents, at the risk of a temporary increase in the child's symptoms. This broad spectrum of differences around a single clinical problem conveys some idea of the differences in the field, and this does not even touch the differences about what goes on in the individual sessions.

Transactional Analysis, Games Theory, Gestalt Theory

These three theoretical concepts are grouped together because all three, though each different in its own right, occupy similar positions in the total scheme of family therapy as it is practiced. These concepts and the therapeutic approaches that go with them were either developed before family therapy or they were developed independent of family therapy. These approaches are not incompatible with individual theory, they provide ingenious ways of conceptualizing relationship systems, and they represent a step toward systems theory. For the therapist attempting to extend his knowledge of family process, these concepts provide ready-made concepts that are more precise for understanding the family and for improvements in therapy. Success with these therapy methods, as with most other methods, depends on the skill of the therapist.

Behavior-Modification Therapy

Almost every experienced family therapist has done some version of behavior-modification therapy, which has now become a well-defined method. The family presents a near-perfect model of a "system" in operation. The family is a system in that each member of the system, on cue, says his assigned lines, takes his assigned posture, and plays his assigned role in the family drama as it repeats itself hour by hour and day by day. This process operates without intellectual awareness. When any principal member of the family can observe and come to know his own part in the family and purposely change his part, the others will immediately change in relation to it. Family members who can become adept at knowing their roles can bring about predictable change in the action-behavior patterns in others. The disadvantage is in the short-term nature of the change. There are two main variables that limit the long-term result. First, the other family members rather quickly catch on and they start their own versions of adapting to it, or they initiate their own changes. Then the process can become "game playing." Secondly, the whole system of reacting and counterreacting is imbedded in the emotional system, and the initiator has to keep on consciously and purposely initiating the change. When there is a lapse, the family system returns to its former level. Long-term change requires a modification in the intensity of the emotional level, at which time such changes can become permanent.

Cotherapist Therapy

The use of two therapists, or several therapists, began very early in the family movement. A high percentage of family therapists have had some experience with it. Originally, it was used to help the therapist become aware of his own emotional overinvolvement with family members. Whitaker[24] routinely used a cotherapist in psychotherapy with schizophrenia long before he started family therapy. He also has become well known for using cotherapists in his long career in family therapy. Others have developed it as a method for including both male and female therapists who serve as a model for the family. Boszormenyi-Nagy[4] is one who has been prominent in perfecting this model in his method of therapy. Still another use of cotherapists is the team approach in which several therapists, representing the various members of the mental-health professions, work together as a team. MacGregor[17] and his group made a major effort to perfect this during his work in Galveston in the early 1960s. He now teaches and trains family therapists with the team approach. Some version of the family-therapy, team approach is now used in most centers that do family therapy. In the broad spectrum of family therapy, cotherapist therapy exists as one of the major innovations and developments in family therapy. It is used both as a method and technique.

Sculpting and Simulated Families

These two innovations are the modern-day descendants of drama therapy. Sculpting is listed first because it has more application to therapy. The simulated family was developed in the early 1960s, more for teaching than for therapy. In teaching, it involves professional people who playact hypothetical family situations. Role playing helps family process become more real to the participants. In therapy, one or more members of a real family have outside people role play the parts of absent family members. People who participate in simulated families discover an uncanny sense of realness to the role-played situation. Sculpting was developed in the late 1960s to help family members become more aware of self in relation to their own families. The therapist helps the family members decide on the functioning position of each family member in relation to the others, following which the family members are put into physical apposition. The sculpting sessions in which family members debate the position of each, plus the living sculpture in which they assume positions such as bossy, meek, clinging, and distant provide both a cognitive and feeling experience that is one of the more rapid ways of helping family members become aware of each other. The sculpting may be repeated during therapy for awareness of change and progress. These two methods are examples of other innovative developments in the field.

Multiple-Family Therapy

The most popular version of this was developed by Laqueur[15] for members of several families who meet together in a form of family-group therapy for discussion of individual and shared family problems. It is most useful for severely impaired or fragmented families. Multiple-family groups have been started around groups of inpatients and families on visiting days at mental hospitals, around families and patients attached to mental-health centers, and families and patients discharged from mental hospitals. This method provides a unique and effective method of support and a relationship system that enables patients to be discharged earlier and to be maintained at home and in the community. New families can replace those who discontinue, while the group continues to serve as an ongoing resource for former families who wish to return. This method has also been used successfully with less impaired people. It is least effective in helping individual family members toward defining a self. The author has devised a method of multiple-family therapy specifically designed to help individual family members toward higher levels of functioning. The therapist works with each family separately, dividing the time between the three or four families and avoiding communication or emotional exchange between the families. The focus on the family emotional process in each family can permit beginning individuation in that family. Emotional exchange between the families encourages group process, which overshadows family process, and individuation is impaired or blocked. Advantages of the method are faster progress in each family from observing the others and a net saving in time. Disadvantages are additional work in scheduling and the energy required of the therapist in maintaining structure.

Network Therapy

This method was devised by Speck[21] in the mid-1960s. It was designed to help "create" families for fragmented, disorganized families. The goal is to include people from the friendship network in addition to relatives. The isolated family may have few available relatives and few close friends. The therapist encourages the family to invite relatives and close friends, and friends of friends, and friends of friends, etc. The meetings often include fifteen to forty people, but Speck has had meetings with up to 200 people. Meetings are held in homes or in other appropriate places in the neighborhood. The therapist begins with discussion about the problem in the central family for which the network was assembled. Discussions soon shift to other problems in the network. Theoretical premises about networks are that people have distorted ideas about problems of others, that distortions are often worse than reality, that friends become distant during stress, and open discussion of problems can stimulate more real relationship activity and helpfulness to network members. Experience with networks tends to support the premises. Some remain to talk for hours after meetings have ended, some do become more helpful around the central problem, and network attitudes about the central problem are modified. When regular network meetings continue, a fair percentage lose interest, attendance at meetings dwindles, and continuation requires enthusiasm by the therapist and those who organize the network. On the negative side, the logistical problems of organizing time-consuming, evening meetings, and the clinical expertise necessary for managing large meetings with divergent emotional forces, makes this a difficult therapeutic method. The network idea has a potential both for the understanding of social networks and the development of therapeutic methods. In practice, the network has come to be a short-term method, or one to achieve a specific goal. One successful application has been for new admissions to mental hospitals. One or two meetings are held to include the family, friends, and people who had contact with the patient before admission.[14] Meetings ease the impact of admission and facilitate discharge. Additional meetings may be called at nodal points during hospitalization.

Encounters, Marathons, Sensitivity Groups

These methods are examples of a trend that has increased in the past decade. Therapists who practice the method are usually not members of the family movement, and the method lends itself to unstructured use by people with little training. The methods are short-term and are based on partial theoretical notions that suppressed feelings are responsible for symptoms, and that the awareness of feelings and the expression of feelings in relation to others is therapeutic. For some, such methods can result in temporary periods of feeling good and exhilaration, which is called growth. For others, the sessions are followed by an increase in anxiety and symptoms. This movement is antithetical to the efforts of the majority of family therapists.

⟨ Experiential and Structured Family Therapy

An increasing number of family therapists are beginning to classify the various family-therapy methods into experiential and structured methods. This is a modification of the A to Z scale in *The Field of Family Therapy*. The experiential approaches put a high premium on becoming aware of feelings, in being able to express feelings directly to others, and in becoming more spontaneous in relationship systems. Most therapists agree that a spontaneous, open relationship system is a desirable result for family therapy, but there is disagreement about the best way to help families achieve this. The structured approach uses theoretical concepts about the nature of the family problem and a therapeutic method that is based on the theory. The method contains a built-in blueprint to guide the course of the therapy. The method knows the problems to be encountered during therapy; it has a methodology for getting through the difficult areas; and it knows when it approaches its goal. This is in contrast to the experiential approaches that emphasize the subjective experience of therapy, that rely on the subjective awareness and intuition of the therapist to guide the therapy, and that consider the development of more open spontaneity in relationships to be the goal. A structure-oriented therapist makes decisions based on theory, and he stays on course in spite of any feelings of his against it. An experiential therapist uses feelings and intuitive, subjective awareness to make his decisions. If all approaches are put on a continuum, the encounter-marathon approaches would be at one end of the continuum. Farther along the continuum would be approaches that offer more and more structure, with less and less emphasis on the expression of feelings as a guiding principle. There is no such thing as an all-feeling situation, or an all-structured situation. The human animal is a feeling being and any approach has to somehow deal with feelings and, also, the realities of relationships with others. The type of approach is not a positive index of success in therapy. There are Indian scouts better qualified to lead an expedition through the wilderness than inexperienced novices with scientific instruments. The structure-oriented therapists believe that knowledge and structure, in addition to experience, will eventually produce a better result. To summarize this point, the experiential orientation says, "Know and express your feelings and the process will break down the unhealthy structure that interferes with your life." The structured orientation says, "Problems are the result of a poorly structured life. The surest approach is the modification of the structure, which will automatically result in free and spontaneous relationships."

The following are some examples of therapists who have worked toward theoretical structures that are different from conventional individual theory. Jackson[13] began working on communication theory in the 1950s. Before his death he had extended his thinking into well-defined systems concepts that clustered around his communication model. His therapy reflected his theoretical thinking. In more recent years, Minuchin,[19] in association with J. Haley who formerly worked with Jackson, has developed a structured approach with theoretical concepts so well-formulated that he has automatic therapeutic moves for any clinical situation. His theoretical concepts view man, and his intrapsychic self, in the context of the relationship system around him. Through his relationships man influences those about him and man, in turn, is influenced by those about him. His therapeutic approach, consistent with his theory, is designed to modify the feedback system of the relationship system through which the whole family is modified. His therapy specifically avoids a focus on the intrapsychic forces. The author has worked toward a family-systems theory of human adaptation and a method of therapy designed to modify the relationship system by modifying the part the individual plays in the relationship system. The therapy also avoids focus on the intrapsychic forces. No one is ever really accurate in describing the work of another. The author's approach will be presented in more detail later.

Conclusions

This survey represents one view of the diversity in theory and practice as it has evolved in the family field during the past two decades. In 1960, the author used the analogy of the six blind men and the elephant to describe a similar situation in the family field. Each blind man felt a different part of the elephant and the assumption of each was accurate within his own frame of reference. The same analogy is accurate today as different family therapists view the family through different frames of reference. The family is a complex organization that remains relatively constant no matter who observes and defines it. At the same time, there can be a wide variety of different concepts that accurately describe the family. Early in the family movement most therapists viewed the family through familiar theories about intrapsychic forces within the individual. This was accurate within limits, but the theory was awkward and inaccurate for conceptualizing the relationship patterns through which the intrapsychic forces in one person were interlocked with the intrapsychic forces in others. Family therapists began using a variety of different concepts to account for the interpersonal forces. This resulted in one theory for the intrapsychic forces and another for the interpersonal forces. A majority of therapists still use this combination of theories, each finding the most compatible combination for himself. There are problems in using two different kinds of theories for the same overall phenomenon. Most of the relationship theories used the functional concepts of systems theory. In the past decade, the term "systems" has been misused to the point of simplistic meaninglessness, but the trend toward systems thinking points to a definite direction. The world of systems thinking has sent men to the moon and back, but systems concepts are poorly defined in areas that apply to man and his functioning. Systems thinking has a tremendous potential for the future, but the "elephant" of systems thinking is far bigger and more complex than the "elephants" of the past. The author's effort at developing a systems theory represents the serious effort of another "blind man." It is presented in the following sections of this chapter.

(A Systems Theory of Emotional Functioning

The main problem in defining a systems theory is in finding a workable collection of functions that can be integrated into a functional whole. The number of choices in the selection of pieces for such a theory is almost infinite. Selection is governed by some overall framework. It is easier to do a theory about a small area of functioning than a large area. Without a framework one can emerge with multiple concepts, each accurate within itself, that do not fit together. The universe is our largest conceptualized system. From a systems model we know there are logical connections between the atom and the organization of the universe and between the smallest cell and the largest known collection of cells, but the development of workable theories are still far in the future. Large areas of specific knowledge are lacking. The conceptual integration of new knowledge can take longer than the original scientific discovery. Into the far distant future man must be content with his lack of knowledge and discrepant, partial theories.

The following are some of the basic notions about the nature of man that guided the selection of the various concepts in this systems theory. Man is conceived as the most complex form of life that evolved from the lower forms and is intimately connected with all living things. The most important difference between man and the lower forms is his cerebral cortex and his ability to think and reason. Intellectual functioning is regarded as distinctly different from emotional functioning, which man shares with the lower forms. Emotional functioning includes the automatic forces that govern protoplasmic life. It includes the force that biology defines as instinct, reproduction, the automatic activity controlled by the autonomic nervous system, subjective emotional and feeling states, and the forces that govern relationship systems. There are varying degrees of overlap between emotional and intellectual functioning. In broad terms, the emotional system governs the "dance of life" in all living things. It is deep in the phylogenetic past and is much older than the intellectual system. A "feeling" is considered the derivative of a deeper emotional state as it is registered on a screen within the intellectual system. The theory postulates that far more human activity is governed by man's emotional system than he has been willing to admit, and there is far more similarity than dissimilarity between the dance of life in lower forms and the dance of life in human forms. Emotional illness is postulated as a dysfunction of the emotional system. In the more severe forms of emotional illness, the emotions can flood the intellect and impair intellectual functioning, but the intellect is not primarily involved in emotional dysfunction. There are varying degrees of fusion between the emotional and intellectual systems in the human being. The greater the fusion, the more the life is governed by automatic emotional forces, despite man's intellectual verbalization to the contrary. The greater the fusion between the emotion and intellect, the more the individual is fused into the emotional fusions of people around him. The greater the fusion, the more man is vulnerable to the emotional forces around him. The greater the fusion, the more man is vulnerable to physical illness, emotional illness, and social illness, and the less he is able to consciously control his own life. It is possible for man to discriminate between the emotions and the intellect and to slowly gain more conscious control of emotional functioning. The biofeedback phenomenon is an example of conscious control over autonomic functioning.

A major concept in this systems theory is developed around the notion of fusion between the emotions and the intellect. The degree of fusion in people is variable and discernible. The amount of fusion in a person can be used as a predictor of the pattern of life in that person. In developing any systems theory it is not possible to develop concepts to cover each piece of the total puzzle. In developing this theory an effort has been made to make each concept harmonious with the overall view of man described here and, above all, to avoid concepts that are discrepant with the overall view.

The Theoretical Concepts

The theory is made up of a number of interlocking concepts. A theory of behavior is an abstract version of what has been observed. If it is accurate, it should be able to predict what will be observed in other similar situations. It should be able to account for discrepancies not included in the formulations. Each concept describes a separate facet of the total system. One may have as many different concepts as desired to describe smaller facets of the system. These concepts describe some overall characteristics of human relationships, the functioning within the nuclear family system (parents and children), the way emotional problems are transmitted to the next generation, and the transmission patterns over multiple generations. Other concepts about details in the extended family and the ways family patterns are interlinked with larger social systems will be added to the theory at a later

time. Since the total theory has been described in other publications,[6,7] the concepts will not be described in detail here.

DIFFERENTIATION OF SELF SCALE

This concept is a cornerstone of the theory. It includes principles for estimating the degree of fusion between the intellect and emotions. The term "scale" conveys the notion that people are different from each other and that this difference can be estimated from clinical information. It is not a scale to be used as a psychological instrument by people not familiar with the theory and the variables in a relationship system. The scale refers to the level of solid self that is within self, which is stable under stress and which remains uninfluenced by the relationship system. The solid self is easily confused by the pseudoself that is determined by the relationship system and can fluctuate from day to day or year to year. The pseudoself can be increased by a congenial relationship and emotional approval and decreased by a negative relationship or disapproval. An index of the pseudoself is the degree to which people act, pretend, and use external appearances to influence others and to feign postures that make them appear more or less adequate or important than they really are. The degree of pseudoself varies so much that it is not possible to make a valid estimate of solid self except from estimating the life patterns over long periods of time. Some people are able to maintain fairly even levels of pseudoself for several decades. With all the variables, it is possible to do a reasonably accurate estimate of the degree of differentiation of self from the fusion patterns in past generations and from the overall course of a life in the present. Estimates of scale levels provide important clues for family therapy and for predicting, within broad limits, the future adaptive patterns of family members.

TRIANGLES

This concept describes the way any three people relate to each other and involve others in the emotional issues between them. The triangle appears so basic that it probably also operates in animal societies. The concept postulates the triangle or three-person system as the molecule or building block of any relationship system. A two-person system is basically unstable. In a tension field the two people predictably involve a third person to make a triangle. If it involves four or more people, the system becomes a series of interlocking triangles. In a multiple-person system, the emotional issues may be acted out between three people, with the others relatively uninvolved, or multiple people clump themselves on the poles of the emotional triangle. Psychoanalytic theory, without specifically naming it, postulates the oedipal triangle between parents and child, but the concept deals primarily with sexual issues, and it is awkward and inaccurate to extend this narrow concept. There are two important variables in triangles. One deals with the level of "differentiation of self"; the other with the level of anxiety or emotional tension in the system. The higher the anxiety, the more intense the automatic triangling in the system. The lower the level of differentiation in the involved people, the more intense the triangling. The higher the level of differentiation, the more the people have control over the emotional process. In periods of low anxiety, the triangling may be so toned down that it is not clinically present. In calm periods, the triangle consists of a two-person togetherness and an outsider. The togetherness is the preferred position. The triangle is rarely in a state of optimum emotional comfort for all three. The most uncomfortable one makes a move to improve his optimum level of emotional closeness–distance. This upsets the equilibrium of another who attempts to adjust his optimum level. The triangle is in a constant state of motion. In tension states the outside position is preferred, and the triangle moves are directed at escaping the tension field and achieving and holding the outside position. The predictable moves in a triangle have been used to develop a system of therapy designed to modify the triangular emotional system. The moves in a triangle are automatic and without intellectual awareness. The therapy focuses on the most important triangle in the family. It is designed to help one or more family members to become aware of the part that self plays in the automatic emotional responsiveness, to control the part that self plays, and to avoid participation in the triangle moves. When one person in the triangle can control self while still remaining in emotional contact with the other two, the tension between the other two subsides. When it is possible to modify the central triangle in a family, the other family triangles are automatically modified without involving other family members in therapy. The therapy also involves a slow process of differentiation between emotional and intellectual functioning and slowly increasing intellectual control over automatic emotional processes.

NUCLEAR FAMILY EMOTIONAL SYSTEM

This concept describes the range of relationship patterns in the system between parents and children. Depending on the relationship patterns each spouse developed in their families of origin and the patterns they continue in marriage, the adaptive patterns in the nuclear family will go toward marital conflict, toward physical or emotional or social dysfunction in one spouse, toward projection of the parental problems to one or more children, or to a combination of all three patterns.

FAMILY PROJECTION PROCESS

This concept describes the patterns through which parents project their problems to their children. This is part of the nuclear family process, but it is so important that an entire concept is devoted to it. The family projection process exists to some degree in all families.

MULTIPLE-GENERATION TRANSMISSION PROCESS

This concept describes the overall pattern of the family projection process as it involves certain children and avoids others and as it proceeds over multiple generations.

SIBLING POSITION

This concept is an extension and modification of sibling-position profiles as originally defined by Toman.[23] The original profiles were developed from the study of "normal" families. They are remarkably close to the observations in this research except that Toman did not include the predictable ways that profiles are skewed by the family-projection process. Knowledge gained from Toman, as modified in this concept, provides important clues in predicting areas of family strength and weakness for family therapy. This is so important that it has been included in a separate concept.

([Family-Systems Therapy

This method of therapy evolved as the theoretical concepts were developed and extended. During the late 1950s, the term "family therapy" was used for the method when two or more family members were present. The deciding factor revolved around the therapeutic relationship when only one family member was present. In the years prior to family research, the author had operated on the premise that the most reliable method for emotional growth was the working out of psychopathology as it was expressed in the relationship with the therapist. Now this basic premise was changed. The new effort was to work out problems in the already existing, intense relationships within the family and to specifically avoid actions and techniques that facilitate and encourage the therapeutic relationship. A change of this magnitude, for one trained in psychoanalysis, is so great that many say it is impossible. The first few years it was difficult to avoid a therapeutic relationship with only one family member and the designation "individual therapy" was accurate for that situation. Gradually, it became impossible to see one family member without automatically thinking about the part played by other family members in this person's life. Transference issues, formerly considered critical for the resolution of problems, were avoided until more family members could join the sessions. By 1960, the technique of working with one family member was sufficiently refined so that it was accurate to begin to talk about family therapy with one family member.

Family therapy for both parents and one child together illustrates another nodal point in the development of this theory and method. These are families faced with school and adolescent-behavior problems in the youngster. Most of the parental anxiety is focused on the symptom in the child. In the family-therapy sessions, in the physical presence of the child, it is difficult to get the parents to focus on themselves. The average good outcome of such therapy would come in about twenty-five to forty appointments covering about a year, with the aggressive mother becoming less aggressive, the passive father less passive, and the child's symptoms much improved. The family would terminate with high praise for family therapy, but with no basic change in the family problem. This experience led to rethinking the theory and developing new techniques to get the focus on the hypothesized problem between the spouses. The triangle concept was partially developed. Now parents were asked to accept the premise that the basic problem was between them, to leave the child out of the sessions, and to try to focus on themselves. The results were excellent and this technique has been continued since 1960. Some of the best results have been achieved when the symptomatic child was never seen by the therapist. In other situations the child is seen occasionally to get the child's view of the family, but not for "therapy." The child's symptoms subside faster when the child is not present in the therapy, and parents are better motivated to work on their own problems. This experience led to the present standard method of family therapy in the triangle consisting of the two parents and the therapist.

Another effort began early in the family movement. This was directed at neutralizing the family emotional process to create the "sick patient" and to make the therapist responsible for treating the patient. Terms such as, "people," "person," and "family member" replaced the term "patient." Diagnoses were avoided, even in the therapist's private thinking. It has been more difficult to replace the concepts of "treatment," "therapy," and "therapist" and to modify the omnipotent position of the therapist to the patient. Most of these changes have to occur within the therapist. Changing the terms does not change the situation, but it is a step. When the therapist has changed himself, the old terms begin to seem odd and out of place. There is the continuing problem of using an appropriate mix of old terms and new terms both in relating to the medical and social institutions and in writing. It has been most difficult to find concepts to replace "therapy" and "therapist" in work with the families and to keep them in the profession. I have found terms such as "supervisor," "teacher," and "coach" helpful. The term coach is probably the best at conveying the connotation of an active expert coaching both individual players and the team to the utmost of their abilities.

One of the most difficult changes has been in finding ways to relate to the healthy side of the family instead of the weak side. It is a slow, laborious task to improve the functioning of the weakest family member. It is many times more effective to work through the healthy side of the family. Opposing this are the family forces to create the patient and the popular notion that psychiatrists are to treat mental illness. One example from a period in the early 1960s will illustrate the point. This came from therapy with conflictual marriages in which each spouse would continue the cyclical, nonproductive report about what was wrong with the other, each trying to prove it was the other who needed to see a psychiatrist. It was effective for the therapist to say he would not continue the cyclical process, that they should decide who was healthiest and he would do the next sessions with the healthiest alone. The focus on both parents, no matter the location of the problem in the family, is a step toward work with the healthy side of the family. The search for the most responsible, most resourceful, and most motivated part of the family can be elusive. It is best determined from knowledge of the family emotional process and the functioning patterns in the past and present generations, in collaboration with the family. The potential source of family strength can be lost in an emotional impasse with a nonproductive family member.

More details about working with a single, motivated family member will be presented later.

With this theoretical, therapeutic system, the term "family therapy" is derived from the way the therapist thinks about the family. It refers to the effort to modify the family-relationship system, whether the effort is with multiple family members, the two spouses together, or only one family member. The term "family-systems therapy" began after the theoretical concepts were better defined. It is more accurate than previous terms, but it is not well understood by those not familiar with systems concepts. The term "systems therapy" is now used more often to refer to the process either in the family or in social systems.

Family-Systems Therapy with Two People

This method is a standard approach for therapists who use this theoretical-therapeutic system. The concept about modifying the entire family in the triangle of the two most important family members and the therapist was well formulated by the mid-1960s. The method has been used with several thousand families by the staff and trainees in a large family training center. It has been used alongside other methods in the effort to find the most productive therapy requiring the least professional time. The major changes since the mid-1960s have been in a better understanding of triangles, clearer definition of the therapist's function in the triangle, and minor changes in techniques. The method was designed as one that would be effective for short-term therapy and that could also go on to long-term therapy. It works best for people who are capable of calm reflection. It is for two people in the same generation with a life commitment to each other. For practical purposes this means husbands and wives. Other twosomes, such as parent and child, two siblings living together, a man and woman living together, or homosexual pairs, are not motivated for significant change in the relationship.

THEORETICAL ISSUES

A relationship system is kept in equilibrium by two powerful emotional forces that balance each other. In periods of calm the forces operate as a friendly team, largely out of sight. One is the force for togetherness powered by the universal need for emotional closeness, love, and approval. The other is the force for individuality powered by the drive to be a productive, autonomous individual as determined by self rather than the dictates of the group. People have varying degrees of need for togetherness, which constitutes the life style (level of differentiation of self) for that person. The greater the need for togetherness, the less the drive for individuality. The mix of togetherness and individuality into which the person was programmed in early life becomes a "norm" for that person. People marry spouses who have identical life styles in terms of togetherness–individuality.

People with lower levels of differentiation of self have greater needs for togetherness and less drive for individuality. The greater the need for togetherness, the harder it is to keep togetherness forces in equilibrium without depriving certain family members. Discomfort and symptoms develop when togetherness needs are not met. The automatic response to anxiety and discomfort is to strive for more togetherness. When this effort fails repeatedly, the family member reacts in ways characteristic to that person. The reactions include dependent clinging, seductiveness, pleading, acting helpless, denial of need, acting strong, dictatorial postures, arguing, fighting, conflict, sexual acting out, rejection of others, drug and alcohol abuse, running away from the family, involving children in the problem, and other reactions to the failure to achieve togetherness.

When a family seeks psychiatric help, they have already exhausted their own automatic mechanisms for achieving more togetherness. Most family-therapy methods put emphasis on the family need for understanding and togetherness. The therapist tries to help the family toward more love, consideration, and togetherness by discarding counterproductive, automatic mechanisms in favor of calmer and more productive mechanisms. These methods are effective in achieving symptom relief and a more comfortable life adjustment, but they are less effective in modifying the life style of family members.

This method is designed to help the family move as rapidly as possible toward better levels of differentiation. It proceeds on the assumption that the forces for individuality are present beneath the emotional reactiveness around togetherness, that the individuality forces will slowly emerge in the favorable emotional climate of the therapy triangle, and that togetherness forces will automatically readjust on a higher level of adaptation with each new gain in individuality.

METHOD

The method was developed from experience with emotional forces in a triangle. Emotional tension in a two-person system immediately results in the twosome involving a vulnerable third person in the emotional issues of the twosome. From earlier family therapy with three family members present, the emotional issues cycled between the family members and evaded the therapist's efforts to interrupt the cycles. This method is designed to put the two most important family members into therapy with the therapist, which makes the therapist a target for family efforts to involve a third person. Progress in therapy depends on the therapist's ability to relate meaningfully to the family without becoming emotionally entangled in the family system.

At the beginning of therapy the two family members are involved in an emotional fusion manifested by a "we," "us," and "our" clinging together, or by an opposite version of the same thing, which is an antagonistic posture against the other. If the therapist can relate to the family over time, without becoming too entangled in emotional issues, and if he can recognize and deal with his entanglements when they do occur, it is possible for two separate selfs to slowly emerge from the emotional fusion. As this occurs, the emotional closeness in the marriage automatically occurs, and the entire family system begins to change in relation to the change in the spouses.

TECHNIQUE

The most important aspect of the therapy depends on the therapist's ability to stay neutral in an emotional field, and his knowledge of triangles. Each therapist has to find his own way to maintain emotional neutrality in the therapy situation. My best operating, emotional distance from the family, even when sitting physically close, is at the point where I can "see" the emotional process flowing back and forth between them. The human phenomenon is usually as humorous and comical as it is serious and tragic. The right distance is the point at which it is possible to see either the serious or the humorous side of things. If the family becomes too serious, I have an appropriate humorous remark to defuse the seriousness. If the family starts to kid and joke, I have an appropriate serious remark to restore neutrality. An example was a wife going into detail about her critical, nagging, bossy mother. The husband was indicating his agreement. If the therapist permitted them to believe he also agreed, he would be in the emotional process with them. His comment, "I thought you appreciated your mother's devotion to you," was enough to change the seriousness to a chuckle and defuse the emotional tension. A calm tone of voice and a focus on facts rather than feelings is helpful in keeping an even, emotional climate. Moves toward differentiation of self are usually not possible in a tense situation.

It is necessary for the therapist to keep his focus on the process between the two. If he finds himself focusing on the content of what is being said, it is evidence that he has lost sight of the process and he is emotionally entangled on a content issue. It is necessary to listen to content in order to follow process, but to keep the focus on process. The greater the tension in the family, the more it is necessary for the therapist to stay constantly active to affirm his neutral position. If he cannot think of anything to say, he is emotionally entangled. Within narrow limits, the therapist may use learned comments for emotional situations. If he is only moderately involved, the comment may be effective. Over the years the "reversal" or "paradoxical comment" has come into use to defuse emotional situations. The reversal is a technique of picking up the opposite side of the emotional issue for a neutralizing comment. If the therapist is deeply involved in the family emotional system, the reversal is heard as sarcasm or hostility and the effort fails.

The principal technique of this method is a structure for each spouse talking directly to the therapist in a factual, calm voice. It is talking about emotional process rather than the communication of emotional process. The therapist avoids a structure in which family members talk directly to each other. Even when the emotional climate is calm, direct communication can increase the emotional tension. This one technique is a major change from earlier methods in which emotionally distant family members were encouraged to talk directly to each other.

A typical session might begin with a comment from the husband to the therapist. To respond directly to the husband involves risk in triangling with the husband. Instead, the therapist asks the wife what she was thinking when she heard this. Then he turns to the husband and asks what was going through his thoughts while the wife was talking. This kind of interchange might go back and forth for an entire session. More frequently, the husband's comment is too minimal for the clear presentation of an idea. The therapist then asks the husband as many questions as necessary to elaborate his thinking into a clearer presentation. Then the therapist turns to the wife for her thoughts while the husband was talking. If her comments are minimal, the therapist might ask a series of questions to more clearly express the wife's views. Then he turns to the husband for his response to the wife's comments. There are numerous other techniques for getting to the private thinking world of each and getting it expressed to the therapist in the presence of the other spouse. For instance, the therapist might ask for a summary of private thoughts about the family situation since the last session, or ask for the most recent thinking about a particular family situation. The therapist asks for thoughts, ideas, and opinions, and avoids asking for feelings or subjective responses. In my opinion, this process of externalizing the thinking of each spouse in the presence of the other is the epitome of the "magic of family therapy." Therapists accustomed to emotional exchanges can find these sessions dull and uninteresting, but the families are interested, and motivated to attend the sessions. It is common for spouses to say how much they look forward to the sessions and how they are fascinated to hear how the other thinks. When asked how they could live with one another so many years without knowing what each thinks, they say they can listen and hear when one of them talks to the therapist in a way they could never listen when talking to each other. It is common to hear these comments about increasing fascination at discovering what goes on in the other after having been in the dark so long. Spouses experience a challenge in being as expressive and articulate as possible. People who have formerly been nontalkers gradually become talkers. Expressions of emotional closeness and increasing affection for each other occur at home. This occurs faster than when the effort is directed at emotional expression in the sessions. Other reports include the ability to deal calmly with children, the ability to listen to others for the first time, and new experiences about being able to work together calmly.

When tears or emotion erupts suddenly in a session, the therapist stays calmly on course, asking what was the thought that stimulated the tears, or asking the other what they were thinking when the feeling started. If feeling mounts and the other spouse responds directly to the first spouse, it is evidence of building emotional tension. The therapist increases the calm questions to defuse the emotion and to bring the issue back to him. The therapist is always in control of the sessions, asking hundreds of questions and avoiding interpretations. By considering each new family as a research project, the therapist always has so many questions there is never time to ask more than a fraction of them. The therapist

avoids acting like a wise man who knows the answers. He asks questions and he listens. His ideas about the family are no more than educated guesses. He might tell the family about his guesses and ask for their ideas that support it or refute it. He might tell the family he thinks a particular area of investigation might be helpful, as a way of telling the family what he is thinking and a way of enlisting their effort in the exploration.

A fair percentage of the therapist's time may go to keeping himself disentangled from the family emotional process. The families use their automatic mechanisms in the effort to involve a third person in the triangle. This is more intense early in the therapy and at periods when anxiety is higher than usual. When the therapist knows the characteristics of triangles, and he is alert, he can often anticipate the triangling move before it occurs. There are situations in which a spouse erroneously assumes the therapist has taken sides on an issue. The process of keeping the therapist emotionally neutral gets first priority in the therapy. The goal of the therapist is to keep active and to make statements or take actions that affirm his neutrality and to avoid transference-type interpretations to the family about it. Systems theory assumes that the triangling move is an automatic emotional response of the people involved, and not personally directed, as it might be interpreted to be in individual-relationship therapy. The casual comment or a calm reversal is effective in helping the therapist maintain his neutral position.

After the family anxiety subsides and the spouses are more capable of calm reflection, individuality forces begin to surface in one spouse. This occurs as the spouse begins to focus more on the part that self plays in the relationship problems, to decrease blaming of the other for one's own discomfort and unhappiness, and to accept responsibility for changing self. The other spouse increases the pressure on togetherness demands, which commonly results in the first spouse falling back into the old togetherness. This process proceeds through a number of false starts, with the differentiating one gradually gaining more strength and the other increasing the tempo of the togetherness pleas. The togetherness pressure includes accusations of lack of love, indifference, not caring, and lack of appreciation. When the differentiating one is sure enough of self to proceed calmly on course, in spite of the togetherness pleading of the other, without defending self or counterattacking, and without withdrawing, the attack subsides and the differentiating process passes through its first major nodal point. It may require a year or two for the first spouse to reach this point. This is followed by a period of calm and a new, higher level of adjustment in both. Then the second spouse begins a similar differentiating effort to change self, and the first spouse becomes the promoter of togetherness. New cycles usually take less time and the steps are not as clearly defined as in the first step.

The individuality force emerges slowly at first and it takes very little togetherness force to drive it back underground for fairly long periods. An average life course of people is one that keeps the togetherness–individuality forces in neutralizing balance. The therapist can facilitate the differentiating process by focusing questions on this new area of family issues, by focusing on responsibility for self, and by avoiding any connotation that he is siding with the more righteous-sounding, togetherness pleading.

Teaching in Family-Systems Therapy

Some kind of didactic teaching is necessary for families who go on to long-term therapy with this method. This kind of knowledge provides the family with a way of understanding the problem, an awareness they are responsible for progress, and a framework in which they can direct their energy on their behalf. A very anxious family is unable to "hear" didactic explanations, and the therapist who attempts such explanations becomes deeply entangled in the family emotional system, with inevitable distortions and impasses in the therapy. Teaching statements are used cautiously until after the family is calm. This applies to

the rationale for sending spouses home for frequent visits with their families of origin, which is part of the effort of encouraging them to "differentiate a self" in their extended families. In the later stages of therapy, all kinds of conferences and didactic sessions can be helpful.

Conclusions

This method is effective as a short-term, mid-term, or long-term process. The length of the therapy is determined by the family. There have been a fair percentage of striking "cures" in five to ten sessions, usually for symptoms that erupted from an overintense relationship. An example was a seven-session "cure" of severe frigidity in a young wife. Mid-term, good results often come in twenty to forty sessions when symptoms have subsided and the togetherness-oriented spouse exerts pressure to discontinue. No other approach has been as effective as this in producing good, long-term results. In 1966, this method was adapted for multiple-family therapy. The therapist does thirty-minute sessions with each of four families while the other families are nonparticipant observers. In these half-hour sessions the average family makes a little faster progress than in one-hour sessions for single families. The difference appears related to the ability to "hear" and learn from the other families without reacting emotionally. When the differentiation of self is the goal, it appears to take a certain amount of time for motivated people to modify their life styles. There have been experiments to spread a given amount of therapy time over longer periods of time with less frequent appointments. A majority of multiple-family-therapy sessions are now held monthly, with results as good, or better, than with more frequent sessions. The families are better able to accept responsibility for their own progress and to use the sessions for the therapist to supervise their efforts. Long-term families continue for an average of five years, which includes about sixty multiple-family sessions and about thirty hours of direct time with the therapist.

❨ Toward the Differentiation of Self in One's Own Family

The turning point in the method came in 1967 after an anonymous paper on the differentiation of self in one's own family was read at a national meeting.[10] The method involved a detailed family history for multiple generations in the past and the developing of a personal relationship with all important living relatives. This activates old family relationships grown latent with neglect. Then, with the advantage of objectivity and the knowledge of triangles, the task is to disentangle themselves from old family triangles as they come to life.

In the spring of 1967, I began using material presented at that conference in teaching family therapy to psychiatric residents and other mental-health professionals. They began to see themselves in their own families and to go home to secretly try out the knowledge on their families. This was followed by reports of inevitable emotional impasses and further conference discussion to help understand the problem and make suggestions for the next trip home.

Also in 1967, the residents were better than previous residents as clinicians in family therapy. At first I thought this was related to the quality of residents that year, but according to them, it was experience with their own families that made the difference. There were comments, such as, "Family theory is just another theory until you see it work with your own family. It is easier to help other families with experience from your own family."

The next awareness came in 1968. The residents were doing so well in their clinical work that no attention had been devoted to personal problems with their spouses and children. The effort had been directed toward the training of family therapists. There had been no mention of problems in their nuclear families. In 1968, I discovered that these residents had made as much progress with spouses and children as similar residents in formal weekly family therapy with their spouses. There was a good sample for comparison. Since the early 1960s, I had been suggesting family therapy for residents and their spouses instead of individual psychotherapy or psychoanalysis for personal problems. There was a volume of clinical experience with formal weekly family therapy for psychiatric residents to compare with residents who were going home to visit their families of origin and who were not in any type of formal psychotherapy. This professional experience with psychiatric residents and other mental-health professionals was the beginning of a new era in my own professional orientation.

There is some speculation about the more rapid change in working with the extended families than with the nuclear family. It is easier to "see" self and modify one's self in triangles a bit outside the immediate living situation than in the nuclear family in which one lives. In the years since 1968, this method of work with the extended family has been used in all kinds of conferences and teaching situations and also in private practice type "coaching." A person working actively can utilize coaching sessions about once a month. Some who have access to teaching sessions do not need private sessions, or they need them less often. Some who live at a distance are seen three or four times a year or as infrequently as once a year. This approach is so different, it is hard to compare results with other approaches. It bypasses the nuclear family and the infinite emotional detail in close-up relationships. It appears to produce better results than the more conventional family therapies.

This method has been used largely for those in training to be family therapists, but it has been used with a growing number of others who hear about it and request it. The results are the same, except that there are few people who seek family therapy until they have symptoms. Once a family starts formal family-therapy sessions, it is harder to find motivation for serious work with the families of origin.

The method of defining a self in the extended family has been used as the only method of therapy for a broad spectrum of mental-health professionals, and for nonprofessional people who hear about the method and request it. Work with the extended family is urged for all families in other types of family therapy, but extended family concepts make little sense when people are anxious. After symptoms subside, it is harder for people to find motivation for serious work with their extended families. Any gain from the extended family is immediately translated into automatic gain with spouses and children. Success in working toward defining self in the family of origin depends on motivation and the family situation. It is easiest with highly motivated people with intact families that have drifted apart. At the other extreme are those who are repulsed by the idea of contacting an extended family and those whose families are extremely negative. In between are different levels of motivation and families with varying degrees of fragmentation and distance. It is not a serious problem when parents are dead if there are other surviving relatives. Reasonable results are possible with those who believe they have no living relatives.

Unique experiences with change in extended families are commonplace. This is in addition to change in the nuclear family. In a course in family therapy for freshman medical students and their spouses, there was a student whose father had been in a state hospital for about twenty years. The hospital was near his home town several hundred miles away. The family had been visiting the father about once a year. I suggested that the student visit his father alone, any time he was home, and that he try to relate through the psychosis to the man beneath the symptoms. I was guessing that the father might be able to leave the hospital by the time the son graduated from medical school. He visited the father about four times that year. The following year, about nine months after the course started, the father visited the son while on a furlough from the hospital. Exactly twelve months after the course started, as the son was starting his sophomore year, the father had been discharged from the hospital and was visiting the son. The father attended the twenty-second meeting of that class in family therapy. After having been in a state institution from the age of thirty to about fifty, he was having adjust-ment and employment problems, but the son, the father, and the family had come far in only one year.

[Systems Theory and Societal Problems

The emotional forces in a triangle operate in the same way in society as in the family. Family therapists have been aware of this for a number of years, but the specific mechanisms involved in this have been elusive and hard to define. The author has made one serious effort at this.[8] The larger societal field, with its multiple emotional forces, is a challenge for the concepts of systems theory.

[Conclusion

This chapter presents an overall view of family therapy as it began almost twenty years ago and as it has developed as part of the changing psychiatric scene. An effort has been made to identify some of the forces that gave rise to the study of the family and other forces that seem to have determined the direction of the growth of family therapy. Family therapists represent such a diversity in theory and therapeutic method that it is difficult to find a frame of reference for either the common denominators or differences in the field. An effort has been made to focus on the broad direction rather than attempting to categorize the work of well-known people in the field. It is factual that the greatest number of family therapists operate from psychiatric theory learned in training, and that they use family therapy as a technique. Another large group of family therapists uses conventional theory for thinking about emotional forces in the individual but another theoretical scheme for thinking about the relationship system between family members. A smaller group of family therapists has moved into completely different theories for conceptualizing and working with families. These differences in theory do not have common denominators in the clinical practice of family therapy. There are skillful therapists who would be masters with any therapeutic method. In this sense, family therapy is still more of an art than a science.

Presented here is the thesis that the study of the family opened the door for the study of relationships between people. There was no ready-made, conceptual scheme for understanding relationships. We are living in the computer age in which systems thinking influences the world about us, but systems concepts are poorly developed in thinking about man and his functioning. Most of the family therapists who have worked on relationships have developed systems concepts for understanding the subtle and powerful ways that people are influenced by their own families, by society, and by their past generations. Those who have developed the most complete systems concepts have developed therapeutic methods that bypass individual theory and practice, not because one is considered better than the other but to experiment with possible new potentials. The author is among those who have worked toward developing systems concepts for understanding emotional illness in the broader family framework. He has presented his theoretical, therapeutic system as one of the many ways that family and social systems may be conceptualized, and to provide the reader with the broadest possible view of the diversity in the practice of family therapy. If the present trend in systems thinking continues, we can reasonably expect even more striking developments in the field in the next decade.

⟨ Bibliography

1. ACKERMAN, N. W. *The Psychodynamics of Family Life*. New York: Basic Books, 1958.
2. BATESON, G., D. JACKSON, J. HALEY et al. "Toward a Theory of Schizophrenia," *Behav. Sci.*, 1 (1956), 251–264.
3. BELL, J. E. *Family Group Therapy*, Public Health Monogr., 64. Washington: Department of Health, Education, and Welfare, 1961.
4. BOSZORMENYI-NAGY, I. and G. SPARK. *Invisible Loyalties*. New York: Harper & Row, 1973.
5. BOWEN, M. "A Family Concept of Schizophrenia," in D. Jackson, ed., *The Etiology of Schizophrenia*, p. 346. New York: Basic Books, 1960.
6. ⸺. "The Use of Family Theory in Clinical Practice," *Compr. Psychiatry*, 7 (1966), 345–374.
7. ⸺. "Family Therapy and Family Group Therapy," in H. Kaplan and B. Sadock, eds., *Comprehensive Group Psychotherapy*, pp. 384–421. Baltimore: Williams & Wilkins, 1971.
8. ⸺. *Societal Regression as Viewed through Family Systems Theory*. Paper presented at the Nathan W. Ackerman Memorial Conf., Venezuela, Feb. 1974.
9. FLÜGEL, J. C. *The Psycho-Analytic Study of the Family*. London: Hogarth, 1960.
10. FRAMO, J., ed. (author of article anonymous) "Differentiation of Self in One's Family," in *Family Interaction*, pp. 111–173. New York: Springer, 1972.
11. FREUD, S. (1909) "Analysis of a Phobia in a Five-Year-Old Boy," in J. Strachey, ed., *Standard Edition*, Vol. 10, pp. 5–147. London: Hogarth Press, 1955.
12. GROUP FOR THE ADVANCEMENT OF PSYCHIATRY. *The Field of Family Therapy*. Report No. 78. New York: Group for the Advancement of Psychiatry, 1970.
13. JACKSON, D. and W. LEDERER. *The Mirages of Marriage*. New York: Norton, 1969.
14. KELLY, V. and M. HOLLISTER. "The Application of Family Principles in a Community Mental Health Center," in J. Bradt and C. Moynihan, eds., *Systems Therapy*, pp. 117–127. Washington: The Groome Center, 1971.
15. LAQUEUR, H. P., H. A. LaBURT, and E. MORONG. "Multiple Family Therapy," in J. Masserman, ed., *Current Psychiatric Therapies*, Vol. 4, pp. 150–154. New York: Grune & Stratton, 1964.
16. LIDZ, T., S. FLECK, and A. CORNELISON. *Schizophrenia and the Family*. New York: International Universities Press, 1965.
17. MacGREGOR, R., A. RITCHIE, A. SERRANO et al. *Multiple Impact Therapy with Families*. New York: McGraw-Hill, 1964.
18. MIDELFORT, C. F. *The Family in Psychotherapy*. New York: McGraw-Hill, 1957.
19. MINUCHIN, S. *Families and Family Therapy*.

Cambridge: Harvard University Press, 1974.

20. SATIR, V. *Conjoint Family Therapy.* Palo Alto, Calif.: Science Behavior Books, 1964.

21. SPECK, R. and C. ATTNEAVE. *Family Networks.* New York: Pantheon, 1973.

22. SPIEGEL, J. Verbal communication.

23. TOMAN, W. *Family Constellation.* New York: Springer, 1969.

24. WHITAKER, C. A. "The Growing Edge in Techniques of Family Therapy," in J. Haley and L. Hoffman, eds., *Techniques of Family Therapy,* pp. 265–360. New York: Basic Books, 1967.

CHAPTER 19

PSYCHIATRY AND THE COLLEGE STUDENT

Robert L. Arnstein

⟮ History

THE CAMPUS as the focus of a psychiatric subspeciality is relatively new. The first psychiatric service at a college is difficult to determine, but there is considerable evidence to suggest that Stewart Paton at Princeton in 1910 first recognized the need for psychiatric help for students and began to do professional counseling in an informal manner.[15,21] The next decade saw slow growth with a few colleges experimenting with part-time psychiatric consultants.[12]

It is of significance, however, that the first meeting of the American Student (now College) Health Association in 1920 heard Frankwood E. Williams state the need for mental health programs in college and elucidate the following goals:

1. The conservation of the student body, so that intellectually capable students may not be forced to withdraw but may be retained.
2. The forestalling of failure in the form of nervous and mental diseases, immediate or remote.
3. The minimizing of partial failure in later mediocrity, inadequacy, inefficiency, and unhappiness.
4. The making possible of a large individual usefulness by giving to each a fuller use of the intellectual capacity he possesses, through widening the sphere of conscious control and thereby widening the sphere of social control.[60]

In the 1920s several colleges responded directly or indirectly to this stated need, but it is probable that the U.S. Military Academy at West Point had the first full-time physician acting as a psychiatrist when Harry Kerns spent a year there, primarily dealing with the emotional problems of the cadets.[40] In 1925, Yale, with the impetus provided by its president, James R. Angell, who himself was a psychologist, established a service that has continued uninterruptedly from that time.[4] In 1926, Clements C. Fry came to Yale as a full-time psychiatrist, and he devoted the next thirty years to pioneering work in the theory and practice of psychiatry with college students.[24]

During the 1920s there were two major theoretical views of work with students. The first was the more or less characteristic medical model that conceived of psychiatric service in terms of dealing with students who had acute or chronic emotional problems that appeared to be interfering with their functioning successfully in college.[44] This concept is implicit in Williams' first two principles above. The second was what may be called "the mental-hygiene model" in which there was emphasis on the growth and development of the student with the ultimate goal the attainment of the fullest realization of potential at some point after college.[5] This model tended to deemphasize the illness concept and is the major thrust of Williams' latter two principles. The two models were summarized in the earliest name given to the Yale service: The Division of College Psychiatry and Mental Hygiene.[24]

In the early programs there were a variety of activities tried out, some of which were abandoned because they did not seem to be successful or economically feasible. For example, screening of all freshmen was tried at some universities with the aim of early identification of susceptible individuals so that treatment could be instituted before problems became too severe.[24] Secondly, there were attempts to institute formal academic courses or lectures dealing with mental health, usually for freshmen, again with the assumption that a better understanding of one's own emotional life and mental functioning would act preventively and forestall the onset of illness as well as help with the general development of the student.

Initially, most of the focus of services seems to have been on the undergraduate student, a fact that is exemplified by the common use of the term "college psychiatry" rather than "university psychiatry." Presumably, the undergraduates were the focus because they seemed to be in a more transitional state (between home and the wider world), because there were more of them, and because the graduate

student's problems may have seemed more like other adult's and less "special." Over the years, however, it has come to be recognized that graduate students have their own particular set of problems, and their problems have increasingly become a matter of concern. In the developmental sense they may be more clearly settled in neurotic patterns that are not uncharacteristic of adults in general, but in the psychosocial sense they face certain particular problems that an adult who is more settled in a work or home situation no longer faces. First, they may be financially dependent, either on the continued flow of fellowships and financial aid or on their parents, at an age when many people are self-supporting. Secondly, they may be in conflict about marriage or have actually married and found that marriage while one or both partners are students is subject to certain kinds of pressures that do not usually occur if marriage is undertaken when career preparation is completed. Furthermore, the number of graduate students has grown immensely, so that this group now represents a large fraction of the student body on many campuses and, as such, is an important segment of the population served.

⟨ Tasks Related to Late Adolescent Development

Four major tasks generally are thought to be the developmental tasks of late adolescence.

Emancipation from the Family

In most instances the late adolescent is in the throes of establishing himself or herself as a person separate from the family. This may involve either more or less disruption in the relationship with the family, but in every case individuals must consciously or unconsciously establish for themselves an identity separate from the family's view of them. As a result of Erikson's use of the term "identity" this process is sometimes referred to as "an identity crisis," a popular phrase that probably does not literally describe the process that goes on, inasmuch as "a crisis" in the usual sense of the word may not occur; rather, certain significant changes occur in the individual's self-definition, and these may occur gradually over time.[17]

Choice of Career

During college most students must choose a career. For some this is a relatively easy choice. They have made up their mind in advance that they wish to go into law or teaching or business, but for others it is a choice that is not only difficult but frequently interacts with the problem of emancipation because one aspect of identity formation may be establishing one's own career direction. There are various popular jokes about parents who have essentially decided for their son or daughter what he or she should pursue in the way of a life career, and obviously families vary greatly in the degree to which they attempt to direct their children's lives. The process of deviating from the parental career choice (stated or only hinted at) may be difficult for the student, but it is essential if the choice is going to be the student's rather than the family's. At times students may go off for a period in a completely different direction, but eventually decide that, for their own reasons, they wish to do what the family suggested initially. Although one can argue whether this is independent choice or capitulation, the chances of the choice being rewarding are greater if it is clearly the student's rather than the family's choice; thus, the path of indirection may be an essential factor in a satisfactory final decision.

Sexual Identity

The student must successfully establish a sexual identity that is satisfactory to him or to her. Although in a broader sense for many this may not appear to be a difficult task, the establishing of a sexual identity involves, in addition to performing sexually as a male or female, the ability to establish a relationship of intimacy that has sexual aspects. In most instances, individuals progress through a series of relationships with varying levels of intimacy and sexual involvement. Some may have considerable difficulty in establishing a relationship that is satisfactory in both aspects. Yet, without the ability to achieve this in some degree, the individual's chance of forming a relationship characterized by sustained involvement with a partner of his or her choice seems unlikely. Although the college period is not necessarily the age in which the final development of this ability will occur, there usually is enough social contact during this period so that the elements of feeling and behavior that go into such a relationship will be tried out and found satisfactory or wanting.

The Establishment of the Ability to Work

Although there are some who might argue that this is not a necessary task of adolescent development, for most people the ability to work successfully and fruitfully will be an important part of their future gratification, and for many the college period is the first in which they must achieve this on their own without parental or other prompting. For many the development of the ability to concentrate, to persevere in various tasks, and to find enjoyment in these tasks is an important aspect of the college experience that can be later transposed into job situations or even home tasks.

(Campus Environment

An obvious fact about all college students is that they are enrolled in a college, and, as such, are related to a particular institution for the general purpose of obtaining an education. Although colleges vary in size, location, and student-body composition, there are certain common characteristics of the college experience that are relevant to psychiatric work with students. Almost without exception colleges involve certain curricular requirements, the majority of which include attending classes, reading and/or laboratory assignments, tests, papers and, in many instances, some kind of final comprehensive exam. Furthermore, the curriculum has a definite periodicity with brief in-term vacations and usually a longer break over the summer. During the longer vacation, most students leave the area of the campus and many undertake jobs quite distinct from their college-based activities or travel to broaden their experience.

Most colleges have a central locus or campus on which the major portion of the curricular work will be done. Campuses, of course, vary considerably. Some are in the midst of a city; these may exist as a kind of enclave within the urban area or may be housed in buildings more or less indistinguishable from other buildings in the area. Others are in rural areas and are relatively isolated and self-contained communities situated within well-defined geographical limits. Some colleges are totally residential and almost all students live in dormitories, often with several roommates, either on an assigned basis or with a certain amount of choice as to roommates, room locations, etc. Other colleges are primarily commuter colleges with students living either at home or in rooms and apartments in the environs of the campus.

Similarly, most colleges have an administrative structure with various regulations and policies that apply to academic matters, student activities, behavior on campus, and sometimes behavior off campus. The college community is made up of a series of constituencies (students, faculty, employees, trustees, etc.) but it is a true community, with each constituency having an integral and usually reasonably well-defined relationship to every other constituency. In many colleges, this structure includes a health service, usually with some sort of infirmary that is responsible for providing health care to the students. The health service is usually supported either by a clearly designated health fee, or by general funds derived from tuition or legislative appropriation, and usually (but not always) has a psychiatic division. In addition, there are frequently on campus a series of other individuals in roles related to counseling and support of students (deans, residence-hall counselors, chaplains, etc.)

⟮ Clinical Problems

Problems that students bring to the health service are related to the tasks of adolescent development, and to stresses of the campus environment. In addition, some students present more classically neurotic or psychotic syndromes. Although there are certainly students who come with relatively minor or transient problems, anyone who works on a campus is impressed by the number who display rather severe psychopathology. The most common symptoms are anxiety and depression, but their causes vary greatly. The campus environment and academic work clearly account for some problems. These tend to be similar in nature regardless of the particular college. Trouble concentrating, anxiety about exams, and difficulty in completing papers, all are "syndromes" related to specific academic tasks. The current competitiveness for admission into graduate and professional schools places a particular strain on the ambitious student with a clear goal of graduate study. Similarly, frictions related to roommates, loneliness at being away from home, and anxiety about sex are rather common symptoms related to the living situation. In addition, difficulties caused either by inadvertent breaking of campus rules or deliberate defiance of "authority" occur on occasion. When environmental pressures lead to emotional upset, one may suspect that the individual is susceptible and would, in different circumstances, also develop problems. But the form they take in college often seems to be clearly related to the specific stresses and may differ from the symptoms of somebody of the same age in the armed forces, even though the basic psychological patterns are quite similar.

Sometimes these symptoms are expressed directly and there is a relatively clear connection that the student is aware of but unable to cope with successfully. At other times there is a kind of intermediate step or symptom, such as insomnia or anorexia, that is the presenting complaint, and the student is not aware of the causal connections. Frequently, the student can identify the precipitant and the effect (e.g., the inability to finish a paper leads to depression and anxiety) but is unaware of the connection of this to more generalized feelings of inadequacy, of being under pressure to perform, and of fear that any effort will be judged unworthy. On occasion, symptoms occur without clear-cut precipitating stress, and the student is aware only of a kind of apathy or lack of direction. It may be quite difficult to elucidate the underlying psychodynamics.

As has already been indicated one of the "tasks" of development is establishing a satisfactory sexual identity. For many this poses problems even in an era when sexual experimentation is relatively acceptable. Inevitably, the individual is influenced by peer pressure and behavior. These may, at times, cause the individual to attempt experiences before being emotionally ready, or to feel inadequate if such opportunities are presented and not seized. Furthermore, students find that despite the fact that they are supposed to feel "emancipated" about sexual activity, they may have uncomfortable feelings that are upsetting simply because they are not "supposed" to have them; this, in turn, may make them wonder about their "normality." In addition, during this period an individual may still be in conflict over homosexual feelings and be uncertain about the significance of such feelings. Although there has been some change in societal attitudes toward homosexual feeling and behavior and more open discussion has helped to diminish the feeling that such impulses are "abnormal," there are still many individuals for whom a homosexual feeling or dream is quite frightening. They are particularly prone to such anxiety during the period when they are still attempting to establish a clear sexual identity. For others who may have strong homosexual impulses, the choice of a homosexual or bisexual life may raise anxieties about the problems that this orientation will create in later life.

Marital difficulties are another frequent area of concern. Although all marriages may have some difficulties in the initial phase, student marriages seem particularly susceptible to certain kinds of problems. Because student status is, by definition, temporary, the marriage must adjust to the transient state of one or both partners. If both are students, life patterns are similar, but there may be money pressures, and, if money comes from one or both families, the money pressure may be compounded by family pressure. If only one partner is a student and the other has a full-time job, there may be significant differences in work patterns so that tensions arise over sleeping hours, household chores, and control of the money earned. If a child is involved, the same problems may be intensified, and may cause more difficulty than in a nonstudent marriage. Most students do not study on a continuous basis and the kind of "puttering" that is viewed as an inevitable part of writing a paper or studying for an exam may be seen by the nonstudent partner as "wasting" time and an avoidance of earning money, taking care of the house, or helping with child care. This can easily lead to resentment on the part of the nonstudent partner—or on the part of the student partner if he or she feels that pressure is being applied to help with these tasks at the expense of academic work. Finally, if both partners are pursuing careers, joint planning may be difficult and lead to the necessity for significant compromises, which may create conflict for either or both partners.

Drug use is a rather specialized problem, which has frequently been associated with college students. For many years the major drug on campus was alcohol. Acute intoxication was a syndrome that on occasion required medical treatment although, more frequently, the student recovered spontaneously, if painfully. Because, however, alcoholism is usually not made as a diagnosis until some years of drinking have occurred, drinking was rarely a presenting problem. Occasionally, a student would be seen for more general problems and, on exploration, it would appear that excessive drinking was accounting for some of the difficulties, but alcoholism as such was a relatively rare diagnosis. In the mid-1960s drinking diminished and the use of marijuana and hallucinogens increased. These drugs sometimes became an acute problem when the user suffered "a bad trip" and required reassurance and/or sedation to aid recovery. Chronic use also, at times, interfered with academic work or other activities, and the student would seek help for this reason although, more often, the role of drug use would be admitted by the student only retrospectively. Because, moreover, drug use was highly disapproved of by administrators and faculty, students suspected of, or known to be, using drugs were at times referred to the psychiatrist for help with what was seen as a psychological difficulty. In addition to hallucinogens, various other drugs were used at times, some of which had high addictive potential and represented serious problems, depending on the individual circumstances of use. As a clinical problem college-student drug use probably does not vary greatly from use by anyone else, except that college students are at a stage in development when experimentation often is highly valued, and, therefore, students may be more susceptible to trying a variety of drugs and may be less likely to weigh and to heed the risks. Furthermore, they may be particularly likely to embrace any new drug that appears, so that the pattern of drug use and potential problems connected therewith are subject to rapid and rather constant change. Recently, there has again been an increase in alcohol use.

In addition to these age-specific or situational problems, students may manifest any of the psychiatric problems that exist in any population. Phobias, obsessions, eating disorders, conversion reactions, and psychophysiologic reactions all appear on occasion. Borderline states are quite frequent, and psychoses severe enough to warrant hospitalization occur not infrequently. Suicidal ideation or threat is a particularly alarming symptom, and constitutes one of the most difficult problems to evaluate and handle. There are enough suicides and attempted suicides so that such a symptom must be taken seriously. Although suicide impulses are always a concern, they seem particularly upsetting in a college student who is considered to have clear-cut abilities and a promising future. Students with severe psychopathology often seem to be able to function at college even in the presence of considerable inner psychological distress, but they remain emotionally shaky and a considerable source of concern to the college psychiatrist, to deans, and often to classmates.

⟦ Types of Clinics and Staffs

Historically, mental-health services on campus have developed in a variety of ways.[19] In many instances "help was where you found it," and services tended to develop under the subtle or not so subtle pressure of students who felt the need for discussion of their emotional problems with professionals or semiprofessionals. One channel was medical. A psychiatrist was employed by whatever health service the college had, and the psychiatric service became a section of the health service, usually staffed by psychiatrists, full-time or part-time. Sometimes psychiatric social workers or clinical psychologists were employed, or a mixed staff developed. In these instances the psychologist or the social worker was frequently full-time and the psychiatrist came in as consultant to deal with particularly difficult cases, cases in which hospitalization might be considered or with problems that had a clearcut "medical" component to them. The second way usually involved gradual development within the college psychology department. Students taking psychology courses would seek out the instructor after class or during office hours for help with their personal problems. Eventually, the instructor found himself or herself spending a fair amount of time in a counseling role, often without any official recognition from the college that this was part of the job. As the instructor spent more and more time in counseling, he or she often asked for formalization of the task and, if enough faculty became involved, their activity became "a counseling service." On many campuses there is a well-developed counseling center, staffed and run by psychologists, sometimes autonomous and sometimes under the aegis of the psychology department. A third model developed similar to the second, but originated in the dean's office. Again, presumably, various deans were approached by students for help with what were ostensibly academic problems. These, on discussion, often turned out to be caused primarily by emotional difficulties. As the counseling load increased, a dean might be designated a counselor, and eventually several people in the dean's office became counselors and an official "service" came into being. On a number of campuses a similar development occurred in offices designed to help students in a variety of ways. Whether the office was initially labeled vocational counseling, study help, job placement, or what-have-you, it gradually began to subsume more and more counseling of a personal nature often because individual staff members became particularly interested in counseling. In time, a major function of the office became the kind of psychological counseling that might have occurred in a counseling center or in the psychiatric service. In addition to these formal services, a number of other "natural" counselors exist, such as chaplains or residence-hall supervisors. Although the counseling may be of a more informal nature, they are important sources of counseling help. Furthermore, in recent years "student" services have been started with a number of senior students acting as counselors after a training program.[28] These have more often than not taken the form of drop-in centers or "hot-line" phone services, but at times they have been relatively formal counseling setups.

Thus, psychological help for the student on campus may be provided by a range of services and the college psychiatrist may be only one of several "helping" resources. Often several types of facilities have appeared on the same campus, and more than one campus has been the scene of considerable interprofessional rivalry. The presence of more than one service or center on a campus, however, may be desirable because it gives a student a choice of types of counselors. Thus, the student who feels that there is a stigma to seeing a psychiatrist may seek out a counselor in the personnel and guidance field while another student feels that no one but a fully trained psychiatrist can help. In most instances, the training backgrounds of staff personnel have been rather broad with psychiatrists, psychologists, social workers, guidance counselors, personnel counselors, vocational counselors, and reading specialists all participating in the counseling process. As noted above, on some campuses students have been utilized very successfully in counseling other students, particularly in speciality counseling of one sort or another, e.g., regarding drugs or sex.

([Current Practice

The post-World-War-II period was characterized by the general growth of available psychiatric services, and, not unnaturally, a number of psychiatrists came to work at colleges. This led to increased stress on the medical approach to problems and for a time the medical model seemed to dominate the psychiatric service offered. The psychiatrists tended to offer a type of nonintensive psychotherapy based on psychoanalytic principles.[10] This was often more formalized than the earlier "counseling" approach. It was based on the belief that relatively short courses of psychotherapy could be very helpful to the student who was perhaps "blocked" in some area of development. If this "block" was circumvented, development could then continue naturally with response to, and assimilation of routine life experiences. Furthermore, because the student, simply by the fact of being in college had demonstrated some ability to function at a relatively high level, it was often possible to adopt an optimistic therapeutic stance even when faced with considerable evidence of distress. Economic considerations (most college clinics are free or covered by a relatively small health fee) limit the duration of therapy, (sometimes to diagnosis and referral), but even brief therapy was found to be helpful at times. The development of psychotropic medications in the 1950s added a dimension to the psychotherapeutic approach that enabled many students to remain functional with relatively infrequent support, although it is probable that medication is used less extensively with students than with some patient groups.

In the 1960s, however, the development of community psychiatry concepts introduced new thinking into the psychiatric field, and it is not surprising that some of these ideas were applied to the campus, which, in some senses, represented a prototype community.[42] Consequently, there was a shift in interest back to the concept of prevention and, at times, to the early mental hygiene concept of "full realization of potential," although this concept was usually presented in a somewhat different form. In some instances, a stress on social action as a mental health measure was developed and the concept of advocacy was advanced. Various "preventive" programs were tried, including orientation sessions with freshman students and their parents, encounter groups for new students, credit or noncredit courses with emphases on problems related to mental health, sex-counseling, and group work with faculty and residence-hall supervisors.[9] The course approach had something of a resurgence, with emphasis on the subjects of drugs and sexuality, both of which were considered to be particular problems for college students and amenable to a quasi-didactic approach. In most courses, however, principles of group dynamics were also introduced and instead of offering just lectures, active participation by the students was encouraged through the use of small discussion groups.[53]

Currently, there is a wide variety in the number of facilities and the amount of service offered on any given campus.[27] As has already been indicated, a given campus may have a single facility offering service, such as the psychiatric unit of the college health service, or it may have a counseling center, or it may have some combination of two or even three such facilities. The ability to establish and maintain a service depends on the personnel that can be attracted to such work, the attitude of the administration toward the provision of mental health support, the financial resources available, and the demands of the students. The development of community psychiatry has broadened the scope of such services. A given service may specialize in psychotherapy with individuals or groups; it may offer only emergency service to individuals and concentrate on a preventive program that may include such activities as are listed above; or it may offer some combination of the two. In addition, some universities maintain an infirmary or even, occasionally, a hospital psychiatric ward that can be utilized in the treatment of individuals with severe problems. This kind of facility often allows such individuals to reintegrate and continue in college.[35]

It is generally estimated that 10 percent of a student body seeks psychiatric or psychological help if such help is available.[19] Smaller colleges are frequently dependent on part-time therapists, who may be psychiatrists, psychologists or social workers. Obviously, the demand may not justify a full-time therapist and the ability to staff a part-time program frequently depends on the proximity to centers that have psychiatrists, psychologists, or social workers available. For the most isolated colleges this may be a considerable problem, but even for small colleges in an urban center it may be difficult to arrange for consultation when it is needed. In an attempt to meet this problem, an unaffiliated service has been developed in Boston that works on a contract basis with colleges in the area.[27] This solution has the advantage of providing both emergency coverage and specific therapeutic service. Major universities often have large, varied programs with multiple facilities: a counseling center on campus, a psychiatric service with an infirmary attached to the student-health service, a psychiatric center with a psychiatric ward staffed by the medical school, and a vocational-testing center, all of which may be available to students. A recent pilot study to collect information for a mental health data bank indicates that some large universities may have as many as fifty-one therapists.[3]

(Organization Support

As college psychiatry has developed over the years, various organizations have been formed that have provided national leadership. The main organization is the American College Health Association (ACHA) and specifically its Mental Health Section. Since its first meeting, the ACHA has been active in asserting the importance of the principles of mental health and has actively encouraged mental health programs on campus. Currently,* the Mental Health Section, in addition to meeting annually and discussing problems of mutual interest, is involved in several activities including the development of standards and the establishment of a system of data collection for exchange of information among various college services.[1]

Over the years the ACHA has held five "national conferences" on the subject of university health. In connection with these, task forces have been established to develop position papers on different aspects of campus-health problems. The Mental Health Task Force Report for the fifth conference in 1970 is an interesting review of current issues in the campus mental health sphere.[2] Written at the height of student protest and at a time when emphasis on student participation in governance was an important "plank" of the protest, there was considerable focus on the use and participation of students in both the planning and provision of services. The impact of political movements on the psychiatric service was also considered. The difficulties inherent in either publicly espousing political positions or, conversely, in *not* espousing them were discussed in relation to the effect that such positions had on the willingness of students to consult the service for emotional problems.

In a different mold, the Committee on the College Student of the Group for the Advancement of Psychiatry has been a small but rather influential group that, over the years, has published several reports on various aspects of mental health in colleges, two or three of which have had particular impact. The initial report of this committee, which outlined the functions of a campus psychiatrist, is still quite pertinent,[30] and a report published in 1965, entitled *Sex and the College Student*, received widespread publicity.[32]

In addition, college psychiatry has been a concern of a committee of the American Psychiatric Association and counseling is a major concern of the American Personnel Guidance Association as well as the American Psychological Association. Furthermore, the American Orthopsychiatric Association has for several years presented a program at its annual meeting on a topic related to college psychiatry, and the American Society for Adolescent Psychiatry has given some attention to the college age.

(International

Understandably, the concern over problems of college-age individuals is not restricted to the United States, and there have been several conferences of an international nature that have been well attended and during which different cultures have compared experiences.[25,61] Obviously, the educational system in each country has some impact on the type and need for service within a given country, but, not surprisingly, the basic principles seem to be quite similar. In Europe, students enter the university and choose a particular area of study at a relatively young age, perhaps nineteen. After a year or two in the university, problems may develop among those students who are dissatisfied with their career choice, but who find it extremely difficult at that point to modify their career plans. In this connection, several European psychiatrists were impressed with the United States system in which a career choice usually is postponed until the junior or senior year of college. It was pointed out, however, that the United States system has the drawback of allowing for, even encouraging, postponement of career decisions, so that frequently juniors or seniors have an acute crisis over the issue of choice.

International comparisons illustrate the role that the political organization may play in the provision of services. In France, for example, a national student organization supports the student outpatient psychiatric services and, during the height of student protest in 1968, the student organization came to the conclusion that the problems of students lay not in the individual but in the society. Thus, it was felt that psychiatrists should be using their energies to change the social system rather than to engage in therapy with individuals. Consequently, financial support was withdrawn for any kind of individual therapeutic efforts. Consideration of such examples helps identify the aspects of the provision of services that have to do with the particular culture and/or educational system. It also tends to highlight those problems of late adolescence which seem more related to the particular educational, political, and social system of a given nation or culture than to psychological development in the more general sense.[47]

(Research

Research has been an ongoing activity of college psychiatry almost since the beginning, although there has been ebb and flow in the findings produced. In the early years, most of the papers either described particular kinds of clinical problems that were seen on the college campus or described ways in which the college psychiatrist performed in the college context.[24,54,57] In the 1930s, somewhat more systematic reviews of particular syndromes were conducted as well as descriptions of therapeutic considerations in working with students.[49] In the 1940s and 1950s, there were two or three major studies that attempted to gather information on aspects of personality development during college.[58] In the 1960s, a variety of research studies appeared, ranging from those focusing on a particular aspect of college psychiatry, such as study problems, to descriptions of problematic kinds of approaches to various student difficulties.[33,46,48] In the early part of the decade, the GAP Committee published a report that focused on the opportunities for psychiatric research and detailed some of the research that had been done.[31]

In addition, there have been a few comprehensive studies of personality development either focusing on an individual's adjustment to college or relating the individual's college experience to prior patterns of psychosocial development. Currently, the American College Health Association is developing a research data bank it hopes to use in codifying information about the kinds of services that are rendered to students, and, if possible, the kinds of problems that are seen in college psychiatric clinics. The Joint Information Service (of the American Psychiatric Association and the National Association of Mental Health) has published a field study by an interdisciplinary team that describes the services on seven college campuses, chosen to provide diversity in regard to size, location, and type.[27] The methods of providing help to students with emotional problems were investigated in some depth, and the report gives a good picture of the type and philosophy of service at different institutions. The Massachusetts Institute of Technology has been particularly interested in studying the impact of institutional organization (i.e., the college) on the student,[56] and Harvard has attempted to trace the adaptation of a particular group of students to college, detailing the changes that occurred in the individual students during their four college years. This has been done through a repeated series of tests and interviews conducted at intervals thoughout the students' college careers.[41] A similar study, conducted at Vassar some years ago, stressed changes that occurred in student attitudes during the four years at college,[52] and a variety of studies at Stanford attempted in-depth descriptions of student attitudes and behavior.[37]

(Training

Although training has gone on for some time in the college setting on an informal basis, probably the first formalized training program was instituted at Yale by C. C. Fry in 1950 as the result of an endowment, part of which was donated specifically to train mental health professionals for work with college students.[7] In the mid-fifties, NIMH established separate speciality training grants for college psychiatry, and programs were started at Harvard and the University of California at Berkeley, as well as expanded at Yale. In the years since, other colleges have instituted similar programs. These programs have flourished when funding has been available, and during residency training a fair number of psychiatrists have spent periods, either full-time or part-time, in college-health services. This gave them experience in conducting brief outpatient psychotherapy for the problems of the college age and in working within the college community. In 1969, a conference was held in Chicago on the subject of training psychiatrists for work with adolescents.[45] Although college students are questionably defined as adolescent, work with college-age individuals was included, and a considerable body of theory was presented about how this is best done. In general, the theory advances a concept of relatively brief therapy, which is often deliberately discontinuous, allowing the individual to respond to the ordinary experiences of life, as well as to the experience of the therapeutic process. It is based on the conviction that emotional development continues at least into the individual's early twenties and psychological patterns up to that point are not necessarily fixed.

(The College as Total Community

Traditionally, the concern of college psychiatrists has almost exclusively been with providing service to students. Recently, however, probably as a result of the intensified interest in community psychiatry, a trend toward extending the service to nonstudents has occurred.[13] Several psychiatrists have felt that the influence of the faculty on the campus climate is very significant and, thus, if a faculty member is emotionally disturbed, he or she may be a rather disruptive influence. The logical corollary to this view is the offering of therapy to faculty and administration as well as to students. Similarly, for some time it has been the practice of some clinics to treat student spouses on the same basis as students on the theory that, if the spouse is very upset, it will inevitably affect the student's ability to

function. Therapy may be offered individually, as couples, or in couples' groups. Some advocates of the community approach have suggested extending service to individuals, officially unconnected with the institution, who live in the area. The argument is similar: if emotionally disturbed "street" people are living with or near students, they may be disruptive to student functioning. Although not many health-service clinics have been able to offer such service, many of the student staffed and operated drop-in centers, rap rooms, and hot lines are available to anyone who wishes to use them.[28] The concept may become even more relevant (and more complicated) when sex-counseling is offered because this service often stresses a therapeutic program that is based on a couple as a unit. If only one is a student and the other is not formally related to the student (i.e., married), it may be difficult to undertake treatment without extending the boundaries of eligibility. This may not be difficult if it just involves "counseling" inasmuch as one can argue that the same amount of staff time is being used whether one or two individuals are in the room, but, if procedures are involved, problems of fees, responsibility, etc. arise.

(Special Operational Problems

For the psychiatrist, working on a campus creates certain special problems. First, while confidentiality is always important in psychiatric practice, in the college community it is vital.[30] In offering psychotherapy it is essential that the confidentiality of the process be established because if students feel that the information they disclose is in any sense available to administrative personnel they will simply not avail themselves of the service. Secondly, one goal of the institution is to provide an education, which each student who enters is supposed to complete. For some students, however, *not* completing the course may at a given time be more appropriate. The therapist may find it difficult to respond therapeutically without appearing either to align himself with the institutional goal or deliberately to eschew it. The patient may be skeptical of the therapist's neutrality and the patient's parents may strongly object to it. Third, inasmuch as the patient constituency is usually the student body, individuals or small student groups may demand or press for certain kinds of therapeutic activity that the therapist does not see as an appropriate function or does not believe is effective. Thus, if students have read a popular article on a relatively unorthodox type of therapy, they may ask for this type of therapy and be disappointed or angry if it is not available. Even if the therapist feels it is a reasonable treatment method, economic factors may limit the range of therapies that can be offered, and the one asked for may be considered less desirable than others by the therapist. Fourth, inasmuch as the therapist is usually a staff member of the health service, and, therefore, paid by the institution, when controversies or confrontations arise, the students may suspect that the therapist is actually acting as an agent of the college. At times, the college administration will feel that the psychiatrist should fill this role, and it may require considerable skill on the part of the psychiatrist to maintain an uncompromised position of independence that is both convincing to the student and acceptable enough to the administration so that funding is not cut off. Fifth, inasmuch as students are frequently being evaluated for post-college study, jobs, fellowships, etc., the psychiatrist may well be asked for an opinion as to the student's emotional fitness for a particular position or occupation. Many services have taken the stand that information gained in therapy should not be used for evaluative purposes and they have refused to answer such requests. It is important, however, to have clear-cut policies about such matters so that students do not feel betrayed either by the provision or nonprovision of information.

health. The consultant role actually represents a considerable opportunity to act as a community psychiatrist, but it also can be a precarious position. There is considerable difference of opinion among psychiatrists as to how strongly the psychiatrist should pursue this role.[6] Some feel that almost any college matter may have an influence on the mental health of students, and, therefore, the psychiatrist should actively conduct research designed to understand these influences and, once data has been obtained, should attempt to apply it as vigorously as possible toward constructive change. This may include curriculum design, rooming arrangements, disciplinary procedures, and residence hall architecture, among other subjects. Others feel that the psychiatirst should be less expansive and restrict consultation to matters that seem to have a more direct medical relationship, such as policies on drugs. Some feel that the psychiatrist should not be involved in the consultant role at all and should simply stand ready to help individuals who seek therapy. One particular role that some psychiatrists have essayed is that of facilitator of communication between adversary campus groups. Justification for this activity is based on the belief that psychiatrists have knowledge about group dynamics and communication and experience in identifying and eliminating difficulty in both these areas.[34] Thus, some feel that these skills can usefully be employed in situations involving a conflict between opposing campus constituencies. In a somewhat similar context on one campus, a psychiatrist was appointed ombudsman for grievances of all types.[36] Although it is not clear that a psychiatrist was essential for this task, it was felt in this instance that his knowledge of people and their psychological functioning would help in the working out of problems that arose.

([Consultant to the College

A difficult role that the college psychiatrist may be asked to fulfill is as consultant to the college on policy matters related to mental

([Conclusion

College students and their particular emotional problems have been a source of concern for the psychiatrist almost since the beginning of the century. The approach has been dual: first, to help with any specific symptoms or difficulties in functioning that the student may manifest while a student, and, second, to aid the student in realizing his or her full potential as an individual. The psychiatrist early recognized the impact of the campus environment on the individual, but initially was more concerned with the individual's inner psychological functioning. During the last decades, under the influence of the community psychiatry movement preventive activities were intensified. Currently, in an attempt to change the campus climate, a psychiatrist may be involved in providing therapy for students, in developing preventive programs, and in acting as consultant to the college on issues that may affect mental health. In addition, the college psychiatrist may be engaged in research efforts to understand factors that affect the psychological adjustment of students and may participate in training other mental health workers and campus advisers to recognize and deal with the emotional problems of students.

❨ Bibliography

1. AMERICAN COLLEGE HEALTH ASSOCIATION. *Recommended Standards and Practices for a College Health Program*, rev. ed. Evanston, Ill.: American College Health Association, 1969.
2. ――. Natl. Conf. Health Coll. Commun. Task Force 3 Report. *Mental Health in the Academic Community*. Evanston, Ill.: American College Health Association, 1970.
3. ――. Data Bank Committee. Mimeographed letter, Jan. 23, 1973, Evanston, Ill.
4. ANGELL, J. R. "Mental Hygiene in Colleges and Universities," *Ment. Hyg.*, 17 (1933), 543–547.
5. APPEL, K. E. and L. H. SMITH. "The Approach to College Mental Hygiene," *Ment. Hyg.*, 5 (1931), 52–71.
6. ARNSTEIN, R. L. "College Psychiatry and Community Psychiatry," *J. Am. Coll. Health Assoc.*, 20 (1972), 257–261.
7. ARNSTEIN, R. L. and J. P. PLUNKETT. "Training of Psychiatric Residents in a Student Mental Health Clinic," in D. Offer and J. F. Masterson, eds., *Teaching and Learn-*

ing Adolescent Psychiatry, pp. 39–53. Springfield, Ill.: Charles C. Thomas, 1971.
8. AXELROD, J., M. B. FREEDMAN, W. R. HATCH et al. *Search for Relevance: The Campus in Crisis*. San Francisco: Jossey-Bass, 1969.
9. BARGER, B. "The Development of a University Mental Health Program," *J. Am. Col. Health Assoc.*, 15 (1966), 80–83.
10. BLAINE, G. B. JR. "Therapy," in G. B. Blaine, JR. and C. C. McArthur, eds., *Emotional Problems of the Student*, pp. 232–249. New York: Appleton-Century-Crofts, 1961.
11. BLAINE, G. B., JR. and C. C. McARTHUR, eds. *Emotional Problems of the Student*. New York: Appleton-Century-Crofts, 1961.
12. BLANTON, S. "A Mental Hygiene Program for College," *Ment. Hyg.*, 9 (1925), 478–488.
13. BLOOM, B. L. "Characteristics of Campus Community Mental Health Programs in Western United States–1969," *J. Am. Col. Health Assoc.*, 18 (1970), 196–201.
14. BLOS, P. *On Adolescence: A Psychoanalytic Interpretation*. New York: Free Press, 1962.
15. CONKLIN, E. G. "Obituary, Stewart Paton," in *Yearbook of the American Philosophical Society*, 1942, p. 354. Philadelphia: American Philosophical Society, 1943.
16. EASTMAN, W., C. B. REIFLER, and M. B. LIPTZIN. "He Loves Me, He Loves Me Not: Student Marital Decisions," *J. Am. Coll. Health Assoc.*, 17 (1969), 230–237.
17. ERIKSON, E. H. "Identity and the Life Cycle," in *Psychological Issues*, Part 1. New York: International Universities Press, 1959.
18. ――. *Youth: Identity and Crisis*. New York: Norton, 1968.
19. FARNSWORTH, D. L. *Mental Health in College and University*. Cambridge: Harvard University Press, 1957.
20. ――. *Psychiatry, Education and the Young Adult*. Springfield: Ill.: Charles C. Thomas, 1966.
21. FARNSWORTH, D. L. and G. B. BLAINE, JR., eds. *Counseling and the College Student*. Boston: Little, Brown, 1970.
22. FREEDMAN, M. B. *The College Experience*. San Francisco: Jossey-Bass, 1967.
23. FREUD, A. *The Ego and the Mechanisms of Defense*. New York: International Universities Press, 1946.
24. FRY, C. C. and E. G. ROSTOW. *Mental Health in College*. New York: Commonwealth Fund, 1942.
25. FUNKENSTEIN, D. H., ed. *The Student and Mental Health: An International View*.

Cambridge: World Federation for Mental Health, 1959.

26. FUNKENSTEIN, D. H. and G. H. WILKIE. *Student Mental Health, An Annotated Bibliography, 1936–1955*. London: World Federation for Mental Health, 1956.

27. GLASSCOTE, R. M., M. E. FISHMAN, C. B. REIFLER et al. *Mental Health on the Campus: A Field Study*. Washington: Joint Information Service of the American Psychiatric Association and the National Association of Mental Health, 1973.

28. GRANT, C. H., K. O. HUBBLE, and C. J. HELM. "The Utilization of Peers in a College Crisis Intervention Program," *J. Am. Coll. Health Assoc.*, 21 (1973), 327–332.

29. GROUP FOR THE ADVANCEMENT OF PSYCHIATRY, Committee on the College Student. Report 32. *Considerations of Personality Development in College Students*. New York: Group for the Advancement of Psychiatry, 1955.

30. GROUP FOR THE ADVANCEMENT OF PSYCHIATRY, Committee on Academic Education. Report 17. *The Role of Psychiatrists in Colleges and Universities*, revised. New York: Group for the Advancement of Psychiatry, 1957.

31. GROUP FOR THE ADVANCEMENT OF PSYCHIATRY, Committee on the College Student. Report 52. *The College Experience: A Focus for Psychiatric Research*. New York: Group for the Advancement of Psychiatry, 1962.

32. GROUP FOR THE ADVANCEMENT OF PSYCHIATRY, Committee on the College Student. Report 60. *Sex and the College Student*. New York: Group for the Advancement of Psychiatry, 1965.

33. HALLECK, S. L. "Psychiatric Treatment of the Alienated College Student," *Am. J. Psychiatry*, 12 (1967), 642–650.

34. ———. "The Changing Nature of Student Psychiatry in an Era of Political Awareness," *Am. J. Psychother.*, 24 (1970), 566–578.

35. JANOWITZ, J. F. "Is this Moratorium Necessary?" *J. Am. Coll. Health Assoc.*, 16 (1968), 378–381.

36. KATCHADOURIAN, H. "The Psychiatrist in the University at Large," *J. Nerv. Ment. Dis.*, 154 (1972), 221–227.

37. KATZ, J., H. A. KORN, V. ELLIS et al. *No Time for Youth*. San Francisco: Jossey-Bass, 1968.

38. KENISTON, K. *The Uncommitted: Alienated Youth in American Society*. New York: Harcourt, Brace, and World, 1965.

39. ———. *Young Radicals: Notes on Committed Youth*. New York: Harcourt, Brace and World, 1968.

40. KERNS, H. M. "Cadet Problems," *Ment. Hyg.*, 5 (1923), 688–693.

41. KING, S. H. "Characteristics of Students Seeking Psychiatric Help during College," *J. Am. Coll. Health Assoc.*, 17 (1968), 150–156.

42. LARSON, E. A. "Community Mental Health on a College Campus," *J. Am. Coll. Health Assoc.*, 15 (1966), 87–91.

43. LIEBERT, R. *Radical and Militant Youth: A Psychological Inquiry*. New York: Praeger, 1971.

44. MENNINGER, K. A. "Adaptation Difficulties in College Students," *Ment. Hyg.*, 11 (1927), 519–527.

45. OFFER, D. and J. F. MASTERSON, eds. *Teaching and Learning Adolescent Psychiatry*. Proc. Conf. Training in Adolescent Psychiatry, University of Chicago, 1969. Springfield: Ill.: Charles C. Thomas, 1971.

46. ORNSTON, D. G., JR. "Academic Decline," *J. Am. Coll. Health Assoc.*, 17 (1969), 458–465.

47. PEARLMAN, S. *University Mental Health: International Perspectives*. Evanston, Ill.: American College Health Association, 1970.

48. PERVIN, L. A., L. E. REIK, and W. DALRYMPLE, eds. *The College Dropout and the Utilization of Talent*. Princeton: Princeton University Press, 1966.

49. RAPHAEL, T. and M. A. GORDON. "Psychoses Among College Students," *Am. J. Psychiatry*, 95 (1938), 659–675.

50. SANFORD, N., ed. *The American College: A Psychological and Social Interpretation of the Higher Learning*. New York: Wiley, 1962.

51. SANFORD, N. *Where Colleges Fail*. San Francisco: Jossey-Bass, 1967.

52. SANFORD, N., M. B. FREEDMAN, H. WEBSTER et al. "Personality Development during the College Years," *J. Soc. Issues*, 12 (1956), 3–70.

53. SARREL, P. M. and H. COPLIN. "A Course in Human Sexuality for the College Student," *Am. J. Public Health*, 61 (1971), 1030–1037.

54. SCHWARTZ, C. G. and M. J. KAHNE. *Conflict*

and Contradiction in College Psychiatry: The Evolution of a Professional Sub-Specialty. Unpublished.

55. SIGGINS, L. "Psychoanalytic Psychotherapy with University Students," in *The Problems of University Life*, pp. 43–51. Canberra, Australia: Australian National University, 1973.

56. SNYDER, B. *The Hidden Curriculum.* New York: Knopf, 1971.

57. THOMPSON, L. J. "Mental Hygiene in a University," *Am. J. Psychiatry*, 8 (1929), 1045–1051.

58. WEDGE, B. M., ed. *Psychosocial Problems of College Men.* New Haven: Yale University Press, 1958.

59. WHITTINGTON, H. G. *Psychiatry on the College Campus.* New York: International Universities Press, 1963.

60. WILLIAMS, F. E. "Mental Hygiene and the College Student," *Ment. Hyg.*, 5 (1921), 283–301.

61. WORLD UNIVERSITY SERVICE. *Report on the Proceedings of the Conference of Experts on Student Mental Health.* State University of Groningen, Netherlands, Jan. 4–11, 1970. Geneva: World University Service, 1972.

CHAPTER 20

SEXUAL-INCAPACITY THERAPY

Edward A. Tyler

THERAPEUTIC MEASURES for human sexual incapacities are as old as recorded history. Documentation usually appeared in vignettes concerning persons of status, fame, or notoriety.[29,34,65,66] These persons were almost exclusively males, since, until this century, women were defined as having low or no sexual,[22] intellectual, or achievement drives. In contrast, the potency and virility of men was believed to be positively correlated with their bravery, leadership ability, competence as soldiers, influence with the gods, etc. Known or rumored impotence in a king or tribal leader could lead to his being expelled, killed, or replaced. Not only were leaders supposed to produce heirs, but crop failures, poor hunting and fishing harvests, lack of rain, losses in battle were often attributed to a male leader's impotence or lack of virility. It was believed that a witch or the devil could cast a spell of impotence on a man. The witch was believed to use such devices as an invisible ligature around the base of the penis of the afflicted male. With this etiology, the logical treatment was to destroy the hapless woman accused of being the guilty witch.

As recently as the first part of the twentieth century, the Christian world subscribed to a moralistic etiology.[66] It was believed to be God's punishment or, at least, a deserved consequence of sexual excesses such as masturbation (self-abuse),[57] "excessive" sexual excitement during courtship, "excessive" coitus, "unnatural" prolongation of coitus (for the alleged greater gratification of the female), "abnormal" coital positions, and sexual activities with lascivious females. "Therapies" were prescribed by priests (penances), mystics (love potions), and by physicians (advice and pharmaceuticals). In 1900, an authoritative book[66] recommended that "the first indication is to determine what is the morbid factor and when discovered to treat it on general medical principles . . . some benefit may follow the judicious installation of strong nitrate of silver solution into the prostatic urethra. . . . In some cases much benefit is produced by the ingestion of a combination of atropine and strychnine. . . . Quinine in three grain doses given three times a day, particularly in combination with strychnine, and in very atonic cases with atropine is sometimes of marked beneficial affect. . . . A preparation composed of various animal extracts, known as phospho-albumen acts as a decided sexual tonic in some cases. . . . Chloride of gold and sodium administered in the form of pills in doses of one-twentieth of a grain, three times a day, have been vaunted by several authors of having marked aphrodisiac power," and so on. Almost every imaginable "witch's brew" and magic "love potion" as well as innumerable physical manipulations of the penis, perineum, prostate, testicles, and rectum were tried without notable or predictable success.

From the early nineteen thirties until the mid-sixties, psychodynamic psychotherapy became the treatment of choice.* Results were neither impressive nor consistent. Insight and/or acceptance of one's incapacities were acceptable outcomes of therapy. During the sixties, Masters and Johnson[50,51] reported on a technique that offered a significantly high and predictable rate of success in improving the sexual interest and performance of sexually incapacited women and men. About the same time there were reports[5,12,28,58] of successful therapy using the behavior-therapy techniques of Wolpe and Eysenck. These two therapeutic regimes have some common objectives that will be discussed later.

⟪ Definitions

Before discussing specific therapeutic principles, objectives, techniques, and outcomes, it is necessary to operationally define such constructs as sexual incapacity, assumed etiologies, and acceptable therapeutic outcome.

* See references 10, 13, 17, 19, 20, 23, and 53.

Sexual Incapacity

Sexual incapacity cannot be measured by any objective or observable tests, scales, or examinations. The diagnosis must be made whenever a patient presents with a subjective complaint of failure to meet her/his† own and/or her partner's sexual-behavioral expectations. The problems about which patients complain are most commonly one, more, or all of the five listed below:

1. Female—infrequent or complete absence of orgasms.
2. Male—impotence, the inability to obtain or maintain an erection.
3. Male—premature ejaculation, prior to or almost immediately after the penis is introduced into the vagina.[61]
4. Female and/or male—infrequent or complete lack of desire for sexual activity on the part of one or both partners.
5. Male and/or female—disgust, fear and/or anxiety at the thought of participating in sexual behavior.

These problems are frequently selective, being experienced primarily or exclusively only in sexual transactions:

1. With a specific person (spouse, fiancé, primary partner, etc.).
2. With a specific class of relationships (i.e., marital partner only, pickups only, obese partners only, nice girls only, etc.).
3. In specific places (i.e., in automobiles, on a beach, in the living room, in the bed, etc.).
4. Under specific conditions (only when drinking, only when fatigued, only when angry, only when playing a passive role, etc.).

The problems may be partial, complete, sporadic, or total and of long or short dura-

† Hereafter in this chapter "her," "she," and "herself" will be used arbitrarily to avoid the repetitive, clumsy use of "her/him," "she/he," "herself/himself."

tion. Typically, once an individual experiences a sexual-response problem, she begins to predict the problem will recur every time a sexual response is desired or required. This fear that failure in sexual response will occur becomes as incapacitating as the inadequate response itself. The isolated, partial, or sporadic symptoms typically increase in frequency and severity with time unless the patient is given prompt, adequate reassurance, education, or the needed therapy.

The above description may seem too constraining to some readers. It is operational for this article only. It does not address itself to such questions as: (a) Is monogomy or having multiple partners the biological norm for human sexual transactions? (b) Should we utilize a descriptive (i.e., telling it like it is) or a prescriptive (i.e., telling it like it ought to be) norm to measure human sexual behavior? (c) Are love and/or legal sanction (marriage) an essential part of adequate sexual response? (d) Is homosexuality a life style or a sexual maladjustment needing therapy? (e) What about wife swapping, swinging, incest, masturbation, sadomasochistic sex, transvestism, transsexualism, etc.? These are not trivial issues on the contemporary human sexual scene, but are more philosophical than therapeutic at this time in human history.[49]

Etiology

Predominantly, patients complain of *their* behavioral failures to meet *their* own expectations for adequate sexual performance and enjoyment.[25,56,72] Patients are problem- not diagnosis- oriented. They hurt and they seek to be relieved rather than classified and labeled. Wershub[73] reports that approximately 5 percent of all sexual-inadequacy complaints have an etiology that is, in part or totally, related to structural, biochemical, and/or physiological disorders. These physical problems should be competently investigated whenever there is good reason to suspect their presence. Listed below are some of the more common structural, biochemical, and physiological causes of human sexual incapacity:[29]

Male:[73]

1. neurological lesions[73] (see also reference[73])
   a. destruction and/or transection of the sacral spinal cord and the cauda equina and parasympathetic plexuses
   b. high lumbar sympathectomy when ganglions below the twelfth dorsal nerve on both sides are removed
2. diabetes Mellitus[8] (see also reference[73])
3. alcoholism[44]
4. drug addictions (narcotic, amphetamines[3]; see also reference[73])
5. heavy-metal poisoning
6. peyronie's disease
7. lerichie's syndrome
8. calcification of the vas deferens (frequently diabetic also)
9. frolich's syndrome
10. phimosis
11. hydrocoele
12. varicocoele
13. crytorchidism
14. orchialgia
15. priapism
16. elephantiasis
17. sebaceous cysts scrotum
18. prostatectomy
19. perineal trauma
20. congenital anomalies (absent, concealed, adherent or double penis, hypospadias, episadias, anorchidism, sexual infantilism)
21. transsexual surgery
22. climacteric[7] (see also reference[73])
23. aging

Female:[59]

1. congenital defects (absent or infantile vagina or clitoris)
2. perineal trauma
3. pubococcygeus muscle relaxations and lacerations[36] (see also reference[59])
4. clitoral adhesions[9] (see also reference[59])
5. atrophic changes after menopause
6. painful infections of vagina

7. pelvic inflammatory disease
8. cysts of labia
9. massive or painful tumors of the genitalia
10. painful rectal disease.

Routine investigation of each of the above in every patient presenting with a chief complaint of sexual inadequacy is an expensive and inconvenient disservice to the patient. The yield is low and the patient with the diseases listed above usually presents first with symptoms of his primary disease. The patient suffering only from a behavioral, sexual-inadequacy problem can become conditioned, by an overzealous search, to believe that there is some remote, as yet undiscovered, structural-biochemical-physiological problem that accounts for his sexual incapacity. Until this nonexistent physical condition is discovered, he refuses the treatment that can successfully influence his problem.

Overwhelmingly, human sexual-incapacity problems that are presented by patients are the consequences of: (1.) faulty learning; (2.) inadequate knowledge; (3.) inexperience; or (4.) anxiety. Only a therapy program addressing itself to these defects has any chance of consistent success.

American child-rearing patterns are eminently suited to the development of sexual-incapacity symptoms. The adolescent female is taught to attract males, exhibit sexiness, and participate in sexually arousing petting, up to a point. She is further taught that it is her job to "cool it" when she experiences a high level of excitement because he won't stop unless she does. When she learns her lesson perfectly, she grows up to be a nonorgasmic woman. Her complaint is expressed as "I get very excited sexually, but when I feel like I am almost there, I just go numb and lose all my sexual feeling."

The adolescent male is warned not to get caught in the act, by catching VD or by impregnating a nice girl. It is implied simultaneously that he is lacking in masculinity if he doesn't seduce a few females. He cannot be caught if he is unable to have an erection, and is less likely to be caught if he only has a "quickie." Anxiety about being caught on the one hand, and fear of not performing like a stud on the other set the stage for the male symptoms of prematurity and impotence.

Since sexual-incapacity symptoms so frequently are specifically related to the sexual interaction between the presenting patient and her primary partner, most successful therapy programs focus on the therapy of both sexual partners and their relationship rather than attempting to treat only the individual who initially complains.[51] At times partners' complaints appear to be reciprocal; as one improves, symptoms appear in the other unless both are in a therapy program together. Brody's successful treatment of 65 percent of 105 females without treating their partners is a notable exception.[6]

Acceptable Therapeutic Outcome

The only acceptable therapeutic outcome is one in which the patient's behavior has changed in the direction of her own stated expectations. The patient initially needs help in explicitly defining her own sexual expectations. Occasionally, she needs help in modifying her expectations into some that are more realistic than those which she brought with her to the therapist. "Insight" without behavioral change cannot be considered an acceptable outcome of sex therapy. Insight with behavioral change is attractive, but is probably of insignificant value to the patient. Knowing why and being able to construct an interrelated etiological-therapeutic model is very important to the researcher. Knowing how to cause a lasting change in the incapacitating behavior is more important to the therapist. The therapist's primary responsibility is to help her patient attain a therapeutic result acceptable to the patient. Sex therapists must decide, before starting with their patients, whether they are primarily therapists or primarily researchers. By first setting up measurable relevant objectives against which the therapeutic outcomes will be measured, therapists can contribute to their own and others knowledge. Having an attractive, internally consistent, abstract model, designing a therapy to fit the model, and explaining away unsuccessful therapeutic outcomes contributes nothing.

❨ Examination of the Sexually Incapacitated Patient

History Taking

Diagnosis and treatment are more dependent on the patient's history[29,51] than the physical or laboratory findings. Therefore, a detailed problem-oriented story of the way in which the patient's sexual behavior doesn't meet her expectations is essential. However, obtaining the needed history doesn't require any special techniques or outlines. The data should describe the symptoms, their frequency and duration, their consistency, the specific circumstances or factors under which symptoms occur, vary, or are absent. It is also important to know whether the symptoms occur with all partners and with all forms of stimulation (genital, oral, manual, self-induced as well as partner induced). If the patient has had any therapy, the type, duration, and outcome should be documented. None of this data base is different from the kinds of data appropriately collected on any medical problem.

Since therapists are trying to change the behavior of their patients, the more a therapist learns about her patients' life styles, personal traits and habits, problem-solving patterns, anxiety levels, life goals, ambitions, values, and fantasies, the better. It is usually valuable to have a gestalt of a patient's total behavioral functioning, but this is especially important when the therapeutic goal is to change behavior.

Eliciting the history is more dependent on a therapist's comfort with human sexuality and her breadth of knowledge about the wide range of human sexual behavior than on any special interviewing techniques or gimmicks.[49,67,69]

Physical Examination

A general physical examination with thorough observation of the genital anatomy is indicated routinely. The examiner is looking for congenital defects, scarring, local infections, degenerative changes, and unusual size. It is perfectly acceptable for the sex therapists to do their own physical examination within the limits of their competence.[27]

When a specific organic disease from the above etiological list is suspected, appropriate physical examinations, and laboratory and x-ray studies must be included. Consultations should be requested when these examinations are beyond the sex therapist's level of competence in the diagnosis and/or management of these diseases.

❨ Specific Therapeutic Goals

Regardless of the therapy strategy or procedures one utilizes, it appears that there are three specific goals. They can be met by any of the following commonly used techniques: (1) reducing anxiety; (2) extinguishing old incapacitating sexual behavior patterns; and (3) conditioning to respond to biological sensual cues.[27,36,57]

1. Before attempting anything else, the therapist must reduce the amount of anxiety that the patient feels about her past and current sexual behavior, performance, and attitudes. It is the author's opinion that the patient usually experiences this sexual anxiety in two forms: shame-and-guilt anxiety, and performance anxiety. Shame-and-guilt anxiety is more commonly seen in persons who had rigid moral or religious upbringing, who are compulsive, who have a general discomfort with messy or "dirty" activities and are uncomfortable with physical and emotional intimacy (e.g., touching another individual). Performance anxiety is more likely to be found in persons who are competitive, ambitious, phys-

ically perfectionistic, and intellectually sharp. A combination of both is seen in persons who try to reduce shame and guilt by turning any performance into work. They believe it's acceptable to participate in pleasurable activities as long as one really works at it.

Tranquilizing drugs[21,24,26] are not the therapy of choice in managing these sexual anxieties. A more effective strategy is a therapy based on the principle that therapists are authority figures and members of the "establishment" who have more humanistic and permissive attitudes on sexuality than the patients have encountered in their past. These authority figures are open to and not fearful of their patients' sexuality. These less fearful and more permissive authoritative figures convey in gesture, manner, tone of voice, and content that it is okay, it is normal and it is not immoral to have sexual feelings, sexual thoughts, and sexual desires. They approve open, honest inquiry and communication about sexual matters between the patient and themselves, patient and friends, patient and potential sexual partners. They encourage the patient to explore and define her sexual expectations. They are not alarmed or judgmental when the patient's desires, expectations, and moral values appear to be in conflict. The patient's anxiety about her sexual behavior, desires, and attitudes is far more effectively reduced by the therapist's gestalt of overall comfort and tolerance about human sexuality than by a relatively uninvolved or even apprehensive exploration of the patient's past as practiced by many traditional psychotherapists.

2. Old patterns of sexual behavior that have not worked in the past need to be extinguished to make the patient more receptive to learning new, more effective patterns. As long as the older, familiar patterns are still available, one tends to repeat them even when these are relatively unsatisfactory. This is particularly true when the patient feels anxious and/or there are no visible alternative patterns of sexual behavior. The initial goal was to reduce anxiety. The reduction of anxiety makes it easier for the patient to avoid returning to her old patterns. Not using the old unsatisfactory pattern reduces the anxiety even more, and both make the patient more receptive to learning new patterns not visible or attainable in the past. Interference with the patient's continued use of her old patterns creates a vacuum and helps to motivate the learning of new acceptable substitutes that evoke less anxiety and incapacity. An effective way to interrupt the older patterns is to make a "contract" with one's patients that, while undergoing therapy, they will refrain from any sexual activity other than that discussed with and prescribed by the therapist. Masters and Johnson[51] simply inform their patients that they are not to have any intercourse until the therapists believe they are ready. It is obvious that both the patients and their therapists must have a great deal of confidence in the therapist's ability if they are to agree to such a "contract" as no intercourse until it is prescribed by the therapist.

3. Conditioning the patient to listen to (i.e., pay attention to and respond to) her own human, biological-sensual cues is the final step. Most patients who are performing sexually in a way that does not meet their own expectations find themselves trying to will an orgasm, erection, or sexual desire. They substitute conscious cortical control for a spontaneous response to proprioceptive-sensory input from the sensual areas of their own bodies. In contemporary society we have discouraged physical exploration of one's own body and tender (as distinguished from competitive and/or violent) physical contact with each other. This has encouraged using cerebration and fantasy to deal with stimuli, desires, and temptations that are taboo. Many modern humans have learned to suppress their biological-sensual cues. Since this inhibition is a taught and learned phenomenon, it can be unlearned. To improve sexually the patient must be taught to listen and respond to her genital, sensual, proprioceptive information and not permit this input to be overruled by "logical," "rational," cortical controls.[51] Lidz says:[45]

The proper carrying out of the sexual act and the enjoyment of it involves an ability to give way to the irrational, the timeless, the purely animal in one: it includes a loss of individuality in a temporary fusion with another. It contains the potentiality of leaving behind the tensions of civilization as one loosens the bonds to reality to float again in the purely sensuous. Here, one needs to be unabashed by the nakedness of impulse and drive, by recrudescence of the infantile and the revealing of much that one has sought to hide from others. The woman in particular requires a capacity to rescind control and give way before an ecstasy that threatens to overwhelm and annihilate her by its very intensity. The sexual act contains a definite and direct relationship to infantile relatedness to the mother, with a renewed interest in sucking, in odor, in skin eroticism; and a reawakening of old forbidden desires to explore and play with orifices. So very much that has been learned needs to be undone; much that has been hidden and long repressed and kept unconscious but that haunted dreams and masturbatory fantasies needs to be released to permit sexual intimacy and enjoyment and to allow fulfillment rather than provoke shame and guilt. The very good sexual adjustment demands such abilities to reverse the socialization process—and yet to permit the individual to be secure in the feeling that the regression and reversal will only be temporary and not reclaim the self. [p. 424]

The therapeutic strategy can now be seen as a combination of: (1) reducing the patient's guilt and performance anxiety by authoritative permissiveness, education and reassurance; (2) reducing the anxiety still further by interfering with the old patterns that originally had been shaped by the anxiety and ultimately became a source of anxiety as well; (3) creating a temporary vacuum to stimulate motivation for learning new patterns, and (4) teaching the patient to respond more spontaneously to her own biological-sensual stimuli.

Low anxiety is optimal for predictable learning. One learns during a state of high anxiety, but what will be learned is less under the control of the teacher (i.e., therapist). When the new patterns to be learned are offered in such a graduated form that the patient never experiences a rapid rise in anxiety and experiences a small but constant measure

of success, what is learned not only increases the patient's competence but reduces the reappearance of performance anxiety. In both behavior therapy[42] and Masters and Johnson sex therapy,[51] attention is given to introducing small but graduated changes, starting in areas the therapist predicts are unlikely to evoke anxiety. Progression is paced, to continue to hold anxiety to a minimum, as the patient is encouraged to move closer and closer to functioning sexually in a biologically natural way.

(Therapeutic Techniques

At the present time, sexual-incapacity-therapy regimes, strategies, techniques, and gimmicks are almost as numerous as the number of therapists.[*] Most therapists identify themselves as using some specific technique described by a well-known therapist. However, most of these are self-trained. Typically, they use an ill-defined blend of their own psychotherapeutic skills with things they have read or heard that other therapists utilize in sex therapy. Too few keep records suitable for audit or reporting in the literature. Most devote only a small percentage of their time to sex therapy, and so any given patient is likely to find herself being shifted back and forth from sex therapy to marital counseling to individual psychotherapy.

Therapists carefully trained in behavior therapy have applied these simple, behavior-modification techniques to the complex of behaviors involved in human sexual interactions.[†] Both behavior-modification therapists and Masters and Johnson oriented therapists have the overall objective of producing a change in the patient's sexual behavior. There are differences in their strategies, techniques, and theoretical models. The other large group, psychodynamic psychotherapists, accept insight and understanding as a major objective.[33] They, therefore, use significantly different

* See references 11, 14, 16, 38, and 72.
† See references 12, 28, 32, 35, and 39.

strategies and techniques. Another strategy is the use of mechanical devices[60] (such as vibrators, penile splints, artificial vaginas, etc.),[46] pharmaceutical agents (hormones,[2,4] [48,62] vitamin E, psychotropic agents,[37] anesthetic ointments), dietary fads (raw oysters, raw eggs, wheat germ, etc.) and surgical procedures.[13,40,47,55] These are used independently or in combination with other therapies. Even direct personal instruction via coitus with the therapists has been recommended.

Variables Influencing Outcome

It now appears that a wide variety of therapeutic strategies and procedures utilized have been influential or coincidental with favorable outcomes. However, serious evaluation of the efficacy of these various therapeutic efforts has been difficult. No well-defined criteria have been established to determine something as simple but essential as how to differentiate between severe cases needing intensive, skilled therapy and mild cases that might have resolved spontaneously or with brief reassurance and accurate information from minimally skilled, warm, tolerant humans with some professional status and credibility. It is the author's observation that choosing a particular procedure seems less important than the therapist's belief that she knows what she is doing will work.[68]

Another significant variable is how much suffering the patient is experiencing from her sexual incapacity problems at the time she seeks therapy. It seems more logical, as well as humane, to conceptualize this as the level of positive motivation toward relief rather than a resistance against change. Oversimplified, the question is whether the patient hurts enough to seek out a therapist who is confident, available, and affordable, and to trust this therapist enough to allow her sexual behavior to be shaped. Additionally, since therapy is directed at the sexual partners, both must be at a similar level of motivation at the same time.

The personality of the therapist is frequently stated to be a crucial factor in any therapeutic procedure. Psychiatric resident applicants are frequently evaluated, sometimes elaborately, in an effort to screen *out* those believed to be poorly qualified. The specific behavioral objectives of residency training for which they are found unqualified is not usually spelled out.

More rarely are evaluations conducted with the goal of "screening *in*" those with specific characteristics desirable in a therapist. Screening in is very important in both self-selection and training-program selection for sex therapists.

Without presuming to set *the* inclusive criteria, it is useful to describe the characteristics observed in a variety of therapists who devote a significant amount of their time treating sexual incapacities.

1. They are careful listeners.
2. They are persistent history takers.
3. They are more problem-oriented than diagnosis-oriented.
4. They help patients conceptualize and define their own sexual expectations.
5. They do not push their own values on their patients as better, healthier, or more "normal."[69]
6. They are aware of and tolerant of a wide range of human sexual behavior.
7. They openly convey warmth, concern for, interest and involvement in, their patients' sexual discomforts and disabilities.
8. They do not hesitate to be firm, directive, and authoritative (not authoritarian).
9. They experiment—i.e., do what "feels right" at the moment.
10. They pay close attention to immediate feedback and modify their techniques, strategies, and communications immediately, as the feedback indicates.

It is worth repeating that this list does not pretend to be a complete or prescriptive guide for selecting sex therapists. It is a description of those characteristics common to several sex therapists who have some consistent degree of success in their sex-therapy practices.

Behavior Therapy[75]

The specific techniques of behavior-modification therapy are adequately described in Chapter 15 of this volume and will not be repeated here. The same basic techniques are applied to changing the unacceptable sexual behavior.* A given therapist may elect to use some of the "sensate-focus" exercises used by the Masters and Johnson disciples, and/or the role-playing, confrontation techniques used by encounter-group leaders.

Psychotherapy

The strategies and techniques used in psychotherapy are adequately described elsewhere in this volume. These are less homogeneous than the behavior therapies. These are also likely to be applied unmodified to the patient's sexual problems. The amount of emphasis on the patients' understanding of their basic psychological problems, "working through" of their conflicts and accepting the therapists' theoretical premises,[64] is highly variable from therapist to therapist. The therapist's comfort with human sexual behavior and her definition of what is "normal" are much more critical factors in psychodynamic psychotherapy than they are to the more ritualized behavior therapies.[49] A given psychotherapist may selectively introduce some of the sensate-focus exercises[51] and encounter-group techniques but, as a rule, is less comfortable with these. Psychotherapists have usually been indoctrinated to be nondirective, unrevealing of how they feel or what they are experiencing, and not to touch their patients. It is difficult to prescribe sensate-focus exercises or to utilize encounter-group techniques without directing, revealing, or touching. When therapists do not routinely use these in their clinical practices, they are initially unsure and hesitant when introducing them in sex therapy. The end result is that they remain

* See references 12, 28, 32, 35, 39, and 41.

uncomfortable as sex therapists or begin to introduce similar techniques in their therapy of other patients. This is usually good if they are comfortable and open about these modifications of their therapy techniques. It is usually bad when they feel guilt about "betraying" their teachers and the theories on which their previous therapeutic techniques have been based.

Hypnosis[52]

Hypnotic therapy is discussed in Chapter 12 of this volume. These techniques are also applied directly to sexual-incapacity symptoms by suggesting relaxation and loss of inhibition in responding to sexual arousal. Hypnosis may be used independently or in combination with any of the other therapies discussed in this chapter.

The Masters and Johnson Approach

Masters and Johnson have developed a human, sexual-inadequacy therapy[51] that has popularized a broad awareness of the problem and has offered the most consistent therapeutic success. This "sensate-focus" approach is presently the therapy of choice among the majority of practitioners who deal with sexual incapacity problems and as such deserves a more detailed presentation.

([Sensate-Focus-Oriented Therapy

The basic concept of sensate-focus-oriented therapy is that the person with sexual problems is not paying attention to and responding to her own natural, biological-sensual cues. Therapy is directed toward freeing the patient to become capable of experiencing the pleasurable and exciting sensory stimuli from her genital anatomy. When this is accomplished, it is believed that these formerly sexually incapacited persons will be permanently able to experience and respond to their own sexual needs without incapacitating symptoms.

A few sex therapists have been trained by Masters and Johnson, but most sensate-focus sex therapists use their own version of the technique. Although variations do exist in the details of the therapeutic attack as employed by different therapists, the similarites are sufficiently widespread to warrant an attempt to extract the basic principles upon which the therapeutic strategies and techniques are based.

Most therapists focus on the therapy of a *sexual unit* rather than an individual. A sexual unit may be defined as a married couple, an engaged couple, or an individual and her primary sexual partner. Masters and Johnson reported on the use of successful surrogate partners when no natural primary partner was available. Therapy is usually conducted in joint interviews with both partners always present.

Coequal male–female cotherapy teams are said to be the ideal model.[51] Unless the therapists are equal in each other's and their patients' eyes, male and female cotherapists add little except cost. Too often a chauvinistic male therapist brings any female he can find into the therapy session and appoints her to be his "cotherapist." She has little background to understand what is taking place, little or no status in either the patients' or the male therapist's eyes and presents a model of male–female inequality to the patient couple. Even two equal cotherapists have to work at presenting themselves as a team not dominated by either the male or the female. This is most likely to occur when each is comfortable with her or his own and each other's sexuality. Verbal encountering to clarify their interpersonal relationship with each other is often helpful.

Therapy typically starts with a long detailed *history*.[29,51] This serves three purposes: (1) establishing communication; (2) understanding most of the patients' sexual patterns of behavior, attitudes, needs, fantasies, and expectations; and (3) exposing the therapists' sexual attitudes and tolerance level to the patients.

Following this a *contract* is negotiated.[51] The therapists share their understanding of the problem with the patients and a therapeutic plan is agreed upon. In addition to cost, duration, and appointment frequency the "contract" includes such items as: availability of therapists beyond the regularly scheduled appointments, how much control of the patients' sexual behavior by the therapists will be required, how much homework is indicated, whether therapy will be limited to sexual behavior or also include counseling about other personal, interpersonal, and marital problems.

Reassurance and support, which have been developing, are now more strongly reinforced. The overall message conveyed is, "I, your therapist, do understand your sexual problems, accept where you are, and am willing and able to help you. I am an authority figure who is more knowledgeable, understanding, and permissive of your sexuality than other authority figures you have known in your past. You are human beings with your own sexual expectations, which I now understand and will respect."

Effective communication skills between the sexual partners have usually deteriorated and therapy moves along more smoothly when therapists focus on this problem early.[43,54] Effective communication may be verbal, paraverbal, or nonverbal, but is always characterized by messages that are equally clear to the sender and the receiver. Sexual communications are most clear when they deal with the "here and now" rather than the past or the future, are statements concerning "where I am," "what I am experiencing," inquire rather than accuse, assume, predict, or guess the partner's motives, wishes, or needs, and are not distortions of reality. The therapist may choose to end the first session with the patient couple by inviting them to try this style of communication for a week before proceeding to work on the sexual behavior itself. Most couples who agree to try this have been moderately successful. They report a reduction in their hostility, their anxiety, and their misunderstanding of each other's messages.

Estimation of motivation for change is necessary. This is less important in the two-week concentrated program offered by Masters and Johnson than in the variations that employ one or two appointments weekly. The latter strategy is quite dependent on the patients' willingness to spend time doing the prescribed homework. When the couple can't find time for thirty minutes of uninterrupted sensate-focus exercises at least every other night, therapy should be discontinued until the patients can arrange their schedules.

Availability by phone is desirable when the therapists choose a once or twice weekly interview strategy. It is the author's experience that the phone-call availability is rarely abused. Mandatory delay of feedback until the next scheduled appointment allows a bad situation to get worse and slows down progress when things are going well.

The *homework* is a sine qua non for successful sex therapy.[51] It consists of carefully prescribed, reciprocating body-massage exercises. The couple is instructed to spend an uninterrupted thirty to forty-five minutes on this activity at least every other night. They take turns at "pleasuring" and "being pleasured by" each other. The primary objective is for each to develop her or his own sensate-focus awareness without moving ahead fast enough to develop incapacitating anxiety. Additionally, each has an opportunity to learn that pleasuring can be as exciting as being pleasured.[51]

The couple is instructed to lie nude beside each other on a bed in a lighted room and relax. When they feel somewhat relaxed, pleasuring starts with gentle massaging of noneroticized areas of the receiver's body. By random selection one has been assigned the role of giver only and the other of receiver only. Halfway through the exercises they will change roles. It is felt that initially concentrating on only one role maximizes awareness and proficiency in that role. Much later blending of the two roles alternately or simultaneously will be a matter of personal preference.

The giver is in charge of what is given as long as pressure is not put on the receiver to respond with anything other than what the receiver is spontaneously experiencing. The goal is to develop an awareness of experiencing the sensory stimuli generated from one's own body being touched and from touching one's partner's body.[31] Premature demand for sexual performance either from oneself or one's partner evokes anxiety and interferes with learning to pay attention to one's own pleasurable sensory cues.

A few nights to a week later the receiver is allowed to indicate preferences in the kind and location of the massaging that is preferred. This is a learning exercise in which the patients teach one another what they have learned about themselves while in the receiving role. Each also learns what pleases the other, and the importance of keeping each other informed. When they do not aggressively make specific demands, both become less fearful of being neglected or of being overwhelmed by the demands of the partner.

Many sexually incapacitated persons do not like to touch "messy," "dirty," "sticky," "slimy," substances, i.e., normal vaginal secretions or semen. Therefore, at this stage, hand lotion is introduced in the massaging exercises.[51] Any "clean," "sterile," water-soluble hand lotion will suffice. It should be used in sufficient quantities as to be experienced as "messy" but paired with the already pleasurable sensation of being massaged.

Next the constraint of limiting the massages to noneroticized areas of the partner's body is removed. This is prescribed when the therapists believe the couple can experience sensual arousal without significant anxiety. Now the goal becomes developing awareness of sensual stimuli originating in one's body rather than that originating primarily in one's head.[36,51] This may be a particularly difficult phase for the less incapacitated partner if she or he is highly aroused sexually but constrained from having sex relations because of an earlier contract with the therapists. The couple is reassured that a spontaneous orgasm is acceptable, but pressuring oneself or one's partner is not. Since the receiver can control how much stimulation she or he accepts and the giver can decide how much she or he is willing to offer, the chance for making anxiety provoking demands is minimized. Independently, or with the help of the therapists, the couple may negotiate to allow the overaroused individual to masturbate for relief.

When the couple is sufficiently comfortable

with experiencing sensual arousal, they are permissively encouraged to experiment with experiencing a full sexual response, dependent primarily on body, not head, stimulation.[51] Initially, this should be experienced by one in the receiver role only. Manual stimulation for this first full sexual turn on is least likely to tempt the previously incapacitated person to return to the older unsatisfactory sexual patterns. However, the therapists must use their clinical judgment about when to prohibit, permit, or encourage oral-genital or genital-genital stimulation. In either case, the previously sexually incapacitated person should be allowed to satisfy herself before trying to satisfy her partner. Learning how to recognize, sort out, and spontaneously respond to sensual body stimuli is necessary before one can effectively participate in simultaneously giving and receiving sexual responses.

After both partners are able to experience desire, arousal, pleasurable excitement, and orgasm when in a receiver role only, the constraint on intercourse is removed. The therapists should help the couple select a time, place, and set of circumstances least likely to evoke anxiety or fear of failure. The couple must be reassured that lack of complete success at this point doesn't mean starting all over again. It is helpful to supportively remind them how far they have already come. Anything that reduces the anxiety of the couple seeing this as the "final exam" is helpful. Demanding good performance of themselves or each other now will have the same counterproductive effect it had in the past.

A failure, even after weeks or months of satisfactory sexual performance, may panic one or both partners into making a self-fulfilling prophesy of a return of the old sexual incapacity.

Interviews, during the sensate-focus homework exercises, are used to explore, clarify, instruct, educate, reassure, praise, support, and maintain the patients' enthusiasm. Primarily, discussions focus on sexual behavior, but, from time to time, exploring some other aspect of the couple's interpersonal relationship may facilitate their ability to interact sexually. Nonverbal encounter-group techniques and role playing can be effective in helping the couple recognize and/or express themselves when verbal communication becomes garbled or blocked. However, therapists who are themselves uncomfortable when interacting with their patients nonverbally will find it difficult to convince their patients to participate.

Sex education is valuable for some patients who have very limited information and very little ingenuity. When they become free enough to experiment, they have no models or guidelines. Reassuring information, reading materials, pictures, models, and movies can be used to stimulate discussion. These are offered permissively and as possible patterns the patients may want to consider for themselves. Setting up a competitive situation must be actively avoided.

When the primary symptom is *premature ejaculation* rather than male impotence or a nonorgasmic female, an addition to the above techniques is indicated. Medication,[22] hypnosis, and psychotherapy have been used, but techniques specific for the symptom[1,51] offer more consistent success. The best-known technique was described by Semans[63] and is called the Semans squeeze technique. Vandervoort[70] has published an illustrated booklet describing its use. Oversimplified, the male recognises his pre-ejaculatory inevitability and informs his partner. She grasps the head of his penis between her thumb and fingers hard enough to hurt. His urge to ejaculate and some of his erection disappear. Sexual activity is resumed and the steps above repeated as frequently as necessary. Over time, the male is conditioned to last longer before ejaculation.

A more humane approach also involves the active, willing cooperation of the partner.[30] She lightly strokes the penis until he experiences prejaculatory inevitability. He indicates this state, and she stops. A minute or two later when the inevitability feeling has passed, she resumes stroking the penis and the process is repeated several times. Masters and Johnson report that this technique can increase duration after intromission from a few seconds to several minutes. The strategy is to increase the male's tolerance for experiencing genital stimulation without adding to his mental excitement and anxieties. Most males spontaneously prescribe the reverse of this for themselves trying to avoid all stimulation until the moment of vaginal entry. This means relying primarily on intellectual and fantasy stimulation to obtain and maintain their erections.

(Conclusions

The therapy of human sexual incapacities is a mixed bag at the time of this writing. The syndromes of sexual problems are ill-defined and vague or operationally defined and arbitrary. The "diagnostic" categories are not well related to specific etiologies, pathologies, prognoses, or therapeutic regimes. Therapies are loosely structured, vary from therapist to therapist, and the model, principles, or strategies are rarely identified. Treatment is most likely to be aimed either at specific symptoms or at overall improvement in the patients' psychological adjustment.

On the positive side, human sexual functioning has become a legitimate concern of those offering health-care services. The newness and as yet poorly defined diagnostic categories make this group of human maladies more patient-oriented than is the case in more traditional medical care. It is accepted that sexual incapacity can only be diagnosed subjectively by the patient herself. This potentially gives the patient options in deciding how much and what treatments she will accept, since the patient defines her own incapacity in terms of a variance from her personal expectations for her own sexual health. In offering the patients these kinds of "diagnosis" and "therapy" options, human sexual health care is more advanced than other areas of health care.

Preventive measures are still poorly understood. The role of sex education in prevention of sexual-inadequacy problems is still very controversial.[71] The August 25, 1969, *AMA News* reported, "When most of the emotion is

stripped away, the basic views of the proponents and opponents of sexual education are these: the *former* hold that sex education courses are designed to answer the 'whys' of children's questions about family life, physiological development and its relationship to the society in which they live. It's taught in a clinical, detailed manner which allows students to make their own moral judgments. *Opponents* hold that sex education courses are really 'how to' courses that teach mechanics of intercourse without morals attached to it." Both are partly right. Courses *should be* designed and delivered to do what proponents aim for, but frequently they are so poorly *conceived* and/or *delivered* as to *accomplish* what the opponents claim. Even when the moral aspects are stripped away, hunch rather than data relates sex education to better sexual functioning.

Most sex therapists believe reassurance about the normality of sexual feelings plus accurate information about patterns, varieties, and frequencies of sexual behaviors, the existence of recreational as well as procreational sex, the relationships between sex, love, and marriage, the relationships between menstruation, menopause, old age, and sexual behavior should be readily available to all humans as they need it. Our current divorce rate and the frequency of sexual incapacities and marital discord suggest that a better preparation for sexual roles is needed before humans reach adulthood. When parents become comfortable with their own sexuality, their children can obtain most of the sex education they need from their own parents in their own homes. Parents need to: (1) encourage their children to be curious about any and everything known to mankind; (2) offer their children a model of two adults who are involved, intimate, and not afraid to show affection for each other; and (3) help their children understand that it's okay to pursue pleasure as a positive goal rather than as something only experienced by breaking the rules.

Basically, this prescription assumes that young humans who are allowed to experience reality as it occurs become those best able to recognize and deal with reality as they grow older. Sexual functioning is a significant part of human reality. As humans become better able to deal with their sexual reality, the need for therapy of sexual incapacities will decrease.

❮ Bibliography

1. AHMED, S. H. "Treatment of Premature Ejaculation," *Br. J. Psychiatry*, 114 (1968), 1197–1198.
2. ANDERSEN, A. P. "Androgenic Treatment of Frigidity," *Geburtshilfe. Frauenheilkd.*, 18 (1958), 632.
3. BELL, D. S. and W. H. TRETHOWAN. "Amphetamine Addiction and Disturbed Sexuality," *Arch. Gen. Psychiatry*, 4 (1961), 74–78.
4. BORELLI, S. "On the Prescription of Sex Hormones in Male Sex Disorder," *Landarzt*, 43 (1967), 476–477.
5. BRADY, J. P. "Brevital-Relaxation Treatment of Fridigity," *Behav. Res. Ther.*, 4 (1966), 71–77.
6. BRODY, H. "Sex Therapy of 105 Women Only—(Ongoing Research)," Personal Communication, Calgary University, 1972.
7. BROWNING, W. J. "Male Climacteric and Impotence," *Int. Rec. Med.*, 173 (1960), 690–694.
8. CHOKYU, K. "Studies on Diabetes Mellitus and Functions of the Male Sexual Glands," *Acta Urol. Jap.*, 11 (1965), 850–876.
9. CLARK, L. "Frigidity," in *101 Intimate Sexual Problems Answered*, pp. 89–97. New York: Signet Books, 1968.
10. CONDRAU, G. "On the Psychotherapy of Male Impotence," *Praxis*, 49 (1960), 641–644.
11. COOPER, A. J. "Outpatient Treatment of Impotence," *J. Nerv. Ment. Dis.*, 149 (1969), 360–370.
12. DENGROVE, E. "Behavior Therapy of the Sexual Disorders," *J. Sex Res.*, 3 (1967), 49–61.
13. DEUTSCH, H. "Frigidity in Women," in *Neurosis and Character Types*. New York: International Universities Press, 1965.
14. DIAMOND, M., ed. *Perspectives in Reproduction and Sexual Behavior*. Bloomington: Indiana University Press, 1968.
15. DITMAN, K. S. "Inhibition of Ejaculation by Chlorprothixene," *Am. J. Psychiatry*, 120 (1964), 1004–1005.
16. FAULK, M. "Factors in the Treatment of Frigidity," *Br. J. Psychiatry*, 119 (1971), 53–56.
17. FERENCZI, S. "The Analytic Interpretation and Treatment of Psychosexual Impotence," in *Sex in Psychoanalysis*. New York: Dover, 1956.
18. FINKLE, A. L. "Trauma and Sexual Impotence," *J. Trauma*, 4 (1962), 60–97.
19. FLICK, L. "Evaluation of Female Orgastic Capacity and Its Disorders from the Psychoanalytic Point of View," *Psyche*, 23 (1969), 58–74.
20. FREUD, S. (1931) "Female Sexuality," in J. Strachey, ed., *Standard Edition*, Vol. 21, pp. 223–243. London: Hogarth, 1955.
21. FREYHAN, F. A. "Loss of Ejaculation During Mellaril Treatment," *Am. J. Psychiatry*, 118 (1961), 171–172.
22. GIBBONS, R. A. "Frigidity (Anaphrodisia)," in *Sterility in Woman*, pp. 167–172. London: Churchill, 1923.
23. GLEN, J. and E. H. KAPLAN. "Types of Orgasm in Women: A Critical Review and Redefinition," *J. Am. Psychoanal. Assoc.*, 16 (1968), 549–564.
24. GREENBERG, H. R. "Erectile Impotence during the Course of Tofranil Therapy," *Am. J. Psychiatry*, 121 (1965), 1021.
25. GUTHEIL, E. H. "Sexual Dysfunctions in Men," in S. Arieti, ed., *American Handbook of Psychiatry*, Vol. 1, 1st ed., pp. 708–726. New York: Basic Books, 1959.
26. HAIDER, I. "Thiodiazine and Sexual Dysfunctions," *Int. J. Neuropsychiatry*, 2 (1966), 255–257.
27. HARTMAN, W. and M. FITHIAN. *Nudist Society*. New York: Crown, 1970.
28. HASLAM, M. T. "The Treatment of Psychogenic Dyspareunia by Reciprocal Inhibition," *Br. J. Psychiatry*, 111 (1965), 280–282.
29. HASTINGS, D. W. *Impotence and Frigidity*. Boston: Little, Brown, 1963.
30. HIRSH, E. W. "The Role of the Female Partner in Premature Ejaculation," *Int. J. Sexol.*, 5 (1951), 1–6.
31. HOLLENDER, M. H., L. LUBORSKY, and J. J. SCARAMELLA. "Body Contact and Sexual Enticement," *Arch. Gen. Psychiatry*, 20 (1969), 188–191.
32. HOLROYD, J. "Treatment of a Married Virgin

by Behavior Therapy," *Obstet. Gynecol.*, 36 (1970), 469–472.

33. HUMMER, W. K. "Frigidity in Women: A Symptom not a Diagnosis," *Minn. Med.*, 49 (1966), 1879–1884.

34. JOHNSON, J. *Disorders of Sexual Potency in the Male.* Oxford: Pergamon, 1968.

35. JONES, W. and P. PARK. "Treatment of Single Partner Sexual Dysfunction by Systematic Desensitization," *Obstet. Gynecol.*, 39 (1972), 411–417.

36. KEGEL, A. H. "Sexual Functions of the Pubococcygeneus Muscle," *West. J. Surg. Obstet. Gynecol.*, 6 (1952), 521.

37. KIEV, A. and E. HACKETT. "The Chemotherapy of Impotence and Frigidity," *J. Sex Res.*, 4 (1968), 220–224.

38. KLEMER, R. H., ed. "Counseling in Sexual Problems," in *Counseling in Marital and Sexual Problems*, pp. 92–186. Baltimore: Williams & Wilkins, 1965.

39. KRAFT, T. and I. AL-ISSA. "Behavior Therapy in the Treatment of Frigidity," *Am. J. Psychother.*, 21 (1967), 116–120.

40. LASH, H. "Silicone Implant for Impotence," *J. Urol.*, 100 (1968), 709–710.

41. LAZARUS, A. A. "The Treatment of Chronic Frigidity by Systematic Desensitization," *J. Nerv. Ment. Dis.*, 136 (1963), 272–278.

42. ———. "Modes of Treatment for Sexual Inadequacies," *Med. Asp. Hum. Sexual.*, 3 (1969), 53–58.

43. LEDERER, W. and D. JACKSON. *The Mirages of Marriage.* New York: Norton, 1968.

44. LEVINE, J. "The Sexual Adjustment of Alcoholics," *Q. J. Stud. Alcohol*, 16 (1955), 675–680.

45. LIDZ, T. *The Person.* New York: Basic Books, 1968.

46. LOWENSTEIN, J. "Treatment of Impotence: A Coitus-Training Apparatus," *Br. Med. J.*, 2 (1941), 49–50.

47. LYDSTON, G. F. "Surgical Treatment of Impotence," *Am. J. Clin. Med.*, 15 (1908), 1571.

48. MARGOLIS, R. and C. H. LESLIE. "Review of Studies on a Mixture of Nux Vomica, Yohimbine and Methyl Testosterone in the Treatment of Impotence," *Curr. Ther. Res.*, 8 (1966), 280–284.

49. MARMOUR, J. "Normal and Deviant Sexual Behavior," *JAMA*, 217 (1971), 165–170.

50. MASTERS, W. and V. JOHNSON. *Human Sexual Response.* Boston: Little, Brown, 1968.

51. ———. *Human Sexual Inadequacy.* Boston: Little, Brown, 1970.

52. MIROWITZ, J. M. "The Utilization of Hypnosis in Psychic Impotence," *Br. J. Med. Hypn.*, 17 (1966), 25–32.

53. MOORE, B. E. "Frigidity: A Review of Psychoanalytic Literature," *Psychoanal. Q.*, 33 (1964), 323–349.

54. O'NEIL, N. and G. O'NEIL. *Open Marriage,* New York: Evans, 1972.

55. PEARMAN, R. "Insertion of a Silastic Penile Prothesis for the Treatment of Organic Sexual Impotence," *J. Urol.*, 107 (1972), 802–806.

56. PETERSON, J. A. "Emotional Factors in Infertility," in E. T. Tyler, ed., *Sterility— Office Management of the Infertile Couple*, pp. 282–299. New York: McGraw-Hill, 1961.

57. PULLIAS, E. V. "Masturbation as a Mental Hygiene Problem: A Study of the Beliefs of 75 Young Men," *J. Abnorm. Psychol.*, 32 (1937), 216–222.

58. RACHMAN, S. "Sexual Disorders and Behavior Therapy," *Am. J. Psychiatry*, 118 (1961), 235–240.

59. ROEN, P. R. "Urologic Causes of Frigidity," *Med. Asp. Hum. Sexual.*, 2 (1968), 20–21.

60. RUSSEL, G. L. "Impotence Treated by Mechanotherapy," *Proc. R. Soc. Med.*, 52 (1959), 872–874.

61. SALZMAN, L. "Premature Ejaculation," *Int. J. Sexol.*, 8 (1954), 69–76.

62. SEID, B. "Gonadotropic (HCG) Treatment of Impotence: Results in Fifty-five Cases," *Va. Med. Mon.*, 89 (1962), 178–181.

63. SEMANS, J. H. "Premature Ejaculation: 'A New Approach'," *South. Med. J.*, 49 (1956), 353–357.

64. SPIEGAL, H. "Is Symptom Removal Dangerous?" *Am. J. Psychiatry*, 123 (1967), 1279–1283.

65. TAYLOR, G. R. *Sex in History.* New York: Vanguard, 1954.

66. TAYLOR, R. W. *A Practical Treatise on Sexual Disorders of the Male and Female.* Philadelphia: Lea Brothers, 1900.

67. TUNNADINE, L. P. D. *Contraception and Sexual Life.* Philadelphia: Lippincott, 1970.

68. TYLER, E. A. "A Simple Working Concept of Psychotherapy," *Med. Times*, 96 (1968), 1022–1027.

69. ———. "A Tolerant Attitude about Human

Sexual Behavior," in S. Lewit, ed., *Advances in Planned Parenthood*, Vol. 8, pp. 51–55. New York: American Elsevier, 1973.

70. VANDERVOORT, H. and T. MCILVENNA. *You Can Last Longer*. San Francisco: Multimedia Resource Center, 1972.

71. VINCENT, C., ed. *Human Sexuality in Medical Education and Practice*. Springfield, Ill.: Charles C. Thomas, 1968.

72. WAHL, C. W., ed. *Sexual Problems: Diagnosis and Treatment in Medical Practice*. New York: Free Press, 1967.

73. WERSHUB, L. P. *Sexual Impotence in the Male*. Springfield, Ill.: Charles C. Thomas, 1959.

74. WOLPE J. and A. A. LAZARUS. *Behavior Therapy Techniques*. New York: Pergamon, 1966.

PART THREE

The Somatic Therapies

CHAPTER 21

ANTIANXIETY DRUGS

Jonathan O. Cole and John M. Davis

⟮ Introduction

MAN has been looking for ways to escape or reduce anxiety for centuries. Alcohol was probably the first drug to be used for this purpose. In common with many modern antianxiety drugs, it not only decreases anxiety at some initial dosages but also acts as a disinhibiting agent, allowing its inbibers to behave in ways which they sometimes regret the next morning. Alcohol raises the convulsive threshold initially. On prolonged chronic administration it produces both psychological and physical dependence. Its abrupt withdrawal can precipitate convulsions (rum fits) and delirium (DTs). Moderate single doses can produce muscle relaxation. Large single doses produce sleep, and very large doses (e.g., a quart of whisky) can produce death through depression of the brain's respiratory center.[62]

All the above actions alcohol shares in principle, and sometimes in practice, with a wide range of sedative, hypnotic, and antianxiety drugs. Alcohol differs chiefly in being easily available, and being subject to a wide range of laws, superstitions, and customs which influence its use. Although as many as 4 percent of

American adult males are said to have a serious drinking problem, fifteen to twenty times as many adult males use the drug without appreciable trouble. It's impossible to assess the real efficacy of alcohol as an antianxiety agent. It is probably useful in acute episodic or reactive anxiety of short duration (e.g., the aftereffects of a bad day at the office), but alcohol's short duration of action and tendency to release catecholamines and elicit some rebound anxiety, interferes with its use in long-term therapy. Chronic alcoholics, consuming alcohol on research wards, appear more anxious and irritable than drunk and happy.[46]

Nevertheless, alcohol has been found useful in some clinical situations. Not surprisingly, efficacy studies have been conducted in institutional settings where elderly patients do not ordinarily have access to alcoholic beverages. Here, alcohol appears to reduce anxiety and tension, and increase cheerfulness and social interaction when given in small daily doses.[4,5] It is possible that in the elderly the vasodilating effect of alcohol may cause slight improvements in organ functioning over and above the drug's benign disinhibiting antianxiety effect at the doses used (one can of beer or one glass of wine). The contribution of social setting and expectations to the clinical drug response to alcohol has not been adequately studied.

Alcohol seemed an excellent drug to consider as an introduction to a discussion of the use of antianxiety drugs in psychiatry since it illustrates the full range of problems encountered in other drugs, plus a few unique ones (e.g., Wernicke's syndrome, cirrhosis of the liver). Some uses, which seem at first to be characteristic of alcohol, like recreational use, are clearly no longer unique. Actually many other sedatives (ether, nitrous oxide, barbiturates, even chloral hydrate) have been used for kicks at one time or another.[17] A major issue, which will be discussed in more detail below, is the issue of the abuse liability of antianxiety drugs.

Terminology

There are serious problems in the terminology, definition and measurement of anxiety which are mainly beyond the scope of this chapter. For present purposes, a combination of free-floating fear or apprehension, psychic and somatic manifestations of anxiety and of tension spreading over into depression, irritability or hypochondriasis must be considered loosely as the target area of antianxiety drugs. Attempts to cluster anxiety symptoms into coherent subgroups and to separate anxious symptoms from depressive symptoms have produced either no separation, confusion, or relatively unhelpful groupings of semantically related items.[7] Since many rating scales which include selections from this mixture of symptoms show clear drug-placebo differences in patients identified by psychiatrists as being "anxious," one almost has to assume that a more detailed delineation of anxiety symptoms is not empirically necessary to determine the efficacy of most drugs.[32]

Major exceptions to this general approach to anxiety are: (1) recurrent severe episodic panic attacks; (2) anxiety clearly secondary to a schizophrenic illness; and (3) severe agitation in a major depressive illness. Under these three conditions antianxiety drugs are not useful, although they may sometimes have a mild palliative effect in low doses and can, in very high doses, render such patients temporarily asymptomatic by putting them to sleep.

Other kinds of patients clearly show anxiety symptoms, such as chronic alcoholics after initial detoxification, or patients with reactive acute first-episode anxiety symptoms of short duration.[13,54] Both groups improve so much on inert placebo plus ordinary supportive therapy that it is difficult to show any need for the use of antianxiety drugs under such conditions.

Drug terminology can be handled with greater clarity. The term "antianxiety agent" is probably preferrable as describing a desired clinical action which can often be achieved. The earlier term "minor tranquillizer" is useless in the United States and only slightly more useful in Europe. In the United States, antipsychotic agents like chlorpromazine, and antianxiety agents like meprobamate, were both initially called "tranquillizers" on the correct but vague assumption that they often made patients more peaceful. Unfortunately, the most important use of chlorpromazine and other phenothiazines is in the treatment of schizophrenic psychopathology, an area in which meprobamate and the antianxiety drugs are essentially ineffective. To call both kinds of drugs "tranquillizers" even if they are segregated into "major" and "minor" tranquillizers implies a nonexistent similarity in the pharmacology and clinical utility of the two groups of drugs. In the United States, the terms "antianxiety drug" and "antipsychotic drug" are becoming more widely used and are much more informative. In Europe the term "neuroleptic" is used instead of "antipsychotic" and the term "tranquillizer" is reserved for drugs which we, in the United States, should call antianxiety agents.

Hollister, in an excellent book on clinical psychopharmacology,[25] neatly handles another dimension of drug classification by dividing agents effective or probably effective in reducing anxiety into two classes:

1. The sedative-hypnotics, into which class alcohol—our prototype anxiety drug—would

fall, as well as meprobamate, barbiturates, and benzodiazepines (e.g., diazepam). As noted above, sedative-hypnotics usually and in varying degrees *decrease* muscle tone, *raise* the convulsive threshold, produce motor ataxia at higher dosages, and elicit tolerance and physical dependence.

2. The sedative-autonomic drugs which decrease anxiety. In contrast to the sedative-hypnotics, they *increase* muscle tone, *lower* convulsive threshold, and do not produce physical dependence. Into this class fall sedative antihistamines (e.g., hydroxyzine or diphenhydramine), phenothiazines when used in low doses to relieve anxiety, and sedative tricyclic antidepressants with antianxiety effects (e.g., doxepin).

Table 21–1 presents antianxiety and seda-

TABLE 21–1.   **Antianxiety and Sedative Agents Used in the United States**

DRUG	HYPNOTIC DOSE*	SEDATIVE DOSE*	ADDICTIVE	
			PS.	PH.
Sedative-Hypnotics				
Benzodiazepines				
Chlordiazepoxide		5–25 mg. tid or qid	+	+
Diazepam		2–10 mg. bid or tid	+	+
Oxazepam		10–30 mg. tid or qid	±	+
Chlorazepate		7.5 mg. qid	+	+
Flurazepam	15–30 mg.	–	?	?
Others				
Meprobamate	800 mg. hs	400 mg. tid	+	+
Solacen		350–500 mg. tid or qid	–	–
Methaqualone	150–300 mg.	75 mg. tid or qid	+	+
Diphenylhydantoin		200 mg./day	–	?
Barbiturates				
Phenobarbital	100–200 mg.	30–60 mg. tid or qid	±	+
Butabarbital	50–100 mg. hs	15–30 mg. tid or qid	±	+
Pentobarbital	100–200 mg. hs	30 mg. tid or qid	+	+
Amobarbital	100–200 mg. hs	30–50 mg. tid or qid	+	+
Secobarbital	100 mg. hs		+	+
Sedative-Autonomic Agents				
Hydroxyzine		25–100 mg. tid	–	–
Diphenhydramine		50 mg. po tid or qid	–	–
Doxepin		50–150 mg.	–	–

LEGEND: tid = three times a day; qid = four times a day; hs = bedtime; Ps. = psychological dependence; Ph. = physical dependence.

* Dose and action recommended by drug company and FDA approved.

tive agents currently in general use in the United States.

To date the only type of possible antianxiety drug under clinical study that does not readily fit into this classification is propanolol, a nonsedative autonomic agent (a beta-adrenergic blocker) which may relieve anxiety symptoms through peripheral blockade rather than through central action on the brain.[18,78]

A question may well be raised at this point. Are barbiturates really the typical hypno-sedatives and are drugs like chlordiazepoxide really very different? Should the newer sedative antianxiety agents be classified separately from the older sedative hypnotics?

Hypnosedative vs. Antianxiety Agents?

Despite almost two decades of advertising by drug companies, the authors are unconvinced that the therapeutic and pharmacological main actions of barbiturates and benzodiazepines are so markedly different as to deserve separate classificatory groupings. Both types of drugs decrease anxiety and elicit sedation or drowsiness as a side effect. At median effective dose (ED-50 in pharmacological jargon) for anxiety reduction, a barbiturate should, in theory, produce more drowsiness and ataxia than a drug similar to diazepam, and at doses of the two drugs producing equal sedation, patients on a benzodiazepine should be less anxious. Although the clinical literature is vague in this direction, the trend is weak and the magnitude of the differences in efficacy and sedation between the two classes of drugs is not large enough to warrant separate classifications. Nevertheless, benzodiazepines are generally judged more effective than barbiturates in controlled studies (at dosages used which are often low for the barbiturates). The really important differences between the two drug classes are to be found elsewhere in this paper.

Benzodiazepines have a much longer half-life in the body than barbiturates like amobarbital, have a slower onset of action when taken orally, and are far far safer when taken with suicidal intent.[25] There is no recorded successful suicide in which only benzo-

diazepines were taken (e.g., in doses as high as 2250 mg. of chlordiazepoxide) while ten short-acting barbiturate capsules can sometimes be lethal. The benzodiazepines are probably also less prone to abuse than short-acting barbiturates because of the benzodiazepines' slower onset, and because of the longer duration of action that deprives spree users of a quick intense "high."

Possible Mechanisms of Action

Although antianxiety drugs have usually been identified and selected by drug companies because, in animals they prolong hexabarbital sleeping time, raise convulsive threshold, and elicit ataxia and reduce motor activity at some dose, these actions are of little psychotherapeutic interest per se. The intriguing action from a psychiatric viewpoint is the ability of the sedative hynotics to disinhibit suppressed behavior in an operant test system. Typically, hungry animals, pressing a lever for an occasional food reinforcement, are taught that, when a red light is on, a lever press may sometimes yield a painful shock as well as a food pellet. Animals treated with saline (or phenothiazine, opiate, or amphetamine) stop pressing the lever while the light is on. Animals treated with barbiturates or benzodiazepines risk the shocks by pressing the lever anyway.

Also, even though sedative-hypnotics can reduce psychomotor activity, at lower doses they often increase exploratory behavior and increase responsiveness to environmental stimuli. They do not suppress conditioned avoidance behavior.

Phenothiazines reduce motor activity at all dosages, decrease exploratory and social behavior, and inhibit conditioned avoidance responses (e.g., acting at a learned warning signal so as to avoid a subsequent imminent shock).

Irwin has extrapolated these animal observations to the clinical situation.[28] He proposes that benzodiazepines should be used to treat anxiety when the patient is shy and underactive and more risk-taking behavior is to be encouraged. Phenothiazines should be used to reduce anxiety when the patient is overactive and takes too many risks, where decreased social responsiveness and physical activity are clinically indicated.

Although no specific clinical trial has tested Irwin's hypothesis, there are some clinical data which tend to support his ideas. Lipman et al.[39] in a study comparing chlordiazepoxide (CDP) with placebo in anxious outpatients found that patients on CDP report significantly more "good things" happening to them during the trial than do placebo patients. Many of the "good" events had an aggressive risk-taking component, e.g., "My wife and I finally had it out and now we understand each other!" DiMascio's observation that benzodiazepines, particularly CDP and diazepam, elicit increased hostility in normal subjects with low pretreatment anxiety levels could also be considered a form of disinhibition.[8] Klein's finding that phenothiazines stabilize and inhibit the behavior of patients with emotionally unstable personality disorders[34] also supports Irwin's thesis.

It is difficult for us to summarize or interpret the neurophysiological effects of the sedative-hypnotic antianxiety agents in any clinically meaningful manner. On the other hand, a recent paper by Stein et al. has intriguing content with relevance for clinical usage.[70] He reports a direct effect by oxazepam on both norepinephrine and serotonin in the brain. He then demonstrates, by the skillful use of research drugs, that the effect of oxazepam on norepinephrine is short-lived and related to sedation while the effect on serotonin lasts for many hours and is relatable to anxiety reduction.

Assuming this differential action is true of man as well as of the rat, an excellent argument can be made for giving the generally long-lasting benzodiazepines at bedtime (hs) rather than on a three-times-a-day (tid) or four-times-a-day (qid) basis. A single hs dose should improve sleep at night while allowing anxiety reduction uncomplicated by ataxia or drowsiness to occur in the daytime. Given half-lives in the body of over twenty-four hours for both chlordiazepoxide and diazepam, this approach should be clinically useful. A study

providing a clear test of the proposition is badly needed.

A recent study of hs butabarbital in elderly psychiatric patients supports this proposition,[72] but with a presumably shorter acting drug. In the course of a study of the efficacy of butabarbital as an hypnotic, ward behavior ratings were collected on general principles. It turned out that during the week on 50 mg. butabarbital hs the patients not only slept better than they did on placebo but also showed improved daytime ward behavior.

Enzyme Induction

There is increasing laboratory evidence about the ability of some drugs to cause the body to make more and more of the enzyme by which they are detoxified. This "induced" extra enzyme will often metabolize other unrelated drugs as well.

The classic example is phenobarbital. A few days' administration of phenobarbital not only increases a person's ability to metabolize that drug but also makes the body metabolize the anticoagulant, warfarin, more rapidly. This effect can have serious consequences in cardiac or other patients who have been stabilized on warfarin. Warfarin blood levels can be reduced by adding phenobarbital or, alternately, elevated after withdrawing phenobarbital.[6,25]

Luckily, the benzodiazepines do not induce metabolic enzymes appreciably.[63] Choral hydrate, interestingly, affects warfarin blood levels by a totally different mechanism. A metabolite of choral hydrate, trichloroacetic acid, kicks warfarin molecules off of their binding sites on plasma proteins, causing a sudden rise in plasma warfarin levels and a drop in prothrombin time, with attendant risk of hemorrhage.

Abuse Liability

Everyone agrees that drugs like secobarbital, amobarbital, and pentobarbital are abused on the "street" illicitly. At an approximate level of daily use of six 100-mg. capsules, physical dependence on these drugs begins to appear.[17,80] Untreated abrupt withdrawal in markedly physically dependent indviduals can lead to severe agitation and tremulousness, convulsions, delirium and, rarely, death. In contrast to opiate withdrawal, which can be terminated at any time by an adequate dose of an opiate agonist, barbiturate withdrawal becomes nonreversable in its more severe stages.

Probably the vast preponderance of sedative-hypnotic addicts—those both physically and psychologically dependent on these drugs —are "street" users and originally took such drugs for "kicks" or possibly as a replacement for heroin or some other drug of abuse. Occasionally a patient becomes markedly dependent on either barbiturates, meprobamate or the benzodiazepines through medical channels by being given—or obtaining by ruse—such pills from one or more physicians. Apparently, the recent quaalude abuse scare arose in that manner.[25,66]

Clearly, physical dependence can be developed to methaqualone,[66] diazepam, chlordiazepoxide,[27] and meprobamate.[26] It can probably be produced by all the agents listed as sedative-hypnotic agents in Table 21–1 except tybamate,[68] the latter being exempted presumably by its short half-life in the body. A steadily elevated drug blood level is apparently needed to induce physical dependence.

The autonomic sedatives do not appear capable of inducing either physical dependence or drug-seeking behavior induced by psychological craving.

To obtain true physical dependence of the barbiturate type, one needs sedative-hypnotic agents available on the street with a real or believed ability to induce an intense, pleasurable "high" and an action long enough to induce real physical dependence. Pentobarbital meets these criteria as, apparently, does methaqualone. It seems possible that longer acting drugs (e.g., chlordiazepoxide, butabarbital, phenobarbital) are less liable to abuse not because they do not induce tolerance or physical dependence but because their "flatter highs" fail to induce much drug-seeking behavior. Currently there is no systematic work in progress to compare older and newer antianxiety agents on these abuse-relevant dimensions in either animals or man.

One last point needs stressing. Nightly ingestion of one or even two sleeping pills will not produce physical dependence. It may well make patients demand such medication vigorously and may induce a little insomnia after the nightly drug is stopped. It may even be therapeutically irrational to continue such medication, since the hypnotic efficacy may drop with successive nightly administrations.[30] It is not clear whether the hangover effects seen after single bedtime doses of hypnotics[30,76] are also seen after regular nightly use. One suspects that some tolerance to these might also develop. Overprescribing or overdependence on nightly hypnotics may be a misuse of such drugs but is probably not a major one.

Overuse of Antianxiety Drugs

The issue of overuse or overprescription of antianxiety drugs in the United States is charged with emotion, with some claiming that the problem is very serious and probably due to undue pressure from unscrupulous drug companies.[37] These claims seem grossly exaggerated. Fortunately, data are becoming available which are relevant to this problem. A 1973 report[48] on a well-conducted national survey of drug use by individuals shows that about one in five adults in the United States had used a prescription psychotherapeutic drug in the twelve months preceding the year. About two-thirds of the drugs used were antianxiety agents. One in five women had used such drugs at some time in that year vs. less than one in ten men. About one in twenty adults had used antianxiety agents daily for two months or more.

It is worth noting that data from the National Disease and Therapeutic Index, a survey of doctors' drug use, indicate that only half the patients for whom antianxiety agents are prescribed are given a psychiatric-type diagnosis. Since antianxiety drugs are used as muscle relaxants and, one of them, phenobarbital, is used in epilepsy, the above use figures may well be a bit inflated. The authors of the survey[48] also obtained comparable data from several European countries and find that the drug use in the United States is comparable to that in other Western nations.

The above information can be interpreted in many ways. We judge it to be generally reassuring, in that antianxiety drug use is not really very rampant. Others could, of course, argue that too many people are being given these drugs. The fact that 77 percent of people surveyed who were using psychoactive drugs felt helped "a great deal or quite a bit," is reasonable evidence of consumer satisfaction. Since about 5 percent of the population surveyed had taken over-the-counter tranquilizers in the past year, the generally lower "improved" rate for all such psychoactive drugs (39 percent vs. 77 percent for prescription drugs) is worth noting. This confirms the highly negative controlled study of Compoz, a major over-the-counter tranquilizer, by Rickels and his group.[53]

The issue of overprescribing by the doctor or overconsumption by the patient must remain moot until some agreement develops as to specific criteria for appropriate or rational use. As Rickels et al.[56] have noted, general-practice patients getting antianxiety drugs are a good deal more symptomatic than patients seen in the same practice with gynecological problems, and only those neurotic patients judged moderately to markedly improved approach, after drug treatment, the subjective distress scores of the gynecologic patients.

Unusual Clinical Actions of Antianxiety Drugs

Before going on to consider the general clinical efficacy of antianxiety drugs, some atypical clinical uses and effects deserve comment.

Sodium amobarbital, IV at 250–500 mg., has some unique properties. It is the fastest way to quiet a wildly disturbed patient if one has enough staff to make access to a vein possible, and if one avoids stopping respiration by injecting the drug too rapidly (e.g., a few seconds vs. two to four minutes). Injected more gradually the same drug often produces a dramatic change in patients in catatonic stupor.[79] Such patients become often fully relaxed, and able to talk and move normally for an hour or two before the stupor and rigidity returns. Interviews with otherwise mute or underresponsive psychotic patients are sometimes made possible by intravenous barbiturates. Sometimes this device makes it possible to get a history and establish identity when the patient is unable to provide the information in an ordinary interview. It is worth noting that information provided under barbiturate sedation (popularly known as "truth serum") is by no means always true. It can be confounded by the patient either consciously or unconsciously.

There is reasonable evidence from research done in World War II that intravenous barbiturate-induced catharsis can produce immediate and dramatic, enduring relief in patients suffering from an acute traumatic neurosis following severe exposure to stress.[19,20]

The value of IV barbiturates in facilitating dynamic psychotherapy in more routine neurotic conditions is less clear. Patients often talk more freely about highly charged material which had previously been either suppressed or repressed. Whether or not this increased verbal fluency leads to clinical improvement is less clear.

Similarly, barbiturate-induced relaxation has been tried along with desensitization and other forms of behavior therapy. Its value in this context is as yet unclear, but tends toward the positive.[41,69]

As Shagass[67] and others have reported, the sedation threshold (the amount of intravenous drug required to produce sedation-related changes in the EEG or GSR) discriminates between neurotics and psychotics, with psychotics developing sedation at significantly *lower* dosages of barbiturate.

Hyperkinetic children are made worse by barbiturates. A history of excitement caused by barbiturates is thought to be an indication of a good clinical response to amphetamine-like agents. Similar sedative-induced excitements occur on occasion in senile or younger organically impaired patients. Organic patients often show marked increases in denial and distortion under the influence of barbiturates.[77]

Two points remain to be made here:

1. Diazepam, available for intravenous use, may be as useful and a bit safer for any or all of the above purposes. Much of the above work was done before diazepam came into use. In a single study of the effect of IV diazepam on anxiety, 10 mg. were infused over a ten-minute period. A clear reduction in subjective and objective components of anxiety was observed but the peak effect appeared ten to twenty minutes after the injection was stopped, which suggests that diazepam has a less immediate onset of action IV than do the fast-acting barbiturates.[36]

2. Intravenous use of barbiturates has one serious side effect besides supression of respiration. Laryngospasm can occur, particularly if the patients' larynx has a preexisting irritation from infection, intubation, or gastric gavage. Laryngospasm can be fatal.

The Efficacy of Antianxiety Drugs

Two sets of apparent facts plague the study of clinical effectiveness in the antianxiety area. The first is that many standard drugs are often found to be more effective than placebo. This is truest of chlordiazepoxide, diazepam, oxazepam, and tybamate (over 80 percent of reported controlled studies show a drug to be significantly better than placebo: chlordiazepoxide 27 of 28, diazepam 16 of 18, oxazepam 8 of 9 and tybamate 15 of 16). In the case of meprobamate and the barbiturates, the proportion of positive controlled studies is about 66 percent (barbiturates 13 of 19, meprobamate 18 of 27). Comparisons between various newer antianxiety drugs, and older drugs like meprobamate or the barbiturates, produce a more mixed picture with no clear superiority emerging overall, though diazepam and tybamate have the best records in a handful of comparative studies.

All this is reasonably clear. A problem arises when one tries to explain the negative studies on any rational basis. Both Rickels[55] and Wheatley[79] present evidence that outpatients with symptoms of only a few months' duration and little previous exposure to antianxiety drugs show over 80 percent improvement on placebo, a figure no current drug can surpass. In chronic cases, an active drug can still give high improvement rates but the placebo response drops to about 25 percent. Large-scale well-designed studies often show less clear drug-placebo differences than more informal private practice studies. Although one can view private practice studies with skepticism, if one so desires, Rickels' data suggest that a real difference exists between private practice and clinic settings.[23] He finds a considerable diazepam-placebo difference in patients seen in general-practice (GP) settings with phenobarbital somewhat less effective than diazepam. In patients seen in a clinic, he found phenobarbital as good as diazepam, and smaller drug-placebo differences. Generally, Rickels has found GP patients to discriminate a drug from placebo better than either poor clinic patients or private psychiatric patients. Wheatley has had equally impressive success with drug studies in general practice in the United Kingdom.[78]

One outstanding failure among the more elaborate attempts to detect drug-placebo differences was an outpatient collaborative study[44] by the Veterans Administration, which ran for eight weeks. Significant differences were found between chlordiazepoxide and placebo mainly at week 5 of the study (if you want to feel better for Christmas, start the drug at Thanksgiving!). This result can be attributed to the general chronicity or schizophrenic coloring of V.A. outpatients, but it can equally be a victim of the curse which pursues collaborative studies.

The NIMH's psychopharmacology program tried a series of studies to identify major variables which might be affecting the results of controlled clinical trials of antianxiety drugs. The first study compared meprobamate vs. placebo in three outpatient clinics. Half the psychiatric resident therapists were trained to be enthusiastic about the effectiveness of the double-blind medication while the other half expressed a cautious neutrality (therapeutic vs. experimental set). An early analysis[12] came out beautifully with the therapeutic doctors obtaining a much bigger drug-placebo difference than the neutral ones. When the results were all in, however, all we had was a statistically significant but confusing mess! There was a triple interaction,[75] and the results differed reliably as a function of drug, set (doctor behavior), and clinic. For example, the biggest drug-placebo difference at Johns Hopkins University occurred with the patients exposed to the experimental set, while at Philadelphia General Hospital the biggest difference occurred with patients exposed to the therapeutic set. In both clinics the other kind of therapist produced no drug-placebo difference at all!

The NIMH-PRB group, of which one of us was a member, next tried to replicate a study by Kast.[31] He found that if you give atropine to produce dry mouth and tell the patients that dry mouths are a good sign, atropine will potentiate the antianxiety effects of antianxiety drugs, presumably by reinforcing suggestibility. Again in three clinics we compared chlordiazepoxide vs. placebo. Half of both drug groups received atropine in their capsules and of the resulting four groups, half of each were told to expect a dry mouth and to expect real improvement if they got a dry mouth. What happened was exactly the opposite of our prediction.[38] The group on librium or placebo plus atropine with positive instructions got dry mouths and did remarkably poorly, while the group told to expect a dry mouth who got no atropine (and no dry mouth) improved very nicely. The study showed (1) chlordiazepoxide is more effective than placebo, and (2) anxious outpatients dislike dry mouths.

The third study compared, in the same three clinics, chlordiazepoxide, meprobamate, and placebo. Two kinds of practicing psychiatrists were recruited to treat study patients: (1) psychiatrists known to favor drug therapy; and (2) those known to be unenthusiastic about drug therapy. It was hoped the graduate psychiatrists with firm therapeutic opinions would influence patient response more than coached residents had. This study mainly showed that actively interacting psychiatrists (independent of drug attitude) elic-

ited more improvement than more reserved therapists.[57] Chlordiazepoxide was again shown to be superior to placebo but meprobamate, for unknown reasons, was less effective than in the three earlier clinical studies.

More promising recent approaches to this problem include McNair's work with an "acquiescence" measure[45] and Goldstein's work with symptomatic normal volunteers.[16]

Predictors of Clinical Response

Uhlenhuth, Rickels, and Lipman separately and together have done most of the work attempting to predict the outcome of patients under treatment with antianxiety drugs. After studying several representative publications[9, 47,74] one finds oneself with a bad case of intellectual dyspepsia. The studies are carefully and sensibly done and employ promising and approved statistical approaches but the results offer little practical advice to the working clinician. Can it be true that chlordiazepoxide is better than hydroxyzine if the doctor likes the patient,[47] while the opposite is true if the doctor's initial reaction to the patient was less favorable? Should a clinician act on this clue? A number of predictors do not discriminate between patients receiving antianxiety drugs and those receiving placebo.

Agoraphobia and Related Conditions

Klein has defined a clear drug-responsive syndrome consisting of primary severe panic attacks, usually associated with secondary phobias about going out or being left alone. This condition—or at least the panic attacks—responds well to imipramine and does not respond to antianxiety or antipsychotic drugs.[33,50] The secondary phobias can then be handled by psychotherapy or behavior therapy and may be blunted by antianxiety agents.

It is unclear whether Klein's patients are within the group that Sargant[65] and co-workers would classify as atypical depressions and treat with monoamine oxidase inhibitors (MAOIs) or MAOIs plus tricyclic antidepressants.[49] More recent studies have reported both iproniazid and phenelzine to be superior to placebo in the treatment of phobic conditions and of atypical depressions.[41,64]

Since many of the patients treated successfully in the above studies do not suffer from typical neurotic or psychotic depressions, it seems as easy to assume that these drugs have special antianxiety properties in phobic or related patients as to assume that phobic states mask hidden depressions.

Mixed Anxiety-Depressions

Klerman and Cole in their review[35] in 1965 observed that controlled studies comparing tricyclic antidepressants with placebo showed a striking drug-placebo difference in outpatients, a very modest drug-placebo difference in acutely depressed inpatients and a large difference in chronic depressions or in depressions manifesting endogenous retarded psychotic features. Since the outpatients cannot have had primarily endogenous psychotic depressions, one is forced to suspect that tricyclics may be useful in anxiety states or mixed anxiety-depression states of neurotic or reactive varieties.

This introduction makes more believable recent studies showing the tricyclic, doxepin, to be quite effective—even better than chlordiazepoxide on occasion—in outpatients being treated by psychiatrists for anxiety and/or depression.[14–16] In fact, the outpatient use of doxepin is much better documented than is this tricyclic drug's efficacy in major inpatient depressions.

Why is doxepin a good outpatient drug in anxiety states mixed with depression? It may be, as Fink[11] suggests, that the drug has central-nervous-system effects in man which resemble both imipramine and diazepam. It may also be that anxiety and depression are almost inseparable in dysphoric psychiatric outpatients,[6] and that any tricyclic drug would be as effective as doxepin. A collaborative controlled study testing the latter proposition is currently in progress.

However, these data plus the data on drugs in phobic states, raise serious questions as to

the simple-minded acceptance of such face-valid drug classes as "antianxiety agents" or "antidepressant drugs."

Phenothiazines in Anxiety

Klein makes a good case for phenothiazines having a useful stabilizing effect in emotionally unstable personality disorders,[34] a case which is weakened by the tendency for such patients to dislike the drug and to stop taking it as soon as they leave the hospital.

Under the Irwin hypothesis[28] one can propose that phenothiazines should be used in low doses in patients who tend to act out or abuse sedative drugs. Most antipsychotics in low dose will probably be shown to be better than placebo in the treatment of anxiety although most were marketed at a time when such evidence was not required by the FDA.

The major deterrant to their use is the remote but present possibility that the phenothiazines might elicit a chronic dyskinesia[10] in vulnerable patients. Since such patients cannot be identified in advance (though age and organic brain defect increase the odds) the energetic and prolonged use of these drugs as antianxiety agents cannot be strongly endorsed.

In abuse-prone patients, tybamate with its inability to produce physical dependence[22,54] or one of the non-phenothiazine "sedative-autonomic" drugs, such as hydroxyzine, diphenhydramine or doxepin, could be used instead of a barbiturate or a benzodiazepine.

Side Effects

The major side effects of hypnosedative antianxiety agents in general clinical use at recommended dosages are oversedation or ataxia. Patients should be warned about driving cars when sleepy and about mixing such drugs with more than very modest amounts of alcohol. Fortunately, such severe toxic or allergic effects as agranulocytosis or acute yellow atrophy of the liver do not seem to be caused by these drugs. As a caution against relaxation on the part of the physician, it should be noted that thalidomide was a good hypnosedative.

It should also be noted that occasional patients on diazepam and perhaps on other disinhibiting drugs, can develop suicidal ideas and severe emotional upsets.[54] This side effect has been noticed in a controlled clinical trial[21] and is confirmed by DiMascio's literature review,[8] but its real frequency in clinical practice is probably low. It is mentioned here to alert clinicians to the possibility of such effects occurring.

Conclusions

Antianxiety drugs are reasonably effective in the treatment of outpatient anxiety. Benzodiazepines are probably more effective than earlier sedative-hypnotics and are clearly safer when taken with suicidal intent. They also appear to lack enzyme-inducing action and may have lower abuse liability than do the barbiturates or other nonbarbiturate hypnosedatives (except tybamate). Tricyclic antidepressants have a place in the treatment of phobic-panic states and in mixed anxious-depressed outpatients.

(Bibliography

1. BERGER, F. "The Relation between the Pharmacological Properties of Meprobamate and the Clinical Usefulness of the Drug," in D. H. Efron, ed., *Psychopharmacology. A Review of Progress*, pp. 139–152. Washington: U.S. Govt. Print. Off., 1960.

2. BOND, A. J. and M. H. LADER. "Residual Effects of Hypnotics," *Psychopharmacologia*, 25 (1972), 117–125.

3. BRILL, N. Q., R. R. KOEGLER, L. J. EPSTEIN et al. "Controlled Study of Psychiatric Outpatient Treatment," *Arch. Gen. Psychiatry*, 10 (1964), 581–595.

4. CHIEN, C. P. "Psychiatric Treatment for Geriatric Patients: 'Pub' or Drug?" *Am. J. Psychiatry*, 127 (1971), 1070–1075.

5. CHIEN, C. P., B. A. STOTSKY, and J. O. COLE. "Psychiatric Treatment for Nursing Home Patients: Drug, Alcohol and Milieu," *Am. J. Psychiatry*, 130 (1972), 5–12.

6. CONNEY, A. H. "Pharmacological Implications of Microsomal Enzyme Induction," *Pharmacol. Rev.*, 19 (1967), 317–366.

7. DEROGATIS, L. R., R. S. LIPMAN, L. COVI et al. "Factorial Invariance of Symptom Dimensions in Anxious and Depressive Neuroses," *Arch. Gen. Psychiatry*, 27 (1972), 659–665.

8. DIMASCIO, A. "The Effects of Benzodiazepine on Aggression: Reduced or Increased?" *Psychopharmacologia*, 30 (1973), 95–102.

9. DOWNING, R. W., K. RICKELS, and H. DREESMANN. "Orthogonal Factors vs. Interdependent Variables as Predictors of Drug Response in Anxious Outpatients," *Psychopharmacologia*, 32 (1973), 93–112.

10. FDA TASK FORCE, American College of Neuropsychopharmacology. "Neurological Syndromes Associated with Antipsychotic Drug Use," *Arch. Gen. Psychiatry*, 28 (1973), 463–472.

11. FINK, M. "EEG Applications in Psychopharmacology" in M. Gordon, ed., *Psychopharmacological Agents*, Vol. 3. New York: Academic, forthcoming.

12. FISHER, S., J. O. COLE, K. RICKELS et al. "Drug-set Interaction: the Effect of Expectations in Drug Response in Outpatients," in P. B. Bradley, F. Fluegel, and P. Hoch, eds., *Neuropsychopharmacology*, Vol. 3, pp. 149–156. Amsterdam: Elsevier, 1964.

13. GALLANT, D. D., M. P. BISHOP, R. GUERRERO-FIGUERO et al. "Doxepin versus Diazepam. A Controlled Evaluation in 100 Chronic Alcoholic Patients," *J. Clin. Pharmacol.*, 9 (1969), 57–63.

14. GOLDBERG, H. L. and R. J. FINNERTY. "The Use of Doxepin in the Treatment of Symptoms of Anxiety Neurosis and Accompanying Depression: A Collaborative Controlled Study," *Am. J. Psychiatry*, 1 (1972), 129–133.

15. ———. "Doxepin in a Single Bedtime Dose in Psychoneurotic Outpatients," *Arch. Gen. Psychiatry*, 31 (1974), 513–520.

16. GOLDSTEIN, B. J., B. BRAUZER, R. M. STEINBOOK et al. "Psychotropic Drug Treatment of Mixed Anxiety and Depression in Non-Psychiatric Office Patients," *South. Med. J.*, 66 (1973), 892–897.

17. GOODMAN, L. S. and A. GILMAN, eds. *The Pharmacological Basis of Therapeutics*, Chaps. 7, 9, 10. New York: Macmillan, 1970.

18. GRANVILLE-GROSSMAN, K. L. and P. TURNER. "The Effect of Propranolol on Anxiety," *Lancet*, 1 (1966), 788–789.

19. GRINKER, R. R. and J. P. SPIEGEL. *War Neuroses in North Africa*. New York: Josiah Macy, Jr., Foundation, 1943.

20. ———. *War Neuroses*. New York: McGraw-Hill, 1945.

21. GUNDLACH, R., D. M. ENGELHARDT, L. HANKOFF et al. "A Double-Blind Outpatient Study of Diazepam (Valium®) and Placebo," *Psychopharmacologia*, 9 (1966), 81–88.

22. HALL, R. and J. JOFFE. "Aberrant Response to Diazepam: a New Syndrome," *Am. J. Psychiatry*, 129 (1972), 738–740.

23. HESBACHER, P. T., K. RICKELS, J. HUTCHINSON et al. "Setting, Patient and Doctor Effects on Drug Response in Neurotic Patients. II. Differential Improvement," *Psychopharmacologia*, 18 (1970), 209–226.

24. HOLLISTER, L. E. "Anxiety, Depression and Psychotropic Drugs," *Drugs*, 1 (1971), 189–227.

25. ———. *Clinical Use of Psychotherapeutic Drugs*. Springfield, Ill.: Charles C. Thomas, 1973.

26. HOLLISTER, L. E. and F. S. GLAZENER. "Withdrawal Reaction from Meprobamate Alone and Combined with Promazine: A Controlled Study," *Psychopharmacologia*, 1 (1970), 336–341.

27. HOLLISTER, L. E., F. P. MOTZENBECKER, and R. O. DEGAN. "Withdrawal Reactions from Chlordiazepoxide (Librium®)," *Psychopharmacologia*, 2 (1961), 63–68.

28. IRWIN, S. "A Rational Framework for the Development, Evaluation and Use of Psychoactive Drugs," *Am. J. Psychiatry* (*Suppl. Drug Ther.*), 124 (1968), 1–19.

29. KAIM, S. C., C. J. KLETT, and B. ROTHFELD. "Treatment of the Acute Alcohol Withdrawal State: A Comparison of Four Drugs," *Am. J. Psychiatry*, 125 (1969), 1640–1646.

30. KALES, A., E. J. MALMSTROM, M. B. SCHARF et al. "Psychophysiological and Biochemical Changes following Use and Withdrawal of Hypnotics," in A. Kales, ed., *Sleep, Physiology and Pathology*, pp. 331–343. Philadelphia: Lippincott, 1969.

31. KAST, E. C. and J. LOESCH. "A Contribution to the Methodology of Clinical Appraisal of Drug Action," *Psychosom. Med.*, 21 (1959), 228–234.

32. KELLNER, R. "Drugs, Diagnosis, and Outcome of Drug Trials with Neurotic Patients," *J. Nerv. Ment. Dis.*, 51 (1970), 85–96.

33. KLEIN, D. F. "Delineation of Two Drug-Responsive Anxiety Syndromes," *Psychopharmacologia*, 5 (1964), 397–408.

34. KLEIN, D. F., G. HONIGFELD, and S. FELDMAN. "Prediction of Drug Effect in Personality Disorders," *J. Nerv. Ment. Dis.*, 156 (1973), 183–192.

35. KLERMAN, G. L. and J. O. COLE. "Clinical Pharmacology of Imipramine and Related Antidepressant Compounds," *Pharmacol. Rev.*, 17 (1965), 101–141.

36. LADER, M. H. and L. WING. *Physiological Measures, Sedative Drugs, and Morbid Anxiety*, Maudsley Monogr. no. 14, p. 1. London: Oxford University Press, 1966.

37. LENNARD, H. L., L. J. EPSTEIN, A. BERNSTEIN et al. "Hazards Implicit in Prescribing Psychoactive Drugs," *Science*, 169 (1970), 438–445.

38. LIPMAN, R. S., L. COVI, L. R. DEROGATIS et al. "Medication, Anxiety Reduction, and Patient Report of Significant Life Situation Events," *Dis. Nerv. Syst.*, 32 (1971), 240–242.

39. LIPMAN, R. S., H. M. M. HAMMER, J. F. BERNARDES et al. "Patient Report of Significant Life Situation Events," *Dis. Nerv. Syst.*, 26 (1965), 586–590.

40. LIPMAN, R. S., L. C. PARK, and K. RICKELS. "Paradoxical Influence of a Therapeutic Side-Effect Interpretation," *Arch. Gen. Psychiatry*, 15 (1966), 462–474.

41. LIPSEDGE, M. S., J. HAJIOFF, P. HUGGINS, L. NAPIER et al. "Management of Severe Agoraphobia: a Comparison of Iproniazid and Systematic Desensitization," *Psychopharmacologia*, 32 (1973), 67–80.

42. LORR, M., D. M. McNAIR, and G. J. WEINSTEIN. "Early Effects of Chlordiazepoxide (Librium) Used with Psychotherapy," *J. Psychiatr. Res.*, 1 (1963), 257–270.

43. LORR, M., D. M. McNAIR, F. J. WEINSTEIN et al. "Meprobamate and Chlorpromazine in Psychotherapy," *Arch. Gen. Psychiatry*, 4 (1961), 389–396.

44. McNAIR, D. M., A. P. GOLDSTEIN, M. LORR et al. "Some Effects of Chlordiazepoxide and Meprobamate with Psychiatric Outpatients," *Psychopharmacologia*, 7 (1965), 256–265.

45. McNAIR, D. M., R. J. KAHN, L. F. DROPPLE-

MAN et al. "Patient Acquiescence and Drug Effects," in K. Rickels, ed., *Non-specific Factors in Drug Therapy*, pp. 59–72. Springfield, Ill.: Charles C. Thomas, 1968.

46. MCNAMEE, H. B., N. K. MELLO, and J. MENDELSON. "Experimental Analysis of Drinking Patterns of Alcoholics: Concurrent Psychiatric Observations," *Am. J. Psychiatry*, 124 (1968), 1063–1069.

47. MAY, P. R. A. and J. R. WITTENBORN, eds., *Psychotropic Drug Response: Advances in Prediction*. Springfield, Ill.: Charles C. Thomas, 1969.

48. PERRY, H. J., M. B. BALTER, G. D. MELLINGER et al. "National Patterns of Psychotherapeutic Drug Use," *Arch. Gen. Psychiatry*, 28 (1973), 769–783.

49. POLLITT, J. and J. YOUNG. "Anxiety State or Masked Depression? A Study Based on the Action of Monoamine Oxidase Inhibitors," *Br. J. Psychiatry*, 119 (1971), 143–149.

50. QUITKIN, F. M., A. RIFKIN, J. KAPLAN et al. "Phobic Anxiety Syndrome Complicated by Drug Dependence and Addiction, *Arch. Gen. Psychiatry*, 27 (1972), 159–161.

51. RICKELS, K., T. W. CLARK, J. H. EWING et al. "Evaluation of Tranquilizing Drugs in Medical Outpatients. Meprobamate, Prochlorperazine and Amobarbital Sodium and Placebo," *JAMA*, 171 (1959), 1649–1656.

52. RICKELS, K., I. CSANALOSI, R. W. DOWNING et al. "Prognostic Indicators of a 4-Week Clinical Improvement with Chlordiazepoxide and Hydroxyzine in Anxious Neurotic Out-patients," *Int. Pharmacopsychiatry*, 6 (1971), 249–253.

53. RICKELS, K. and P. T. HESBACHER. "Over-the-Counter Daytime Sedatives, a Controlled Study," *JAMA*, 223 (1973), 29–33.

54. RICKELS, K., P. HESBACHER, W. VANDERVORT et al. "Tybamate: A Perplexing Drug," *Am. J. Psychiatry*, 125 (1968), 320–324.

55. RICKELS, K., P. T. HESBACHER, C. T. WEISE et al. "Pills and Improvement, a Study of Placebo Response in Psychoneurotic Out-patients," *Psychopharmacologia*, 16 (1970), 318–326.

56. RICKELS, K., R. S. LIPMAN, C. GARCIA et al. "Evaluating Clinical Improvement in Anxious Outpatients: a Comparison of the Normal and Treated Neurotic Patients," *Am. J. Psychiatry*, 128 (1972), 1007–1009.

57. RICKELS, K., R. S. LIPMAN, L. C. PARK et al. "Drug, Doctor Warmth and Clinic Setting in the Symptomatic Response to Minor Tranquillizers," *Psychopharmacologia*, 20 (1971), 128–152.

58. RICKELS, K., R. LIPMAN, and E. RAAB. "Previous Medication, Duration of Illness and Placebo Response," *J. Nerv. Ment. Dis.*, 142 (1966), 548–554.

59. RICKELS, K., I. RAAB, R. DESILVERIO et al. "Drug Treatment in Depression. Antidepressant or Tranquilizer," *JAMA*, 201 (1967), 675–680.

60. RICKELS, K. and L. SNOW. "Meprobamate and Phenobarbital in Neurotic Psychiatric Patients and Medical Clinical Outpatients," *Psychopharmacologia*, 5 (1964), 339–346.

61. RICKELS, K., C. H. WARD, and L SCHUT. "Different Population, Different Drug Responses; a Comparative Study of Two Antidepressants, Each Used in Two Different Patient Groups," *Am. J. Med. Sci.*, 247 (1964), 328–337.

62. RITCHIE, J. M. "The Aliphatic Alcohols," in L. S. Goodman and A. Gilman, eds., *The Pharmacological Basis of Therapeutics*. New York: Macmillan, 1970.

63. ROBINSON, D. S. and E. L. AMIDON. "Interaction of Benzodiazepines with Warfarin in Man," in S. Garattini, E. Mussini, and L. O. Randall, eds., *The Benzodiazepines*, pp. 641–644. New York: Raven Press, 1973.

64. ROBINSON, D. S., A. NIES, C. L. RAVARIS et al. "The Monoamine Oxidase Inhibitor, Phenelzine, in the Treatment of Depressive-Anxiety States," *Arch. Gen. Psychiatry*, 29 (1973), 407–413.

65. SARGANT, W. "The Treatment of Depressive States," *Int. J. Neurol.*, 6 (1967), 53–71.

66. SCHWARTZBURG, M., J. LIEB, and A. H. SCHWARTZ. "Methaqualone Withdrawal," *Arch. Gen. Psychiatry*, 29 (1973), 46–47.

67. SHAGASS, C. *Evoked Brain Potentials in Psychiatry*. New York, Plenum, (1972).

68. SHELTON, J. and L. E. HOLLISTER. "Simulated Abuse of Tybamate in Man: Failure to Demonstrate Withdrawal Reactions," *JAMA*, 199 (1967), 338–340.

69. SILVERSTONE, T. "The Use of Drugs in Behavior Therapy," *Behav. Ther.*, 1 (1970), 485–497.

70. STEIN, L. S., C. D. WISE, and B. D. BERGER. "Antianxiety Action of Benzodiazepines: Decrease in Activity of Serotonin Neurons

in the Punishment System," in S. Garattini, E. Mussini, and L. O. Randall, eds., *The Benzodiazepines*, pp. 299–308. New York: Raven Press, 1973.

71. STEPHENS, J. H. and J. W. SHAFFER. "A Controlled Study of the Effects of Diphenylhydantoin on Anxiety, Irritability and Anger in Neurotic Outpatients," *Psychopharmacologia*, 17 (1970), 169–181.

72. STOTSKY, B. A., J. O. COLE, Y. T. TANG et al. "Sodium Butabarbital (Butisol Sodium) as an Hypnotic Agent for Aged Psychiatric Patients with Sleep Disorders," *J. Am. Geriatr. Soc.*, 19 (1971), 860–870.

73. TYRER, P., J. CANDY, and D. KELLY. "Preliminary Communication: Phenelzine in Phobic Anxiety: A Controlled Trial," *Psychol. Med.*, 3 (1973), 120–124.

74. UHLENHUTH, E. H., L. COVI, K. RICKELS et al. "Predicting the Relief of Anxiety with Meprobamate, an Attempt at Replication," *Arch. Gen. Psychiatry*, 26 (1972), 85–91.

75. UHLENHUTH, E. H., K. RICKLES, S. FISHER et al. "Drug, Doctors' Verbal Attitude and Clinic Setting in the Symptomatic Response to Pharmacotherapy," *Psychopharmacologia*, 9 (1966), 392–418.

76. VON FELSINGER, J. M., L. LASAGNA, and H. K. BEECHER. "The Persistence of Mental Impairment following a Hypnotic Dose of a Barbiturate," *J. Pharmacol. Exp. Ther.*, 109 (1953), 284–291.

77. WEINSTEIN, E. A. and R. L. KAHN. *Denial of Illness. Symbolic and Physiological Aspects*. Springfield, Ill.: Charles C. Thomas, 1955.

78. WHEATLEY, D. "Comparative Effects of Propranolol and Chlordiazepoxide in Anxiety States," 115 (1969), 1411–1412.

79. ———. *Psychopharmacology in Family Practice*. London: Heinemann Medical Books, 1973.

80. WIKLER, A. *The Relation of Psychiatry to Pharmacology*. Baltimore: Williams & Wilkins, 1957.

CHAPTER 22

ANTIPSYCHOTIC DRUGS

John M. Davis and Jonathan O. Cole

MODERN clinical psychopharmacology was ushered in by the almost simultaneous discoveries that two chemically very different drugs were able to alter psychotic behavior in hospitalized psychiatric patients.[169] The ultimately less important of the two drugs, reserpine, had been observed to have antianxiety effects in hypertensive patients and taming effects in the rhesus monkey. Furthermore, its source, the rauwolfia serpentina root had been used in Hindu native medicine for centuries as a treatment for insanity. Its initial trial on disturbed psychotics in 1952 was well controlled and showed that the active drug caused a statistically larger decrease in hours spent in restraint or seclusion than resulted from placebo treatment.[131] The major defect in the design, in retrospect, was the failure of the investigators to establish the effective dose of reserpine before beginning the trial. At the dose used (1 mg. per day) the drug's effect might have been missed had not relatively large numbers of patients been employed in a quantitative experiment. Reserpine's discovery was, therefore, the outcome of a relatively methodical procedure of scientific investigation. Unfortunately, it proved to be slower acting and less effective than chlorpromazine, a drug discovered purely by chance, as have been all new classes of psychoactive drugs discovered since that time.

Chlorpromazine (CPZ) was, in fact, originally synthesized as an antihistamine. Animal tests revealed it to be rather sedative. Pierre Laborit, a French anaesthesiologist was looking for just such a drug to add to the pharmacological agents in his "lytic cocktail," an intravenous mixture with which he was trying to block the overresponse of the human body to surgical stress. He readily obtained it from the French firm which had synthesized it, and soon observed that CPZ produced a behavioral change which might most accurately be described as tranquilization. Soon thereafter, in 1952, two French psychiatrists, J. P. Delay and P. Deniker administered the drug to schizophrenic patients.[51] Once again, the tranquilizing effects were observed but, in addition, there seemed to be a striking reduction of psychosis.

Since the discovery of these drugs and their antischizophrenic effects, psychiatric practice has been profoundly altered. For although the use of CPZ did not usually produce a permanent cure in the schizophrenic, It did produce major benefits in many patients, in a way no other treatment had ever accomplished (Figure 22–1).[50] The news of Delay's and Deniker's clinical observations spread quickly and resulted in the wide use of CPZ on thousands of schizophrenic patients throughout the world.*

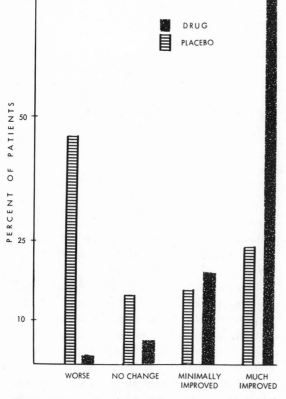

Figure 22–1. Doctors' global rating of improvement in patients after treatment with phenothiazines or placebo.

The discovery of CPZ heralded the beginning of a therapeutic revolution which extended far beyond the pharmacological actions of the drug.[48] For the first time, public mental institutions could be regarded as true treatment centers, rather than as primarily custodial facilities. Since clinically significant therapeutic effects could be produced by this drug, an atmosphere was created in which other therapies, including milieu therapy, psy-

chotherapy, group therapy, and occupational therapy could be applied simultaneously to patients who, prior to drug treatment, were too disturbed and required too much custodial supervision to be offered such treatments on any regular basis.[48,163,164,145] Thus, the widespread use of these social therapies is possible, due to the control, through pharmacological agents, of the more disruptive and destructive aspects of the patient's illness. This has profoundly altered the fate of many patients who would have otherwise languished in the custodial wards of our mental institutions. In fact, some were so improved that they were discharged from the hospital and returned to their communities as functioning members. For other patients whose illness still required inpatient treatment, the hospital became more humane and tolerable. Today schizophrenic patients can often be treated effectively with antipsychotic agents without ever being hospitalized. For patients who do need to be hospitalized for a first illness or for recurrent psychotic episodes, the duration of hospitalization is sometimes a few days or, at most, weeks.[28,47,148]

One result of this new therapy has been a major reduction in the number of hospitalized schizophrenic patients. This is an especially remarkable development, because, until the introduction of these new drugs, there had been a steady, large increase in the population of hospitalized mental patients (see Figure 22–2).[48] This marked change in the fate of mental patients is, perhaps, the most convincing proof of the efficacy of these agents. Indeed, the improvement produced by CPZ and related drugs in schizophrenia is unlike anything produced by earlier somatic or psychotherapies; these drugs represent a major therapeutic breakthrough.[48]

Skeptics raised the possibility that the improvement might be due to placebo effects, particularly since it was quickly evident that uncontrolled studies of CPZ gave systematically more positive results than controlled studies.† Moreover, it was found that false positive findings with other CPZ-like drugs

* See references 23, 59, 138, 147, and 179.

† See references 29, 47, 71, 72, and 148.

No. of Patients
(in thousands)

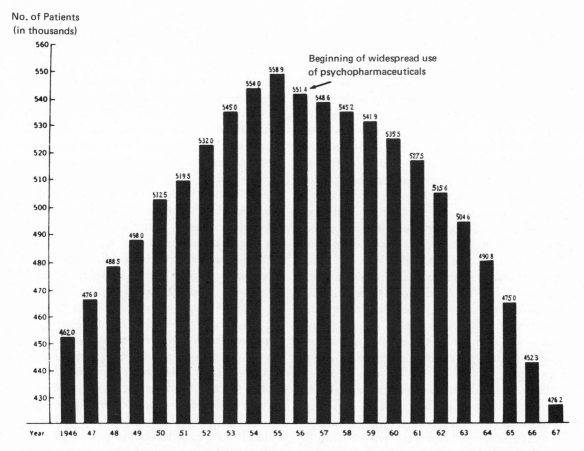

Figure 22–2. Population of public mental hospitals in the United States, 1946–1967. Note the progressive decline in the number of patients beginning in 1956 corresponding to the widespread introduction of the phenothiazines, followed shortly thereafter by other psychoactive agents. Based on data from the United States Public Health Service.

had been obtained—findings in which some drugs (e.g., mepazine) which were later found to be therapeutically ineffective were thought initially to be effective because of favorable results obtained in early uncontrolled evaluation. In addition, false negative results also occurred, in which skeptical investigators found CPZ-like drugs to be ineffective when they were later proven to be effective. Results such as these led to considerable controversy in psychiatry as to the real efficacy of these agents. Some physicians, regarding these tranquilizers as merely fancy sedatives, had little use for them, or thought they might actually be harmful, whereas other doctors endorsed them without critical reservations. Well-controlled studies using adequate drug dosages, appropriate treatment periods and criteria of change have proved like drugs of the CPZ type to be highly effective. In conjunction with this we should point out that development of the methodology to carry out the controlled trials of these drugs was, in itself, an important advance in psychiatry.

Heretofore, radically new treatment approaches in psychiatry within a wide range of modalities, e.g., psychoanalysis, insulin coma therapy, or behavior therapy, have generally been greeted with a mixture of popular enthusiasm and professional skepticism, or even outright and hostile rejection. New treatments were evaluated by a mixture of testimonials by proponents and criticism by opponents. Such evaluations sometimes resembled religious controversies more than objective scientific assessments of efficacy.

However, during the past twenty years it has become standard practice in psychopharmacology to have drugs tested by controlled randomized double-blind trials in which the drug is compared to placebo or a standard comparison drug. This is reflected in the widespread use of this methodology, the funding of such studies by both drug companies and the National Institute of Mental Health, and the insistance on controlled studies by the Food and Drug Administration. Indeed, the practice of treatment evaluation in psychiatry has been profoundly altered. An increasing number of controlled studies of psychological and social therapies in psychiatry have been completed since the mid-1960s. The paradigm for treatment evaluation, particularly in psychopharmacology, has changed from testimonial to controlled trial. This is a consequence of the discovery of chlorpromazine. In our judgment, this new paradigm of the controlled clinical trial is itself a psychiatric advance of major significance.

In this context, the concept of placebo effect requires discussion. The placebo (or inert medication) is used in clinical drug studies to eliminate several phenomena, one or more of which might influence the outcome of a drug study. The patient might get better simply because he believes the pill helps him. This is the conventional, narrow conception of the placebo effect. In addition, however, a placebo-treated group can be used to control spontaneous improvement as well as the effects of other treatments (e.g., milieu or psychotherapy) upon the patient's status. It can remove also or reduce the effects of observer bias, i.e., the expectation of the doctor or nurse that the drug *must* be helpful, leading to objectively unwarranted ratings of improvement. The other aspects of rigorous treatment evaluation are the random assignment of patients to treatments—so that all the good prognosis patients are not placed in the drug (or in the placebo) treated groups—and, the double-blind technique—whereby neither the elevators nor the patients know which patients are receiving the drug and which the placebo.*

* See references 29, 47, 71, 72, 148, and 169.

General Considerations of Efficacy

Chlorpromazine and the other antipsychotic drugs have now been examined in hundreds of double-blind studies, the results of which are summarized in Table 22–1. The vast majority of these studies indicate, as the table clearly shows, that antipsychotics are superior to placebo in the treatment of both acute and chronic schizophrenic patients. In some of the smaller studies, which failed to show a reliable drug–placebo difference, it becomes clear, on detailed evaluation that the dosage was too low for a demonstrable effect. Such results occurred most frequently in the earlier studies of chlorpromazine. However, when adequate doses were administered, chlorpromazine was consistently shown to be superior to placebo, the magnitude of improvement being quite considerable. An NIMH study showed that approximately 75 percent of the phenothiazine-treated patients involved improved significantly under phenothiazine therapy; only 5 percent failed to be helped to some degree and only 2 percent worsened.†[27,29,79] This is certainly in marked contrast to the placebo-treated group in which only one fourth of those involved showed moderate to marked improvement, while half of the group failed to improve or became worse (see Figure 22–1). In addition, this same study showed that new schizophrenic symptoms often emerged in the placebo-treated group, even when these patients were simultaneously receiving individual psychotherapy, group therapy, or other social therapies. This worsening was prevented by phenothiazines.[79] Lehman[137] has used the word "psychostatic" to describe the effects of the phenothiazines because they seem to prevent the emergence of new psychotic symptomatology as well as suppressing the preexisting symptom of schizophrenia.

In the average patient, most of the therapeutic gain occurs in the first six weeks of phenothiazine therapy, although further gains

† In this study chlorpromazine was compared with fluphenazine and thioridazine. No differences were found between the three drugs in a wide range of clinical measures of psychopathology.

TABLE 22–1. **The Comparative Efficacy of Antipsychotic Drugs**

DRUG	MORE EFFECTIVE THAN PLACEBO	EQUAL TO PLACEBO	MORE EFFECTIVE THAN CHLORPROMAZINE	EQUAL TO CHLORPROMAZINE	LESS EFFECTIVE THAN CHLORPROMAZINE
		PERCENTAGE OF STUDIES IN WHICH DRUG WAS			
Chlorpromazine	82.00%	17% (66)*	—	—	—
Acetophenazine	—	—	0.	100.0 (1)	0.0
Butaperazine	100.0	0.0 (4)	0.0	100. (2)	0
Carphenazine	100.0	0 (2)	0.	100.0 (2)	0.
Fluphenazine	100.0	0 (15)	0.0	100.0 (9)	0.0
Mepazine	40	60 (5)	0.0	0.0 (4)	100.0
Mesorizadine	100.0	0 (3)	0.	100. (7)	0.
Perphenazine	100.0	0.0 (5)	0.0	100.0 (6)	0.0
Piperacetazine	—	—	0	100.0 (3)	0.
Prochlorperazine	77.8	22.2 (9)	0.0	100.0 (10)	0.0
Promazine	43	57 (7)	0.0	33.3 (6)	66.7
Thiopropazate	—	—	0.	100.0 (1)	0.
Thioridazine	100.0	0.0 (7)	0.0	100.0 (12)	0.0
Trifluoperazine	88.9	11.1 (18)	0.0	100.0 (11)	0.0
Triflupromazine	90.0	10.0 (10)	0.0	100.0 (10)	0.0
Chlorprothixene	100.0	0.0 (4)	0	100. (6)	0
Thiothixene	100.0	0.0 (2)	0	100. (4)	0
Haloperidol	100.0	0.0 (9)	0	100. (3)	0
Phenobarbital	0.0	100.0 (3)	0	100. (6)	0
Reserpine	69.0	31.0 (29)	—	—	—

	MORE EFFECTIVE THAN THIORIDAZINE	EQUAL TO THIORIDAZINE	LESS EFFECTIVE THAN THIORIDAZINE
Carphenazine	0.0%	100.0 (1)	0.0
Haloperidol	0.0	100.0 (2)	0.0
Mesoridazine	0.0	100.0 (2)	0.0
Piperacetazine	0.0	100.0 (3)	0.0

	MORE EFFECTIVE THAN TRIFLUOPERAZINE	EQUAL TO TRIFLUOPERAZINE	LESS EFFECTIVE THAN TRIFLUOPERAZINE
Acetophenazine	0.0%	100.0 (1)	0.0
Butaperazine	0.0	100.0 (3)	0.0
Carphenazine	0.0	100.0 (3)	0.0
Chlorprothixene	0.0	100.0 (1)	0.0
Haloperidol	0.0	100.0 (4)	0.0
Mesoridazine	0.0	100.0 (1)	0.0

* The numbers in parentheses indicate the number of studies on which the percentages are based.

are made during the subsequent twelve to eighteen weeks as well.[28,29,47] Individual differences do occur, with some patients showing a very rapid improvement in a single day or a few weeks, and some patients exhibiting a very gradual rate of improvement over several months. The course of improvement for the average patient is illustrated in Figure 22–3.

While it is important to know that the phenothiazines benefit psychotics, it is equally important to know the quality and nature of this effect. This information, combined with an increased understanding of the etiology and pathogenesis of schizophrenia, should lead to a more rational pharmacotherapy of this illness.

The data available show that phenothiazine therapy brings about a cognitive restoration with a decrease in psychotic thinking, projection, suspiciousness, perplexity, and ideas of reference, as well as a normalization of psychomotor behavior in slowed and retarded, as well as hyperactive, patients.* Rating scales

* See references 27–29, 80, 82, 126, and 171.

show a reduction of both the fundamental symptoms of schizophrenia (i.e., thought disorder, blunted affect, indifference, autistic withdrawal, psychotic behavior, and mannerisms) and in accessory symptoms (i.e., hallucinations, paranoid identification, hostility, belligerence, resistiveness, and uncooperativeness). Specific aspects of schizophrenic thought disorder, such as overinclusive thinking (as measured by categorizing tasks), and in bizarre, inappropriate responses have been shown to respond to these drugs.[88,170] This is so particularly in process schizophrenia.[136–138] Thus, the symptoms which are reduced by the phenothiazines are typical of schizophrenia in particular and psychosis in general, and, therefore, these agents are most correctly called "antischizophrenic" or "antipsychotic" drugs.[27–29] They do not, in any real sense, produce a state of tranquility in either normal or psychotic individuals.[57,58] The term "tranquilizer" is, therefore, inappropriate. Normal subjects usually dislike the effects of these drugs which tend to produce unpleasant sedation and fatigue.

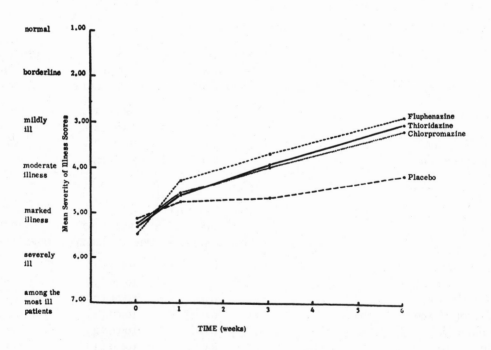

Figure 22–3.   Improvement over time of patients treated with phenothiazines, measured by the severity of illness scores. Data from NIMH-PSC Collaborative Study I.

(Comparative Effects

The advent of chlorpromazine as a novel and effective antipsychotic agent stimulated the search for better antipsychotic drugs with fewer side effects and, as a result, a number of new phenothiazine derivatives were synthesized. In addition, animal screening for chemically unrelated but pharmacologically similar drugs resulted in the development of a number of new classes of antipsychotic compounds. These include the thioxanthene derivatives, which are structural analogs of the phenothiazines, and the butyrophenones, a class of effective antipsychotic compounds with very different chemical structures,[134] as well as several other classes of currently experimental agents with antipsychotic properties. Inasmuch as we can now choose from a variety of drugs with antipsychotic properties, the question arises as to whether any of these drugs are better than chlorpromazine in treating the average schizophrenic patient or any particular schizophrenic symptoms, or any subtype. Furthermore, we must ask whether these agents all produce the same quality of improvement.

In response to these questions we can say that, with the exception of promazine and mepazine, all the phenothiazine drugs are clearly superior to placebo. Controlled trials have shown that both mepazine and promazine are clearly inferior to chlorpromazine (see Table 22–1) and, in addition, that all the other antipsychotic agents are equal to chlorpromazine in their therapeutic efficacy. There is considerable evidence, then, from many controlled studies that the antipsychotic drugs, excepting promazine and mepazine are equal to chlorpromazine in therapeutic efficacy.

It would, of course, be possible for one drug to be slightly superior to another in several studies, while showing statistically significant difference in no single study. We therefore inspected all the original studies to see if, indeed, there were any trends. This inspection revealed that if a given antipsychotic compound were slightly better than another in one trial, it would be likely to be less effective in a second trial. There was no consistent trend for any drug to be superior to any other drug. Inspection of the changes of the symptoms of schizophrenia brought about by the various drugs revealed that all the antipsychotic compounds produced changes consistently on the same dimensions. We found the similarity of these results to be quite striking and supportive of the hypothesis that these drugs act through a common and specific mechanism of action. Differences exist between the drugs, of course, but these lie primarily in the nature of the side effects produced. For example, some may produce more sedation than others, but they all reduce psychotic retardation to a significant extent. In fact, even the most sedating agents reduce psychotic retardation and produce normalization which, in this context, means increased activity and apparent alertness. Similarly, even the least sedating of the drugs produces a calming of psychotic agitation, and does so to an extent equal to that of the most sedating member of this class (see Table 22–2). In summation, then, all the antipsychotic compounds exhibit this paradoxical effect through which they normalize patient behavior: psychomotor activity is *increased* in the retarded patient but *reduced* in the agitated patient.

All antipsychotic drugs being about equally efficacious, we now face the problem of individual differences among patients in attempting to choose the best drug for a given patient.* That is, can we predict how a given patient will react to a specific antipsychotic medication? Certainly, it could be argued, since the antipsychotic action of the drug is related to those features of the molecule which are shared by all the antipsychotics. There is no reason, therefore, to expect that a subtype of patient would respond better to a particular phenothiazine. Nevertheless, the possibility does exist that subtypes of patients may indeed respond better to a particular phenothiazine than to others, due to differential absorption, accumulation at neuronal receptor sites, or differences in the metabolism of one derivative or another. It is further hypo-

---

* See references 75, 81, 82, 128, 129.

TABLE 22–2.   Comparison of Sedative Properties and
Antipsychotic Activity

DRUG	SEDATIVE ACTION	ANTIPSYCHOTIC EFFECT
Chlorpromazine	+ +	+ + + +
Promethazine	+ +	0
Phenobarbital	+ + + +	0
Trifluoperazine	+ −	+ + + +

LEGEND: + to + + + + indicate varying degrees of sedative or antipsychotic activity, with + + + + indicating the greatest and + indicating
the least amount of activity. + − indicates that the effect may or may
not be sedating depending upon the circumstances.

thesized that the patient's psychological response to side effects, such as sedation, could
play a role in differential responsiveness. For
example, there is some clinical evidence that a
patient who uses activity as a defense mechanism may become quite alarmed if he is sedated
and should do better on a nonsedating drug.
In any case, determining whether a subtype
of patient responds differentially to a given
drug is a legitimate empirical question, but
one which cannot be answered positively
given the existing relevant clinical data.

A myth presently extant in psychiatry is that
hyperexcitable patients respond best to chlorpromazine (Thorazine) because it is a sedating phenothiazine, while withdrawn patients
respond best to an altering phenothiazine,
such as fluphenazine (Prolixin) or trifluoperazine (Stelazine), but this has never been
proven to be true.[81] In fact, evidence from
NIMH multihospital collaborative studies suggests that a second-order factor labelled
"apathetic and retarded" predicts a differentially *good* response to chlorpromazine.[78,81]
Even though attempts to replicate this finding
have failed, it is noted since the trend runs
against the popular clinical impression of
chlorpromazine's special properties. It is particularly important to remember, when evaluating predictive studies, that with many predictors, variables, and outcome measures, a
statistical analysis of the data often yields statistically significant predictions by chance
alone. It is therefore most important that results be cross-validated before they be accepted as gospel truth. This statement is confirmed by the fact that most reported
predictions in this field have failed to survive
cross-validation. Specifically, several systems
have been developed to predict which class of
schizophrenic will respond best to which antipsychotic drug.[78] But subsequently, studies
which tested these empirically defined predictions have invalidated them. However, it
should be noted that despite the absence of
clear differential indications for one or another
antipsychotic in a particular patient or class of
patients, psychiatrists continue to observe clinically that patients who fail to respond to one
phenothiazine occasionally do show a good
response to another. Of course it is unwise to
change antipsychotic drugs every few days.
Certainly one must try to find the optimal
dosage of a single drug and, having found said
dosage, allow the drug a reasonable time to
exert its behavioral effect. However, after a
reasonable period of administration—perhaps
a few days in a severely disturbed acute patient, a few weeks in a less dramatically impaired patient—a trial with a different antipsychotic agent is warranted.

The aim of drug treatment is to achieve the
maximum therapeutic improvement in the patient. Thus, one must treat the whole patient,
including the underlying disease process, and
not merely a given symptom. This is particularly noteworthy when treating a depressed
schizoaffective or retarded schizophrenic patient, for these patients often respond dramatically to antipsychotic drugs even though
troublesome target symptoms, such as agitation or aggression, are completely absent.

Luckily, existing antipsychotic drugs tend to produce a generalized reduction in a broad range of schizophrenic psychopathologies rather than working only on a specific isolated target symptom. In sum, the therapeutic goal is for maximum cognitive reorganization and a lessening of the underlying schizophrenic process and, hence, of all symptoms.

⟦ Dosage

Different patients respond to different dosage levels, hence there is no set dose for any given antipsychotic agent. Table 22–3 gives an idea of the clinical dose used in some of the better controlled studies, as well as the cost of the various antipsychotic medications. Columns 1 and 2 are based on empirical data drawn from double-blind studies, in which the different drugs were given in identical appearing tablets to samples of schizophrenic patients. From these results the number of mg. of a given neuroleptic that produces the same therapeutic response in comparison to 100 mg. of chlorpromazine can be calculated. Thus, in column 1 are the number of mg. of each drug equivalent to 100 mg. of chlorpromazine. These double-blind studies were generally based on severely ill hospitalized patients. The average dose of chlorpromazine was 734 mg. a day. In column 2 the average daily dose of all the neuroleptics are given. Thus, column 1 gives the equivalent dose to 100 mg. of chlorpromazine and column 2 gives the equivalent daily dose of the various drugs. Since equivalent doses are known one can compute the cost of the drugs from retail pharmacy catalogs. This is expressed as the total cost for a typical patient of the average daily dose of the given drug in the largest possible tablet size. One could also think of it as the total cost of

TABLE 22–3.   **Comparable Doses of Antipsychotic Drugs**

GENETIC NAME	TRADE NAME	EMPIRICAL DEFINED DOSE IN MG. EQ. TO 100 MG. CHLORPROMAZINE	AVERAGE DAILY DOSE, MG.	AVERAGE COST FOR ONE MONTH AT ACUTE DOSE SCHEDULE
Chlorpromazine	Thorazine	100	734	$15.31
Thioridazine	Mellaril	97 ± 7	712	37.29
Mesoridazine	Serentil	56 ± 6	411	30.68
Chlorprothixine	Taractan	44 ± 8	322	18.03
Triflupromazine	Vesprin	28 ± 2	206	38.71
Carphenazine	Proketazine	25 ± 2	184	20.55
Acetophenazine	Tindal	23 ± 1	169	23.34
Prochlorperazine	Compazine	14 ± 2	103	30.09
Piperacetazine	Quide	11	81	22.27
Butaperazine	Repoise	9 ± 1	66	19.63
Perphenazine	Trilafon	9 ± 0.6	66	27.11
Molindone	Moban	6 ± 0.9	44	12.06
Thiothizene	Navane	4.4 ± 1	32	22.39
Trifluoperazine	Stelazine	2.8 ± 0.4	21	16.91
Haloperidol	Haldol	1.6 ± 0.5	12	28.04
Fluphenazine	Prolixin, 5 mg.	1.2 ± 0.1	9	15.84
Fluphenazine	Permitil, 10 mg.	1.2 ± 0.1	9	6.92
Fluphenazine	Prolixin Enanthate	0.67		20.91
Fluphenazine	Prolixin Decanoate	0.61		18.24

treating thirty patients for one day where the group receives the average daily dose.

It should be pointed out that these dose figures are averaged dose. For reasons explained in the text, one must adjust the dose to the individual patient. The average dose or the dose compared to 100 mg. chlorpromazine is as only a guide to the average dose. This should not be confused with maximal dose. It should also not be confused to suggest that the average dose is appropriate for every patient. With psychotropic drugs the average dose is just that and indeed is not appropriate for most patients, since a little less than half the patients require a slightly smaller dose and roughly half the patients require a slightly higher dose.

A number of points should be made about dosage regulation in the acute patient.* There is a wide therapeutic range between effective dose and toxic overdose with the antipsychotic agents. In research studies, patients have been safely treated with between ten and 100 times the recommended therapeutic dose. Although we do not advocate routinely treating patients with 100 times the dose recommended in the company brochure (e.g., 700 mg./day of perphenazine, or 1000 mg./day of fluphenazine), we wish to go on record as having stated that one can administer a substantially higher dosage of such agents than that recommended, without danger to the patient.[115,149,173] Consequently, the physician should not be concerned about increasing the dose of an antipsychotic drug for good clinical reasons. Evidence for the efficacy of very high dose therapy will be discussed below.

Institution of antipsychotic drug therapy varies widely, in both manner and level, from one psychiatric setting to another. Generally, crisis-oriented facilities start drug therapy in the emergency room, using IM medication freely in turbulent or severely withdrawn patients. The dosage is rapidly increased over two or three days to a high level (perhaps 1200 mg./day of chlorpromazine), and reduced only after the patient is clearly much

* See references 4, 83, 149, 152, and 173.

less aroused and agitated and is beginning to look quiet and even sleepy. In better staffed, more selective, private facilities, a more thoughtful drugfree evaluation period of days or even weeks may precede a rather gradual initiation of drug therapy, with levels of 600 mg./day of chlorpromazine being much more common than levels of 1200 mg./day. However, there is really no reasonable evidence to indicate which regimen leads to a better long-term remission, and regardless of the procedure, the goals of therapy remain unchanged, i.e., reduction of overt psychotic symptoms and gradual cognitive reorganization. However, it should be recognized that the dosage level attainable is sometimes limited by the side effects and may necessitate shifting to another drug.

The most common side effects concomitant with administration of antipsychotic drugs are sedation and extrapyramidal symptoms. However, the appearance of these effects does not usually necessitate shifting to another drug.

The patients generally develop tolerance to the sedative properties so that this side effect disappears after a few days or weeks. Persistent sedation can be handled by dosage reduction or giving most of the drug at bedtime. But neurological side effects present a bigger problem. Generally it is clinically necessary to treat the psychosis with phenothiazines so that one controls the extrapyramidal side effects by antiparkinsonian medication. When there is a question as to whether one needs such a high dose of antipsychotic medication, one can control the extrapyramidal side effects by dosage reduction.

In general, clinicians gradually reduce the dosage of the antipsychotic drug once the patient appears maximally improved, raising the dose again if the symptoms recur. In addition, the dosage is often elevated prophylactically when the patient is about to undergo a special stress, such as returning home or starting a new job.

There are some practical matters relevant to dosage which deserve special attention. The antipsychotic effect of the phenothiazines is of relatively long duration, on the order of days rather than hours, while the sedative effect generally lasts only a few hours. For this reason the common medical practice of administering medication three times a day may leave the patient oversedated when he should be working, learning, or participating in psychotherapies. The same total dose given at bedtime may well promote better sleep while leaving the patient calm, though not sedated, during the day.

Another argument in favor of once-a-day dosage is that the cost of these drugs is not a function of dose, a 25-mg. chlorpromazine tablet costing almost as much as a 100-mg. tablet (see Table 22–4).

There are substantial differences in the cost per mg. of the various drugs depending on the size of the tablet or capsule which was prescribed. For example, if a physician prescribed twenty 10-mg. tablets of Thorazine a day to one patient, it would cost the patient essentially ten times as much (or 1060 percent) as the same amount in one 200 mg. tablet (100 percent) would cost. Similarly, if one prescribed a patient one 200-mg tablet of Thorazine at bedtime vs. 25 mg. chlorpromazine tablets (two tablets four times a day) it would

cost the patients five times as much (or 500 percent). Table 22–4 gives the comparative cost figures for different tablet or capsule sizes of the various neuroleptics. The largest tablet size marketed is given the arbitrary rating of 100 percent and the percent figure of the other tablet sizes are calculated. It should be pointed out that different pharmacies have different pricing policies. Just as auto dealerships in different parts of the country might sell cars at slightly different average prices, so different pharmacies might sell the same drug at slightly different prices. The information given in Table 22–4 is from a general pricelist and is only an approximation of what a given pharmacy may charge.

Thus, giving the largest available indicated dosage form once a day will save considerable money over a long time, substantially reducing nursing time and cost to the hospital. For patients in aftercare, a bedtime or evening dose, once it becomes routine, should be harder to forget and easier for the family to monitor, than a three-times-a-day regimen. Finally, although spansules or other delayed-release oral forms are available for some of the phenothiazines, there is no evidence that these

TABLE 22–4. **Cost per mg. for Different Tablet Size in Percent of Cost of Most Inexpensive Tablet Size**

	TABLET SIZE													
	200	100	50	25	16	125	10	8	5	4	25	2	1	0.5
Chlorpromazine	100	180	300	500			1060							
Triflupromazine			100	150			250							
Thioridazine	100	138	231	415			762							
Prochlorperazine				100			210		323					
Perphenazine					100			149		246		358		
Fluphenazine									100		154		270	
Trifluoperazine							100		153			353	553	
Carphenazine		100	165		277									
Butaperazine				100			197		310					
Mesoridazine		100	167	289			545							
Piperacetazine				100			167							
Haloperidol									100			178	238	332
Chlorprothixene		100	165	271			494							
Thiothixene							100		151			291		450

more expensive formulations have any advantage over the standard tablet preparations.

❮ Chlorpromazine Blood Levels

As mentioned previously, different patients respond to widely different dosage levels, as illustrated in Table 22–5 which condenses studies of the effectiveness of chlorpromazone at different dose levels. In practice, one sees patients who do not respond to a low or moderate dose but who do respond to a high dosage and, conversely, one sees patients who respond quite well to very low doses but who do poorly on moderate doses. Some degree of understanding of this phenomenon may be derived from studies relating blood chlorpromazine to therapeutic improvement and side effects.* Patients exhibit wide differences in blood chlorpromazine levels with comparable doses of the drug.[40] Some patients receiving a moderate dose are found to have an extremely high level of blood chlorpromazine and to be excessively sedated; with reduction of the dosage the patient improves remarkably.[37,39,40,43] Such a patient may have a metabolic deficit and consequently built up a psychotoxically high level of blood chlorpromazine. Quite in contrast to this are the patients who exhibit extremely low blood levels, even on very high doses.[32,39,40] Such patients may metabolize chlorpromazine so rapidly that

* See references 16, 35–44, 90, 91, 109, 132, and 139.

even with very high doses, adequate amounts of chlorpromazine do not reach the brain. Preliminary evidence suggests that antiparkinsonian administration may lower blood CPZ levels.

There are wide individual differences in the metabolism of other phenothiazines. Patients on the same dose may have a thirtyfold variation in serum butaperazine levels or a twentyfold variation in serum thioridazine levels. Curry and his co-workers found that chlorpromazine is metabolized to a significant extent in the gut. If an individual is a rapid metabolizer, he may metabolize CPZ too completely in the gut, with the result that the CPZ which reaches the blood is already an inactive metabolite and is excreted without effect.[40] The patient who is a nonresponder and has low blood levels is shunting the active drug out through excessive metabolism in the gut. It would follow that these patients may respond to intramuscular medication such as depo fluphenazine.

Curry and Adamson[39] screened chronic schizophrenic patients and found a number whose blood chlorpromazine levels were lower on oral dosage than on parenteral dosage. A significant number of these patients responded differentially and more favorably to fluphenazine enanthate (a long-acting, parenterally administered phenothiazine), a finding which would be consistent with the above hypothesis.[39,44] It may be that some patients never build up adequate blood levels of the drug due to excessive metabolism in the gut.

Curry has also shown that the property of

TABLE 22–5.   **The Effectiveness of Different Dose Levels of Chlorpromazine**

DOSE MG./DAY	PERCENT OF STUDIES IN WHICH CHLORPROMAZINE WAS		
	MORE EFFECTIVE THAN PLACEBO	SLIGHTLY MORE EFFECTIVE THAN PLACEBO	EQUAL TO PLACEBO
300 or less	42	23	35
301–400	50	38	13
401–500	80	0	20
501–800	100	0	0
800	100	0	0

chlorpromazine to produce central behavioral toxicity in hepatic coma is due to an enhanced response of the brain to the drug's sedative properties, rather than to an impairment of metabolism as reflected in chlorpromazine blood levels.[143] For optimal results, empirical variation of dosage, routes of administration, and different types of antipsychotic agents should be tried. Unfortunately, however, methods for measuring blood levels of antipsychotic drugs remain technically complex, and it may be several years before it will be possible for psychiatrists to routinely check unresponsive patients to make sure that appropriate antipsychotic drug levels have been achieved.

⟦ High-Dosage Phenothiazine Treatment

Some patients do not benefit significantly from any antipsychotic drug medication and therefore the question naturally arises as to whether abnormally high doses would have brought about a remission.[83,165]

Two collaborative studies were performed by the NIMH in order to test the efficacy of "mega" dose strategy.[157,158] In both studies chronically hospitalized patients were used. In one study the drug administered was chlorpromazine (2000 mg./day), in the other study the drug of choice was trifluoperazine (70 mg./day). Both studies compared the drug to normal dose and to placebo. Results showed that while the younger, more acute patients seemed to improve with the higher dose, the older, chronic "burned-out" schizophrenics exhibited no benefit from the "mega" dose. Led by these results, Clark et al.[24,25] reexamined data from dose-response studies of maintenance treatment in chronic schizophrenics. Subsequent to a drugfree washout period chlorpromazine was administered to patients in doses of 150, 300, or 600 mg./day. The result of this study was that while younger subacute patients responded best to 600 mg./day the older chronic patients (more than forty years old, hospitalized more than ten years)

exhibited no improvement beyond that achieved with a 300 mg./day dose. Of course, one must note that in these, as in any statistical study, one is looking at a mean or average effect. Therefore, it is quite possible that some individual patients in the older, more chronic group may have responded to massive doses of the drug and, conversely, that some of the semiacute patients would have been better off with lower doses. Controlled studies give a good indication of how the majority of the patients respond. However, in treating individual patients one must adjust the dosage within these general guidelines, to achieve optimal effect.[115,160]

Several groups[115] have performed exploratory studies using massive doses of fluphenazine, 300–1200 mg./day. These groups found that chronic as well as acute schizophrenics resistant to treatment exhibited a good to excellent response. Moreover, they found that while the predominant side effects at low doses were extrapyramidal, the predominant side effect at the higher doses was sedation. The Hillside group performed a double-blind study comparing fluphenazine at 30 mg./day to fluphenazine at 1200 mg./day (personal communication). They found little difference in therapeutic outcome between the two groups. Of course, one must differentiate between the use of moderately high doses, such as double the normal dose used by Prien and Cole,[157] and the "mega" dose strategy used by Rifkin and his co-workers,[160] which was sixty times the normal dose. Nevertheless, the controlled study noted above would tend to caution against undue optimism that megadose antipsychotic drug treatment will cure many drug-resistant schizophrenic patients. However, since patients can receive mega doses of drugs such as fluphenazine without undue toxicity, it would seem that there need be little worry about administering doses which are moderately higher than recommended. In our view, treatment-resistant patients deserve a trial on moderately high-dose treatment. Perhaps, in selective cases megadose treatment might be indicated on an experimental basis. However, because of the larger clinical literature on the use of megadose fluphenazine therapy, it seems reasonable to consider this drug when high-dosage treatment is to be attempted.[6,7]

([Maintenance Treatment with Antipsychotic Medication

Once the patient has exhibited substantial improvement with pharmacotherapy the question arises as to how long he should be maintained on antipsychotic drugs.* To the best of our knowledge, every properly controlled double-blind study (with twenty-four countries reporting such studies) has shown that significantly more patients relapsed on placebo than on continued pharmacotherapy.[136] This is a consistent finding in double-blind studies on a variety of populations, in the United States, Canada, and Great Britain. For example, Leff and Wing[136] studied patients who recovered from an acute schizophrenic illness and found that of those randomly placed on placebo 83 percent relapsed, while only 33 percent relapsed who were maintained

* See references 19, 20, 56, 61–66, 99, 100, 103, 136, 141, 147, 161, 162, and 181.

on drugs. Recently Hogarty and Goldberg[103] performed a particularly important study dealing with the problem of maintenance treatment. A group of 374 schizophrenics was discharged from state hospitals upon recovery and, after a stabilization period on maintenance outpatient phenothiazine, half of these patients were assigned to maintenance chlorpromazine and half to placebo. Half of each group received psychotherapeutic sessions consisting of individual case work and vocational rehabilitation counseling. The results (see Figure 22–4) showed that 73 percent of the patients on placebo without psychotherapy and 63 percent on placebo plus psychotherapy had relapsed. In contrast, only 33 percent of the drug maintenance group relapsed and a "mere" 26 percent of the group on drug maintenance plus psychotherapy relapsed. Thus, this study exhibits a substantial drug-placebo difference, i.e., 31 percent of the drug treated group relapsed in comparison to 68 percent of the placebo group.[103] Furthermore, if we eliminate from the drug-maintenance group those patients who had spontaneously stopped taking their drugs, the relapse rate for drug patients over twelve

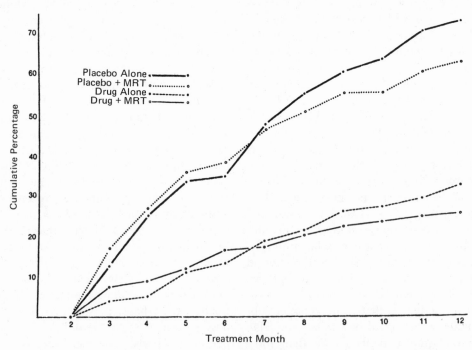

Figure 22–4. Cumulative relapse rates. MRT indicates major role therapy.

months drops to approximately 16 percent. In contrast, patients maintained on placebo generally relapse at an approximately linear rate. However, because individual patients showed few signs of schizophrenic symptomatology until their relapse occurred, at which time they abruptly became markedly more psychotic, the necessity of maintenance of phenothiazine for the prevention of otherwise rather unpredictable relapses is dramatically demonstrated.

The Veterans Administration (VA) performed a major study on maintenance therapy. After sixteen weeks, 5 percent of the patients relapsed who were on drugs, and about 45 percent of the patients relapsed who were on placebo (see Figure 22–5).[19,21]

Engelhardt and his collaborators[60-66] performed an earlier major study of maintenance phenothiazine treatment of ambulatory schizophrenic outpatients. They found that phenothiazines produced better adjustment in the community, lessened the number of relapses, and decreased the time spent in the hospital. Thus, although phenothiazines do not in any sense cure the patients, they do alter the course of the disease in a quantitative way. The result is a shortened hospitalization together with an improvement of behavior outside the hospital.

In all of the studies we have evaluated, treatment with phenothiazines did prevent some relapses. Of course, the number of relapses within a given time period varies with the sickness of the patient population studied, the sicker patients having a greater number of relapses within a time span than the less seriously ill. Thus, about 50 percent of a moderately ill population of chronic, hospitalized schizophrenics will relapse within six months after discontinuance of drug therapy. These data produce a rather ambiguous situation in the argument for phenothiazine maintenance. For, although 50 percent of these moderately

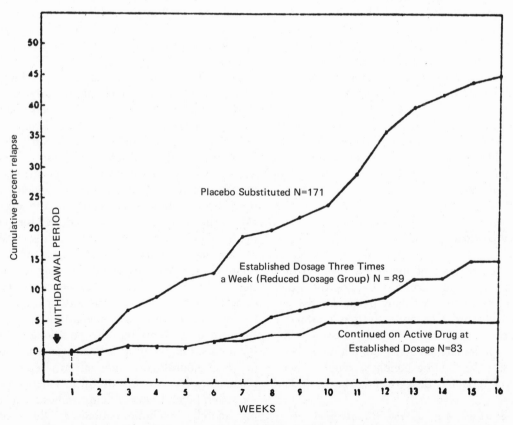

Figure 22–5. Cumulative percentage of clinical relapses during discontinuation study.

ill patients do relapse, the corollary is equally true, namely, 50 percent do not relapse. Thus, half of this patient population are taking a drug they do not need. On the other hand, in regard to the 50 percent who do relapse, a relapse can often have a very serious impact on a patient and his family.

It is our view that the decision to continue a patient on the drug for a long period of time should be arrived at clinically for each individual, based upon a knowledge of his illness and his life situation. In general, it is reasonable to continue most patients on phenothiazines for six months to one year after a psychotic episode. However, for longer periods, treatment should be individualized.

In practice, the decision to maintain or discontinue phenothiazine treatment is based upon clinical common sense.* A history of relapse following discontinuation of phenothiazines would be an indication for a longer period of maintenance, whereas evidence that phenothiazines may not have helped the patient originally, or that their discontinuation in the past has not led to relapse, would be indications for the gradual reduction of dosage leading to termination of drug treatment. Very chronic patients, such as patients who have been hospitalized continuously for fifteen years, are less likely to relapse than more acute patients. We would like to emphasize that psychotherapeutic and social interventions during the recovery phase and in posthospital care are very important in prompting improved social adjustment.

Drug Holidays

There are risks of long-term toxicity with the antipsychotic drugs, although the exact factors associated with any particular risk are rather obscure. Consequently it is reasonable to seek ways of maintaining a remission while using minimal amounts of antipsychotic drugs.[74,76,99,139] Drug holidays, which are one way of reducing dosage, have been studied

---

* See references 17, 99, 136, 161, 162, and 172.

---

chiefly by the VA in extensive studies of chronic inpatients.[19] The VA group has shown that drugs can be omitted on weekends or on an every-other-day basis, either with no increase in the frequency of relapse or a very modest one. If omitting one or several days of drugs does not lead to relapse, it would certainly follow that once-a-day schedules would not lead to relapse. In addition, drug holidays may be useful on minimally staffed maintenance wards. Furthermore, there is considerable time saved on once-a-day medication, i.e., almost forty minutes of staff time per patient.

Depo Intramuscular Medication

There are a number of long-acting antipsychotic agents which are being studied at present; two are currently available in the United States for general use, fluphenazine enanthate and fluphenazine decanoate. These two intramuscular depo forms provide a very useful treatment approach for patients who do not take their oral medication and, on the basis of evidence presently available from double-blind studies, depo fluphenazine is as effective as oral fluphenazine. There have been clinical reports of patients who were particularly benefited by the depo medication in open trials. Although it is presumed that this benefit is due to the fact that these patients had failed to take their oral medication it is also reasonable to suppose that improvement occurred in part due to the IM administration, which bypasses gut metabolism. Therefore, the depo IM medication should be considered for patients who do not manifest optimal responses to oral medication or who, because of frequent relapses, are suspected of failing to take the medication. Thus, the existence of the depo phenothiazines is an important addition to our therapeutic armamentarium, specifically for outpatients but also occasionally for inpatients. Finally, despite their propensity for inducing neurological side effects, depo fluphenazines can be very useful in emergency-room and home-treatment approaches to treating acutely psychotic patients in the community without resorting to inpatient admission.[10,74,176]

A new long-acting (one week) oral agent, penfluridol,[13,73] is in use in Europe.[177]

([Antipsychotic Drugs and Somatic Therapies

The paucity of evidence supporting the efficacy of insulin-shock therapy and electroconvulsive therapy (ECT) in the treatment of schizophrenics has led to the use of phenothiazine and other antipsychotic drugs.* In a controlled study of treatment efficacy Ackner and Oldham[2] failed to find any beneficial effect with insulin shock. Other studies have shown that the effectiveness of ECT and insulin shock is certainly no greater than that of the phenothiazines. Furthermore, although some clinicians are of the opinion that ECT is helpful in the treatment of selected schizophrenics when given concurrently with phenothiazine therapy, there has been no extensive investigation of this point.[127,135] However, Smith et al.[174] found in a controlled study that ECT may be helpful, and that ECT plus phenothiazine led to a more rapid remission than phenothiazine alone. More precisely, they found that the number of inpatient days during the year following hospitalization for the drug group was 159 days as compared to 102 days for the drug–ECT group. Two months after admission, 84 percent of the drug group remained inpatients compared to 48 percent of the ECT–drug group which remained hospitalized.[174] In six months 40 percent of the drug group had not been discharged compared to 14 percent of the ECT–drug group. Until cross-validated appropriate caution should be applied in interpreting these results.

Drug Combinations

The therapeutic value of combining one phenothiazine with another has yet to be demonstrated experimentally. Of course, for any study of combinations to be valid it is important that all treatment groups have an equal amount of antipsychotic medication. Obviously, treatment of the combination group with double the amount of antipsychotic medication used in either of the single-drug groups demonstrates only a dose-response relationship.

It is necessary to have answers for the following questions: Do combinations of antidepressants and phenothiazines help the depressed schizophrenic patient or the apathetic schizophrenic patient? Does a minor tranquilizer with anticonvulsive activity help a schizophrenic with suspected psychomotor epilepsy or one with episodes of violent behavior? A large VA collaborative study[20,22] found that the addition of imipramine, or a monoamine oxidase inhibitor, to chlorpromazine did *not* benefit chronic schizophrenics more than chlorpromazine alone. The addition of an amphetamine to chlorpromazine may have been slightly harmful.

The Spring Grove group[133,146] tested several combinations. Since sedation can be a target symptom and because one is adding a sedating minor tranquilizer to an antipsychotic one might actually undertreat with the antipsychotic medication to avoid excessive sedation.[133] Data from the Spring Grove group and other studies relating to combinations of tricyclic antidepressants with phenothiazines suggest that this mixture may benefit some schizo-affective depressed patients, as well as patients with catatoniclike symptoms.[146] However, the results are not uniform and the differences exhibited are small.† Thus, we strongly emphasize that a trial-and-error approach to obtain maximum benefit from a single drug or combination of drugs is indicated for the individual patients.

When working with drug combinations it is usually best to prescribe each medicine individually, until one obtains the optimal ratio. Certainly, if there exists a proprietary prepara-

---

* See references 8, 12, 70, 94, 127, 135, and 144.

† See references 18, 101, 116, 146, 164, and 166.

tion which contains the optimal ratio, one might use it for convenience. However, one should not assume that all patients respond best to such a preparation.

(Drug, Psychological, and Social Treatments

Drug treatments have been much more thoroughly assessed than have psychotherapeutic methods. May[144] studied a group of newly hospitalized schizophrenics who were divided into four treatment groups: control, psychotherapy alone, phenothiazines alone, and psychotherapy plus phenothiazine. His results are presented in Table 22–6. In general, maximal

TABLE 22–6.   **Comparison of Four Methods of Therapy of Acute Schizophrenia**

TREATMENT	PERCENTAGE OF PATIENTS RELEASED IN STUDY PERIOD
Control	65
Psychotherapy alone	70
Drug alone	90
Drug and psychotherapy	95

improvement was produced by phenothiazines alone or by phenothiazines plus psychotherapy. Psychotherapy alone was decidedly worse than drug therapy alone. In another study performed at the Massachusetts Mental Health Center (MMHC) by Grinspoon et al.[96–98] a small group of chronically ill schizophrenic patients were treated by senior psychoanalysts. When placebo was substituted for thioridazine the behavior of these patients deteriorated, yet there was no evidence from this study that the drug therapy made the patients unresponsive to the psychoanalytically oriented psychotherapy. Rather the opposite was the case. When receiving phenothiazines the patients seemed more involved with their psychoanalysts, indeed, they seem more involved with the outside world in general and more aware of events such as President Ken-

nedy's death, the absence of the psychoanalysts or the ward physician during vacations, etc.

At Massachusetts Mental Health Center (MMHC) Greenblatt, et al.[95] compared four variations in drug and social therapies. High social therapies were administered at the MMHC and consisted of a variety of psychotherapies, social work, occupational therapies, psychodrama, etc. The low social therapies were administered at a state hospital. Some of these chronic schizophrenic patients were transferred from a state hospital to the MMHC and were divided into two groups, one group receiving high social therapy with drugs and the other group receiving high social therapy without drugs. Those remaining at the state hospital were also divided into two groups and once again, one group received low social therapy with drugs and the other group received low social therapy without drugs. The results showed that both groups of patients who received drugs exhibited greater improvement (drug plus high social therapy group 33 percent) (drug plus low social therapy 23 percent) than that observed in the nondrug groups in the state hospital milieu (10 percent) or at the MMHC (0 percent). Finally, regarding the ultimate fate of these patients, Table 22–7 shows that those who were able to leave the hospital because of symptomatic improvement were those who had received both drug and the social therapies. Moreover, high social therapies without drugs seem to mitigate against improvement since this group, when placed back on drugs after having been off them for six months never did catch up with the group continuously treated with drugs plus social therapies.

In a large double-blind study comparing group therapy alone, group therapy with phenothiazine therapy, and phenothiazine therapy alone performed by the VA, it was found that in most symptom areas typical of psychosis phenothiazine therapy with or without group therapy produced maximum improvement. There were, however, several interactions of phenothiazine with group therapy and several effects which were due to group therapy alone.[89]

TABLE 22–7.   Drug Versus Social Therapies in Chronic Schizophrenia. Results of Four Treatment Regimes[95]

REGIME	PERCENT HIGHLY IMPROVED AFTER 6 MOS.	PERCENT DISCHARGED AFTER 6 TO 9 MOS.	PERCENT HIGHLY IMPROVED AFTER 36 MOS.
Drug + high social therapy	33	27	35
Drug + low social therapy	23	9	19
No drug + high social therapy	0	7	26
No drug + low social therapy	10	5	6

It is important to remember that these therapies are complimentary.[46,67,89] The social therapies do not have the antipsychotic activities of the drugs. Conversely, phenothiazine therapies may be beneficial in reducing the patient's psychotic symptomatology, but they do not help him to get a job, adjust to his family situation, or give him the motivation and judgement to stay out of the hospital.[46,67,96–98]

([Side Effects

A physician must be familiar with possible side effects produced by the drugs that he prescribes.[28] Moreover, since psychotropic agents are some of the most frequently prescribed, he must be acquainted with the side effects of all of these agents, since there is a reasonable likelihood that he will have to diagnose and treat side effects produced by drugs prescribed by other doctors or taken on the patient's own initiative.[104–107]

The sharing of common pharmacological modes of action by many of the psychotropic drugs has made it convenient to consider categories of related side effects.[*] For example, the antipsychotic and tricyclic antidepressant medications block biogenic amines reuptake and also cholinergic receptors. This can produce a family of autonomic side effects, such as blurred vision, dry mouth, constipation, urinary retention, etc. Also, all of the antipsychotic agents produce extrapyramidal side

* See references 20, 55, 104–107, and 134.

effects because of their central blockage of dopamine receptors. It is useful to think of side effects as belonging to categories, because it is easier to remember general patterns than it is to think of thirty to forty individual side effects. We can classify the effects of the antipsychotic drugs as: autonomic, extrapyramidal, other central-nervous-system effects, allergic, endocrine, and long-term skin and eye side effects.

Autonomic Side Effects

The autonomic side effects of the antipsychotic agents are a result of their anticholinergic and antiadrenergic properties. Among autonomic side effects which may present themselves are: dry mouth and throat, blurred vision, cutaneous flushing, constipation, urinary retention, paralytic ileus, mental confusion, miosis, mydriasis, and postural hypotension.

Dry mouth is one of the most frequently occurring complaints. For relief, the patient can be advised to rinse his mouth out frequently with water. However, he should not be advised to chew gum or candy since adding sugar to the mouth provides a good culture medium for fungal infestions such as moniliasis and, in addition, may increase the incidence of dental caries. Pharmacologically, pilocarpine can be administered to reduce this side effect, although the relief it provides is sometimes transitory. In any case, patients develop a tolerance to dry mouth, as well as to other autonomic side effects.

Orthostatic (postural) hypotension[122] occurs most frequently during the first few days of treatment and patients readily adapt to it. It develops more frequently when acute, high doses of IM medication are administered. It can be occasionally troublesome, the chief dangers being that the patient may faint, fall and injure himself, although such events are very rare. In susceptible patients (i.e., those taking a high dose of parenteral medication), it is sometimes prudent to take the patient's blood pressure (lying and standing) during the first few days of treatment. Such a practice will present the clinician with the need to make arbitrary judgements. A patient may show a blood pressure of 85/50 but be asymptomatic. Should one worry or change dose? The authors think not. Asymptomatic blood pressure decreases have to be handled differently than symptomatic drops in patients who become faint, weak, or dizzy upon standing up. On a more pedestrian level, support hose may provide some relief to patients with chronic mildly symptomatic hypotension.

The patient should be warned of this side effect when appropriate, and the usual instructions should be given: rise from bed gradually, sit with legs dangling, wait for a minute, and sit or lie down if you feel faint. In general, postural hypotension is not troublesome. However, when it occurs it can usually be managed by having the patient lie down with his feet higher than his head. On very rare occasions, vasopressor agents may be indicated. Obviously, since phenothiazines are alpha-adrenergic blockers, they block the alpha-stimulating properties of epinephrine, while leaving the beta-stimulating properties untouched. Consequently, the administration of epinephrine results in a paradoxical hypotension and this is contraindicated in phenothiazine-induced hypotension. For persons with cardiovascular disease, the doses should be increased more slowly and the blood pressure carefully monitored.

A predrug ECG for baseline purposes is sometimes indicated in patients with preexisting heart conditions, and is probably desirable in all patients in the geriatric age range (over sixty-five).

An electrocardiogram abnormality, consisting of broadened, flattened, or cloven T-waves and an increased Q–R interval of uncertain clinical significance has been described in patients receiving thioridazine at doses as low as 300 mg./day.[180] This abnormality does not seem to be associated with clinical electrolyte disturbances, but, nevertheless, has been reversed by potassium supplements, isosorbidodinatrate, and ergotamine tartrate, as well as by discontinuation of the drug. In addition, ST-segment depression has been observed in patients treated with a number of other phenothiazines, as have alterations in heart rate, both bradycardia and tachycardia.

Very rarely, sudden death has been reported in patients receiving phenothiazine treatment.[111] However, one cannot make an accurate assessment as to whether or not these drugs were the causal agent involved in such a death, since sudden death, in the absence of drugs, can occur even in young, apparently healthy, adolescents. Sudden deaths were reported in healthy hospitalized young schizophrenics long before antipsychotic drugs were ever invented.[154] Mechanisms proposed for such sudden deaths are: ventricular filbrillation, asphyxia caused by regurgitated food, and endobronchial mucus plug in an asthmatic schizophrenic, shock in patients with acquired megacolon, and convulsive seizures or their complications.

Extrapyramidal Side Effects

Extrapyramidal effects fall into three arbitrary categories: (1) parkinsonian syndrome, (2) dyskinesias, and (3) akathisia. The parkinsonian syndrome involves tremor of resting muscles, masklike face, a slowing of voluntary movements, a festinating gait, and rigidity. In symptomatology, it bears much resemblance to idiopathic parkinsonism. Dyskinesia is characterized by a variety of peculiar movements of the neck, face, and tongue, such as torticollis, oculogyric crisis, opistohotonus, and buccofacial movements with salivation. Akathisias are marked by the fear of sitting down and by the inability to stay still, a semi-involuntary motor restlessness most marked in the lower extremities.

Diagnosis of this family of side effects can

occasionally present problems. The parkinsonian syndrome can sometimes be mistaken for schizophrenic apathy, especially when motor retardation is prominent, the dyskinesias can appear to be the bizarre mannerisms of psychotic patients, and akathisia strongly resembles agitation.

It is important to diagnose these symptoms correctly so that proper treatment can be administered.[129] A therapeutic trial of antiparkinsonian agents, such as benztropine (Cogentin), procyclidine (Kemadrim), or diphenhydramine (Benadryl), is especially useful in making an accurate diagnosis.[129] Dramatic dyskinesias, in particular, respond readily to intravenous or intramuscular treatment with antiparkinsonian medication. Comparative quantitative data on these side effects is imprecise.[129] The greatest incidence of extrapyramidal effects if produced by butaperazine, fluphenazine, haloperidol, thiothixene, and trifluoperazine. Acetophenazine, chlorpromazine, and chlorprothixene produce a moderate number of such effects, and thioridazine produces the fewest neurological side effects.

Even patients receiving small amounts of phenothiazine can experience the acute dyskinetic reaction which normally occurs during the first several days or weeks of treatment. The same reaction often occurs in children who have been treated for nausea with a single dose of prochlorperazine (Compazine). The reaction causes the patient to be brought hastily to the emergency room. Patient and family often fail to recognize the relationship between the symptoms and the previously administered antimimetic drug. Consequently, they usually fail to inform the examining physician that the patient has been using a phenothiazine-type medication. Dyskinesias can disappear of their own accord after minutes or hours but since they are frequently painful and psychologically distressing to the patient, it is best to administer antiparkinsonian medication.

Occasionally one encounters an acute dyskinetic reaction which is resistant to treatment with typical antiparkinsonian medication. In these cases, caffeine, diazepam, or methylphenidate (Ritalin) may be effective. Dystonic reactions are more likely to occur in patients suffering from hypoparathyroidism.

Akathisia and the parkinsonian syndrome can also occur early in treatment and continue for a few weeks until tolerance develops. Sometimes patients can exhibit a very subtle form of parkinsonian disease. This presents itself as zombielike appearance or emotional blunting. One must be cautious not to confuse these symptoms with emotional withdrawal or retardation. Antiparkinsonian medications readily alleviate such symptoms.

The akathisias, the third branch of parkinsonian side effects, can be confused with psychotic agitation. An akathisia patient is driven by motor restlessness. Antiparkinsonian drug treatments often bring dramatic results in akathisia patients. However, those who are resistant to such treatment can be aided by reducing dosage or changing to a different phenothiazine.

There has been debate among psychiatrists as to whether antiparkinsonian medication should be administered (1) prophylactically to all patients under antipsychotic treatment, or (2) to only those patients exhibiting a given side effect. Physicians opposing the routine method of treatment argue that (1) extrapyramidal symptoms do not occur in most patients; (2) high doses of parkinsonian medication cause side effects such as blurring of vision, dry mouth and *very rarely* paralytic ileus and/or urinary retention; (3) cost of treatment rises; (4) there is no conclusive evidence that routine use of antiparkinsonian medication prevents parkinsonian symptoms; and (5) patients can develop albeit rarely what is essentially an atropine-type psychosis. In the most severe form, this could be the central anticholinergic syndrome characterized by loss of immediate memory, disorientation, vivid hallucinations, etc.[49]

Those in favor of routine or prophylactic administration of antiparkinsonian medication point out that the extrapyramidal effects are often distressing to the patient, especially when he is not in the hospital. For example, a case of dramatic dystonia is frequently interpreted as a medical emergency and the patient is rushed to the hospital, a disturbing incident for the patient and his family. The proponents go on to note the existence of some clinical manifestations of parkinsonian extrapyramidal effects, such as apathy, drowsiness, lack of spontaneity, relative inability to participate in social activity, and lifelessness, which are sufficiently indistinct to make diagnosis difficult. Avoidance of the dramatic and unpleasant side effects which tend to alarm the patient and alleviation of the more subtle manifestations of extrapyramidal syndromes are, thus, the arguments used by those in favor of routine administration of antiparkinsonian medication.

For every 400 mg. of chlorpromazine or its equivalent, approximately 5 mg. of procyclidine or an equivalent antiparkinsonian medication can be prescribed. Initially, procyclidine is given on a three-times-a-day schedule, because it has a short-term effect. Later on in treatment, however, it can be administered twice daily or at the hour of sleep. Dosage need not be increased beyond a 15 mg. daily total.

Despite the fact that there is a lack of quantitative data on this point, it is the opinion of the authors that patients develop a degree of tolerance to extrapyramidal side effects. We would not recommend routine administration of antiparkinsonian drugs in a hospital situation. For some outpatients, we would favor judicious use of preventive antiparkinsonian medication in the minimum dosage. Adjustment of the dose is often required. After several weeks or months of phenothiazine treatment, the patient may no longer require antiparkinsonian medication.[130,153] In two studies in which antiparkinsonian medication was systematically withdrawn from chronic patients, it was found that approximately only 20 percent of the patients showed any neurological side effects after withdrawal. The other 80 percent had apparently received the medication without needing it. We therefore suggest that antiparkinsonian medication be gradually reduced after phenothiazine treatment has continued for a few months.

Given that extrapyramidal effects are produced by all antipsychotic drugs, the hypothesis is raised that the qualitative presence of the effects may bear a relationship to the antipsychotic properties of the drugs. One author has gone on to suggest that the optimal therapeutic dose of phenothiazine is reached when a certain minimal type of extrapyramidal effect begins. This so-called "neuroleptic threshold" is manifested by certain subtle changes in handwriting. No solid evidence has been found to support this hypothesis. That extrapyramidal side effects and therapeutic effects should be related is not surprising, however, for the two are dose related. There is no correlation between therapeutic improvement and the presence of extrapyramidal effects. Thioridazine (Mellaril), which produces only minimal extrapyramidal side effects, has as much therapeutic effect as butyrophenones such as haloperidol, and phenothiazines such as fluphenazine and trifluoperazine, which produce far more extrapyramidal effects.[27]

Tardive Dyskinesia

Tardive dyskinesia, or terminal extrapyramidal insufficiency, is an extrapyramidal syndrome which emerges late in the course of treatment with antipsychotic drugs.* It occurs particularly in cases in which high doses of the medication have been used for years. The syndrome is present only when the patient is awake.[32–34] It consists of buccofacial mandibular or buccolingual movements such as "smacking" of the lips, sucking, lateral or "fly catching" movements of the tongue, grimacing, lateral jaw movements, tonic contractions of the neck and back, and choreic movements of the upper extremities of fingers, ankles, and toes.[32] The symptoms may appear during antipsychotic treatment. They may also recur or become intensified several days or weeks after the drug treatment has been reduced or ceased. When this happens, the symptom may be unmasked, since dystonic movements can be suppressed by phenothiazine induced rigidity. Paradoxically, then, if the patient is given high doses of butyrophenones and phenothiazines, the syndrome may be undetectable. In

---

* See references 32–34, 124, and 125.

some patients, symptoms disappear soon after treatment ceases, while in others they persist at length. Antiparkinsonian medication is not beneficial. Reserpinelike medications[77,124,125] may prove helpful. Attention is called to an FDA-ACNP Task Force Statement in the *AMA Archives of General Psychiatry* [28 (1973), 463–467], and to a series of systematic studies by Crane[31–34] and Cole.[124,125] In populations who have not had long-term, high-dose treatment with phenothiazine, tardive dyskinesia appears less frequently; for example, incidence among chronic schizophrenic patients in Turkey is low.

⟮ Other Central Nervous System Effects

The threshold of seizures in animals is decreased by most antipsychotic compounds. When humans are given antipsychotic medication in high doses, seizures can occur but do so only rarely. It is usually clinically observed that psychotic epileptic patients who are given antipsychotic drugs show improvement of both their seizure disorder and their behavioral disorder. If seizures do occur, they are generally single and isolated and occur with high doses of the medication. Obviously the patient should receive the appropriate medical workup. Dosage can often be decreased slightly without fear of seizures. Occasionally, when a seizure occurs on phenothiazine medication, an anticonvulsant such as diphenylhidantoin (Dilantin) can be added to the treatment program and antipsychotic medication can be continued without further seizures, even at high doses.

Behavioral Toxicity

The term "behavioral toxicity" refers to adverse behavioral changes, including performance decrements, produced by the ingestion of an antipsychotic drug. It is exceedingly difficult to evaluate behavioral toxicity severely in schizophrenic patients since to do so accurately would require the separation of the

symptoms of drug-induced toxicity from non-drug-related increase in schizophrenic symptoms. Patients treated with psychotropic drugs can display such symptoms as somnambulism, insomnia, toxic confusional states, bizarre dreams, hindered psychomotor activity, and aggravation of schizophrenic symptoms. Since some of these effects may be dose-related, they can be treated by changing dosage, switching drugs, adding or deleting drugs, etc. Within minutes, IM antiparkinsonian drugs can reverse akathisia or an organic psychosis which is thought to be an ideational concomitant of extrapyramidal disorder. The anticholinergic properties of the drugs may be related to some of the confusional states.[50] Also, the rates of metabolism of a specific drug vary from patient to patient; consequently, slow metabolizers may build up psychotoxic amounts of drug or metabolites and manifest excessive sedation.

⟮ Allergic Reactions

When chlorpromazine treatment was first being used, jaundice occurred about once in every 200 cases. For some unknown reason, the occurrence of this side effect has lessened considerably.[106] Today the incidence is approximately one per 1000 chlorpromazine-treated patients, although no precise data on incidence is available; only one case was observed in an active public mental hospital over a five-year period where about 400 new patients a year probably received the drug. Jaundice usually follows one to seven days of flulike symptoms, including nausea, vomiting, fever, malaise, abdominal pains, and diarrhea.[11,54,105,106] It occurs during the first five weeks of phenothiazine treatment. Indicators of phenothiazine-induced jaundice are the timing of the jaundice in relation to phenothiazine treatment, lack of a tender, enlarged liver, and chemical indications of choleostasis, including increase in alkaline phosphatase, decrease in esterified cholesterol, greater increase in direct relative to indirect bilirubin, a modest increase in the liver enzymes SGPT

(Serum Glutamate Pyruvic Transaminase) and SGOT (Serum Glutamate Oxaloacetic Transaminase). Eosinophilia can be observed on peripheral blood smears. Liver biopsy can reveal bile plugs in the canaliculi wth eosinophilic infiltration in the periportal spaces. Chlorpromazine jaundice usually disappears in a few days to several weeks. The majority of such cases are benign and normal liver function returns entirely. Plasma bilirubins do not generally exceed 15 mg./100 mg. Very rarely, the more prolonged exanthomatous billiary cirrhosis can occur. If this does happen, it clears, but sometimes with a chronic course of six to twelve months. Indications that chlorpromazine jaundice may be an allergic reaction (in a broad sense) are its temporal association with treatment, its relationship with eosinophilic infiltrations in the liver and with peripheral eosinophilia, its not infrequent relationship with other allergic reactions, and its long-lasting retention of sensitivity on the challenge test. On occasion, patients have contracted chlorpromazine jaundice five to ten years after their first jaundice has developed. Although most cases of phenothiazine induced jaundice are reported to have occurred with chlorpromazine, the condition is also associated with thioridazine,[11] mepazine, promazine, fluphenazine, and prochlorperazine. It has not been proven that chlorpromazine jaundice can be produced by haloperidol. Since infectious hepatitis is not uncommon in psychiatric patients, not all of these reported associations between psychoactive drugs and jaundice can be assumed to be clearly drug caused.

Routine weekly or biweekly liver-function tests are neither useful nor indicated. When a patient contracts chlorpromazine jaundice, the chlorpromazine treatment should be discontinued.

Agranulocytosis

The most serious, but very rare, side effect of phenothiazines is agranulocytosis. When it occurs, the mortality rate is often 30 percent or higher. Agranulocytosis usually appears suddenly during the first two months of treatment. It is characterized by the abrupt appearance of fever, sore throat, and sometimes mouth ulceration. When it occurs, the patient should enter a medical facility for reverse isolation procedure and phenothiazine treatment should be immediately halted. The infection should be treated rigorously.[30,114,155,156] Adrenal corticosteroids are said to contribute nothing to speeding recovery from agranulocytosis. Although accurate data are lacking, some patients may show cross-sensitivity to other phenothiazines. Again, concrete data are not available, but agranulocytosis occurs probably once in every 500,000 cases. It also has been reported to occur very rarely with mepazine, prochlorperazine, promazine, and thioridazine.

Phenothiazine-related agranulocytosis tends to strike older women. It is certain that routine blood counts are not of value in spotting agranulocytosis. Hence these are not indicated. The condition develops at such a pace that only daily blood counts could detect an unusually uncommon complication.

It is not uncommon for chlorpromazine and other phenothiazines to temporarily reduce a normal white count by 40–80 percent. The hematological phenomenon is not that of agranulocytosis, however. This leukopenia is a benign phenomena and requires no special treatment or deletion of the drug.

Rarely patients taking phenothiazines may develop hemolytic anemias, thrombocytopenic or nonthrombocytopenic purpura or pancytopenia. In such cases, the medication may be deleted or changed.

Dermatologic Side Effects

Skin eruptions of a petechial, maculopapular, urticarial, or edematous character may occur in patients receiving phenothiazine treatment. These effects generally develop in the first weeks of treatment. Those who handle chlorpromazine may also be susceptible to contact dermatitis of the hands and face.

Chlorpromazine treatment can cause a phototoxic photosensitivity reaction similar to severe sunburn.[9] Physicians should make sure that patients are aware of this possible side effect; patients on CPZ should avoid sunlight, using sun screens when appropriate.

Long-Term Eye and Skin Effects

When chlorpromazine was first introduced, phenothiazines were assumed to be entirely safe, even on a long-term, high-dose basis. Since then, however, longitudinal studies plus even longer clinical experience have made it possible to notice long-term side effects such as long-term skin and eye effects.[28,14]

Skin discoloration of areas exposed to sunlight is one such effect. Face, nose, and other open areas may turn tan and proceed to turn slate gray, metallic blue or purple, or even a vivid purple. In such cases, histological examination of skin biopsies reveals pigmentary granules similar to, but histochemically not identical to, melanin.

Long-term, high-dose chlorpromazine (over 1–3 kg.) treatment has also been associated with whitish brown, granular deposits localized in the posterior cornea and anterior lens. These deposits eventually progress to opaque white and yellow-brown, and are often star-shaped. They are visible only by slit-lamp examination. The conjunctiva will occasionally become discolored by a brown pigment. These opacities are in no way related to senile cataracts.

According to statistical data, lens changes are found more often in patients with skin discoloration. Such patients do not display retinal damage and do not have impaired vision. Statistics on the incidence of skin and eye effects vary among hospitals, from under one to over 30 percent. One reason for this variance may be the amount of sun to which a hospital generally exposes its patients.

Since skin and eye effects are related to sunlight, it is suggested that patients exhibiting these effects be treated by curtailing exposure to the sun and shifting patients still requiring antipsychotic drugs to haloperiodol or low-dose phenothiazines, since both eye and skin changes are probably a function of total phenothiazine dose taken over time.

Retinopathy

Thioridazine is the only phenothiazine really dangerous to the eye. Retinitis pigmentosa develops when dosage exceeds 800 mg./day. Serious visual impairment or even blindness may result. Therefore, one must strictly avoid thioridazine doses exceeding 800 mg./day.

Endocrine Effects and Impotence

Although there exists a large basic literature relating to the effects of antipsychotic agents, given in large doses, on the endocrine systems of a wide variety of obscure species, in practical terms the clinically important effects for the human species are lactation and male impotence. Of these, the latter is presumably autonomic, not endocrine, in origin. In addition, these drugs may result in a shift in glucose tolerance curves in a diabetic direction. Finally, false positive hormonal (not immunological) pregnancy tests have been reported among females receiving antipsychotics.

Breast engorgement and lactation in female patients is a well-known effect of these drugs and, although figures are lacking, if every patient were checked for lactation by manual pressure on the breast, an incidence of as high as 20–40 percent might be found. However, subjective complaints of overt lactation are quite rare, less than 5 percent. When such spontaneous lactation does occur, however, it is usually adequately handled by dose reduction or by shifting the patient to another drug. Finally, drug-related gynecomastia in male patients has been described.

Clinical studies of the effects of these drugs upon other sex hormones and upon adrenocortical, thyroid, or pituitary hormones have produced negligible and/or inconsistant results. In addition, marked weight gain is sometimes associated with phenothiazine treatment.

Thioridazine, among all the antipsychotics, produces the most frequently reported incidence of sexual impotence in male patients. This impotence begins with delayed ejaculation and, ultimately, to loss of erectile ability. The reason for this special effect of thioridazine is, perhaps, that the drug has more autonomic (and fewer extrapyramidal) side effects than do the higher-potency antipsychotic agents.

The physician should be aware that drug-induced impotence is a potentially disturbing side effect which he may miss simply because the patient is too embarrassed to speak of it. He should therefore be alert for such a possibility and attempt to mitigate some of the embarrassment by providing a general statement as to the possibility of such an effect.

Side Effects in the Elderly

For unknown reasons, elderly psychotic patients tolerate and require lower dosages of antipsychotic drugs than do younger adult schizophrenics.[112,113,129,178] Lower dosages are indicated; for example, a dose of 10 or 25 mg. of thioridazine or 0.25 mg. haloperidol is a safe dose in elderly patients. Clinically effective dosages are 100 mg. or less of the former, or 1.0 mg. of the latter per day.[112,113] Caution is advised in establishing initial dosage levels, since hypotension or ataxia, with high risk of falls and hip fractures, can result if elderly patients are placed rapidly on high drug levels.[178] Nevertheless, these drugs can prove most effective in psychotic geriatric patients. Finally, where hyperarousal clearly exists at the modest dose levels suggested above, careful and gradual raising of the dose, until symptomatic relief is obtained, is clearly indicated.

⟨ Theoretical Implications

There is a wide variety of drugs which seem to benefit schizophrenic patients. These include the phenothiazine and the thioxanthene derivatives, the butyrophenones, and reserpine, as well as several experimental antipsychotic agents. Thus, it is reasonable to ask whether these antipsychotic agents act through a common mechanism and, furthermore, whether

this mechanism would provide a clue as to the organic causes of schizophrenia. Certainly there are a great many postulated causes of schizophrenia, the more important of which are reviewed in other chapters of this *Handbook*. In this chapter we are restricting ourselves to a discussion of drug-related findings which point toward a biological theory of schizophrenia.

It is noteworthy that all antipsychotic drugs cause parkinsonian side effects. Inasmuch as Parkinson's disease has been shown to be a dopamine deficiency disease, one would assume that these side effects are produced through dopaminergic mechanism. In addition, it is also true that all the antipsychotic agents block central dopamine receptors and, compensatorily increase dopamine synthesis. Consequently, it is reasonable to hypothesize that the common denominator which underlies all the drugs which benefit schizophrenia is their property of blocking central dopamine. Both reserpine and tetrabenazine exhibit antipsychotic properties, but neither seems to be as effective an antipsychotic agent as the phenothiazine derivatives.[1,5,140,168] Both interfere with the storage of biogenic amines, thus one would assume that the beneficial effect they produce in schizophrenics is accomplished through the mechanism of decreasing the level of dopamine in the brain. Theoretically, if one reduced the dopamine level in the brain through the administration of an inhibitor of dopamine synthesis, one might potentiate the action of the antipsychotic drug. This in fact seems to be the case. If dopamine synthesis is blocked with alpha-methyl-*p*-tyrosine, the result is a reduction in the amount of antipsychotic agent necessary to achieve a beneficial effect in schizophrenics. This observation is evidence that the neuroleptics produce their antipsychotic action by means of an interaction with a catecholamine. Thus, we have several lines of evidence that the antipsychotic drugs may benefit schizophrenia through blocking the receptors for the catecholamines, or interfering with catecholamine storage, the former being potentiated by catecholamine synthesis inhibitors. Alpha-methyl-*p*-tyrosine is itself ineffective in treating schizophrenia.

Inasmuch as decreasing dopaminergic activity benefits schizophrenics, it is reasonable to ask whether the schizophrenic process can be produced, or exacerbated where it already exists, by increasing dopamine activation. In this regard psychomotor stimulants such as amphetamine and methylphenidate are potent releasers of dopamine and it is further known that large doses of amphetamine can cause a paranoid schizophrenic episode and IV doses can exacerbate schizophrenia.[118-121] The administration of a number of psychostimulant drugs, including amphetamine and methylphenidate, quickly results in stereotyped activity in rats, consisting of repetitive sniffing and gnawing behavior. This behavior is generally thought to be caused by increased dopaminergic stimulation in or near the neostriatum or tuberculum olfactorium. It is believed to be the animal model of human psychosis since many of the agents which cause it have also precipitated or intensified psychotic behavior in man, and since all existing antipsychotic drugs anatagonize and prevent it in rats probably by causing receptor blockades or by the depletion of central dopamine (DA).

Janowsky and Davis[118-121] have shown that psychomotor stimulants administered IV can markedly exacerbate schizophrenic symptomatology producing in a well-controlled schizophrenic a florid exacerbation of his illness for about one to two hours. Furthermore, methylphenidate is roughly two to three times as potent as L-amphetamine in worsening schizophrenic symptoms, and D-amphetamine is almost twice as potent as methylphenidate (see Figure 22–6). This differs from the order of potency in the rat, for D-amphetamine is two to three times more potent than L-amphetamine or methylphenidate. It is reasonable then to ask the question: Why is methylphenidate more potent in schizophrenia and less potent in causing stereotyped behavior, an animal model for schizophrenia? Methylphenidate and D-amphetamines both produce stereotyped behavior by releasing the dopamine; however, they do so through somewhat different mechanisms. It is thought that

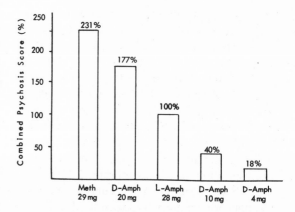

Figure 22–6. Comparison of the ability of various intravenously administered psychostimulants to increase the psychosis score in psychiatric patients expressed as percentage of the effect of L-amphetamine (28 mg.). Methylphenidate (Meth), D-amphetamine (D-Amph), and L-amphetamine (L-Amph) are equimolecular.

they represent two different types of psychomotor stimulants, i.e., (1) methylphenidate releasing dopamine from the stores and (2) amphetamines releasing dopamine from the newly synthesized source. In addition, alpha-methyl-p-tyrosine does not benefit schizophrenia by itself and inhibits synthesis, hence, would be more effective on a newly synthesized pool of amine. Reserpine, which depletes stores of dopamine does have some antipsychotic properties. This evidence would be consistent with stored DA being more important in schizophrenia. Janowsky and Davis have shown[118-121] that there may be an antagonism on many types of behavior between dopaminergic (or noradrenergic) activation and cholinergic stimulation. It is of interest that the worsening in schizophrenia produced by methylphenidate can be reversed or prevented by physostigmine, a drug which increases brain acetylcholine.[118-121] Thus, the worsening of schizophrenia produced by methylphenidate is under control of cholinergic and presumed dopaminergic balance.

Amine released from stores would be expected to be released to some extent intracellularly and thus be vulnerable to destruction by monamine oxidase, an intracellular enzyme. If methylphenidate is differentially more potent in schizophrenia, it may be that schizophrenic patients have a deficit in monamine oxidase. Empirically, schizophrenic patients have low platelet monoamine oxidase (MAO) and furthermore, the great similarity between platelets and adrenergic neurons has led to the suggestion that platelets are a model for the neuron.[150] The observation that platelet MAO may be under hereditary control, may provide an explanation for the hereditary predisposition to schizophrenia. If schizophrenia were simply dopaminergic overactivity, phenothiazines should turn it off as rapidly as they block amphetamine psychosis; that is in hours or a few days. In fact the improvement with antipsychotic drugs takes place more slowly than this. One can easily formulate, as the authors have, a two-factor theory of schizophrenia. It is hypothesized that dopaminergic stimulation can turn up the gain and hence worsen schizophrenia and that the antipsychotic drugs turn down the gain and thus suppress the schizophrenic process. The schizophrenic process, however, could be related to some "second" factor, as yet undefined, either biological and/or psychological. When a patient is treated with antipsychotic drugs, these agents tone down their psychosis and give normal reparative processes a chance to work. D. X. Freedman has termed such theories to be metapsychopharmacological theories. This term serves to emphasize that these theories are speculative. They might be considered as strategies for research more than as well substantiated theories. They are included here to give examples of the fact of the pharmacological properties shared by these antipsychotic agents and may provide clues as to the underlying cause of the disorder. It is important that such theorizing be kept in perspective, e.g., pneumococcal pneumonia is not a penicillin deficiency disease. With the increased understanding of the mechanisms by which these drugs work, it would be unreasonable not to look for common denominators in these mechanisms, as long as one does not prematurely conclude that the cause of schizophrenia has been discovered. Aside from these theoretical considerations, appreciation of the mechanism of these drugs is also useful in understanding side effects and hence, leads to more effective medical management of our patients.

⟮ Bibliography

1. ABSE, D. W., T. E. CURTIS, W. G. DAHLSTROM et al. "The Use of Reserpine in the Management of Acute Mental Disturbance on an Inpatient Service," *J. Nerv. Ment. Dis.*, 124 (1956), 239–247.

2. ACKNER, B., and A. J. OLDHAM. "Insulin Treatment of Schizophrenia," *Lancet*, 1 (1962), 504–506.

3. ANGRIST, B., B. SHOPSIN, and S. GERSHON. "The Comparative Psychotomimetic Potency of Stereoisomers of Amphetamine," *Nature*, 234 (1971), 152.

4. APPLETON, W. "The Snow Phenomenon: Tranquilizing the Assaultive," *Psychiatry*, 28 (1965), 88–93.

5. ASHCROFT, G. W., E. J. MACDOUGALL, and P. A. BARKER. "A Comparison of Tetrabenazine and Chlorpromazine in Chronic Schizophrenia," *J. Ment. Sci.*, 107 (1961), 287–293.

6. AYD, F. J., JR. "Fluphenazine: Its Spectrum of Therapeutic Application and Clinical Results in Psychiatric Patients," *Curr. Ther. Res.*, 1 (1959), 41–48.

7. ———. "Low- vs High-Dose Fluphenazine," *Int. Drug Ther. Newsl.*, 7 (1972), 25–28.

8. BAKER, A. A., J. A. GAME, and J. G. THORPE. "Physical Treatment for Schizophrenia," *J. Ment. Sci.*, 104 (1958), 860–864.

9. BAN, T. A., H. E. LEHMANN, Z. GALLAI et al. "Relationship between Photosensitivity and Pathological Pigmentation of the Skin with Large Doses of Chlorpromazine," *Union Med. Can.*, 94 (1965), 305–307.

10. BANKIER, R. G. "A Comparison of Fluspirilene and Triflusperazine in the Treatment of Acute Schizophrenic Psychosis," *J. Clin. Pharmacol.*, 13 (1973), 44–47.

11. BARANCIK, M., L. L. BRANDENBORG, and M. J. ALBION. "Thioridazine-Induced Cholestasis," *JAMA*, 200 (1967), 69.

12. BARKER, J. C. and A. A. BAKER. "Deaths Associated with Electroplexy," *J. Ment. Sci.*, 105 (1959), 339–348.

13. BARO, F., R. VAN LOMMEL, and R. DOM. "Pimozide Treatment of Chronic Schizophrenics as Compared with Haloperidol

and Penfluridol Maintenance Treatment," *ACTA Psychiatr. Belg.*, 72 (1972), 199–214.

14. BARSA, J. A., J. C. NEWTON, and J. C. SAUNDERS. "Lenticular and Corneal Opacities during Phenothiazine Therapy," *JAMA*, 193 (1965), 10–12.

15. BARTHOLOMEW, A. A. and N. F. HOLT. "A Long-Acting Phenothiazine (Fluphenazine Enanthate): A Preliminary Communication," *Med. J. Aust.*, 1 (1966), 12–18.

16. BERMAN, H. and M. SPIRTES. "Gas Chromatographic Analysis of Chlorpromazine and Its Metabolites Formed by Hepatic Micrones," *Biochem. Pharmacol.*, 20 (1971), 2275–2286.

17. BROOKS, G. W. "Withdrawal from Neuroleptic Drugs," *Am. J. Psychiatry*, 115 (1959), 931–932.

18. BUFFALOE, W. J. and M. G. SANDIFER. "A Study of Combined Therapy with Stealizine and Parnate (SKF–385) in Chronic Anergic Schizophrenics," *Am. J. Psychiatry*, 117 (1961), 1030–1031.

19. CAFFEY, E. M., L. S. DIAMOND, T. V. FRANK et al. "Discontinuation of Reduction of Chemotherapy in Chronic Schizophrenics," *J. Chronic Dis.*, 17 (1964), 347–358.

20. CAFFEY, E. M. and C. J. KLETT. "Side Effects and Laboratory Findings during Combined Drug Therapy of Chronic Schizophrenics," *Dis. Nerv. Syst.*, 22 (1961), 370–375.

21. CAFFEY, E. M., M. P. ROSENBLUM, and C. J. KLETT. "Side Effects and Laboratory Findings in a Study of Antidepressant Drugs," *VA Cooperative Studies in Psychiatry*, Report no. 31. Washington: VA Administration, 1962.

22. CASEY, J. F., L. E. HOLLISTER, C. J. KLETT et al. "Combined Drug Therapy of Chronic Schizophrenics. Controlled Evaluation of Placebo Dextro-Amphetamine, Imipramine, Isocarboxazid and Trifluoperazine Added to Maintenance Doses of Chlorpromazine," *Am. J. Psychiatry*, 117 (1961), 997–1003.

23. CHILDERS, R. T. and R. THERRIEN. "A Comparison of the Effectiveness of Trifluoperazine and Chlorpromazine in Schizophrenia," *Am. J. Psychiatry*, 118 (1961), 552–554.

24. CLARK, M. L., W. K. HUBER, J. SULLIVAN et al. "Evaluation of Loxapine Succinate in Chronic Schizophrenia," *Dis. Nerv. Syst.*, 33 (1972), 783–791.

25. CLARK, M. L., H. R. RAMSEY, D. K. RAHHAL et al. "Chlorpromazine in Chronic Schizophrenia," *Arch. Gen. Psychiatry*, 27 (1972), 479–483.

26. CLARK, M. L., T. S. RAY, and R. E. RAGLAND. "Chlorpromazine in Chronic Schizophrenic Women: Rate of Onset and Rate of Dissipation of Drug Effects," *Psychosom. Med.*, 25 (1963), 212–217.

27. COLE, J. O., G. L. KLERMAN, and S. C. GOLDBERG. "Phenothiazine Treatment of Acute Schizophrenia," *Arch. Gen. Psychiatry*, 10 (1964), 246–261.

28. COLE, J. O. and J. M. DAVIS. "Antipsychotic Drugs," in L. Bellack and L. Loeb, eds., *The Schizophrenic Syndrome*, pp. 478–568. New York: Grune & Stratton, 1969.

29. COLE, J. O., S. C. GOLDBERG, and J. M. DAVIS. "Drugs in the Treatment of Psychosis: Controlled Studies," in P. Solomon, ed., *Psychiatric Drugs*, pp. 153–180. New York: Grune & Stratton, 1966.

30. COUNCIL ON PHARMACY AND CHEMISTRY. "Blood Dyscrasias Associated with Chlorpromazine Therapy," *JAMA*, 160 (1956), 28.

31. CRANE, G. E. "A Review of Clinical Literature on Haloperidol," *Int. J. Neuropsychiatry*, 3 (1967), S110–S129.

32. ———. "Tardive Dyskinesia in Patients Treated with Major Neuroleptics: A Review of the Literature," *Am. J. Psychiatry*, 124 (1968), 40–48.

33. ———. "Pseudoparkinsonism and Tardive Dyskinesia," *Arch. Neurol.*, 27 (1972), 426–430.

34. CRANE, G. E. and G. PAULSON. "Involuntary Movements in a Sample of Chronic Mental Patients and Their Relation to the Treatment with Neuroleptics," *Int. J. Neuropsychiatry*, 3 (1967), 286–291.

35. CURRY, S. H. "Plasma Protein Binding of Chlorpromazine," *J. Pharm. Pharmacol.*, 22 (1970), 193–197.

36. ———. "Theoretical Changes in Drug Distribution Resulting from Changes in Binding to Plasma Proteins and to Tissues," *J. Pharm. Pharmacol.*, 22 (1970), 753–757.

37. ———. "Chlorpromazine: Concentrations in Plasma, Excretion in Urine and Duration of Effect," *Proc. R. Soc. Med.*, 64 (1971), 285–289.

38. ———. "Relation between Binding to Plasma Protein, Apparent Volume of Distribution, and Rate Constants of Disposi-

tion and Elimination for Chlorpromazine in Three Species," *J. Pharm. Pharmacol.*, 24 (1972), 818.

39. CURRY, S. H. and L. ADAMSON. "Double Blind Trial of Fluphenazine Decanoate," *Lancet*, 2 (1972), 543–544.

40. CURRY, S. H., J. M. DAVIS, D. S. JANOWSKY et al. "Factors Affecting Chlorpromazine Plasma Levels in Psychiatric Patients," *Arch. Gen. Psychiatry*, 22 (1970), 209–215.

41. CURRY, S. H., A. D'MELLO, and G. P. MOULD. "Destruction of Chlorpromazine during Absorption in the Rat in vivo and in vovo," *Br. J. Pharmacol.*, 42 (1971), 403–411.

42. CURRY, S. H., M. H. LADER, G. P. MOULD et al. "Clinical Pharmacology of Chlorpromazine," *Br. J. Pharmacol.*, 44 (1972), 370–371.

43. CURRY, S. H. and J. H. L. MARSHALL. "Plasma Levels of Chlorpromazine and Some of Its Relatively Non-polar Metabolites in Psychiatric Patients," *Life Sci.*, 7 (1968), 9–17.

44. CURRY, S. H., J. H. L. MARSHALL, J. M. DAVIS et al. "Chlorpromazine Plasma Levels and Effects," *Arch. Gen. Psychiatry*, 22 (1970), 289.

45. DALLY, P. *Chemotherapy of Psychiatric Disorders*. London: Logan Press, 1967.

46. DAVIS, A. E., S. DINITZ, and B. PASAMANICK. "The Prevention of Hospitalization of Schizophrenia," *Am. J. Orthopsychiatry*, 42 (1972), 375–388.

47. DAVIS, J. M. "The Efficacy of the Tranquilizing and Antidepressant Drugs," *Arch. Gen. Psychiatry*, 13 (1965), 552–572.

48. DAVIS, J. M., E. BARTLETT, and B. A. TERMINI. "Overdosage of Psychotropic Drugs," *Dis. Nerv. Syst.*, 29 (1968), 157–164.

49. DAVIS, J. M., M. K. EL-YOUSEF, D. S. JANOWSKY et al. "Treatment of Benztropine Toxicity with Physostigmine," *Abstr. 5th Int. Congr. Pharmacol.*, 5 (1972), 52.

50. DAVIS, J. M. and N. S. KLINE. "Therapeutic Efficacy of the Phenothiazines and other Antipsychotic Agents," P. Black, ed., *Drugs and the Brain*, pp. 173–184. Baltimore: The Johns Hopkins Press, 1969.

51. DELAY, J. and P. DENIKER. "Le Traitement des psychoses par une méthode neurolytique dérivée de l'hibernothérapie," Congrès de Médecins Aliénistes et Neurologistes de France, Luxembourg, pp. 497–502, 1952.

52. DEMAIO, D. and A. CLOZAPINE. "A Novel Tranquilizer," *Arzneim.-Forsch.*, 22 (1972), 919–923.

53. DENBER, H. C. "Tranquilizers in Psychiatry," in A. Freedman and H. Kaplan, eds., *A Comprehensive Textbook of Psychiatry*, pp. 1251–1263. Baltimore: Williams & Wilkins, 1967.

54. DENBER, H. C. and D. TURNS. "Double Blind Comparison of Thiothixene and Trifluoperazine in Acute Schizophrenia," *Psychosomatics*, 13 (1972), 100–104.

55. DEWAR, R. and H. ROSS. "The Use and Abuse of Tranquilizing Drugs for Mental Patients," *Canad. Med. Assoc. J.*, 87 (1962), 1375–1377.

56. DIAMOND, L. S. and J. B. MARKS. "Discontinuance of Tranquilizers among Chronic Schizophrenic Patients Receiving Maintenance Dosage," *J. Nerv. Ment. Dis.*, 131 (1960), 247–251.

57. DiMASCIO, A., L. L. HAVENS, and G. L. KLERMAN. "The Psychopharmacology of Phenothiazine Compounds: A Comparative Study of the Effects of Chlorpromazine, Promethazine, Trifluoperazine and Perphenazine in Normal Males: I. Introduction, Aims and Methods," *J. Nerv. Ment. Dis.*, 136 (1963), 15–28.

58. ———. "The Psychopharmacology or Phenothiazine Compounds: A Comparative Study of the Effects of Chlorpromazine Promethazine, Trifluoperazine, and Perphenazine in Normal Males: II. Results and Discussion," *J. Nerv. Ment. Dis.*, 136 (1963), 168–186.

59. ELKES, J. and C. ELKES. "Effect of Chlorpromazine on the Behavior of Chronically Overactive Psychotic Patients," *Br. Med. J.*, 2 (1954), 560–565.

60. ENGELHARDT, D. M. and N. FREEDMAN. "Maintenance Drug Therapy: The Schizophrenic Patient in the Community," in N. S. Kline and H. E. Lehmann, eds., *International Psychiatry Clinics*, pp. 933–960. Boston: Little, Brown, 1965.

61. ENGELHARDT, D. M., N. FREEDMAN, B. S. GLICK et al. "Prevention of Psychiatric Hospitalization with the Use of Psychopharmacological Agents," *JAMA*, 173 (1960), 147–149.

62. ENGELHARDT, D. M., N. FREEDMAN, L. D. HANKOFF et al. "Changes of Social Be-

havior in Chronic Schizophrenic Outpatients under Phenothiazine Treatment," *Compr. Psychiatry*, 1 (1960), 313–316.

63. ———. "Longterm Drug Induced Symptom Modification in Schizophrenic Outpatients," *J. Nerv. Ment. Dis.*, 137 (1963), 231–241.

64. ENGELHARDT, D. M., N. FREEDMAN, B. ROSEN et al. "Phenothiazines in Prevention of Psychiatric Hospitalization. III. Delay or Prevention of Hospitalization," *Arch. Gen. Psychiatry*, 11 (1964), 162–169.

65. ENGELHARDT, D. M., B. ROSEN, N. FREEDMAN et al. "Phenothiazines in Prevention of Psychiatric Hospitalization. II. Duration of Treatment Exposure," *JAMA*, 186 (1963), 981–983.

66. ENGELHARDT, D. M., B. ROSEN, N. FREEDMAN et al. "Phenothiazines in Prevention of Psychiatric Hospitalization. IV. Delay or Prevention of Hospitalization—a Reevaluation," *Arch. Gen. Psychiatry*, 16 (1967), 98–101.

67. EVANGELAKIS, M. G. "De-institutionalization of Patients," *Dis. Nerv. Syst.*, 22 (1961), 26–32.

68. FAULKNER, M. and E. A. BURKITT. "Pimozide," *Br. Med. J.*, 3 (1972), 643.

69. FELDMAN, P. E., B. S. LACY, A. E. WALKER et al. "A Controlled Blind Study of Effects of Thorazine on Psychotic Behavior," *Bull. Menninger Clin.*, 20 (1956), 25–47.

70. FINK, M., R. SHAW, G. E. GROSS et al. "Comparative Study of Chlorpromazine and Insulin Coma in Therapy of Psychosis," *JAMA*, 166 (1958), 1846–1850.

71. FOULDS, G. A. "Clinical Research in Psychiatry," *J. Ment. Sci.*, 104 (1958), 259–265.

72. FOX, B. "The Investigation of the Effects of Psychiatric Treatment," *J. Ment. Sci.*, 107 (1961), 493–502.

73. FREEMAN, H. "Controlled Trial of Penfluridol in Acute Psychosis," *Br. Med. J.*, 2 (1972), 442.

74. ———. "Long Acting Phenothiazines in Schizophrenia," *Lancet*, 2 (1972), 245–246.

75. GALBRECHT, C. R. and C. J. KLETT. "Predicting Response to Phenothiazines: The Right Drug for the Right Patient," *J. Nerv. Ment. Dis.*, 147 (1968), 173–183.

76. GALLANT, D. M., C. G. EDWARDS, M. P. BISHOP et al. "Withdrawal Symptoms after Abrupt Cessation of Antipsychotic Compounds: Clinical Confirmation in Chronic Schizophrenics," *Am. J. Psychiatry*, 121 (1964), 491–493.

77. GILLIGAN, B. S., J. WODAK, J. L. VEALE et al. "Tetrabenazine in the Treatment of Extrapyramidal Dyskinesia," *Med. J. Aust.*, 2 (1972), 1054–1056.

78. GOLDBERG, S. C., W. A. FROSCH, A. K. DROSSMAN et al. "Prediction of Response to Phenothiazines in Schizophrenia," *Arch. Gen. Psychiatry*, 26 (1972), 367–373.

79. GOLDBERG, S. C., G. L. KLERMAN, and J. O. COLE. "Changes in Schizophrenic Psychopathology and Ward Behavior as a Function of Phenothiazine Treatment," *Br. J. Psychiatry*, 111 (1965), 120–133.

80. GOLDBERG, S. C. and N. MATTSSON. "Symptom Changes Associated with Improvement in Schizophrenia," *J. Consult. Psychol.*, 31 (1967), 175–180.

81. GOLDBERG, S. C., N. MATTSSON, J. O. COLE et al. "Prediction of Improvement in Schizophrenia under Four Phenothiazines," *Arch. Gen. Psychiatry*, 16 (1967), 107–117.

82. GOLDBERG, S. C., N. SCHOOLER, and N. MATTSSON. "Paranoid and Withdrawal Symptoms in Schizophrenia," *J. Nerv. Ment. Dis.*, 145 (1967), 158–162.

83. GOLDMAN, D. "The Results of Treatment of Psychotic States with Newer Phenothiazine Compounds Effective in Small Doses," *Am. J. Med. Sci.*, 235 (1958), 67–77.

84. GOLDSTEIN, M. J. "Psychophysiological Reactions to Films by Chronic Schizophrenics," *J. Abnorm. Psychol.*, 71 (1966), 335–344.

85. GOLDSTEIN, M. J., L. L. JUDD, and E. H. RODNICK. "Psychophysiological and Behavioral Effects of Phenothiazine Administration in Acute Schizophrenics as a Function of Premorbid Status," *J. Psychol. Res.*, 6 (1969), 271–287.

86. GOLDSTEIN, M. J., E. H. RODNICK, N. P. JACKSON et al. "The Stability and Sensitivity of Measures of Thought, Perception and Emotional Arousal," *Psychopharmacologia*, 24 (1972), 107–120.

87. GOODMAN, L. S. and A. GILMAN. *The Pharmacological Basis of Therapeutics*. New York: Macmillian, 1970.

88. GORHAM, D. R. and J. E. OVERALL. "Dimensions of Change in Psychiatric Symptoma-

tology," *Dis. Nerv. Syst.*, 22 (1961), 576–580.

89. GORHAM, D. R. and A. D. POKORNY. "Effects of a Phenothiazine and/or Group Psychotherapy with Schizophrenics," *Dis. Nerv. Syst.*, 25 (1964), 77–86.

90. GRAM, L., J. CHRISTIANSEN, and K. F. OVERO. "Pharmacokinetic Interaction between Neuroleptics and Tricyclic Antidepressants," *Nord. Psykiatr. Tid.*, 26 (1972), 364.

91. GRAM, L. and K. F. OVERO. "Drug Interactions: Inhibitory Effects of Neuroleptics on Metabolism of Tricyclic Antidepressants in Man," *Br. Med. J.*, 1 (1972), 463–465.

92. GREENBLATT, M., D. J. LEVINSON, and G. L. KLERMAN. *Mental Patients in Transition.* Springfield, Ill.: Charles C. Thomas, 1961.

93. GREENBLATT, M., R. F. MOORE, and R. S. ALBERT, eds. *The Prevention of Hospitalization: Treatment without Admission for Psychiatric Patients.* New York: Grune & Stratton, 1963.

94. GREENBLATT, M., R. F. MOORE, and R. S. ALBERT. "Differential Response of Hospitalized Depressed Patients to Somatic Therapy," *Am. J. Psychiatry*, 120 (1964), 935–943.

95. GREENBLATT, M., M. H. SOLOMON, A. S. EVANS et al., eds. *Drug and Social Therapy in Chronic Schizophrenia.* Springfield, Ill.: Charles C. Thomas, 1965.

96. GRINSPOON, L., J. R. EWALT, and R. I. SHADER. "Psychotherapy and Pharmacotherapy in Chronic Schizophrenia," *Am. J. Psychiatry*, 124 (1968), 1645–1652.

97. ———. *Schizophrenia: Pharmacotherapy and Psychotherapy.* Baltimore: Williams & Wilkins, 1972.

98. GRINSPOON, L. and M. GREENBLATT, "Pharmacotherapy Combined with other Treatment Methods," *Compr. Psychiatry*, 4 (1963), 256–262.

99. GROSS, M., T. L. HITCHMAN, W. P. REEVES et al. "Discontinuation of Treatment with Ataractic Drugs," *Am. J. Psychiatry*, 116 (1960), 931–932.

100. GWYNNE, P. H., M. HUNZIAK, J. KAUTSCHITSCH et al. "Efficacy of Trifluoperazine on Withdrawal in Chronic Schizophrenia," *J. Nerv. Ment. Dis.*, 134 (1962), 451–455.

101. HANLON, T. E., K. NUSSBAUM, B. WITTIG et al. "The Comparative Effectiveness of Amitriptyline, Perphenazine and Their Combination in the Treatment of Chronic Psychotic Female Patients," *J. New Drugs*, 4 (1964), 52–60.

102. HARDEMAN, W. J. and S. J. BAKER. "Double Blind Comparative Study of the Effects of Thiothixene and Thioridazine in Twenty Chronic Schizophrenic Patients," *Psychiatr. Neurol. Neurochir.*, 73 (1970), 1–71.

103. HOGARTY, G. E. and S. C. GOLDBERG. "Drugs and Sociotherapy in the Aftercare of Schizophrenic Patients," *Arch. Gen. Psychiatry*, 28 (1973), 54–64.

104. HOLLISTER, L. E. "Allergy to Chlorpromazine Manifested by Jaundice," *Am. J. Med.*, 23 (1957), 870–879.

105. ———. "Allergic Reactions to Tranquilizing Drugs," *Ann. Intern. Med.*, 49 (1958), 17–29.

106. ———. "Chlorpromazine Jaundice," *JAMA*, 169 (1959), 1235–1236.

107. ———. "Adverse Reactions to Phenothiazines," *JAMA*, 189 (1964), 311–313.

108. ———. "Mental Disorders—Antipsychotic and Antimanic Drugs," *N. Engl. Med. J.*, 286 (1972), 984–987.

109. HOLLISTER, L. E. and S. H. CURRY. "Urinary Excretion of Chlorpromazine Metabolites following Single Doses and in Steady State Conditions," *Res. Commun. Chem. Pathol. Pharmacol.*, 2 (1971), 330–338.

110. HOLLISTER, L. E., G. V. ERICKSON, and F. P. MOTZENBECKER. "Trifluoperazine in Chronic Psychiatric Patients," *J. Clin. Exp. Psychopathol.*, 21 (1960), 15–24.

111. HOLLISTER, L. E. and J. D. KOSEK. "Sudden Death during Treatment with Phenothiazine Derivatives," *JAMA*, 192 (1965), 1035–1038.

112. HONIGFELD, G. and P. N. NEWHALL. *Hemodynamic Effects of Acetophenazine, Imipramine and Trifluoperazine in Geriatric Psychiatry.* Report no. 61. Perry Point, Md.: VA Central Neuropsychiatric Research Laboratory, 1964.

113. HONIGFELD, G., M. P. ROSENBLUM, I. J. BLUMENTHAL et al. "Behavioral Improvement in the Older Schizophrenic Patient: Drug and Social Therapies," *J. Am. Geriatr. Soc.*, 8 (1965), 57–72.

114. HUGHLEY, C. M., JR. "Drug-Induced Blood Dyscrasias. II. Agranulocytosis," *JAMA*, 188 (1964), 817–818.

115. ITIL, T. M., A. KESKINER, and M. FINK.

"Therapeutic Studies in 'Therapy Resistant' Schizophrenic Patients," *Compr. Psychiatry*, 7 (1966), 488–493.

116. JANECEK, J., B. C. SCHIELE, T. BELLEVILLE et al. "The Effects of Withdrawal of Trifluoperazine on Patients Maintained on the Combination of Tranylcypromine and Trifluoperazine: a Double Blind Study," *Curr. Ther. Res.*, 5 (1963), 608.

117. JANKE, W. and G. DEBUS. "Double Blind Psychometric Evaluation of Pimozide and Haloperidol versus Placebo in Emotionally Labile Volunteers under Two Different Work Load Conditions," *Pharmakopsychiatr. Neuro-Psychopharmakol.*, 5 (1972), 33–51.

118. JANOWSKY, D. S. and J. M. DAVIS. "The Elucidation of Psychotic Symptomatology by Methylphenidate," in J. O. Cole, ed., *Drugs and Psychopathology*, pp. 113–132. Baltimore: The Johns Hopkins University Press, 1973.

119. JANOWSKY, D. S., M. K. EL-YOUSEF, and J. M. DAVIS. "The Elucidation of Psychotic Symptomatology by Methylphenidate," *Compr. Psychiatry*, 13 (1972), 83.

120. JANOWSKY, D. S., M. K. EL-YOUSEF, J. M. DAVIS et al. "Cholinergic-adrenergic Balance and Affect," Paper presented 125th Ann. Meet. Am. Psychiatr. Assoc., San Francisco, 1972.

121. JANOWSKY, D. S., M. K. EL-YOUSEF, J. M. DAVIS et al. "Psychologic Effects of Physostigmine in Psychiatric Patients and Normal Volunteers," *Abstr. 5th Int. Congr. Pharmacol.*, 5 (1972), 115.

122. JEFFERSON, J. W. "Atypical Manifestations of Postural Hypotension," *Arch. Gen. Psychiatry*, 27 (1972), 250–251.

123. JUDAH, L. N., Z. M. JOSEPHS, and O. D. MURPHREE. "Results of Simultaneous Abrupt Withdrawal of Ataraxics in 500 Chronic Psychotic Patients," *Am. J. Psychiatry*, 118 (1961), 156–158.

124. KAZAMATSURI, H., C. CHIEN, and J. O. COLE. "Treatment of Tardive Dyskinesia," *Arch. Gen. Psychiatry*, 27 (1972), 95–103.

125. ———. "Therapeutic Approaches to Tardive Dyskinesia," *Arch. Gen. Psychiatry*, 27 (1972), 491–499.

126. KILLAM, E. K. and K. F. KILLAM. "Neurophysiological Approaches to an Understanding of the Action of Tranquilizing Drugs," in N. S. Kline and H. E. Lehmann, eds., *International Psychiatry Clinics*, pp. 845–859. Boston: Little, Brown, 1965.

127. KING, P. D. "Chlorpromazine and Electroconvulsive Therapy in the Treatment of Newly Hospitalized Schizophrenics," *J. Clin. Exp. Psychopathol.*, 21 (1960), 101–105.

128. KLEIN, D. F. "Importance of Psychiatric Diagnosis in Prediction of Clinical Drug Effects," *Arch. Gen. Psychiatry*, 16 (1967), 118–126.

129. KLEIN, D. F. and J. M. DAVIS. *Diagnosis and Drug Treatment of Psychiatric Disorders*. Baltimore: Williams & Wilkins, 1969.

130. KLETT, C. J. and E. CAFFEY. "Evaluating the Long-term Need for Antiparkinson Drugs by Chronic Schizophrenics," *Arch. Gen. Psychiatry*, 26 (1972), 374–379.

131. KLINE, N. S. "Use of Rauwolfia Serpentina Benth in Neuropsychiatric Conditions," *Ann. N.Y. Acad. Sci.*, 59 (1954), 107–132.

132. KUPFER, D. J., R. J. WYATT, F. SNYDER et al. "Chlorpromazine Plasma Levels and Sleep in Psychiatric Patients," *Commun. Behav. Biol.*, 6 (1971), 237–240.

133. KURLAND, A. A., G. D. BETHON, M. H. MICHAUX et al. "Chlorpromazine-Chlordiazepoxide and Chlorpromazine-Imipramine Treatment: Side Effects and Clinical Laboratory Findings," *J. New Drugs*, 6 (1966), 80–95.

134. LAFAVE, H. G., A. STEWART, and G. SEGOVIA. "Haloperidol. New Addition to the Drug Treatment of Schizophrenia," *Can. Psychiatr. Assoc. J.*, 12 (1967), 597–602.

135. LANGSLEY, D. G., J. D. ENTERLINE, and G. X. HICKERSON. "A Comparison of Chlorpromazine and EST in Treatment of Acute Schizophrenic and Manic Reactions," *Arch. Neurol. Psychiatry*, 81 (1959), 384–391.

136. LEFF, J. and J. WING. "Trial of Maintenance Therapy in Schizophrenia," *Br. Med. J.*, 2 (1971), 599–605.

137. LEHMANN, H. E. "Drug Treatment of Schizophrenics," *Int. Psychiatr. Clin.*, 2 (1965), 717–752.

138. LEHMANN, H. E. and G. E. HANRAHAN. "Chlorpromazine," *Arch Neurol. Psychiatry*, 71 (1954), 227–237.

139. LEWIS, D. M., S. H. CURRY, and G. SAMUEL. "Long-Acting Phenothiazines in Schizo-

phrenia," *Br. Med. J.*, 1 (1971), 671–672.

140. LINGJAERDE, O. "Tetrabenazine (Nitoman) in the Treatment of Psychoses," *Acta Psychiatr. Scand.*, 39 *Suppl.* 170 (1963), 1–109.

141. MARJERRISON, G., D. IRVINE, C. N. STEWART et al. "Withdrawal of Long-term Phenothiazines from Chronically Hospitalized Psychiatric Patients," *Can. Psychiatr. Assoc. J.*, 9 (1964), 290–298.

142. MCNEILL, D. L. M. and J. R. A. MADGWICK. "A Comparison of Results in Schizophrenics Treated with (1) Insulin, (2) Trifluoperazine (Stelazine)," *J. Ment. Sci.*, 107 (1961), 297–299.

143. MAXWELL, J. D., M. CARRELLA, J. D. PARKES et al. "Plasma Disappearance and Cerebral Effects of Chlorpromazine in Cirrhosis," *Clin. Sci.*, 43 (1972), 143–151.

144. MAY, P. R. A. *Treatment of Schizophrenia.* New York: Science House, 1968.

145. MICHAUX, M. H. "Day and Full Time Psychiatric Treatment: A Controlled Comparison," *Curr. Ther. Res.*, 14 (1972), 279–292.

146. MICHAUX, M. H., A. A. KURLAND, and D. AGALLIANOS. "Chlorpromazine-Chlordiazepoxide and Chlorpromazine-Imipramine Treatment of Newly Hospitalized, Acutely Ill Psychiatric Patients," *Curr. Ther. Res.*, 8 (1966), 117–152.

147. MITCHELL, P. H. "Chlorpromazine in the Treatment of Chronic Disturbed Schizophrenic Patients," *J. Ment. Sci.*, 102 (1956), 151–154.

148. MOFFAT, J. and E. C. MACLEOD. " 'Discontinuous' Thioproperazine," *Br. J. Psychiatry*, 110 (1964), 851–854.

149. MOLCAN, J., L. FLOREANOUA, H. KUKUCOVA et al. "Therapeutic Effects of Fluphenazine in Various Doses and Forms," *Activitas Nervosa Superior (Praha)*, 13 (1971), 182–183.

150. MURPHY, D. L. and R. J. WYATT. "Reduced Monamine Oxidase Activity in Blood Platelets of Schizophrenic Patients," *Nature*, 238 (1972), 225–226.

151. OLSON, G. W. and D. B. PETERSON. "Sudden Removal of Tranquilizing Drugs from Chronic Psychiatric Patients," *J. Nerv. Ment. Dis.*, 131 (1960), 252–255.

152. PARK, S., E. I. BURDOCK, and S. GERSHON. "Importance of Adequate Dose Determination of Drug Efficacy: Trial of a New Butyrophenone Compound on Acute Schizophrenics," *Pharmakopsychiatr. Neuro-Psychopharmakol.*, 5 (1972), 191–197.

153. PECKNOLD, J., J. V. ANANTH, T. A. BAN et al. "Lack of Indication for Use of Antiparkinson Medication," *Dis. Nerv. Syst.*, 32 (1971), 538–541.

154. PEELS, R. and I. VON LOETZEN. "Phenothiazine Deaths: A Critical Review," Paper presented Annu. Meet., Am. Psychiatr. Assoc., Dallas, May 4, 1972.

155. PISCIOTTA, A. V., S. S. EBRE, E. J. LENNON et al. "Agranulocytosis following Administration of Phenothiazine Derivatives," *Am. J. Med.*, 25 (1958), 210–223.

156. PRETTY, H. M., G. GOSSELIN, G. COLPRON et al. "Agranulocytosis: A Report of 30 Cases," *Can. Med. Assoc. J.*, 93 (1965), 1058–1064.

157. PRIEN, R. F. and J. O. COLE. "High Dose Chlorpromazine Therapy in Chronic Schizophrenia," *Arch. Gen. Psychiatry*, 18 (1968), 482–495.

158. PRIEN, R. F., J. J. LEVINE, and J. O. COLE. "High-Dose Trifluoperazine Therapy in Chronic Schizophrenia," *Am. J. Psychiatry*, 126 (1969), 305–313.

159. RAJOTTE, P., J. M. BOURDELEAU, and L. TETREAULT. "Etude comparative de la butapérazine et de la prochlorpromazine chez le schizophrène chronique," *Can. Psychiatr. Assoc.*, 10 (1965), 25–34.

160. RIFKIN, A., F. QUITKIN, C. CARRILLO et al. "Very High-Dose Fluphenazine for Nonchronic Treatment in Refractory Patients," *Arch. Gen. Psychiatry*, 25 (1971), 398–402.

161. ROTHSTEIN, C. "An Evaluation of the Effects of Discontinuation of Chlorpromazine," *N. Engl. J. Med.*, 262 (1960), 67–69.

162. ROTHSTEIN, C., I. ZELTERMAN, and H. R. WHITE. "Discontinuation of Maintenance Dosage of Ataractic Drugs on a Psychiatric Continued Treatment Ward," *J. Nerv. Ment. Dis.*, 134 (1962), 555–560.

163. SARETSKY, T. "Effects of Chlorpromazine on Primary-Process through Manifestations," *J. Abnorm. Psychol.*, 71 (1966), 247–252.

164. SCHIELE, B. C. "The Unique Therapeutic Properties of Tranylcypromine and Trifluoperazine (Parstelin)," *Am. J. Psychiatry*, 117 (1960), 245–246.

165. SCHIELE, B. C., A. S. MANDELSOHN, A. S. DENMAN et al. "Comparison of Low and High Dosage Procedures in Chlorproma-

zine Therapy," *Psychiatr. Q.*, 33 (1959), 252–259.

166. SCHIELE, B. C., N. D. VESTRE, and D. V. MACNAUGHTON. "Treatment of Hospitalized Schizophrenics with Trifluoperazine plus Tranylcypromine. A Double Blind Controlled Study," *Compr. Psychiatry*, 4 (1963), 66–79.

167. SHARPLEY, P., G. HEISTAD, and B. C. SCHIELE. "Comparison of Butaperazine and Perphenazine: A Double Blind Controlled Study," *Psychopharmacologia*, 5 (1964), 209–216.

168. SHAWVER, J. R., D. R. GORHAM, L. W. LESKIN et al. "Comparison of Chlorpromazine and Reserpine in Maintenance Drug Therapy," *Dis. Nerv. Syst.*, 20 (1959), 452–457.

169. SHEPHERD, M., M. LADER, and R. RODMIGHT. *Clinical Psychopharmacology*. London: English Universities Press, 1968.

170. SHIMKUNAS, A. M., M. D. GYNTHER, and K. SMITH. "Abstracting Ability of Schizophrenics before and during Phenothiazine Therapy," *Arch. Gen. Psychiatry*, 14 (1966), 79–83.

171. SIMPSON, G. M., M. AMIN, J. W. ANGUS et al. "Role of Antidepressants and Neuroleptics in the Treatment of Depression," *Arch. Gen. Psychiatry*, 27 (1972), 337–345.

172. SIMPSON, G. M., M. AMIN, and E. KINZ. "Withdrawal Effects of Phenothiazines," *Compr. Psychiatry*, 6 (1965), 347–351.

173. SIMPSON, G. M., M. AMIN, E. KUNZ-BARTHOLINI et al. "Problems in the Evaluation of the Optimal Dose of a Phenothiazine (Butaperazine)," *Dis. Nerv. Syst.*, 29 (1968), 478–484.

174. SMITH, K., W. R. P. SURPHLIS, M. D. GYNTHER et al. "ECT Chlorpromazine and Chlorpromazine Compared in the Treatment of Schizophrenia," *J. Nerv. Ment. Dis.*, 144 (1967), 284–290.

175. STEINBOOK, R. M., R. M. GOLDSTEIN, B. BRANZER et al. "Loxapine: A Double Blind Comparison with Chlorpromazine and Acute Schizophrenic Patients," *Curr. Ther. Res.*, 15 (1973), 1–7.

176. SVESTKA, J. and K. NAHUNEK. "Flupenthixol Depot in the Maintenance Treatment of Psychoses," *Activitas Nervosa Superior (Praha)*, 4 (1972), 2.

177. TANGHE, A. and J. L. VEREECKEN. "Fluspirilene, an Injectable, and Penfluridol, an Oral Long-Acting, Neuroleptic," *Acta Psychiatr., Scand.* 48 (1972), 328–331.

178. TSUANG, MIN-MIN, B. A. STOTSKY, and J. O. COLE. "Haloperidol versus Thioridazine for Hospitalized Psychogeriatric Patients," *J. Am. Geriatr. Soc.*, 19 (1971), 593–600.

179. WECKOWICZ, T. E. and T. WARD. "Clinical Trial of Stelazine on Apathetic Chronic Schizophrenics," *J. Ment. Sci.*, 106 (1960), 1008–1015.

180. WENDKOS, M. H. "The Significance of Electrocardiographic Changes Produced by Thioridazine," *J. New Drugs*, 4 (1964), 322–332.

181. WHITTAKER, C. B. and R. M. HOY. "Withdrawal of Perphenazine in Chronic Schizophrenia," *Br. J. Psychiatry*, 109 (1963), 422–427.

CHAPTER 23

ANTIDEPRESSANTS*

Arthur J. Prange, Jr.

DEPRESSION is a common syndrome, especially in middle life,[98] and the treatment of depressed patients absorbs a large share of the professional effort of general physicians and psychiatrists alike. Although it is convenient to speak of the pharmacological treatment of depression, drugs are only components, though often the main ones, of total management. When we "treat" depression we really preside over its course. We try to guard our patients from death and lesser complications, and we try to hasten the remission process.

Several modalities can be used with or in place of drugs, electric convulsive treatment (ECT) being the most important. I regard psychotherapy as adjunctive to the management of the depressive attack, though it may be very important in fortifying the patient against later attacks. During the attack, psychotherapy and milieu therapy set the stage

on which drugs play their part. The stage setting can, in fact, exert considerable importance, but I see no reason to rely on it exclusively. Antidepressant drugs, however, tend to show a troublesome latency in exerting their therapeutic effects, and it is during this period that the patient should be counseled about delay and reassured that treatment is in progress.

With the combined use of ultrafast and ultrabrief barbiturates and muscle relaxants, ECT has become both safer and less unpleasant. However, it remains cumbersome, and is a procedure best limited to hospitalized patients. At present, ECT rarely is used to commence treatment; it is generally reserved for patients who have not responded adequately to drugs, or for the rare patient for whom drugs are contraindicated. At our clinic, we do advocate its initial use for one type of patient, the agitated patient, often middle-aged and usually a man, who presents frank suicidal intention. We give ECT to such a patient as soon as necessary tests of physiological function are performed. We may give it daily until mental

* This work was supported in part by U.S. Public Health Service Career Scientist Award MH-22536 (A.J.P.).

confusion supervenes and reduces the ability of the patient to carry out his suicidal drive.

〔 Theoretical Considerations

In defending theory to clinicians, Fuller Albright[2] argued that rules can apply to only 90 percent of patients and that rigid adherence to rules will produce more harm in the remaining 10 percent than good in the majority to whom they apply. He recommended theory in place of rules.

In large measure, drugs have given us the notions by which our use of them is guided. Relying on drug effects and referring to our least important antidepressants, I shall state a theoretical position. Within this context I shall then discuss the use of our most important antidepressants, the tricyclics.

In the phylogenetically old parts of the mammalian brain there are found in high concentrations certain small molecules known as biogenic amines.[55] They concentrate in nerve ends and are released by nerve impulses.[60] They enter the synaptic cleft, reach sensitive areas of the adjacent cell body, tend to alter its polarization, and thus influence the likelihood of transmission. The synthesis, storage, release, and inactivation of these substances are more or less complicated[37] and can be affected by drugs.[3] The biogenic amines are of two chemical types: (1) catecholamines, i.e. dopamine (DA), norepinephrine (NE), and epinephrine; and (2) indoleamines, i.e., tryptamine (TA) and 5-hydroxytryptamine (5-HT, serotonin). With regard to depression, and probably mania as well, NE and 5-HT seem the most important.

Several authors have drawn attention to the importance of NE,[10,74] but Schildkraut[89] has put the matter most lucidly by stating the catecholamine hypothesis of affective disorders: "Some, if not all, depressions are associated with an absolute or relative deficiency of catecholamines, particularly norepinephrine, at functionally important adrenergic receptor sites in the brain. Elation conversely may be associated with an excess of such amines." The role of 5-HT has not been so formally stated, but several authors[14,34,63] have garnered evidence suggesting that 5-HT activity is deficient in depression. These two hypotheses have provided considerable leverage for the understanding, chemical remedy, and further investigation of affective disorders. However, they appear insufficient as theoretical positions, as I have tried to indicate elsewhere.[76]

Several authors believe that we should broaden our focus to include receptor sensitivity as well as biogenic amine changes,[79,83,84] since together they determine synaptic transmission. Moreover, we would be wise not to disregard cholinergic mechanisms, which govern most of the brain.[50] Janowsky et al.[51] have for example shown that physostigmine, a cholinesterase inhibitor, has a remarkably prompt beneficial action in mania.

Even within the realm of biogenic amines there are unsolved problems. Chief among these is how to combine the catecholamine hypothesis and the indoleamine hypothesis. Kety[56] made a suggestion that our group has stated formally:[78] "A deficit in central indoleaminergic transmission permits affective disorder but is insufficient for its cause. Changes in central catecholaminergic transmission, when they occur in the context of a deficit in indoleaminergic transmission, act as a proximate cause for affective disorders and determine their quality, catecholaminergic transmission being elevated in mania and diminished in depression." This can reasonably be called *the biogenic amine permissive hypothesis of affective disorder*, or simply the *permissive hypothesis*. See Figure 23–1.

This unifying notion rests on the similarities between mania and depression, phenomenological,[19] physiological,[107] chemical[16] and pharmacological.[1,94] In particular, the end product of 5-HT, 5-hydroxyindoleacetic acid (5-HIAA), seems diminished in cerebrospinal fluid in both mania and depression, and at least in depression the diminution persists after remission.[16] Agreement on these points, however, is far from perfect.[73]

With these thoughts in mind, we can profitably examine the mood-active substances listed below.

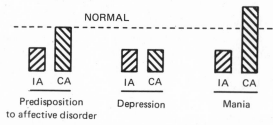

IA, Indoleaminergic Transmission

CA, Catecholaminergic Transmission

Figure 23–1. Alterations in biogenic amines in affective disorders according to the permissive hypothesis.

Mood-Active Substances

A. MAO Inhibitors
1. hydrazines
e.g., phenelzine (Nardil)
2. non-hydrazines
e.g., tranylcypromine (Parnate)
B. Tricyclics
1. nonsedating
a. methylated
e.g., imipramine (Tofranil)
b. demethylated
e.g., desipramine (Pertofran, Norpramin)
2. sedating
a. C = C, ring to side-chain
e.g., amitriptyline (Elavil)
b. C = C, ring to side-chain; oxygen in ring
e.g., doxepin (Sinequan)
C. Stimulants
1. potent but addicting
e.g., d-amphetamine (Dexedrine)
2. nonaddicting but impotent
e.g., methylphenidate (Ritalin)
D. Lithium salts
E. Amino acids
e.g., L-Dopa, L-tryptophan
F. Phenothiazines
e.g., chlorpromazine (Thorazine)

Monoamine oxidase (MAO) inhibitors inhibit the enzyme monoamine oxidase. This enzyme inactivates biogenic amines within the nerve end. When we inactivate (with a drug) an inactivator (the enzyme), we increase the amount of biogenic amines ready for release upon receipt of the nerve impulse. The difficulty with MAO inhibitors, whether they are hydrazines or nonhydrazines, is the wide distribution of monoamine oxidase, or oxidases, in the body. Their substrate specificity and drug sensitivity may vary from tissue to tissue[97] and even within the brain.[32] However, if we inhibit one in the brain, we are likely to inhibit all in all sites, at least to some extent. As a consequence, the MAO-inhibited patient stands in toxic jeopardy. If he eats otherwise innocuous foods,[40,100] or if he ingests certain amine-active drugs,[40,67,100,103] including other antidepressants,[95] he is subject to serious toxicity. Moreover, MAO inhibitors are inherently toxic, and several have therefore been removed from the U.S. market.[66] Probably the pharmacotherapy of depression should not begin with a MAO inhibitor unless the patient gives a clear history of excellent response during past attacks coupled with a history of poor response to tricyclics. The MAO inhibitors may reasonably be used, after a drugfree interval, when tricyclics have failed.

It has recently been shown in man that MAO activity in the brain increases with age while biogenic amine levels diminish.[82] This suggests that MAO inhibitors would be specific remedies for depression in elderly patients. While this idea is appealing, it does nothing to decrease the toxicity of these drugs. A related finding has been reported by Jones et al.[52] These authors gave MAO inhibitors to moribund elderly patients. At autopsy they found that fixed doses of drugs had exerted extremely variable effects on the brain enzyme.

Stimulants, lithium salts, amino acids, and phenothiazines can also be dealt with summarily. The stimulants appear to be not so much antidepressants as psychomotor activators. While some of them, notably amphetamine, may induce a degree of euphoria in normal subjects, depressed patients may perceive their action as unpleasant. The stimulants tend to be either potent and addicting or, on the other hand, nonaddicting but impotent. Amphetamine causes the prompt release of NE and DA from nerve ends.[12,39]

Lithium salts, principally the carbonate, are used to control manic attacks.[93,21] They probably reduce the incidence of manic recurrence[5] and may also diminish the incidence of depressive relapse.[15] One would expect this effect to be especially manifest in bipolar patients prone to recurrent depression. However, Coppen et al.[15] found that lithium prevented the recurrence of unipolar and bipolar depressions about equally. Lithium may be effective in some depressive attacks,[26] but this is uncertain. Lithium, through a number of complex actions, decreases brain NE activity[92] and increases brain 5-HT activity.[96,102] According to the permissive hypothesis, we should expect lithium to remove "permission" for both mania and depression. By reducing NE activity it should be an excellent treatment for mania but might be less effective or even fail in depression, depending on the balance of its effects.

L-Dopa is an amino acid precursor of catecholamines (see Figure 23–2). When ingested in large amounts it produces a rise in brain catecholamines, DA more than NE.[49] Its use has led to great progress in the management of Parkinson's disease.[53] In this disorder L-Dopa can produce a medley of mental effects or none at all.[6,111] It seems to have antidepressant value in only a few depressed patients,[11] and they have not yet been identified prospectively. The antidepressant value of L-Dopa is unreliable and I have cited this as a criticism of the catecholamine hypothesis.[76]

The effects of L-Dopa are, however, consistent with the permissive hypothesis. By increasing catecholamine activity without increasing indoleamine activity L-Dopa might only change the sign of affective disorder, and indeed swings from depression to mania during L-Dopa treatment have been reported.[70] Moreover, L-Dopa probably reduces central indoleamine activity, quite apart from failing to increase it. After administration of L-Dopa there is a sharp drop in cerebrospinal fluid levels of 5-HIAA.[42] Amino acids compete for transport into cells,[7] and an excess of one pre-

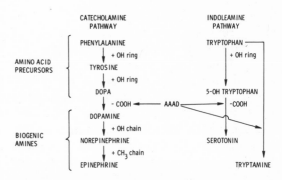

Figure 23–2. Synthetic pathways of biogenic amines.

cursor may exclude others. Moreover, L-Dopa requires only the ubiquitous enzyme, aromatic amino acid decarboxylase (AAAD), to be transformed to the active amine DA, which may displace 5-HT, thus acting as a false transmitter.[61]

L-tryptophan (L-TP) is a more physiological substance to use as a precursor than L-Dopa and, for that matter, more psysiological than 5-hydroxytryptophan (5-HTP). L-TP requires the discretely localized tryptophan hydroxylase to be converted to 5-HT. Thus, a loading dose of L-TP is unlikely to lead to the formation of 5-HT where it does not normally occur. The possibility must be kept in mind, however, that L-TP may be widely decarboxylated to TA, and that this substance could displace other amines. However, this may not occur to an important degree. Dunner and Goodwin[25] have shown that in man a L-TP loading dose causes only a slight decrement in cerebrospinal fluid homovanillic acid, the end product of DA metabolism, while the decrease of 5-HIAA after L-Dopa is substantial.

The effects of 5-HTP administration are often compared directly to the effects of L-TP administration. Each procedure may yield its own species of information and the two may be usefully compared, but they are not equivalent procedures. Figure 23–2 shows that 5-HTP can form only 5-HT but, as mentioned, it can form this substance anywhere that AAAD occurs. On the other hand, L-TP can form 5-HT only where tryptophan hydroxylase and AAAD occur together, i.e., in physiological locations. It is interesting to note, however, that pyridoxine, an AAAD cofactor, seems to have an important influence on the effects of L-TP. Under Hall's leadership, our group showed that neither L-TP nor pyridoxine alone has any effect in Parkinson's disease, while the combination markedly aggravates this condition.[44] From this it appears that TA formation may, after all, be important, whether as a physiological or as a false transmitter. It should be recalled that Dewhurst[22] has based a biochemical theory of affective disorder partly on alterations in TA metabolism. The theory was criticized in part on the ground that TA was difficult to identify in mammalian brain even after L-TP loading and MAO inhibition.[29] Although other criticisms remain,[104] this objection was largely removed when Saavedra and Axelrod,[86] using a sensitive method, identified TA in the brains of untreated rats.

Coppen and his colleagues have found that L-TP with pyridoxine is an effective treatment for depression whether[17] or not[18] an MAO inhibitor is given concomitantly. Pare[71] and Glassman and Platman[36] confirmed this response when an MAO inhibitor is used, and Broadhurst[8] confirmed the finding when the drug is omitted. On the other hand, Bunney et al.,[9] and Carroll et al.[13] found that the amino acid without an MAO inhibitor is ineffective. These discrepancies may reflect differential responses of unipolar and bipolar patients.[41] Results with 5-HTP are uniformly disappointing in depression.[35,39]

According to the permissive hypothesis, L-TP should be a better treatment for mania than for depression. In depression, a 5-HT increment would be beneficial but an NE decrement (from L-TP crowding out endogenous L-Dopa) could be harmful. In mania, on the other hand, both actions of L-TP would be beneficial. To test these notions, we treated ten patients with moderately severe mania with a small dose of L-TP (plus pyridoxine), then chlorpromazine or the substances in reverse order.[108] We found L-TP superior. Its advantage was clearest in, but not limited to, the control of activity. We sug-

gested that the motor phenomena of mania and the agitation of depression, when it is present, may form a connecting link between the two disorders. Kotin and Goodwin[62] recently reappraised the notion that the mental content of depression may be present during mania. Our concept concerning motor phenomena is analogous.

It is instructive to compare L-TP and lithium in the treatment of affective disorders. The former appears to be useful in depression and in mania, while lithium is useful in mania and may be in depression. This similarity of clinical activity seems quite likely related to the two substances sharing both "proindoleaminergic" and "anticatecholaminergic" properties. It is of parenthetical interest that in preliminary work our group has found both substances useful in the treatment of tardive dyskinesia,[78] and that Dalen[20] has confirmed the value of lithium.

Phenothiazines have been reported to exert antidepressant effects. These appear limited to agitated depressions,[47] perhaps to the agitation aspects of depression. Since phenothiazines are also useful in mania,[64] this nexus of observations may support the notion that motor phenomena form a link between mania and depression.

⟮ A View of Drug Treatment

Tricyclics are the most important antidepressant drugs; imipramine is the prototype of this class. Imipramine is not the best tricyclic for all patients but it is the standard to which others are compared.

Figure 23–3 shows the chemical structure of imipramine, as a point of reference, and Table 23–1 characterizes the chemical differences between the six tricyclic antidepressants currently available to physicians in the United States. The tricyclics differ from the phenothiazines and the thioxanthenes by having seven rather than six atoms in the central ring. The ring in doxepin contains an oxygen atom. All tricyclics are tertiary or secondary amines;

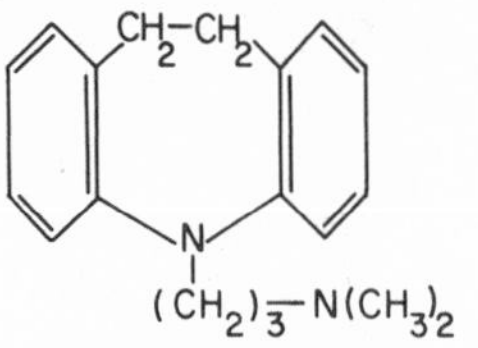

IMIPRAMINE

Figure 23–3. The molecular structure of imipramine.

some have doublebonds between the central ring and the side chain. These differences in molecular structure are only poorly correlated with differences in clinical activity. Klerman and Cole[58] and Gyermek[43] have given full accounts of the pharmacology of imipramine.

The mechanism of action of tricyclics was an enigma and their clinical efficacy was troublesome to theorists of affective disorders until Hertting et al.[45] showed that imipramine blocks the reuptake of NE into the nerve end following its release. Inactivation by reuptake is probably the major physiological means of terminating the action of both NE[60] and 5-HT.[65] Thus, by showing an action of a tricyclic on NE which would prolong the life of the amine in the synaptic cleft, Hertting et al. solved an enigma and gave powerful support to the catecholamine hypothesis. The matter is probably more complicated than it first appeared, as Schildkraut suggested, and his later findings may help explain the clinical latency of tricyclic antidepressant action.[90]

Reuptake blockade by tricyclics is not limited to NE but pertains as well to 5-HT. A series of elegant studies have demonstrated that tricyclics which are tertiary amines block mainly the reuptake inactivation of 5-HT; tricyclics which are secondary amines block mainly the reuptake inactivation of NE.[65] It is a criticism of the single-amine hypotheses of affective disorders that imipramine, a tertiary amine, and desipramine, a secondary amine, are equally effective clinically in unselected patients.[57]

The notion was widely held that imipramine, with a side chain containing two terminal methyl groups and which is, therefore, a tertiary amine, had to be partly demethylated

in the body to become an active antidepressant. Since slow onset of action was a drawback of imipramine, the demethylated product, desipramine, was synthesized in the hope that it would be a faster-acting drug. The data, however, that have been adduced to demonstrate that desipramine acts faster than imipramine, or that nortriptyline acts faster than amitriptyline are not persuasive.[57] Tertiary amine tricyclics are now considered to be active substances themselves.

An important difference was produced when a carbon atom was substituted for the nitrogen atom in the central ring of imipramine and when it was linked to the first side-chain carbon by a double bond. The result was amitriptyline (see Table 23–1). Amitriptyline is more sedating than imipramine or desipramine and so are its congeners, doxepin and nortriptyline. Amitriptyline, doxepin and nortriptyline, in addition to their sedative properties, possess anxiolytic properties, but so does imipramine and, for that matter, desipramine. The distinguishing feature of the newer tricyclic drugs, then, is primarily their sedative properties and only secondarily their anxiolytic properties. Doxepin may be an exception, for its tranquilizing effect has been compared favorably with that of chlordiazepoxide.[99] Protriptyline, on the other hand, is a stimulating agent. It is remarkable that all tricyclics, with the exception of protriptyline and the partial exception of nortriptyline, are about equally potent on a weight basis, and that their dose range is so narrow, barely threefold, compared to that of other psychotropic drugs.

Choice of a Drug

Tricyclic antidepressants have more similarities than differences. If this is true, it follows that choosing between them is difficult but often unimportant. In making a choice, depressive typology is often used as a guide.

If one classifies depressed patients as neurotic or psychotic, implying that the neurotic is less depressed but more likely to show anxiety, then a drug with sedating properties is

TABLE 23–1.   **Characteristics of Chemical Structure in Antidepressants**

CHARACTERISTICS	IMP	AMI	DOX	DMI	NOR	PRO
Tertiary amine	X	X	X			
Secondary amine				X	X	X
Ring-to-side-chain bond						
nitrogen-to-carbon						
single bond	X			X		
carbon-to-carbon						
single bond						X
double bond		X	X		X	
Oxygen in central ring			X			

LEGEND: IMP = imipramine; AMI = amitriptyline; DOX = doxepin; DMI = desipramine; NOR = nortriptyline; PRO = protriptyline.

more likely to be useful in neurotic depression. If a contrast is made between agitated and retarded patients, it is the former who are more apt to profit from a phenothiazine than the latter, though imipramine is an effective remedy for both.[81,109] If one refers to history rather than description of the current attack, a unipolar-bipolar dichotomy can be made. It is in bipolar depression that lithium may be of some value, though even here it is probably less useful than more accepted treatments, such as imipramine. It is of theoretical interest, but little practical help, to know that bipolar patients are more likely than unipolar patients to respond to L-Dopa[70] and to imipramine[18] with hypomanic excursions. Perhaps this phenomenon includes most other antidepressant agents as well. If the permissive theory is accurate, however, L-TP should not produce hypomania. Coppen et al.[18] did not observe it in a small series of patients.

The endogenous-reactive dichotomy is not useful, in my experience, as a guideline in choosing a drug, let alone in choosing between tricyclics. Some clinicians employ it, but I think they are responding to information that more aptly pertains to severity or to a neurotic-psychotic dichotomy. In any case, patients tend to become "more reactive" as their history unfolds. To the extent that patients can be assigned to one or the other moiety, endogenously depressed patients do seem to respond better to drugs.

If choosing a drug by clinical characteristics is risky, choosing one according to psychodynamics is dangerous. It can even lead to the selection of a drug from the wrong class of psychotropics. If, for example, a middle-aged woman has sustained a series of object losses but presents manifest anxiety, not depression, and if she needs a psychotropic drug, it is an anxiolytic, not an antidepressant. Chemical characteristics of the patient are no more valuable in drug selection, though Schildkraut et al.[91] have suggested in a preliminary study that amitriptyline is more useful than imipramine in patients who show high excretion rates of 3-methoxy-4-hydroxy phenylglycol.

Some of the obvious differences between depressed patients are somewhat helpful in drug selection. A few patients are men while most are women,[98] and we have found that men respond better than women to imipramine.[75] While this may serve as an investigational lead, it does not tell us what to prescribe for a specific woman. Just as obviously some depressed patients are elderly, while most are middle-aged.[98] This observation also does not help us to choose drugs according to their therapeutic qualities, though Klein and Davis[57] suggested that differences between studies by Sandifer et al.[87] and by Hordern et al.[48] can be understood by assuming from Hordern's evidence that amitriptyline is a more effective drug in the aged than imipramine. The consideration of age introduces a complementary approach, i.e., choosing between tricyclics according to side effects.

Side Effects

Tricyclics cannot be classified more sharply according to side effects than according to therapeutic effects. Nevertheless, a consideration of both can often lead to the rational choice of a tricyclic for a given patient. Sedation offers a convenient link between the two types of drug effects. Sedation, like many drug effects, is therapeutic when we desire it and a nuisance when we do not.

All tricyclic drugs exert anticholinergic actions. They produce dry mouth, which is generally only a transient nuisance, and minor cardiovascular effects such as palpitations and tachycardia. Orthostatic hypotension is less common. Tricyclics may also produce toxic confusion and urinary retention, and may aggravate glaucoma.

These side effects are most apt to occur and to be serious in elderly patients. For this reason a drug that seems to have a somewhat reduced anticholinergic potential, such as doxepin,[4] may be of special value in the elderly when other considerations do not countervail. For related reasons the elderly are rarely given full doses of tricyclics, unless they are gradually attained while side effects are watched. It is probably unwise to give an elderly patient his entire daily dosage at bedtime,[77] as has been recommended for younger patients.[57]

The cardiovascular effects of tricyclics are probably due not only to their anticholinergic properties but also to their ability to block the reuptake inactivation of NE and 5-HT. The responses of a given patient probably represent the sum of these various actions. Amine theories of affective disorders depend mostly on the observation that tricyclics prolong or intensify the activity of released biogenic amines. This occurs in the periphery,[45] as well as in the brain.[38] Therefore one would expect hypertension, not orthostatic hypotension, to be a consequence of tricyclic administration. Indeed, hypertensive events have been related to imipramine ingestion,[46] though orthostatic hypotension is much more frequent. Another hypothesis derived from current theory in its simplest form is this: depression and hypertension are incompatible disorders, i.e., one cannot suffer from a lack of amines and from their excessive presence at the same time. In fact, depression and hypertension frequently do coexist and this combination in a given patient tests the pharmacotherapist. Were it not for the variety of antihypertensive drugs such patients are usually taking, one might regularly recommend the cautious use of pargyline, an MAO inhibitor which may have been used in the psychiatric rather than the antihypertensive clinic, had not MAO inhibitors fallen into disfavor with psychiatrists. The main alternative to drugs, ECT, should be reconsidered in this situation.

⟮ Remaining Problems

The foregoing is relevant mainly to the 75 percent of depressed patients who respond favorably to a program of treatment centered around currently available antidepressant drugs. The refractory 25 percent are but one of the problems in this field, and I will return to them after taking up some other issues.

The physician is never presented with a *depressed* patient, only with a patient. He must make his own diagnosis. This depends upon recognition, which in turn depends upon suspicion. Diagnosis, though often easy, is sometimes difficult. I refer to what an earlier generation of psychiatrists termed "depressive equivalents."[28,68] I do not mean, for example, the patient who is manifestly anxious but demonstrates the psychodynamic constellation usually associated with depression. I refer to the patient who presents somatic complaints, usually vague but persistent, seems gloomy, verbalizes poorly, and may present a history that typically is antecedent to depression. I do not think these patients, who are the bane of both the general physician and the psychiatrist, respond very favorably to antidepressant drugs. A trial of one such drug, however, is at least as rational as the variety of drugs that generally have previously been directed to this or that complaint.

The general physician, as much as the psychiatrist, must remember that depression of serious, even suicidal, proportions can be present even when it is not the chief complaint. The medical profession needs to be reminded of this periodically, Fawcett[30] has performed this service most recently.

Another problem, as I have indicated, is the need for a subclassification of patients with manifest depression that would serve as a guide to drug treatment. I have mentioned a few guidelines, but they are of limited practical value. The unipolar-bipolar dichotomy seems reliable and appears to tally with a number of physiological distinctions.[24] It offers little predictive leverage on drug treatment, however, and even if it did we would not have advanced very far. The vast majority of depressed patients fall in the unipolar group, and we would still need to distinguish between them. It is possible, of course, that no valid distinctions exist. Conceivably all, or nearly all, the variations in depression to which we are witness are idiosyncratic elaborations of a basic, more or less uniform midbrain dysfunction variously achieved. If this is true, we should seek more nearly universal remedies and in the meantime try to enhance by milieu therapy or any other means the remedies at hand. I have no convictions about the venerable problem of typology.* In fact, if broad diagnostic criteria are applied, many depressions are atypical.[85]

Although it would be a convenience for the theorist if anxiety and depression did not coexist, in fact they often do. With drugs one tries to treat the dominant constellation of symptoms. An antidepressant with sedative-anxiolytic properties is indicated if depression seems uppermost. When the symptoms of anxiety and depression are nearly counterbalanced a drug combination becomes advisable. A tricyclic and a phenothiazine, for example, can be useful, but their combination should be reserved for this specific instance and not routinely prescribed with a "just in case" attitude. There is an advantage in starting drugs a few days apart to learn, if possible, some of the wanted and unwanted effects of the first before confounding the clinical situation with the second.

Various adjuncts have been used to accelerate the clinical action of tricyclics. Our group has found that the addition of a small amount of L-triiodothyronine (T_3) to a usual tricyclic regimen is effective,[79,109] at least in women.[75] This has been confirmed by Wheatley[106] and by Coppen et al.,[18] but not by Feighner et al.[31] Methylphenidate appears to be effective.[105] This drug interferes with the enzymatic destruction of imipramine[72] and thus given doses of tricyclic produce higher tissue levels.

What can one do about depressed patients who are refractory to usual drug programs? The first approach is to insure adequate dosage. Some previously unresponsive patients respond if they are given 250–300 mg. of imipramine or its equivalent. Side effects are more or less related to dosage, however, and one should watch for them carefully.[110] An alternative is to administer ECT. In my opinion, exclusive reliance on drugs is not sensible in the management of depression.

There are, of course, several pharmacological means of dealing with the refractory patient. In England, MAO inhibitors have been combined with tricyclics in the treatment of patients who failed on either class of drugs alone.[33] Weight gain was striking, but toxicity was slight. Recently, Schuckit et al.[95] have challenged the notion—refuted it, perhaps—that MAO inhibitors and tricyclics, given in usual doses, are intolerably toxic. They indicated the need for more research on this point. However, it bears repetition that MAO inhibitors are toxic drugs, inherently as well as interactively, and the simultaneous use of a tricyclic cannot reduce this hazard. Reserpine and tetrabenazine can be added to imipramine treatment. In animals this causes excitement while reserpine alone causes lethargy.[101] In depressed patients it can correct refractoriness but it is accompanied by cardiovascular toxicity.[23]

Earle,[27] in a single-blind study, gave T_3 to

* See references 54, 68, 69, 85, and 88.

depressed patients who had not responded to one or another tricyclic; most responded favorably. It is also worth mentioning that while we have shown that T3 accelerates imipramine response only in women, it is possible that it is useful in the occasional man who is imipramine-refractory.

Finally, the question arises as to how long to continue tricyclic treatment. Information on this point is insufficient, but it seems reasonable to attempt dose reduction one month after remission is complete, reinstating full doses if symptoms recur. It is accepted practice to give half doses for six months after remission.[57]

⟮ Concluding Remarks

Drugs are useful in the management of depression. The most useful are the tricyclics. Various means are available to accelerate their effects and to treat the patient who is refractory to usual regimens. Sound practice depends upon sound theory. Knowledge about drugs has contributed substantially to theories about affective disorders, and theory should guide drug administration.

⟮ Bibliography

1. AKIMOTO, H., M. NAKAKUKI, and Y. MACHIYAMA. "Clinical Experiences with MAO Inhibitors," *Dis. Nerv. Syst.*, 21 (1960), 645–648.

2. ALBRIGHT, F. "Introduction to Diseases of the Ductless Glands," in R. L. Cecil and W. McDermott, eds., *A Textbook of Medicine*, 7th ed. Philadelphia: Saunders, 1948.

3. AXELROD, J. "The Fate of Catecholamines and the Effect of Psychoactive Drugs," in G. J. Martin and B. Kirsch, eds., *Enzymes in Mental Health*. Philadelphia: Lippincott, 1966.

4. AYD, F. J. "Recognizing and Treating Depressed Patients," *Mod. Med.*, 39 (1971), 80–86.

5. BAASTRUP, P. C., J. C. POULSEN, M. SCHOU et al. "Prophylactic Lithium: Double Blind Discontinuation in Manic-Depressive and Recurrent-Depressive Disorders," *Lancet*, 2 (1970), 326–330.

6. BARBEAU, A., H. MARS, and L. GILLO-JOFFROY. "Adverse Clinical Side Effects of Levodopa Therapy," in F. H. McDowell and C. H. Markham, eds., *Recent Advances in Parkinson's Disease*, Contemporary Neurology Series, Vol. 8. Philadelphia: Davis, 1971.

7. BARTHOLONI, G., M. DA PRADA, and A. PLETSCHER. "Decrease of Cerebral 5-Hydroxytryptamine by 3,4-Dihydroxyphenylalanine after Inhibition of Extracerebral Decarboxylase," *J. Pharm. Pharmacol.*, 20 (1968), 228–229.

8. BROADHURST, A. D. "Tryptophan versus ECT," *Lancet*, 1 (1970), 1392–1393.

9. BUNNEY, W. E., JR., H. K. H. BRODIE, D. L. MURPHY et al. "Studies of Alpha-CH₃-Para-Tyrosine, L-Dopa, and L-Tryptophan in Depression and Mania," *Am. J. Psychiatry*, 127 (1971), 872–881.

10. BUNNEY, W. E., JR., and J. M. DAVIS. "Norepinephrine in Depressive Reactions," *Arch. Gen. Psychiatry*, 13 (1965), 483–494.

11. BUNNEY, W. E., JR., D. L. MURPHY, H. K. H. BRODIE et al. "L-Dopa in Depressed Patients," *Lancet*, 1 (1970), 352.

12. CARR, L. A. and K. E. MOORE. "Norepinephrine: Release from Brain by d-Amphetamine in vivo," *Science*, 164 (1969), 322–323.

13. CARROLL, B. J., R. M. MOWBRAY, and B. DAVIS. "Sequential Comparison of L-TP with ECT in Severe Depression," *Lancet*, 1 (1970), 967–969.

14. COPPEN, A. "The Biochemistry of Affective Disorders," *Br. J. Psychiatry*, 113 (1967), 1237–1264.

15. COPPEN, A., R. NOGUERA, and J. BAILEY. "Prophylactic Lithium in Affective Disorders," *Lancet*, 2 (1971), 275–279.

16. COPPEN, A., A. J. PRANGE, JR., P. C. WHYBROW et al. "Abnormalities of Indoleamines in Affective Disorders," *Arch. Gen. Psychiatry*, 26 (1972), 474–478.

17. COPPEN, A., D. M. SHAW, and M. B. FARRELL. "Potentiation of the Antidepressive Effect of a Monoamine-Oxidase Inhibitor by Tryptophan," *Lancet*, 1 (1963), 79–81.

18. COPPEN, A., P. C. WHYBROW, R. NOGUERA. "The Comparative Antidepressant Value of L-Tryptophan and Imipramine with and without Attempted Potentiation by Liothy-

ronine," *Arch. Gen. Psychiatry*, 26 (1972), 234–241.

19. COURT, J. H. "Manic-Depressive Psychosis: An Alternative Conceptual Model," *Br. J. Psychiatry*, 114 (1968), 1523–1530.

20. DALEN, P. "Lithium Therapy in Huntington's Chorea and Tardive Dyskinesia," *Lancet*, 1 (1973), 107–108.

21. DAVIS, J. E., D. S. JANOWSKY, and M. K. EL-YOUSEF. "The Use of Lithium in Clinical Psychiatry," *Psychiatr. Ann.*, 3 (1973), 78–99.

22. DEWHURST, W. G. "On the Chemical Basis of Mood," *J. Psychosom. Res.*, 9 (1965), 115–127.

23. DICK, P. and P. ROCH. "The Interaction of Tricyclic Antidepressants and Tetrabenazine. Its Clinical Use and Therapeutic Results," in S. Garattini and M. N. G. Dukes, eds., *Proc. 1st Int. Symp. Antidepressant Drugs*. Amsterdam: Excerpta Medica Foundation, 1966.

24. DUNNER, D. L., C. K. COHN, E. S. GERSHON et al. "Differential Catechol-O-Methyltransferase Activity in Unipolar and Bipolar Affective Illness," *Arch Gen. Psychiatry*, 25 (1971), 348–353.

25. DUNNER, D. L. and F. K. GOODWIN. "Effect of L-Tryptophan on Brain Serotonin Metabolism in Depressed Patients," *Arch. Gen. Psychiatry*, 26 (1972), 364–366.

26. DYSON, W. L. and J. MENDELS. "Lithium and Depression," *Curr. Ther. Res.*, 10 (1968), 601–609.

27. EARLE, B. V. "Thyroid Hormone and Tricyclic Antidepressants in Resistant Depressions," *Am. J. Psychiatry*, 126 (1970), 1667–1669.

28. EARLEY, L. W. "The Clinical Signs and Early Recognition of Depressions as They Are Met with in General Practice," *Penn. Med. J.*, 59 (1956), 1355–1358.

29. ECCLESTON, D., G. W. ASHCROFT, T. B. B. CRAWFORD et al. "Some Observations on the Estimation of Tryptamine in Tissues," *J. Neurochem.*, 13 (1966), 93–101.

30. FAWCETT, J. "Suicidal Depression and Physical Illness," *JAMA*, 219 (1972), 1303–1306.

31. FEIGHNER, J. P., L. J. KING, M. A. SCHUCKIT et al. "Hormonal Potentiation of Imipramine and ECT in Primary Depression," *Am. J. Psychiatry*, 128 (1972), 1230–1238.

32. FULLER, R. W., B. J. WARREN, and B. B. MOLLOY. "Selective Inhibition of Monoamine Oxidase in Rat Brain Mitochondria," *Biochem. Pharmacol.*, 19 (1970), 2934–2936.

33. GANDER, D. R. "The Clinical Value of Monoamine Oxidase Inhibitors and Tricyclic Antidepressants in Combination," in S. Garattini and M. N. G. Dukes, eds., *Proc. 1st Int. Symp. Antidepressant Drugs*. Amsterdam: Excerpta Medica Foundation, 1966.

34. GLASSMAN, A. "Indoleamines and Affect Disorders," *Psychosom. Med.*, 31 (1969), 107–114.

35. GLASSMAN, A. and J. JAFFEE. Personal communication.

36. GLASSMAN, A. and S. R. PLATMAN. "Potentiation of a Monoamine Oxidase Inhibitor by Tryptophan," *J. Psychiatr. Res.*, 7 (1969), 83–88.

37. GLOWINSKI, J. "Some New Facts about Synthesis, Storage, and Release Processes of Monoamines in the Central Nervous System," in S. S. Snyder, ed., *Perspectives in Neuropharmacology*. London: Oxford University Press, 1972.

38. GLOWINSKI, J. and J. AXELROD. "Inhibition of Uptake of Tritiated Noradrenaline in the Intact Rat Brain by Imipramine and Related Compounds," *Nature*, 204 (1964), 1318–1319.

39. GLOWINSKI, J., J. AXELROD, and L. L. IVERSEN. "Regional Studies of Catecholamines in the Rat Brain. IV. Effects of Drugs on the Disposition and Metabolism of H^3-Norepinephrine and H^3-Dopamine," *J. Pharmacol. Exp. Ther.*, 153 (1966), 30–41.

40. GOLDBERG, L. I. "Monoamine Oxidase Inhibitors," *JAMA*, 190 (1964), 132–138.

41. GOODWIN, F. K. and W. E. BUNNEY, JR. "A Psychobiological Approach to Affective Illness," *Psychiatr. Ann.*, 3 (1973), 19–53.

42. GOODWIN, F. K., D. L. DUNNER, and E. S. GERSHON. "Effect of L-Dopa Treatment on Brain Serotonin Metabolism in Depressed Patients," *Life Sci.*, 10 (1971), 751–759.

43. GYERMEK, L. "The Pharmacology of Imipramine and Related Antidepressants," *Int. Rev. Neurobiol.*, 9 (1966), 95–143.

44. HALL, C. D., E. A. WEISS, C. E. MORRIS et al. "Rapid Deterioration in Patients with Parkinsonism following Tryptophan-Pyri-

doxine Administration," *Neurology*, 22 (1972), 231–237.

45. HERTTING, G., J. AXELROD, and L. G. WHITBY. "Effect of Drugs on the Uptake and Metabolism of H³-Norepinephrine," *J. Pharmacol. Exp. Ther.*, 134 (1961), 146–153.

46. HESSOV, I. B. "Hypertension during Imipramine Treatment," *Lancet*, 1 (1970), 84–85.

47. HOLLISTER, L. E. and J. E. OVERALL. "Reflections on the Specificity of Action of Antidepressants," *Psychosomatics*, 6 (1965), 361–365.

48. HORDERN, A., N. F. HOLT, C. G. BURT et al. "Amitriptyline in Depressive States: Phenomenology and Prognostic Considerations," *Br. J. Psychiatry*, 109 (1963), 815–825.

49. HORNYKIEWICZ, O. D. "Physiologic, Biochemical, and Pathological Backgrounds of Levodopa and Possibilities for the Future," *Neurology* (*Minneap.*,) 20, Part 2 (1970), 1–5.

50. IVERSEN, L. L. "Neurotransmitters, Neurohormones, and Other Small Molecules in Neurons," in F. O. Schmitt, ed., *The Neurosciences: Second Study Program*. New York: Rockefeller University Press, 1970.

51. JANOWSKY, D. S., M. K. EL-YOUSEF, J. M. DAVIS et al. "A Cholinergic-Adrenergic Hypothesis of Mania and Depression," *Lancet*, 2 (1972), 632–635.

52. JONES, A. B. B., C. M. B. PARE, W. J. NICHOLSON et al. "Brain Amine Concentrations after Monoamine Oxidase Inhibitor Administration," *Br. Med. J.*, 1 (1972), 17–19.

53. KEENAN, R. E. "The Eaton Collaborative Study of Levodopa Therapy in Parkinsonism: A Summary," *Neurology* (*Minneap.*), 20, Part 2 (1970), 46–59.

54. KENDELL, R. E. "The Problem of Classification," in A. Coppen and A. Walk, eds., *Recent Developments in Affective Disorders: A Symposium*. Ashford, England: Headley Brothers, 1968.

55. KETY, S. S. "The Central Physiological and Pharmacological Effects of the Biogenic Amines and Their Correlations with Behavior," in G. C. Quarton, T. Melnechuk, and F. O. Schmitt, eds., *The Neurosciences: A Study Program*. New York: Rockefeller University Press, 1967.

56. ———. "Brain Amines and Affective Disorders," in B. T. Ho and W. M. McIsaac, eds., *Brain Chemistry and Mental Disease*. New York: Plenum, 1971.

57. KLEIN, D. F. and J. M. DAVIS. *Diagnosis and Drug Treatment of Psychiatric Disorders*. Baltimore: Williams & Wilkins, 1969.

58. KLERMAN, G. L. and J. O. COLE. "Clinical Pharmacology of Imipramine and Related Antidepressant Compounds," *Pharmacol. Rev.*, 17 (1965), 101–141.

59. KLINE, N., W. SACKS, and G. M. SIMPSON. "Further Studies on: One Day Treatment of Depression with 5-HTP," *Am. J. Psychiatry*, 121 (1964), 379–381.

60. KOPIN, I. J. "Disposition and Metabolic Fate of Catecholamine Hormones," in G. Litwack and D. Kritchevsky, eds., *Actions of Hormones on Molecular Processes*. New York: Wiley, 1965.

61. ———. "False Aminergic Transmitters," in S. S. Snyder, ed., *Perspectives in Neuropharmacology*. London: Oxford University Press, 1972.

62. KOTIN, J. and F. K. GOODWIN. "Depression during Mania: Clinical Observations and Theoretical Implications," *Am. J. Psychiatry*, 129 (1972), 679–686.

63. LAPIN, I. P. and G. F. OXENKRUG. "Intensification of the Central Serotoninergic Processes as a Possible Determinant of the Thymoleptic Effect," *Lancet*, 1 (1969), 132–136.

64. LEHMANN, H. E. and G. E. HANRAHAN. "Chlorpromazine, New Inhibiting Agent for Psychomotor Excitement and Manic States," *Arch. Neurol. Psychiatry*, 71 (1954), 227–237.

65. LIDBRINK, P., G. JONSSON, and K. FUXE. "The Effect of Imipramine-Like Drugs and Antihistamine Drugs on the Uptake Mechanisms in the Central Noradrenaline and 5-Hydroxytryptamine Neurons," *Neuropharmacology*, 10 (1971), 521–536.

66. LIFSHITZ, K. and N. KLINE. "Pharmacology of the Aged," in J. T. Freeman, ed., *Clinical Principals and Drugs in the Aging*. Springfield, Ill.: Charles C. Thomas, 1963.

67. MASON, J. "Fatal Reaction with Parnate and Methylamphetamine," *Lancet*, 1 (1962), 1073.

68. MENDELS, J. *Concepts of Depression*. New York: Wiley, 1970.

69. MENDELS, J. and C. COCHRANE. "The Nosology of Depression: The Endogenous-Reactive Concept," *Am. J. Psychiatry*, 124 (1968), 1–11.

70. MURPHY, D. L., H. K. H. BRODIE, and F. K. GOODWIN. "Regular Induction of Hypomania by L-Dopa in 'Bipolar' Manic-Depressive Patients," *Nature*, 229 (1971), 135–136.

71. PARE, C. M. B. "Potentiation of Monoamine-Oxidase Inhibitors by Tryptophan," *Lancet*, 2 (1963), 527–528.

72. PEREL, J. M. and N. BLACK. "In vitro Metabolism Studies with Methylphenidate," *Fed. Proc.*, 29 (1970), 345.

73. POST, R. M., J. KOTIN, F. K. GOODWIN et al. "Psychomotor Activity and Cerebrospinal Fluid Amine Metabolites in Affective Illness," *Am. J. Psychiatry*, 130 (1973), 67–72.

74. PRANGE, A. J., JR. "The Pharmacology and Biochemistry of Depression," *Dis. Nerv. Syst.*, 25 (1964), 217–221.

75. ———. "Discussion of 'Hormonal Potentation of Impramine and ECT in Primary Depression'," [reference 31], *Am. J. Psychiatry*, 128 (1972), 1235–1238.

76. ———. "Discussion of Dr. Schildkraut's Paper," [reference 90], in J. Zubin and F. A. Freyhan, eds., *Disorders of Mood*. Baltimore: The Johns Hopkins Press, 1972.

77. ———. "The Use of Antidepressant Drugs in the Elderly Patient," in C. Eisendorfer and W. E. Fann, eds., *Psychopharmacology and Aging*. New York: Plenum, 1973.

78. PRANGE, A. J., JR., J. L. SISK, I. C. WILSON et al. "Balance, Permission, and Discrimination among Amines: A Theoretical Consideration of L-Tryptophan in Disorders of Movement and Affect," in J. D. Barchas and E. Usdin, eds., *Serotonin and Behavior*. New York: Academic, 1973.

79. PRANGE, A. J., JR., I. C. WILSON, A. E. KNOX et al. "Thyroid-Imipramine Clinical and Chemical Interaction: Evidence for a Receptor Deficit in Depression," *J. Psychiatr. Res.*, 9 (1972), 187–205.

80. PRANGE, A. J., JR., I. C. WILSON, C. E. MORRIS et al. "Preliminary Experience with Tryptophan and Lithium in the Treatment of Tardive Dyskinesia," *Psychopharmacol. Bull.*, 9 (1973), 36–37.

81. PRANGE, A. J., JR., I. C. WILSON, A. M. RABON et al. "Enhancement of Imipramine Antidepressant Activity by Thyroid Hormone," *Am. J. Psychiatry*, 126 (1969), 457–496.

82. ROBISON, D. S., A. NIES, J. M. DAVIS et al. "Ageing, Monoamines, and Monoamine-Oxidase Levels," *Lancet*, 1 (1972), 290–291.

83. ROSENBLATT, S., J. D. CHANLEY, and W. P. LEIGHTON. "The Investigation of Adrenergic Metabolism with 7H^3-Norepinephrine in Psychiatric Disorders: I. Temporal Change in the Distribution of Urinary Tritiated Metabolites and the Effects of Drugs," *J. Psychiatr. Res.*, 6 (1969), 307–319.

84. ———. "The Investigation of Adrenergic Metabolism with 7H^3-Norepinephrine in Psychiatric Disorders: II. Temporal Changes in the Distribution of Urinary Tritiated Metabolites in Affective Disorders," *J. Psychiatr. Res.*, 6 (1969), 321–333.

85. ROTH, M. "The Phenomenology of Depressive States," *Can. Psychiatr. Assoc. J.*, 4 (1959), 532–583.

86. SAAVEDRA, J. M. and J. AXELROD. "A Specific and Sensitive Enzymatic Assay for Tryptamine in Tissues," *J. Pharmacol. Exp. Ther.*, 182 (1972), 363–369.

87. SANDIFER, M. G., I. C. WILSON, and J. M. GAMBILL. "The Influence of Case Selection and Dosage in Antidepressant Drug Trial," *Br. J. Psychiatry*, 111 (1965), 142–148.

88. SANDIFER, M. G., I. C. WILSON, and L. GREEN. "The Two-Type Thesis of Depressive Disorder," *Am. J. Psychiatry*, 123 (1966), 93–97.

89. SCHILDKRAUT, J. J. "The Catecholamine Hypothesis of Affective Disorders: A Review of Supporting Evidence," *Am. J. Psychiatry*, 122 (1965), 509–522.

90. ———. "Neuropharmacological Studies of Mood Disorders," in J. Zubin and F. A. Freyhan, eds., *Disorders of Mood*. Baltimore: The Johns Hopkins Press, 1972.

91. SCHILDKRAUT, J. J., P. R. DRASKOCZY, E. S. GERSHON et al. "Effects of Tricyclic Antidepressants on Norepinephrine Metabolism: Basic and Clinical Studies," in B. T. Ho and W. M. McIsaac, eds., *Brain Chemistry and Mental Disease*. New York: Plenum, 1971.

92. SCHILDKRAUT, J. J., S. M. SCHANBERG, and

I. J. KOPIN. "Effects of Lithium Ion on H³-Norepinephrine," *Life Sci.*, 5 (1966), 1479–1483.

93. SCHOU, M. "Biology and Pharmacology of the Lithium Ion," *Pharmacol. Rev.*, 9 (1957), 17–58.

94. ――――. "Normothymotics, 'Mood-Normalizers.' Are Lithium and the Imipramine Drugs Specific for Affective Disorders?" *Br. J. Psychiatry*, 109 (1963), 803–809.

95. SCHUCKIT, M., E. ROBINS, and J. FEIGHNER. "Tricyclic Antidepressants and Monoamine Oxidase Inhibitors," *Arch. Gen. Psychiatry*, 24 (1971), 509–514.

96. SHEARD, M. H. and G. K. AGHAJANIAN. "Neuronally Activated Metabolism of Brain Serotonin: Effect of Lithium," *Life Sci.*, 9 (1960), 285–290.

97. SHIH, J.-H. C. and S. EIDUSON. "Multiple Forms of Monoamine Oxidase in Developing Tissues: The Implications for Mental Disorder," in B. T. Ho and W. M. McIsaac, eds., *Brain Chemistry and Mental Disease.* New York: Plenum, 1971.

98. SILVERMAN, C. *The Epidemiology of Depression.* Baltimore: The Johns Hopkins University Press, 1968.

99. STERLIN, C., T. A. BAN, H. E. LEHMANN et al. "A Comparative Evaluation of Doxepin and Chlordiazepoxide in the Treatment of Psychoneurotic Outpatients," *Curr. Ther. Res.*, 12 (1970), 195–200.

100. STOCKLEY, I. H. "Interactions of Monoamine Oxidase Inhibitors with Foods and Drugs," *Pharmac. J.*, 203 (1969), 174–179.

101. SULSER, F., J. WATTS, and B. B. BRODIE. "Antagonistic Actions of Imipramine and Reserpine on Central Nervous System," *Fed. Proc.*, 19 (1960), 268.

102. TAGLIAMONTE, A., P. TAGLIAMONTE, J.

PERET-CRUEZ et al. "Effect of Psychotropic Drugs on Tryptophan Concentration in the Rat Brain," *J. Pharmacol. Exp. Ther.*, 177 (1971), 475–480.

103. TONKS, C. M. and A. T. LLOYD. "Hazards with Monoamine-Oxidase Inhibitors," *Br. Med. J.*, 1 (1965), 589.

104. WEIL-MALHERBE, H. "Amines, Alerting, and Affect," *Lancet*, 2 (1968), 219–220.

105. WHARTON, R. N., J. M. PEREL, P. G. DAYTON et al. "A Potential Clinical Use for Methylphenidate with Tricyclic Antidepressants," *Am. J. Psychiatry*, 127 (1971), 1619–1625.

106. WHEATLEY, D. "Potentiation of Amitriptyline by Thyroid Hormone," *Arch. Gen. Psychiatry*, 26 (1972), 229–233.

107. WHYBROW, P. C. and J. MENDELS. "Toward a Biology of Depression: Some Suggestions from Neurophysiology, *Am. J. Psychiatry*, 125 (1969), 1491–1500.

108. WILSON, I. C. and A. J. PRANGE, JR. "Tryptophan in Mania: Theory of Affective Disorders," *Psychopharmacologia* (Suppl.) 26 (1973), 76.

109. WILSON, I. C., A. J. PRANGE, JR., T. K. McCLANE et al. "Thyroid Hormone Enhancement of Imipramine in Non-Retarded Depressions," *N. Engl. J. Med.*, 282 (1970), 1063–1067.

110. WILSON, I. C., J. T. VERNON, T. GUIN et al. "A Controlled Study in the Treatment of Depression," *J. Neuropsychiatry*, 4 (1963), 331–338.

111. YARYURA-TOBIAS, J. A., M. DIAMOND, and S. MERLIS. "The Action of L-Dopa on Schizophrenic Patients (a Preliminary Report)," *Curr. Ther. Res.*, 12 (1970), 528–531.

CHAPTER 24

LITHIUM

Samuel Gershon

❲ Introduction

THE INTRODUCTION of lithium into psychiatry in 1949 initiated modern psychopharmacology. It predated chlorpromazine or reserpine, the compounds usually associated with this revolution in psychiatric treatment. Thus, the first report on the use of lithium in psychiatric states sets a pattern of firsts for this agent and for its important role in psychopharmacology. Lithium, like the agents to follow, was introduced by a clinician, and serendipity seems to have been the midwife to its birth, as was the case later with the phenothiazines and the antidepressants of both the MAOI and tricyclic types. Furthermore, no reliable predictions based on preclinical pharmacological studies could have been made about the profile of clinical activity of lithium. This problem of clinical predictability, based on current preclinical pharmacological studies, still applies to lithium and many new psychoactive drugs.

If we look back further, we see that lithium has had a checkered—although unique—history since its discovery in 1818. Arfwedson[6] demonstrated that this mysterious element resembled sodium and potassium in some reactions but not in others. Lithium salts were later detected in some spa waters in Europe, and thus, about 100 years ago, it was first launched on its therapeutic career. During the latter half of the nineteenth century and the early part of this century, claims were made for the therapeutic value of lithium salts in a vast array of disorders, such as hypertension, gout, rheumatic gout, urinary calculi, and epilepsy. It was also reported to have diuretic, tonic, and sedative properties. None of these applications became established and most are now considered ineffective. Its next appearance was in the late 1940s in the United States, when lithium chloride became a popular salt substitute for patients on sodiumfree diets. It was being taken by patients with heart and kidney disease and some fatalities and serious poisonings resulted.[27]

This background would not appear to be an auspicious one for any new therapeutic claims for lithium. However, in looking at the first report in 1949 by Cade[24] on the use of lithium in mania, we find that the study suggests a remarkable effectiveness, in that clear and marked improvement occurred in every one of the ten cases treated. The report includes a trial of lithium on six patients suffering from dementia praecox with no fundamental improvement noted in any of them, except some decrease in restlessness in three. It was also tried on three patients suffering from chronic depressive psychosis, again without any improvement. Thus, it is these uncontrolled observations by an astute clinician that have been explored since this report,

If we can, for a moment, move on to the present and look at some of the claims for lithium in psychiatry and if in fact they prove to be true, we have, for the first time, a relatively simple compound that controls a major mental illness. The claim includes an aspect of therapeutic specificity which is extraordinary in that the drug acts against the various aspects of manic-depressive disorder and is not restricted to any one or more symptomatic manifestations. It is claimed that lithium will resolve a manic episode without exhibiting other secondary effects on behavior such as drowsiness and sedation that accompany treatment with neuroleptics in this disorder. Furthermore, when lithium is given in nontoxic doses to normals, no such effects on behavior appear, nor is there any impairment on psychological test parameters.[92]

Such a claim would almost satisfy the goals of chemotherapeutic specificity sought by Paul Ehrlich in his work on specific drug action and would have widespread consequences on psychiatric thinking for several reasons. Conclusive findings would strengthen the hypothesis of genetically inherited biochemical defect or defects in the affective disorders that might in some ways be corrected by this ion. It also raises the important and crucial need for careful and accurate diagnostic categorization. Confusion in diagnosis and classification of the affective disorders will militate against maximum therapeutic utility, as well as present a major obstacle to biological research in these disorders. This is highlighted by the findings that lithium responders are far more likely to

have a genetic history of bipolar illness than lithium non-responders.[71]

(Lithium in Affective Disorders

Mania

The use of lithium salts for the treatment of mania was the first and single indication reported by Cade in 1949.[24] Since then, it is estimated that over fifty published reports for this usage have appeared, almost all of them reporting widespread agreement on its efficacy. However, this literature includes trials in manic patients, schizophrenic patients of various subtypes, and those in other diagnostic categories.[42] Even in those studies where the population is restricted to clearly defined and diagnostically typical manic cases, it is difficult to assess the therapeutic efficacy of lithium because no rating scales were employed and other medications were used concomitantly or because there was a lack of an adequate drug-washout period. The dosage range of lithium varies widely among studies and plasma levels were often not reported. However, diagnostic problems are considerable in reviewing this literature, and the large variation in reports of incidence of the disease tends to support the possibility of a large variation in diagnostic criteria. Methodological problems are perhaps greater in the study of mania than in any other psychiatric condition, but additional problems arise from the management difficulties presented by these patients and in the self-limiting and recurrent nature of the disease. These methodological questions are of considerable importance in evaluating published reports in this area and are discussed in more detail elsewhere.[43]

With these reservations and the fact that only a few of the trials in mania have employed a controlled design, a composite of all reported studies gives an improvement rate of 60 to 100 percent in mania treated with lithium. From these data one might conclude that lithium is an effective agent in the treatment of mania.

To date, there have been nine controlled studies of lithium in mania, five comparing lithium with placebo* and four lithium with chlorpromazine.[61,79,82,107]

Schou et al.[95] studied thirty-eight patients; thirty were described as "typical" manics; the other eight (called "atypical") had schizophreniform symptoms. The experimental design consisted of two weeks of trial of lithium or placebo.

Among the thirty typical manic patients, twelve were judged as showing a positive response, fifteen a possible response, and three no response. For the eight atypical patients, two had a positive response, three a possible response, and three no response. The shifts from active drug to placebo, or vice versa, also indicated drug efficacy and superiority to placebo.

A crossover design with lithium or placebo for two weeks on each was utilized by Maggs.[67] In this study twenty-eight manic patients were randomly assigned to lithium and placebo. A fixed dose of lithium carbonate, 1.5 g./day, was used, and psychiatric assessments were made using the Wittenborn scale. Because of toxicity, uncooperativeness, or unmanageability, only eighteen of twenty-eight patients completed the entire study. The exclusion of these dropouts may present a methodological problem in the analysis of the results. However, the statistical assessment of the findings on cluster 3 (manic state) and cluster 5 (schizophreniform excitement) of the Wittenborn scale showed that the degree of mania diminished significantly more during the second week of treatment with lithium than after similar treatments with placebo. In studies by Bunney et al.[23] and Goodwin et al.,[46] placebo was substituted for lithium at predesignated periods in a blind fashion. In the former, two manic patients were observed, both were normalized by lithium, and both relapsed on its withdrawal. In ten out of ten trials, manic behavior increased within twenty-four hours following substitution of placebo.

* See references 23, 46, 67, 95, and 111.

In the latter, the study was extended to include twelve manics. Nine were rated as "unequivocal responders," and the remaining three failed to improve.[46]

A double-blind study, comparing lithium with placebo in mania, has been reported by Stokes.[111] A double-blind crossover design was employed with alternating periods of seven to ten days on each drug. The population consisted of thirty-eight manic-depressive inpatients. The initiation of the drug sequence, or the order of the drugs, was not randomized. Lithium chloride was administered in syrup at a dose of 0.5 mEq./per kg. body weight per day, divided in four daily doses producing a mean serum level of 0.93 mEq./l. In analyzing the manic treatment periods, 75 percent of the patients improved after seven to ten days of lithium treatment, while only 18 percent worsened. During the placebo periods an equal number of patients improved and worsened. These differences were statistically significant by chi-square analysis. Several problems appear with this study, such as the lack of randomization, and the fact that the lithium trial period was quite short and would not have been an adequate test of lithium's antimanic properties in some of the patients, especially as a fixed upper limit of dosage was established. The rating instruments employed were made up by these investigators and it is difficult to compare their validity or reliability with those of other studies. It would appear then that the value of lithium in the treatment of mania is generally apparent from the numerous open studies. Furthermore, each of the five controlled studies comparing lithium with placebo in the treatment of mania has its own methodological strengths and weaknesses. However, it is important to note that, despite these differences, the results are remarkably concurrent, that is, lithium is clearly superior to placebo in the acute treatment of mania.

The comparison studies with chlorpromazine are of greater practical importance in the assessment of therapeutic utility of lithium in this disorder, and will be considered individually. Johnson et al.[62] studied twenty-eight bipolar manic-depressive patients treated with lithium and chlorpromazine and compared their response with a second group of thirteen excited schizo-affective patients. A consensus on diagnosis was reached by three psychiatrists, and the diagnostic criteria employed indicate that the schizo-affective group was made up of individuals who would be included in the APA classification of the schizophrenia-schizo-affective type. After a baseline placebo period of five days, the patients were assigned randomly to lithium carbonate or chlorpromazine. The blood level of lithium was maintained between 1.0 and 2.5 mEq./l. Dosage of chlorpromazine began at 400 mg. and was adjusted upwards, according to clinical judgment, to 1800 mg. Clinical change was assessed on several different rating instruments. The nurses observation scale for inpatient evaluation (NOSIE) was completed by the nurses; the structured clinical interview (SCI) was completed by a psychologist; the brief psychiatric rating scale (BPRS), the treatment rating assessment matrix (TRAM), and the clinical global impressions (CGI) were taken by two psychiatrists at base line and during treatment. The results of this study indicate a superior therapeutic effect of lithium carbonate in manic states. The global remission rates obtained with lithium were 78 percent, as compared with 36 percent of those patients treated with chlorpromazine. It was clear that chlorpromazine produced a decrease in motor activity more rapidly, and improved manageability earlier than did lithium. Similar improvement with lithium did not occur until an average of eight days of treatment had passed. In the nonmanic states, a striking dissimilarity of action was noted. The chlorpromazine-treated schizo-affective patients all showed varying degrees of improvement, with 80 percent attaining marked or moderate levels of improvement, whereas only seven of fourteen patients treated with lithium showed moderate improvement. The remainder manifested varying degrees of worsening of their condition. This outcome may be attributed in part to several disputable issues in the experimental design. The dosage plan called for an attempt at matching the approximate number of capsules given per day for each medication and dosage was increased until clinical improvement or toxicity appeared. This may have given rise to the use of too high doses of lithium with a high degree of toxicity and aggravation of the pathology in schizophrenics and, on the other hand, the maximum dose of chlorpromazine, 1800 mg., may be considered to be too low in some cases. In the manic-depressive group the SCI profile of the subscales revealed that specific features of psychopathology in the manic patients were affected selectively by lithium but not by chlorpromazine, suggesting that lithium has a more specific effect on mania.

Spring et al.[108] were not able to show a statistically significant difference between the two drugs. They observed a total of twelve patients—seven on lithium, five on chlorpromazine—for a three-week period. Lithium carbonate was given up to 1800 mg./day and chlorpromazine 1600 mg./day. Six of the seven patients started on lithium responded to the drug, compared with three out of five who started on chlorpromazine. The two chlorpromazine failures were crossed over to lithium carbonate and both had a remission. However, the one lithium failure was crossed over to chlorpromazine and failed to respond. Thus, in terms of total drug trials, responses to lithium were noted eight out of nine times, whereas responses to chlorpromazine occurred three out of six times. Spring et al.[108] concluded that lithium is not significantly superior to chlorpromazine. Their treatment of their data is somewhat confusing in that they do not define how they determine whether a patient had responded or not. A comparison of mean relative improvement of the target symptoms in each group shows that there is a much greater response for lithium than for chlorpromazine for the target symptoms of motor hyperactivity, flight of ideas, euphoria, expansiveness, and pressured speech. However, when the total list of target symptom response is analyzed by the Mann-Whitney test, the difference does not achieve statistical significance.[108]

Platman[80] assigned thirteen manic patients to lithium carbonate, and ten to chlorpromazine in a double-blind randomly selected drug-trial period. It was preceded by a two-week placebo period, followed by three weeks of lithium or chlorpromazine. Mean dose of lithium carbonate was 1800 mg. with plasma levels maintained at a mean of 0.8 mEq./l; mean chlorpromazine dose was 870 mg. Platman concludes that at the third week of receiving the test drugs, lithium carbonate was superior on all scales on the psychiatric evaluations (PEF) developed by Spitzer et al.[107] but this was not statistically significant on any individual parameter. Platman further states that the general state of the patients on lithium carbonate was markedly superior and, in fact, the majority of the patients were discharged on this drug while none of the patients on chlorpromazine were sent home. This result is closely akin to the reports by Johnson et al.[62] and Spitzer et al.[107] Two other reports attempt to deal with this question. Johnson et al.[61] studied thirteen manics on lithium and eight on chlorpromazine; seven schizo-affectives (excited phase) were treated with lithium and six with chlorpromazine using an array of behavioral rating instruments. On the TRAM scale only the lithium-treated manic-depressives were significantly improved at termination. The other treatment groups demonstrated no significant change on this scale. On the CGI, lithium and chlorpromazine had a statistically significant effect on all the groups, except on the schizo-affectives treated with lithium. On the BPRS, the manic group treated with lithium showed significant changes in more areas of psychopathology. The lack of significant change with chlorpromazine on those items concerned with ideation is in agreement with clinical impressions. Analysis of the SCI scores using the Penrose technique reveals that the greatest improvement, over 1 standard deviation, was shown by the manic patients treated with lithium.[61,79]

A related study by Shopsin et al.[102] underscores lithium's specificity of action. In a double-blind controlled study of lithium vs. chlorpromazine in acute schizophrenic patients, a clear distinction between the effects of these agents indicated that lithium appears to be without any sedative or neuroleptic

properties and, in fact, can precipitate or contribute to further decompensation of schizophrenic symptomatology.[103]

From these studies the question of the efficacy of lithium compared with a standard form of treatment such as chlorpromazine is not clearly resolved. Therefore, the NIMH and the Veterans Administration began a collaborative project on lithium conducted at eighteen hospitals. For three weeks two hundred fifty-five manic patients were assigned to either lithium or chlorpromazine.[82,83] During a base-line period of three to five days the patients were evaluated on the BPRS, the inpatient multidimensional psychiatric scale (IMPS), and the psychotic inpatient profile (PIP) rating scale, and randomly assigned to medication with individualized dosage. The mean dosage of medications was 1800 mg. lithium carbonate and 1000 mg. chlorpromazine. They were divided into a highly active group of 125, and a mildly active one of 130 cases. In the former group, 38 percent of the lithium patients were dropped, as compared with 8 percent of the chlorpromazine patients. In the highly active group, comparing lithium completers with chlorpromazine completers (by covariance analysis), there was no major difference between the groups. A similar conclusion was reached in the mildly active group. The study certainly provides adequate numbers of cases for study and, in fact, is the largest controlled study in the world literature on the chemotherapy of mania. This report goes further in stating that there was no evidence that the treatments acted differentially on the underlying manic process. The findings are somewhat at variance with clinical impressions presented in some of the above studies, which cannot be compared with each other from almost any point of view. This latter one also differed in several respects: (1) no history of cyclic episodes in the previous two years was requisite for inclusion in the study; (2) it was carried out in a regular hospital setting in most cases and not in a research facility; and (3) no minimum plasma lithium level was demanded as a treatment requisite. Other questions are raised by the relatively high dropout rate. It is somewhat surprising that there were almost as many terminaters among the mildly active patients (nineteen) as there were among the highly active patients (twenty-six). It also seems probable that a large multihospital sample might be diagnostically more heterogeneous.

Thus, even after more than twenty years of study, the conclusions that can be reached on the efficacy of lithium in acute mania are not absolutely resolved. It is probably safe to say that lithium is an effective agent in the treatment of mania and is superior in efficacy to placebo. With regard to its comparison with chlorpromazine, the smaller controlled studies suggest its equivalence with or superiority to chlorpromazine, whereas the larger study of Prien et al.[83] indicates a superiority of chlorpromazine over lithium. The fact that lithium takes approximately a week to produce a significant therapeutic effect indicates that for practical purposes some neuroleptic is the preferred agent for rapid control of disturbed behavior and the production of a manageable patient. However, in addition to chlorpromazine and related phenothiazines, haloperidol, a butyrophenone, has been widely used in the treatment of acute mania, but to date there have been no controlled studies comparing its efficacy with that of lithium. These issues are more extensively considered in a book by Gershon and Shopsin.[43]

Prophylactic Activity

The above material indicates that it has been difficult to establish the efficacy of lithium in current manifest manic episodes. The task in establishing the prophylactic efficacy of lithium in recurrent mania has been considerably more difficult. Furthermore, no controlled studies have been carried out on the problem of prophylactic activity of any other form of chemotherapy in recurrent affective disorders. The claim for prophylactic activity emerges from some of the earlier longitudinal studies. Such references appear in reports of Noack and Trautner,[76] and Schou et al.[91,94] which suggest primarily activity in the manic

phase and the prophylaxis for recurrent mania. In a report of Gershon and Yuwiler,[45] a similar suggestion of prophylactic activity for recurrent mania is presented. During the use of lithium for the treatment of mania the medication was continued in the expectation that it might prevent recurrent episodes of the manic disorder. Then, in 1963, Hartigan[55] concluded that a prophylactic action of lithium against recurrent mania occurs and added a claim for its prophylaxis against recurrent depressive cycles. It is important to note that Hartigan adds the reservation that in "atypical cases in which there was diagnostic doubt because of conspicuous schizophrenic or paranoid features they did not do as well as the pure classical forms of mania." It appeared in some of these studies that the medication led not only to diminution of the manic episodes, but also to attenuation of the depressive symptoms.[91,92] This seemed to indicate that lithium might exert a prophylactic action in depression as well as in mania.

Independently, Baastrup and Schou[11] also reported that this continued medication of patients seemed to produce a beneficial effect on the prevention of recurrences of both the manic and depressive episodes. They studied eighty-eight patients who had had two or more manic-depressive episodes during one year, or one or more episodes during two years. Patients were observed for one to six years without lithium, and for one to five years with lithium.

Among the first to claim prophylactic effects of lithium in bipolar manic-depressive illness were Hartigan,[55] and Baastrup and Schou.[11] The latter study indicated that lithium reduced the frequency of hospitalizations and length of psychotic episodes. The design employed was not strictly double-blind controlled; the analyses were based on the frequencies of episodes before and during lithium treatment and were compared intraindividually. Of the eighty-eight patients studied, five showed an increase in frequency of episodes from the period before to the period of lithium treatment, in two the frequency remained the same, and in eighty-one patients it decreased. On the assumption of equal chance of increases and decreases, the sign test revealed a highly significant difference (p<0.001). Factors, such as the age of the patients and the duration of the illness, did not influence the results, but patients with schizo-affective disorder responded less well than those with bipolar and unipolar affective disorder. The last point is of considerable importance and will be discussed again later. The other lithium placebo comparison was a small-sample discontinuation study by Melia[70] which also found lithium to be more effective than placebo, but not significantly so.

Following on the initial report by Baastrup and Schou[11] these investigators developed a cooperative study[4,53,94] with colleagues in Prague and in Zurich, with the aim to see whether the findings could be confirmed in different clinical settings, and to employ a larger sample for detailed statistical analysis. A total of 244 patients were included in this study; design and selection criteria were similar to those employed by Baastrup and Schou.[11] Diagnostic types were manic-depressive disorder, recurrent endogenous depressions, or recurrent schizo-affective disorder. The results were tested with Wilcoxon's Matched Pairs Signed Ranks Test for the null hypothesis that the chances of increases and decreases in frequency would be equal. The data showed that the null hypothesis must be rejected; the majority of the patients with lithium treatment showed a pronounced reduction in the number of episodes. This was demonstrated at all three clinics involved and for each of the three diagnostic categories. In addition to the various groups of patients, regression analyses of the duration of cycles and episodes were carried out, with lithium administration as one of the variables. This confirmed for all three diagnostic groups the prolongation of cycles during lithium treatment, and, furthermore, showed that it was the intervals between the psychotic episodes that were prolonged. The episodes themselves were shortened in the manic-depressive patients and unchanged in duration in the patients with recurrent depressions and schizo-affective disorder. These diagnostic distinc-

tions derived from this study are of considerable importance and should be kept in mind.

In a longitudinal single-blind prophylactic study by Fieve et al.[34] on forty-three bipolar manic-depressive patients, lithium produced a slight decrease in intensity of depression scores, but no significant change in frequency of bipolar depressive attacks. The study compared the patients on lithium over seven months with those on lithium less than seven months. In this study there was no alteration of frequency of attacks produced by lithium.[5,34,53,94] Stancer et al.[109] studied twenty-one recurrent endogenous patients, periodic as well as nonperiodic, and found only a mild prophylaxis in the nonperiodic patients.

In a somewhat similar study, Hullen et al.[59] saw a lapse within six months in one of eighteen lithium patients, and in six of eighteen placebo patients, again indicating a significant superiority for lithium over placebo. The prophylactic effect of lithium was studied double-blind in a group of sixty-five patients with recurrent affective disorders, collected in four centers.[26] Patients were randomly assigned to lithium or placebo for periods of up to 112 weeks. In addition, they received additional medication thought necessary by the treating psychiatrist when a failure occurred on either lithium or placebo. Patients receiving lithium had significantly less affective illness than those on placebo. Also, the amount of antidepressants or antimanic additional medication prescribed was significantly less in the lithium group. The conclusion reached was that lithium seemed to be as effective in patients with unipolar recurrent depressive illness as in patients with both mania and depression.

In an attempt to resolve some of the issues raised by the longitudinal design trials, Baastrup et al.[10] initiated a double-blind comparison of lithium with placebo, using a discontinuation design. The study group consisted of eighty-four females who had been on maintenance lithium therapy for at least one year. There were two diagnostic groups: (1) manic-depressives (N = 50) with a history of both manic and depressive episodes; and (2) recurrent endogenous depressives (N = 34) with no history of mania. Patients were paired within each diagnostic group. One member of each pair was randomly taken off lithium and given identically appearing placebos. Each patient was evaluated periodically by clinicians unaware of the patient's treatment assignment. The patient was considered relapsed if he had a manic or depressive episode severe enough to require hospitalization or supplementary drug therapy. The results indicated that in both diagnostic groups lithium was significantly superior to placebo after five months; 55 percent of the manic-depressives on placebo had relapsed as compared with none of the patients on lithium. In the recurrent depression group, relapse occurred in 53 percent of the placebo patients and in none of the lithium patients. In this study the differences in relapse frequency between periods without lithium and with lithium were statistically significant at the $p < 0.001$ level. This study is an important and well-controlled one, and even though not without criticism in regard to methodology, provides us with a study plan which is acceptable in most respects. It provides the first clear-cut evidence for the prophylactic efficacy of any psychotropic agent in recurrent affective disorders. Furthermore, it presents the view that lithium has a prophylactic effect in manic-depressive, manic, and recurrent depressive relapses. One important issue, however, is the fact that this was a carefully selected sample of female lithium responders, who had been maintained on the program with positive therapeutic effects for at least one year.

It is possible that the prophylactic effects of lithium may be less pronounced in a randomly selected group of manics and recurrent depressives. This appears to be borne out in another study where a more random selection of cases was used. For example, Platman[81] compared lithium with imipramine and demonstrated a major prophylactic effect. Van der Velde[114] reported on seventy-five patients maintained on lithium carbonate. Here again the prophylactic efficacy was not as marked as reported in the Danish study.[10]

The most recent exploration of prophylactic efficacy of lithium carbonate in manic-depressive illness was carried out as part of the joint NIMH-VA collaborative study and is reported by Prien et al.[84] This study included patients who had been hospitalized with acute mania and were treated upon discharge with either lithium carbonate or placebo for a two-year period. Patients were stabilized on maintenance doses of lithium carbonate which yielded serum lithium levels of 0.5–1.4 mEq./l. At discharge, the patients were randomly assigned to lithium carbonate or placebo. The sample consisted of 133 men and seventy-two women. Assessment of clinical change was evaluated primarily in terms of frequency and severity of relapse. Outcome for the total sample, including the completers of the full two years plus early terminators, showed that 67 percent of the placebo patients had at least one severe relapse compared with only 31 percent of the lithium patients. This difference is statistically significant by chi-square analysis ($p < 0.001$). Twenty-nine percent of the patients in the placebo and 12 percent in the lithium group had two or more severe relapses (that is, were hospitalized two or more times). There was no major difference between treatments in the incidence of moderate relapses. The proportion of patients without relapses was significantly higher in the lithium group than in the placebo group ($p < 0.001$). Furthermore, there was no major difference between results obtained during the first and second years. Lithium was superior to placebo during both periods. The nature of relapse did not differ significantly between the groups. In the lithium group, 64 percent of the relapsers were manic, 24 percent were depressive, 3 percent were mixed manic and depressive, and 9 percent were schizo-affective. In the placebo group, 75 percent of the relapses were manic, 20 percent depressive, 3 percent mixed, and 3 percent schizo-affective. Comparing the relapse incidence with the prestudy incidence, in the lithium group there was a significant reduction in the incidence of relapse during the study period, i.e., 31 percent of lithium patients had one or more relapses during the study, compared with 58 percent before the study ($p < 0.001$). In the placebo group, there was no significant difference in the incidence of relapse before and during the study. The significant improvement of the lithium group was due mainly to the reduction in manic relapses. Relatively few patients had depressive relapses in the lithium group; 8 percent of the patients had depressive relapses during the study, compared with 16 percent before the study, which does not attain statistical significance. In the placebo group, 13 percent showed depressive relapses during the study and 11 percent before the study, which is also not significant.

An important additional result in the analysis in this study was a closer look at patients with a history of schizophrenia. A survey of psychiatric history data revealed that fourteen patients had been hospitalized with a diagnosis of schizophrenia during the two years preceding the study. Of the fourteen, twelve had no recorded history of affective illness preceding the manic episode that resulted in their inclusion in the study. This raises the question as to whether these patients can be legitimately classified as manic-depressive. Of the fourteen patients eleven were in the lithium group. Their response to treatment was relatively poor and five of the eleven were dropped before the end of three months. Of the three placebo patients, one was dropped for schizo-affective behavior, one required supplementary drug therapy, and one showed no symptomatology. These results suggest that patients with a history of schizophrenia are not suitable candidates for a program of lithium prophylaxis.[81,84,115] Although the findings in this study indicate prophylactic activity, an unresolved question remains whether recurrences might have been reduced if the lithium dosage had been increased.[84] Only about half of the severely relapsed patients on lithium had their dosage increased during the weeks preceding hospitalization, whereas about one sixth of the nonrelapsed patients on lithium had their dosage increased for poor clinical response. This probably prevented relapse in some cases.

In addition to this unresolved issue, another important point is the definition or description of the effect that is observed. It might be stated that relatively large doses of lithium are required to resolve the acute manic episode, followed by lower doses for maintenance. In these cases it appears that the prophylactic activity, when present, modifies the magnitude of the amplitude of the manic or the depressive phase rather than abolishing absolutely the endogenous episode. For example, it was noted that when a manic episode begins to appear, the patient experiences some of the same features that heralded previous episodes. These may include mild restlessness, insomnia, overactivity, or some more individual specific alteration in behavior. This has been described as a hypomanic alert by Jacobsen.[60] At such times, the dosage of lithium needs to be increased to produce an abatement of symptoms. Thus, the maintenance medication produces a marked diminution in the amplitude of symptomatology and enables the patient and his family to detect and appreciate the onset of the cyclic episode. The patient then can usually be maintained as an outpatient without requiring admission to the hospital. Therefore, it may be more appropriate to apply a different term, other than prophylactic, to the effect of lithium in these disorders. Alternative terms have been offered, such as stabilization or normalization.

Thus, the various studies comparing prophylactic lithium with placebo indicate that lithium carbonate combined with regular clinical appraisals is a safe and effective treatment for preventing relapse in manic-depressive illness. Whether it is more effective than other psychopharmacological treatments remains to be answered.[60]

It should be stressed that these conclusions are based upon Jacobsen's appraisal of the available data. However, it should be pointed out that other reviewers of literature have drawn quite contrary conclusions. For example, Shull and Sapira[105] concluded that the available data demonstrate neither efficacy nor inefficacy, primarily because of inadequate experimental design. Other issues have been raised by Blackwell and Shepard,[20] suggesting that a similar negative appraisal of these data could be reached. The issues debated are of considerable academic interest and for a more extensive analysis of this material, reference to recent reviews on the subject would be of value.[20,105,44] Notwithstanding this debate, it would seem that for a satisfactory result with prophylactic lithium maintenance treatment the drug should be administered on proper diagnostic indications. The typical "affective disorder" group is predicted to show the highest response. In the opinion of some investigators, some effect may be seen on the affective element of schizo-affective disorder. This is contested by others, but there is unanimity that thought disturbances are not influenced.

Depression

Central to the problem of manic-depressive disease is the question of the effect of lithium in a current manifest depressive illness. The first attempt to evaluate the effectiveness of lithium in the treatment of depression was included in Cade's[24] original report. Three patients suffering from chronic depressive psychosis were given lithium for several weeks and neither improvement nor aggravation of depression was noted. A similar conclusion was reached after a trial in several depressed patients in the report by Noack and Trautner.[76] Similar conclusions were reported by Gershon and Trautner[44] and Gershon and Yuwiler.[45] However, several European investigators reported improvement of depression with lithium in a small number of cases. Vojtechovsky,[116] as quoted by Schou,[91] reported that eight of fourteen depressed patients who had failed to respond to ECT subsequently improved with lithium. Andreani et al.[2] reported that ten out of twenty-four depressed patients improved on lithium.

More recently, Dyson and Mendels[31] observed the successful treatment of a number of depressed patients with lithium carbonate. A group of thirty-one patients with depression were treated, seventeen were outpatients and fourteen inpatients; nineteen of the patients showed a favorable response to lithium; seven were diagnosed as suffering from manic-depressive illness, bipolar type; ten patients who improved had a history which suggested

cyclothymic personality. Thus, it would appear that responders in this study had a history of recurrence and that a diagnosis of manic-depressive illness would apply, together with a high incidence of family history of affective type.

Fieve et al.,[35] in a double-blind study of twenty-nine moderately depressed patients diagnosed as having manic-depressive psychosis, compared the effect of lithium with that of imipramine. After three weeks, lithum patients were slightly improved, while imipramine patients were moderately to markedly improved. It is the conclusion of these authors that the therapeutic response was restricted to the group that might be characterized as the endogenous depressive group. However, Van der Velde[115] noted that in eight of seventy-five depressed patients a precipitation of depressive episode occurred in association with lithium administration. This observation is in accord with the earlier report of Noack and Trautner.[76]

Nahunek et al.[75] treated ninety-eight patients with a diagnosis of either endogenous depression or involutional melancholia with lithium and report a favorable result in 54 percent. Patients received 300 to 2100 mg. of lithium carbonate daily for an average of 26.4 days. Clinical improvement emerged mainly at the end of the first week and during the second week of treatment. A controlled study of lithium in depression has been reported by Hansen et al.[54] In studying twelve patients diagnosed as severe endogenous depressives, they found no significant improvement during the two-week trial on lithium. The study involved a crossover between lithium and placebo. The authors concluded that lithium was not effective in the treatment of this group of patients.

Goodwin et al.[46,47] investigated hospitalized depressed patients, using the alternation of placebo and lithium on a double-blind basis, and concluded that lithium was effective in the treatment of selected depressed patients. It should be noted that the number of patients here is quite small.

The controlled study by Stokes et al.[111] reports on eighteen patients who were treated with lithium or placebo for thirty-eight depressive periods. Lithium was administered during seventeen of these and placebo during twenty-one. They found a statistically significant alleviation of depression during the periods of lithium treatment, as compared with depression ratings on the day prior to the institution of lithium treatment. But they also found improvement during the placebo periods and note that there was no significant difference between lithium and placebo changes.

The most recent attempt to resolve this problem is a double-blind controlled study reported by Mendels et al.[72] They concluded that lithium carbonate was as effective as desipramine in the treatment of selected depressed patients. Twenty-four patients were included on the basis of having a score on the Hamilton depression rating scale of at least fifteen. Desipramine was given in daily doses of 100–200 mg., lithium carbonate in daily doses of 1–2 g. A significant critical issue in this study is the absence of a placebo group for comparative purposes. The only conclusion that can be reached at this stage in regard to the effect of lithium in recurrent manifest depressive episodes, is that the possibility of this activity exists but has not been satisfactorily established. The situation may be clouded by diagnostic considerations rather than by other variables. For example, it may conceivably be—as some authors contend—that it is effective only for a certain and specific subcategory of depressive disorders. Studies carried out to date have been pooling different subcategories of depression and this may have impaired clarification of this issue.

([Lithium in Other Psychiatric Disorders

Unfortunately, lithium has suffered the same fate as many other compounds introduced into psychiatric therapy. Initially based on uncontrolled clinical observations, therapeutic efficacy is claimed for a compound that affects a wide variety of disorders and, on occasions, the entire spectrum of psychopathology. Patients with schizo-affective schizophrenia have been investigated in three controlled studies. Johnson et al.[62] compared the efficacy of chlorpromazine over lithium in schizo-affective schizophrenia and divided this population into highly active and mildly active subsamples. The highly active patients treated with chlorpromazine did significantly better than lithium-treated patients on a total of twenty-two items on the BPRS. There were no significant changes between BPRS scores before and after lithium treatment. However, for the forty-one mildly active schizo-affective patients, both treatment groups did significantly better when compared with pretreatment levels.

In a collaborative study by Angst et al.[5] it was concluded that lithium had prophylactic value in schizo-affective illness but that this effect was not as profound as in manic-depressive disease. Their finding of greater morbidity of schizo-affectives with time would appear to relate to the implications of Prien et al.[83,84] and Johnson et al.[61,62] that there is more residual pathology after three weeks of treatment of an acute schizo-affective episode on lithium than there is of manic-depressive psychosis. In the most recent study referred to above by Prien et al.[84] there is some contradiction of the positive prophylactic finding reported by Angst.[4] Thus, a tentative conclusion seems to suggest that schizo-affective schizophrenia and manic-depressive illness do not respond identically to medication and therefore may not be the same disorder.

Lithium has also been explored in a variety of neurotic illnesses and personality disorders. Anecdotal reports of the use of lithium have appeared for obsessive-compulsive personality,[9] obsessive-compulsive neurosis,[37] phobias,[48] and as an anti-anxiety agent.[66] In reviewing this material, it would appear that no strong case can be offered for the efficacy of lithium in any of the above disorders, although this matter has not been conclusively resolved. However, a special subsample of this population with a clear or presumptive affective component has been studied in a controlled fashion by Rifkin et al.[85] Twenty-one inpatient adolescents, diagnosed as having emotionally unstable character disorder (EUCD), were selected. In this study, lithium or placebo was administered in a random manner for six weeks followed by a crossover to the other drug. The serum level of lithium was maintained between 0.8 and 1.5 mEq./l. The hypothesis that lithium would dampen affective fluctuation was confirmed. Lithium was significantly better than placebo on two measures of mood fluctuation, namely, global judgment and a rating of the daily range of mood. The other issue here is whether lithium has a superior effect over chlorpromazine or other agents. This study is of interest in view of the fact that Baastrup,[9] and Gershon and Trautner[44] both report from open trials that unmanageable antisocial disorders, which did not respond to a variety of treatments, did seem to respond favorably to lithium.

In another area, an important study carried out by Sheard,[97] presented encouraging results on the use of lithium in explosive personalities. The subjects were twelve male prisoners. On a single-blind random-assignment design, subjects treated with lithium rated themselves lower on aggression and had significantly fewer official reports due to aggressive acts. This report is of considerable interest and warrants further exploration in more comprehensive controlled studies.

Because of the often clear affective component and inherent periodicity in premenstrual tension syndrome, it appeared that lithium would warrant exploration in this disorder. Such a trial was carried out by Sletten and Gershon.[106] Only eight patients were studied and a positive response was elicited in all eight cases. This study was a completely uncontrolled and open clinical trial and therefore does not permit any definitive conclusions to be reached. However, adequately designed studies in this area would be of considerable academic and practical importance.

Trials of lithium in childhood disorders have been reported by a number of investigators.[30,38,116] However, none of these studies indicates any clear-cut or specific indications for its use in the disorders investigated to date.

(Therapeutic Regimen

The treatment procedure must take into account the two areas involved in the interaction, that is, the clinical aspect, and the physiological and pharmacological properties of the drug. In the former, there are two considerations as to whether the treatment is for the control of the current manic episode or for maintenance during interphase. One must also take into account an important fact, that this drug, lithium, is of most value in a specific diagnostic entity: manic-depressive disease.

The first issue then is proper selection of patients to whom lithium is to be prescribed; the patient must be in reasonably good physical condition to handle the lithium ion adequately upon its introduction into the body. Significant renal disorder such that adequate elimination of the lithium ion in the urine might be impaired is an absolute contraindication for treatment. Other factors that militate against treating a patient with lithium include significant cardiac disease, organic brain damage, and regimens requiring restriction of dietary intake of salt. Therefore, after selection of the patient for treatment, the therapeutic regimen may be considered in two phases. The initiation of lithium treatment in a manic needs to be considered, like the institution of insulin in controlling a diabetic patient. The stabilization of a manic episode may take from five to ten days.

Any of the lithium salts may be used, but the most readily available is lithium carbonate in tablets or capsules of 250 or 300 mg. each, equivalent to 6.75 or 8 mEq. of elemental lithium, respectively. The range of daily dosage during this phase varies between 1 and 3 g. in multiple divided doses over twenty-four hours. This initial higher dosage is given until the manic symptoms have abated. The size of the dose is determined by several factors, such as the severity of the clinical condition, body weight, age, physical condition, and rate of renal clearance of lithium. The steady state between intake and elimination is reached in five to six days; thereafter the serum lithium concentration in blood samples drawn approximately twelve hours after the last intake of lithium should be within the range of 0.8 to 1.8 mEq./l. Plasma levels may be determined approximately every three or four days during the stabilization phase. In addition to such chemical surveillance, careful clinical observation and chemical assays are mandatory and may indicate the appearance of any toxic manifestations. If toxic symptoms appear or if the plasma lithium level approaches 2 mEq/l. the dose of lithium should be reduced, or if the toxicity is severe, the drug temporarily withdrawn.

In cases where the disruptive behavior becomes a significant management problem, a manic attack may also be treated with a combination of lithium and a major neuroleptic such as chlorpromazine or haloperidol. The neuroleptic drug usually controls the more violent manifestations of the mania more rapidly, but when the effect of lithium becomes apparent, the former drug may be gradually withdrawn.

(Maintenance Phase

After the manic episode remits, the initial high dosage of lithium may be reduced. The dosage should be lowered and plasma levels continued until a stable plasma is established. When the clinical condition is fully under control and a constant dose of lithium has been established, the patient can be safely managed at that level with continued ingestion, a regular check of plasma lithium levels, and clinical surveillance. During maintenance the intake of lithium must equal the elimination, and since lithium is excreted almost exclusively through the kidneys, it is primarily the renal lithium clearance which determines the maintenance dosage. The renal lithium clearance is usually a fixed proportion, about one-fifth of the creatinine clearance, and like it, varies a great deal among individuals and decreases with advancing years. Accordingly, the optimum maintenance dosage varies a good deal from person to person. In general, this maintenance level of plasma lithium is between 0.5

and 1.2 mEq./l., although maintenance dosage must be adjusted to each individual case in accordance with symptomatology and occurrence of adverse effects. Because of the usefulness of lithium medication as a prophylactic agent in manic-depressive disease, this medication may need to be continued for many years. As far as has been ascertained, the addition of other psychotropic drugs to lithium in the treatment of either the manic or the depressive phase may be given without producing problems of drug interaction or increasing toxicity.

(Toxicology

The Acute Effects of Excessive Dosage

The most common features associated with mild toxicity and with slightly elevated plasma lithium levels, usually over 1 mEq./l., include anorexia, gastric discomfort, diarrhea, vomiting, thirst, polyuria, and hand tremor.[45] These often coincide with serum lithium peaks. The effects may be related more to the steepness of the rise of the lithium levels than to the height of the peak. Often they disappear or diminish without reduction of dose. However, some may persist, such as polyuria and tremor. The tremor induced by lithium does not respond to antiparkinsonian medication. The polyuria may continue and give rise to a diabetes insipiduslike syndrome which usually responds on withdrawal of medication.[3] Toxic effects seen at blood levels above 1.5 mEq./l. are more serious and may include muscle fasiculation and twitching, hyperactive deep-tendon reflexes, ataxia, somnolence, confusion, dysarthria, and (rarely) epileptiform seizures. These effects are often associated with reversible electroencephalographic alterations.

There is no specific antidote for severe lithium intoxication. From the studies carried out to date, treatment should consist of general measures to correct the effects induced on water and electrolyte balance. Schou et al.[94] suggested that forced diuresis should aid significantly in the elimination of lithium.

(Chronic Effects

Chronic effects may be of considerable interest and have only recently been described. Side effects appearing with chronic ingestion of lithium include diabetes insipiduslike syndrome, elevation of blood sugar, thyroid disturbances, and elevated white blood cell counts. The occurrence of goiter in patients on lithium was first observed by Schou et al.[93] Of 330 patients on maintenance therapy from five months to two years, twelve developed diffuse, nontender thyroid enlargements while remaining clinically euthyroid. Abnormal iodine metabolism was revealed in several patients as indicated by increased tracer uptake and thyroid iodine clearance. The goiters usually disappear when lithium is discontinued or thyroid hormone is administered concurrently with lithium medication. The appearance of this side effect does not necessitate the discontinuation of lithium medication. Hyperthyroidism, with enlargement of the thyroid, has also been reported.[99,118]

Carbohydrate metabolism has been modified by lithium ingestion. Several reports, some at variance with each other, present this material.[57,115] Recent studies carried out by Shopsin et al.[104] indicate that increased blood glucose levels resulted after lithium administration in different diagnostic categories and reached statistical significance at the sixty-minute interval of the glucose tolerance test (GTT). The implications of these studies are that decreased glucose tolerance accompanying lithium administration is due to a physiological effect of lithium and is not related to psychiatric diagnosis, change in clinical state, or duration of treatment with a drug. A "consistent and striking" elevation in white blood cell count accompanying lithium administration was first reported by Mayfield and Brown.[69] Subsequently Johnson et al.,[62] Shopsin et al.,[102] and O'Connell[77] reported similar findings. Significant elevation of blood glucose occurred during periods of lithium ingestion. This phenomenon was reversible, apparently innocuous, and not related to psychiatric diagnosis or the many variables of hospitalization. While the elevations in white blood cell count appear to be due to drug effect, they are not dose-related or dependent on the concentration of lithium found in the peripheral blood.

Another special aspect of lithium toxicity has been described in several reports dealing with lithium-induced neurotoxicity. Reports of lithium-induced delirium have appeared sporadically throughout the literature since 1950. However, in a series of controlled studies on lithium by Johnson et al.[63] it was found that most of the schizo-affective patients treated with lithium carbonate showed an overall worsening of their clinical status. A significant feature of this group was the appearance of symptoms of organicity, such as disorientation, confusion, and reduced comprehension. Along with these changes, there was an increase in the severity of the basic psychopathology; thought disturbance often became more pronounced as did psychomotor excitation, delusional thought, and hallucinations. These apparent toxic effects occurred at blood levels usually not associated with severe toxic phenomena. These central effects occurred in those cases without the usual lithium effects or toxic manifestations. The most consistent laboratory abnormalities consisted of EEG changes which included alterations in the alpha activity, diffuse slowing, accentuation of previous focal abnormalities, and/or the appearance of previously absent focal changes. The occurrence of neurotoxicity corresponds, therefore, to the presence and severity of EEG changes. This drug-induced neurotoxicity will clear on cessation of lithium administration but the course of events following withdrawal is that the plasma lithium level falls first, and the clinical state and EEG follow; the latter two are related.

It is important to consider the possible teratogenic effects of lithium that might arise in considering whether the patient should be maintained on this medication if a pregnancy intervenes. There is no easy way to calculate the true incidence of lithium-induced teratology from the available literature, since no systematically randomized sample or even representative sample of births to mothers on lithium medication is available for analysis. However, a large number of perfectly normal children have been born, but some incidences of abnormalities have also been reported. Bearing in mind the possibility of potential risk, it might be wisest to suggest that women treated with lithium should not routinely be carried through a pregnancy and maintained on medication. Furthermore, it would appear even more imperative that breast feeding by lithium-treated women should not be permitted as lithium appears in the breast milk in concentrations approaching those of the mother's serum. These topics are considered more extensively in a volume by Gershon and Shopsin.[43]

⟪ Mode of Action

Although a considerable amount of work has been undertaken in order to seek the mode of action of the lithium ion in affected disorders, one must conclude that this has not yet been determined. Lithium has been shown to affect electrolytes.[15,89,101] Questions still unresolved are: which of these effects are primary in regard to its effect on behavior, and are any of them central to its effects in manic-depressive disease?

Aspects of absorption, distribution, and excretion of the lithium ion in man are of considerable significance. Before reviewing some of the studies that deal with possible alterations therein and whether they appear to be related either to clinical state or toxicity, a brief outline of its physiology will be given. Lithium is rapidly absorbed by the gastrointestinal tract. It is not protein-bound and it is distributed throughout the body water, both intra- and extra-cellularly. Lithium can be actively transported across cell membranes but cannot be pumped out of cells as efficiently as sodium.[68] Thus, tissue lithium concentration depends on at least three factors: (1) serum lithium concentration; (2) the water content of the tissues; and (3) the rates at which lithium penetrates into and is removed from intracellular fluids.

In early clinical studies the effects of lithium and other electrolytes in man were reported by Trautner et al.[112] On the first day of lithium treatment, urine flow as well as the excretion of sodium and potassium are increased. During the next few days sodium is retained. The third phase follows in which a homeostatic level is again attained. These studies have been extended by other workers using an important methodological control, the controlled diet.[7,12,14,15] The mechanisms responsible for the fluid and electrolyte changes appear independent of the glomerular filtration rate as no significant changes in creatinine clearance were noted.[13] A second mechanism that could account for some of these changes is a lithium effect on the renin, angiotensin, and aldosterone systems. Aronoff et al.[7] found urine aldosterone remarkably increased on the second day after the initiation of lithium treatment, returning toward normal on the fourth and fifth days. Long-term studies of aldosterone during lithium treatment revealed increased levels of aldosterone. These findings are consistent with increased aldosterone production seen in rats treated with lithium.[64] Murphy et al.[74] found an increase in aldosterone excretion occurring during the first week of lithium administration in man.

Trautner et al.[112] observed that the lithium dosage required for the acute manic treatment was generally higher than that tolerated by normal subjects; furthermore, once the mania subsided, the patient could no longer tolerate such high doses without showing toxic complications. The manic patients also seem to excrete less lithium at the beginning of treatment. These results suggest that lithium may be handled differently in manic patients when they are manic and when they are not manic, and differently also in normals. Thus, one may postulate that many patients retain more lithium than controls. It should also be pointed out that the capacity to retain excessive amounts of lithium may exist only in patients during the acute phase of their illness or during a major relapse of their manic-depressive disease, and appears not to be present when the disease is in remission. In another study using patients maintained on a controlled sodium intake, Greenspan et al.[51] found similar patterns of lithium retention in acutely manic patients as compared with normothymic patients. The manic patients retained greater amounts of the lithium in the manic phase than they did in a normothymic phase of the illness. Furthermore, after patients began to improve they went into a phase of negative lithium balance.[16,32,51]

The Differential Distribution of Lithium in the Body

From animal studies it has been found that lithium concentration is higher in some tissues and lower in some than in serum, but the concentration gradients across the cell wall are of the order of two to four times as great and never approach those found for either sodium or potassium. Analyses of tissues from animals given lithium for long periods of time give no indication that lithium is accumulated to any considerable amount in specific organs. This discrepancy in regard to the brain is of particular interest for a compound that primarily effects mood and behavior.[90] In studies of the cerebrospinal fluid (CSF) from patients to whom lithium was administered for a long time, it was shown that the CSF level of lithium is indefinitely maintained at approximately 50 percent of the plasma level, even under toxic conditions.[45]

Studies carried out in rats indicate that with lithium administration for twenty-eight days, the total brain lithium level is of the order of about 50 percent of that of the plasma.[58] The relationship among lithium, sodium, and potassium in plasma and human saliva has been studied. Following oral administration of lithium carbonate, lithium was found in the serum and saliva of all patients within an hour of its ingestion. The data indicate that lithium is present in the saliva at concentrations of approximately twice its serum level.[102] These effects of lithium on fluid and electrolytes may be related to lithium's mechanism of action in psychiatric disturbances. The inability of lithium to substitute for sodium in functional renal transport systems might parallel its action in the central nervous system (CNS).

Accordingly, replacement of electrolytes by lithium in cells and its inefficient pumping out of cells could alter electrical transmission. Lithium has altered the cortical potential in man and the electroencephalogram.[39] The recent demonstrations of interactions between electrolyte metabolism and catecholamine metabolism further emphasize the importance of the findings of altered electrolyte metabolism during lithium treatment.[21]

The other major area of biochemical interest concerning affective disorders deals with catecholamine metabolism, and this work is essential in consideration of the possible mode of action of lithium. These catecholamine data imply a bipolarity in which depression and mania represent related but opposite states; the former is associated with decreased and the latter with increased functional norepinephrine at central adrenergic nerve receptors. This bipolar theoretical framework cannot easily be invoked with lithium because it appears to exert a similar prophylactic effect in both mania and depression. Moreover, it becomes more difficult to reconcile this hypothesis with the report that lithium is effective in the treatment of mania and may also be effective in the treatment of a current manifest depressive episode.

Schildkraut et al.[89] investigated the effects of lithium on the fate of intracisternally injected ^{3}H-norepinephrine. In rats they administered lithium at 50 mg./kg., one, two, and three hours after the injection and found an increase in the level of ^{3}H-deaminated catechols, a small decrease in ^{3}H-normetanephrine, and a nonsignificant increase in ^{3}H-O-methylated deaminated metabolites.[87] In a subsequent experiment Schildkraut et al.[89] reported that there was a nonsignificant decrease in ^{3}H-normetanephrine and a significant but small decrease in ^{3}H-norepinephrine. Lithium chloride, 2.4 mEq./kg., was given intraperitoneal (i.p.) twice daily for a week at two periods, just after the injection of ^{3}H-norepinephrine and 150 minutes later. In the former, there was a non-insignificant decrease in ^{3}H- and endogenous norepinephrine. In the latter time period, there was a decrease in the levels of tritiated norepinephrine, normetanephrine, and total deaminated O-methylated metabolites. Stern et al.[110] studied the effect of lithium at 3.75 mg./kg. on norepinephrine turnover in rat brain and found that there was almost a 95 percent increase in brain norepinephrine turnover without altering the steady-state levels of norepinephrine in the brain. Corrodi et al.[28] showed that the administration of lithium to rats in single doses does not change the tissue levels of norepinephrine, dopamine, or serotonin. Sedvall[96] was not able to show any difference in norepinephrine and dopamine turnover in brain. Greenspan et al.[49] gave lithium for ten days in doses up to 3 mEq./kg. and found that the lithium more than doubled the influx of ^{3}H-norepinephrine from the brain. Coburn et al.[25] isolated nerve-ending particles from controlled rats pretreated with lithium and found that the rate of net uptake of norepinephrine into the neuron was increased, a finding confirmed by Kuriyama and Speken,[65] and Baldessarini and Yorke.[17] This increase in net uptake was also presented in nerve-ending particles treated with reserpine, even though the reserpine inhibited storage of norepinephrine.[25]

Ho et al.[58] gave lithium chloride 2 mEq./kg.-i.p. daily for twenty-eight days to rats. In the lithium-treated rats, the content of 5-HT in the hypothalamus and brain stem showed a significant reduction of 46 and 26 percent, respectively, as compared with the controls. Tissue concentration of both dopamine and norepinephrine showed no significant change in each of the brain areas studied. In the lithium-treated rats, values obtained for the rate of synthesis using whole brain homogenate were 0.37 µg./g. per hour, compared with the control value of 0.42 µg./g. per hour. This change was not significant. However, in another series of experiments in which the effect was examined on discrete brain areas this change was significant. There was an increase of 37 percent in the cerebellum, but decreases were found in all other areas with the highest reduction of 57.5 percent in the hypothalamus. Findings of Corrodi et al.[28] are in accord with the above data and tend to support the importance of both regional studies and chronic administration to assess psychotropic drug effects. Corrodi et al.[28] found that 5-HT and 5-HIAA levels were higher in lithium-treated animals than in controls.

In clinical studies, Haskovec and Rysanek[56] examined the effects of lithium on catecholamine metabolism in human subjects. After three control days, lithium carbonate, 900–1200 mg./day was administered to ten non-psychotic patients for five days. The increase in vanillyl mandelic acid (VMA) excretion in urine was statistically significant during the first ten days of the treatment with lithium carbonate but not on the subsequent two days. Significant decreases in the excretion of normetanephrine and metanephrine occurred on the fourth and fifth days of treatment with lithium carbonate but not on the first three days.

Greenspan et al.[50] observed statistically significant decreases in the excretion of normetanephrine and metanephrine in manic-depressive patients undergoing treatment with lithium carbonate. However, one cannot exclude the possibility that these biochemical effects measured in the urine were peripheral and secondary to changes in clinical state. Wilk et al.[119] reported that levels of 3-methoxy-4-hydroxyphenylglycol (MHPG) present in the CSF were increased in the small group of manic patients compared with controls. A pronounced decrease in MHPG was subsequently observed in two patients when the mania had subsided during treatment with lithium carbonate. A moderate increase in levels of homovanillic acid deaminated-O-methylated metabolite of dopamine in the CSF was concurrently observed in these two patients during treatment with lithium. Bowers et al.[22] examined levels of homovanillic acid (HVA) in the CSF in four manic patients before and after treatment with lithium. A nonsignificant decrease of HVA in the CSF was observed during the administration of lithium. Messiha et al.[73] studied the urinary excretion of dopamine which was found to be higher prior to lithium carbonate administration in the manic group than in controls, but decreased during treatment with lithium. The urinary excretion of dopamine which was not different from that of controls prior to the administration of lithium in the depressed group was not changed significantly following treatment with lithium carbonate. These findings with regard to the effects of lithium on catecholamine metabolism have been replicated in most cases and therefore are effects of lithium on these amines. However, these findings do not add up to a coherent story of how lithium produces its therapeutic effects in manic-depressive disease.

Recently, certain studies exploring the relationship of cyclic AMP (adenosine monophosphate) to affective disorders as well as to the effects of medication have been reported. Other studies have correlated urinary levels of cyclic AMP with the clinical status of patients in affective disorders.[1,78] Depressives showed low twenty-four-hour urine levels of cyclic AMP while manic patients had high levels. In addition, Abdulla and Hamadah[1] have shown that clinical improvement of the depression and mania resulted in a change toward normal levels of urinary cyclic AMP. However, Paul et al.[78] found that the urinary output in the manic group was significantly higher than the outputs of the control and depressed groups, and it was calculated that in the manic the twenty-four-hour urinary cyclic AMP level was not significantly higher than normal values. Some investigators have suggested that the alteration in urinary cyclic AMP levels observed in patients during the different states of affective illness may be related to their physical activity rather than being a reflection of their mood.[18,86] Furthermore, it is far from clear whether the urinary levels of cyclic AMP are in any way indicative of the levels of the nucleotide in the CNS, since it is highly insoluble in lipids and will not cross cell membranes. Furthermore, Robison et al.[86] have measured cyclic AMP levels in the cerebrospinal fluid of patients in affective disorders in an attempt to obtain direct information on the origin of cyclic AMP in affective disorders. These investigators have found that CSF levels of cyclic AMP in depressive and manic patients do not differ from those measured in neurological and epileptic patients. These data, therefore, support a peripheral source of the urinary cyclic AMP. Paul et al.[78] studied the effect of lithium treatment on cyclic AMP excretion in a small population of manic-depressive patients. They reported that a clinical response to lithium was associated with a decrease in cyclic AMP in the urine of manic patients, and an increase in urinary levels in the depressed patients. These authors suggested that the changes in urinary cyclic AMP are secondary to the clinical state rather than a direct effect of the lithium ion. However, the studies in various animal species indicate a direct effect of lithium on the cyclic AMP-synthesizing enzyme, adenyl cyclase.[29,36]

Again, we note some interesting effects of lithium, but as yet its effects and its possible relationship to mode of action or clinical state are unclear. Thus, the intensive studies on the mode of action of lithium still do not provide an explanation of lithium's mode of action in the treatment of manic-depressive disease.

([Conclusion

Lithium was introduced into psychiatry as the first psychoactive drug in this era of psychopharmacology. Its proposed indication at that time was acute mania. At its introduction it was condemned as dangerous. Now, after more than twenty years, it is often reported as a panacea for many forms of mental illness, and a clearer and more specific definition of its role in treatment must be found. The controlled studies that have been carried out since its introduction, on the whole, tend to support the claim that it is an effective agent in the treatment of mania. From studies of lithium against a placebo control group, it would appear that lithium is clearly significantly superior to placebo in the treatment of mania.

The second comparative issue, the relative effects of lithium vs. another established neuroleptic, is not clearly resolved. Some of the smaller controlled studies suggest a qualitative superiority of lithium over chlorpromazine in regard to its effects on the psychopathology of the manic disorder, in that lithium, within a two-week period, affects more of the ideational components than does chlorpromazine whereas chlorpromazine has a faster, more rapid onset of activity in controlling the psychomotor overactivity of disturbed manic patients. Claimed efficacy in the published studies of lithium in the treatment of mania ranges from 60 to 100 percent. It would appear from some of the genetic studies that the therapeutic activity of lithium increases in those cases that have a bipolar affective disorder and, further, in those cases with a family history of this condition.

In regard to prophylactic studies, it would appear from the early longitudinal studies that lithium exerted its therapeutic activity against recurrent episodes of both mania and depression. Two of the controlled studies using different designs tend again to support the higher therapeutic efficacy for lithium in the prophylaxis of both mania and depression than for placebo groups. Although this is borne out in the larger NIMH-VA study, the order of activity is not as marked as in the earlier studies. The bulk of the evidence from all sources would tend to indicate that lithium maintenance does have a useful prophylactic effect. Some studies use the term "prophylactic" to suggest prevention of the manifestations of a subsequent manic or depressive episode, while others, including this reviewer, mean only that it affects the amplitude of the cycles and does not clearly modify the inherent cyclic nature of the disorder. This requires an increase in maintenance dose to diminish further the incipient hypomanic manifestations and to cut the episode short. This action is considered capable of preventing the need for further hospitalization, and to this extent the word "prophylactic" might be fairly applicable although other words, such as "stabilization," might be more acceptable.

In the handling of depressive recurrences, the best method of treatment is not resolved. The alternates that are open for consideration are either the maintenance of lithium together with the addition of an effective antidepressant agent, or the increase of lithium dosage at the time of the appearance of depressive symptomatology. In regard to the effect of lithium in a current manifest depressive epi-

sode, no final conclusions can be reached from the data available to date. The claimed effects of lithium in other psychiatric disorders have not been clearly resolved but the areas of considerable interest are its use in premenstrual syndrome and its action on aggressive behavior.

The clinical reports on lithium have prompted many studies on its mode of action. It clearly affects water and electrolyte balance. Effects on hormones have also been documented and there is a possibility that these effects are secondary to the initial electrolyte shifts. It has also been clearly documented that the lithium ion effects monoamine metabolism. The questions that are unresolved are whether these changes are primary or secondary to the electrolyte changes and whether they may vary over time as the electrolyte changes do. Furthermore, even though these changes on amines do occur, no final resolution is yet available as to their effects on behavior. The matter is made more complicated because of the many reservations that must, of necessity, apply to the interpretation of data from studies of animals and isolated tissues. Thus no satisfactory explanation of the mode of action of lithium in the treatment of affective disorders has emerged from the studies to date. Therefore, the possibility of using lithium ion as a research tool to explore the etiology of manic-depressive disease is perhaps the most exciting aspect of its introduction into psychopharmacology.

(Bibliography

1. ABDULLA, Y. and K. HAMADAH. "3'5' Cyclic Adenosine Monophosphate in Depression and Mania," *Lancet*, 1 (1970), 378–381.
2. ANDREANI, G., G. CASELLI, and G. MARTELLI. "Rilieri Clinici ed Electroencefalografici Durante il Trattamento con Sali di Litio in Malati Psichiatrici," *Gen. Psychiatr. Neuropathol.*, 86 (1958), 273–328.
3. ANGRIST, B., S. GERSHON, S. LEVITAN et al. "Lithium-Induced Diabetes Insipidus-like Syndrome," *Compr. Psychiatry*, 11 (1970), 141–146.

4. ANGST, J. "Die Lithium Prophylaxe Affektiver Psychosen," *Ars Medici*, 60 (1970), 29–40.

5. ANGST, J., P. WEIS, P. GROF, et al. "Lithium Prophylaxis in Recurrent Affective Disorders," *Brit. J. Psychiatry*, 116 (1970), 599–619.

6. ARFWEDSON, A. "Undersokning af Nagra vid Uto Jernmalmsbrott Forekommande Fossilier, och af ett deri Funnet eget Eldfast Alkali, Afhandl," *Fysik, Kemi, Mineral*, 6 (1818), 145–176.

7. ARONOFF, M., R. EVANS, and J. DURELL. "Effect of Lithium Salts on Electrolyte Metabolism," *J. Psychiatr. Res.*, 8 (1971), 139–159.

8. BAASTRUP, P. "The Use of Lithium in Manic Depressive Psychosis," *Compr. Psychiatry*, 5 (1964), 396–408.

9. ———. "Practical Clinical Viewpoints Regarding Treatment with Lithium," *Acta Psychiatr. Scand. (Suppl.)*, 207 (1969), 12–18.

10. BAASTRUP, P., A. AMDISEN, J. POULSEN et al. "A Prophylactic Lithium—Double-Blind Discontinuation in Manic and Recurrent Depressive Disorders," *Lancet*, 2 (1970), 7668.

11. BAASTRUP, P. and M. SCHOU. "Lithium as a Prophylactic Agent: Its Effect Against Recurrent Depressions and Manic Depressive Psychosis," *Arch. Gen. Psychiatry*, 16 (1967), 162–172.

12. BAER, L., J. DURELL, E. W. BUNNEY, JR. et al. "Sodium²² Retention and 17-Hydroxycorticosteroid Excretion in Affective Disorders," *J. Psychiatr. Res.*, 6 (1969), 289–297.

13. BAER, L., S. KASSIR, and R. FIEVE. "Lithium-Induced Changes in Electrolyte Balance and Tissue Electrolyte Concentration," *Psychopharmacologia*, 17 (1970), 216–224.

14. BAER, L., S. PLATMAN, and R. FIEVE. "The Role of Electrolytes in Affective Disorders: Sodium, Potassium and Lithium," Paper presented 50th Annu. Meet. Am. Coll. Physicians, Chicago: April, 1969.

15. BAER, L., S. PLATMAN, and S. KASSIR. "Mechanisms of Renal Lithium Handling and Their Relationship to Mineralocorticoids: A Dissociation between Sodium and Lithium Ions," *J. Psychiatr. Res.*, 9 (1971), 91–105.

16. BAKER, M. and G. WINOKUR. "Cerebrospinal Fluid Lithium in Manic Illness," *Br. J. Psychiatry*, 112 (1966), 163–165.

17. BALDESSARINI, R. and G. YORKE. "Effects of Lithium and of pH on Synaptosomal Metabolism of Noradrenaline," *Nature*, 228 (1970), 1301.

18. BERG, G. and W. GLINSMAN. "Cyclic AMP in Depression and Mania," *Lancet*, (1970), 834.

19. BLACKWELL, B. "Lithium," *Lancet*, 2 (1970), 875.

20. BLACKWELL, B. and M. SHEPARD. "Prophylactic Lithium: Another Therapeutic Myth? An Examination of the Evidence to Date," *Lancet*, 1 (1968), 968–971.

21. BOGDANSKY, D. and B. BRODIE. "Role of Sodium and Potassium Ions in Storage of Norepinephrine by Sympathetic Nerve Endings," *Life Sci.*, 5 (1966), 1563–1569.

22. BOWERS, M., JR., G. HENINGER, and F. GERBODE. "Cerebrospinal Fluid 5-Hydroxyindoleacetic Acid and Homovanillic Acid in Psychiatric Patients," *Int. J. Neuropharmacol.*, 8 (1969), 255.

23. BUNNEY, W. E., JR., F. GOODWIN, J. DAVIS et al. "A Behavioral-Biochemical Study of Lithium," *Am. J. Psychiatry*, 125 (1968), 499–512.

24. CADE, J. F. J. "Lithium Salts in the Treatment of Psychotic Excitement," *Med. J. Aust.*, 36 (1949), 349–352.

25. COBURN, R. F. GOODWIN, E. W. BUNNEY, JR. et al. "Effect of Lithium on the Uptake of Noradrenaline by Synaptosomes," *Nature*, 215 (1967), 1395–1397.

26. COPPEN, A., R. NOGUERA, J. BAILEY et al. "Prophylactic Lithium in Affective Disorders," *Lancet*, (1971), 275–279.

27. CORCORAN, A. C., R. D. TAYLOR, and I. H. PAGE. "Lithium Poisoning from the Use of Salt Substitutes," *JAMA*, 139 (1949), 685–688.

28. CORRODI, H., K. FUXE, and M. SCHOU. "The Effect of Prolonged Lithium Administration on Cerebral Monoamine Neurons in the Rat," *Life Sci.*, 8 (1969), 643–651.

29. DOUSA, T. and O. HECHTER. "Lithium and Brain Adenyl Cyclase," *Lancet*, 1 (1970), 834–835.

30. DYSON, W. L. and A. BARCAI. "Treatment of Children of Lithium-Responding Parents," *Curr. Ther. Res.*, 12 (1970), 286–290.

31. DYSON, W. L. and J. MENDELS. "Lithium

and Depression," *Curr. Ther. Res.*, 10 (1968), 601–608.

32. EPSTEIN, R., L. GRANT, M. HERJANIC et al. "Urinary Excretion of Lithium in Mania," *JAMA*, 192 (1965), 409.

33. EVANS, R. and J. DURRELL. "Effect of Lithium Salts on Electrolyte Metabolism," *J. Psychiatr. Res.*, 8 (1971), 139–159.

34. FIEVE, R., S. PLATMAN, and R. PLUTCHIK. "The Use of Lithium in Affective Disorders: I. Acute Endogenous Depression," *Am. J. Psychiatry*, 125 (1968), 487–491.

35. ———. "The Use of Lithium in Affective Disorders: II. Prophylaxis of Depression in Chronic Recurrent Affective Disorder," *Am. J. Psychiatry*, 125 (1968), 492–498.

36. FORN, J. and F. VALDECASAS. "Effects of Lithium on Brain Adenyl Cyclase Activity," *Biochem. Pharmacol.*, 20 (1971), 2773–2779.

37. FORSSMAN, H. and J. WALINDER. "Lithium Treatment on Atypical Indication," *Acta Psychiatr. Scand. (Suppl.)*, 207 (1969), 34–40.

38. FROMMER, E. "Depressive Illness in Childhood," *Br. J. Psychiatry, Spec. Pub.*, 2 (1968), 117–136.

39. GARTSIDE, I., O. LIPPOLD, and B. MELDRUM. "The Evoked Cortical Somatosensory Response in Normal Man and Its Modification by Oral Lithium Carbonate," *Electroencephalogr. Clin. Neurophysiol.*, 20 (1966), 382–390.

40. GERSHON, S. "Lithium in Mania," *Clin. Pharmacol. Ther.*, 2 (1970), 168–187.

41. ———. *Methodology of Psychiatric Drug Evaluation*, HEW Public Health Serv. Publ., no. 2138. Washington: U.S. Govt. Print. Off., 1971.

42. ———. "Lithium Salts in the Management of the Manic-Depressive Syndrome," *Ann. Rev. Med.*, 23 (1972), 439–452.

43. GERSHON, S. and B. SHOPSIN. *Lithium Ion, Its Role in Psychiatric Treatment and Research.* New York: Plenum, 1973.

44. GERSHON, S. and E. TRAUTNER. "The Treatment of Shock-Dependency by Pharmacological Agents," *Med. J. Aust.*, 43 (1956), 783–787.

45. GERSHON, S. and A. YUWILER. "Lithium Ion: A Specific Psychopharmacological Approach to the Treatment of Mania," *J. Neuropsychiatry*, 1 (1960), 229–241.

46. GOODWIN, F., D. MURPHY, and E. W. BUNNEY, JR. "Lithium Carbonate Treatment in Depression and Mania," *Arch. Gen. Psychiatry*, 21 (1969), 486–496.

47. GOODWIN, F., D. MURPHY, D. DUNNER et al. "Lithium Response in Unipolar vs. Bipolar Depression," *Am. J. Psychiatry*, 129 (1972), 44–47.

48. GOTTFRIES, C. "The Effect of Lithium Salts on Various Kinds of Psychiatric Disorders," *Acta Psychiatr. Scand. (Suppl.)*, 44 (1968), 199–204.

49. GREENSPAN, K., M. ARONOFF, and D. BOGDANSKY. "Effect of Lithium Carbonate on Turnover and Metabolism of Norepinephrine in the Rat Brain," *Pharmacology*, 3 (1970), 129–136.

50. GREENSPAN, K., F. GOODWIN, and E. W. BUNNEY, JR. "Lithium Retention and Distribution: Patterns during Acute Mania and Normothymia," *Arch. Gen. Psychiatry*, 19 (1968), 664–673.

51. GREENSPAN, K., R. GREEN, and J. DURELL. "Lithium: Pharmacological Tool in Studying the Pathophysiology of Manic-Depressive Psychosis: Retention and Distribution Patterns," *Am. J. Psychiatry*, 125 (1968), 512–519.

52. GROF, P., P. CAKULS, and T. DOSTAL. "Lithium Drop-Outs—A Follow-Up Study of Patients who Discontinued Prophylactic Treatment," *Int. Pharmacopsychiatry*, 5 (1970), 162–169.

53. GROF, P., M. SCHOU, J. ANGST et al. "Methodological Problems of Prophylactic Trials in Recurrent Affective Disorders," *Brit. J. Psychiatry*, 116 (1970), 599–619.

54. HANSEN, C., W. RETBULL, and M. SCHOU. Unpublished data, quoted by M. Schou, in "Lithium in Psychiatric Therapy and Prophylaxis," *J. Psychiatr. Res.*, 6 (1968), 67–95.

55. HARTIGAN, G. "The Use of Lithium Salts in Affective Disorders," *Br. J. Psychiatry*, 109 (1963), 810–814.

56. HASKOVEC, L. and K. RYSANEK. "Die Wirkung von Lithium auf den Metabolismus der Katecholamine und Indoalkylamine beim Menschen," *Arzneim. Forsch.*, 19 (1969), 426–427.

57. HENINGER, C. and P. MUELLER. "Carbohydrate Metabolism in Mania: Before and after Lithium Treatment," *Arch. Gen. Psychiatry*, 23 (1970), 310–319.

58. HO, A., H. LOH, I. CRAVES et al. "The Effect of Prolonged Lithium Treatment on the

Synthesis, Rate, and Turnover of Mono-amines in Brain Regions of Rats," *Eur. J. Pharmacol.*, 10 (1970), 72–78.

59. HULLEN, R., R. McDONALD, and M. ALL-SOPP. "Prophylactic Lithium in Recurrent Affective Disorders," *Lancet*, 1 (1972), 1044–1046.

60. JACOBSEN, J. "Hypomanic Alert; Program Designed for Greater Therapeutic Control," *Am. J. Psychiatry*, 122 (1965), 295–299.

61. JOHNSON, G., S. GERSHON, E. BURDOCK et al. "Comparative Effects of Lithium and Chlorpromazine Treatment of Acute Manic States," *Br. J. Psychiatry*, 119 (1971), 267–276.

62. JOHNSON, G., S. GERSHON, and L. HEKIMIAN. "Controlled Evaluation of Lithium and Chlorpromazine in the Treatment of Manic States: An Interim Report," *Compr. Psychiatry*, 9 (1968), 563–573.

63. JOHNSON, G., M. MACCARIO, S. GERSHON et al. "The Effects of Lithium on Electroencephalogram Behavior and Serum Electrolytes," *J. Nerv. Ment. Dis.*, 151 (1970), 273–289.

64. KRULIK, R. "Effect of Lithium on Aldosterone Production by Rat Adrenals," *Arzneim.-Forsch.*, 6 (1971), 889–890.

65. KURIYAMA, K. and R. SPEKEN. "Effect of Lithium on Content and Uptake of Norepinephrine and 5-Hydroxytryptamine in Mouse Brain Synaptosomes and Mitochondria," *Life Sci.*, 9 (1970), 1213–1220.

66. LACKROY, G. and H. VAN PRAAG. "Lithium Salts as Sedatives," *Acta Psychiatr. Scand.*, 47 (1971), 163–173.

67. MAGGS, R. "Treatment of Manic Illness with Lithium Carbonate," *Br. J. Psychiatry*, 109 (1963), 56–65.

68. MAIZELS, M. "Cation Transfer in Human Red Cells," in A. Kleinzeller and A. Kutyk, eds., *Membrane Transport and Metabolism.* New York: Academic, 1961.

69. MAYFIELD, D. and R. BROWN. "The Clinical Laboratory and Electroencephalographic Effects of Lithium," *J. Psychiatr. Res.*, 4 (1966), 207–219.

70. MELIA, P. "Prophylactic Lithium: A Double-Blind Trial in Recurrent Affective Disorders," *Br. J. Psychiatry*, 116 (1970), 621–624.

71. MENDELEWICZ, J., R. FIEVE, F. STALLONE et al. "Greater History of a Prediction of Lithium Response in Manic-Depressive Illness," *Lancet*, 2 (1972), 599–600.

72. MENDELS, J., S. SECUNDA, and W. DYSON. "A Controlled Study of the Antidepressant Effects of Lithium," *Arch. Gen. Psychiatry*, 26 (1972), 154–157.

73. MESSIHA, F., D. AGALLIANOS, and C. CLOWER. "Dopamine Excretion in Affective States and Following Li_2CO_3 Therapy," *Nature*, 225 (1970), 868–869.

74. MURPHY, D., F. GOODWIN, and E. W. BUNNEY, JR. "Aldosterone and Sodium Response to Lithium Administration in Man" *Lancet*, 2 (1969), 458–461.

75. NAHUNEK, K., J. SVESTKA, and A. RODOVA. "Zur Stellung des Lithiums in der Gruppe der Antidepressiva in der Behandlung von akuten Endogener und Involutions-depressionen," *Int. Pharmacopsychiatry*, 5 (1970), 249–257.

76. NOACK, C. and E. TRAUTNER. "The Lithium Treatment of Maniacal Psychosis," *Med. J. Aust.*, 2 (1951), 219–222.

77. O'CONNELL, R. "Leukocytosis during Lithium Carbonate Therapy," *Int. Pharmacopsychiatry*, 4 (1970), 30–34.

78. PAUL, M., B. DITZION, G. PAUK. et al. "Urinary Adenosine 3',5'-Monophosphate Excretion in Affective Disorders," *Am. J. Psychiatry*, 126 (1970), 1493–1497.

79. PENROSE, L. S. "Distance, Size and Shape," *Ann. Eug.*, 18 (1954), 337–343.

80. PLATMAN, S. "A Comparison of Lithium Carbonate and Chlorpromazine in Mania," *Am. J. Psychiatry*, 127 (1970), 351–353.

81. ———. "Comparison of Lithium Carbonate and Imipramine in Prevention of Manic-Depressive Disease," *Dis. Nerv. Syst.*, 31 (1970), 132–134.

82. PRIEN, R., E. CAFFEY, and C. KLETT. A *Comparison of Lithium Carbonate and Chlorpromazine in the Treatment of Mania.* Cooperative Studies in Psychiatry, Prepub. Rep. 86. Perry Point, Md.: Central Neuropsychiatric Research Lab., 1971.

83. ———. "Comparison of Lithium and Chlorpromazine in the Treatment of Mania," *Arch. Gen. Psychiatry*, 26 (1972), 146–153.

84. ———. *Prophylactic Efficacy of Lithium Carbonate in Manic-Depressive Illness.* Report of the VA and NIMH Collaborative Study Group. Perry Point, Md.: Central Neuropsychiatric Research Lab., 1972.

85. RIFKIN, A., F. QUITKIN, C. CARRILLO et al. "Lithium in Emotionally Unstable Charac-

ter Disorder," *Arch. Gen. Psychiatry*, 27 (1972), 519–523.

86. ROBISON, G., A. COPPEN, P. WHYBROW et al. "Cyclic AMP in Affective Disorders," *Lancet*, 2 (1970), 1028–1029.

87. SCHANBERG, S., J. SCHILDKRAUT, and I. KOPIN. "The Effects of Psychoactive Drugs on Norepinephrine Metabolism in the Brain," *Biochem. Pharmacol.*, 16 (1967), 393–399.

88. SCHILDKRAUT, J., M. LOGUE, and G. DODGE. "Effects of Lithium Salts on Turnover and Metabolism of Norepinephrine," *Psychopharmacologia*, 14 (1969), 135–141.

89. SCHILDKRAUT, J., S. SCHANBERG, and I. KOPIN. "The Effects of Lithium Ion on H³ Norepinephrine Metabolism in Brain," *Life Sci.*, 5 (1966), 1479–1483.

90. SCHOU, M. "Lithium Studies. 3: Distribution between Serum and Tissues. *Acta Pharmacol. Toxicol.*, 15 (1958), 115–124.

91. ———. "Lithium in Psychiatric Therapy and Prophylaxis," *J. Psychiatr. Res.*, 6 (1968), 67–95.

92. ———. "Lithium in Psychiatry—A Review," in D. H. Efron, ed., *Psychopharmacology: A Review of Progress 1957–1967*, pp. 701–718. Am. College of Neuropsychopharmacology. Washington: U.S. Govt. Print. Off., 1968.

93. SCHOU, M., A. AMDISEN, S. JENSEN et al. "Occurrence of Goitre during Lithium Treatment," *Br. Med. J.*, 3 (1968), 710–713.

94. SCHOU, M., P. BAASTRUP, P. GROF et al. "Pharmacological and Clinical Problems of Lithium Prophylaxis," *Br. J. Psychiatry*, 116 (1970), 615–619.

95. SCHOU, M., N. JUEL-NIELSEN, F. STROMGREN et al. "The Treatment of Manic Psychoses by the Administration of Lithium Salts," *J. Neurol. Neurosurg. Psychiatry*, 17 (1954), 250–260.

96. SEDVALL, G. "Discussion," *Acta Psychiatr. Scand.* (Suppl.) 207 (1969), 57.

97. SHEARD, M. "Effect of Lithium on Human Aggression," *Nature*, 230 (1971), 113–114.

98. SHEARD, M. and G. AGHAJANIAN. "Neuronally Activated Metabolism of Brain Serotonin: Effect of Lithium," *Life Sci.*, 9 (1970), 285–290.

99. SHOPSIN, B., M. BLUM, and S. GERSHON. "Lithium-Induced Thyroid Disturbance: Case Report and Review," *Compr. Psychiatry*, 10 (1969), 215–223.

100. SHOPSIN, B., R. FRIEDMANN, and S. GERSHON. "Lithium and Leukocytosis," *Clin. Pharmacol. Ther.*, 12 (1971), 923–928.

101. SHOPSIN, B., S. GERSHON, and L. PINCKNEY. "The Secretion of Lithium in Human Mixed Saliva: Effects of Ingested Lithium on Electrolyte Distribution in Saliva and Serum," *Int. Pharmacopsychiatry*, 2 (1969), 148–169.

102. SHOPSIN, B., G. JOHNSON, and S. GERSHON. "Neurotoxicity with Lithium: Differential Drug Responsiveness," *Int. Pharmacopsychiatry*, 5 (1970), 170–182.

103. SHOPSIN, B., S. KIM, and S. GERSHON. "A Controlled Study of Lithium vs. Chlorpromazine in Acute Schizophrenics," *Br. J. Psychiatry*, 119 (1971), 435–440.

104. SHOPSIN, B., S. STERN, and S. GERSHON. "Altered Carbohydrate Metabolism during Lithium Treatment in Hospitalized Psychiatric Patients: Absence of Diagnostic Specificity," *Arch. Gen. Psychiatry*, 26 (1972), 566–571.

105. SHULL, W. and J. SAPIRA. "Critique of Studies of Lithium Salts in the Treatment of Mania," *Am. J. Psychiatry*, 127 (1970), 136–140.

106. SLETTEN, I. and S. GERSHON. "The Premenstrual Syndrome: A Discussion of Its Pathophysiology and Treatment with Lithium Ion," *Compr. Psychiatry*, 7 (1966), 197–206.

107. SPITZER, R., J. ENDICOTT, and J. FLICH. "Instrumental Recording Times for Evaluating Psychiatric States and History; Rational Method of Development and Description," *Compr. Psychiatry*, 8 (1967), 321–343.

108. SPRING, G., D. SCHUCID, C. GRAY et al. "A Double-Blind Comparison of Lithium and CPZ in the Treatment of Manic States," *Am. J. Psychiatry*, 126 (1970), 1306–1309.

109. STANCER, H., W. FURLONG, and D. GADAZ. "A Longitudinal Investigation of Lithium as a Prophylactic Agent for Recurrent Depressions," *Canad. Psychiatr. Assoc. J.*, 75 (1970), 29–40.

110. STERN, D., R. FIEVE, N. NEFF et al. "The Effect of Lithium Chloride Administration on Brain and Heart Norepinephrine Turnover Rates," *Psychopharmacologia*, 14 (1969), 315–322.

111. STOKES, P., B. SHAMOIAN, P. STOLL et al. "Efficacy of Lithium as Acute Treatment

of Manic Depressive Illness," *Lancet*, 1 (1971), 1319–1325.

112. TRAUTNER, E., R. MORRIS, C. NOACK et al. "The Excretion and Retention of Ingested Lithium and Its Effect on the Ionic Balance of Man," *Med. J. Aust.*, 2 (1955), 280–291.

113. VAN DER VELDE, C. "Effectiveness of Lithium Carbonate in the Treatment of Manic-Depressive Illness," *Am. J. Psychiatry*, 127 (1970), 345–351.

114. ———. "Toxicity of Lithium Carbonate in Elderly Patients," *Am. J. Psychiatry*, 127 (1971), 1075–1077.

115. VAN DER VELDE, C. and M. GORDON. "Manic-Depressive Illness, Diabetes Melli-

tus and Lithium Carbonate," *Arch. Gen. Psychiatry*, 21 (1969), 478–486.

116. VOJTECHOVSKY, M. "Zkusenosti s lecbou Solemi Lithia," in *Problem y Psychiatrie v Praxi a ve Vyskumu*. Praha, 1957.

117. WHITEHEAD, P. and L. CLARK. "Effect of Lithium Carbonate, Placebo and Thioridazine on Hyperactive Children," *Am. J. Psychiatry*, 127 (1970), 824–825.

118. WIGGERS, A. "Lithiumpavirkning af Glandela Thyreoidea?" *Ugeskr. Laeger*, 130 (1968), 1523–1524.

119. WILK, S., B. SHOPSIN, S. GERSHON et al. "Cerebrospinal Fluid Levels of MHPG in Affective Disorders," *Nature*, 235 (1972), 440.

CHAPTER 25

RESTITUTIVE THERAPIES

Arnold M. Ludwig and Frida G. Surawicz

RESTITUTIVE THERAPIES encompass the variety of techniques used to produce altered states of consciousness (ASC) in patients for therapeutic purposes. For some of these techniques, healing or curative powers are attributed to the experience per se of the ASC (e.g., mystical, peak, or transcendental states, postanesthetic amnestic states, etc.); for other techniques, the production of the ASC purportedly renders the mind susceptible to specific psychological maneuvers on the part of the therapist (e.g., narcoanalysis, narcosynthesis, abreaction, etc.). In general, these therapies, which aim toward reintegration of the personality, the controlled release of inhibitions, relief of nuclear conflicts, and renewed hope, are applied over a relatively short-time span, covering one to twenty sessions. While these ASCs can be evoked by a variety of means,[44] this chapter will be limited solely to those techniques utilizing pharmacological agents.

⟦ History

Restitutive therapies have been an important tool in medicine from antiquity to the present.

Primitive man knew that sickness could be influenced by suggestion. Since mental disease as such was not acknowledged but was attributed to spirit influences or demoniacal possession, the treatment, of necessity, fell into the hands of priests and shamans. In the times before Hippocrates, treatment for the mentally sick took place in Aesculapian temples, starting with impressive religious ceremonies during which suggestions of healing were monotonously repeated. The patients were encouraged to dream of healing miracles and, depending upon the dream content, different drugs concocted from herbs were used. Not all patients were accepted and some patients were chased away with stones: however, the selection criteria are irretrievably buried in the vaults of time.[43,77] In the reign of Augustus, Celsus, a Roman with encyclopedic medical knowledge, described the use of total darkness as well as drugs for the treatment of mental disease. Among the drugs used were purgatives, like black hellebore, sedatives derived from poppies and henbane, emetics (white hellebore) and enemas. Excessive bloodletting to the point of fainting has also been an honored practice in the treatment of mental disease. Followers of Asclepiades prescribed large doses of alcohol and sexual exercises for mental patients.[77]

Alcohol

This is probably the oldest drug used by man for social, religious, and medical purposes. References to the use of wine have been discovered in Babylon and Egypt.[42] Vines were seen as godly plants and the juice of the grape was equated with divine blood. The priest drank in order to establish a closer relationship with the gods, especially Osiris, the wine god. The Hebrews also drank for religious and medical purposes. The *Book of Proverbs* states "Give strong drink unto him that is ready to perish and wine unto those that be of heavy hearts, let him drink and forget his poverty and remember his misery no more." In ancient Greece, wine was used generously for religious, festive, and social occasions, including the symposium.[7] The Greeks drank wine to seek communion with Dionysus. The religious and social use of alcohol found its way to Rome, where wine was used for libation and religious ceremonies devoted to Bacchus, which often deteriorated into orgies. The rise of Christianity put a stop to the excessive use of alcohol for religious purposes. However, it remained as a therapeutic drug. In the thirteenth century, a professor of medicine, Arnaldus de Villanova stated: "It purifies the five wits of melancholy and of all uncleanness."[67] The priest devoted to the cult of Bacchus, administering to his intoxicated followers, has been replaced in our times by the bartender who listens and gives advice to his drinking customers.

Peyote, Mescaline

Peyote is the dried top of the cactus *Lophophora williamsii* and its active principle is mescaline. When the Spanish explorers traveled to the southwest of America, they noted that the Indians "eat a root which they call peyote, and which they venerate as though it were a deity."[26,75] Subsequent investigators made similar observations and described the peyote cult during which food, drink, and cigarettes were offered to Peyote. Peyote has been used for 2000 years by the Aztecs and southwestern Indian tribes for religious ceremonies, to cure disease such as snake bites and arthritis and for intoxication.[69] The use of peyote for social and recreational purposes by young people in the Western world is a well-known phenomenon of the 1960s and 1970s.[10,15,73,74]

Psilocybin

Psilocybin falls in the same category as peyote and is one of the sacred plants of Mexico. The Psilocybin mushroom is called "god's flesh" or "the sacred mushroom"[10,61] and is used, like peyote, to produce visions as a part of religious rites. There are some indications that mushrooms were also used to produce hallucinogenic states in India and Siberia. As with peyote, psilocybin has been used widely from the 1960s on among young adults in the Western world for cultural and social purposes.

Marijuana

In contrast, *cannabis sativa*, the marijuana plant, which originated in Asia, has had no definite religious connotations. Marijuana, which is derived from the dried tops, leaves, or resin of the female hemp plant has been used as a medical drug for approximately five millennia.[19] Although it has been widely used all over the world, its use for psychoactive purposes came into the national limelight in the 1960s, when it became the drug par excellence of the counterculture, young adults, and artists.

The above-mentioned drugs all change the mental states of their users. The assumption that mental illness is caused by the gods or by supernatural beings carries with it the implication that such substances are equally imbued with supernatural powers. The bacchantes and maenads, guided by their priests and soused with wine, underwent a complete personality change and had visions of heaven. Many a user of the hallucinogenic drugs claim to have experienced entirely novel insights or knowledge about themselves as well as about the universe.[26] Purportedly, they experience an "expansion of consciousness" and a transcendental relationship with the universe where perspectives of time and space have ceased to exist. They discover an inner world that appears as infinite and holy as the transfigured outer world.

All these drugs, therefore, produce profound subjective changes that cause persons to view themselves and their environment in a totally different manner. This can be effected directly through administration of psychotropic drugs or indirectly through the use of purgatives, emetics, and bloodletting, which result in electrolyte disturbances and anemia. The latter experiences, by the way, can be compared with exorcism rites for spirit possession since both leave the patient physically weakened and emotionally depleted. All these drug-induced experiences lead to a catharsis, mental and sometimes physical, during which the patient bares his soul, opens his inner mind to the world and displays, in general, a decrease in inhibitions.

The close association of psychiatry and religion throughout civilization prompts us to draw a parallel between these therapies and religious or ideological conversion experiences. In a classical religious conversion, the subject appears dejected, guilt-ridden, and generally unhappy. The priest and other worshippers produce a highly emotional state, supported by rhythmic hand clapping, singing, dancing, etc. The subject is gradually induced into a state of intense emotional excitement, with lack of inhibitions, in which he confesses and acknowledges his sins and transgressions. This may, at times, be accompanied with dissociative reactions and followed by an emotional collapse, during which the subject feels that he is cleansed and free of all old feelings of tension, guilt, and sin. In this phase, the patient is vulnerable, defenseless, and ready to accept new patterns and reconditioning. He is, so to say, "reborn" and ready to be integrated into a different and new way of life.

(Specific Techniques

Carbon Dioxide

Loevenhart et al.[40] discovered in 1929 that withdrawn psychotic patients, upon inhalation of a mixture of carbon dioxide and oxygen for three to ten minutes, became relaxed and were able to relate and talk in a coherent way. It was noted that no lasting improvement resulted, but the temporary improvement was attributed to "cerebral stimulation." Meduna[49,50] applied the technique to psychoneurotics and found the treatment successful in patients with conversion symptoms, anxiety neurosis, spastic colitis, and alcoholism. Stutterers, homosexuals, and patients suffering from personality disorders also benefited from this technique. Peck[52] found carbon dioxide and oxygen inhalation superior to psychotherapy in the treatment of phobic patients. Meduna postulated that psychoneurosis was caused by an abnormally low threshold to normal stimuli and that carbon dioxide normalized the threshold to stimuli from within or from without.

Carbon dioxide should be administered with care in patients over forty-five years of age. The patient wears loose-fitting clothes and dentures are removed. The treatment is given on an empty stomach. A mixture of 30 percent carbon dioxide and 70 percent oxygen is inhaled through a tight-fitting face mask and a breathing bag with an expiratory valve to prevent a rise in pressure. After a few breaths, the patient may feel uncomfortable and become short of breath, but, with continued reassurance, should be told to take a few more breaths at every subsequent treatment session. The introductory phase may last anywhere up to twenty-four respirations, whereupon the patient enters into the phase of anesthesia. During this phase, the patient may display motor phenomena such as struggling movements to escape discomfort, flexor hypertonus, and occasional carpal spasms. Abreaction with severe motor excitement takes place during the transitional phase, after the mask has been removed. Good results have been reported when the patient goes through a strong cathartic abreaction. The method is considered ineffective for obsessive-compulsive neurosis, hypochondriasis, and anxiety states with obsessional features. Modifications have been made by Kindwall[29] who sets a limit to the number of inhalations and Wilcox[76] who uses the method for "psychopenetration." Milligan[51] starts out with pure oxygen and uses a smaller percentage of carbon dioxide, whereas LaVerne[31] produces a quick anesthesia by using 70 percent carbon dioxide in oxygen for one to seven respirations. Because of its unpleasant side effects, carbon dioxide is frequently combined with other drugs such as ether and nitrous oxide to cut short the discomfort.

After the initial enthusiasm, several investigators expressed doubts about the efficacy of this treatment.[6,22,23] Carbon dioxide is nowadays rarely used.

Nitrogen and Nitrous Oxide

Alexander and Himwich[4] reported in 1939 on the beneficial effects of nitrogen inhalation in the therapy of schizophrenia, and explained this as a short-lasting anoxia that produced depression of the cerebral metabolism. Lehman and Bos[32] reported positive results with nitrous-oxide inhalation, using it almost exclusively in psychotic patients. The procedures for both nitrogen and nitrous oxide are similar. The patient breathes through a Connell inhalator while the breathing bag is filled with nitrous oxide (or nitrogen) until his respiration becomes rapid, irregular, and automatic. At this point, the bag is emptied of nitrous oxide and filled with pure oxygen. After four to five respirations, the mask is removed. The patient loses consciousness about a minute later, and the whole procedure lasts between two and three minutes. After this experience, the patient feels euphoric. He displays a facilitation of his mental processes and appears to have gained insight. The method is reportedly safe and convenient and was especially recommended for the treatment of manic episodes. Nitrous oxide is more pleasant for the patient than carbon dioxide since it does not produce the fear of losing consciousness and the shortness of breath.

Ether

The induction of a narcotic state with ether was described by Sargant and Slater[62] and Shorvon.[66] It was used for patients with previous stable personalities who suffered from depressive and hysterical symptoms and persistent anxiety after traumatic incidents, but who were refractory to barbiturates. The investigators reported that the treatment was more effective if a state of violent emotional excitement was produced, especially in a previously stable personality.

As to method, ether is poured on a mask, which is held slightly away from the patient's face. The patient is encouraged to talk about those past experiences which may be expected to arouse powerful emotions, especially anger and fear. As he becomes absorbed in his story, the mask is brought nearer to his face. When he becomes slightly intoxicated, the excitement is deliberately stimulated by the therapist until the patient begins shouting and struggling. Additional personnel to hold the patient down and physical restraints add to his excitement, which steadily rises until a climax occurs. The patient subsequently passes into a state of collapse and exhaustion during which he becomes limp and unresponsive. This treatment is not recommended for chronically anxious patients, severe constitutional hysterics, obsessive-compulsive neurotics, or endogenous depressions.

Trichlorethylene

A similar method using trichlorethylene was developed by Rees,[53] who considered this anesthetic superior to ether, carbon dioxide, sodium amytal, or nitrous oxide. The patient sits on a chair or lies on a couch and breathes steadily through a mask connected to an Oxford vaporizer. During this procedure, he becomes more communicative, but, at times, may become emotionally uninhibited. This method is recommended for narcoanalysis, abreaction, relaxation, hypnosis, narcosuggestion as well as for diagnostic purposes. The method purportedly works in acute situational reactions like war neurosis, but is ineffective in lifelong personality or chronic neurotic disorders.

Sodium Amytal, Pentothal, and Other Barbiturates

In 1930, Bleckwenn,[9] followed by Lorenz[41] and Solomon,[70] reported beneficial effects in psychotic patients after a prolonged narcosis with intravenous barbiturates. This finding intrigued Erich Lindemann[38] who gave between three and seven grains of sodium amytal, slowly, intravenously, to noncommunicative psychotic patients. This dose was insufficient to produce prolonged sleep or narcosis. However, during these injections the patients became cooperative and communicative and were able to relate important material. A controlled series of normal subjects reported a sense of well-being, freedom from inhibitions, and an increased desire to communicate, sometimes about intimate personal matters. Lindemann postulated that the drug removed certain inhibitions so that more primitive tendencies were displayed. Hoch[24] developed the concept of narcodiagnosis and used sodium amytal, seconal, and pentothal to disclose hallucinations and delusions in suspected schizophrenic patients who had appeared to be nonpsychotic during regular interviews. He felt that the drugs removed secondary manifestations of the mental state and uncovered the essential primary disturbance, as well as the psychodynamics. He differentiated between narcosuggestion and narcocatharsis or abreaction. During narcosuggestion the patient received, primarily, reassurance and support, with suggestions that he was going to get better. In narcocatharsis, the interviewer aimed to uncover and to let the patient react to repressed materials. Hoch reported benefits of narcosuggestion and narcocatharsis in patients with conversion hysteria, simple anxiety, fatigue states, and in some psychosomatic diseases. When the method was applied to patients suffering from

a war neurosis, Hoch reported a return to duty of 75 percent. Obsessive, aggressive, and ruminative hypochondriacal patients did less well. The treatment was not recommended for alcoholics, drug addicts, and character neuroses.

Grinker and Speigel[21] used sodium amytal for their modified version, called narcosynthesis. They felt that narcocatharsis was not sufficient and that the abreaction during the pentothal or amytal interview did not necessarily lead to improvement, especially since the patient was frequently amnestic for what transpired during the interview. Instead, they proposed narcosynthesis in which the patient not only expressed and relived the repressed painful or traumatic event but was taught by the therapist to deal with it in a more economical and realistic fashion so that the repressed or forgotten feelings could be synthesized by the ego. This also implied the synthesis of related feelings to the traumatic period that had occasionally been separated through the process of dissociation. Grinker reported a return to some sort of military duty after treatment for 97.7 percent for officers and 79.1 percent for enlisted men. The best candidates for this treatment were young soldiers with a sense of guilt and depression. Patients with psychoticlike reactions also had a fairly good prognosis. The poorest prognosis was reserved for patients with hostile, aggressive, and psychopathiclike reactions. Sargant and Slater[58,62] used intravenous barbiturates during World War II as a front-line technique for functional amnesic states and acute conversion symptoms and recommended its use in peacetime for hysterical conversion reactions.

Method

Sodium pentothal is administered in a 2.5 or 5 percent solution. The average dose for a satisfactory interview is between 0.25 and 0.5 g. but doses up to 0.75 to 1.0 g. have been used. It is essential that the patient be given a brief description of the protocol and be asked to sign a permit. The patient is placed in a semidarkened, quiet room and the drug is injected at a slow rate, not to exceed 0.1 g. per minute while the patient is asked to count. He soon starts to complain of lightheadedness or of feeling drunk. At this point one should interrupt the injection while the needle is left in place. The patient commonly speaks with a slow voice and his speech may be somewhat thick. The therapist in most cases will have to initiate the conversation and lead the interview in the direction of assumed conflicts. The therapist should remain calm, soothing, and supportive. Sometimes a patient may go into a severe terror state and it is advisable to have a few people present during the interview to control the patient and to protect him from injury. Following the abreaction, the patient typically appears exhausted and depleted. Many therapists make positive suggestions, then increase the pentothal dose after having told the patient that he will have a healthy sleep from which he will recover refreshed and free from conflicts.

The same procedure is used for sodium amytal, which comes in ampules of 7.5 gr. in 5 or 10 cc. The injection rate is not to exceed 1.5 gr. per minute. This method is contraindicated in severe medical illness, such as liver and kidney disease, cardiac failure, and porphyria.

Methedrine, Methylphenidate, and Droperidol

Following World War II different groups of drugs found their way into the armamentarium for narcoanalysis. Simon and Taube[67] reported on the use of methedrine, which made the patients more communicative and verbal and at times produced an abreaction. They also recommended the use of methedrine to disclose psychotic material. In Great Britain, Sargant[58] and Shorvon[64,65] reported positively on the use of methedrine for patients suffering from war neurosis and other neurotic reactions. Shorvon used methedrine in dosages up to 20 mg. intravenously to treat skin disorders, phobic states, depersonalization, traumatic anxiety states, psychosomatic diseases, and mixed hysterical states and

found it to be superior to ether in the treatment of patients with obsessive trends. Rothman and Sward[54] described excellent results in a group of patients who had been refractory to other treatments, with a minimum dosage of thiopental sodium followed by 5 to 15 mg. of methamphetamine hydrochloride, and Davison[16] described good results in cases with episodic depersonalization.

Methylphenidate in doses up to 15 mg. IV has been reported by Freed[18] to increase verbalization and to bring repressed material to the surface. Freed[18] prefers this over a combined program of sodium amytal and methamphetamine, mostly because the patient is easier to manage and does not suffer from insomnia. More recently, methylphenidate has been given intravenously following an IV drip of 0.1 percent solution of methohexital, an ultra short-acting barbiturate. With this method the depth of the inhibition reduction can be easily controlled.[20]

Droperidol, a butyrophenone derivative, has been used with reported good results in delinquent adolescents by Jauch et al. in dosages between 10 and 15 mg. IV.[27]

LSD (d-Lysergic Acid Diethylamide)

Following its accidental discovery in 1943, LSD was first used to induce time-limited, psychotic reactions (model psychoses). Subsequently, this controversial and dramatic drug, as well as comparable agents (e.g., psilocybin, DMT), found its way as an aid to psychotherapy for a variety of conditions. Different methods of treatment with LSD have been developed.

In psycholytic therapy, low doses of LSD (30–200 μg.) are used as an adjunct to a form of regular insight-oriented psychotherapy.[11,33] The therapist uses the hallucinogenic potential of LSD to heighten symbolic dream images, regression, and transference, but the focus is on insight pertaining to reality problems.

In psychedelic therapy, in contrast, the patient receives high dosages of LSD (400–

1500 μg.) to undergo an intense mystical peak or transcendental experience.[63] The patients are prepared for this in previous sessions and the LSD experience is aided and supplemented by paraphernalia such as strobe lights, music, incense, etc. This type of therapy, which carries with it the trappings of a religious conversion, is restricted to one or, at best, a few sessions.

Hypnodelic therapy was developed by Ludwig and Levine as a method to control and modify the LSD experience through hypnosis in psychotherapy.[34–36,45,46] The average dose is 150–350 μg. and upon administration of the drug, before it takes effect, the patient is hypnotized. Subsequently, the patient is encouraged to discuss and relive major conflictual experiences. This treatment model is dynamic and insight-oriented and utilizes play acting, abreaction, and posthypnotic suggestions based on the obtained insight.

The use of LSD in psychotherapy was widely hailed in the 1950s as an important breakthrough in the treatment of refractory cases. Many investigators and clinicians used the drug in individual and group therapy and reported excellent results in the treatment of psychoneuroses, acute and chronic character disorders, including sociopathy, homosexuality, and sexual perversions.[*] Statistics combining all these reports reveal "marked improvement" rates of 45 percent and "improved by treatment" rates of 70 percent. The early reports of treatment of alcoholics employing LSD claimed a 94 percent improvement rate. It was generally accepted that a one-time, intense, mind-expanding psychedelic experience would restitute or reintegrate previously pathological personalities and, therefore, was superior to years of traditional psychotherapy. Not until the 1960s were some voices raised to dampen the unbridled enthusiasm and point out the potential dangers of indiscriminate use of hallucinogenic agents. The fate of LSD in restitutive therapies was sealed in 1970 by the controlled study of LSD in the treatment of alcoholism.[47] Despite the above-mentioned, impressive claims of improvement, the authors

[*] See references 1–3, 5, 8, 12–14, 17, 37, 39, 48, 55–57.

found no lasting short- or long-term benefits after hypnodelic or psychedelic therapy compared to ordinary therapy. Other investigators obtained comparable results.[25,28]

⟨ Mechanisms

The following major theories are offered to explain the underlying mechanisms of action of the restitutive therapies. It is felt that the theoretical explanations at times overlap and are not mutually exclusive.

Altered States of Consciousness

This concept, as developed by Ludwig,[44] has become increasingly relevant in contemporary research in psychiatry, and implies subjective as well as objective changes from the normal psychological functioning during alert, wakeful consciousness. During an altered state of consciousness, the subject frequently experiences a change in the sense of time as well as a loss of control. The subject succumbs to this latter change with the hope that some special knowledge or communion will be established. Perceptual distortions, such as hallucinations, illusions, as well as heightened or diminished sensitivity to stimuli, are part of most altered states of consciousness. Many subjects attach an increased meaning and significance to their perceptions, ideas, and experiences during such states, feeling that they are undergoing a very unique or important event that reveals to them a very special truth or insight. Because of the unusual quality of the subjective experiences, characterized by transcendental, oceanic, mystical, or universal feelings, the individual is often unable to describe or relate these experiences. These very qualities add to the patient's feeling that he has obtained the ultimate in knowledge or insight and that his sense of reality has deepened to a level never before experienced.

Following most profound alterations of consciousness, whether they be abreactive states, mystical experiences, consciousness expansion, religious conversion, or just plain sleep, patients report a sense of rejuvenation and a sense of being reborn.

Neurophysiological Mechanisms

Sargant[59-61] developed a theory, based on Pavlovian principles, to explain catharsis abreaction, possession, conversion, and similar intense emotional states. Various degrees of external or internal stress bring about changes in brain function, starting with "protective inhibition," where all strengths of outside stimuli produce the same brain responses independent of their differences in strength. This is followed by the "paradoxical phase" in which the brain overreacts toward a small stimulus and remains indifferent toward overwhelming stimuli. In the ultraparadoxical phase, all positive conditioned reflexes become negative and vice versa. This is combined with the hypnoidal state of inhibitory brain activity, in which new expressions, ideas, and philosophies are uncritically and unconditionally accepted without any processing or screening by the brain. The benefit of restitutive therapy is attributed to this last event.

Psychoanalytic Theories

The effectiveness of cathartic therapy has been explained according to psychoanalytic principles by Kubie and Margolin.[30] According to their theory, a dynamic relationship between patient and therapist is maintained, provided the drug dose does not lead to narcosis. Because of this dynamic relationship the patient relates pertinent data and events and is able to relive extreme affection, both positive or negative, toward significant people. In addition, the patient often displays a marked transference reaction toward the therapist in an obvious and direct way rather than in the subtle transference during regular therapy sessions. This, then, makes it easier to use the transference process therapeutically.

It was further postulated that certain highly emotional and traumatic events stand out like high centers. The drug brings the conflictual centers into high relief in a more direct way than through the usual pathways of free association. The drugs, in essence, produce a controlled delirious state and, therefore, like organic delirious reactions, bring to the surface latent depressions, elations, fear reactions, or paranoid states.

⟨ Conclusion

In this chapter, we have described the historical development and present status of restitutive therapies. These intriguing and dramatic techniques, which take root from naturalistic healing practices either of a religious or medical nature, still have their place in modern psychiatric practice. While most of the impressive claims made for these therapies are anecdotal or descriptive in nature, the state of psychiatry is such that any promising or even controversial approach for refractory patients should be given a thorough test. There is a desperate need for continued, controlled evaluation of the different techniques employed, as well as of the different categories of patients who may benefit from them.

Some restitutive approaches, notably sodium amytal and pentothal interviews, are still widely used in clinical practice, whereas other controversial approaches have fallen into disfavor or have been shown scientifically to have little efficacy. From the long history of these approaches, it is likely that they or newer variations of them will always have a place in psychiatry. It behooves eclectic psychiatrists to be familiar with the potential applications of these techniques and, perhaps, to include them in their therapeutic armamentarium.

⟨ Bibliography

1. ABRAMSON, H. A. "Lysergic Acid Diethylamide (LSD-25): III. As an Adjunct to Psychotherapy and Elimination of Fear of Homosexuality," *J. Psychol.*, 39 (1955), 127–155.

2. ———. "Lysergic acid diethylamide (LSD-25): XIX. As an Adjunct to Brief Psychotherapy with Special Reference to Ego

Enhancement," *J. Psychol.*, 41 (1956), 199–229.

3. ——. *The Use of LSD in Psychotherapy*, New York: Josiah Macy, Jr. Found., 1960.

4. ALEXANDER, F. A. D. and H. E. HIMWICH. "Nitrogen Inhalation Therapy for Schizophrenia," *Am. J. Psychiatry*, 94 (1939), 643–655.

5. ARENDSEN-HEIN, F. W. "Hallucinogenic Drugs, Specific Problems," *Lancet*, 1 (1961), 445.

6. ARTHURS, R. G. S., D. CAPPON, E. DOUGLASS et al. "Carbon Dioxide Therapy with Stutterers," *Dis. Nerv. Syst.*, 15 (1954), 123–126.

7. ATHENAEUNS. *The Deipnosophists*. Translated by C. B. Gulick. Loeb Classical Library, Vols. 1, 4, and 5. London: Heineman, 1927.

8. BALL, J. R. and J. J. ARMSTRONG. "The Use of LSD-25 (d-Lysergic Acid Diethylamide) in the Treatment of the Sexual Perversions," *J. Can. Psychiatr. Assoc.*, 6 (1961), 231–235.

9. BLECKWENN, W. J. "Narcosis as Therapy in Neuropsychiatric Conditions," *JAMA*, 95 (1930), 1168–1171.

10. BLUM, E., R. ALPERT, and J. FORT. *Utopiates*. New York: Atherton, 1964.

11. BUCKMAN, J. "Theoretical Aspects of LSD Therapy," in H. A. Abramson, ed., *The Use of LSD in Psychotherapy and Alcoholism*, pp. 83–100. New York: Bobbs-Merrill, 1967.

12. BUTTERWORTH, A. T. "Some Aspects of an Office Practice Utilizing LSD-25," *Psychiatr. Q.*, 36 (1962), 734–753.

13. CAMERON, K. "Hallucinogenic Drugs, Specific Problems," *Lancet*, 1 (1961), 445.

14. CHANDLER, A. L. and M. A. HARTMAN. "Lysergic Acid Diethylamide (LSD) as a Facilitating Agent in Psychotherapy," *Arch. Gen. Psychiatry*, 2 (1960), 286–299.

15. CHOLDEN, L. *LSD and Mescaline in Experimental Psychiatry*. New York: Grune & Stratton, 1956.

16. DAVISON, K. "Episodic Depersonalization," *Br. J. Psychiatry*, 11 (1964), 505–513.

17. FREDERKING, W. "Intoxicant Drugs (Mescaline and Lysergic Acid Diethylamide) in Psychotherapy," *J. Nerv. Ment. Dis.*, 121 (1955), 262–266.

18. FREED, H. "The Use of Ritalin Intravenously as a Diagnostic Adjuvant in Psychiatry," *Am. J. Psychiatry*, 114 (1958), 944.

19. GOODE, E. *The Marijuana Smokers*. New York: Basic Books, 1970.

20. GREEN, D. O. and D. R. REIMER. "The Methohexital-Methylphenidate Interview," *Bull. Menninger Clin.*, 38 (1974), 76–77.

21. GRINKER, R. R. and J. P. SPIEGEL. *Men Under Stress*. Philadelphia: Blakiston, 1945.

22. HARGROVE, E. A., A. E. BENNETT, and M. STEELE. "An Investigation of Carbon Dioxide as an Adjunct to Psychotherapy in some Neuroses," *Am. J. Psychiatry*, 110 (1954), 844–847.

23. HAWKINGS, J. R. and R. W. TIBBETTS. "Carbon Dioxide Inhalation in Neuroses, Controlled Clinical Trial," *J. Ment. Sci.*, 102 (1956), 52–59.

24. HOCH, P. H. "The Present Status of Narcodiagnosis and Therapy," *J. Nerv. Ment. Dis.*, 103 (1946), 248–259.

25. HOLLISTER, L. E., J. SHELTON, and G. KREIGER. "A Controlled Comparison of Lysergic Acid Diethylamide (LSD) and Dextroamphetamine in Alcoholics," *Am. J. Psychiatry*, 125 (1969), 1352–1357.

26. HUXLEY, A. *The Doors of Perception*. New York: Harper & Row, 1963.

27. JAUCH, T. E., J. LOCH, J. EARL et al. "Droperidol, a Preferred Neuroleptic in Narcoanalysis," *Dis. Nerv. Syst.*, 34 (1973), 259–262.

28. JOHNSON, F. G. "LSD in the Treatment of Alcoholism," *Am. J. Psychiatry*, 126 (1969), 481–487.

29. KINDWALL, J. A. "Carbon Dioxide Narcosis Therapy," *Am. J. Psychiatry*, 105 (1949), 682–685.

30. KUBIE, L. S. and S. MARGOLIN. "The Therapeutic Role of Drugs in the Process of Repression, Dissociation and Synthesis," *Psychosom. Med.*, 7 (1945), 147–151.

31. LAVERNE, A. A. "Narcostimulation," *Am. J. Psychiatry*, 115 (1959), 738.

32. LEHMANN, H. and C. BOS. "The Advantages of Nitrous Oxide Inhalation in Psychiatric Treatment," *Am. J. Psychiatry*, 104 (1947), 164–170.

33. LEUNER, H. "Present State of Psycholytic Therapy and Its Possibilities," in H. A. Abramson, ed., *The Use of LSD in Psychotherapy and Alcoholism*, pp. 101–116. New York: Bobbs-Merrill, 1967.

34. LEVINE, J. and A. M. LUDWIG. "Alterations in Consciousness Produced by Combinations of LSD, Hypnosis and Psychotherapy," *Psychopharmacologia*, 7 (1965), 123–137.

35. ———. "The Hypnodelic Treatment Technique," *Int. J. Clin. Exp. Hypn.*, 14 (1966), 207–215.

36. LEVINE, J., A. M. LUDWIG, and W. H. LYLE, JR. "The Controlled Psychedelic State," *Am. J. Clin. Hypn.*, 6 (1963), 163–164.

37. LEWIS, D. J. and R. B. SLOAN. "Therapy with Lysergic Acid Diethylamide," *J. Clin. Exp. Psychopathol.*, 19 (1958), 19–31.

38. LINDEMANN, E. "Psychological Changes in Normal and Abnormal Individuals under the Influence of Sodium Amytal," *Am. J. Psychiatry*, 11 (1932), 1083–1091.

39. LING, T. M. and J. BUCKMAN. "The Use of Lysergic Acid in Individual Psychotherapy." *Proc. R. Soc. Med.*, 53 (1960), 927–929.

40. LOEVENHART, A. S., W. F. LORENZ, and R. M. WATERS. "Cerebral Stimulation," *JAMA*, 92 (1929), pp. 880–883.

41. LORENZ, W. F., H. H. REESE, and A. C. WASHBURNE. "Physiological Observation during Intravenous Sodium Amytal Medication," *Am. J. Psychiatry*, 90 (1934), 1205–1212.

42. LUCIA, S., ed. *Alcohol and Civilization.* New York: McGraw-Hill, 1963.

43. LUDWIG, A. M. "An Historical Survey of the Early Roads of Mesmerism," *Int. J. Clin. Exp. Hypn.*, 12 (1964), 205–217.

44. ———. "Altered States of Consciousness," *Arch. Gen. Psychiatry*, 15 (1966), 225–234.

45. ———. "A Model for Evaluating the Clinical and Therapeutic Effects of Psychedelic Agents," in D. H. Efron, J. O. Cole, J. Levine et al. eds., *Psychopharmacology: A Review of Progress 1957–1967*, pp. 1263–1268. Washington: Public Health Services Publ., 1968.

46. LUDWIG, A. M. and J. LEVINE. "A Controlled Comparison of Five Brief Treatment Techniques Employing LSD, Hypnosis, and Psychotherapy," *Am. J. Psychother.*, 19 (1965), 417–435.

47. LUDWIG, A. M., J. LEVINE, and L. H. STARK. *LSD and Alcoholism, A Clinical Study of Treatment Efficacy.* Springfield, Ill.: Charles C. Thomas, 1970.

48. MARTIN, A. J. "LSD (Lysergic Acid Diethylamide) Treatment of Chronic Psychoneurotic Patients under Day-Hospital Conditions," *Int. J. Soc. Psychiatry*, 3 (1957), 188–195.

49. MEDUNA, L. J. "Physiological background of

50. ———. *Carbon Dioxide Therapy.* Springfield, Ill.: Charles C. Thomas, 1958.

51. MILLIGAN, W. L. "Treatment of Psychoneurosis—Modified Carbon Dioxide Abreaction Technique," *Br. Med. J.*, 1 (1951), 1426–1428.

52. PECK, R. E. "Carbon Dioxide Therapy—A Cooperative Statistical Study," in L. J. Meduna, *Carbon Dioxide Therapy*, pp. 444–496. Springfield, Ill.: Charles C. Thomas, 1958.

53. REES, L., M. W. ANNEAR, and G. CROSSE. "Trichlorethylene Narcosis as a Therapeutic Aid in Psychiatry," *J. Ment. Sci.*, 94 (1950), 502–508.

54. ROTHMAN, T. and K. SWARD. "Studies in Pharmacological Psychotherapy," *Arch. Neurol. Psychiatry*, 75 (1956), 95–105.

55. SANDISON, R. A. "Psychological Aspects of the LSD Treatment of the Neuroses," *J. Ment. Sci.*, 100 (1954), 508–515.

56. SANDISON, R. A., A. M. SPENCER, and J. D. A. WHITELAW. "The Therapeutic Value of Lysergic Acid Diethylamide in Mental Illness," *J. Ment. Sci.*, 100 (1954), 491–507.

57. SANDISON, R. A. and J. D. A. WHITELAW. "Further Studies in the Therapeutic Value of Lysergic Acid Diethylamide in Mental Illness," *J. Ment. Sci.*, 103 (1957), 332–343.

58. SARGANT, W. "Some Observations on Abreaction with Drugs," *Digest Neurol. Psychiatry*, 16 (1948), 193–206.

59. ———. *Battle for the Mind.* Garden City, New York: Doubleday, 1957.

60. ———. "The Physiology of Faith," *Br. J. Psychiatry*, 115 (1969), 505–518.

61. ———. *The Mind Possessed.* Philadelphia: Lippincott, 1974.

62. SARGANT, W. and E. SLATER. *An Introduction to Physical Methods of Treatment in Psychiatry.* Edinburgh: Livingston, 1963.

63. SAVAGE, C. and S. WOLF. "An Outline of Psychedelic Therapy," in H. Brill et al. eds., *Proceedings Fifth International Congress of Neuropsychopharmacology*, Int. Congr. Ser. 129, pp. 405–410. Amsterdam: Excerp. Med. Found. 1967.

64. SHORVON, H. J. "Discussion on Abreaction." *Proc. R. Soc. Med.*, 46 (1953), 158–160.

65. SHORVON, H. J., A. J. ROOK, and D. S. WILK-

the Carbon Dioxide Treatment of the Neuroses," *Am. J. Psychiatry*, 110 (1954), 664–667.

INSON. "Psychological Treatment in Skin Disorders," *Br. Med. J.*, 2 (1950), 1300.

66. SHORVON, H. J. and W. SARGANT. "Excitation Abreaction with Special Reference to Its Mechanism in the Use of Ether," *J. Ment. Sci.*, 93 (1947), 709–732.

67. SIGERIST, H. E. *The Earliest Printed Book on Wine, Now for the First Time Rendered into English and with a Historical Essay by H. E. Sigerist with Facsimile of Original, 1478 Edition.* New York: Schuman, 1943.

68. SIMON, J. L. and H. TAUBE. "A Preliminary Study on the Use of Methedrine in Psychiatric Diagnosis," *J. Nerv. Ment. Dis.*, 104 (1946), 593.

69. SLOTKIN, J. S. *The Peyote Religion.* Glencoe, Ill.: Free Press, 1956.

70. SOLOMON, H. C. et al. "Some Effects of the Inhalation of Carbon Dioxide and Oxygen, and of Intravenous Sodium Amytal in Certain Neuropsychiatric Conditions," *Am. J. Psychiatry*, 10 (1931), 761–769.

71. SPENCER, A. M. "Permissive Group Therapy with Lysergic Acid Diethylamide," *Br. J. Psychiatry*, 109 (1963), 37–45.

72. TENNENBAUM, B. "Group Therapy with LSD-25," *Dis. Nerv. Syst.*, 22 (1961), 459–462.

73. UNGER, S. M. "Mescaline, LSD, Psilocybin and Personality Change," *Psychiatry*, 26 (1963).

74. UNITED NATIONS. "Peyote," *Bull. Narc.*, 11 (1959), entire issue.

75. WASHBURN, C. *Primitive Drinking.* New Haven: College and University Press, 1961.

76. WILCOX, P. H. "Psychopenetration," *Dis. Nerv. Syst.* 12 (1951), 35–38.

77. ZILBOORG, G. and G. W. HENRY. *A History of Medical Psychology.* New York: Norton, 1971.

CHAPTER 26

INSULIN COMA THERAPY

H. Peter Laqueur

Insulin coma therapy (ICT) for severe forms of schizophrenia, and for some anxiety and tension states, and for cases which fall under Hoch and Polatin's[9] description of "pseudoneurotic schizophrenia," was one of the most helpful tools for psychiatry until the advent of tranquilizing drugs of the phenothiazine class. Some authors (Arnold,[2] Dussik,[7] Kalinowsky,[10] and the author[11,12]), as well as psychiatrists in East-European countries (Russia, Czechoslovakia, Estonia) are of the opinion that it is still capable of producing results which are far beyond the capability of other psychopharmacological agents. Most patients who are treated with antipsychotic drugs must remain on such a regime for the rest of their life, while a good many of our patients treated with ICT for a sufficient period, can subsequently lead normal lives, work, marry, and enjoy their friends, without having to take a daily pill in order to "remain normal."

Foremost in the minds of families and patients who fall ill with severe schizophrenia or intense anxiety-tension states is the question, whether this condition can be improved, cured and prevented from recurring.

In 1926, before Sakel,[17,18] one of the first psychiatrists engaged in experiments with insulin, which seemed to change a hitherto bleak prognosis, there was little hope in the opinion of most psychiatrists consulted about schizophrenia and related states. This chapter is, of course, largely retrospective, since much to our regret insulin coma therapy in this country is virtually abandoned and many young professionals in the field, who have never worked with it, repeat the message to each other that it is dangerous and ineffectual.

However, it must be said that there are very few people today who have seen the powerful and lasting effects of this treatment when it was given with good technique and observation, by patient, highly trained crews of physicians, nurses, and aides who patiently dedicated their time to obtain optimal continued results for their patients, minimizing the potential dangers by continuous conscientious observation of the treatment in progress, and adapting the technique so that in the end there were no fatalities and only very exceptional undesired side reactions.

It is easy to condemn something that one does not wish to do anyway, but it must be said that a totally negative attitude deprives the patients of a last-resort treatment that could be very beneficial when other methods fail.

To the best of my knowledge, Russian, Czech, and Estonian hospitals have kept trained workers and proceed with ICT (this was also reported from Japan and India), while American and Western European countries have decided that it is too expensive to train and maintain workers and centers for a treatment that overcomes the failures of chemical treatment in patients, thus allowing them to become chronic sufferers.

Research into the reasons for the effectiveness of insulin by Himwich[8] and others is not conclusive, but might provide further information about the nature of schizophrenia which will only become available to researchers now when active study of the effect of hypoglycemia, thiamine and adrenalin, and glucagon (an antiinsulin hormone) is again undertaken.

When Sakel found insulin helpful in not only raising appetite in morphinists but overcoming schizophrenic symptoms after accidentally having caused coma, he decided that it was necessary to take risks to find lucidity and healthy mental functions, rather than chronic abject avoidance of reality through schizophrenic thought processes.

(Insulin Coma Therapy

Insulin coma therapy is a more adequate name than insulin shock therapy, since in the most modern and effective versions, neither a state usually described as *shock*, nor a state of *convulsions* is considered necessary, desirable or, if it occurs too often, acceptable.

Time and Personnel Necessary for Treatment

The patient has to be treated five days a week from 6 or 6:30 A.M. till noon. It became possible with the safer introduction of coma (multiple insulin doses) and with the easier termination (adrenalin thiamine or glucagon IM injection) to have one registered nurse

with three male and three female trained aides to observe fifty patients in ICT. Before the IM injections and with the older (Sakel or Shurley–Bond) techniques at least three registered nurses and five male and five female aids were necessary to give safe treatment.

Insulin Coma Combined with Electroconvulsive Therapy (ECT)

This combination was sometimes used in order to get quickly through a catatonic refusal to eat, or other conditions when the patient's recovery was in danger, because he made it difficult for himself. (It is important to have patients drink after hypoglycemic coma, even though tube-feeding can replace this function temporarily.) As a rule we did not want or need convulsive conditions because they force us to terminate the treatment early and thus lose part of a treatment day.

Bond and Shurley[3] who tried to reach coma quicker, took more risks and increased the dose after reactions and side reactions. The patients sometimes developed protracted coma which seemed to help them for the moment but it was difficult with this method to give enough comas to produce lasting results.

The "zig-zag" method of inducing coma by von Braunmühl[4,5] was an early modification of Sakel's technique which he himself called the "classic method." Von Braunmühl observed that a patient who with daily increasing doses could not yet go into coma with 200 units of insulin and who the next day received only thirty units, could reach a deep coma on a subsequent day with 200 units easily.

Multiple Insulin Doses

Assuming that the resistance of human organisms to insulin could be the product of adrenal outpourings which are set off by administration of a large insulin dosage, this author[13] tried small insulin amounts administered over more time (one third of the planned amount every fifteen minutes or every half hour in order to produce less adrenal stimulation). This proved effective in nearly 50,000 comas administered from 1951–1968; practically no prolonged coma of more than one hour was seen in our unit.

Advantages of Modern (Safe) ICT Technique

1. We can treat more patients with the same crew.
2. We need not fear protracted coma and secondary complications and risks.
3. The patients feel well enough to engage in other activities (occupational therapy, psychotherapy, group and family treatment, recreation, patient government, and milieu therapy.)
4. The slow awakening permits the study of the patients in preconscious states and influencing them therapeutically.[19]

Stages of Insulin Coma

1. Precoma: patient in drowsy somnolent condition, some cold perspiration, lowering of body temperature.
2. Coma (green stage): cortical loss of function, patient restless, not responding to questions but will respond to pain. May be used for several hours.
3. Coma (yellow or warning stage): *midbrain symptoms*, loss of pain sense except for supraorbital pressure, wide pupil, myoclonic and myotonic contractions. This stage allowed for fifteen to twenty minutes only.
4. Coma (red stage): medullary symptoms, miosis, complete affect medulla oblongata, loss of pain sense and reflexes, to be terminated in five minutes; positive Babinski reflex, slow pulse.

Colors are teaching devices, derived from traffic signals. By carefully observing the following rules, ICT can be made perfectly safe:

1. *Precoma* and
2. *Green* stage coma permitted if necessary all morning.
3. *Yellow* stage: not to last more than fifteen to twenty minutes before termination is begun.
4. *Red* stage: not to last more than five minutes until termination begins. This will avoid the

5. Blue stage (spinal phase) and complications.

Termination of Hypoglycemic Reactions

There are four possibilities:
1. Tube feeding with orange juice plus sugar or with a mixture of molasses and sugar.
2. Slowly administering 33 percent glucose (50–100 cc) intravenously.
3. Administering 0.5–1 mg. adrenalin mixed with 100 mg. thiamine intramuscularly.
4. Injecting 0.33–1 mg. glucagon (an anti-insulin hormone) intramuscularly.

Laqueur[14,15] found that 0.50 mg.–1.0 mg. adrenalin by itself may awaken about one half of the coma patients and enable them to drink sugar solutions by mouth. By adding 100 mg. thiamine (a substance that enables sugar to pass the blood-brain barrier but that does not have an effect on low blood sugar by itself) 80–90 percent of our deep-coma cases could be "lightened" enough so they were able to drink sugar water with molasses (which people in deep hypoglycemia like to take).

Afternoon Observations

With one aide for the males and one for the females (with one registered nurse on call) all "possible afternoon reactions" following that the introduction of the small multiple insulin doses could be handled. The patients could be outside, take part in sports, or have occupational and group therapy; they only could not be allowed to fall asleep in the shade by themselves without being observed, because then a dangerous hypoglycemic reaction might overcome them.

❲ Indications

Insulin coma therapy worked very well with:

1. Paranoids.
2. Catatonics.
3. Mixed forms of schizophrenia.
4. True hebephrenic conditions (they occur

rarely and ICT was very effective in some).

5. Anxiety and tension states (both neurotic and psychotic).

6. In schizoaffective depressed conditions where drugs and ECT had failed to bring results.

Contraindications

1. While there is no real evidence of damage done, it has been suggested that insulin coma should not be used in pregnant women, because of possible injury to the unborn child in the early phase when its own pancreas is not yet fully developed.

2. Cardiovascular disease may constitute a risk, and is always considered as such in persons older than fifty years.

3. Upper *respiratory* infections.

4. Lung diseases.

5. Renal diseases.

6. Other severe medical conditions are usually a reason against the use of ICT.

⟪ Insulin Coma Combined with Other Forms of Treatment

It is regrettable that this country appears to have abandoned the training of personnel and the organization of at least a few treatment centers (one for each region) where patients can receive this safe and helpful treatment when other approaches (psychopharmacology, milieu therapy, psychotherapy, ECT, etc.) fail. These patients are now again in the desperate situation that existed before the discovery of insulin coma therapy.

Insulin Coma and Milieu Therapy

Post-ECT patients, unless they were treated with the slower-working unilateral applications of electrodes, are often drowsy and little inclined to take part in afternoon and evening activities. The same is true for patients heavily medicated with phenothiazines, thiothixine, haloperidol, etc. Post-ICT patients are fit and eager on the same treatment day to take part in therapeutic activities.

Results

ICT "took," as the saying went, if patients left their psychotic state of apparent unconnectedness with reality for a "lucid" period after a coma. The first lucid period might only last five minutes, after a few comas it might increase to thirty minutes and, as the treatment progressed it might last all afternoon and evening. We learned that, if the treatment was disrupted at that point, relapses might occur, but if forty to fifty continued ICT's were given after full "lucidity" was reached, we could count on permanent results. Continuity was very important.

⟪ Conclusions

Insulin coma therapy must be considered a useful form of treatment which has helped many schizophrenic patients. It is not used any more because other forms of treatment have taken its place for the greater part.

There are, however, cases where pharmacodynamic and milieu therapy, and many forms of group and individual therapy do not attain the full degree of remission which previous authors have seen and which permitted patients to return to normal living without having to use drugs continuously to remain free of symptoms (and having to fear that they would relapse if medications were interrupted.)

The costs of insulin coma treatment were not insuperable during the last few years of its use in the United States and Canada. Trained crews with the help of electronic controls and with the considerably higher degree of safety which the most modern methods of treatment (multiple insulin doses and glucagon termination) permitted, could treat more patients simultaneously than in earlier years.

·With these modern methods this author treated fifty patients daily with a crew designed for the treatment of only twenty-five patients by the older method. In most patients deep coma was attained and not a single fatality occurred in more than 50,000 comas over seventeen years. Very few undesirable secondary reactions were observed, and all gave way immediately to secondary application of intravenous glucose or glucogen, or adrenalin–thiamine intramuscularly.

Subcoma insulin treatment is still occasionally used in the United States, as recommended by Leonard Cammer,[6] mostly in anxiety and tension states and subsequent neurotic depressions.

The pre- and postcoma states have been explored and used therapeutically by Wallach,[19] who used to observe this author's patients during their awakening from coma and talked with them during these preconscious phases before they returned to full lucidity. This is another safe way of reaching early memories and awareness; some of this psychotherapy has been performed by this author in many cases with the help of sodium amytal desoxyn interviews which were tape-recorded and played back to the patients. But we feel that deep hypoglycemia is in schizophrenics a better tool to reach such early and deep levels of repressed data held back in adult conscious states.

We must wait for information from other countries what the ultimate fate of insulin coma therapy shall be. In this country, revival of at least three or four reliable regional centers, where psychiatrists and nurses could perform this treatment, would be in the best interest of scientific and clinical psychiatry and is recommended by this author and by Lothar Kalinowsky in his writings.

We should not end this article without referring to the splendid review by J. Angst, of the University Psychiatric Clinic in Zurich (under Manfred Bleuler), who reviewed 227 recent publications in the field of insulin therapy and who left the question of its usefulness in today's somatotherapies open.[1]

❨ Bibliography

1. ANGST, J. *Die Somatische Therapie der Schizophrenie*. Stuttgart: Georg Thieme, 1969.
2. ARNOLD, O. H. "Results and Efficacy of In-
sulin Shock Therapy," in M. Rinkel, ed., *Insulin Treatment in Psychiatry*, pp. 199–221. New York: Philosophical Library, 1959.
3. BOND, E. D. and J. T. SHURLEY. "Insulin Shock Therapy in Schizophrenia," *V.A. Tech. Bull.*, 10 (1948), 501.
4. BRAUNMÜHL, A. VON. "Fünf Jahre Schock- und Krampfbehandlung in Eglfing-Haar," *Arch. Psychiatr.*, 114 (1942), 410.
5. ———. *Insulinschock und Heilkrampf in der Psychiatrie*. Stuttgart: Wissenschaftliche Verlagsgesellschaft, 1947.
6. CAMMER, L. "Treatment of Anxiety through Conditioning with Low-dose Insulin," in M. Rinkel, ed., *Biological Treatment of Mental Illness*, pp. 768–777. New York: Farrar, Straus & Giroux, 1966.
7. DUSSIK, K. T. "The Place of Sakel's Insulin Coma Therapy in an Active Treatment Unit of Today," in M. Rinkel, ed., *Insulin Treatment in Psychiatry*, pp. 316–331. New York: Philosophical Library, 1959.
8. HIMWICH, H. E., K. M. BOWMAN, C. DALY et al. "Changes in Cerebral Blood Flow and Arteriovenous Oxygen Difference during Insulin Hypoglycemia," *Proc. Soc. Exp. Biol. Med.*, 45 (1940), 468.
9. HOCH, P. H. and P. POLATIN. "Pseudoneurotic Forms of Schizophrenia," *Psychiatr. Q.*, 23 (1949), 248.
10. KALINOWSKY, L. B. and H. HIPPIUS. *Somatic Treatments in Psychiatry*. New York: Grune & Stratton, 1969.
11. LAQUEUR, H. P. "Manfred Sakel, Karl Dussik, Max Rinkel and the Development of Biological Psychiatry," in S. Bogoch, ed., *The Future of the Brain Sciences*, pp. 575–581. New York: Plenum, 1969.
12. LAQUEUR, H. P., K. T. DUSSIK, H. A. LaBURT et al. "Tactical and Strategical Considerations in the Use of Insulin Therapy: A Joint Study of Two Mental Hospitals," in M. Rinkel, ed., *Biological Treatment of Mental Illness*, pp. 731–760. New York: Farrar, Straus & Giroux, 1966.
13. LAQUEUR, H. P. and H. A. LaBURT. "Coma Therapy with Multiple Insulin Doses," *J. Neuropsychiatry*, 1 (1960), 135–147.
14. ———. "Experiences with Low-Zinc Insulin, with Semi-Lente Insulin, with Glucagon and Adrenalin-Thiamine in Insulin Coma Treatment," *J. Neuropsychiatry*, 2 (1960), 86–92.
15. ———. "Use of Glucagon in Insulin Coma

Therapy," *Dis. Nerv. Syst., Monogr. Suppl.* 22 (1961), 1–3.

16. ———. "The Therapeutic Community on a Modern Insulin Ward," *J. Neuropsychiatry,* 3 (1962), 139–149.

17. SAKEL, M. "Neue Behandlung der Morphinsucht," *Z. Gesante Neurol. Psychiatr.,* 143 (1933), 506.

18. ———. "The Nature and Origin of the Hypoglycemic Treatment of Psychoses," *Am. J. Psychiatry,* 94 (Suppl.): (1938), 24.

19. WALLACH, M. B. "Interviews with Schizophrenics after Insulin Coma," *Dis. Nerv. Syst.,* 25 (1964), 597–600.

CHAPTER 27

ELECTRIC AND OTHER CONVULSIVE TREATMENTS

Lothar B. Kalinowsky

CONVULSIVE THERAPY was introduced by Meduna[36] in Hungary in 1935. It was a strange coincidence that this event took place less than two years after the first reports on insulin coma treatment (ICT) appeared. It was based on the belief that schizophrenia and epilepsy do not occur together and, thus, may be antagonistic to each other. It was, furthermore, based on old clinical observations that psychotic syndromes may temporarily disappear after spontaneous convulsions. The same considerations which led Meduna to the induction of actual convulsions had led another Hungarian, Nyiro,[37] to attempts at treating schizophrenia with blood from epileptics. There are some references in the older literature concerning the beneficial use of convulsions in mental patients. Convulsions in the previously discovered insulin coma treatment had originally been considered as dangerous, and, therefore, had not contributed to the discovery of convulsive treatment. The theoretical

basis of convulsive therapy became doubtful when later studies questioned the antagonism between schizophrenia and epilepsy, and even more so when it was noticed, several years after the introduction of convulsive therapy, that its best results were not obtained in schizophrenia but in depressions.

Meduna[36] used a pharmacological means to induce convulsions. In 1938 Cerletti and Bini,[12] in Italy, replaced pharmacological convulsive treatment with electrically induced convulsions, whereby they introduced the most widely applied shock treatment in psychiatry. In 1957 Krantz,[31] an American pharmacologist, and his co-workers,[32] as clinicians, introduced an inhalant, Indoklon, which produces convulsions.

The common feature of these three discoveries is that their inventors did not see the essential feature of their method in the chemical or physical properties of the convulsant used, but in the convulsion itself. This important fact should be remembered even if slight differences in various drugs or various types of current were occasionally claimed.

⟪ Techniques

Pharmacological Convulsive Therapy

Meduna[36] first produced convulsions with intramuscular injection of 25 percent camphor in oil. Convulsions could be obtained with 10–40 cc. (2.5–10 cc. of camphor), according to the convulsive threshold of the individual. Camphor proved to be unreliable, because frequently the desired convulsion did not occur at all, or it happened as late as one or two hours after the injection. There also could be several convulsions. Camphor in oil was, therefore, replaced by a soluble synthetic camphor preparation, pentamethylenetetrazol, known in original European publications as Cardiazol, and in the United States as Metrazol. Metrazol is injected intravenously in a 10 percent aqueus solution. The relatively large amount of fluid injected is a necessary inconvenience, because more concentrated solutions easily coagulate the vein at the site of injection. Quick injection is necessary to obtain a convulsion with the minimum amount, and poor veins are one of the difficulties in this type of convulsive treatment.

Metrazol treatment is usually started with an initial intravenous injection of 5 cc. (0.5 g.). If no convulsion ensues within one or two minutes, subsequent injections can be given. Other convulsive drugs have been recommended, among them picrotoxin and triazol 156 or azoman (cyclohexylethyltriazol). These are less reliable in the provocation of convulsions and are more slowly eliminated. Therefore, Metrazol proved to be the best convulsive drug.

A pharmacologically induced convulsion differs from a spontaneous as well as from an electrically induced convulsion by some clonic movements preceding the tonic phase of the convulsion. It has this so-called "first-clonic phase" in common with the convulsion induced by means of the inhalant Indoklon. During the initial irregular clonic movements, the patient becomes pale and frequently coughs. He then loses consciousness and presents a tonic contraction of all muscles. This tonic phase, which lasts an average of ten seconds, goes over into a clonic phase lasting thirty to forty-five seconds. Irregular clonic movements can still occur after the convulsion is over and are peculiar to the pharmacologically induced convulsion as is the first clonic phase. Neither of these phenomena occur in electrically induced convulsions. They are probably due to a direct cortical stimulation by the drug. Occasional second convulsions occur with Metrazol, as well as in convulsions induced by inhalation but apparently never in electrically induced convulsions.

Inhalation Convulsive Treatment

Pharmacological convulsive therapy, largely replaced by electric convulsive therapy, received a revival through the introduction of convulsions with an inhalant drug, Indoklon (hexafluorodiethyl ether). The discovery of Indoklon stemmed from studies on the anesthetic action of aliphatic fluorinated ethers. One of these was found to have a convulsive action upon inhalation in laboratory animals. It was recommended by Krantz et al.[31] under the name of Indoklon, for the treatment of psychiatric patients in whom convulsive therapy was indicated. Indoklon is a colorless, mobile liquid which is readily volatile and has a mild, pleasant odor similar to ether. It is noninflammable. In the first clinical trials inhalers, similar to those used for nasal inhalation, were used. Later, a Stephenson mask, modified appropriately with an activated charcoal exhalant absorber, was used. The mask is close-fitted with one-way flow, with the drug dispersed in a measured amount over absorbent gauze contained in a plastic reservoir with air inlets. This is fastened into the inlet valve of the mask.

Today Indoklon is given with the anesthesia technique which will be described later for electric convulsive treatment. When the patient is sufficiently relaxed, 0.25–0.5 cc. of Indoklon are injected into the vaporizer through a rubber diaphragm, and the Indoklon is forced into the lungs by repeatedly squeezing the bag. Some myoclonic movements appear soon, but Indoklon has to be administered until sustained plantar flexion indicates the tonic phase. Only then is the mask taken off, the Indoklon blown out, and oxygen supply resumed. It is a frequent mistake that the myoclonic movements are taken for a convulsive seizure which actually starts only when the tonic phase sets in. If this is not the case, the application remains therapeutically ineffective.

There is no doubt that Indoklon inhalation treatment is equally effective as ECT. Its superiority in treatment-resistant schizophrenics has been claimed but not proven. A technical advantage is that it protects loose teeth better because the direct stimulation of the jaw muscles by the electrodes is eliminated. Indoklon did not fulfill the hope that the absence of electric application may reduce posttreatment confusion. Furthermore, it produces more nausea, and requires routine medication with Compazine in most patients. All this explains why Indoklon has not replaced ECT, although it is useful to have an alternative to ECT in patients who are afraid of a treatment with the name "electric shock."

Electric Convulsive Treatment, ECT

The standard technique by Cerletti and Bini[12] is still extensively used, although different types of current have been recommended. The original technique uses alternating current from the electric-light circuit at a frequency of 50 or 60 cycles. The voltage applied varies between 70 and 150 V. applied for 0.1 to 1 second. There is no need for measurement of the resistance, because the resistance of the skin changes considerably. Stimuli of less than 50–70 volts do not produce unconsciousness, cause a painful sensation, and should be avoided. Stimuli of 70 or 80 V. may produce unconsciousness but not lead to a convulsion.

They are then called subconvulsive stimuli. Increasing the current further, one may obtain a delayed convulsion. The current that produces an immediate generalized seizure varies considerably, according to the convulsive threshold of the individual patient. In general, it can be stated that young people have a lower convulsive threshold than older ones, and that women have a slightly higher threshold than men. Some machines permit the setting of the actual milliamperage which flows through the patient's head. This and other devices are controversial, however, because their reliability is questioned, and they are unnecessary, as the electric stimulus must be sufficient to produce a convulsion. It will be shown later that there is no harm in applying too large an amount of current, and, therefore, hesitancy on the part of the therapist in giving an adequate stimulus only results in the failure to elicit the proper response.

The current is applied through electrodes placed on both temples. The electrodes originally used consisted of a meshwork mounted on a rubber sponge which, by means of a forceps, permits strong pressure and the best possible adaptation to the patient's head. Other electrodes, such as simple metal disks, can be attached with rubber bands to the patient's head, but they slip off more easily and are more apt to produce burns on the patient's skin. Permeability of the skin can be improved by an electrojelly, as used in electrocardiography, or by a saline solution.

Therapeutic efficacy does not depend on the choice of any particular type of machine. Some machines try to avoid the immediate flow of the entire current for which the machine is set and, rather, step it up slowly to the maximum (glissando technique). Other machines do not measure the time but only provide a button which is pressed until the patient goes into the convulsion. The techniques of stepping up the current more slowly were based on the assumption that the occurrence of fractures in electrically induced convulsions and their absence in epileptics is explained by the sudden onset of most electric convulsions.

Great efforts have been made to avoid memory impairment, by using different types of current. The first modifications were recommended by Friedman[17] and Wilcox,[45] who both used a unidirectional wave form eliminating the alternating oscillations of the current. It was claimed that such half-waves rectified the 60-cycle current and produced a convulsion with lesser intensity, but workers who used this and other newer types of current usually applied the current for a longer period of time than did Cerletti and Bini with their standard technique. Therefore a comparison can hardly be made. The same is true for the brief-stimuli technique by Liberson,[35] who used stimuli lasting from $\frac{1}{6}$ to $\frac{1}{3}$ millisecond. Some manufacturers use a combination of unidirectional and brief-stimuli currents. Therapeutic superiority by any of these currents has never been proved. There is some evidence that the temporary memory impairment of the treatment is diminished by smaller amounts of current used with these modified techniques.

The so-called "electronarcosis treatment" was recommended by several workers from California, who used alternating current and maintained the convulsive stimulus for thirty seconds, thereby suppressing the development of clonic movements. After thirty seconds the current was reduced. At this point some clonic movements still appeared, which shows that they had been only suppressed by the continued stimulation of the brain. There is no proof that this treatment prevents any of the complications or side effects. It has been claimed, though, that its results in paranoid schizophrenia are better than those of simple electric convulsive treatment and come closer to results obtained with insulin coma treatment. Epstein[15] recommended unipolar electrocerebral stimulation with one electrode on the head and one indifferent electrode on the forearm, using spiked unidirectional current. Others tried focal stimulation producing unilateral seizures by applying both electrodes to one side of the head. This is contrary to the experience of most clinicians who consider unilateral convulsions, which sometimes occur in regular ECT, as therapeutically ineffective, and who repeat the stimulation if such a unilateral convulsion occurs.

A true electronarcosis or electric sleep is not obtained with any of these techniques. In 1902, the French physiologist Leduc[34] described electric sleep induced by applying general anesthesia by means of a unidirectional pulsating current of high frequency. Similar electronarcosis without convulsion has been reported by some Russian investigators. The closest approximation to such electric sleep treatment can be seen in methods of nonconvulsive electrostimulatory treatment.

Attempts to treat mental patients with electricity without producing a convulsion were made long ago. Shortly before the introduction of ECT, Berkwitz,[8] in this country, recommended a "faradic shock treatment" for functional psychoses. The complications which occurred in electrically induced convulsions were the reason that, soon after the introduction of ECT, attempts were made to avoid the convulsion. The so-called "subconvulsive petit-mal response" was used in a series of our patients, however, without therapeutic results. Later, several workers used even smaller amounts of current than we did, and, since the patient would have felt such low currents, intravenous injections with pentothal sodium preceded these stimulations. Improvements were claimed mostly in neurotic conditions, but not in those conditions which respond to ECT, such as depressions. Hirschfeld,[25] like many others, used special currents such as the spiked unidirectional current of the Reiter machine, but later achieved the same effect with other machines. Stimulation of the diencephalon by special placing of the electrodes above the ear and nasal electrodes as discussed by Breitner,[10] were also tried with these nonconvulsive stimulations. Another nonconvulsive application, used primarily to relieve anxiety, goes under the name of Sedac and is given for half an hour to neurotic patients.

Unilateral ECT with application of the electrodes over the nondominant hemisphere was first used by Thenon[44] in Argentina, and then by Lancaster et al.[33] in Great Britain. It leads to a generalized bilateral seizure which can be hardly distinguished from a seizure due to bilateral stimulation. There is definite agreement that this method avoids the usual posttreatment confusion and forgetfulness. There is, however, disagreement about the therapeutic effectiveness of the unilateral approach. While the studies of the original workers[33] claim identical therapeutic efficacy (Abrams and de Vito in a first paper[2] came to a similar conclusion), Abrams in his later work[1] found that more treatments are necessary with unilateral than with bilateral ECT in order to achieve identical results. He later recommended multiple treatments with unilateral application in the same session. Some clinicians reported the occasional need of subsequent bilateral ECT which means that the patient who did not recover under unilateral ECT would have done so with bilateral application even if no unilateral treatments had preceded them. The same conclusions were drawn in studies by Strain et al.[43] Interesting work by Abrams et al.[3] showed differences in the EEG changes in the sense that unilateral ECT slow waves were more pronounced over the sides of treatment electrode placement, whereas the slowing of bilateral ECT was mostly seen on the left (i.e., on the dominant hemisphere).

At the present time, the conclusion must be drawn that while the unpleasant memory impairment by ECT can be avoided with unilateral ECT, the therapeutic effect is inferior.

Another modification of the treatment which helped to reduce the memory impairment seems to be what Blachley and Gowing[9] described, in 1966, as multiple-monitored ECT. Whether or not the treatment is monitored, multiple treatments are given in the same session. They, as well as Strain and Bidder,[42] found that after two sessions with eight to ten convulsions recovery of a depression sets in with memory impairment less pronounced than when that many treatments were given in the usual three-times-a-week routine.

Preparation of the patient for ECT consists in a general medical check-up. It will be shown later that very few, if any, contraindications exist for ECT, but there might be reasons to modify anesthesia techniques in patients with cardiac or pulmonary conditions. Medico-legal considerations are also a frequent reason for physical investigation taken prior to ECT.

The preparation of the patient for each individual treatment consists in limiting his food intake. If treatment is given in the morning, no food and no medication should be taken. If treatment is given later in the day, a light breakfast of coffee or tea, and one slice of toast four hours before the treatment should not be exceeded. More food could easily lead to nausea and vomiting. The latter is especially dangerous if treatment is given under anesthesia, which abolishes the gag reflex and permits flow of gastric material into the lungs. The bladder should be voided. Dentures should be removed, although, in patients with only a few irregularly spaced teeth, it may be safer to leave the denture in to protect these teeth. Sedation does not have to be withheld except for some drugs with hypotensive effect, such as neuroleptics. It is true that some workers combine these drugs with ECT without untoward results, but some reports on unexplained fatal accidents seem to suggest the potential danger of such a combination. Although no such instances are known in connection with antidepressants, the hypotensive effect of these drugs also suggests caution. It became customary to withhold such medication on the morning of a treatment. In particular, these drugs should not be used by injection in acutely disturbed patients before the treatment; here barbiturates are preferable. If a patient is under Rauwolfia drugs, it is advisable to postpone treatment for a week, although this is sometimes not possible for psychiatric reasons.

The treatment is usually given to the patient while he is lying on a table in the most relaxed and comfortable position. A mouth gag is used for the prevention of tongue bite and for the protection of the teeth. A looplike mouth gag is the best safeguard against pressure on the valuable front teeth. However, a soft sponge is the most reliable means to protect all teeth in patients with a poor bite or irregular teeth.

Premedication with muscle-relaxant drugs for the prevention of fractures was first recommended by Bennett[7] who used curare

(Intocostrin). Later, curarelike drugs such as tubocurarine were tried. Curare and the other drugs paralyze the muscles, owing to their action on the neuromuscular junction. Prostigmin can be used as an antidote after the convulsion to shorten the effect of the curare. In spite of this antidote, fatalities with all of the curare preparations were frequent, and cases became known in which the patient died before the electroshock had been given. Therefore curare as well as the other drugs were abandoned.

In 1952 succinylcholine, discovered by the Nobel Prize winner Bovet, was introduced[5,26] for the same purpose of relaxing the muscles before an electrically produced convulsion. Succinylcholine has no antidote, but it has the great advantage over curare that the effect of an injection usually does not last more than two or three minutes, which is sufficient for the duration of a convulsion. Succinylcholine produces a block by depolarization with an acetylcholinelike effect. Muscular fasciculations, which may be quite painful, are the first effect, and a feeling of suffocation indicates the beginning of respiratory paralysis. It is for this reason that pentothal sodium or similar short-acting barbiturates are injected before the injection of succinylcholine. Our technique,[28] developed and used by the anesthesiologist S. dell'Aria, applies the drip method using a 0.2 percent solution of methohexital (Brevital) in 5 percent dextrose solution after insertion of an 18-gauge thin-wall needle. Approximately 40 or 50 mg. of Brevital induces sleep. Then the Brevital drip is followed by infusion of 0.2 percent succinylcholine chloride in 5 percent dextrose solution. While the patient is oxygenated, muscle fasciculations set in, followed by complete relaxation of the muscles. A good sign that paralysis has set in is the disappearance of knee and other reflexes. It is at this point that the convulsive stimulus should be given.

Succinylcholine appears to be less dangerous than the preceding barbiturate anesthesia. This is suggested by clinical experience since the introduction of anesthesia in ECT, as well as by some cardiovascular complications in

ECT, when pentothal sodium was used prior to the advent of muscle relaxants. Therefore, Impastato[27] devised a technique of giving the patient succinylcholine, followed by an immediate subconvulsive stimulus to prevent the feeling of suffocation. The subconvulsive stimulus is followed, after complete muscle relaxation, by the convulsive stimulus. This technique shows two disadvantages, namely, that the subconvulsive stimulus may be either too weak so that the patient feels the current, or too strong so that an immediate convulsion takes place before the patient is relaxed. Therefore, this technique is reserved for patients with myocardial damage or pulmonary diseases such as asthma or emphysema, where barbiturate anesthesia might be dangerous.

Constant oxygenation before, during and after the convulsion is necessary. The possibility of prolonged apnea, possible cardiovascular disturbances, and the unexpected occurrence of vomiting with flow of gastric material into the lungs, while the gag reflex is absent, make the assistance of an anesthetist preferable, although it is not considered obligatory. Reports on fatalities are rare, but in the author's opinion higher than in unmedicated ECT. However, prevention of the frequent bone complication with these techniques is so reliable that today premedicated ECT with muscle relaxants is generally accepted as a routine procedure.

Electric convulsive therapy is usually given three times a week. It can, however, be administered every day, and even several treatments a day are recommended by those who wanted to produce a severe organic reaction as a possible way to achieve better results. Such "regressive," "confusional," or "annihilation" treatment was first suggested for psychoneuroses but later also for other conditions. We tried this method in relapsing schizophrenics without convincing results, but we could confirm the observation of others that such intense treatment does not lead to lasting memory impairment or other damage. Glueck et al.[22] found this procedure in which the patient's regression is brought to the point of incontinence of urine and feces, superior to ordinary ETC. Cameron and Pande[11] used it under the term of "depatterning" and combined it with prolonged barbiturate sleep treatment and with neuroleptics. Sargant[40] also combines ETC with prolonged sleep and neuroleptics.

Ambulatory treatment can be given in outpatient departments of hospitals as well as in properly equipped offices. Here the patient should be kept in the office for at least one hour. He should be treated only if he is accompanied by someone who can take him home. Furthermore, supervision at home must be requested. The patient should also be warned against driving a car while there is the possibility of organic side effects. The social importance of ambulatory treatment is undeniable, especially in cases such as depressions, where a few treatments can be expected to remove the condition, and where hospitalization may be an unnecessary hardship on the patient. He and the relatives should be warned against business activities during the time of memory impairment following ECT.

Medical observations[28] during an electrically induced convulsion are numerous but mostly of theoretical interest. The heart rate is usually increased during the clonic phase, whereas during the tonic phase the pulse can hardly be felt. Arrhythmias are frequent in the postconvulsive phase. Observations of the circulatory system show inconsistencies, however. There is evidence that the blood pressure does not depend on the muscular contraction but is due to central stimulation. Electrocardiographic changes are negligible, showing mostly arrhythmias of very short duration. Numerous metabolic studies have been made without clarifying the therapeutic agent of ECT. The same is true for studies of blood biochemistry and spinal-fluid studies. Endocrine changes have also been studied. Plasma steroid elevation has been reported. It was claimed that the more normal the adrenal cortex response to ECT, the better the therapeutic effect. The most important clinical manifestations of an endocrine nature are disturbances of weight and menstruation. Pa-

tients responding well to ECT gain weight. Since the same is true for patients with spontaneous improvements, however, it can be questioned whether the ECT, as such, or the clinical improvement led to the gain in weight. Menstruation is also affected and often ceases during a long course of ECT, if it had not ceased already during the psychosis before the treatment. Amenorrhea often continues for a month or two after ECT, even in clinically improved cases. The same is true for temporary impotence during and shortly after ECT. Sleep disturbances are usually concomitant with weight disturbances and are often the first to disappear in patients successfully treated by ECT. The autonomic nervous system has been studied in various ways, but again it must be said that, aside from such signs as epinephrine increase after each convulsion, most changes can be explained equally by improvement of the mental syndrome for which the patient is being treated.

Funkenstein et al.[18] studied the response of electroshocktreated patients to epinephrine and mecholyl chloride and found differences in these responses valuable for prognostication in patients undergoing ECT. The authors described various reactions in what is commonly referred to as the Funkenstein test. Details must be studied in the authors' original work. Contradictory results limited the value of this prognostic test.

Psychiatric changes manifesting themselves during ECT are manifold, and can be explained as organic-reaction types. They are unrelated to the improvement of the underlying psychiatric condition for which the patient is treated. All patients show confusion immediately after a convulsion, and a retrograde amnesia which usually clears up in one or two hours. Patients never remember any sensations from the electric shock even if no anesthesia is given. The memory impairment becomes longer in duration after several treatments. The intellectual impairment is always accompanied by some emotional disturbances, and the patient is dull or sometimes silly. Fear develops almost invariably after a certain number of treatments, and no satisfactory explanation has been found for this fear which the patient also is unable to explain. Some people are frightened by the wakening and the ensuing difficulty in orienting themselves, and by a very characteristic feeling that everything looks either strange and unfamiliar or, to the contrary, that all strangers look familiar. Postconvulsive excitement is not infrequent and may lead to dangerous aggressiveness, which may last for fifteen to thirty minutes. Patients always have a complete amnesia for such postconvulsive excitement states. If they occur once, they usually occur after every treatment, but they can be avoided by a twenty-minute drip of Brevital. Less severe excitement can be prevented by an intravenous injection of 1–2 cc. of Diazepam (Valium) after the convulsion.

A rare organic psychotic reaction occurring during or shortly after a series of ECT is represented by disorientation with vivid auditory and sometimes visual hallucinations, a syndrome which differs from the original psychosis for which the patient is being treated. Such symptomatic psychoses may last for several days but always clear up spontaneously. Another important observation is the activation of the patient's original psychosis. This is mostly seen in quiet, blocked, or depressed schizophrenics in whom, after the first treatment, an acute delusional and hallucinatory syndrome emerges. In these cases the underlying schizophrenic psychosis, previously unrecognized, becomes overt, leading to the statement by Halpern[24] that ECT can serve as a diagnostic aid in schizophrenia.

Psychological investigations by Zubin[47] and many others have shown convincingly that the most constant psychiatric side effect of ECT, i.e., memory impairment, is not permanent. Learning and retention return within a few weeks after termination of treatment. Testing of patients with more than 100 treatments by Rabin,[39] Perlson,[38] and other authors showed that no organic patterns remain. More insistent complaints of memory impairment are sometimes heard from neurotic patients who are overconcerned with all side effects of the treatment, and many complain of forgetful-

ness long after tests have shown a return of normal memory function. The Swedish workers Cronholm and Ottosson[13] found that successfully treated patients had less memory difficulty than those with only limited therapeutic results.

Neurological observations contributed little to the understanding of ECT. The manifestations do not differ from those observed in other convulsions. Electroencephalographic findings are quite similar to those seen in spontaneous convulsions. After several treatments the electroencephalographic record remains abnormal, being characterized generally by slow waves which disappear within one or two months after termination of treatment. The question of brain damage has been thoroughly investigated since early papers mentioned petechial hemorrhages and other bleedings in the brain. Later, studies in animals and in humans after fatalities did not confirm such hemorrhages, nor did they reveal any cell changes in the brain. In our experimentation on monkeys treated with the same technique used in our patients, no changes were found that were not likewise present in the brains of control animals. Alexander and Loewenbach[4] demonstrated that morphologically recognizable tissue reactions are limited to the parts of the brain which lie in the direct path of the current and are limited to vasoconstriction, not accompanied by cell changes. Most studies confirmed the absence of "brain damage" in ECT. Although the presence of memory impairment and electroencephalographic changes is undoubtedly proof of reversible organic changes in the brain, it does not express itself in any neuropathology visible with present-day methods.

Complications and Contraindications

In the past, the most important complications of convulsive therapy were represented by fractures. Some difference between spontaneous convulsions in epileptics and pharmacologically, as well as electrically, induced convulsions must be considered responsible for these fractures, because they hardly ever occur in epileptics. Knowledge concerning these fractures is useful today only in order to understand why muscle relaxants are necessary. The most frequent fractures were those in the middorsal spine which, however, aside from some temporary pain never led to any neurological complications because they were limited to the rigid part of the spine. Less frequent were fractures of the neck, of the humerus, and of the femur, the latter occurring only in male patients. The same was true of the rare fractures of the acetabulum.

The absence of other complications is easily understood, when we realize that epileptics never have any complications from their seizures or any aggravation of preexisting diseases.

Fatalities are extremely rare. Those few which did occur, usually concerned patients whose pretreatment examination did not indicate a particularly great risk. In most fatalities autopsies did not show any explanation for the death. In over 100,000 treatments given in one treatment unit a fatality rate of 0.003 percent was found in spite of a large percentage of old patients with cardiovascular disease.[30]

The discussion of complications has shown that the contraindications established for ECT in the beginning of our experience cannot be maintained. There is general agreement that arterial hypertension does not represent a contraindication, all the more as most psychotic episodes lead to a rise in blood pressure which is reduced immediately when the patient improves under ECT. The rise of systolic pressure to 300 in one of our patients with an agitated depression, and its reduction to 160 after the first clinical improvement, shows that any attempt to lower the blood pressure as a preparation for ECT is ill-advised. Cardiovascular diseases had been considered as a complication until more and more such patients had to be treated because their mental condition and their agitation endangered the cardiovascular system. There is now an almost general agreement that such cases stand ECT extremely well, and the only precaution may consist in replacing the barbiturate anesthesia

with a subconvulsive stimulus as described above. Recent coronary thrombosis is a great problem, when ECT is indicated. Variable waiting periods have been postulated,[27] but where treatment had to be given for psychiatric reasons as early as a few weeks after a coronary infarction, it was tolerated surprisingly well. Patients have been treated after previous heart surgery, and those with a pacemaker do not even show the normally observed asystole or arrythmia during the treatment.

Aneurysms, especially of the aorta, tolerated even unpremedicated ECT very well, as demonstrated by Wolford[46] with a patient who received 275 ECT over a five-year period in spite of a large aneurysm which finally ruptured in a treatmentfree interval. Patients with the history of an arachnoid hemorrhage or bleeding ulcers can be treated with muscle relaxant drugs without hesitation.

Pulmonary tuberculosis is no contraindication. This was important because of the frequent simultaneous occurrence of tuberculosis and schizophrenia. Fever in itself is no contraindication as seen in those severe cases of pernicious catatonia in which ECT is life-saving. Eye complications are not considered a contraindication since it was found that a convulsion does not increase but rather decreases intraocular pressure. Glaucomas are more a contraindication for antidepressant drugs than for ECT. However, the use of succinylcholine suggests eserine or other eye drops prior to the treatment.

Pregnancy is definitely no contraindication which is again in accordance with the known fact that pregnant epileptic women are not threatened by abortion or premature birth. Even in patients treated at termination of pregnancy convulsions do not produce labor pain or rupture of the membrane. Followups also did not show any damage to the child.

Age is no contraindication as has been amply demonstrated in patients treated at the age of over eighty. Children have been treated without harm as shown by the extensive experience of Bender.[6]

Bone diseases, even recent fractures, are no

contraindication if muscle relaxants are given in adequate dosage. Arthritis of the spine, spinal curvature, and even recent laminectomies do not represent contraindictions as was shown by such cases even before muscle relaxants were available.

(Indications and Results

Pharmacological convulsive therapy and its later modification of electrically induced convulsions were introduced for the treatment of schizophrenia. However, a few years later, it was recognized that the most spectacular results were obtained in the treatment of the affective psychoses, and here mainly in depressions. Insulin coma treatment, which had also been introduced for the treatment of schizophrenia, remains limited to this disease. The indications for convulsive therapy and its most widely used technique of electric convulsive therapy include both affective disorders and schizophrenic psychoses, as well as a number of other psychiatric disorders. There are many statistical evaluations of results. They are so numerous that their individual listing would go beyond the scope of this contribution, but they can be found in a monograph on the subject.[28]

Depression and Manic States

The most favorable results in ECT are undoubtedly obtained in depressions. Some statistics for ECT in typical psychotic depressions come close to 100 percent recoveries of the episode for which the patient was treated, although future episodes of depression cannot be prevented. The patients usually respond after two or three treatments, but it is necessary to give a few more to stabilize the improvement. However, it is hardly ever necessary to give more than six to eight treatments in depressions. The first three treatments should be applied within a week, whereas the subsequent ones may be spread over longer intervals. They may be spaced more closely in cases of serious suicidal danger. Depressions respond equally well whether they are manic-depressive, involutional, or those of old age.

Today the most important decision for the psychiatrist is whether to treat a depression with pharmacotherapy or with ECT. Most patients referred to a specialist are already under antidepressant medication, although often in inadequate amounts. An attempt with increased dosage is usually the first step if there are no reasons to institute ECT immediately. The overriding consideration is suicidal danger which is present in every psychotic depression. There are no reliable ways to estimate suicidal danger. It is true that patients of the older age group are statistically more apt to commit suicide in a depression. However, all of us have misjudged this danger, and such accidents are the reason why ECT in depressions is again more widely used. Other considerations are time and money. The lack of job protection and the limited period of insurance for psychiatric hospitalization often rule out time-consuming use of drugs. There is ample proof that ECT remains the most reliable treatment for endogenous depressions.

Combination of ECT and antidepressant drugs is of little value. If pharmacotherapy has failed, its combination with ECT has no advantage and the hypotensive effect of antidepressants might be potentially dangerous for the barbiturate anesthesia during ECT.

In neurotic or reactive depressions ECT has less convincing results. However, if the depressive affect in a neurotic patient is very deep and neither psychotherapy nor antidepressant drugs were successful, ECT should be tried. Side effects, such as complaints of memory impairment, are more frequent in this group of patients.

Depressive episodes occurring in manic-depressives cannot be prevented by treatment of the individual episode. Prophylactic ECT as demonstrated by Geoghegan and Stevenson[21] is useful in patients who have very frequent episodes. It could be shown convincingly that in such cases one ECT in monthly intervals prevents future episodes. Today antidepressant drugs can be tried for the prevention of future episodes. More promising is lithium carbonate in patients with bipolar depressions. In monopolar depressions results with prophylactic lithium are less convincing, and monthly ECT is still indicated if the depressions are frequent enough to warrant it.

Toward the end of a depressive episode, patients sometimes show a slight hypomanic state which usually clears up within one or two weeks. The same has been observed in spontaneous remissions. There are also patients whose depression is immediately followed by a true manic phase of the disease.

The manic phase of a manic-depressive psychosis also responds to ECT. Treatments are successful only if they are given close together, one or two treatments a day. This often leads to the remission of a manic phase with the same number of treatments as in depressions (six to eight). Sometimes longer series of treatments are necessary in manics. It should be realized that manic syndromes are often unrecognized schizophrenic syndromes and are less responsive to a short series of ECT. The indication for ECT in manic patients has changed since the introduction of lithium carbonate. This type of medication is certainly superior to ECT in milder manic episodes. In severe manic excitement, ECT is still useful in removing the acute symptomatology within a few days until simultaneously started lithium carbonate becomes effective and is then continued as long-term medication.

Involutional melancholia also clears up spontaneously, but the duration of the illness is usually much longer than in depressive episodes of manic-depressive patients. Therefore, these patients should be subjected to ECT as soon as possible. Fortunately, even a longer duration of illness does not interfere with a favorable outcome. Results are equally as good in retarded as in agitated depressions, a statement which is also valid for manic-depressive and senile depressions. Failures are usually due to schizophrenic and paranoid symptoms of an involutional psychosis, a group which actually belongs to the schizophrenic psychoses.

Depressions of old age respond equally well to convulsive therapy. The importance of this cannot be overemphasized, because patients in this age group, when they become psychotic, are usually diagnosed as senile psychoses, and such cases are considered organic reactions to an irreversible brain condition. Careful diagnostic appraisal of all old-age patients reveals that many of them do not show the typical intellectual impairment of senile or presenile psychoses but the symptomatology of a retarded or agitated depression which could have likewise occurred at an earlier age. Sometimes more careful anamnestic searching will reveal that such patients did have depressions at an earlier age. These persons stand ECT very well, and clinical experience shows that they recover with a smaller number of convulsive treatments than do many cases of depression in the younger age groups.

Schizophrenia

In the group of schizophrenics, results with ECT are far less spectacular than in the affective disorders. Patients with acute symptomatology may also become symptomfree after the same number of treatments (three or four) that clear up a depression. After such few treatments, however, schizophrenics invariably relapse. Therefore, many workers have requested that in pharmacological and electric convulsive treatment a minimum of fifteen or more convulsions be given even in patients who appear symptomfree after a few treatments.

Pharmacotherapy with neuroleptics has changed the indications for ECT in schizophrenics. This is particularly true in chronic schizophrenics for whom ECT never had much to offer. The symptomatic improvement of disturbed behavior is today almost entirely the domain of neuroleptic drugs. There are, however, still some indications for ECT in chronic schizophrenics. One example are those patients whose illness runs in episodes and who are known to respond to a very few treatments. A second group are those who show some irreversible changes in the sense of Bleuler's primary symptoms but who, in spite of neuroleptic medication, have acute exacerbations with psychomotor excitement, paranoid or other symptoms which respond to ECT. A third group are chronic schizophrenics with symptoms that do not respond well to drugs, such as catatonic stupor. If these patients begin to slow down and withdraw, a few ECT's or an occasional maintenance treatment can keep them functioning. Finally, there is a considerable number of chronic patients who do not take their medication, either because of negligence or because of subjective side effects. Here ECT in an ambulatory setting can be of great value.

Acute schizophrenia continues to be an important indication for ECT. In these patients the indications for ECT and neuroleptic drugs overlap. If an acute catatonic excitement responds to pharmacotherapy, there is no reason to give ECT. However, often the symptoms are only covered up by the medication. Therefore, these acute patients who have a good chance for a full and lasting remission, should be withdrawn tentatively from neuroleptic medication before they are discharged from the hospital. If they then relapse into their previous symptomatology, ECT instead of drugs should be instituted in the hope that the patient achieves a full remission and can be discharged without medication. One reason for this recommendation is that these acute schizophrenics should be given the opportunity of a treatment which is most effective during the first year of illness but may lose efficacy later. If chronicity cannot be prevented, continued pharmacotherapy can still be of great symptomatic value after years of illness.

The various subtypes of schizophrenia respond differently to convulsive therapy. It has often been said that catatonic stupors respond best. This is true from a symptomatic standpoint because even chronic catatonics respond well to two or three treatments. The results, though, are not lasting, and these patients tend to relapse. Catatonic excitement and acute paranoid states respond best to ECT. In catatonic excitements the treatment is often life-saving and should be instituted immediately even in patients with dehydration and high fever. Three treatments, given within twenty-four hours, remove the threatening

condition. Here, neuroleptic drugs are often contraindicated in the required large amounts, particularly when the disturbed behavior makes injection of the drug necessary. The hypotensive effect of neuroleptics may lead to vasomotor collapse, a complication which may even occur spontaneously in these patients, who, therefore, were described as having "pernicious catatonia." Here, ECT has its best results and is well tolerated even if these patients are in extremely poor physical condition.

Chronic paranoid schizophrenia with insidious onset in the middle-aged patient respond less well and usually require a long series of treatments. Hebephrenics and the simple type of schizophrenia show the poorest results. This confirms the often repeated fact that the primary symptoms of schizophrenia do not respond in a convincing way to any of our treatments, and that the secondary symptoms are the ones that are amenable to treatment. It also makes it understandable that even schizophrenics in remission frequently show some "scarring" in the sense of loss of emotional responsiveness or other primary symptoms of schizophrenia. The pseudoneurotic type of schizophrenia also responds poorly to ECT, except if complicated by acute panic states or depressive features which clear up after a few treatments but leave the basic illness untouched.

Postpartum psychoses are usually schizophrenic episodes occurring after childbirth. Depressive features are frequently in the foreground and may explain the favorable prognosis of many of these cases. There are, however, some postpartum psychoses which are particularly resistant to shock therapy. On the whole, the response of these patients to ECT does not differ much from the results in other schizophrenic patients.

Other Indications for ECT

Other indications for convulsive therapy are rare or unsatisfactory. The most important fact is that ECT has hardly any indications in the large group of the neuroses. Much of the objection to ECT stems from its indiscriminate use in this type of patient. Anxiety, the most frequent symptom in neuroses, is often aggravated by such side effects of ECT as memory impairment and a feeling of unreality. Cases of conversion hysteria frequently add the side effects to the already-existing symptoms. Psychosomatic symptoms occasionally benefit from the blurring effect of ECT. This is particularly true when psychosomatic symptoms occur episodically with some degree of depressive mood, a group of patients which today is often described as "masked depression," and which Foster Kennedy[29] labeled as "manic-depressive equivalent." In most neurotic and psychosomatic conditions ECT has nothing to offer, and it should be added that attempts to use it as an adjunct to psychotherapy in the sense of making patients more accessible, are bound to fail. A notable exception are psychoneurotic or reactive depressions, which may respond well to a few convulsive treatments. This supports the view held by many that depressions in such patients are actually unrelated to the neurosis, and it is seen again and again that such a patient's depression clears up, but that his neurotic symptoms persist. The fact that obsessive-compulsive neuroses and anxiety neuroses do not respond to ECT in any lasting way is in accordance with the experience that such symptoms in depressions or in schizophrenia tend to mar even an otherwise favorable prognosis for ECT. Some claims have been made for favorable results in psychoneurotics who had been treated with the intense method of regressive shock. Nonconvulsive electrostimulation treatment was found to be more valuable in psychoneurotics, but the simultaneous use of barbiturate anesthesia in nonconvulsive treatment may account for these results.

Organic psychiatric disorders offer some indications for symptomatic ECT. They have, however, been mostly replaced by the newer drugs. The most frequent, although purely symptomatic, use of ECT is made in the organic psychoses of old age. In these patients such disturbing symptoms as agitation, depression, and paranoid delusions can often be removed with a few ECT's which are often better tolerated by very old patients than psychotropic drugs in large doses. In mental deficiency, epilepsy, and other organic conditions, disturbed behavior can be influenced by ECT. In general paresis, depressive, manic, and paranoid syndromes can be removed symptomatically by ECT, but the basic treatment of the underlying pathology is penicillin or malaria. The practical value of ECT in general paresis is that it quickly removes symptoms which often make the treatment of these patients in neurological wards so difficult. In Parkinson's disease the noninfrequent depressions or paranoid episodes respond very well to ECT, and the neurological impairment in these and other patients with neurological ailments often improves remarkably after the removal of the emotional disorder. In epileptics, ECT has some interesting indications: clouded states, which usually clear up after spontaneous convulsions, can be equally shortened by two or three electrically induced seizures. The rise of the convulsive threshold, which is observed after each convulsive treatment, also led to attempts to decrease the number of spontaneous convulsions in epileptics. The practical importance of such attempts, even though successful, is minimal. In some neurological conditions such as hyperkinetic manifestations, results have been contradictory. A few psychosomatic disorders may respond to ECT. Favorable results have been reported in neurodermatitis, bronchial asthma, and other conditions. Intractable pain of various kind, including trifacial neuralgia and pain of phantom limbs, may respond well, though certainly not in any predictable way. A last indication to be mentioned is the possibility of preventing withdrawal symptoms in drug addiction. This method has been quite successful in the treatment of morphine and barbiturate addiction in open hospitals. But it has lost importance since the introduction of the new drugs. The same is true for toxic and postinfectious psychoses, where ECT was successful but is today replaced by drugs.

The clinician will make occasional use of ECT in various conditions,[20] but it should be repeated once more that the actual indications lie in the field of the major psychoses.

◖ General Remarks

Although the place of ECT in the therapeutic armamentarium of the psychiatrist is definitely established for the treatment of psychotic patients, there are those who feel that any disease expressing itself in psychological symptoms can be treated only by psychological means and that convulsive therapy is only an adjunct to psychotherapy. That this is not the case is clearly proved by the excellent results of ECT in depressions, and particularly in involutional melancholia, for which most patients are treated without psychotherapy. The question as to what extent future depressive episodes can be prevented with psychotherapy after ECT is an open one. Again, another problem is the use of ECT to improve the patient's accessibility to psychotherapy. This has been tried, especially in neuroses, with one or a few ECT's but results remained unconvincing.

My own experience includes two parallel series of patients, one treated in a large institution without psychotherapy, and the second in a teaching institute with intensive psychotherapy for each patient. The comparative results did not support the view that psychotherapy is indispensable to obtain favorable results with ECT. This, of course, does not contradict the advantage of proper supportive psychotherapy in any patient treated for a psychological disturbance. It should also be emphasized that, in hospital patients, occupational and work therapy as well as a progressive hospital management are important factors contributing to good results in the rehabilitation of patients.

Discussions of the theoretical aspects of convulsive treatment largely reflect the concepts of different authors. Gordon[23] was able to publish fifty different theories on ECT. They can be classified as partly psychodynamic and partly somatic. The shock therapies represent a somatic approach to the treatment of psychological disease, and, therefore, a somatic explanation of their mode of action seems to be more probable than a psychological one. Yet psychological theories have been advanced in considerable number. Whereas in insulin coma treatment the more intimate contact with physicians and nurses has been considered as psychotherapeutically valuable, ECT, with its post-treatment amnesia, does not offer itself to such theories. The concept of the "psychic shock" caused by any treatment that makes the patient unconscious, has been promoted, however, by a number of authors. In Metrazol treatment, the sensation of deathly fear before the convulsion was considered an important psychotherapeutic factor. This concept, however, had to be abandoned when this sensation was eliminated in the electrically induced method. The experience of coming close to death, though, followed by the feeling of rebirth, was common to all shock treatments and was thought to break the patient's autism and to counteract his regression and narcissism. It has also been claimed that the threat of death helps to mobilize the patient's vital instincts.

The especially good results in depressions with guilt feelings led to the theory that the treatment works because it represents a well-deserved punishment for the patient's sins. Experience with many depressed patients suggests, however, that most of them do not consider this treatment as a punishment; even if one assumes that they do consider it as such, there are many valid objections against such expanations of the therapeutic effect of ECT.

It appears that all psychological theories connected with the frightening experience of the treatment could not explain the uniformity of results, for instance in depressions, because many patients do not have any fear, or they develop fear only after they are improved. It should also be borne in mind that ECT remains unsuccessful if the patient is treated only with stimuli which render him unconscious but do not produce convulsions. The ineffectiveness of nonconvulsive treatment in conditions where the convulsion proves to be beneficial is the most convincing evidence against any psychological theory, because the patient's psychological experience is the same, whether or not he convulses during his state of unconsciousness. It may also be added that barbiturate anesthesia without electric convulsion, and nitrogen anesthesia, to mention another therapeutic attempt, do not have the same results. Another point to be made against purely psychological theories is the fact that psychoneurotics for whom the experience of the treatment has the greatest psychological impact show the poorest results. A combination of psychogenic and organic concepts was tried by Schilder,[41] who stated that the victory over the death threat in any epileptic seizure and the perceptual and aphasic difficulties of the postconvulsive state enable the patient to start life and normal relations all over again. He emphasizes, however, that, although the results of the treatment can be psychologically understood, this does not mean that it acts primarily as a psychological agent in the common sense. The same should be said about some psychoanalytical theories of shock treatments, which are interesting attempts to describe the phenomena during shock treatments in analytical terms but hardly explain satisfactorily why a convulsion rather than simple unconsciousness is necessary for therapeutic results.

Unfortunately, somatic theories of convulsive therapy are also far from being satisfactory. There is actually not one somatic theory that could not be easily disproved. It has been stated already that the theory of the antagonism between schizophrenia and epilepsy, which led to the discovery of convulsive therapy, could not be maintained. The assumption that a convulsion eliminates toxic substances from the nerve cell was suggested in convulsive treatment by the old concept that an epileptic seizure has the purpose of eliminating toxic substances.

Attempts to localize the effect of convulsive therapy concentrated on the diencephalic centers. Stimulation of the diencephalon locally rather than with a generalized convulsion was tried. The importance of the diencephalic region for the effect of ECT is supported by symptoms such as weight gain, improved sleep, menstrual changes, and other manifestations. Such concepts logically follow ideas on the origin of psychiatric syndromes in the diencephalon. The influence of ECT on the vegetative centers of the brain also played an important part in the theoretical concepts of some French authors[14] who devoted monographs to the subject. Theories of reduced oxygenation as a therapeutic agent became obsolete after the introduction of anesthetic techniques in ECT. Oxygenation before and after the convulsion in patients premedicated with succinylcholine rather tends to overoxygenate patients under ECT. Work on changes of the vegetative nervous system did not lead to more convincing theories than did many of the other laborious studies on the biochemistry of convulsive treatment. Attempts to explain the therapeutic effect with organic brain changes have also been made. Although neuropathological changes are absent, the electroencephalographic and psychological changes would support such a view. These changes, however, are still practically absent when, for example, depressions clear up after two or three treatments. The purely empirical nature of convulsive therapy cannot be denied. This is not surprising in a treatment of disorders for which no etiology is established, and it should not be a reason to withhold such treatment where clinical experience has demonstrated its usefulness.

Electroconvulsive therapy, as the most widely used form of convulsive treatment, continues to be a very effective therapeutic measure in psychiatry. This is so in spite of many misconceptions listed by Furlong[19] in an article on "The Mythology of Electric Convulsive Therapy," in which he concluded that neither the treatment nor the myths have left us yet. The advent of pharmacotherapy raised the hope that medication would replace this and other complicated procedures. Many reports on neuroletpic drugs in schizophrenia and on antidepressant drugs claimed that the new psychotropic drugs have replaced ECT. Later, comparative studies and, more so, clinical experience demonstrated that the hope of replacing ECT was premature. In recent years, ECT is again on the increase in spite of its frightening name, persistent theoretical objections, and its poorly understood mode of action. The number of publications on ECT is again growing, the difficulty of using anesthesia techniques for a psychiatric treatment has been overcome in many hospitals, and the public has become increasingly aware of the effectiveness of this somatic treatment in psychiatry.

⟮ Bibliography

1. ABRAMS, R. "Recent Clinical Studies of ECT," *Semin. Psychiatry*, 4 (1972), 3–12.
2. ABRAMS, R. and R. A. DE VITO. "Clinical Efficacy of Unilateral ECT," *Dis. Nerv. Syst.*, 30 (1969), 262–263.
3. ABRAMS, R., M. FINK, R. DORNBUSH et al. "Unilateral and Bilateral ECT: Effects on Depression, Memory, and the Electroencephalogram," *Arch. Gen. Psychiatry*, 27 (1972), 88–91.
4. ALEXANDER, L. and H. LÖWENBACH. "Experimental Studies on Electroshock Treatment: 1. The Intracerebral Vascular Reaction as an Indicator of the Path of the Current and the Threshold of Early Changes within the Brain Tissue," *J. Neuropathol. Exp. Neurol.*, 2 (1944), 139–140.
5. ARNOLD, O. H. and W. BÖCK-GREISSAU. "Elektroschock und Muskelrelaxantien," *Wien. Z. Nervenheilk.*, 4 (1951), 326.
6. BENDER, L. "One Hundred Cases of Childhood Schizophrenia Treated with Electric Shock," *Trans. Am. Neurol. Assoc.*, 72 (1947), 165.
7. BENNETT, A. E. "Preventing Traumatic Complications in Convulsive Shock Therapy by Curare," *JAMA*, 114 (1940), 322–324.
8. BERKWITZ, N. J. "Faradic Shock Treatment of the 'Functional' Psychoses," *Lancet*, 59 (1939), 351–355.
9. BLACHLY, P. H. and D. GOWING. "Multiple Monitored Electroconvulsive Treatment," *Compr. Psychiatry*, 7 (1966), 100–109.
10. BREITNER, C. "Localized Electric Stimulation of the Diencephalon in the Treatment of Mental Disorders," *Dis. Nerv. Syst.*, (Suppl.), 18 (1957), 14.
11. CAMERON, D. E. and S. K. PANDE. "Treatment of the Chronic Paranoid Schizophrenic Patient," *Can. Med. Assoc. J.*, 78 (1958), 92–96.
12. CERLETTI, U. and L. BINI. "L'Elettroshock," *Arch. Psicol. Neurol. Psichiatr.*, 19 (1938), 266.
13. CRONHOLM, B. and J. O. OTTOSSON. "The Experience of Memory Function after Electroconvulsive Therapy," *Br. J. Psychiatry*, 109 (1963), 251–258.
14. DELAY, J. *L'Electro-choc.*, Paris: Masson, 1946.
15. EPSTEIN, J. and L. WENDER. "Alternating Current vs. Unidirectional Current for Electroconvulsive Therapy—Comparative Studies," *Confin. Neurol.*, 16 (1956), 137–146.
16. FINK, M. "The Mode of Action of Convulsive Therapy," *J. Neuropsychiatry*, 3 (1962), 231.
17. FRIEDMAN, E. "Unidirectional Electro-Stimulated Convulsive Therapy," *J. Nerv. Ment. Dis.*, 109 (1949), 540.
18. FUNKENSTEIN, D., M. GREENBLATT, and S. ROST. "A Test which Predicts the Clinical Effects of Electroshock Treatment on Schizophrenic Patients," *Am. J. Psychiatry*, 106 (1950), 889–901.
19. FURLONG, F. W. "The Mythology of Electroconvulsive Therapy," *Compr. Psychiatry*, 13 (1972), 235–239.
20. GALLINEK, A. "Controversial Indications for Electric Convulsive Therapy," *Am. J. Psychiatry*, 109 (1952), 361–365.
21. GEOGHEGAN, J. J. and G. H. STEVENSON. "Prophylactic Electroshock," *Am. J. Psychiatry*, 105 (1949), 494–496.
22. GLUECK, B. C., H. REISS, and L. E. BERNARD. "Regressive Electric Shock Therapy," *Psychiatr. Q.*, 31 (1957), 117.
23. GORDON, H. L. "Fifty Shock Therapy Theories," *Milit. Surgeon*, 103 (1948), 397–401.
24. HALPERN, L. "Electroshock as a Diagnostic Aid in Schizophrenia," *Monatsschr. Psychiatr. Neurol.*, 118 (1949), 61–64.
25. HIRSCHFELD, G. R. "Nonconvulsive Electrostimulation," *J. Nerv. Ment. Dis.*, 117 (1953), 323–328.
26. HOLMBERG, G. and S. THESLEFF. "Succinylcholine Iodide as a Muscular Relaxant in Electroshock Therapy," *Am. J. Psychiatry*, 108 (1952), 842–846.
27. IMPASTATO, D. J. "The Safer Administration of Succinylcholine without Barbiturates—a New Technic," *Am. J. Psychiatry*, 113 (1956), 461.
28. KALINOWSKY, L. B. and H. HIPPIUS. *Pharmacological, Convulsive and Other Somatic Treatments in Psychiatry.* New York: Grune & Stratton, 1969.
29. KENNEDY, F. "The Neuroses Related to the Manic-Depressive Constitution," *Med. Clin. North Am.*, 28 (1944), 452.

30. KING, E. Personal Communications, to be published.

31. KRANTZ, J. C., JR., E. B. TRUITT, JR., L. SPEERS et al. "New Pharmacoconvulsive Agent," *Science*, 26 (1957), 353.

32. KURLAND, A. A., T. E. HANLON, A. J. ESQUIBEL et al. "Comparative Study of Hexafluorodiethyl Ether (INDOKLON) and Electroconvulsive Therapy," *J. Nerv. Ment. Dis.*, 129 (1959), 95.

33. LANCASTER, N. P., R. R. STEINERT, and I. FROST. "Unilateral Electroconvulsive Therapy," *J. Ment. Sci.*, 104 (1958), 221–227.

34. LEDUC, S. "Production du sommeil et de l'anesthésie générale et locale par le courant eléctrique," *Compt. Rend. Acad. Sci. U.R.S.S.*, 135 (1902), 199.

35. LIBERSON, W. T. and P. H. WILCOX. "Electric Convulsive Therapy: Comparison of 'Brief Stimuli Technique' with Friedman-Wilcox-Reiter Technique," *Dig. Neurol. Psychiatry*, 8 (1945), 292–302.

36. MEDUNA, L. J. "General Discussion of the Cardiazol Therapy," *Am. J. Psychiatry* (Suppl.), 94 (1938), 40.

37. NYIRO, J. "Beitrag zur Wirkung der Krampftherapie der Schizophrenie," *Schweiz. Arch. Neurol. Psychiatr.*, 40 (1937), 180.

38. PERLSON, J. "Case of Schizophrenia Treated with 248 Electric Shock Treatments," *Arch. Neurol. Psychiatry*, 54 (1945), 409.

39. RABIN, A. L. "Patients who received more than 100 Electric Shock Treatments," *J. Pers.*, 17 (1948), 42.

40. SARGANT, W., E. SLATER, and D. KELLY. *An Introduction to Physical Methods of Treatment in Psychiatry*, 5th ed. London: Churchill, Livingstone, 1972.

41. SCHILDER, P. "Notes on Psychology of Metrazol Treatment of Schizophrenia," *J. Nerv. Ment. Dis.*, 89 (1939), 133.

42. STRAIN, J. J. and G. T. BIDDER. "Transient Cerebral Complication Associated with Multiple Monitored Electroconvulsive Therapy," *Compr. Psychiatry*, 32 (1970), 95–100.

43. STRAIN, J. J., L. BRUNSCHWIG, J. P. DUFFY et al. "Comparison of Therapeutic Effects and Memory Changes with Bilateral and Unilateral ECT," *Am. J. Psychiatry*, 125 (1968), 294–304.

44. THENON, J. "Electrochoque monolateral," *Acta Neuropsiquiatr. Argent.*, 2 (1956), 292.

45. WILCOX, P. H. "Electroshock Therapy. A Review of Over 23,000 Treatments Using Unidirectional Currents," *Am. J. Psychiatry*, 104 (1947), 100–112.

46. WOLFORD, J. A. "Electroshock Therapy and Aortic Aneurysm," *Am. J. Psychiatry*, 113 (1957), 656.

47. ZUBIN, J. "Memory Functioning in Patients Treated with Electric Shock Therapy," *J. Pers.*, 17 (1948), 33.

CHAPTER 28

SURGICAL CONTRIBUTIONS TO PSYCHIATRIC TREATMENT

Kenneth E. Livingston

❨ Introduction

VIEWED in historical perspective it is clear
that surgical contributions to psychiatric treatment were developed parallel with advancing insight into how the brain
"works." Since the 1930s surgical contributions fall into three distinct but overlapping
epochs, representing successive levels of insight into the central mechanisms that govern
emotion and behavioral activity.

During the first epoch which began in 1935,
the surgical approach was entirely empirical.
The objective was disconnection of a major
portion of the anterior frontal lobe from the
rest of the brain. Since no physiological function was then ascribed to the isolated regions,
the procedures were referred to as "psycho"
(mind) surgery.

Within ten years however, limitations of this
empirical frontal-lobe lesion were apparent.
During this period it was demonstrated in
animal studies, and confirmed in man, that
there were two discrete areas within the so-
called "silent" zone of frontal disconnection
from which strong autonomic responses could
be elicited by electrical stimulation. This suggested that a more selective and physiological
approach to surgical treatment might be developed.

By 1950, the empirical frontal transection of
"psychosurgery" was being replaced by physiologically defined and anatomically limited
lesions of the frontal lobe. With this advance
the epoch of empirical "psychosurgery" drew
rapidly to a close.

During the second epoch, attention focused
on the anatomically restricted target areas of
autonomic representation in the posterior orbital and anterior cingulate regions of the

frontal lobe. Selective frontal lesions in these areas have proven to be clinically effective in alleviating otherwise intractable disorders of affect, but have not proven effective in modifying the schizophrenic psychoses which represent the major burdens of chronic psychiatric illness.

Clinical studies of temporal-lobe epilepsy have provided persuasive evidence that temporal-lobe circuits must be involved in many of the manifestations of the schizophrenialike psychoses. In addition, it has become increasingly clear that the central mechanisms governing visceral, emotional, and psychic activity are not arranged in separate and specific structural and functional packages, but rather as integrated circuits in a larger dynamic complex—the limbic system.

Thus, during the third and current epoch of surgical contribution to psychiatry, the frame of reference has extended beyond the frontal lobes to encompass the more complex territories of the temporal-lobe and limbic system. Therapeutic strategies appropriate to the current "limbic" era of biological psychiatry are still developing.

In the following brief review we will trace the development of surgical contributions to psychiatry from an opening "empirical" phase to an increasingly refined physiologial orientation; from a fixed focus concept to a balanced "systems" approach; and from an anatomically ablative to a functionally modulative methodology.

⟮ Empirical Frontal-Lobe Transection: "Psychosurgery"

The principal events leading to the development of surgical therapy for psychiatric illness are well known. In 1935, Fulton and Jacobsen[35] presented to the International Congress of Neurology in London, observations on two now famous chimpanzees, *Becky* and *Lucy*, who were relieved of experimentally induced frustrational and neurosislike behavior by extensive frontal-lobe ablation. Viewing the film records of this animal study, the Portuguese neuropsychiatrist, Egaz Moniz, visualized the striking changes in the animal's behavior in terms of specific psychiatric patients under his care. Together with his neurosurgical colleague, Almeida Lima, Moniz designed a surgical lesion which transected connections of the anterior frontal lobe with other parts of the brain.[82] This frontal lobotomy or leucotomy (cutting of white matter) was considered functionally equivalent to the technically more formidable ablations carried out in the laboratory studies. This frontal disconnection produced striking improvement in some patients with previously intractable psychiatric disability.[82]

In America clinical interest in this empirical surgical approach to psychiatric therapy was stimulated by the monograph, *Psychosurgery*,[32] by Freeman and Watts, published in 1942. This study presented clinical data on eighty surgically treated patients, and raised widespread expectations that this new mode of therapy might substantially reduce much of the individual and social burden of chronic psychiatric illness. With rapidly rising public interest and demand "psychosurgery" was widely undertaken.

Although the frontal disconnection resulting from the standard lesion of psychosurgery was frequently followed by strikingly beneficial changes in otherwise unremitting disability[*] some limitations of this extensive frontal transection soon became apparent.[21,110] Although the negative effects following operation were often relatively minor in degree compared with the extent of clinical improvement, they sometimes constituted a serious and irreversible deficit. In 1948, Fulton[33] expressed this concern in "an earnest plea for caution on the part of the neurosurgeon, lest, in the absence of basic physiological data, he unwittingly do irremediable harm to human beings who might be benefitted by a far less radical operation than is now being performed."

Thus, although the potential value of frontal intervention had been established by the early results of the standard lobotomy procedure,

---

[*] See references 32, 41, 97, 111, and 125.

further refinement was clearly needed, first to define the minimal anatomical lesion that would be clinically effective, and second to establish, if possible, some physiological rationale for the procedure.

It was soon established that a more limited lesion, interrupting only the medial frontal pathways,[34,41,97] was as effective as the standard frontal transection, and carried much less risk of unwanted side effects. Pathological correlations[9] indicated that it was injury to connections of the frontal polar convexity that accounted for the principal blunting effects on personality and intellect. By 1952 it was established on the basis of clinical studies that frontal lesions limited to the cingulate[57,60,129,132] or orbital[43,115,124] areas of the frontal lobe were equally or more effective in relieving severe psychiatric disability than the earlier standard transection, and that these lesions could be applied with some degree of clinical selectivity particularly in the affective psychoses. Most important, this limited intervention carried a much lower risk of undesirable side effects than the more extensive lesions of psychosurgery. In 1951, Fulton[34] was able to state "in the light of information we now possess, I believe that the radical lobotomy as carried out by Freeman and Watts should be abandoned in favor of a more restricted lesion."

The evolution in concept and practice which made psychosurgery obsolete clearly reflected increasing insight into how the brain "works." Unfortunately, awareness of this orderly evolution from an empirical to a physiological rationale for surgical intervention was obscured by the dramatic introduction of chlorpromazine therapy.[20] The almost immediate assumption that pharmacotherapy would provide the definitive solution for severe chronic psychiatric illness, produced a backlash of criticism directed not only at the empirical procedure of psychosurgery, but, in effect, at all types of surgical intervention.

Historically the period of surgical empiricism in psychiatric therapy was brief. Its limitations were recognized early, and through continued clinical and laboratory efforts a rational physiological approach to selective fron-tal-lobe surgery was rapidly established. In retrospect, it is clear that psychosurgery was only a brief initial step in the sequence of surgical contributions to psychiatric treatment.

❲ Selective Frontal-Lobe Intervention

At the time that frontal lobotomy was introduced in America, all of the territory anterior to the plane of section of the surgical lesion was regarded as physiologically "silent." Historically however, nearly fifty years earlier Spencer[120] had demonstrated cardiovascular and respiratory responses from stimulation of the orbital frontal cortex in the cat, rabbit, dog, and monkey. Spencer's findings were confirmed by Bailey and Sweet[6] in 1940, and by Livingston and his collaborators in Fulton's laboratory in 1947.[68,69] The possible clinical implications of these observations, however, were not discussed.

In 1945 Smith[116] elicited a full range of autonomic responses from stimulation of the anterior cingulate gyrus in the monkey, and particularly noted that the responses "are those which are generally recognized as occurring in emotional expression, necessarily implicating this cortical region in the emotive process." See Figure 28–1.

Two years later Ward[129] confirmed Smith's observations, and stated that the most striking change following bilateral ablation of the cingulate gyrus in the monkey was a change in social behavior, characterized by a loss of fear and absence of aggression.

Thus, by 1947, on the basis of animal studies, the possible role of two powerful autonomic effector areas of the frontal lobe, in modifying emotional activity and behavior had been clearly established. Clinical application of these experimental studies followed promptly.

In 1948 and 1949 clinical studies of selective lesions of the anterior cingulate gyrus were undertaken in England, France, and America. In 1951 and 1952, initial reports of these studies[57,60,132] showed that selective cingulate lesions were highly effective in relieving some

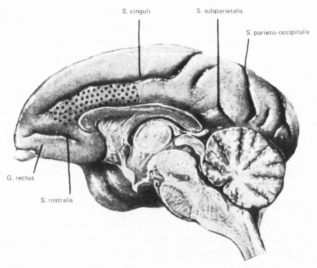

Figure 28–1. The medial surface of the brain of macaca mulatta showing the area of the anterior cingulage gyrus from which autonomic responses are elicited by electrical stimulation.[116]

patterns of previously intractable restless hyperactivity, irritability, excitement, anxiety, and obsessive compulsive behavior. With various types of cingulate disconnection there was little or no evidence of loss of intellect or blunting of personality.

Concurrent studies of selective lesions of the orbital cortex and its underlying white matter[43,124] demonstrated that disconnection of this area of autonomic representation is particularly effective in relieving the intractable depressive syndromes.

In physiological terms, the reduction of psychic and motor hyperactivity following cingulate disconnection suggests the removal of an overdriving facilitatory mechanism, while the release of psychic and motor activity following orbital disconnection suggests the removal of overactive inhibitory mechanisms.

It is of interest that although direct electrical stimulation of these areas both in man and animals produces patterns of autonomic outflow that are quite similar, the response to ablation or disconnection in chronic psychiatric disorders is quite different. This suggests that although the final outlet pathways may be identical, the intermediate circuit relationships are unique. In ongoing activity one can visualize that constellations of neurones in the cingulate and orbital cortex exert a quite different tonic bias on the central mechanisms

regulating the affective state. In this context "normalcy" of affect represents a dynamic balance between these and other circuits, while persistent imbalance is expressed as affective disorder. The anatomical basis for such a functional hypothesis has been described by Nauta.[91,93,94]

Since the 1950s, there has been no basic change in the surgical approach to the treatment of the affective disorders. There is now extensive documentation of the clinical effectiveness of lesions limited to the frontal areas of autonomic representation in modifying intractable affective disorders.* New stereotaxic methods have been developed for lesion placement together with new techniques of lesion production using radio frequency,[7,11,12,29] cryogenic,[19] and radioactive instrumentation.[56] Open methods of surgical ablation or tract section under direct vision are less frequently employed, but the target areas remain essentially the same.

During this period, the conceptual framework within which surgical contributions to psychiatry were evolving had extended beyond the frontal lobes to include the more complex territories of the temporal-lobe and limbic system.

The transition from a frontal to limbic ori-

* See references 4, 7, 12, 17, 29, 52, 54, 57–60.

entation has been facilitated by the fact that the patterns of limbic-system representation and the topography of autonomic projection in the frontal lobe are identical.

⟨ The Evolution of the Limbic-System Concept

The designation "limbic system" was first used in its current context by MacLean in 1952.[72] The terminology was derived from Broca's description in 1878[10] of "la grand lobe limbique" made up of the cingulate gyrus superiorly, and the hippocampal gyrus inferiorly, joined anteriorly beneath the genu of the corpus callosum by the "olfactory" lobe. These prominent structures on the medial wall of the hemisphere formed a "limbus" or hemlike ring around the foramen of Munro at the point of lateral evagination of the embryonic neural canal from which the cerebral hemispheres develop.

The structures of Broca's limbic lobe were traditionally considered to be part of the rhinencephalon or smell-brain. In 1901, Ramón-y-Cajal challenged this assumption. "Since the memorable works of Broca, the general opinion has been that the limbic convolutions are the station for the distribution of primary and secondary olfactory fibers," but "all our efforts . . . persuade us that these conductors represent centrifugal or descending pathways passing near the olfactory centers, but that they have nothing more than neighborly relations with them." [pp. 117–118][106]

In 1933, Herrick[47] made the suggestion that these "olfactory parts of the cerebral cortex" might be components of a nonspecific arousal mechanism for all cortical activity.

Shortly thereafter, Papez[96] posed the question "Is emotion a magic product or is it a physiological process?" He answered by postulating that the structures of Broca's limbic lobe are part of a "harmonious central mechanism of emotion." Papez included not only the cingulate gyrus and hippocampus but their interconnections with the hypothalamic and anterior thalamic nuclei as well (see Fig-

ure 28–2). Although these structures of the *Papez circuit* constitute only the medial components of what we now visualize as the *limbic system*, the basic relationships, which Papez postulated in 1937, have required little modification in subsequent years.

The first direct evidence providing physiological support for the Papez postulate came in 1945, when Smith[116] demonstrated that a full spectrum of autonomic responses could be elicited by stimulation of the anterior cingulate gyrus in the monkey. It was pointed out that this display of pupillary, cardiovascular, respiratory, and pilomotor response was identical with that accompanying states of emotional activation in the intact animal.

Similar autonomic representation had been demonstrated earlier[6,68,69] in the orbital frontal cortex, an area not included in the Papez "central mechanism of emotion."

Evidence that these two discrete areas of the frontal lobe exert modulatory control over patterns of autonomic outflow from lower brain-stem centers provided the basic physiological rationale for selective surgical intervention in the therapy of some patterns of affective psychiatric illness. The elaborate interplay between autonomic activity and all forms of emotion and behavior requires that the central regulatory mechanisms serving internally expressed (visceral) behavior, and externally expressed (emotional) behavior, be fully integrated at higher levels.

In 1948, Yakovlev[133] extended the Papez concept to include a major group of basolateral mesopallial structures, i.e., the orbital, insular, and anterior temporal cortical areas, together with their interconnections with the amygdala and dorsomedial nucleus of the thalamus (see Figure 28–3). Within this circuit, the orbital cortex might play a role in the regulation of autonomic-emotional interaction parallel to that of the cingulate cortex in the Papez circuit. Although the patterns of autonomic response elicited by electrical stimulation of the cingulate and orbital frontal cortex are similar, indicating that they act on the same motor outflow pathways, the intermediate connections are strikingly different.

In 1952, MacLean[72] proposed that the

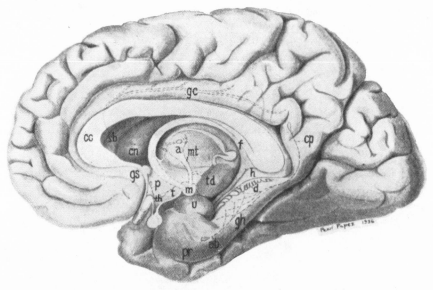

Figure 28–2. The medial surface of the right cerebral hemisphere showing the principal structures included in Papez "central mechanism of emotion."[96] (Copyright 1937, American Medical Association.)

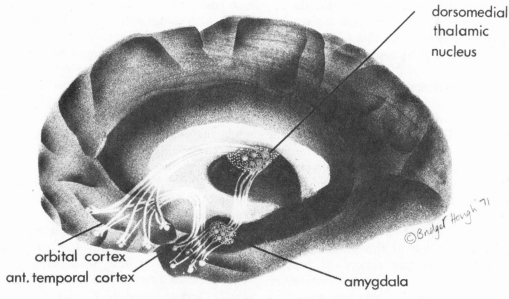

dorsomedial
thalamic
nucleus

orbital cortex
ant. temporal cortex

amygdala

Figure 28–3.   The basolateral limbic circuit.

structures of the medially oriented circuit described by Papez,[96] and the basolaterally oriented circuit added by Yakovlev[133] be given the common designation "limbic system."

The basic relationships, as defined in 1952, have been fully confirmed by subsequent studies. There has been increasing emphasis on the major linkage of the medial circuit with the reticular core of the brain stem (see Figure 28–4). Fibers from the great fornix bundle pathway are distributed widely from the septal preoptic level throughout the length of the hypothalamus to the limbic-midbrain area of Nauta in the tegmentum.[91–94]

If the medial limbic circuit were to be characterized in terms of this prominent anatomical orientation, it might be said that the medial circuit listens to and interacts particularly with the reticular core of the brain stem. Through these pathways the medial limbic

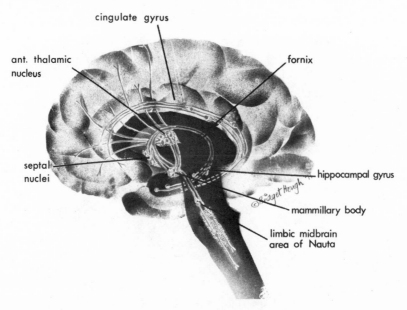

Figure 28–4.   The medial limbic circuit.

circuit receives the major input from the internal (visceral) world, and from the mechanisms of alerting and attention represented in the reticular activating apparatus of the brain stem.*

Clinical experience indicates that destructive lesions of structures within this medial limbic circuit are characterized principally as states of motor and psychic hypoactivity, in effect a "turning off" of activating mechanisms. Clinical syndromes of apathy, akinesia, and mutism are seen with a variety of lesions (tumor, aneurysm, trauma, etc.) at all levels of this circuit from the medial frontal cortex to the midbrain tegmentum. Conversely, irritative disturbance within this circuit can be visualized as producing motor and psychic hyperactivity, i.e., an excessive driving of alerting and activating mechanisms. Syndromes of restlessness, irritability, excitement, anxiety, obsessive-compulsive behavior, etc., fall in this category. This type of clinical disturbance is most likely to be benefitted by selective lesions of the cingulate and medial frontal areas.

In contrast to the medial circuit, the basolateral limbic circuit receives its major volume of input from the great sensory receiving and

association areas of the neocortex via pathways which converge in parallel on the transitional cortex of the anterior temporal lobe (see Figure 28–5). This circuit then appears to be listening particularly to sensory information from the body surface and the outer world. The disorganization of normal activity in this limbic sector, can be visualized as producing misinterpretation of sensory information from the body surface and from the environment, leading to the complex delusional systems, patterns of hallucination, and thought disorder that characterize the schizophrenic psychoses.[15,101]

If the dysfunctions that characterize the schizophrenic psychoses involve particularly temporal-limbic circuits, what evidence is available as to the effects of temporal-lobe lesions in these major psychiatric disorders?

⟨ Temporal-Lobe Lesions

The role of temporal-lobe surgery in the management of the major psychoses is not yet defined. Clinical information is largely indirect, since up to the present time most temporal-lobe intervention has been focussed on the problems of epilepsy and pathological aggression.

* See references 16, 61, 62, 64, 93, 94, and 101.

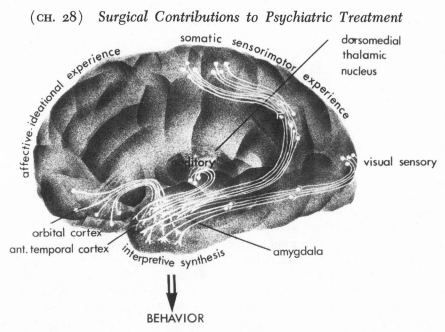

somatic sensorimotor experience

dorsomedial thalamic nucleus

affective-ideational experience

auditory

visual sensory

orbital cortex

ant. temporal cortex

interpretive synthesis

amygdala

BEHAVIOR

Figure 28–5. Convergence of information from neocortical sensory receiving and association areas on the limbic cortex of the anterior temporal lobe.

Temporal-lobe epilepsy is of particular interest since many of its manifestations suggest a transient psychosislike dysfunction.[26-28] During an attack the patient may appear detached from reality, have hallucinatory sensory experience (olfactory, visual, auditory, somatic, etc.), often with a strong emotional content, and may carry out complex psychomotor performance for which there is no subsequent memory.[36] This miniature "psychosis" is commonly time-locked to the period of electrographic seizure discharge.* Of greatest interest, however, is the fact that with longstanding temporal-lobe epilepsy there is increasingly frequent interictal psychiatric disturbance extending from a mild change in personality to gross and continuous manifestations of psychosis. At this end point, the psychiatric characteristics of the "organic" psychosis associated with epilepsy may be indistinguishable from the "idiopathic" psychosis.[8,37] The clinical association between the seizure disorder and the complex psychic phenomena is accepted, but the extent to which they share a common pathophysiological substrate has not been established.[26]

If the seizures and the schizophrenialike psychosis in temporal-lobe epilepsy are ex-

pressions of focal dysfunction in a common substrate, unilateral temporal lobectomy in patients with a well defined seizure focus should be followed by parallel improvement in the psychotic as well as epileptic manifestations. Unfortunately this has not proven to be the case. Indirect benefits do occur as a result of improved social function in individuals who are free of seizures, but the basic characteristics of the psychotic disorder are not changed. As Falconer[25] has stated, "the psychosis persists, although mellowed."

On the basis of clinical experiences and considerable experimental evidence it seems likely that the mechanisms responsible for the psychoses are multicentric and seldom dependent on the surgically resectable structures of a single temporal lobe.

What clinical information is available as to the effects of bilateral lesions in the temporal-limbic circuits?

Most of the relevant clinical data in this area are derived from the study of patients showing recurrent unprovoked aggressive behavior. The surgical approach utilized in most of the latter cases has been bilateral stereotoxic lesioning of the amygdala. The initial studies by Narabayashi[88] were carried out on individuals with extensive brain damage or severe impairment from longstanding intract-

* See references 8, 26, 27, 37, and 117.

able epilepsy. Here the operation had a marked quieting effect on behavior. In patients with no other evidence of brain defect than the seizure disorder and the unprovoked aggressive behavior, bilateral lesions of the amygdala consistently reduce emotional tension and affective response.[77,87,127] Although these patients are emotionally more stable and function better socially, there is flattening of normal emotional responsiveness, together with decreased spontaneity and productivity.

Vaernet[127] carried out bilateral amygdalotomies in a series of twenty schizophrenic patients, all of whom had had bilateral frontal lobotomy between ten and fifteen years earlier, but continued to be violently aggressive. Following amygdalotomy all of these patients were improved in terms of their aggressive behavior but their psychoses were not altered. They were described as quiet and generally cooperative but still deeply schizophrenic, in poor contact, and hallucinating.

The conclusion from clinical experience with bilateral amygdalotomy must be that this surgical lesion does not significantly alter the mechanisms responsible for the schizophrenias. Similarly, the combination of bilateral amygdalotomy with basolateral frontal tractotomy[127] apparently fails to relieve the schizophrenic syndromes. In addition, earlier evidence established the fact, that bilateral lesions of the hippocampus are not acceptable since they impose a disabling defect in memory.[81]

Focal hypothalamic lesions have been shown to have a general "sedative" effect on some patterns of hyperactive behavior[112] and, in combination with thalamic lesions, to modify some patterns of abnormal sexual behavior.[108]

Multiple lesions of the thalamus[23] and combinations of hypothalamic, thalamic, and amygdala lesion[57] also modify behavior, but none of the changes described suggest that such lesions would be effective in the treatment of the schizophrenic psychoses.

Can other lesions or combinations of lesions in the temporal lobe and limbic circuits effectively modify the schizophrenic psychoses without imposing serious deficit?

At present there is little clinical evidence on which to base an answer to this question. Limited experience of Turner,[126] Brown,[11] and Crow[19] suggests that in some carefully selected cases multifocal destructive lesions may be effective in relieving schizophrenic symptoms, but the data are insufficient to permit any conclusion regarding the applicability of such surgical intervention in the general therapeutic management of major schizophrenic illness.

Thus, although it is established that the affective components of intractable psychiatric illness can be benefited by precise and limited surgical intervention, no comparable formula for the treatment of the schizophrenic syndromes has yet emerged. Since schizophrenic illness reflects a much more profound and extensive disorder of emotional, psychic, and behavioral activity than the imbalances of the affective disorders, it is quite possible that no type of ablative intervention will substantially relieve the disorder without sacrificing essential qualities of intellect, motivation, and personality.

There is now very good evidence to suggest that new nonablative approaches to the treatment of the major psychoses may prove fruitful in the future.

⟮ The Future Outlook

The most desirable approach to therapy of the major psychoses would be through nondestructive manipulations which could, over a period of time, permit the central mechanisms of emotional-behavioral control to return to a state of "normal" homeostatic balance.

If the schizophrenic syndromes reflect biochemical as well as neurophysiological imbalances, various noninvasive manipulations may be employed to modify the abnormal activity. This general approach to therapy is exemplified by the long established use of physical (EST) and pharmacological (phenothiazine) modes of therapy. The potential effectiveness of this approach increases dramatically with growing insight into the basic chemistry and physiology of brain function. This is illustrated by the striking improvement in the clinical management of Parkinson's disease following the discovery of the role of dopamine in the nigrastriatal pathway.[51] Similar investigations of serotonin, dopamine, noradrenaline, acetylcholine, and other putative neurotransmitters, may produce equally dramatic breakthroughs in psychiatric therapy.* Some of the ultimate therapeutic possibilities from this rapidly expanding field of investigation, have been suggested in important reviews by Axelrod[3] and Snyder, et al.[119]

Some biochemical and pharmacological measures may be applied systemically by oral and parenteral routes, but counterbalancing peripheral and central effects, together with problems of blood brain barrier, differential actions of the same agent in different parts of the nervous system, and dosage requirements for whole body administration may seriously restrict the use and effectiveness of potentially valuable agents. It is now possible, using stereotactic techniques for both electrophysiological and biochemical interventions to be direct to specific targets, and applied with precise control of timing and intensity.

The possibility of selectively changing the balance of activity in specific limbic circuits by introducing different patterns of facilitatory or inhibitory input, without imposing a "lesion," may open new avenues to effective therapy. Clinical information in this area is still very limited. Repeated low-intensity electrical stimulation of particular limbic loci has been given some clinical trial,[46] but has not yet produced lasting benefit. It is now possible to implant permanent receivers that will deliver patterned electrical stimulation to such electrode sites, using apparatus comparable to cardiac pacemaker systems. However, such electrophysiological techniques should be applied with considerable caution since there is substantial experimental evidence[21,39,84,103] suggesting that repeated stimulation of limbic and neocortical structures may induce widespread changes in threshold and may establish a persisting "mirror focus."

* See references 3, 78, 114, 118, and 119.

Controlled biochemical intervention may carry less risk and offer greater potential for benefit. Some bits of relevant information are available. More than twenty years ago, as a screening test for patients under consideration for frontal lobotomy, Van Wagenen carried out direct infiltration of procaine hydrochloride into the white matter of the frontal lobe through frontal burr holes in a series of twenty chronic schizophrenic patients.[128] A striking reduction in psychic symptoms occurred in thirteen of the twenty patients, lasting in several cases for twenty-four to forty-eight hours, and in one case, after a second injection, persisting for two weeks, although the drug is completely hydrolysed in brain tissue and plasma in less than thirty minutes.[5,65] In many of these cases the qualitative as well as the quantitative change in long-standing schizophrenic symptoms and behavior was remarkable. More recently, Bucci reported using procaine systemically as a monamine oxidase inhibitor in a series of twenty patients with chronic schizophrenia.[13] In sixteen of the twenty cases there was a well defined sequence of clinical improvement over a period of six months. In four cases the drug had to be discontinued early because of aggravation of psychotic symptoms. These observations suggest that significant modification of the schizophrenic syndromes may be possible by using nondestructive biochemical and pharmacological modes of therapy.

Recent evidence from our experimental laboratory[105] suggests that there may be a definable electrophysiological basis for such changes in the emotional-behavioral state. In the kindling model of temporal-lobe epilepsy induced by repeated low-intensity stimulation of the amygdala, there is a progressive buildup of after-discharge which spreads widely throughout the limbic structures before overflowing into the motor pathways as a convulsive seizure.[38,39,102,103] Once established, the pattern of seizure response to the amygdalar stimulus is stable over long periods.[38,104] In rat-killing cats, concurrent with the appearance of motor seizures, there is a striking and long-lasting change in predatory behavior.[1] This provides a useful model to study the electrographic correlates of limbic-induced motor seizure and behavioral change, and their modification by various pharmacological and biochemical agents.[104]

In recent studies[104] it has been shown that procaine administered systemically facilitates after-discharge in the limbic structures but has an opposite, inhibitory, effect on electrical excitability at the cortical level. In the same study, diazepam (valium) was found to have a strikingly suppressant effect on limbic excitability, but little effect at the cortical level. Diphenylydantoin (dilantin) had effects very similar to procaine, i.e., blocking discharge at the cortex, but facilitating discharge in the limbic structures. Such well-defined and selective inhibition or facilitation of electrical excitability in different cortical and limbic loci raises the possibility of therapeutic modulation of central dysfunction in some of the psychotic states. Other drugs may have equally or more selective effects, and can perhaps be used in various combinations to suppress some of the physiological dysfunction underlying the schizophrenic syndromes. Specific transmitter substances may be utilized in a similar manner, systemically or by more precise presentation to particular loci, using stereotactic techniques for placement and fine implanted canula-reservoir systems for delivery.

The possibility of modifying disordered limbic activity and restoring a more normal cortico-limbic balance through nondestructive inhibitory or facilitatory biochemical "tuning" opens new avenues to therapy for the major psychoses.

Much additional important information will be forthcoming from many laboratories working at both basic science and clinical levels. The final therapeutic assessments must be clinical since there is as yet no adequate experimental model for chronic schizophrenia. The initial clinical trials must be carried out under the most thoughtful and careful scientific control, with reference to all of the social and legal restraints relating to clinical research and informed consent.

Although no therapeutic "formula" can yet be defined, there is reason to hope that the massive problem of the schizophrenic psychoses will not remain forever totally impregnable, and that through increasingly close collaboration with the basic neurosciences, surgical approaches will contribute to the breaching of its walls.

([Bibliography

1. ADAMEC, R. "Neural Correlates of Long Term Changes in Predatory Behavior in the Cat." Ph.D. Thesis, McGill University, 1974.

2. ANDY, O. "The Neurosurgical Treatment of Abnormal Behavior," *Am. J. Med. Sci.*, 252 (1966), 232–238.

3. AXELROD, J. "Neurotransmitters," *Sci. Am.*, 230 (1974), 58–65.

4. BAILEY, H. R., J. L. DOWLING, C. H. SWANTON et al. "Cingulo-Tractotomy in the Treatment of Severe Affective Illness," *Med. J. Aust.*, 1 (1971), 8–12.

5. BAILEY, O. T., W. T. SMALL, and F. D. INGRAHAM. "Procaine Block of Frontal Lobe White Fibers as a Means of Predicting the Effect of Prefrontal Lobotomy. I. Experimental Studies," *J. Neurosurg.*, 9 (1952), 21–29.

6. BAILEY, P. and W. H. SWEET. "The Effects on Respiration, Blood Pressure, and Gastric Motility, of Stimulation of the Orbital Surface of the Frontal Lobe," *J. Neurophysiol.*, 3 (1940), 276–281.

7. BALLANTINE, H. T., W. L. CASSISDY, N. B. FLANAGAN et al. "Stereotaxic Anterior Cingulotomy for Neuropsychiatric Illness and Intractable Pain," *J. Neurosurg.*, 26 (1967), 488–495.

8. BEARD, A. W. "The Schizophrenia-like Psychosis of Epilepsy," *Br. J. Psychiatry*, 109 (1963), 113–129.

9. BECK, E., T. McLARDY, and A. MEYER. "Anatomical Comments on Psychosurgical Procedures," *J. Ment. Sci.*, 96 (1950), 157–167.

10. BROCA, P. "Anatomie comparée des enconvulutions cérébrales: le grand lobe limbique et la cissure limbique dans la série des mammifères," *Rev. Anthropol.*, 1 (1878), 385–498.

11. BROWN, M. H. "Further Experience with Multiple Limbic Targets for Schizophrenia

and Aggression," in L. Laitinen and K. E. Livingston, eds., *Surgical Approaches in Psychiatry*, pp. 189–195. Lancaster, England: Medical and Technical Publ., 1973.

12. BROWN, M. H. and J. A. LIGHTHILL. "Selective Anterior Cingulotomy: a Psychosurgical Evaluation," *J. Neurosurg.*, 29 (1968), 513–519.

13. BUCCI, L. "Procaine: a Monoamine Oxidase Inhibitory in Schizophrenia," *Dis. Nerv. Syst.*, 34 (1973), 389–391.

14. CHOPPY, M., M. ZIMBACCA, and J. LeBEAU. "Psychological Changes after Selective Frontal Surgery (Especially Cingulotomy) and after Stereotactic Surgery of the Basal Ganglia," in L. Laitinen and K. E. Livingston, eds., *Surgical Approaches in Psychiatry*, pp. 174–181. Lancaster, England: Medical and Technical Publ., 1973.

15. CLEMENTE, C. "The Neurological Substrates of Aggression Behavior," *Annu. Rev. Physiol.*, 35 (1973), 329–356.

16. CHUTE, C. C. D. "Cholinergic Pathways of the Brain," in L. Laitinen and K. E. Livingston, eds., *Surgical Approaches in Psychiatry*, pp. 282–292. Lancaster, England: Medical and Technical Publ., 1973.

17. COLUMBIA-GREYSTONE ASSOCIATES. *Selective Partial Ablation of the Frontal Cortex: A Correlative Study of Its Effects on Human Psychotic Subjects*, F. A. Mettler, ed. New York: Hoeber, 1949.

18. CRAWFORD, M. P., J. F. FULTON, C. F. JACOBSEN, et al. "Frontal Lobe Ablation in Chimpanzee: a Resume of Becky and Lucy," *Res. Publ. Assoc. Res. Nerv. Ment. Dis.*, 27 (1947), 3–58.

19. CROW, H. J. et al. "Progressive Leucotomy," *Curr. Psychiatr. Ther.*, 13 (1963), 98–113.

20. DELAY, J., P. DENIKER, and J. M. HARL. "Utilisation en thérapeutique psychiatrique d'une phénothiazine d'action centrale eléctive," *Ann. Med. Psychol. (Paris)*, 110 (1952), 112–117.

21. DELGADO, J. and N. SEVILLANO. "Evolution of Repeated Hippocampal Seizures in the Cat," *Electroencephalogr. Clin. Neurophysiol.*, 13 (1961), 722–733.

22. DiCARA, L. V. "Learning in the Autonomic Nervous System," *Sci. Am.*, 222 (1970), 30–39.

23. DYNES, J. B. and J. L. POPPEN. "Lobotomy for Intractable Pain," *JAMA*, 140 (1949), 15–19.

24. FALCONER, M. A. "Temporal Lobe Epilepsy in Children and Its Surgical Treatment," *Med. J. Aust.*, 1 (1972), 1117–1121.

25. ———. "Pathological Substrates in Temporal Lobe Epilepsy with Psychosis," in L. Laitinen and K. E. Livingston, eds., *Surgical Approaches in Psychiatry*, pp. 121–124. Lancaster, England: Medical and Technical Publ., 1973.

26. FLOR-HENRY, P. "Schizophrenic-like Reactions and Affective Psychoses Associated with Temporal Lobe Epilepsy: Etiological Factors," *Am. J. Psychiatry*, 126 (1969), 148–152.

27. ———. "Ictal and Interictal Psychiatric Manifestations of Epilepsy: Specific or Non-specific," *Epilepsia*, 13 (1972), 773–783.

28. ———. "Psychiatric Syndromes Considered as Manifestations of Lateralized Temporal-Limbic Dysfunction," in L. Laitinen and K. E. Livingston, eds., *Surgical Approaches in Psychiatry*, pp. 22–26. Lancaster, England: Medical and Technical Publ., 1973.

29. FOLTZ, E. L. "Cingular Lesions. Current Status and Use of Rostral Cingulotomy," *South. Med. J.*, 61 (1968), 899–908.

30. FONBERG, E. "Control of Emotional Behavior through the Hypothalamus and Amygdaloid Complex," *Ciba Found. Symp.*, 8 (1972), 131–150.

31. FREEMAN, W. "Transorbital Leucotomy: the Deep Frontal Cut," *Proc. R. Soc. Med. (Suppl.)*, 4 (1949), 8–12.

32. FREEMAN, W. and J. W. WATTS. *Psychosurgery: Intelligence, Emotion, and Social Behavior Following Prefrontal Lobotomy for Mental Disorders*. Springfield, Ill.: Charles C. Thomas, 1942.

33. FULTON, J. F. *Functional Localization in the Frontal Lobes and Cerebellum*. The William Withering Memorial Lectures, 1948. Oxford: Clarendon Press, 1949.

34. ———. *Frontal Lobotomy and Affective Behavior*. New York: Norton, 1951.

35. FULTON, J. F. and C. F. JACOBSEN. "The Functions of the Frontal Lobes, a Comparative Study in Monkeys, Chimpanzees and Man," *Adv. Mod. Biol. (Moscow)*, 4 (1935), 113–123.

36. GESCHWIND, N. "Disconnection Syndromes in Animals and Man," *Brain*, 88 (1965), 237–294, 585–644.

37. GLITHERO, E. and E. SLATER. "The Schizo-

phrenia-like Psychoses of Epilepsy. IV.,"
Br. J. Psychiatry, 109 (1963), 134–142.

38. GODDARD, G. V. and D. McINTYRE. "Some
Properties of a Lasting Epileptogenic
Trace Kindled by Repeated Electrical
Stimulation of the Amygdala in Mammals," in L. Laitinen and K. E. Livingston,
eds., *Surgical Approaches in Psychiatry*,
pp. 109–117. Lancaster, England: Medical
and Technical Publ., 1973.

39. GODDARD, G. V., D. McINTYRE and C.
LEECH. "A Permanent Change in Brain
Function Resulting from Daily Electrical
Stimulation," *Exp. Neurol.*, 25 (1969),
295–330.

40. GOLLA, F. L., E. C. DAC, E. J. RODLEY-
SMITH et al. "Prefrontal Lobotomy with
Reference to Indications and Results,"
Proc. R. Soc. Med., 39 (1946), 443–458.

41. GRANTHAM, E. G. "Prefrontal Lobotomy for
Relief of Pain, with Report of a New
Operative Technique," *J. Neurosurg.*, 8
(1951), 405–410.

42. GRAY, J. A. "The Structure of Emotions and
the Limbic System," *Ciba Found. Symp.*, 8
(1972), 87–120.

43. GREEN, J. R., R. E. H. DUISBERG, and W. S.
McGRATH. "Orbitofrontal Lobotomy with
Reference to Effects on 55 Psychotic Patients," *J. Neurosurg.*, 9 (1952), 579–587.

44. HASSLER, R. and G. DIECKMAN. "Relief of
Obsessive Compulsive Disorders, Phobias,
and Tics by Stereotaxic Coagulation of the
Rostral Intralaminar and Medial Thalamic
Nuclei," in L. Laitinen and K. E. Livingston, eds., *Surgical Approaches in Psychiatry*, pp. 206–212. Lancaster, England:
Medical and Technical Publ., 1973.

45. HEATH, R. G. "Electrical Self-Stimulation
of the Brain in Man," *Am. J. Psychiatry*,
120 (1963), 571–577.

46. HEATH, R. G. and W. A. MICKEL. "Evaluation of Seven Years Experience with Depth
Electrode Studies in Human Patients," in
E. R. Ramey and D. S. O'Doherty, eds.,
*Electrical Studies of the Unanesthetized
Brain*, pp. 214–247. New York: Hoeber,
1960.

47. HERRICK, J. G. "The Function of the Olfactory Parts of the Cerebral Cortex," *Proc.
Natl. Acad. Sci. USA*, 18 (1933), 7–14.

48. HEUSER, G., P. H. CRANDALL, J. HUNTLEY
et al. "Clinical Neurophysiology. Newer
Diagnostic and Therapeutic Methods in
Neurological Disease and Behavior Dis

orders," *Ann. Intern. Med.*, 71 (1969),
619–645.

49. HOCKMAN, C. H., K. E. LIVINGSTON, and
J. TALESNIK. "Supramedullary Modulation
of Autonomic Reflexes," in C. H. Hockman,
ed., *Limbic System Mechanisms and Autonomic Function*, pp. 152–166. Springfield,
Ill.: Charles C. Thomas, 1972.

50. HOCKMAN, C. H., J. TALESNIK, and K. E.
LIVINGSTON. "Central Nervous System
Modulation of Baroreceptor Reflexes," *Am.
J. Physiol.*, 217 (1969), 1681–1689.

51. HORNYKIEWICZ, O. "The Subcortical Monaminergic Systems," in L. Laitinen and
K. E. Livingston, eds., *Surgical Approaches
in Psychiatry*, pp. 293–301. Lancaster,
England: Medical and Technical Publ.,
1973.

52. KELLEY, D., A. RICHARDSON, and N. MIT-
CHELL-HEGGS. "Technique and Assessment
of Limbic Leucotomy," in L. Laitinen and
K. E. Lvingston, eds., *Surgical Approaches
in Psychiatry*, pp. 165–173. Lancaster,
England: Medical and Technical Publ.,
1973.

53. KILLAM, E. E. "Drug Actions on the Brain-
stem Reticular Formation," *Pharmacol.
Rev.*, 14 (1962), 175–223.

54. KIM, Y. K. and W. UMBACH. "Combined
Stereotactic Lesions for the Treatment of
Behavior Disorders and Severe Pain," in
L. Laitinen and K. E. Livingston, eds.,
Surgical Approaches in Psychiatry, pp.
182–188. Lancaster, England: Medical
and Technical Publ., 1973.

55. KNIGHT, G. C. "The Orbital Cortex as an
Objective in the Surgical Treatment of
Mental Illness," *Br. J. Surg.*, 51 (1964),
114–124.

56. ———. "Stereotaxic Tractotomy in the
Surgical Treatment of Mental Illness,"
J. Neurol. Neurosurg. Psychiatry, 28
(1964), 304–310.

57. LeBEAU, J. "The Cingular, and Pre-cingular
Areas in Psychosurgery (Agitated Behavior, Obsessive Compulsive States, Epilepsy)," *Acta Psychiatr. Neurol. Scand.*, 27
(1952), 304–317.

58. LEWIN, W. "Selective Leucotomy," *Proc. R.
Soc. Med.*, 53 (1960), 732–734.

59. ———. "Observations on Selective Leucotomy," *J. Neurol. Neurosurg. Psychiatry*,
24 (1961), 37–44.

60. LIVINGSTON, K. E. "Congulate Cortex Isolation for the Treatment of Psychoses and

Psychoneuroses," *Proc. Assoc. Res. Nerv. Ment. Dis.*, 31 (1951), 374–378.

61. ———. "The Frontal Lobes Revisted: The Case for a Second Look," *Arch. Neurol.*, 20 (1969), 90–95.

62. ———. "Neurosurgical Aspects of Primary Affective Disorders," in J. Youmans, ed., *Neurological Surgery*, pp. 1881–1899. Philadelphia: Saunders, 1973.

63. LIVINGSTON, K. E. and A. ESCOBAR. "The Anatomical Bias of the Limbic System Concept: A Proposed Reorientation," *Arch. Neurol.*, 24 (1971), 17–21.

64. ———. "Tentative Limbic System Models for Certain Patterns of Psychiatric Disorders," in L. Laitinen and K. E. Livingston, eds., *Surgical Approaches in Psychiatry*, pp. 245–252. Lancaster, England: Medical and Technical Publ., 1973.

65. LIVINGSTON, K. E. and R. G. PERRIN. "The Central Physiological Effects of Experimental Intravenous Procaine Hydrochloride," *J. Neurosurg.*, 37 (1972), 188–194.

66. LIVINGSTON, R. B. "Central Control of Receptors and Sensory Transmission Systems," in J. Field, H. W. Magoon, and V. E. Hall, eds., *Handbook of Neurophysiology*, Sect. 1, Vol. 1, pp. 741–760. Washington: Am. Physiol. Soc., 1959.

67. ———. "Brain Circuitry Relating to Complex Behavior," in G. C. Quarton, T. Melnechuk, and F. O. Schmitt, eds., *Neurosciences Study Program*, pp. 499–515. New York: Rockefeller University Press, 1967.

68. LIVINGSTON, R. B., W. P. CHAPMAN, and K. E. LIVINGSTON. "Stimulation of the Orbital Surface of Man Prior to Frontal Lobotomy," *Proc. Assoc. Res. Nerv. Ment. Dis.*, 27 (1947), 421–432.

69. LIVINGSTON, R. B., J. F. FULTON, J. M. R. DELGADO et al. "Stimulation and Regional Ablation of the Orbital Surface of the Frontal Lobe," *Proc. Assoc. Res. Nerv. Ment. Dis.*, 27 (1947), 405–420.

70. LORENTE DE NO, R. "The Summation of Repulses Transmitted to the Neurones through Different Synapses," *Am. J. Physiol.*, 113 (1935), 524–528.

71. MACLEAN, P. D. "Psychosomatic Disease and the 'Visceral Brain,' Recent Developments Bearing on the Papez Theory of Emotion," *Psychosomatic Med.*, 11 (1949), 338–353.

72. ———. "Some Psychiatric Implications of

Physiological Studies on the Frontotemporal Portion of the Limbic System (Visceral Brain)," *Electroencephalogr. Clin. Neurophysiol.*, 4 (1952), 407–418.

73. ———. "Contrasting Functions of Limbic and Neocortical Systems of the Brain and Their Relevance to Psychophysiological Aspects of Medicine," *Am. J. Med.*, 25 (1958), 611–626.

74. MAGOON, H. W. "Bulbar Inhibition and Facilitation of Motor Activity," *Science*, 100 (1944), 549–550.

75. ———. "Caudal and Cephalic Influences of the Brain Stem Reticular Formation," *Physiol. Rev.*, 30 (1950), 459–474.

76. MALAMUD, N. "Psychiatric Disorder with Intracranial Tumors of the Limbic System," *Arch. Neurol.*, 17 (1967), 113–123.

77. MARK, V. and R. NEVILLE. "Brain Surgery in Aggressive Epileptics," *JAMA*, 226 (1973), 765–772.

78. MARGULES, D. L., M. J. LEWIS, J. A. DRAGOVICH et al. "Hypothalamic Noradrenaline Circadian Rhythms and the Control of Feeding Behavior," *Science*, 178 (1972), 640–642.

79. MAZARS, G. "Criteria for Identifying Cingulate Epilepsies," *Epilepsia*, 11 (1970), 41–47.

80. MILLER, N. E. "Learning of Visceral and Glandular Responses," *Science*, 163 (1969), 434–445.

81. MILNER, B. "Psychological Defects Produced by Temporal Lobe Excision," *Assoc. Res. Nerv. Ment. Dis., Proc.*, 36 (1958), 244–257.

82. MONIZ, E. *Tentatives Operatoires dans le traitement de certaines psychoses.* Paris: Masson, 1936.

83. ———. "Prefrontal Leucotomy in the Treatment of Mental Disorders," *Am. J. Psychiatry*, 93 (1937), 1379–1385.

84. MORRELL, F. "Physiology and Histochemistry of the Mirror Focus," in H. H. Jasper, A. A. Ward, and A. Pope, eds., *Basic Mechanisms of the Epilepsies*. Boston: Little, Brown, 1969.

85. MORUZZI, G. and H. W. MAGOON. "Brain Stem Reticular Formation and Activation of the E.E.G.," *Electroencephalogr. Clin. Neurophysiol.*, 1 (1949), 455–473.

86. MULLAN, S. and W. PENFIELD. "Illusions of Comparative Interpretation and Emotion; Production by Epileptic Discharge and by Electrical Stimulation of the Temporal

Cortex," *Arch. Neurol. Psychol.*, 81 (1959), 269–284.

87. NÁDVORNÍK, P., J. POGÁDY, and M. SRAMKO. "The Results of Stereotaxic Treatment of the Aggressive Syndrome," in L. Laitinen and K. E. Livingston, eds., *Surgical Approaches in Psychiatry*, pp. 125–128. Lancaster, England: Medical and Technical Publ., 1973.

88. NARABAYASHI, N. et al. "Stereotaxic Amygdalotomy for Behavior Disorders," *Arch. Neurol.*, 9 (1963), 1–25.

89. NASHOLD, B. S., JR., B. STEWART, and W. P. WILSON. "Depth Electrode Studies in Centroencephalic Epilepsy," *Confin. Neurol.*, 34 (1972), 252–263.

90. NASHOLD, B. S., JR. et al. "Stereotactic Evaluations of Bitemporal Epilepsy with Electrodes and Lesions," *Confin. Neurol.*, 35 (1973), 94–100.

91. NAUTA, W. J. H. "Hippocampal Projections and Related Neural Pathways to the Midbrain in the Cat," *Brain*, 81 (1958), 319–340.

92. ———. "Some Neural Pathways Related to the Limbic System," in E. R. Ramey and D. S. O'Doherty, eds., *Electrical Studies of the Unanesthetized Brain*, pp. 1–16. New York: Hoeber, 1960.

93. ———. "The Problem of the Frontal Lobe: A Reinterpretation," *J. Psychiatr. Res.*, 8 (1971), 167–187.

94. ———. "Connections of the Frontal Lobe with the Limbic System," in L. Laitinen and K. E. Livingston, eds., *Surgical Approaches in Psychiatry*, pp. 303–314. Lancaster, England: Medical and Technical Publ., 1973.

95. OLDS, J. and P. MILNER. "Positive Re-inforcement Produced by Electrical Stimulation of the Septal Area and Other Regions of the Rat Brain," *J. Comp. Physiol. Psychol.*, 47 (1954), 419–427.

96. PAPEZ, J. W. "A Proposed Mechanism of Emotion," *Arch. Neurol. Psychiatry*, 38 (1937), 725–743.

97. PAUL, N. L., M. A. FITZGERALD, and M. GREENBLATT. "Five Year Follow-up of Patients Subjected to Three Different Lobotomy Procedures," *JAMA*, 161 (1956), 715–719.

98. PENFIELD, W. "Engrams in the Human Brain," *Proc. R. Soc. Med.*, 61 (1958), 831–840.

99. ———. "The Interpretic Cortex: the Stream of Unconsciousness in the Human Brain Can Be Electrically Re-activated," *Science*, 129 (1959), 1719–1735.

100. POPPEN, J. L. "Technique and Complications of the Standard Prefrontal Lobotomy," in M. Greenblatt et al., eds., *Studies in Lobotomy*, New York: Grune & Stratton, 1950.

101. POWELL, T. P. S. "Sensory Convergence in the Central Cortex," in L. Laitinen and K. E. Livingston, eds., *Surgical Approaches in Psychiatry*, pp. 266–281. Lancaster, England: Medical and Technical Publ., 1973.

102. RACINE, R. J. "Modification of Seizure Activity by Electrical Stimulation, I: After-Discharge Threshold," *Electroencephalogr. Clin. Neurophysiol.*, 32 (1969), 269–279.

103. ———. "Epileptiform Activity and Neural Plasticity in Limbic Structures," *Brain Res.*, 47 (1972), 262–268.

104. ———. "Modification of Seizure Activity by Electrical Stimulation, II: Motor Seizure," *Electroencephalogr. Clin. Neurophysiol.*, 32 (1972), 281–294.

105. RACINE, R. J., K. E. LIVINGSTON, and A. JOAQUIN. "The Effects of Procaine Hydrochloride, Diazepam, and Diphenylhydantoin on Seizure Development in Cortical and Subcortical Structures," *Electroencephalogr. Clin. Neurophysiol.*, 38 (1975), 355–365.

106. RAMÓN Y CAJAL, S. *Studies on the Cerebral Cortex (Limbic Structures)*. Translated by L. M. Kraft. London: Lloyd-Luke, 1955.

107. REISS, D. J., N. DOBA, M. A. NATHAN et al. "Predatory Attack, Grooming and Consumatory Behaviors Evoked by Electrical Stimulation of Cat Cerebellar Nuclei," *Science*, 182 (1973), 845–847.

108. ROEDER, F., H. ORTHNER, and D. MULLER. "The Stereotactic Treatment of Pedophilic Homosexuality and Other Sexual Deviations," in E. Hitchcock et al., eds., *Psychosurgery*, pp. 87–111. Springfield, Ill: Charles C. Thomas, 1972.

109. RUTLEDGE, L. T., C. WRIGHT, and J. DUNCAN. "Morphological Changes in Pyramidal Cells of Adult Mammalian Cerebral Cortex Associated with Increased Use," *Exp. Neurology*, 44 (1974), 209–228.

110. RYLANDER, G. "Personality Analysis before and after Frontal Lobotomy," *Res. Publ. Ass. Res. Nerv. Ment. Dis.*, 27 (1948), 691–705.

111. ———. "The Renaissance of Psychosurgery," in L. Laitinen and K. E. Livingston, eds., *Surgical Approaches in Psychiatry*, pp. 3–12. Lancaster, England: Medical and Technical Publ., 1973.

112. SANO, K., M. YOSKIOKA, M. OGASHIWA et al. "Posterolateral Hypothalamotomy in the Treatment of Aggressive Behavior," *Confin. Neurol.*, 27 (1966), 164–167.

113. SCHILDKRAUT, J. J. "Neuropharmacology of Affective Disorders," *N. Engl. J. Med.*, 281 (1969), 197–201, 248–255, 302–308.

114. SCHILDKRAUT, J. J. and S. KETY. "Biogenic Amines and Emotion," *Science*, 156 (1967), 21–37.

115. SCOVILLE, W. B. "Selective Cortical Undercutting," *Proc. R. Soc. Med. (Suppl)*, 42 (1949), 3–8.

116. SMITH, W. K. "Functional Significance of Rostral Cingulate Cortex as Revealed by Its Responses to Electrical Excitation," *J. Neurophysiol.*, 8 (1945), 241–253.

117. SMOCYGNSKI, S. "Clinical Investigations on Chronic Psychic Disturbances in Patients with Temporal Lobe Epilepsy," *Pol. Med. J.*, 11 (1972), 1706–1715.

118. SMYTHIES, J. R. "Brain Mechanisms and Psychiatry," in L. Laitinen and K. E. Livingston, eds., *Surgical Approaches in Psychiatry*, pp. 13–17. Lancaster, England: Medical and Technical Publ., 1973.

119. SNYDER, S. H., S. P. BANERJEE, H. I. YAMAMURA et al. "Drugs, Neurotransmitters, and Schizophrenia," *Science*, 184 (1974), 1243–1253.

120. SPENCER, W. G. "Effect Produced upon Respiration by Farodic Excitation of the Cerebrum in the Monkey," *Philos. Trans.*, 185b (1894), 609–657.

121. SPIEGEL, E. A. and H. T. WYCIS. *Stereoencephalotomy*, Sect. II. Thalamotomy, I. Basic Considerations, pp. 72–106. New York: Grune & Stratton, 1962.

122. STEVENS, J. R., V. H. MARK, F. ERWIN et al. "Deep Temporal Stimulation in Man," *Arch. Neurol.*, 21 (1969), 157–169.

123. TAYLOR, D. C. "Mental State and Temporal Lobe Epilepsy," *Epilepsia*, 13 (1972), 727–765.

124. TOW, P. M. and W. LEWIN. "Orbital Leucotomy (Isolation of the Orbital Cortex by Open Operation)," *Lancet*, 2 (1953), 644–649.

125. TUCKER, W. "Results of Lobotomy," *J. Neuropsychiatry*, 2 (1961), 153–157.

126. TURNER, E. "A New Approach to Unilateral and Bilateral Lobotomies for Psychomotor Epilepsy," *J. Neurol. Neurosurg. Psychiatry*, 26 (1963), 285–299.

127. VAERNET, K. "Stereotactic Amygdalotomy in Temporal Lobe Epilepsy," *Confin. Neurol.*, 34 (1972), 176–183.

128. VAN WAGENEN, W. P. and C. T. LIU. "Procaine Block of Frontal Lobe White Fibers as a Means of Predicting the Effect of Prefrontal Lobotomy. II. Clinical Evaluation," *J. Neurosurg.*, 9 (1952), 31–50.

129. WARD, A. A., JR. "The Cingular Gyrus, Area 24," *J. Neurophysiol.*, 11 (1948), 13–23.

130. WALKER, A. E. "The Libidinous Temporal Lobe," *J. Neurophysiol.*, 111 (1972), 473–484.

131. WEST, K. A. "Treatment of Psychomotor Epilepsy with Stereotaxic Amygdalotomy," *Ann. Clin. Res.*, 5 (1973), 60–64.

132. WHITTY, C. W. M., J. E. DUFFIELD, P. M. Tow et al. "Anterior Cingulectomy in the Treatment of Mental Disease," *Lancet*, 1 (1952), 475–481.

133. YAKOVLEV, P. I. "Motility, Behavior, and the Brain; Stereodynamic Organization and Neural Coordinates of Behavior," *J. Nerv. Ment. Dis.*, 107 (1948), 313–335.

PART FOUR

*Management and Care
of the Patient*

CHAPTER 29

PSYCHIATRIC EMERGENCIES: EVALUATION AND MANAGEMENT

Gary J. Tucker

PHENOMENOLOGICALLY a psychiatric emergency is a request by a person, family, or agent of society to *immediately evaluate* the behavior of an individual. Theoretically, an emergency is the occurrence of a "sudden change" and a crisis is a "turning point" that may have potentially adverse consequences. Defined in such a way, almost any disturbance of human behavior can confront the clinician as an emergency or crisis situation. Consequently, the skills and knowledge required to treat these varied problems may seem overwhelming. The emergency situation not only demands diverse knowledge but also implies intervention or action. This is true of any emergency situation, medical or psychiatric. The demands of making insulin and diet changes over a prolonged period in a known diabetic are very different from treating the same patient in diabetic acidosis. In the same way, a patient who has been in long-term

psychotherapy for a depression becomes a very different treatment problem should he become acutely and seriously suicidal. While one can say that in these emergency situations everything must be known, the management of emergency situations is, in actuality, simpler. It is simpler because the time perspective needs only be brief, only those interventions which alleviate the immediate situation are necessary; although long-term goals and treatment can be aimed at, these facets of treatment may be reserved for some future time. This chapter, of necessity, must deal with many disparate topics, but its intent is to deal with the discrete variables that have proved most useful in emergency situations. Although as noted, the emergent situation can encompass almost any aspect of human behavior, general guidelines for emergency psychiatric management can be clearly delineated. These guidelines, coupled with specific information of the more common emergency problems, can lend competence and skill to the management and treatment of these difficult and, for the clinician, frequently anxiety-provoking situations. However, all that any text can provide is a skeleton that must be fleshed out with experience, judicious judgment, knowledge, and a sense of humanity.

The psychiatrist has always been confronted with urgent situations, but until recently psychiatry, as a profession and a body of knowledge, has shown little cognizance of emergency and crisis situations. Sixty-nine percent of emergency psychiatric services in this country have been established since 1950.[70] Perhaps as long as most psychiatric care for seriously ill patients was undertaken in large, isolated rural state hospitals, there was little need for psychiatrists, unrelated to these hospitals, to concern themselves with emergency care. If the patient did not respond to immediate verbal intervention or sedation, the only resource for the emergency situation was the state hospital. Consequently, the major emergency intervention was hospitalization. In fact, one of the first articles that took cognizance and delineated some principles of emergency psychiatric management was by Lindemann in 1944,[49] on a population not traditionally considered psychiatric, e.g., the bereaved families of the victims of a disaster situation. However, as the care of the psychiatric patients moved closer to the community it became apparent that neither our institutions nor theories were capable of handling emergency situations. From the early 1950s to the present, many new types of psychiatric facilities as well as a vast theoretical framework for the management of psychiatric emergencies have arisen.[67]

❴ The Rise of Psychiatric Facilities for Emergency Care

As the state hospital systems shifted their orientation from custodial to therapeutic, they, in part, forced the communities to develop facilities for care of discharged patients and outpatients, and soon emergency functions followed. In the middle and late 1950s, in order to treat the returning patients from the state hospitals, we saw the development of large outpatient clinics set up primarily as aftercare clinics. These clinics soon became inadequate for the demands put upon them. In 1959, Coleman and Zwerling noted that their clinic was soon overrun with demands for service.[12] They described the development of a six-to-twelve-month waiting list and, consequently, a marked inability to provide treatment when the person most needed it, that being during the crisis or emergency situation. They then go on to describe an "innovative" psychiatric emergency clinic that provided "a flexible way of meeting community mental-health needs." Concomitantly, as general hospitals began to develop their own psychiatric units, the psychiatrist became available to general hospital emergency rooms. In part, the Community Mental Health Center Act of 1963 explicitly defined this increasing need by making emergency care one of the essential services of a community mental health center. Consequently, some type of walk-in or emergency psychiatric consultation is presently available in most communities.[1]

Paralleling the geographic changes in the handling of psychiatric emergencies, one is impressed with the increasing variety of treatment modalities that have become available to the psychiatrist. The advent of the tranquilizing and antidepressant agents coupled as well with the theoretical developments of family and group therapies, brings an increasing range of effective treatment modalities and capabilities within reach of those treating psychiatric emergencies. However, for the psychiatrist to utilize these techniques great shifts in training were required.

In the recent past the major focus of psychiatric training has been on the development of individual psychotherapeutic skills. These skills emphasized the psychotherapeutic relationship, analyzing, over time, intrapsychic problems and the necessity for the relative exclusion of others from the treatment.[18,93]

With this emphasis we developed a generation of psychiatrists who seemed ill prepared to deal with emergency situations. When all the psychiatrist had to offer was an intense and prolonged delving into intrapsychic conflicts it became quite difficult for him to deal with the problems presented in an emergency situation. The dictionary definition of an emergency covers such things as "an unlooked for contingency," "a sudden demand for action," "a pressing need." An emergency requires both intervention and some action. The psychodynamic theories, as noted, offered little theoretical help in the handling of emergencies and crisis situations. Into this vacuum moved the theories of Lindemann,[49] Caplan[7] and Erikson,[22] relating in varied ways to the concept of "crisis." Caplan defined a crisis as a state "provoked when a person faces an obstacle to important life goals that is, for a time, insurmountable through the utilization of customary methods of problem solving."[7] Much of the early literature on crisis intervention was devoted to demonstrating that crisis management could be either reconciled or made relevant to psychoanalytic principles.[2,13,39,78] Although subtle, this viewing of an emotional crisis as an "obstacle" to important life goals put the "crisis or emergency" into a conceptual framework that allowed the clinician to examine aspects of the emergency situation other than the intrapsychic. The therapist was now doing "crisis intervention work" during which it was legitimate to examine the social matrix of the situation and even temporarily rearrange it. The person treating "the crisis" no longer felt that an intervention fell short of the mark unless it revised the person's total personality. However, with the advent of crisis theory the definition of a crisis and the areas of intervention were expanded greatly to allow almost any change in life, such as the "crisis of adolescence, early marriage, change of jobs, entrance into nursery school, retirement,"[8] to be viewed as an area in which to intervene. While these would certainly be classified as what Caplan has called primary prevention, they are not the usual emergencies with which a psychiatrist is confronted.

Psychiatric Emergencies— A Perspective

If one reviews the literature on the kinds of psychiatric problems that come to the emergency rooms of general hospitals, one is impressed with several things.* Although there are few such studies in the literature, it is clear that the emergency situation is most often defined by people other than the psychiatrist. The clinician charged to deal with the emergency can state after evaluating the patient that it is or is not an emergency, but the psychiatrist is not usually noted as the initiator of the emergency contact. In this country a high proportion of the patients seen as emergencies (55 percent) are referred by themselves.[68,96] This contrasts with England[5] where only 35 percent of the patients are self-referred, and 59 percent come from general practitioners, which may in part reflect the low availability of primary medical care in this country for lower socioeconomic groups. The general proportion of psychiatric emergencies seen in emergency rooms varies from 3 percent to 12 percent[9,96] of the total patients seen. About 50 percent of the psychiatric patients are seen between 8:00 A.M. and 5:00 P.M., 20 to 40 percent are seen from 5:00 P.M. to midnight, and about 8 to 12 percent are seen from midnight to 8:00 A.M in large metropolitan centers.[68]

A survey of psychiatric emergencies done by Muller, Chafetz, and Blane,[68] summarized data gathered on close to 5000 emergency psychiatric contacts seen in Helsinki, New Haven, Boston, and Cleveland. It noted that diagnostically the problems that present on an emergency basis are equally divided among: (1) psychotic, (2) neurotic, (3) alcoholic, and (4) personality disorders and situational reactions. These proportions varied slightly from location to location as do most studies that rely primarily on clinical diagnosis and, as such, are often difficult to interpret. However, if we look at the behavior manifested by these

* See references 1, 9, 11, 23, 68, 79, 80, 89, and 96.

patients, we see consistent patterns that necessitate emergency psychiatric consultation. The kinds of behavior seen most often as emergencies primarily are agitation, suicide (both threats and attempts), episodes of excessive drinking, and emotional withdrawal or isolation. Contrary to the popular notion, assault and other forms of violence were the least common patterns of behavior presenting for emergency consultations. The majority of the patients also represented episodic outbreaks of chronic problems. Of those seen in emergency rooms, about 23 percent had had prior inpatient treatment, and about 13 percent previously had had outpatient treatment. Unfortunately, there is almost no data on the types of emergencies handled by private practitioners. Descriptively, the patients necessitating emergency consultation usually manifest chronic problems, are often of a low social class, and are usually young adults. While this data may also be viewed as more representative of those who use emergency rooms of urban general hospitals, clinical experience seems to confirm that the nature of the presenting symptoms is similar in other populations and settings.

The majority of patients studied were felt to be valid emergencies in that between 30 and 50 percent were immediately hospitalized. The remainder were referred to outpatient treatment of some sort, and under 10 percent were discharged as either not needing treatment or because the contact was sufficient. Those most likely to receive no treatment were patients who primarily manifested longstanding character problems.

❲ General Aspects of the Evaluation Process of Psychiatric Emergencies

A psychiatric emergency may then be defined by its components: (1) either the patient or those surrounding the patient perceive that there has been a sudden change in the patient's behavior, or the consequences of this behavior; (2) there is a request made to a socially designated expert in behavior for assistance and evaluation of this behavior, and (3) the socially designated expert agrees or disagrees that this behavior or the resulting situation is one that needs immediate psychiatric intervention or care. In this sense, the clinician is frequently confronted with a patient whose *behavior* has been judged by others as either changed, disruptive, or deemed no longer appropriate to a specific setting. The person charged with evaluating this behavior is usually confronted with a person who has "done" something. It is the process of evaluation to determine what "is" happening to the person as well as what "is" disrupting the equilibrium of the patient's life and/or others' lives. Probably the most helpful parameters in evaluating behavior and most critical in determining the emergency status of the behavior are the *form, intensity,* and *frequency* of the behavior.[46]

Behavior by its formal characteristics alone can be deviant, repugnant, or serious. Consider a suicide attempt. A patient who has ingested three aspirin tablets is treated and evaluated differently than the patient who has shot himself in the chest. The intensity of the behavior relates more to the degree of control over the behavior the patient manifests, e.g., the difference between suicidal thoughts, a suicide plan, and an actual suicide attempt. The frequency of the behavior is the actual frequency of the occurrence of a behavior and the context it occurs in, e.g., the constant occurrence of suicidal thoughts after any rejection or personal affront (it may at times also relate to the deficiency of behavior in specific contexts).

Behavior does not occur in isolation. There is a constant interplay between the individual and the social network surrounding him. This interactive process can also be affected by the presence of either or both psychopathology or impairment of biologic function. The request for an emergency consult can best be viewed as a disturbance in a "system."[72] While all the components of this system are constantly interacting, this interaction can be best evaluated by arbitrarily looking at its three major components. These are: (1) the psychologic status, (2) the social network surrounding the patient, and (3) the biologic functions.

The evaluation of the *psychological status* has often been considered the main task of the evaluation, but in the emergency setting it is only one component and in part often obtained from others. It encompasses the traditional mental-status examination and psychiatric history. It is here that knowledge of specific categorical psychiatric syndromes are necessary to the evaluation. Those aspects of categorical problems necessary for emergency evaluation will be dealt with subsequently. While the psychiatrist traditionally has gained this information from the patient himself, and this evaluation of the patient is of extreme importance, in an emergency situation the examination is often confirmatory, in the sense that history and symptoms are frequently gained from those who requested the emergency evaluation, e.g., the family, the police, etc. The patient, for a variety of reasons, may be unwilling or unable to reveal the entire history, so it is often necessary to gather data from other sources about present and past psychologic status. For example, a fifty-eight-year-old man was seen as a walk-in patient for an initial interview. He manifested symptoms of a mild to moderate depressive reaction (both biological and psychological) but denied any suicidal ideation. Although the physician was somewhat concerned about the patient, he felt that it would compromise his relationship with the patient to consult anyone else, and when confronted by the patient's wife in the waiting room at the conclusion of his interview, he suggested that she might discuss some of her anxieties with a social worker at the next visit. By this time, the husband had left the waiting room and the wife, who had tried to be with the patient initially, asked the physician if he "had told him about the noose" (which the patient had not). The patient was sought out, but could not be located. Later that day he committed suicide.

While the psychological status may reveal little symptomatology during mental-status examination, the clue to the nature of an emergency situation is frequently gained by an evaluation of the social relationships surrounding the person. It is critical as part of an emergency evaluation to determine significant relationships in the person's life, particularly, patterns of relationship and changes in these relationships. In several recent studies, one of the most critical life-stress factors noted was entrances and exits from the person's immediate life. Usually these were entrances and exits of significant people in the person's life.[38] The family is only one aspect of the person's life, the other important aspect is the work situation.

The evaluation of the biological status of the patient is perhaps the most crucial evaluation in the emergency situation. This evaluation is critical in that it is easy to overlook physical or biological causes of behavior when seen by those clinicians with primarily a psychological "set." Certainly, there are many organic syndromes (epilepsy,[83] encephalitis),[37] prescribed and nonprescribed medications that can often precisely mimic primarily psychological conditions.[15,71] This distinction becomes even more difficult in patients who are seen for the first time and are relatively unknown to the person doing the evaluation. While these conditions, fortunately, are rare, they must be kept in mind when doing emergency evaluations, for it is easy to prescribe not only the wrong treatment but to overlook a potentially life-threatening situation.

It is also important to recognize that organic problems may not only coexist but contribute to emotional symptoms. Several studies of admissions to psychiatric hospitals have noted that anywhere from 18 to 44 percent of the patients were suffering from some form of physical disorder.[20,21] In one hundred patients seen as psychiatric emergencies, Eastwood et al. noted that 24 percent were suffering from physical disorders already known to the physicians and 16 percent had physical abnormalities that had not previously been recognized.[20]

While in contemporary times there is much concern about the role and identity of the psychiatrist, it is in the area of emergency evaluations that medical knowledge is crucial. However, it does not mean these conditions cannot be determined by nonphysicians who are trained in evaluation but that the complete evaluation may necessitate physical examination and subsequent medical consultation. Several clinical observations may prove helpful in indicating that organic problems may be present: (1) there is an abrupt history of personality change, in that the patient's premorbid behavior and personality are in marked contra-distinction to the presenting behavior; (2) a good premorbid history of social functioning and achievement, and a family situation that is warm and supportive; (3) rapid or periodic fluctuations in behavior and mental status; and (4) the patient seems to struggle against the symptoms rather than giving in to or believing them. In addition to these, certainly any history of a recent central-nervous-system trauma such as a fall, head trauma, etc., or a history of drug use or abuse is critically important to the evaluation of many behavior disorders. A family history of central-nervous-system disease is also pertinent.[37,71]

The complexity of the evaluation process is further enhanced by the fact that the request itself is an important part of the psychiatric emergency. The request may simply be related to the fact that the behavior observed was either misunderstood or inappropriate to a specific situation. It may also be a request to remove an unwanted family member (frequently the aged) or label someone mentally ill.[84] The request itself may have many meanings. In an evaluation of 200 patients requesting treatment from a "walk-in service," Lazare et al.[45] defined four major types of requests from patients applying for immediate treatment: (1) *Support*—including such things as aiding self-control, reality contact, succor, institutional contact, confession, ventilation, and advice; (2) *psychotherapy*—a desire to clarify the recent events in their life or provide insight into some intrapsychic problem. (3) *request to an authority figure*—medical, administrative requests in order to meet and fulfill social needs; and (4) *miscellaneous requests*—related to community triage, e.g., where the person uses the clinic evaluation in

order to be directed to what they really want —to no requests at all. The latter category, interestingly, includes patients frequently brought to the clinic against their will.

While the behavior, the psychobiologic aspects, and the meaning of the request for emergency evaluation can usually be determined through interview and observation, the emotional aspects of the emergency may color this information.

Emotional Aspects of Dealing with Psychiatric Emergencies

As noted previously, the psychiatric emergency by definition and fact puts immediate emotional pressure on the person requested to do the evaluation. This pressure is related primarily to the necessity of making rapid decisions in what most often presents as a chaotic situation. Contributing to this anxiety and also affecting action sometimes is the threat of physical violence. Although relatively rare in psychiatric emergencies,[68] the possibility or fantasy of violence is often present in the mind of the person doing the evaluation. Another factor that contributes to the anxiety of the person charged with dealing with emergencies, particularly those working in general hospital emergency rooms, walk-in clinics, etc., is the feeling of having very little, or actually no, control over what type of patients present themselves for evaluation. The consequent anticipation of problems that "could" present themselves often leads to great anxiety. In the face of the anxiety-provoking situation of dealing with psychiatric emergencies, particularly on a continuing basis, several aspects of the preparation of the staff are important. (It is probably important to recognize that some people will never be able to function well in these situations also.)

The evaluation of emergencies requires not only skilled but knowledgeable decisions. One of the best general ways to prevent anxiety from unduly influencing decisions is to equip emergency personnel with clear guidelines for dealing with and evaluating many of the common problems they will confront. For example, many types of check lists for evaluating suicidal behavior have been developed and others should be.[53,62,69,99] The need for guidelines relates more to a way of organizing knowledge and making sure that the person, while acting under pressure, will not leave out pertinent aspects of the evaluation. Certainly, the gathering of information in itself has a calming effect on everyone. The person who presents as an emergency frequently has been the focus of chaotic interactions with others in his environment. An attempt to sit down and clarify this situation often has a calming effect in itself. In this sense, it is best if the emergency can be evaluated in a calm surrounding. A crisis in a person's life is not best handled in the heart of the emergency ward or the halls of a psychiatric unit: there should be a private place in which to deal with the situation. The manner of the interviewer in terms of equanimity, calmness, and composure, even under the greatest stress, is important to the patient. The manner should also be sympathetic, firm, consistent, and reassuring. The person doing the evaluation should also try to convey that if the patient assists him he, the clinician, may be able to sort out some critical factors that will be helpful to the patient. In this sense, the person doing the evaluation is certainly more active than the traditional psychotherapeutic "blank-screen" stance. He shows that he is willing to aid in the resolution of the problem as much as he can.

Hankoff,[34] in his book on the treatment of psychiatric emergencies, condenses the above into three phases of emergency treatment: (1) assessment of symptoms and the critical aspects of the patients life; (2) an exploration of the patient's environment either by interview, phone calls, or even a home visit; and (3) the relief of acute symptoms through either verbal communication or pharmacologic means. Perhaps a key to the assessment of the emergency situation is the question, "Why now?" Why is this patient here at this point in time? What has happened in his immediate life that has made this situation an emergency? Many of the interpersonal and social problems that present as emergency requests for consultation

can be markedly alleviated, and much of the pressure of the situation removed, through the process of clarification and evaluation itself.

From the foregoing survey of emergency problems it seems clear that it is the patient's *behavior* or other people's reactions to that behavior that usually constitute the emergency, and that traditional diagnostic labels are not as valuable as one might think for either evaluation or intervention. From the same data it is apparent that three classes of categorical behavior appear to most frequently necessitate emergency consultations: (1) *behavior that threatens life,* such as suicide, assault, or generally violent behavior; (2) *behavior that disturbs existing patterns of life,* such as depressive symptoms, overwhelming anxiety, interpersonal conflicts, or what would be considered classic psychopathology; and (3) *behavior that makes it impossible to negotiate life,* such as senility, toxic psychosis, or what would usually be considered organic disturbances of the brain. For most of these categories of behavior there are clear guidelines for evaluation and intervention. We intend to focus on those aspects of emergencies which are the most difficult to evaluate and manage and to spend less time on those aspects most familiar to the daily work of psychiatrists, other than to present some recent work in the more familiar area. These specific guidelines, blended with the above general guidelines, can facilitate emergency evaluation and treatment. (This process is summarized in Table 29–1.)

(Categorical Kinds of Behavior Necessitating Emergency Intervention

Life-threatening Behavior

Certainly, the evaluation of life-threatening behavior such as suicide, assault, or even homicide are some of the most difficult and anxiety-provoking kinds of behavior confronting the clinician. Depending upon the findings

TABLE 29–1.   The Process of Evaluation of the Psychiatric Emergency

CATEGORIES OF BEHAVIOR THAT MOST OFTEN CONSTITUTE PSYCHIATRIC EMERGENCIES	THE EMERGENCY MAY BE DEFINED OR CALLED TO ATTENTION BY THE FOLLOWING
1. Behavior that threatens life (e.g., suicide, assault). 2. Behavior that disturbs patterns of life (e.g., depression, overwhelming anxiety). 3. Behavior interfered with so that it is impossible to negotiate life (e.g., senility, toxic psychosis).	1. Patient. 2. Family, friends. 3. Physician. 4. Social agencies (police, etc.)

These combine to request emergency consultation.

Emergency evaluation (from patient and person who defined the emergency or those necessary to the evaluation).

Factors evaluated:

1. Evaluation of psychologic status (mental status), previous patterns of behavior, the intensity and frequency of the behavior.
2. Determine significant relationships in patient's life and recent changes in these relationships and patterns of behavior.
3. Assess organic or biologic factors (medical, neurologic illness, drug usage, etc.) that could cause such behavior.

Possible outcome of evaluation.

No intervention (or the evaluation itself has made further intervention unnecessary).

Psychiatric treatment.

Nonpsychiatric treatment.

Outpatient treatment.

Hospitalization (Inpatient treatment).

Other agency referrals.

Legal assistance.

Religious counseling, etc.

of the evaluation, the decision will be made as to whether the patient can be treated as an outpatient or whether he should be hospitalized immediately. The crucial decision is one of the few life-and-death decisions that confront those who evaluate psychiatric emergencies. Perhaps the most crucial, overall predictive factor in the evaluation of life-threatening behavior is the past history.[24,26,51,77] It has been demonstrated in numerous studies that those who have acted violently or suicidally in the past will have a higher incidence of such behavior in the future. It is also in this area that questions of morality and legality, in terms of the physician's responsibility to the patient and to society, may come into conflict with the civil rights of the patient. It is of interest that a court or judge cannot imprison someone as a potential criminal. The court of law must act on fact, including previous behavior, whereas, those who evaluate psychiatric emergencies often act in an opposite manner. The person evaluating the psychiatric emergency, if he feels there is a high potential for either violence or suicide related to emotional problems, can, in most states and countries, institutionalize or effect institutionalization as a preventative measure against life-threatening behavior. Certainly, this responsibility must be taken seriously and cannot be abused. However, it is also important to note that this responsibility and power is legislated by the society through the advice of the medical or psychiatric profession.

With regard to life-threatening behavior, there are usually two aspects: (1) there are patients who threaten such behavior, and (2) those patients who have actually carried out such behavior. The other dichotomy are those patients who participate in life-threatening behavior while not in treatment and those who participate in such behavior while in treatment, either outpatient or inpatient treatment. Successful completion of life-threatening behavior while in treatment often relates to denial on the part of the therapist.[50] However, at times, clues to these kinds of behavior are not clear. Regardless of these distinctions,

a history of such behavior in the past remains as one of the best predictors.

Suicide and Suicide Attempts

Recently, a whole range of kinds of suicidal behavior has been delineated. Groups of patients who threatened suicide have been contrasted with those who have successfully committed suicide, as well as those patients who have made multiple suicide attempts.[10,60,81,92] All categories of suicidal behavior are higher in patients who have primary diagnoses of depression[26] and alcoholic problems,[61] as well as some schizophrenic patients in the posthospital phase.[26] With the recent interest in suicide, it is easy to overlook the fact that suicide is a symptom and its occurrence is usually related to the above diagnostic entities. The typical suicide attempt is by a person described as a white, female, twenty to forty years of age, who ingests pills, usually after an interpersonal conflict. The successful suicide is usually forty-five years of age or older, male, white, often separated, widowed, or divorced, who lives alone and may be unemployed or retired. Historical factors of poor physical health, and medical care within the past six months, some evidence of psychiatric disturbance as noted above, and a previous history of attempts or threats are usually cited as being more common in those who have successfully committed suicide.[81] However, it is of note that there are many people who fit these demographic characteristics who have no suicidal behavior.

In the evaluation of patients immediately after suicide attempts, several scales have been devised that attempt to predict the lethality of suicide. One study delineates the risk of the attempt by evaluating the method and actual damage done.[99] Specific factors looked at are the agent used, whether these resulted in impairment of consciousness, the lesions or toxicity produced, the reversibility of the method used, and the treatment required. The more severe and irreversible these factors, the higher the risks. The other component is the rescue factor. This is based on whether the suicide attempt was made in observable circumstances and how available resources for rescue were at the time of the attempt. The latter include such things as location of the suicide attempt, the people around to initiate rescue, the probability of discovery, and the accessibility and delay until rescue. Other psychological factors have been delineated. Probably the most pertinent are the following:[27] (1) interpersonal capacity—the person's ability to relate to other people, and the quality of their relations. Interestingly, this interpersonal capacity probably relates also to the occurrence of other violent acts, as well as suicide attempts; (2) marital isolation; (3) the use of distorted communications; and (4) help negations—the person that feels that no help is available and also goes out of his way to negate any help. Stengel has talked about the Janus-faced quality of suicide wherein one part of the person actually wants to die and the other part is looking toward life.[85] But, in part, all of this comes down to the most critical factor—*the patient's explicit intent to die.* After assessing this factor by means of the above guidelines, one can then institute a treatment program for the patient. However, it is important to note that patients who are seen during the immediate postsuicide-attempt period may manifest a brief (hours to several weeks) period of lifting of a depressive reaction. So, the evaluation must be made on the previous depth of symptoms and lethality as well as the immediate clinical status, with an awareness that the presenting clinical picture maybe short-lived. It is also important at this point to assess the presence of any factors of an organic nature in the mental status that may have resulted from the suicide attempt.[14] While most of these are acute, their presence may affect the immediate disposition and if chronic, the long-term disposition as well.

Certainly, in the process of the evaluation of the suicidal patient, an attempt should be made to establish a relationship with the patient. It is also essential to gather information from people in the person's environment. As a critical part of the assessment includes the evaluation of the type of suicidal plan, e.g.,

the use of a gun, pills, etc., one should then attempt to remove these agents of destruction from the person's environment. An attempt should also be made to reduce the isolation of the patient in terms of involving friends and family, and even through hospitalization.

The suicidal patient usually feels helpless and is somewhat in an inert or anergic state. Some attempt to break this inertia can be achieved by giving the patient specific tasks such as to call at certain times, take specific medications, etc. A follow-up during this period is crucial and a contact should be maintained with the patient both over the phone and at frequent, short intervals in person. Some therapists attempt to discover any reason at all that the patient has for living and use this in their dealings with the patient. With respect to medication, no more should be given than a brief supply, and, certainly, the maximal lethal dose should not be exceeded.[4] It is also important to institute treatment for any other associated symptoms, e.g., depression, alcoholism, schizophrenia, etc.

VIOLENCE

Violent and impulsive behavior in general can be defined as threatening or destructive acts or ideation to animate or inanimate objects.[24] While violence is no stranger to psychiatrists, it is probably less of a problem in psychiatric populations than one would expect. Violence is not an exclusive problem of the emotionally ill, and, in general, it is more prominent in those who are not emotionally ill than those who are. Kalogerakis noted recently that in a survey of psychiatric inpatients violence against the staff was a most uncommon phenomena.[40] Messinger noted that less than 5 percent of all major crimes are committed by people with overt psychosis or mental retardation.[65] Brill and Malzberg are frequently cited to demonstrate that the crime rate for psychiatric patients was lower than that of the general population.[3] Recently, Rappeport and Lassen noted that for some serious offences (robbery and rape) there is a higher incidence in discharged male psychiatric patients than in the general population.[73] For discharged females, aggressive assault was higher than in the general population.[74] This is of some interest, for one must recognize that this is only for discharged patients and not those still hospitalized. Still, the majority of violent people, which includes most criminal offenders, reckless and drunken drivers and so on, will not be seen by the psychiatrist.[24]

Several studies have been done on emergency-room psychiatric patients, seen primarily for violent behavior.[50,51,90] These patients were almost exclusively male (94 to 98 percent). Their age range was between fifteen and forty-five years and their social class conformed to usual emergency-room populations. Aside from these demographic factors, the most consistently cited predictive factor is a *past history of violent or impulsive behavior.* The sociologic factors cited in many studies are of interest, but of less use to the clinician. Recently, Rubin[77] delineated some of the more pertinent psychologic historical patterns in violent patients: (1) their life experiences have created bitterness or resentment; (2) they have frequent quarrels with family members; (3) their associations with significant figures who are violent are greater than usual; (4) there is generally an absence of a source of self-esteem and a defective self-image; (5) interest in weapons; and (6) violent fantasies and daydreams. Specific symptoms that have also been correlated with violent behavior (but are also found in nonviolent patients) are such things as temper tantrums, hyperactivity, stuttering, and holding of breath. The specific constellation of pyromania, enuresis, and cruelty to animals has also been noted to be predictive of adult crime.[36] Typical family constellations that have been noted in violent patients are those marked by parental hostility and overt violence and/or seductiveness. Alcohol and drug use are factors indicated in a large number of violent episodes.[24]

As with any life-threatening behavior, it is no diagnostic feat to determine that an act has been committed. However, it is crucial to try to predict during an emergency consultation who will, in the immediate future, engage in such activity. It seems clear that there are at least two major groups that engage in violent behavior. One is a group of patients that has lifelong histories of acting out aggressively and violently in response to varied, and often any, stress. The other comprises a smaller group.[17] It is those who act aggressively in relation to the onset of some clear-cut emotional disorder, such as psychosis, affective disturbance, etc.

Violence or violent thoughts are either diffusely directed or directed at a specific person. Those with diffusely directed violence are frequently more difficult to treat as to finding a focus for immediate psychotherapeutic intervention. The self-referred patient who comes about questions of self-control or loss of control should be taken quite seriously in that he perceives himself to be a definite danger.[50] Mental status is of some assistance in evaluating violent patients. Particularly noteworthy are the following: acute anxiety, fears of loss of control, ambivalent feelings toward those in the environment, and undisguised, straightforward hatred and anger. The more severe these symptoms are the more possible is the occurrence of violent behavior.[24]

It has been noted in prison populations and in those with impulsive behavior that there is a high incidence of EEG abnormality, but the exact role of neurologic factors in violent behavior is relatively unclear.[66,91] Certainly, many physiologic factors have been shown to be a contributing factor in violent behavior, such as brain injury, seizure-like behavior, and even some of the recent genetic defects such as XYY.[24,59] While these can be contributing factors in lowering impulse control, the part they play in the immediate treatment plan is minimal other than in the utilization of specific medications for seizure disorders, etc. The majority of the patients seen for violent behavior are hospitalized, at least briefly, for further evaluation and many have previously been hospitalized for similar complaints.[51,90]

In general, the treatment of these patients involves some attempt to clarify the precipitants of the violent behavior, and to increase their capacity to tolerate stress and depression. Stress tolerance, at least in the acute state, can be increased pharmacologically. Many of these patients require immediate sedation in order to even further evaluate (see Table 29–2). Ervin recommends developing a type of institutional cathexis so that when the patient is under stress, he can either return to the emergency room or call the physician who saw him initially. Most violent acts are directed at family members, or those with whom the patient has close contact. Some assistance in alleviating the stress can be gained by treating the recipient of the violent behavior either alone or with the patient, and clarifying what is stressful and what isn't stressful. In most studies, continued contact with these patients is of some necessity and seems to be helpful.[24]

In the initial phase of treatment, when an agitated patient is brought to an emergency room, it is important to convey that he is in a place where he is safe and can be controlled and will be able to do no harm. In this respect, restraints, although distasteful, are often useful initially, for a brief period of time.

For the very agitated, a "show of force" is recommended as a very calming influence. As an example, a manic patient who was reluctant to either take medication or remain in the hospital, and was quite dangerous to himself and others, was being restrained, not too successfully, by some of the psychiatric staff when a security guard entered who was at least six feet four inches and 250 pounds. The patient, who had been struggling violently and had assaulted one of the staff members, looked at this man, put out his hand, and said, "Hello. I'm Joe. Would you like to play chess?" and was quiet and took his medication.

In general, the assessment of the violent patient probably depends upon three main factors: (1) the previous history of violent behavior; (2) the type of violence either contemplated or actually undertaken; and (3) the degree of control that the patient manifests both verbally and physically during the interview. When all of these kinds of behavior are clearly present and not well-controlled, the likelihood of violence is high. It also behooves the psychiatrist to recall the statement of Rubin: "The term dangerousness to others cannot be simply a way of singling out anyone

who we would prefer not to meet on the streets. Possibility of injury is not enough, it must be likely, and the threatened harm must be substantial . . . thus, the psychiatrist must define 'likely' as meaning 'virtual certainty' rather than mere chance."[77]

HOMICIDE

The problem of homicide may be considered as a difference of degree in relation to violence. However, there are some aspects of the evaluation that are different. The demographic data reveals that the typical person who commits homicide is a male between the ages of eighteen and forty-three years. It is interesting that risk of committing homicide decreases with age unlike the suicide rate, which increases with age. The male to female ratio is five to one. While there is a higher Negro to white homicide rate, this seems more related to the American culture than to racial distinction, in the sense that the homicide rate of the American Negro is several times higher than that of the African. Certainly, the great majority of homicides is not related to classic psychiatric illness. However, MacDonald has stated that acutely psychotic schizophrenic patients and delirious patients who make homicidal threats should be hospitalized. The chronicity of paranoid delusions should provide the clinician with no assurance against homicide in that the paranoid delusions of those who actually assaulted or killed someone were present for at least four and a half years.[56]

Among the many factors associated with homicide potential are: (1) parental brutality, (2) parental seduction, (3) arson, (4) cruelty to animals, (5) enuresis after age five, (6) arrest record, (7) arrest for assault, (8) alcoholism, and (9) attempted suicide. MacDonald, in an attempt to evaluate these predictors, studied a group of patients who made homicidal threats and compared them to a group of patients who had actually committed homicide and to a group of nonviolent psychiatric patients. None of these patients studied was psychotic, and each was matched for age,

TABLE 29–2.   **Types and Doses of Medications Frequently Prescribed for Psychiatric Emergencies***

1. Acute Agitation—no organicity—usually psychotic
   A. Severe—immediate sedation desired, patient usually not arousable postdrug
      (a) Sodium Pentothal, 250–500 mg. IV
      (b) Sodium Amobarbital 200–800 mg. IV
      (c) ECT
   B. Severe—sedation desired rapidly, usually within 1 hour—patient usually arousable postdrug
      (a) Chlorpromazine: male (70kg.) 100 mg. p.o. every 30 min., or 50 mg. IM and repeat in 45 min.
      (b) Haloperidol: 3–5 mg. IM every hour
      (c) Perphenazine: 5 mg. IM every hour
   C. Moderate—oral doses of above, tranquilizers and minor tranquilizers with regular maintenance schedule if indicated
   D. Prolonged Sleep Treatment (Dauerschauf)
      (a) Chlorpromazine: 150 mg. p.o. and 150 mg. every 4 hours
      (b) Sodium Amobarbital: 500 mg. p.o. and 250 mg. p.o. every 4 hours if awake

2. Acute Agitation—organic etiology
   A. Toxic psychosis secondary to hallucinogenic drug use (sedation seems the most important factor)
      (a) No marked anticholinergic symptoms
         1. Chlorpromazine as above depending on severity of agitation
         2. Sodium Pentothal or Amobarbital, as above depending on agitation
         3. Diazepam: 10 mg. IM or IV and then 5–10 mg. every hour, or 20–40 mg. p.o. and then 10 mg. every hour

   4. Chlordiazepoxide: 100 mg. IM or p.o. every hour until sedated and p.o. or IM every 4 hours
   B. Presence or suspicion of anticholinergic-like drug or symptoms of—do not use phenothiazines
      (a) Diazepam, as above
      (b) Chlordiazepoxide, as above
      (c) Barbiturates, as above but smaller doses
      (d) Paraldehyde, as stated
      (e) Physostigmine salicylate, 2–4 mg. IM or p.o. and then p.o. every hour

3. Drug Withdrawal
   A. Alcohol—Delirium Tremens
      (a) Paraldehyde 10 cc p.o. or IM and every 2–4 hours; chloral hydrate (may be added) 0.5–1 gm. every 4–6 hours
      (b) Chlordiazepoxide, as stated
      (c) Chlorpromazine, as stated in slightly smaller doses
      (d) ECT
   B. Barbiturate and other central nervous system depressants
      (a) Reintoxication with 200 mg. pentobarbital, (see text for dose schedule)
   C. Narcotic Withdrawal
      (a) Acute intoxication—can be treated with Nalorphine 2–10 mg. every 2 hours to restore mildly depressed respirations
      (b) Withdrawal with 10–20 mg. p.o. Methadone in divided doses to a total of 40–60 mg. daily with gradual reduction (10%/day)

4. Organic Brain Syndromes
   A. Minimal initial doses of major tranquilizers either p.o. or IM with careful observation of effects, and gradual increasing of doses as needed.

---

* It is assumed in the use of these medications that the physician is familiar with the potential adverse reactions, side effects, and their treatment prior to administration.

sex, race, and social class. While there was evidence that parental brutality, parental seduction, childhood arson, cruelty to animals, and enuresis were slightly higher in the actual homicide group, the groups could not be statistically differentiated. The only parameter that was significant was attempted suicide in the homicide-threat group. The study concluded that "the risk of homicide is higher in the absence of attempted suicide. Those who have attempted suicide are more likely to kill themselves than to commit homicide." A follow-up study of 100 patients who were admitted to a hospital for homicidal threats found that the subsequent rate of homicide or suicide was more than 7 percent during the five-year, follow-up period. This study indicates that the incidence of life-threatening behavior is much higher in the group that makes these threats than in the general population.[56]

While the above-cited parameters of controlled studies do not differentiate those who are homicide prone from those who will actually kill someone, they should alert the clinician to the person's potential for violence. As with suicide, one should not hesitate to ask questions about either homicidal thoughts, potential, plans, or past hisotry when the potential for violence to others is suggested by a patient's history or clinical examination. As homicide seems to involve those the patient sees regularly (85 percent of murder victims were known by the murderer) there is reason for not only evaluating patients but the family as well and even treating them together.[24] While all patients who make threats cannot be hospitalized or detained for long periods, when there is a history of violent behavior—a patient agitated enough by mental-status examination to engage in such acts, with a history of poor impulse control—hospitalization is indeed indicated until the situation is mitigated or the patient is further evaluated. Lion,[51] Ervin,[24] MacDonald[56] and others who have had a great deal of experience with such patients, all note the value of long-term follow-up and accessibility of a therapist for patients who manifest such problems, so that they might talk out rather than act out their feelings.

Behavior that Upsets the Patterns of Life

Many of the problems that constitute psychiatric emergencies are perceived by the patient or others. What is perceived is that something different, or some dramatic change, has occurred. Into this area fall most major categories of acute and chronic psychiatric illness, particularly psychosis. While there is no intent to review every major psychiatric syndrome, it is acknowledged that general guidelines of management exist. Any change in the behavior of even a chronic patient that is perceived as markedly different by the patient or others often leads to an emergency psychiatric consultation. In actuality, the problems that most often present in this manner can be grouped into four categories: (1) primary symptoms of conceptual disorganization (usually schizophrenia); (2) primary symptoms of affective disturbance (depression, manic depression, etc.); (3) primary symptoms of anxiety (panic); and (4) primary physical or somatic symptoms (conversions). These conditions are considered together, as they usually represent disruptions in the life of the patient; these disruptions effect almost all systems (social, family, and work) with which the patient has contact. The patient usually presents as the focus of a chaotic situation and the emergency consultation often provides a structured forum whereby some of the chaos can be mitigated. In dealing with these particular psychiatric problems, it is often easier to group them into the above categories instead of in diagnostic categories. In the emergency situation, one is mainly interested in the target symptoms and the primary complaint of the patient. At this point the diagnosis may not be at all clear. The short-term focus of the emergency situation allows one to focus on immediate alleviation of symptoms and precipitating events, and to initiate treatment. As many organic conditions can mimic these states, organicity must be considered and ruled out before the institution of any medication. While there is great diversity in the clinical picture of the above conditions, there are some overall principles of management that are generally useful. Sedation and tranquilization may be necessary in order to even evaluate the patient. Specific attempts should be made to clarify the situation with regard to any activity of the patient or family that may be adding to the chaos. There is some value, in the initial phase of contact with the patient, in attempting to instill some hope with respect to a resolution of the situation. The interpersonal aspects of the relationship during the initial interview are extremely important. Perhaps most helpful is the acknowledgement on the part of the interviewer of the degree of distress or discomfort the patient feels. Statements such as "how upsetting" or "how frightening these experiences are" are much more useful than attempting to confront the patient, particularly the psychotic patient, with reality.[6] It is not reassuring to the patient to try to deny his discomfort or unhappiness. Perhaps the most important message to convey to the patient is a spirit of collaboration. While the decision to hospitalize such patients is often easier than continued outpatient treatment, the major factor that seems to determine the choice of intervention relates to the structure and accessibility of environmental supports and treatment facilities.[60,63,102] Even the most psychotic patient can often be sent home to a supportive family, while someone less ill may need to be hospitalized because he has no supports in the community. Particularly, one should be careful about sending a heavily medicated patient out of the emergency room without supervision except when his response to the medications is known.

While the above initial pharmacologic and psychotherapeutic guidelines are appropriate for most major emergency behavioral disturbances, specific behavior requires differentiation. Although by no means comprehensive, the following summary lists the pertinent symptoms and historical factors that are useful in determining the emergency management of these problems, particularly with regard to medications. Also cited are the more important conditions they must be differentiated from.

PRIMARY SYMPTOMS OF CONCEPTUAL DISORGANIZATIONS

The symptoms most often noted are those of bizarre and idiosyncratic speech, delusions, hallucinations, without disturbances of orientation or memory. Also absent are primary or noticeable affective symptomatology. Certainly, the major condition that presents in this manner is the acute schizophrenic reaction. However, such entities as sleep deprivation,[55] gross-stress reactions,[33] and particularly hallucinogenic-drug reactions[29] can present in this manner, so a careful history must be taken to differentiate these conditions. The history should provide precise information on premorbid social functioning, family history, and the immediate precipitants to the episode. The predominant pharmacologic intervention for disorders that present with the above picture are the major tranquilizers.[41]

PRIMARY SYMPTOMS OF AFFECTIVE DISTURBANCE

The most common symptoms associated with these conditions are depression, retardation, manic or hypomanic behavior, guilt, hopelessness and self-deprecation. These conditions, particularly retarded depressions, can often be mistaken for organic states, especially in older patients. Conversely, the organic dementias and senility can often be mistaken for severely retarded depressions. In this instance, it is especially important to perform a neurologic examination in cognitive and motor-retarded patients. A careful history of premorbid functioning will often assist in differentiating a dementia from the onset of a depressive reaction, the former being more gradual and slow, and the latter usually being more distinct at its onset. Certainly, there is very little difficulty in recognizing hypomanic and manic conditions, again being careful to differentiate them from various types of hallucinogenic-drug ingestions and other self-medications. Strokes or cerebrovascular accidents can often present in either manner, e.g., either depressed or hypomanic. When this is suspected a neurologic examination is often of use. Almost as a subgroup of these reactions are acute grief reactions, as described by Lindemann.[49] This includes symptoms of somatic distress, preoccupation with the image of the deceased, guilt, hostile reactions, and, in general, loss of usual life patterns. In these conditions, while initial medication for agitation may be necessary, the major pharmacologic interventions are those that affect mood, e.g., antidepressants, lithium, etc.[41]

PRIMARY SYMPTOMS OF ANXIETY

In these instances, we see the patient expressing symptoms mainly associated with anxiety, such as feeling nervous, tense, an inability to concentrate, along with various symptoms of autonomic-nervous-system arousal—palpitations, diaphoresis, and an inability to focus attention. These symptoms may be treated by the minor tranquilizers or, if the agitation is severe, the major tranquilizers for immediate sedation.[41]

In this section it might also be useful to discuss the group of reactions seen in survivors of a disaster situation.[54,64,94] While natural disasters such as fires, floods, and earthquakes, etc. are rare, the survivors of these occasions are frequently seen en masse in emergency rooms and psychiatrists may be called in as part of a general medical mobilization. While major psychiatric problems are rare, there is a typical pattern of emotional response to be aware of. The crucial factor most of the survivors of disaster situations experience is an abrupt shift from a familiar environment to a strange or unfamiliar environment. In disaster situations, 12 to 25 percent of the patients remain calm and collected, and can be used for various leadership roles. Another 10 to 25 percent will react in an inappropriate, hysterical, and overwhelmed fashion. This group usually represents the majority of the psychiatric casualties. These patients are best managed by sedation. The majority of survivors of disaster situations, usually about three-quarters, will act in a stunned, bewildered, confused fashion, and, in fact, often appear sedated. They are usually passive and compliant. They respond to simple directions and clarification of ru-

mors. After the initial shock phase of the disaster situation, there is usually a desire for compulsive talking and repetition of the story. However, this is accompanied, frequently, by physical fatigue and lassitude. At this time, leadership and direction are important, as well as rumor control. The whole cycle takes place in twenty-four to forty-eight hours, with complete recovery in most cases.[77]

PRIMARY PHYSICAL OR SOMATIC SYMPTOMS

These patients frequently present with conversion reactions, paralysis, hysterical blindness, somatic symptoms such as nausea and vomiting, amnesia, and fugue states. While these are not classically considered psychiatric emergencies they often present to emergency rooms or as emergency consultations. Certainly many of the patients who have these symptoms may belong to other diagnostic groups as well, but, in terms of the emergency management, these are the primary-target symptoms that need alleviation. In these patients interview and clarification often are more helpful than medication.

MANAGEMENT OF THE ABOVE CONDITIONS— THE USE OF MEDICATIONS

All of the above conditions, depending on their severity, may necessitate varying amounts of medication. These amounts may range from none to a great deal of parenteral medication. The criteria for the administration of medication usually depend upon the severity of the symptoms, but more particularly on the severity of what can be termed "biological symptoms." Biological symptoms we would consider are: (1) psychomotor disturbance in terms of either extreme agitation or extreme retardation; (2) extreme conceptual disorganization; (3) marked symptoms of anxiety; and (4) sleep disturbances that are protracted. While any of these symptoms may be present, they frequently are present as an admixture of all of them. Depending on the severity of symptoms and the capacity of the patient to be interviewed and evaluated, one may use these medications rapidly or at a gradual pace.

Although the phenothiazines and other

tranquilizing agents have been in use for close to twenty years, there is very little in the way of prescribing or directions for the emergency use of these medications. The major psychotropic agents have most often been prescribed for the target symptoms of agitation, excitement, anxiety, ideas of persecution, and hostility.[30,41] While the phenothiazines have become one of the most useful pharmacologic agents in the psychiatrist's armamentarium, there are still other agents such as barbiturates, paraldehyde, chloral hydrate, and minor tranquilizers that are useful in sedating agitated patients (see Table 29–1).

The decision to use medications is based on the level of biologic symptoms of the patient and his response to the interview attempts. For example, if the patient calms down appreciably during the interview, then sedation may not be necessary at that point but may be necessary if the patient is to return home. However, if the patient either remains very agitated during the interview or is initially so agitated that he cannot be interviewed, then medications are certainly in order. While medication should not be administered without examining the patient, in rare instances the patient will be so agitated that physical examination is difficult. At this time, pertinent history must be gained from either the patient or most often from others as to possible organic causes and, specifically, as to drug ingestion. An attempt should be made to take at least the vital signs. While the systolic blood pressure is often high in an agitated, struggling patient, the diastolic is usually not that elevated. If the history is clear and there are no organic findings in the physical examination to contraindicate, then medications should be instituted, usually by the parenteral route. With regard to the major tranquilizers, the use of chlorpromazine (parenteral dose range 50–100 mg.), perphenazine (parenteral dose 5 mg.) or haloperidol (5 mg.) are all effective in initially sedating the patient.[16,41,76,82] If there is no response or diminishing of excitement, the dose may be repeated at thirty-to-forty-five-minute intervals until the patient is either asleep or calm enough to talk (see Table 29–1). At times, the very act of giving

medication parenterally calms the patient. Aside from its pharmacologic effect, it signifies to the patient that safeguards or external controls have now been instituted to stop his behavior. In cases of extreme agitation, where the patient needs immediate sedation, intravenous sodium amobarbital in ranges from 400 to 800 mg. IV slowly, is also quite effective. The proper dose is enough to sedate or calm, and most problems relate to not giving enough of the medication.[41] In prolonged contact it is important to continue the medication orally after the time of effectiveness of the intramuscular dose is over.[16] It is important to remember that the prior state of the organism, where the level of excitement or arousal is quite high, will usually allow the person to tolerate much higher doses of medications than he would in a less agitated state. In other words, 100 mg. of sodium amobarbital may be used as a hypnotic for a person in a normal state, and the same person in an agitated state may take close to 800 mg. of sodium amobarbital to produce the same soporific effect.[101]

MANAGEMENT OF ABOVE CONDITION— PSYCHOTHERAPEUTIC GOALS

With regard to psychotherapeutic interventions, many of the objectives of the emergency interview have already been listed. Depending upon the severity of the symptoms of either conceptual disorganization or affective disturbance, the primary intervention is medication. After a period of sedation and some alleviation of symptoms, the scheduling of psychotherapeutic sessions can be done at a more leisurely pace, either on an outpatient or inpatient basis. This is in contrast to the situation where symptoms of anxiety, and the physical and somatic symptoms predominate. Then talking and psychotherapeutic intervention are almost the main intervention, especially in mild cases, and medications are adjunctive. Lindemann's principles for the treatment of acute grief reactions are useful in many emergency situations other than grief reaction.[49] He outlined that in acute grief reactions psychotherapeutic intervention should focus on: (1) a sharing (of the grief work); (2) reviewing the relationship with the important people in the environment (deceased); (3) accepting the pain of the grief as well as working through and mobilizing some of their own feelings and fears about such things as insanity, anger, etc.; (4) acquainting the patient with their own present alteration of modes of emotional reaction; (5) attempting to establish some acceptable formulation of future relationships (to the deceased) and, in general, to others in the environment; and (6) finding new persons around whom the patient can develop new patterns of contact. In the emergency situation many of these topics can only be touched on, but they do provide good guides for inquiry. The gathering of information and the reflection back to the patient of the implications of the information go a long way to reassuring the patient that there is not only a cause for the state he is in but a possible solution. The use of insights gained in these contacts may be superficial, but they are often perceived by the patient as the beginning of a helping process. Interestingly, for some they may even be lastingly effective, becoming "rules of life" for their future activities.

Impairments to Performing Effective Behavior

While previously we looked for classic symptoms of emotional illness, in this section the class of symptoms that are manifested primarily are those considered to indicate organic brain dysfunction. Disturbances of memory, orientation, and level of awareness are the most frequent symptoms that one would note. In other words, we are dealing with phenomena that interfere almost mechanically with the person's ability to negotiate life. In most instances the emergency situation that will confront the clinician relates primarily to three areas: (1) specific central nervous system damage, (2) too much of a drug (intoxication) or too little of a drug (withdrawal) or (3) drugs with primary-behavior-altering properties or idiosyncratic reactions to drugs or toxins. Whatever the cause, the symptoms usually manifest themselves as some type of cerebral dysfunction

either in the form of a delirious state or in classic-acute or chronic-organic brain syndrome.[52] When the mental-status examination reveals evidence of cerebral dysfunction, it is almost mandatory that the patient have a detailed physical examination, looking for such things as pneumonia, subdural hematoma or cerebral laceration, meningitis, diabetes, and any of the other myriad metabolic conditions that can cause delirium and even psychosis.[37,71] Of contemporary concern would be noting, in the physical examination, evidence of injections of various drugs, particularly narcotic drugs. The vital signs (temperature, blood pressure, and pulse) are also of critical importance in the evaluation, particularly temperature. The other most important part of the examination of patients with any type of evidence of cerebral dysfunction in the mental status is a detailed exploration of the history for past drug use and abuse as well as current medications, both prescribed and self-prescribed.

The majority of these problems can be grouped into the following three categories: withdrawal reactions from chronic use of some pharmacological agent, toxic or idiosyncratic reactions, and, lastly, cerebral dysfunction related to traumatic, vascular, infectious, metabolic, or neoplastic disease of the central nervous system.

WITHDRAWAL REACTIONS

The classic withdrawal reaction is that usually associated with the use of alcohol. The syndromes (all of which may present for emergency evaluation) associated with the abuse of alcohol have been most clearly delineated by Victor.[98] He noted: (1) *alcohol intoxication*, which is simple drunkenness and includes such entities as pathological intoxication. Pathological intoxication may be defined as an abnormal, psychoticlike reaction related to small amounts of alcohol. Some people have felt this is related to temporal-lobe epilepsy; (2) *abstinence or withdrawal syndrome*, including tremulousness, hallucinosis, "rum fits," and delirium tremens; (3) *nutritional diseases* associated with alcoholism, such as Wernecke Korsokov syndrome, neuropathies, pellagra; and (4) *degenerative diseases* of uncertain pathogenesis. The syndromes related to abstinence and withdrawal are those most commonly seen as psychiatric emergencies. Alcoholic hallucinosis may present without tremulousness and may be seen as a withdrawal symptom or while the patient is still drinking. However, its close association with the ingestion of alcohol and the lack of a history of schizophrenia make it a fairly distinct entity.[97] The classical syndrome of delirium tremens, with increased motor and autonomic activity, confusion, disorientation, hallucinations and illusions, is familiar to most physicians. The syndrome is classified as a medical emergency. Its treatment necessitates proper hydration as well as vitamin supplementation. The pharmacologic management of this entity has changed in the recent past, initially being treated by the phenothiazines when they first became popular, moving to chlordiazepoxide (Librium) when it became available; now there has been a return to paraldehyde and chloral hydrate in the treatment of these alcohol withdrawal syndromes. In the sixties, a study by Golbert demonstrated that paraldehyde and chloral hydrate were the most effective and best-tolerated drugs in the treatment of patients with delirium tremens.[31] With the use of these drugs, there were fewer complications noted in terms of pneumonia, convulsions, and hypertension. The schedule recommended in the regimen was 10 cc. of paraldehyde orally, and 0.5 to 1 g. of chloral hydrate orally. The paraldehyde could also be given intramuscularly. The paraldehyde was given at four-hour intervals and the chloral hydrate at six-hour intervals. If the agitation increased, the 10 cc. of paraldehyde could be given every two hours, and a gram of chloral hydrate every four hours until the patient was sedated. Librium in doses of 50–100 mg. every hour until sedation was reached has also been recommended as adequate treatment. The onset of the withdrawal syndrome occurs, usually within the first twenty-four to forty-eight hours, but may occur as long as seven to ten days after the cessation of alcohol. However, this is rare. Eighty percent of the cases will respond within three days of treatment.[98] A few years ago, Dudley presented data that a single ECT was also often effective in the treatment of delirium tremens.[19]

Barbiturate withdrawal, or for that matter any central-nervous-system-depressant drug, can present frequently with either seizures or psychotic symptoms as part of the withdrawal syndrome.[25,87] In fact, of those taking more than 900 mg. of barbiturate a day about 80 percent will have seizures and the majority psychotic symptoms upon abrupt withdrawal. The barbiturate addict (also found in patients addicted to other types of central-nervous-system depressants) may present in an intoxicated state. Usually, they are ataxic (often they show bruises on legs and body due to ataxia) with slurred speech and slowed and confused mentation. The intoxicated patient is often brought in by his family or friends. They say that the patient's behavior has changed and that he is either acting differently now or sleeping most of the time.

While an addict of central-nervous-system depressants, in the intoxicated state, may present as a diagnostic problem, the patient, in withdrawal, may present as a self-referral for treatment, for partial treatment to make his habit cheaper, or because he has run out of drugs. Physical signs that often confirm barbiturate-addiction withdrawal are insomnia, blepharospasm, nystagmus, and postural hypotension with a pulse rise on standing of greater than twelve to fifteen beats. Seizures do not usually occur before thirty-six hours. The usual treatment of the withdrawal state from depressant drugs is by reintoxication with a depressant drug. Ewing has suggested a demonstration of drug tolerance with the use of a test dose of 200 mg. of pentobarbital orally on an empty stomach.[25] The patient is then observed in one hour, and if he shows no sign of intoxication at the end of this hour, there is probably indication of extreme tolerance (addiction of more than 1000 mg./day) to barbiturates; if the patient is asleep but arousable, there is probably no dependence on these types of drugs. There is a great deal of cross-tolerance in these drugs and even though the patient may be addicted to such things as meprobamate, glutethimide, etc., the patient may be withdrawn with pentobarbital or phenobarbital on a decreasing schedule of 10 percent a day until withdrawal is complete. With regard to opiate use, the withdrawal usually starts thirty-six to seventy-two hours after cessation of drug use, with symptoms progressing from a craving for drugs and anxiety to yawning, perspiration, lacrimation, mydriasis to goose flesh (pilo-motor erection) etc. The withdrawal can usually be tolerated without substitution of other drugs. However, the addiction may be mixed and one then must withdraw the patient depending on the addiction. While pure opiate withdrawal is not life threatening, most physicians will use methadone for withdrawal.[87] It is also important to note that many drug abusers are addicted or use many different drugs so that both withdrawal and intoxicated states may present confusing clinical features. Consequently, in any patient with drug-abuse problems multiple drug use should be considered.

DRUGS THAT ALTER BEHAVIOR. TOXIC AND IDIOSYNCRATIC REACTIONS TO DRUGS

Of interest today are the reactions to hallucinogenic drugs. In the past decade the increase in number and availability of compounds that have hallucinogenic effects has been nothing short of remarkable (Table 29–3).* The willingness of people to take unknown compounds, which may or may not be adulterated and may have any number of unknown contaminants, is no less astounding.[29] The effects of these drugs, often taken in varying combinations and routes of administration, are dramatic. However, some indication of what drug the patient has taken can often be obtained from some of the physiological symptoms (see Table 29–3). The confused, highly anxious, often fearful, hallucinating youth, with a history of hallucinogenic drug use, often surrounded either by his frightened family or by friends who may be in a similar condition, has been all too common in our emergency rooms. Lately, this trend has seemed to

* See references 29, 32, 42, 47, 48, and 95.

diminish. However, these reactions are still common and, as our pharmacological armamentarium increases, so are behavioral and toxic reactions to a wide variety of new and old compounds.

The form of treatment for the patient who has taken these drugs usually consists of: (1) decreasing the stimulation in the immediate environment: treating the person in a quiet room out of the mainstream of the emergency room or hospital activities; (2) attempting to establish some type of verbal contact with the patient with a minimum use of tranquilization; (3) reassurance and attempts to make reality concrete with repetitive, simple statements; and (4) reassuring the patient that the temporary waxing and waning of his mental status is typical. As a last resort, sedation is often necessary. If the agitation is severe, the phenothiazines in moderate doses have been quite effective parenterally or orally as an initial intervention. If there is some evidence that the patient has taken a drug with a strong anticholinergic component, then diazepam (Valium) 10 mg. intramuscularly (I.M.), repeated every thirty to forty minutes usually brings about sedation. (The use of phenothiazines with patients who have taken drugs with strong anticholinergic components may bring on a central, hypotensive crisis.) In general, the treatment guidelines for these reactions, when medications are indicated, are sedation. In this respect, either phenothiazines, barbiturates, paraldehyde, or diazepam have all been noted to be effective.[86,87]

However, there are a wide variety of toxic and/or idiosyncratic behavioral reactions that can occur with any type of central-nervous-system stimulant or depressant, anticholinergics, tranquilizers, halogenated hydrocarbons (glue, gasoline, cleaning fluids) and commonly used medicines. Thus, the possibility of their use should never be ruled out.[43,44] This is especially true if neither the past history nor clinical picture are consistent with typical diagnosis categories. Careful questioning about drug use is extremely important as patients may not only be reluctant to reveal regular use but may also have taken a drug for so long that it has almost become a way of

TABLE 29–3. Physiological Effects* of Drugs that have Acute Behavioral Effects

DRUG	CONSCIOUSNESS	SKIN	PUPILS	TEMPERATURE	PULSE	BLOOD PRESSURE	REFLEXES	MOTOR ACTIVITY
Stimulants								
Amphetamines Methylphenidate, etc.	Hyperaroused, hallucinations	Sweating, dry mouth	Dilated, reactive	↑	↑	↑	→↑	↑
Hallucinogens								
LSD Mescaline	Hyperaroused, visual hallucinations, often no confusion	Slight sweating	Dilated, reactive	↑	↑	↑	↑	↑
Anticholinergics								
Scopolamine Atropine Methapyrilene, trihexyphenidyl	Confused, hallucinating, memory impairment	Flushed, dry, hot, mucous membranes also dry	Dilated, unreactive	↑	↑	→↓	↑	→↑ Urinary retention
Marijuana THC†	Clear, distorted perceptions, drowsy	Dry mouth	Normal, conjunctive dilated vessels	→	→↑	→	→	→
Opiates								
Intoxication	Depressed, slight	Warm, sweating	Pinpoint unreactive	→↓	→↓	→↓	→↓	↓
Withdrawal	Alert, anxious	Sweating, gooseflesh	Dilated, decreasingly reactive, lacrimation	→↑	↑	↑	↑	Restless, muscle aches
Barbiturates								
Intoxication	Drowsy, confused, slurred speech		Normal, nystagmus	→↓	→	→↓	↓	↓ Ataxia
Withdrawal	Anxiety, psychosis, delirium	Sweating	blepharospasm	→↑	→↑	Postural ↓	↑	Restless, tremors, seizures
Halogenated hydrocarbons	Giddy, tinnitus		Diplopia, dilated, reactive		→↑	→↑	↑	→↑ Restless, ataxia
Phenothiazines	Drowsy	Dry, mucous membranes dry	Dilated, reactive	↓	→↓	Postural ↓→	↓	↓ Akathisia dystonias, Parkinsonism (seizures with high doses)
Tricyclic antidepressants‡	Confusion, disorientation, hallucinations	Dry, mucous membranes dry	Dilated, unreactive	→↑	↑	Postural →↓	↑	Restless, seizures, tremors, urinary retention

* Physiological effects may be mixed due to multiple simultaneous drug injections.
† Tetrahydrocannibinal. ‡ High doses or idiosyncratic responses. LEGEND: → = Normal; ↑ = Elevated; ↓ = Decreased.

life. Any medication the patient is taking, including digitalis, aspirin, even antidepressant medication and phenothiazines, can cause toxic, confusional-type syndromes by themselves or through electrolyte imbalance.[52] The majority of these reactions can be treated simply by withdrawing or omitting the offending agent, and sedation. The history of any current drug use is often important. Even a person who has stabilized a drug habit may show evidence of withdrawal with intercurrent infections, changes in tolerance to the drug, or a less potent new drug supply. All can cause some type of behavioral reaction.

When there is a clear history of drug use that could explain the clinical picture, the clinician tends to drop the diagnostic process. In any intoxication it is important to remember that head trauma is a distinct possibility, either from the patient falling or from attempts at "sedation" by those accompanying the patient. An adolescent, who had jumped through a ground floor window while under the influence of LSD, was brought in by his parents with a history of the father having to "hit" the patient to quiet him. When routine skull x-rays revealed a depressed skull fracture, it was then noted by the father that the "hitting" was done with a hammer.

Cerebral Dysfunctions

Disturbances of memory, verbal ability, spatial psychomotor functioning, numerical ability, and fluctuating or diminished levels of consciousness are usually taken as symptoms of the presence of cerebral dysfunction (organic-brain syndrome). As these conditions are discussed more fully in Volume 4, Chapters 2–9, they will only be touched upon here.

Etiologically, organic-brain syndromes unrelated to drug reactions are usually associated with fever, bacterial toxins, or other cerebral insults such as cerebrovascular accidents, trauma, etc. In general, the diagnosis of these conditions rests again on getting an accurate history, particularly an accurate medical history. The treatment rests on dealing with the underlying causes. It is important, also, to assess the electrolyte balance, hydration, nutrition, and vitamin supply of the confused patient.

Treatment of organic-brain syndromes consists of: (1) treatment of underlying condition if possible; (2) attempts to orient the patient through regular, simple sensory inputs by staff, stating at each contact who they are, what hospital the patient is in, etc. Also such things as clocks and calendars for time orientation; even a radio tuned to a station with hourly news breaks is helpful; and increasing lighting so visual illusions are not as possible due to shadows or indistinct objects; and (3) sedation with a major tranquilizer in small doses may be helpful for the more agitated patients.[16,80] The use of cortical depressants such as barbiturates should be avoided because they may exacerbate the condition.

Repetitive Behavior Patterns

In many of the studies of psychiatric emergency rooms, patients with personality disorders who manifest chronic patterns of behavior that cause themselves and those about them repeated difficulties are a small percentage of all patients seen. These patients are usually discharged from the emergency room with no follow-up arrangements. The diagnostic labels of psychopath, antisocial personality, or behavior disorder are most frequently used for these patients. While they may manifest acute symptoms of anxiety or depression, what is most prominent in their histories is a prolonged story of consistent maladaptive responses to stress. Usually after or during the interview, it becomes apparent why they have come at this particular time, and their enthusiasm for further treatment usually depends on the response of the interviewer in promising or offering some type of help for the immediate situation. Most often treatment or prolonged contacts are broken off as soon as the acute situation is over, and these patients tend to return only at times of a repeated stress. Although their behavior is more of a pattern, they do, at times, have difficulty in negotiating their lives due to these repetitive patterns.[57]

⟨ Conclusion

From the foregoing it is quickly apparent that the psychiatric emergency can encompass almost any behavior. To write comprehensively on each topic would require a complete textbook of psychiatry. However, the problems that constitute the emergency can usually be treated by careful evaluation and judicious decisions. In many settings staff (nonpsychiatrists) have been trained to do at least the initial screening, using psychiatric consultation as needed.[35,63] As soon as standardized interview schedules and rapid computer analysis become available, it would seem that more nonpsychiatrists will be doing the emergency evaluations.

What is also apparent is that the evaluation of the psychiatric emergency is often the initiation of the treatment process. As such, the place where emergency evaluations are performed should be part of a system for continued care with a diversity of facilities, e.g., hospital, outpatient, day care, etc. If facilities are not provided for whatever follow-up is necessary from the emergency consultation, then the quality of service is distinctly compromised.[75,88,100] It would also seem important that if an emergency consultation service or walk-in service is to function efficiently, then it should have facilities for medical and diagnostic consultations.

⟨ Bibliography

1. BLANE, H. T., J. J. MULLER, and M. E. CHAFETZ. "Acute Psychiatric Services in the General Hospital: II. Current Status of Emergency Psychiatric Services," *Am. J. Psychiatry*, 124 (1967), 37–45.
2. BRANDON, S. "Crisis Theory and Possibilities of Therapeutic Intervention," *Br. J. Psychiatry*, 117 (1970), 627–633.
3. BRILL, H. and B. MALZBERG. *Mental Hospital Service*, Suppl. 153. Washington: Am. Psychiatric Assoc., 1962.
4. BROPHY, J. J. "Suicide Attempts with Psychotherapeutic Drugs," *Arch. Gen. Psychiatry*, 17 (1967), 652–657.
5. BROTHWOOD, J. "The Work of a Psychiatric Emergency Clinic," *Br. J. Psychiatry*, 111 (1965), 631–634.
6. BULLARD, D. M. "Psychotherapy of Paranoid Patients," *Arch. Gen. Psychiatry*, 2 (1960), 137–141.
7. CAPLAN, G. *An Approach to Community Mental Health*. New York: Grune & Stratton, 1961.
8. CAPLAN, G. and H. GRUNEBAUM. "Perspectives on Primary Prevention," *Arch. Gen. Psychiatry*, 17 (1967), 331–346.
9. CHAFETZ, M. E., H. T. BLANE, and J. J. MULLER. "Acute Psychiatric Services in the General Hospital: I. Implications for Psychiatry in Emergency Admissions," *Am. J. Psychiatry*, 123 (1966), 664–670.
10. CLENDENIN, W. W. and G. E. MURPHY. "Wrist Cutting," *Arch. Gen. Psychiatry*, 25 (1971), 465–469.
11. COLEMAN, J. V. and P. ERRERA. "The General Hospital Emergency Room and Its Psychiatric Problems," *Am. J. Public Health*, 53 (1963), 1294–1300.
12. COLEMAN, M. D. and I. ZWERLING. "The Psychiatric Emergency Clinic: A Flexible Way of Meeting Community Mental Health Needs," *Am. J. Psychiatry*, 115 (1959), 980–984.
13. DARBONNE, A. "Crisis: A Review of Theory, Practice and Research," *Psychotherapy*, 4 (1967), 371–379.
14. DAVIS, J. M., E. BARTLETT, and B. TERMINI. "Overdosage of Psychotropic Drugs," *Dis. Nerv. Syst.*, 29 (1968), 157–164.
15. DAVISON, K. and C. R. BAGLEY. "Schizophrenia-like Psychoses Associated with Organic Disorders of the Central Nervous System: A Review of the Literature," in R. N. Herrington, ed., *Current Problems in Neuropsychiatry*, pp. 113–184. Ashford, Kent: Headley, 1969.
16. DETRE, T. and H. JARECKI. *Modern Psychiatric Treatment*. Philadelphia: Lippincott, 1971.
17. DETRE, T., D. J. KUPFER and S. TAUB. "The Nosology of Violence." Paper presented Houston Neurol. Symp., March 1972.
18. DETRE, T. and G. J. TUCKER. "Psychotherapy for the Mentally Ill: A Redefinition of Goals." in N. S. Greenfield and G. E. Abrams, ed., *New Hospital Psychiatry*, pp.

57–65. New York: Academic, 1970.

19. DUDLEY, W. H. C. and J. G. WILLIAMS. "Electroconvulsive Therapy in Delirium Tremens," *Compr. Psychiatry*, 13 (1972), 357–360.

20. EASTWOOD, M. R., R. H. S. MINDHAM, and T. G. TENNENT. "The Physical Status of Psychiatric Emergencies," *Br. J. Psychiatry*, 116 (1970), 545–550.

21. EILENBERG, M. D. and P. B. WHATMORE. "Physical Disease and Psychiatric Emergencies," *Compr. Psychiatry*, 2 (1961), 358–363.

22. ERIKSON, E. H. *Childhood and Society*. New York: Norton, 1950.

23. ERRERA, P., G. WYSHAK, and H. JARECKI. "Psychiatric Care in a General Hospital Emergency Room," *Arch. Gen. Psychiatry*, 9 (1963), 105–112.

24. ERVIN, F. R. and J. R. LION. "Clinical Evaluation of the Violent Patient," in Staff Report to the Natl. Commiss. on the Causes and Prevention of Violence, Appendix 24, pp. 1163–1188. Washington: U.S. Govt. Print. Off., 1969.

25. EWING, J. A. and W. E. BAKEWELL. "Diagnosis and Management of Depressant Drug Dependence," *Am. J. Psychiatry*, 123 (1967), 909–917.

26. FARBEROW, N. L. and E. S. SHNEIDMAN. *The Cry for Help*. New York: McGraw-Hill, 1961.

27. FAWCETT, J., M. LEFF, and W. E. BUNNEY. "Suicide," *Arch. Gen. Psychiatry*, 21 (1969), 129–137.

28. FRANKEL, F. H., M. E. CHAFETZ, and H. T. BLANE. "Treatment of Psychosocial Crises in the Emergency Service of a General Hospital," *JAMA*, 195 (1966), 626–628.

29. FREEDMAN, D. X. "On the Use and Abuse of LSD," *Arch. Gen. Psychiatry*, 18 (1968), 330–347.

30. GOLDBERG, S. C., G. L KLERMAN, and J. O. COLE. "Changes in Schizophrenic Psychopathology and Ward Behavior as a Function of Phenothiazine Treatment," *Br. J. Psychiatry*, 111 (1965), 120–133.

31. GOLBERT, T. M., C. J. SANZ, D. D. ROSE et al. "Comparative Evaluation of Treatments of Alcohol Withdrawal Syndromes," *JAMA*, 201 (1967), 99–102.

32. GOWDY, J. M. "Stramonium Intoxication: Review of Symptomatology in 212 Cases," *JAMA*, 221 (1972), 585–587.

33. GRINKER, R. and J. P. SPIEGEL. *Men Under Stress*. New York: McGraw-Hill, 1963.

34. HANKOFF, L. D. *Emergency Psychiatric Treatment—A Handbook of Secondary Prevention*. Springfield, Ill.: Charles C. Thomas, 1969.

35. HANKOFF, L. D., C. J. RABINER, and C. ST. GEO. HENRY. "Comparison of the Satellite Clinic and the Hospital-Based Clinic," *Arch. Gen. Psychiatry*, 24 (1971), 474–478.

36. HELLMAN, D. S. and N. BLACKMAN. "Enuresis, Firesetting, and Cruelty to Animals," *Am. J. Psychiatry*, 122 (1965), 1431–1435.

37. HIMMELHOCH, J., J. PINCUS, G. J. TUCKER et al. "Sub-Acute Encephalitis: Behavioral and Neurological Aspects," *Br. J. Psychiatry*, 116 (1970), 531–538.

38. HOLMES, T. S. and T. H. HOLMES. "Short-term Intrusions into the Life Style Routine," *J. Psychosom. Res.*, 14 (1970), 121–132.

39. JACOBSEN, G. F. "Crisis Theory and Treatment Strategy: Some Sociocultural and Psychodynamic Considerations," *J. Nerv. Ment. Dis.*, 141 (1965), 209–218.

40. KALOGERAKIS, M. G. "The Assaultive Psychiatric Patient," *Psychiatr. Q.*, 45 (1971), 372–381.

41. KLEIN, D. F. and J. M. DAVIS. *Diagnosis and Drug Treatment of Psychiatric Disorders*. Baltimore: Williams & Wilkins, 1969.

42. KRAMER, J. C., V. S. FISCHMAN, and D. C. LITTLEFIELD. "Amphetamine Abuse: Pattern and Effects of High Doses Taken Intravenously," *JAMA*, 201 (1967), 305–309.

43. LAMY, P. P. and M. E. KITLER. "Untoward Effects of Drugs—Part I. (Including Non-Prescription Drugs)," *Dis. Nerv. Syst.*, 32 (1971), 17–23.

44. ———. "Untoward Effects of Drugs—Part II. (Including Non-Prescription Drugs)," *Dis. Nerv. Syst.*, 32 (1971), 105–114.

45. LAZARE, A., F. COHEN, A. JACOBSEN et al. "The Walk-In Patient as a Customer: A Key to Evaluation and Treatment," *Am. J. Orthopsychiatry*, 42 (1972), 872–883.

46. LEBOW, M. D. *Behavior Modification*. Englewood Cliffs, N.J.: Prentice-Hall, 1973.

47. LEFF, R. and S. BERNSTEIN. "Proprietary

Hallucinogens," *Dis. Nerv. Syst.*, 29 (1968), 621–626.

48. LIEBERMAN, C. M. and B. W. LIEBERMAN. "Marihuana—A Medical Review," *N. Engl. J. Med.*, 284 (1971), 88–91.

49. LINDEMANN, E. "Symptomatology and Management of Acute Grief," *Am. J. Psychiatry*, 101 (1944–45), 141–148.

50. LION, J. R., G. BACH-Y-RITA, and F. R. ERVIN. "The Self-Referred Violent Patient," *JAMA*, 205 (1968), 503–505.

51. ———. "Violent Patients in the Emergency Room," *Am. J. Psychiatry*, 125 (1969), 1706–1711.

52. LIPOWSKI, Z. J. "Delirium, Clouding of Consciousness and Confusion," *J. Nerv. Ment. Dis.*, 145 (1967), 227–255.

53. LITMAN, R. E. and N. L. FARBEROW. "Emergency Evaluation of Self-destructive Potentiality," in N. L. Farberow and E. S. Shneidman, eds., *The Cry for Help*, pp. 48–59. New York: McGraw-Hill, 1961.

54. LOWENBERG, R. "Psychologic Reactions in an Emergency (Earthquake)," *Am. J .Psychiatry*, 109 (1952), 384–385.

55. LUBY, E. D., C. E. FROHMAN, J. L. GRISELL et al. "Sleep Deprivation: Effects on Behavior, Thinking, Motor Performance, and Biological Energy Transfer Systems," *Psychosom. Med.*, 22 (1960), 182–192.

56. MACDONALD, J. M. *Homicidal Threats*. Springfield: Ill.: Charles C. Thomas, 1968.

57. ———. "The Prompt Diagnosis of Psychopathic Personality," *Am. J. Psychiatry*, 122 (1966), 45–50.

58. McHUGH, P. R. and H. GOODELL. "Suicidal Behavior—A Distinction in Patients with Sedative Poisoning Seen in a General Hospital," *Arch. Gen. Psychiatry*, 25 (1971), 456–464.

59. MARK, V. H. and F. R. ERVIN. *Violence and the Brain*. New York: Harper & Row, 1970.

60. MAXMEN, J. S., G. J. TUCKER, and M. D. LEBOW. *Rational Hospital Psychiatry*, pp. 117–125. New York, Brunner/Mazel, 1974.

61. ———. "No Exit: The Persistently Suicidal Patient," *Compr. Psychiatry*, 14 (1973), 71–79.

62. MAYFIELD, D. G. and D. MONTGOMERY. "Alcoholism, Alcohol Intoxication, and Suicide Attempts," *Arch. Gen. Psychiatry*, 27 (1972), 349–353.

63. MENDEL, W. M. and S. RAPPORT. "Determinants of the Decision for Psychiatric Hospitalization," *Arch. Gen. Psychiatry*, 20 (1969), 321–328.

64. MENNINGER, W. C. "Psychologic Reactions in an Emergency (Flood)," *Am. J. Psychiatry*, 109 (1952), 128–130.

65. MESSINGER, E. and B. APFELBERG. *A Quarter Century of Court Psychiatry*. 26th Annual Report. New York: Psychiatric Clinic, Court of General Sessions, 1958.

66. MONROE, R. R. *Episodic Behavioral Disorders—A Psychodynamic and Neurophysiologic Analysis*. Cambridge: Harvard University Press, 1970.

67. MORRICE, J. K. W. "Emergency Psychiatry," *Br. J. Psychiatry*, 114 (1968), 485–491.

68. MULLER, J. J., M. E. CHAFETZ, and H. T. BLANE. "Acute Psychiatric Services in the General Hospital: III. Statistical Survey," *Am. J. Psychiatry*, 124 (1967), 46–57.

69. MURPHY, G. E. "Clinical Identification of Suicidal Risk," *Arch. Gen. Psychiatry*, 27 (1972), 356–359.

70. MYERS, E. S. "Conference on Handling Psychiatric Emergencies," *Am. J. Psychiatry*, 122 (1965), 224–225.

71. PINCUS, J. and G. J. TUCKER. *Behavioral Neurology*. New York: Oxford University Press, 1974.

72. POLAK, P. "Social Systems Intervention," *Arch. Gen. Psychiatry*, 25 (1971), 110–117.

73. RAPPEPORT, J. R. and G. LASSEN. "Dangerousness—Arrest Rate Comparisons of Discharged Patients and the General Population," *Am. J. Psychiatry*, 121 (1965), 776–783.

74. ———. "The Dangerousness of Female Patients: A Comparison of the Arrest Rate of Discharged Psychiatric Patients and the General Population," *Am. J. Psychiatry*, 123 (1966), 413–419.

75. RHINE, M. W. and P. MAYERSON. "Crisis Hospitalization within a Psychiatric Emergency Service," *Am. J. Psychiatry*, 127 (1971), 1386–1391.

76. RITTER, R. M., D. E. DAVIDSON, and T. A. ROBINSON. "Comparison of Injectable Haloperidol and Chlorpromazine," *Am. J. Psychiatry*, 129 (1972), 79–81.

77. RUBIN, B. "Prediction of Dangerousness in Mentally Ill Criminals," *Arch. Gen. Psychiatry*, 27 (1972), 397–407.

78. SCHULBERG, H. and A. SHELDON. "The Probability of Crisis and Strategies for Preventive Intervention," *Arch. Gen. Psychiatry*, 18 (1968), 553–558.

79. SCHWARTZ, M. D. and P. ERRERA. "Psychiatric Care In A General Hospital Emergency Room: II. Diagnostic Features," *Arch. Gen. Psychiatry*, 9 (1963), 113–121.

80. SENAY, E. C. and F. P. MCKEGNEY. "Common Psychiatric Emergencies in the General Hospital," *Am. Acad. Gen. Prac.*, 37 (1968), 102–109.

81. SHNEIDMAN, E. S. and N. L. FARBEROW. "Statistical Comparisons between Attempted and Committed Suicides," in E. S. Shneidman and N. L. Farberow, eds., *The Cry for Help*, pp. 19–47. New York: McGraw-Hill, 1961.

82. SHOPSIN, B., L. J. HEKIMIAN, S. GERSHON et al. "A Controlled Evaluation of Haloperidol, Chlorpromazine, and Sodium Amobarbital: Intramuscular Short-term Use in Acute Psychotic Patients," *Cur. Ther. Res.*, 11 (1969), 561–573.

83. SLATER, E., A. W. BEARD, and E. GLITHERO. "Schizophrenia-like Psychoses of Epilepsy," *Br. J. Psychiatry*, 109 (1963), 95–150.

84. SMITH, C. G. and K. SINANAN. "The 'Gaslight Phenomenon' Reappears," *Br. J. Psychiatry*, 120 (1972), 685–686.

85. STENGEL, E. *Suicide and Attempted Suicide.* Baltimore: Penguin, 1967.

86. TAYLOR, R. L., J. I. MAURER, and J. R. TINKLENBERG. "Management of 'Bad Trips' in an Evolving Drug Scene," *JAMA*, 213 (1970), 422–425.

87. THE MEDICAL LETTER ON DRUGS AND THERAPEUTICS. "Diagnosis and Management of Reactions to Drug Abuse," 12 (1970), 65–68.

88. THOMAS, C. S. and G. K. WEISMAN. "Emergency Planning: The Practical and Theoretical Backdrop to an Emergency Treatment Unit," *Int. J. Soc. Psychiatry*, 16 (1970), 283–287.

89. TISCHLER, G. L. "Decision-Making Process in the Emergency Room," *Arch. Gen. Psychiatry*, 14 (1966), 69–78.

90. TUASON, V. B. "The Psychiatrist and the Violent Patient," *Dis. Nerv. Syst.*, 32 (1971), 764–768.

91. TUCKER, G. J., T. DETRE, M. HARROW et al. "Behavior and Symptoms of Psychiatric Patients and the Electroencephalogram," *Arch. Gen. Psychiatry*, 12 (1965), 278–286.

92. TUCKER, G. J. and E. R. GORMAN. "The Significance of the Suicide Gesture in the Military," *Am. J. Psychiatry*, 123 (1967), 854–861.

93. TUCKER, G. J. and J. S. MAXMEN. "The Practice of Hospital Psychiatry: A Formulation," *Am. J. Psychiatry*, 130 (1973), 887–891.

94. TYHURST, J. S. "Individual Reactions to Community Disaster," *Am. J. Psychiatry*, 107 (1950), 764–769.

95. ULLMAN, K. C. and R. H. GROH. "Identification and Treatment of Acute Psychotic States Secondary to the Usage of Over-the-Counter Sleeping Preparations," *Am. J. Psychiatry*, 128 (1972), 1244–1248.

96. UNGERLEIDER, J. T. "The Psychiatric Emergency," *Arch. Gen. Psychiatry*, 3 (1960), 593–601.

97. VICTOR, M. and J. M. HOPE. "The Phenomenon of Auditory Hallucinations in Chronic Alcoholism," *J. Nerv. Ment. Dis.*, 126 (1958), 451–481.

98. ———. "Treatment of Alcoholic Intoxication and the Withdrawal Syndrome," *Psychosom. Med.*, 28 (1966), 636–650.

99. WEISMAN, A. D. and J. W. WORDEN. "Risk-Rescue Rating in Suicide Assessment," *Arch. Gen. Psychiatry*, 26 (1972), 553–560.

100. WEISMAN, G., A. FEIRSTEIN, and C. THOMAS. "Three-Day Hospitalization—A Model for Intensive Intervention," *Arch. Gen. Psychiatry*, 21 (1969), 620–629.

101. WILDER, J. M. "Modern Psychophysiology and the Law of Initial Value," *Am. J. Psychother.*, 12 (1958), 199–221.

102. WOOD, E. C., J. M. RAKUSIN, and E. MORSE. "Interpersonal Aspects of Psychiatric Hospitalization," *Arch. Gen. Psychiatry*, 3 (1960), 632–641.

CHAPTER 30

ADMINISTRATION OF THE STATE HOSPITAL

Milton Greenblatt

S TATE HOSPITALS are complex systems that function to admit, treat, and follow up mentally ill patients. They have also been used to segregate individuals who are dangerous to society, where the dangerousness may be attributable to emotional disorder. Many other individuals have been hospitalized who do not necessarily suffer full-blown mental derangement, but, inasmuch as they may be homeless and without friends and society provides no better place for them, they have been accepted on "humanitarian" grounds as inpatients.

Throughout history mental hospitals have varied dramatically in both structure and function while generally pursuing their social task of segregating and treating the emotionally disturbed. History, in fact, teaches us that the primary therapeutic methods and goals of our mental hospitals have largely reflected society's philosophical view of man and his willingness and ability to muster resources on behalf of the destitute, poverty-stricken, and

downtrodden sector of humanity. The mentally ill in state hospitals constitute one of the disfranchised minority groups to which society now appears to be addressing itself with renewed vigor. Indeed, the mentally ill come from the poverty stratum; and the conditions of their hospitalization, throughout most of our nation's history, have reflected, again, poverty, discrimination, and neglect.

(History

The *first hospital* for the mentally ill in America, founded in 1817 by Pennsylvania Quakers, was named the Friends Asylum. Patterned after the York Retreat, it was opened expressly for the purpose of practicing moral treatment —an enlightened form of patient care based on kindness, forebearance, and understanding together with social, recreational, and occupational diversions directed toward restoring balance in their lives. Many more privately endowed hospitals conducted along similarly enlightened lines were constructed in the ensuing years. The *first state-supported institution* was built in Lexington, Kentucky, in 1824, the Eastern State Hospital. It was followed in 1825 by the Manhattan State Hospital in New York; in 1828 by the Western State Hospital in Staunton, Virginia; in 1828, also, by the South Carolina State Hospital in Columbus; and the Worcester State Hospital in Massachusetts in 1833. State hospital construction burgeoned, particularly after 1841, when that Massachusetts school teacher, Dorothea Dix, aflame with anguish at the suffering and abuse of the mentally ill in the jails and almshouses, appealed directly to the legislatures of Massachusetts and other states to provide humane care and treatment for the afflicted. In 1904, the State Care Act in Massachusetts relieved the towns of their obligations for patient support in state hospitals; this, in turn, was followed by another large influx of patients into hospitals from jails and almshouses.

The early state hospitals of the moral treatment era were small communities in which close relationships existed among the superintendent, his staff and the patient population.[1] The superintendent and his family, according to the description by Charles Dickens in 1842, sat down to dinner every day with the patients, whom they knew intimately and personally.

In the labour department, every patient is as freely entrusted with the tools of his trade as if he were a sane man. . . . In the garden and on the farm, they work with spades, rakes, and hoes. For amusement, they walk, run, fish, paint, read, and ride out to take the air in carriages provided for the purpose. They have amongst themselves a sewing society to make clothes for the poor, which holds meetings, passes resolutions, never comes to fisticuffs or Bowie knives as some assemblies have been known to do elsewhere; and conducts all its proceedings with the greatest decorum. . . . Immense politeness and good breeding are observed throughout. . . . It is obvious that one great feature of this system is the inculcation and encouragement, even among such unhappy persons, of a decent self-respect. [pp. 105–111][2]

Thus, administration in the moral treatment era was directed to establishing within the hospital an enlightened society, with great respect for each individual. Careful attention was directed to his psychological and social needs, and opportunities were provided for occupational and social activities of all sorts. The assumption was that the patient could be trusted, that he would get better, and that he could contribute both to the inner community of the hospital and eventually to the outer community. This optimism was reflected in actual statistics of improvement and discharge.

The philosophy, mission, and dedication of the superintendent was poignantly stated by Isaac Ray, superintendent of the Augusta State Hospital in 1873.[12]

He constantly striveth to learn what is passing in the mind of his patient, by conversation and inquiry of those who see him in his unguarded moments. He also maketh diligent inquiry respecting the bodily and mental traits of his kindred, knowing full well that the sufferer is generally more beholden to them than himself, for the evil that has fallen upon him. He endeavoreth so to limit the number committed to his care, as to obtain a personal knowledge of every wandering spirit in his keeping. He boasteth not of the multitude borne on his registers, but rather, if he boasteth at all, of the many whose experience he has discovered, whose needs he has striven to supply, whose moods, fancies, and impulses he has steadily watched. To fix his hold on the confidence and good will of his patients, he spareth no effort, though it may consume his time and tax his patience, or encroach, seemingly, on the dignity of his office. A formal walk through the wards, and the ordering of a few drugs, compriseth but a small part of his means of restoring the troubled mind.

Moral treatment did not survive the radical changes in the socioeconomic structure of the nation that came with the industrial revolution after 1860.[9] Hospitals increased rapidly in size as population growth turned into its exponential phase. Patients were no longer treated directly by the superintendent but by attendants, low in the hospital hierarchy, poorly paid, lacking in professional instruction or standards, and themselves handled impersonally by the ever-enlarging system in which they worked. Influx of foreign-born immigrants to our shores, who lived impoverished lives and frequently fell prey to emotional disorders, increased the inpatient population of hospitals. They were considered undesirable by the "intelligent yeomanry" of the early American villages; and as staff–patient ratios fell, so did wages of attendants and nurses in mental hospitals as compared to general hospitals. The most unfortunate consequence of all these developments was that as patients were increasingly treated as impersonal objects, discharge rates fell decade by decade so that some distinguished psychiatrists of the late 1800s, like Pliny Earle, began to argue that mental disease was becoming incurable.[11]

During this period new philosophical-intellectual themes were sounded. In the sphere of sociology, William Graham Sumner[15] expounded on the theory of social Darwinism, which regarded social laws as fixed and immutable as physical laws; he advised strongly against support of the "hopelessly degenerate members of society" as a waste of effort and money. "Let it be understood that we cannot go outside this alternative: liberty, inequality, survival of the fittest; not—liberty, equality, survival of the unfittest."

In the field of medicine a great to-do was being made of so-called "lesions of the brain" associated with mental disorder. That these dicta came from the neuropathologist's bench carried great weight, for the science of neuropathology was being extolled as the last court of appeals in diagnosis. History has since demonstrated that although some of the damage noted in the brains of mental patients at post-mortem was due to cerebral nervous system syphilis, trauma, or encephalitis, nevertheless, most of the post-mortem changes were due to autolytic processes following upon the death of tissues, and could not properly be attributed to premortem disease.

However, as neuropathologists began to reign in mental hospitals, the concept of insanity caused by a physical lesion began to hold sway, directing therapeutic emphasis to such factors as rest, diet, room temperature regulation, and physical well-being, and away

from sociopsychological factors in the causation of emotional disease. The climate of institutions reflected custodialism; punitive and restrictive practices were directed to control bizarre and aggressive behavior; and accounting systems were designed to house "incurables" at lowest cost and with administrative efficiencies to rival the great businesses growing up in the outside economy. Interest shifted to the niceties of diagnosis, the refinements of legal medicine, and of brain pathology. Quite consistent with this picture was the fact that leadership in American psychiatry passed to John P. Gray, superintendent of the Utica State Hospital in New York, the largest hospital in the land. He introduced the microscope into American mental hospitals and taught that insanity "is simply a bodily disease in which the mind is disturbed more or less profoundly, because the brain is involved in the sickness either primarily or secondarily. The mind is not, in itself, ever diseased."[4]

The optimism, enthusiasm, and psychological sensitivity of moral treatment that dominated administrative philosophy of the first half of the nineteenth century gave way to custodialism, pessimism, warehousing, and overemphasis on neuropathology. Now we are on the road back. In rapid succession, since World War I, *custody* has given way to *therapy*, whilst responsibility for the common man from cradle to grave has replaced rugged individualism and social Darwinism. Following repeated public disclosures of "snake-pit" conditions in our mental institutions, state and federal governments have committed themselves to attempting a final resolution of the problems of neglect and dehumanization. The Freudian enlightenment, which has gained such great influence in all intellectual circles, has made it once again fashionable to discover the details of the inner life of man and to plan therapeutic programs with due consideration for the deeper psychological and experiential forces affecting his adaptation. Administration of mental hospitals since the 1930s has emphasized "eclectic" philosophy, taking advantage of new insights of psychoanalysis, social psychiatry, somatic therapy, and psychopharmacology that have emerged as the terrible plight of the mentally ill has stirred the nation. Many mental hospitals have made effective affiliations with medical schools, and have developed significant research and training potentialities to enliven and stimulate the therapeutic climate of our institutions.

As therapy replaced custody, the evils of excessive seclusion, wet-sheet packs, overmedication, and physical and mental restraint have disappeared, and the motif of the *therapeutic community*, which mobilizes the total potential of all the hospital citizenry toward progressive improvement of the social-psychological-physical environment, has spurred the imagination of administrators.

This, in turn, has been supplemented by the concept of the *mental-health center*, wherein barriers between hospital and community are broken down and administrators seek to encourage a flow of students, families, volunteers, and community officials across the hospital-community interface. They strive also to set up transitional and extramural facilities, such as outpatient departments, aftercare services, day-care services, halfway houses, cooperative apartments, and specialized community rehabilitation centers for patients now being discharged in increasing numbers.

Since the 1960s, concomitantly with the rise of social medicine, public-health ideology and practice, health insurance, and renewed national resolve to alleviate poverty and attack disease on a grand scale, a new slogan and concept, the *comprehensive mental-health center*, has come to the fore. Once again, as in the Moral Treatment era, the small hospital is the model; intensive personal concern for the whole individual and his family is the mode, and utilization of every means to restore the troubled mind is the goal. In addition, the superintendent of today assumes responsibility for a *defined geographic area*; he tries to think and plan actively in terms of the mental-health needs of all the citizens of that area, and to explore the community resources that might give formal or informal help to his clients. He thinks in terms of home care, family and network treatment, and the interplay between his hospital and community satellites.

His language is sprinkled with terms such as "risk groups," "preventive intervention," "incidence," "prevalence," "community partnership," "cross-cultural and minority psychiatry" —terms that were heard infrequently before. We are, in effect, in the midst of a virtual social revolution in both mental-health philosophy and practice.

In the foregoing, we have compressed many decades of history into a capsule, in order to show that mental-hospital administration tends to be molded and swayed by changing social and cultural conditions. The superintendent of today is at the pinnacle of this history, able to utilize a great variety of ideas and programs; yet there are expectations that he cannot ignore. For example, if he is a manager of a large state hospital, he will experience great pressures to reduce the census, rehabilitate his patients into community settings, encourage citizen partnership in many of his endeavors, and promote participation in direct therapeutic care of a spectrum of professionals, paraprofessionals, and nonprofessionals. Moreover, he should be attuned to the voice of minority groups; he should be a strong advocate of equal employment and affirmative action; and he should be an ardent student of legal medicine and of patient rights. His hospital will give much service to alcoholics and to drug-dependent individuals, and he will strive to broaden his therapeutic activities to include proper attention to geriatric cases, adolescents, children, and retarded individuals —these categories having been overlooked or slighted in past allocations of therapeutic resources.

❲ Structure of the Mental Hospital

The chief officer, who has maximum responsibility and authority, is usually the superintendent. In turn, he is accountable to a board of trustees or similar body, usually made up of laymen, that may be either advisory or policy setting. In some states boards of trustees are appointed by the governor; in others, they or their counterparts may be elected by county jurisdiction or, in turn, appointed by elected county officials. The superintendent is also accountable in most states to a commissioner of mental health—who is usually a gubernatorial appointee.

As the chief officer of the hospital, the superintendent appoints subordinates and generally defines their duties. Chief subordinates are usually an assistant superintendent, with authority over nursing service, personnel, the business office, and administrative operations; and a chief medical officer, responsible for all clinical services, research, and training. Direct patient care, therefore, comes under the chief medical officer, whereas all supporting services come under the assistant superintendent.

For the most part, mental-hospital superintendents are physician-psychiatrists, although in recent years there has been a tendency to appoint nonphysicians with experience in administration, or formally trained hospital administrators.

The staff, usually numbering in the hundreds, is divided into departments, each with its own head, spanning the whole complex of areas that have to do with management of a system responsible for the total care of patients—engineering, food service, laundry, personnel, grounds, etc., as well as all professional services such as social work, psychology, nursing, occupational therapy, rehabilitation, pastoral counseling, etc.

Approximately 70 to 80 percent of the average budget of a state hospital goes into personnel, the remainder into administrative overhead. Large institutions have major administrative expenditures related to repairs and renovations of buildings, heating, clothing, food services, etc., which in recent years have led management experts to favor community care wherever possible over institutionalization, on the theory that the former is not only more humane and therapeutically more effective but also more economical.

Though the mental hospitals in America spend huge sums of money for their patients, the fact is that rarely are these monies sufficient to provide adequate and appropriate care and treatment. The per-diem costs in state-owned institutions rarely approach costs in good private institutions, or in general hospitals with satisfactory psychiatric services. This discrepancy, and the discontent generated in all parties concerned, has been the cause of great distress and strain, a source of innumerable critical investigations and media exposés; and a perennial thorn in the side of legislators and community groups. This "Shame of the States" has been the motivation for much legal action, including *class actions* on behalf of the mentally ill and retarded that now threaten to shake the foundation of institutional care in the United States.

(Stresses and Demands on Administration

Superintendents, who in the last analysis set administrative policy, are too often ill prepared for the tasks they face. Not only do they require mastery of a variety of purely supportive or administrative functions, but also, they must have command of clinical programming so as to give the institution reasonable direction and guidance. They should have more than passing knowledge of the law in order to conform the work of the hospital to legal requirements and to assure patients their legal rights and privileges. In addition to internal operational demands of the institution and his role as its social leader, the superintendent is subject to a variety of extramural demands for public appearances in which he interprets the work of the hospital to people and tries to gain support for its programs and goals.

Administrative officers in public institutions are subjected to numerous strains:

1. The necessity to master new concepts and information related to management functions of a complex therapeutic system, very little of which has been taught to them either in medical school or in subsequent postgraduate training.

2. The high vulnerability of the office due to (a) their responsibility for large sums of public money; (b) the large number of seri-

ously ill patients in their charge; and (c) the generally poor level of care and treatment provided patients in relation to standards of private institutions as well as the general standards for care of the sick acceptable to any informed public.

3. The unusual demands on time, effort, and physical and mental vitality that reduce energy available for self, family, and friends. In addition to high vitality and robust health, administrators must recuperate quickly from disappointments and losses.

4. Public exposure and criticism are frequently the lot of administrators of public mental hospitals, and this phenomenon is likely to increase in the future.

5. Financial remuneration is not commensurate with private practice or university full-time employment.

6. Short tenure and uncertain future is the rule. Administrative jobs are subject to the whims of political fortune. A job well done in the professional sense does not necessarily guarantee tenure. As a result, many security-minded professionals shun the responsibility of administrative office.

⟮ Rewards of the Administrator

The rewards of the administrative life, nevertheless, are many:[7]

The intellectual challenge and joy of mastering new material, the broadening of one's horizons over a larger sector of one's field, the perspective on large areas of health in relation to its sociopolitical determinants, centrality in the arena of action and decision, the power to do a great deal of good for patients, families, and colleagues, the control of vast resources, the honing of one's judgment, the greater call upon one's personal capacities for performance and achievement.

Beyond these is the opportunity to look after the cherished values of the mental health profession—the freedom to treat patients and to teach and to do research in a favorable climate, the elevation of the health and welfare of the citizens to first value in the thinking of the body politic, the opportunity to represent the health of the poor among the multitude of projects clamoring for government attention.

Finally, as Mary P. Follet has pointed out so brilliantly, our success as a civilization depends largely on how well we can solve the functional problems of large organizations in serving the welfare and happiness of the individual.

⟮ Basic Decisions of Administration

The hospital is a system dedicated to the goal of serving society through the treatment of mental patients. Within this broad framework, decisions will have to be made that relate both to the philosophy of patient care, the availability of resources, and the administrator's view of management. In the long run administrators tend to fashion their systems in their own image.[6] Most of the major decisions depend on instinct and judgment; very often there exists no adequate data base to support any given direction. Part of the difficulty is that both psychiatry and management are relatively young sciences, and in psychiatry, in particular, research on administration is meager.

Regarding the overall allocation of resources, the administrator will have to make a decision as to how to cut the pie for service, training, and research. In the service area he will be faced with judgments on how much should be done for patients extramurally as opposed to intramurally. He will ponder whether major emphasis should be on acute versus chronic patients; whether the intake of patients should be controlled by the institution or directed by extra hospital forces. Should waiting lists be tolerated? How long should patients be hospitalized? What is the balance between long-term and short-term therapies, between psychotherapy, somatic therapy, social therapy? Should one or a few approaches to treatment be emphasized as opposed to a broad eclectic, try-everything attitude? Is therapy to be practiced only by trained psychiatrists or perhaps opened up to nonpsychiatrists, even nonprofessionals? Further problems that require profound judgment concern choice of a unified philosophy of treatment versus multiple ideologies; centralization of organizational structure versus decentralization into autonomous units; organizational stability as against dynamic change.[8]

In the pursuit of organizational change with respect to any specific set of goals, the administrator has to make up his mind what areas to motivate first toward reorganization or reform and how fast changes or progress should be expected; how many areas to activate at any one time; who may be supported as his delegates in creating change; how much effort should be put into working through personnel stresses and strains; and how broad a base of participation in planning and implementing change should be encouraged.

Sayre[13] has offered four theoretical views of administration. All have to be taken into account with operations of the institution, though one or more may be stressed or favored by a given administrator.

Administration as a technological system wherein cost effectiveness is the primary emphasis. This approach, highly suitable in the business world, where commodities are discrete and easy to identify, is applied with difficulty to the mental hospitals whose commodity is relatively vague—the mental health of clients. Nevertheless, as health costs rise in the future and the public becomes more and more interested in how its money is spent, this aspect of management is sure to become more and more important.

Administration as a system for policy formation and decision making. Where many difficult decisions are to be made, and where participation of staff that will eventually carry out the decisions is required, a broad base of policy formulation and development is desirable. Administrators trained in group dynamics will find this approach highly consonant with their experience.

Administration as a system of responsibility and accountability. More and more the mental hospital finds itself accountable to outside agencies; first, to the mental-health department of the state that has to render reports to executive and legislative branches; second, to its board of trustees; then to the relatives, friends, and constituents in the community; to the formal citizen organizations promoting mental health; to the professional societies with which the staff is affiliated; to the universities that assist in training and research and confer academic titles upon selected staff; and, finally, to the courts that refer cases for evaluation and consultation.

Further accountability is to a disparate variety of standard-setting or monitoring agencies: the Joint Commission on Accreditation of Hospitals, without whose endorsement the institution cannot maintain its reputation within the family of hospitals serving the nation; the public-safety inspection board of state and/or local level; federal government monitoring regarding Medicare and Medicaid standards; public-health inspection of sanitation, food handling, management of infections and contagious disease. In modern times, the organization is accountable also to the courts which, in one state after another, are imposing standards for adequate and appropriate care and treatment; for proper education of inmates of hospitals and schools for the retarded, and for proper compensation to hospitalized patients for work done that would otherwise require paid employees.

Administration as a social process. In this view the individuals that shape the organization are more important than technology; therefore, participation, cooperation, morale, and consensus are all important. Leadership, then, is the skill necessary to create the proper climate for individuals and groups to exercise their creativity and to make their maximum contribution.

Miller and Rice[10] in their studies of task-oriented human systems emphasize discrepancies between sentient systems and organizational tasks as the basis of organizational strain. We have elsewhere stressed the social-process dimension of the organization in attempting to view the administrator's role as one of "social system clinician,"[5] comparing this function with that of the "individual clinician" in psychotherapy. In both, identification of areas of anxiety and strain is essential, followed by working through of tensions, release of inner strivings and creative forces, and assumption of greater autonomy and responsibility. Mental-health professionals who assume the task of administrators of mental-health systems will often feel more comfortable with emphasis on social process.

(Personality and Style of Administration

It is generally recognized that the *personality* of the administrator in large measure determines administrative *style*, and that both of these factors profoundly affect the fate of the institution under the administrator's command. Administration requires maturity, energy, creativity, humanism, intelligence—a host of virtues that, mixed in proper proportions, spell the character of the man or woman with leadership qualities. For many years it was taken for granted that the director of a mental-health facility must be a psychiatrist-physician. No doubt, when the functions of the administrator involved intimate knowledge of each patient and personal attention to his medical-psychological needs, as in the Moral Treatment era, that administrator would most properly be a physician. However, with the growth of institutions both in size and complexity, and the necessity for the superintendent to be concerned largely with more administrative details, this requirement has become less crucial. Nowadays, administrators of mental-health facilities may come from a variety of backgrounds where training and experience in institutional management are an important part of their preparation. This has become increasingly true for schools for the mentally retarded, in VA facilities, and in mental-health facilities of those states where psychiatric administrators are difficult to recruit.

Where nonmedical administrators are in charge, administration of all clinical functions is delegated to a chief medical officer or physician-psychiatrist, who is then the chief arbiter of matters affecting the medical and psychiatric well-being of patients. There has been much anxiety in some professional ranks that if final decision making is left in the hands of nonmedical administrators, cost-effectiveness considerations will take precedence over humanitarianism. Whatever the truth of the matter, and perhaps the problem has been exaggerated, the fact is that with sharply rising costs of medical-psychiatric care and sharply increased expectations of the public for total health insurance, cost-effectiveness factors will be increasingly important in the future.

Personality in part determines the administrator's basic priorities concerning such matters as the welfare and morale of employees, the concern for the image of the hospital vis-à-vis his own image in the community, his philosophy with respect to research and training, his interest in reform and innovation, and so on. Even more basic to the morale of an institution are those intangible qualities which give people a feeling that they are working for a man of strength, integrity, reliability, and warmth. Workers would like to say, "I am pleased to work with such a person." Patients and family feel that with this type of person "someone up there cares for them."

The United Nations technical report links the character of the administrator to the therapeutic effectiveness of the institution, in these words:

The most important single factor in the efficacy of the treatment given in a mental hospital appears to the committee to be an intangible element which can only be described as its atmosphere. . . . As in the community at large, one of the characteristic aspects of the psychiatric hospital is the type of relationship between people that are to be found within it. The nature of the relationships between the medical director and his staff will be reflected in the relationship between the psychiatric staff and the nurses, and finally in the relationship not only between the nurses and the patients, but between the patients themselves [pp. 17–18].[16]

Administrative style seems to flow from the basic character training, particularly early training, of the individual. This area has not been well conceptualized and certainly research is scarce. Sharaf and Kotin,[14] however, have conceptualized one dimension of administrative style that they call "tight–loose." At the tight end, an administrator is concerned with careful definition of role and authority, orderly and hierarchical chain of command, reliance on formal communications, and explicit rules. Loose administrative style favors less explicit delineation of authority and responsibility, tolerance of role ambiguity, informal communications, informal exercise of power, and little reliance on rules and regulations.[14]

Readers will see at once a relationship between tight–loose administrative style and authoritarianism-equalitarianism in ideology and personality functioning. For example, those who adopt authoritarian attitudes toward politics, family relationships, religion, and ethnic groups are more likely to be interested in structure, precise role delineation, and rigid-role boundaries in organizational functioning.[3]

Most significant with regard to style is the administrator's ability to adapt flexibly and creatively, means to ends—the use of a variety of approaches, concepts, and styles in solving problems and reaching goals.

(Training for Administration

Few specialized training courses exist for psychiatric administrators of mental hospitals. Usually, preparation consists of experience in one or another leadership position in a hospital, such as clinical director, director of education, chief of outpatient department, or head of a day hospital. Apprenticeship to an administrator of known reputation as an assistant superintendent is very useful.

A more formal training in administrative psychiatry and more specifically for the role of administrator of a mental hospital ought to begin with increased awareness and emphasis on the administrative-executive role from the beginning of postgraduate training. Instead of taking for granted the organization in which he is being trained, the graduate should be made aware of the history, goals, methods of operation, personnel relations, business and legal problems of his institution and how and why his postgraduate-education opportunity developed the way it has.

Then, as the postgraduate student or psychiatric resident begins to work with patients, staff, and family, he proceeds with greater awareness that he is part of a *system* and that the treatment he intends to give on behalf of his patients depends on efficient operation of that system. When he becomes a senior resident, ward chief, head of an outpatient department, or clinical director, he is even more involved in, and responsible for, that therapeutic system.

In the resident years, administrative seminars could enlighten and broaden the resident's grasp of the total scene. In advanced residency years, he could take on a project in the hospital that administration is trying to push forward, under supervision. Increased awareness of the forces in the community that shape the institution and his role in it could be developed by visits to important facilities in his area involved in health care of patients. Knowledge of the roles of welfare, corrections, youth services, and public-health agencies is vital. It is particularly enlightening to talk with important legislators responsible for health legislation and to watch the process of legislative enactment at the state or federal level.

In the case of a resident especially interested in concentrating on administrative science, special courses could be offered through local university auspices in systems management, institutional change, social psychology of groups, health standards, public relations, personnel relations, and legal medicine. Most pertinent to the preparation for the administration responsibility would be field experience, or apprenticeship, to administrators of long experience and known effectiveness. Here it should be noted that our best administrators in the field are not fully utilized as models or teachers. Those who teach often do not teach administration; those who write often write about professional matters other than administration. Many would be delighted to help younger and less experienced persons with their careers, through regular supervision and guidance similar to that which is offered residents learning psychotherapy.

Finally, the training of the young administrator should include a period of executive responsibility under supervision. A period of training as assistant superintendent to two or more fine superintendents would be advisable. Added to this would be frequent trips to the central office of the state administration of mental health where he learns who is responsible for the various departmental divisions to which he must relate, how they operate, how he and they can work together to the best advantage. In one such department in my experience over twenty units were identifiable, each under a separate chief with special expertise. These included nursing, psychology, social work, occupational therapy, retardation, children's disorders, speech and hearing, legal medicine, drug rehabilitation, alcoholism, geriatrics, volunteering, business administration, farm and grounds, engineering, personnel, liaison with the legislature, public relations, work rehabilitation, hospital inspection, and laundry.

Upon the assumption of the definitive role as director of a mental hospital, the incumbent cannot be left to flounder; he needs supports; opportunities to meet with fellow directors of other institutions to share experiences; refresher courses; visits to other facilities grappling with and possibly solving problems similar to his own; brief vacations planned for maximum stress relief; periods of role interchange with administrators higher or lower in the chain; and sabbaticals with the opportunity to pursue further education and experience consistent with his intellectual needs.

Too many fine administrators lose their spark as a result of the high chronic strain to which they are subjected. This strain is greater today than at any time in history due to the acceleration of change, the growing complexity of organizations, and the increasing demand for performance by the public. Tenure of administrators in high office may not exceed four to five years on the average. Probably official recognition should be given to this fact by prearranged job changes, sabbaticals, and "recycling" so as to help highly trained individuals to remain in the public service for the longest possible time.

⟨ Areas of Concern of the Public Hospital Administrator

The administrator of the state hospital must of necessity gain a mastery in several areas. As mentioned before, it is unlikely that any of these areas have been adequately covered in his previous education. Even when considerable intellectual mastery exists, the administrator will find that *operating mastery* is a different kettle of fish, requiring repeated practical experience in the arena of *action*.

Law and Psychiatry

It will be necessary to have a thorough knowledge of the rights of patients, the rights of personnel, and to know intimately the power of the superintendent and his administrative subordinates as well as the limits of this power. The whole fabric of law, departmental rules and regulations (which when properly processed have the force of laws) and traditional practices governing the exercise of his office must be understood. This is the day of active redress, of quick litigation, and of citizen and legislative monitoring of the actions of their public servants. To get caught outside the law, particularly where it affects patient rights or the proper use of money is to court professional disaster as well as legal punishment. The wise administrator will not only *know* the law to the best of his ability; he will also have legal advice close at hand and avail himself of the legal expertise of departmental officials at a higher level.

Knowing the law regarding patient rights and privileges puts the administrator in a position to "normalize" his patients' hospitalization to the maximum, and to plan further privileges as the behavior of the patient group improves and the trust of staff rises. Patient rights relate not only to admission procedures, social privileges on the ward, testimentary capacity, use of money, maintenance of various licenses but also to their life in the community, temporarily halted by hospitalization. They have landlords who expect rents and may want to evict them for nonpayment; they may have claims on welfare; they may have dependents temporarily unsupported or business partnerships in jeopardy. Many states have recently restricted the criteria for involuntary hospitalization, mandating periodic reviews and placing the burden of proof on the superintendent to plead before the courts for continued retention of a client.

Laws governing the rights of personnel are equally important. The administrator will quickly learn that one or more labor groups are dedicating their entire efforts to protecting employees' rights and pressing for higher wages, better conditions of work, and more union privileges. Well-worked-out union contracts with superintendents and employee representatives negotiating across the table on a man-to-man basis may set the stage for good employee morale. The administrator will find himself a signator to labor contracts, personally responsible for guaranteeing the rights and privileges contained therein.

Recently, class-action forms of redress have come to the fore, approximately thirty such actions now being before the state and federal courts in various stages of development. These are in three primary areas:

1. Actions relating to proper standards of care and treatment of hospitalized patients of mental institutions or residents of schools for the retarded. In effect, the petitioners ask for "adequate and appropriate" care and treatment for involuntarily held individuals.

2. Actions related to the right to education of patients in institutions who are missing that opportunity because they are hospitalized.

3. Actions proposing compensation of hospitalized patients for work done for the institution that replaces paid employees.

Present indications are that much progress will be made on behalf of the mentally ill and retarded through the use of the class-action vehicle. Having been denied humane treatment for many decades, appeal now via the courts promises a return to greater "humanism" of the type enjoyed in the Moral Treatment era.

Business Administration

Every hospital director needs a good business manager—honest, loyal, and dedicated to support the clinical services and to help the director adapt means to ends. This budget officer should see his role as secondary to patient care, never one of controlling or directing patient care or competing with top management. He should be skilled in the utilization of every technical means to make his budget flexible, responsive, and effective in the face of changing demands.

Budget preparation is a skill that the director and his aides must master. Given the general priorities established by the administrator, it is then necessary to obtain inputs from all hospital section heads and many of their subordinates. In other words, budget development is both "top down" and "bottom up."

Budgets may be "line item," with minimum transferability between categories, or they may be "block grants," with much autonomy left to the director, or something in between. The administrator always seeks to obtain maximum flexibility within the allowed rules. Usually, it is also a good idea to spend the budget annually down to the last penny, if possible, because requests for additional allotment are difficult to justify if substantial "surpluses" have been shown in previous years.

The strongest fiscal position that the administrator can enjoy is to have funds coming from a variety of sources—state, university, federal government, and private. The good administrator seeks to diversify, thus becoming less dependent on any one fiscal resource.

Labor Relations

Labor groups are a part of the modern scene. Bargaining, contracts, arbitration are recurrent areas of activity. How the administrator gets along with labor will determine to a large extent employee morale. In his negotiations with labor he must never bargain away his management rights to run his organization according to the best interests of patients. At the same time, labor is always determined to win ever larger wages and improved conditions. The administrator will have to participate in this progress. Strikes, work slowdowns, sit-ins, sick-ins, and picketing are to be avoided if at all possible. However, the good administrator will give some thought as to what he would do should a strike be called some day, even if illegal. How will he take care of his patients? He will need a plan as precise as his plan for protection against fire, thefts, or natural disasters.

Citizen Involvement

Increasingly, citizens want to know about mental health. They want to understand the functions of their institutions, and to help in the planning and implementation of treatment. At times they may wish to share the responsibilities of the executive role.

Most hospitals involve citizens at several levels:

1. Volunteers who give direct aid to patients. This movement has grown immensely in recent years. Volunteers have become a recognized means of adding to staff effectiveness. Every modern hospital will have a volunteer director and division heads tuned to recruiting, orienting, training, and utilizing volunteers within their general mandate. Patients appreciate that volunteers provide a link to the community and that their interest is not based on job or remuneration. Student volunteers, in particular, bring to the institution youth, enthusiasm, and optimism—priceless ingredients in any therapeutic climate.

The administrator will take active steps to contact schools and community groups, and to establish a bridge to many community activities through volunteers.

2. Citizens serve on mental-health boards as appointed or elected officials, usually advisory, sometimes policy setting, but always significant members of the planning-implementing team. Many have distinguished records of accomplishment in the world and can be of great assistance to the manager in interpreting his institution to the public, identifying

sources of support, assisting in relations with the central office and with the legislature.

3. An important set of citizen roles relates to their membership in community associations dedicated to raising the standards of care and treatment of the mentally ill and retarded. They can be most vociferous in recommendations as to how the institution ought to utilize its resources. Some of these groups are very "activistic," seeking their ends through sharp public criticism of the administration, enactment of special laws, or pressure on governors and councils. Their tactics may include destruction of property, threats, and personal vilification.

Problems arise in ghetto communities, or communities with mixed social or socioeconomic groups, as to who in fact represents the people. Those groups which are most activistic may not necessarily represent the majority; nevertheless, they may be intent on getting their way. Some of the most difficult problems facing administrators today are in attempts to provide service to such communities of discontent.

Public Relations

A good deal of effort and attention will have to go into public relations. The administrator's image with his staff and with the outside community are both important.

Instrumentalities for communication with the employee group, not merely their labor representatives, should be developed—newsletters, social gatherings, group activities of various sorts—through which the feelings and problems of employees may be identified and, at least to an extent, expressed. The way the administrator conducts himself, and his reputation for courtesy, caring, and helping his staff will play a great role in morale and in creating a proper therapeutic climate.

Public relations directed toward the community should be on a planned and continuing basis. Many different sectors of the community will have to be dealt with—families, interest groups, university affiliates, legislators, the press, and other media. All this will be directed toward interpreting the work and goals of the hospital, fostering a climate of acceptance by the public of mental illness and mental patients, and encouraging contributions of personal service, material, and funds on behalf of the mentally ill.

(Special Problems Facing the State Mental Hospital in the Future

Although it is risky to predict the future, particularly in a field so subject to change as health services, we may identify current trends that, for some time at least, may continue to be manifest.

1. Decreasing the number of patients in mental hospitals is still going on in most of the state hospitals in the nation. Administrators, in fact, have shown pride in their ability to move patients into the community. Concomitant with this trend has been the movement of staff into hospital-generated community services such as satellite clinics, halfway houses, cooperative apartments, and work-rehabilitation centers.

2. Decentralization of hospitals into semiautonomous units, each with its own therapeutic team responsible for a designated "catchment" area will probably be explored further. Patients from a given geographic area are admitted, treated, discharged, and followed up by the same team. Differentiation between acute and chronic patients is reduced. Population reduction is accelerated, and community liaison via bridging activities is increased.

3. Planning of services to the catchment area, jointly with community facilities that have sprung up independent of the hospital, and together with citizen representatives of the geographic area, will certainly be increased in the future.

4. There will be greater utilization of mobile home-treatment services, family therapy, network therapy; and greater dependence upon collaboration with both formal and informal care givers in the community.

5. There will be greater utilization of volunteers and paraprofessionals, both in the hospitals and in the community.

6. As the hospital population decreases, the trend toward admission of clinically more severe cases will continue with increasing representation of drug dependent, alcoholic, geriatric, brain-damaged and retarded individuals.

7. There will be greater efforts to provide total services for disturbed and delinquent adolescents and mentally ill children through a variety of newly developed modalities—such as day care, home care, nurseries, and schools.

8. The treatment of the emotionally disturbed offender will receive greater emphasis in the future. Mental-health administrators will collaborate with correctional administrators in ascertaining the common ground for their joint efforts.

9. There will be greater emphasis on work rehabilitation and the value of compensated-sheltered workshop employment as well as community-employment training in the treatment of mentally ill patients.

10. The phase out, or closing, of some state hospitals is likely to continue.

11. Conversion, in whole or in part, of some state hospitals serving the mentally ill to schools for the retarded, or training centers for juvenile delinquents and adult offenders may be expected.

12. Collaboration with public-health agencies toward developing total-health, rather than simply mental-health, services to sick individuals will increase.

13. Upgrading of care and treatment in state mental hospitals to more humanistic and acceptable levels will occur as the public, aided by the courts, becomes increasingly determined to provide adequate and appropriate treatment to all indigent ill persons.

14. Increasing experimentation by state government with nonmedical cabinet-level administration of mental-health systems by executives lacking direct service experience will occur concomitantly with the rising need for greater efficiency and economy in management of large governmental organizations.

15. There will be increased monitoring of the functions of mental hospitals both by state

and federal government officials and by interested citizens from the private sector.

⦅ Bibliography

1. BOCKOVEN, J. S. *Moral Treatment in Community Mental Health.* New York: Springer, 1972.
2. DICKENS, C. *American Notes for General Circulation,* Vol. 1, 3rd ed. London: Chapman & Hall, 1842.
3. GILBERT, D. C. and D. J. LEVINSON. "Performance, Ideology, and Personality in Mental Hospital Aides," in M. Greenblatt, D. J. Levinson and R. H. Williams, eds., *The Patient and the Mental Hospital,* pp. 197–208. New York: Free Press, 1957.
4. GRAY, J. P. "Insanity; Its Frequency, and Some of Its Preventable Causes," *Am. J. Insanity,* 42 (1885–1886), 1–45.
5. GREENBLATT, M. "The Psychiatrist as Social System Clinician," in M. Greenblatt, D. J. Levinson, and R. H. Williams, eds., *The Patient and the Mental Hospital,* pp. 317–323. New York: Free Press, 1957.
6. ———. "The Elongated Shadow," *Compr. Psychiatry,* 12 (1971), 293–301.
7. ———. "Administrative Psychiatry," *Am. J. Psychiatry,* 129 (1972), 384–385.
8. GREENBLATT, M., M. SHARAF, and E. STONE. *Dynamics of Institutional Change.* Pittsburgh: University of Pittsburgh Press, 1971.
9. GREENBLATT, M., R. H. YORK, and E. L. BROWN. *From Custodial to Therapeutic Patient Care in Mental Hospitals,* pp. 408–409. New York: Russell Sage Found., 1955.
10. MILLER, E. J. and A. K. RICE. *Systems of Organization: The Control of Task and Sentient Boundaries.* New York: Social Service Paperbacks, 1970.
11. PINEL, P. *A Treatise on Insanity,* translated by D. D. Davis, p. 5. London: Cadell & Davies, 1806.
12. RAY, I. "Ideal Characters of the Officers of a Hospital for the Insane," *Am. J. Insan.,* 30 (1873), 67.
13. SAYRE, W. S. "Principles of Administration," *Hospitals,* 30 (1956), 34–35.
14. SHARAF, M. and J. KOTIN. "Management Succession and Administrative Style," *Psychiatry,* 30 (1967), 237–248.
15. SUMNER, W. G. *Essays of William Graham Sumner,* Vol. 2, p. 107. New Haven: Yale University Press, 1934.
16. WORLD HEALTH ORGANIZATION. *Expert Committee on Mental Health,* 3rd Rep., Techn. Rep. Ser. no. 73. Geneva: WHO, 1953.

CHAPTER 31

GENERAL HOSPITAL PSYCHIATRIC SERVICES

Thomas P. Detre and David J. Kupfer

(Historical Background

Considerations of a social nature quite outside the scientific or medical aspect of the subject have led to patients suffering from mental disorders being kept separate from other patients and dealt with in an exceptional manner.

Some social reasons for the separation have ceased to exist. The superstitious ideas which less than a hundred years ago were associated with the occurrence of insanity have ceased to be entertained or, at least, to have any practical influence.

THUS wrote Sir John Sibbald in the first issue of the *Review of Neurology and Psychiatry* published in England in 1903. Sibbald continued.

Let us now look for a moment at some of the reasons which make the treatment of mental disease in general hospitals desirable. Such wards have an advantage over an asylum of saving the patient from the mental shock which is often felt upon entering an institution largely devoted to the care of the incurably insane. . . . Wards for mental disease need not be distinguishable from other wards and residence in such wards does not entail the industrial and social injury which follows residence in an asylum.

Almost sixty years later in 1961, the Joint Commission on Mental Illness and Health of the United States[21] took a nearly identical position, declaring that: (1) no community hospital can render complete medical services unless it accepts mental patients; and (2) each hospital should become a focal point of a community-oriented psychiatric program. This endorsement has given further impetus to the development of general hospital psychiatric services, a trend which started in the 1920s and accelerated quite rapidly after World War II.

As far as we know, it was in 1755 when the first psychiatric beds were set aside for the "cure and treatment of lunatics" at the Pennsylvania Hospital in Philadelphia; but it was not until 1902 that the first autonomous inpatient unit, the famous Pavilion F, was established at the Albany Hospital. Its director, J.

Mosher, claimed considerable success when he announced in 1922 that 15 percent of all psychiatric patients admitted were able to return to the community. By 1942, when the Pavilion was under the direction of Dr. E. Cameron, 82 percent of the patients admitted and treated were said to have returned to the community.

These early experiments notwithstanding, the majority of general hospital psychiatric services prior to World War II were subdepartments of neurology or neurosurgery, and functioned primarily as diagnostic centers and triage stations. The excellent results achieved in Army hospitals, most of which had provisions for the treatment of psychiatric patients, rapidly dispelled the prevailing concern that the treatment of mentally ill patients in a general hospital was impractical or disruptive. Statistics compiled from various military hospitals in the 1940s showed that while the average stay of their psychiatric patients was approximately sixty days, patients presenting symptoms of panic, depression, confusion, and other acute psychiatric problems required only brief hospitalization. Thus, such units functioned in a manner analogous to other units caring for acutely ill patients. Moreover, there was no evidence that the presence of psychiatric patients was in any way disturbing to the rest of the hospital. On the contrary, the hospital staff from other specialties acquired considerable sophistication in dealing with psychological problems encountered in medical practice which proved particularly beneficial in the management of the so-called psychosomatic disorders.[7]

Public acceptance of such inpatient psychiatric services grew rapidly. By 1952, 205 of the 1600 larger hospitals in the United States had fairly adequate units with fifteen or more beds[4] and less than ten years later psychiatric beds in general hospitals exceeded the number of beds in mental hospitals.[34] The rise in the number of psychiatric inpatient units in general hospitals since that time has been even more striking: in 1964, there were 536 such units; in 1967, there were 694; and in 1970, there were 766 with the greatest increase occurring (71 percent of the total) in the voluntary hospital.

A survey undertaken jointly by the American Psychiatric Association and the National Association for Mental Health in 1965,[19] revealed that approximately 85 percent of all general hospitals had inpatient psychiatric units, and that the majority of these units had broadened the scope of services they provided. While some of these units still had seclusion rooms, over two-thirds of the units were "open" services. Relatively liberal admission policies were practiced in 85 percent of all general hospital psychiatric services in that they were admitting patients who were assaultive, suicidal, abused alcohol or other drugs, or had problems which fell into the domain of geriatric psychiatry. Despite the fact that over one-half of the hospitals reporting had no explicit limitations on the length of stay, the average duration of hospitalization was about twenty days. Only in university-based teaching hospitals was the average stay longer. Increasing confidence in the effect of these units was also reflected by third-party payers. At least one-half of the patients admitted had some kind of health insurance which covered a substantial portion of their charges.

From a statistical point of view the treatment approach to patients admitted to these inpatient services appeared quite eclectic and included chemotherapy (91 percent), individual psychotherapy (72 percent), occupational therapy (70 percent), electroshock (67 percent), recreational therapy (60 percent), and group psychotherapy (25 percent). Nonetheless, until about 1960 treatment programs essentially followed two models: patients would receive either psychoanalytically oriented treatment or a therapeutic regimen consisting primarily of the so-called biological therapies (such as drugs, electric shock and, in some instances, insulin coma) with little else in the way of psychological care.

This particular polarization in treatment philosophies has easily identifiable historical roots. During the late 1930s the Meyerian psychobiological approach was superseded by the far more etiologically oriented psychoanalytic approach whose proponents believed that, given sufficient time and proper training, definitive treatment of psychiatric disorders was possible. This view stood in sharp contrast to the organically oriented approach whose proponents believed that symptomatic relief rather than "cure" was the only realistic aim of treatment. What both camps had in common was the conviction that the physician is the only important therapeutic agent, a conviction that was clearly reflected by the staffing patterns in nearly all hospital psychiatric units. Although many of these units had at least a part-time psychiatrist-administrator, with the exception of occupational and recreational therapy, all treatment was primarily administered by the patient's own psychiatrist, rather than by a psychiatrist retained by the hospital.

One logical outcome of this trend was the lack of concern for aftercare facilities since in principle, at least, the doctor who took care of the patient while he was hospitalized was supposed to provide all treatments after discharge as well. Up to the mid 1960s, 36 percent of those hospitals which had inpatient psychiatric units did not have outpatient facilities. Partial hospitalization or other types of aftercare services were made available to only a selected few; even patients who could afford psychiatric care after discharge from the hospital had difficulties getting outpatient treatment at the same facility. Nor were hospital administrators very eager to develop outpatient facilities; at the time health insurance provided little or no incentive to the establishment of ambulatory services.

With the growing recognition that the patient's needs were not met by either a strictly insight-oriented psychotherapeutic approach or a purely organic approach, the polarization which characterized the psychiatric scene during the 1940s and 1950s began to diminish in the 1960s. Moreover, as advances in psychopharmacological treatment made the management of even severely disturbed patients feasible, it became clear that merely hospitalizing the patient in his own community rather than in a state facility did not automatically diminish the adjustment problems he had to face upon discharge. It became no less obvious that we could not simply transplant the psychotherapeutic approach, which was being utilized with varying degrees of effectiveness

in private practice, to a hospital setting. The purely organic approach also proved disappointing, for it was soon discovered that unless the clinician is prepared to deal with the patient's social and family-support structure to insure compliance even biological treatments of proven value are doomed to failure.

Gradually the emphasis shifted to an approach which aimed to clarify the patient's relationship with his family and community, and provide him with social clues around which he could orient himself and increase his adaptive skills.[14] By the mid-to-late 1960s, many hospitals had intricate and often well thought-out social treatment programs which were generally classified as "therapeutic communities." This development resulted in a deemphasis of individual psychotherapy and increasing participation of staff nurses, social workers, psychologists, and other health professionals in the life of these units. With the counterculture then in full swing, it became possible or even fashionable to talk about one's self with a greater degree of frankness than was ever possible in the past. Therapy for couples and families, and various group therapies became acceptable modes of treatment, thereby adding a new dimension to psychiatric care and actively involving the patients, their family, and the community at large.

The Role of the General Hospital in Mental-Health Care

In less than three decades the concept of treating psychiatric patients in the general hospital has been enthusiastically endorsed and implemented throughout the United States. As health professionals and the public began to regard it as the most desirable setting for the care of the mentally ill, the general hospital became for several reasons a community resource of unparalleled medical and psychological importance. Its primarily urban environment made recruitment of competent personnel easier. The availability of sophisticated diagnostic facilities, together with a multidisciplinary approach to patient care and a wide range of services, were not easily matched by a psychiatric "specialty hospital." Then, too, the public image of the general hospital has always been very different from that of a mental hospital. Never the kind of "last resort" where people went only when they were very ill, the general hospital was also a place of joy where one's children and grandchildren were born. Families, already accustomed to receiving help for "physical" illnesses were less fearful of being admitted to the general hospital for psychiatric care than to other mental-health facilities. Families, friends, and employees were less reluctant to visit and maintain contact with the patient, and were more inclined to help his reentry into the community when he was discharged.

The acceptance of psychiatric services by other medical specialties has also rapidly increased. Psychiatrists became available and responsive to requests for consultations on difficult diagnostic and management problems throughout the hospital, demonstrating convincingly that psychological care is basic to the comprehensive care of all patients. As the psychiatrist became a more active participant on the hospital medical staff, administrators of small institutions, rather than erecting specialized units, began to show a willingness to experiment by admitting psychiatric patients to medical services, and found it a less costly and successful alternative.[29,10]

Paradoxically, along with the innovations that seemed to broaden the scope and increase the effectiveness of psychiatric services in the general hospital, there came expressions of concern about problems that were not solved or might even have been aggravated by the establishment of these units. Despite a substantial decrease in the average length of inpatient stay and a more realistic determination of treatment goals, the early hopes that the number of patients admitted to state hospitals would diminish remained unfulfilled. A thoughtful study comparing the psychiatric services of the Strong Memorial Hospital and the Rochester State Hospital found that the general and the state hospital did indeed serve different segments of the population.[17] Many patients suffering from chronic organic brain syndromes associated with arteriosclerosis and

other disorders of the senium, as well as patients who were first treated in a university hospital but subsequently relapsed, tended to drift to the state hospitals. Soon accusations were leveled at general hospital psychiatric services charging that the only advancement they had made was to siphon away "good patients," leaving the state hospitals with increasing numbers of deteriorated patients, and lending further credence to their already dubious distinction as "warehouses of the unwanted."

That the general hospital tended to concentrate on those patients who are most amenable to short-term intensive care, largely ignoring those whose prognosis was guarded or poor, also raised questions about the quality of training provided in these settings. Many medical educators felt that being exposed primarily to patients who tended to improve in a matter of days or weeks would cause health personnel to become less tolerant of frustrating and difficult cases; this would, in turn, result in less learning about the chronically ill who are in greatest need of effective care. Criticism was also directed at those general hospitals operating in close proximity to ghettos and other socioeconomically deprived neighborhoods as they seemed to be ignoring the mental-health needs of the poor. Although patient-flow statistics have revealed that these accusations were not without foundation, the causes were often fiscal. Many hospitals found themselves unable to absorb the cost of patients who did not have health insurance and made exceptions only when there was a concomitant need for medical and surgical services.

To complicate matters further, at this time in the 1960s, the community mental-health-center movement also became a potent health-delivery force and began to compete actively for patients. The community mental-health centers were mandated to develop certain essential services which included, besides inpatient services, partial hospitalization and extensive aftercare services. The aim of these centers was to change the locus of treatment from the state mental hospital to a new type of health facility in the hope that they could, within a decade or so, cut the census of the state mental hospital by 50 percent. Since the general hospital has been accused of losing sight of socioeconomic factors and emphasizing the medical aspects of psychiatric care, the community mental-health centers moved rapidly to establish outreach services and, making use of community workers, managed to reach a whole new group of "consumers" who previously would not have thought to avail themselves of psychiatric services. But the mental-health centers tended to be dominated by an almost exclusively psychosocial view of the etiology and pathogenesis of mental illness and concentrated primarily on social intervention; hence, they usually fell short of assuring the poor what they needed most—comprehensive health care.

To recapitulate, we ended up with the community mental-health-center program in addition to the already existing state psychiatric hospitals, the private specialty hospitals, and the general hospital psychiatric-care system. Although all four were competing for the acutely ill, some movement toward consolidation began as general hospital psychiatric services (and to a lesser extent, specialty hospitals) became essential components of the community mental-health centers. In fact, by 1973, in almost 40 percent of all the 353 community mental-health centers, general hospital psychiatric services provided at least one segment of their mandated services.

One deplorable consequence of this haphazardly developed program of psychiatric care has been an economically bifurcated system of care. Rather than a selection based on the patient's needs and the availability of specialized facilities, the general hospital and specialty hospital tended to admit patients who could afford hospital care, while the community mental-health centers concentrated primarily on the poor. Furthermore, since all three preferred to care for the acutely ill, each continued to refer their chronically ill patients to the state hospital system. Neither the general hospital nor the community mental-health system were suitably organized to provide care for children. The separatist attitude prevailing in child psychiatry tended to minimize joint planning efforts in both general hospitals and community mental-health centers, and as a result very disturbed children and young adolescents continued to be sent to the state hospitals. Thus, while the overall population in these state institutions has been steadily declining for the past twenty-five years, practically all their new buildings have been devoted to the care of children. Embarrassingly little has been done to assure adequate care for patients with long-standing disabilities as well. To be sure, many patients with chronic schizophrenia, a personality disorder, or an organic brain syndrome now find their way into acute treatment facilities and have a better chance than in the past to receive an adequate evaluation. Given the scarcity of aftercare facilities and the lack of coordination between hospital and community facilities, however, these patients have been compelled to continue their pilgrimage together with many elderly patients for whom the state hospital is often the only accessible facility.

Not even the alcohol and drug-abuse programs, that have been rather lavishly funded by the federal government over the past few years, are free of problems. While these programs do provide psychiatric care, they seldom offer the quality general health care so sorely needed by this kind of patient.

As mentioned earlier, the reasons for these inadequacies were rooted in poor planning. What little systematic planning was done was based on the erroneous assumption that most of the psychiatric patients are acutely ill and need help for a limited period when, in fact, the majority of patients who are ill enough to be hospitalized tend to have a long history of marked social dysfunctioning and cannot easily reinsert themselves into the community without a vast, well-organized and well-funded network of human services.

The uncritical application of social psychiatric principles became still another source of problems. For instance, the finding that schizophrenia, particularly in its chronic form, most frequently occurs in the socioeconomically disadvantaged led to the erroneous conclusion that the single most effective treatment for this disorder is psychosocial with the result that many centers were reluctant to provide drug-maintenance therapy for their patients. Another version of this psychosocial view, which blended a bit of psychoanalytic thinking into its fabric, produced the conviction, again without proof, that "intensive" family therapy was effective in treating and maintaining schizophrenic patients in the community.

We sang the praises of therapeutic communities and liked being part of them, but despite our pleasant experiences we learned that the milieu in itself is no panacea for the treatment of severe disorders. We have been reminded by insurance commissioners that not everyone who likes to be in them needs them. We also came to realize that the Community Mental Health Center Act did not provide sufficient funds to cure the urban ills of poverty and inadequate housing, poor nutrition and general health care, and that even if such economic and social measures should come to pass and succeed in altering the "urban picture," it is still uncertain whether we would have substantially reduced the number of individuals in need of specialized care because they are mentally ill.

Finally, some of the facilities and services we have designed were fiscally unsound. The eternal dilemma of any health facility located in an urban area, be it a mental-health center or a general hospital, is the cost of operating such institutions on expensive real estate. Funds needed for extensive reeducation and occupational rehabilitation are prohibitive and often consume the budget intended for specialized services, ultimately diminishing the quality of care offered and the numbers of well-trained professionals who are responsible for health care.

(Treatment Model for A General Hospital Psychiatric Unit

Since a national plan for psychiatric care is still lacking, the role to be played by the general hospital psychiatric services in the care of the mentally ill remains to be defined. We now have a number of pressing questions which we will never be able to answer fully until such a national plan is put forth. What psychiatric services can the general hospital provide and for what kinds of patients? What role will it play in the early identification of cases and the rehabilitation of patients in the area it serves? How would it relate to other facilities in and outside the community? Which of its functions will it perform directly and in what others would its responsibility be primarily a coordinating one? And what kind of organization would be most consistent with its designated role?

The Point of Entry

It would seem logical to look at the general hospitals as regional centers and the gate of entry for all patients entering the mental-health delivery system. This approach would stress the overall quality of general health care and would lead to the identification of nonpsychiatric problems that may be associated with, aggravated by, or even causing what appears to be psychological distress. While a screening system of this kind may appear unnecessarily cumbersome and expensive—regardless whether individuals with a long-standing psychiatric disorder are more subject to all forms of nonpsychiatric morbidity or, conversely, that a certain percentage of the population show a generalized propensity to disease—there is ample evidence that a significant percentage of patients with psychiatric problems come with a previously unidentified nonpsychiatric disorder that requires medical attention.[16,34]

If indeed the general hospital is a logical point of entry for all patients in the mental-health-treatment system, it follows that one of the principal gates for entry, the emergency room of the general hospital, is not suitable for the task as it is currently structured. The utilization of emergency rooms is very high for all types of problems. This is due to the increasing "ghettoization" of the urban population and the flight of the middle and upper classes to the suburbs. This outward movement has left a medical-care vacuum for the slum poor. Yet the need to serve this urban populace cannot be met by an environment which underemphasizes the stresses of life, and the resulting reactions to it, by pretending that psychiatric emergencies are like other medical emergencies.

Among those who seek help there is a large group in which poor impulse control, antisocial behavior, promiscuous use of drugs, and personality disorders are quite common. Since this group as a whole has enormous difficulty using any set of supportive services appropriately, providing care for unscheduled admissions is a very important community need. Although storefront clinics may have their place in consumer education, attempts to reduce the number of unscheduled admissions by setting up outreach services have not been particularly successful. Rather than constructing outreach facilities in the relative vicinity of a well-equipped hospital, it may make far more sense to operate home-care services for problem-ridden areas directly from the hospital and provide transportation to and from the facility for those who have to be evaluated in a medical setting without delay.

The majority of those who come to an emergency room for psychiatric treatment are in the midst of an immediate crisis and are seeking human contact, not active treatment in the conventional sense. The health-care delivery system's inappropriate emphasis on medical expertise and its underemphasis upon social support and human services has prevented it from providing considerate and thoughtful attention to patients in need.[11] This lack of understanding of the patient's life situation is also reflected in current clinical procedures. Although the individuals who present themselves to the emergency room tend to be unreliable informants, the history is traditionally taken from the patient alone and all decisions are usually made on the basis of the data he provides.

If the psychiatric services in general hospitals were to be designated regional centers tied to satellite units with a clear mandate to make management and treatment decisions for a specific geographic area, all scheduled and unscheduled requests for psychiatric con-

sultations and admissions should be processed through an information-reception center (IRC), rather than through a traditional emergency room or outpatient admission unit. The purpose of the single-portal entry would be: (1) to register the patient upon entering the treatment system, collect the necessary demographic, fiscal, and clinical data, and pursue appropriate sources for additional information when necessary; (2) to have personnel available capable of assessing the patient's needs and referring the patient to the appropriate treatment facility within or outside of the system; (3) to assure that all data relevant to diagnostic and treatment decisions reaches the facility to which the patient has been referred; (4) to monitor the patient's movements throughout the various treatment systems and maintain a continuously updated central record system; (5) to coordinate all auxiliary assistance from the community, public welfare, family, physicians, visiting nurse, and other personnel, thus insuring optimal care and preventing wasteful, multiple utilization of community resources; and (6) to conduct research to identify backup facilities and initiate action where the appropriate facilities are lacking.

It is important that the clinical assessment completed in the IRC provide the information necessary to determine the actual treatment plan and/or disposition. In addition, the IRC should be appropriately staffed to provide consultation to the nonpsychiatric divisions in the general hospital as well as to staff, and coordinate home-service teams capable of providing assistance or consultations whenever the patient or the family is unable or unwilling to come to the hospital. The degree to which consultation services should be extended to include consultation and education activities for schools and social agencies depends upon the community's interest and willingness to provide the necessary budget, and also upon the availability of manpower.

In accordance with its multiple mandate, the manning of the IRC must be multidisciplinary in composition and include at least a part-time psychiatrist, a physician's associate or a nurse practitioner trained in physical examinations and other diagnostic procedures, a social worker with experience in family therapy and crisis intervention techniques, and a community worker who is preferably a cultural and ethnic representative of the neighborhood.

One of the important decisions that an IRC makes is whether or not the patient needs inpatient care and, if so, whether the setting of the general hospital is a suitable facility. Again, assuming that the general hospital is a regional center with its satellite units, a list of indications for a relatively brief hospitalization (defined as ranging from two to three days to two to three months) might include *suicidal ideation* or activity; an abrupt and significant *deterioration in social judgment* (as for instance, overt sexual behavior in public, spending sprees during hypomanic or manic episodes); *organic brain syndrome* requiring neurological and neuropsychological studies; the *initiation of pharmacotherapeutic measures* requiring continuous observation either because of the type of medication administered or because of complicating nonpsychiatric conditions; the *withdrawal* from drugs a patient is abusing if such a program is too hazardous to be implemented outside of the hospital setting; and *decompensation* of a patient with a long-standing psychiatric illness requiring active resocialization in addition to pharmacological measures. In addition to deciding admissions to the inpatient unit, the IRC would also be expected to maintain contact with the patient throughout hospitalization, plan his discharge, and arrange for the delivery of aftercare services.

Inpatient Service

The general hospital functions best as a regional center if only those patients requiring prolonged or indefinite residential care are referred to the state hospitals or other specialty hospitals. Thus, the IRC should refer the patient to the general hospital's psychiatric inpatient service if the accepted plan of treatment is consistent with the optimal short-term

care mandate of the unit. The treatment plan should be interdisciplinary and reflect the staff's judgment regarding: (1) diagnosis(es) on admission; (2) additional diagnostic procedures indicated; (3) psychological and social target symptoms requiring modification; (4) treatment of current nonpsychiatric problems, if any; and (5) recommendations for drug treatment, electroshock treatment, or psychotherapeutic modalities including occupational and recreational treatments. Included also should be an assessment of the social, familial, and other environmental support available to the patient and his estimated length of stay in days. If the inpatient staff, after additional observation, finds it necessary to modify the treatment plan the IRC team should be notified.

Although the staffing pattern obviously depends upon the size of the inpatient unit, it is best to have a separate team (or teams) to deal with very brief hospitalization and to allocate approximately one-third of the available beds for patients who are likely to require less than one week of hospitalization. Very brief hospitalization can be particularly effective following suicide attempts, unauthorized discontinuation of maintenance drug treatment in a previously compensated patient, and also for the rapid assessment of patients who are likely to be referred to another facility for more extensive rehabilitation or even permanent care (e.g., senile, deteriorating organic brain syndromes).

The teams responsible for brief hospitalization should also assume responsibility for those patients requiring partial (day, night, or weekend) hospitalization. At any one time, probably 20 percent of the total number of psychiatric patients requiring admission live in a sufficiently supportive environment to benefit from partial hospitalization services. The partial hospitalization unit can serve: (1) as a transitional treatment center for those moving from inpatient services to full community life; (2) as a resocialization facility for impaired patients whose families are able to take care of them some of the time; and (3) as a treatment program for those who have not responded to previous psychiatric outpatient treatment.

Utilizing the same physical facility for "crisis intervention," short-term and partial hospitalization makes it financially feasible to maintain a high staff–patient ratio and also assures a high rate of occupancy, thereby contributing to the facility's economic viability.

Ultimately, the only aim of hospitalization is to alleviate the reasons for which hopitalization was necessary. All other treatment goals should be pursued after the patient is discharged. Accordingly, and in view of its multiple mandate, maximum use should be made of peer group, leaderless group, family group, and community meetings in order to recreate a microcosm of the outside world and provide the patient with opportunities to practice those skills on which his autonomy in the outside world will depend. Although acutely ill patients generally do not require resocialization, multidimensional groups still perform a useful function by discouraging regressive tendencies and by making it possible to evaluate accurately both the patient's adaptive repertoire and his readiness to reenter the community outside the hospital. Families, whenever possible, should be considered important allies in carrying out the treatment plan; their collaboration may assure that the patient utilize outpatient and aftercare facilities to the fullest extent. This is particularly important for patients whose hospitalization is very brief, or for those who are likely to benefit from partial hospitalization. Without a close collaborative relationship with the family, most efforts at "crisis intervention" or partial hospitalization are likely to fail.

In addition to group therapeutic modalities, behavior modification techniques may be utilized to deal with specific difficulties associated with socialization, such as impairment of impulse control, self-care and other isolated problems of independent living.

Outpatient Services

Ambulatory services should be organized into two relatively autonomous, though overlapping divisions. One division should provide for the administration of various sociotherapies, including the different kinds of individual psychotherapy, group, and family therapies. While most patients obtain sufficient support from the various forms of group and family therapies, time-limited individual psychotherapy and behavior modification techniques, it is estimated that approximately 10 percent may need rather extensive long-term individual psychotherapy.

The second division should be devoted to patients who can by and large be treated within the medical model and should concern itself with the evaluation, treatment, and follow-up of inpatients whose psychiatric disorders have responded to medication or whose condition may require drug-maintenance treatment. In addition to brief supportive psychotherapeutic contacts, major emphasis in this second division should be placed upon educating the patient and his family with regard to signs and symptoms of impending relapse in order to prevent rehospitalization.

Obviously, indications for the psychotherapeutic and medication-maintenance programs of treatment overlap at times, but administrative experience has reinforced the importance of separating the psychotherapies section from the section emphasizing psychotropic medication. While most psychotherapy clinics can operate on a regularly scheduled basis, the division of medication maintenance needs to operate clinics several times a week at hours which are convenient for working patients and will also need to be readily available for emergency consultations.

The third component of an outpatient clinic, a social-service unit to coordinate rehabilitation efforts, plays an especially important role in the aftercare of the chronically ill patient. Our failure in the past to provide adequate aftercare programs for the large numbers of chronically ill patients returning to the community had nearly disastrous effects upon the entire mental-health establishment in that it eroded public confidence in our efforts. What was once growing support for the care of the mentally ill in the community has been partially obliterated by the socially undesirable behavior of these "carelessly discharged" patients, now often living in transitional facilities and "halfway" houses, where inadequately trained personnel in insufficient numbers have been vainly attempting to oversee their haphazard reentry into society. At this moment, without training in even the simplest resocialization techniques, patients discharged into the metropolitan areas soon reenter acute treatment centers, starting a vicious cycle of patient movement. Thus, the need for well-developed and thought-out aftercare programs is all too obvious.

Such an aftercare program must stress allegiance to an institution, rather than to a particular individual such as the patient's physician or social-service counselor. This is necessary because the teams taking care of patients rapidly change their composition, especially the ones located in community general hospitals or university-based teaching hospitals. These hospital settings are particularly conducive to the organization of self-care groups which are capable, with adequate patient supervision, of assuring some degree of socialization without exorbitant costs.[2]

(Conclusion

Practically all of our large-scale plans in mental-health-care delivery have been implemented posthaste, but few of them have been subjected to proper scrutiny. To be sure, the principles underlying short hospitalization, brief treatment and community orientation are laudatory but it is still uncertain whether these programs are truly effective.

The ineffectiveness of aftercare programs has resulted in the emergence of a new type of patient ghetto which has cast a long shadow over all of our services.[5] Society served notice on us that the desire of mental-health professionals to get rid of undesirable patients has come to an end. Our major concern today is focused on delivery of better psychiatric care to the chronically ill but while this is a task of highest priority, it is, as yet, also an unproven skill of modern psychiatry.

(Bibliography

1. ABRAM, H. S. "Interpersonal Aspects of Psychiatric Consultations in a General Hospital," *Psychiatry Med.*, 2 (1971), 321–326.
2. ANDERSON, C., S. MEISEL, and J. L. HOUPT. "Training Former Patients as Task Group Leaders," *Int. J. Group Psychother.*, 25 (1975), 32–43.
3. ASTRACHAN, B. M. and T. P. DETRE. "Posthospital Treatment of the Psychotic Patient," *Compr. Psychiatry*, 9 (1968), 71–80.
4. BENNETT, A. E., E. A. HARGROVE, and B. ENGLE. *The Practice of Psychiatry in General Hospitals.* Berkeley: University of California Press, 1956.
5. BENNETT, D. "Community Mental Health Services in Britain," *Am. J. Psychiatry*, 130 (1973), 1065–1070.
6. BLAIN, D. "General Hospital Psychiatric Unit," *Ment. Hosp.*, 7 (1956), 18–19.
7. BRILL, N. Q. "Army Experience Proves that Psychiatric Patients Belong in General Hospitals," *Mod. Hosp.*, 66 (1947), 238–239.
8. BROWN, G. W., M. BONE, B. DALISON et al. *Schizophrenia and Social Care.* Maudsley Monograph, no. 17. London: Oxford University Press, 1966.
9. CAMERON, D. E. "The Psychiatric Unit of the General Hospital," *Ment. Hosp.*, 8 (1957), 2–7.
10. CASTELNUOVO-TEDESCO, P. "Care of Female Psychiatric Patients, Including the Acutely Disturbed, on an Open Medical and Surgical Ward," *N. Engl. J. Med.*, 257 (1957), 748–752.
11. COLEMAN, J. V. "Aims and Conduct of Psychotherapy," *Arch. Gen. Psychiatry*, 18 (1968), 1–6.
12. DANIELS, R. S. "Changing Human Service Delivery Systems: Their Influences on Psychiatric Training," *Am. J. Psychiatry*, 130 (1973), 1232–1236.
13. DETRE, T. P., D. R. KESSLER, and H. G. JARECKI. "The Role of the General Hospital in Modern Community Psychiatry," *Am. J. Orthopsychiatry*, 33 (1963), 690–700.
14. DETRE, T. P., J. SAYERS, N. N. NORTON et al. "An Experimental Approach to the Treatment of the Acutely Ill Psychiatric Patients in the General Hospital," *Conn. Med.*, 25 (1961), 613–619.

15. DETRE, T. P. and G. TUCKER. "Psychotherapy for the Mentally Ill: A Redefinition of Goals," in G. M. Abroms and N. S. Greenfield, eds., *The New Hospital Psychiatry*, pp. 57–65. New York: Academic, 1971.

16. EASTWOOD, M. R. and M. H. TREVELYAN. "Relationship between Physical and Psychiatric Disorder," *Psychol. Med.*, 2 (1972), 363–372.

17. GARDNER, E. A., A. K. BAHN, and H. C. MILES. "Patient Experience in Psychiatric Units of General and State Mental Hospitals: First Admission Rates and Two-Year Followup," *Public Health Rep.*, 79 (1964), 755–767.

18. GAYLE, R. F. "Some Thoughts on Psychiatric Units in General Hospitals," *Ment. Hosp.*, 7 (1956), 5–8.

19. GLASSCOTE, R. M. and C. K. KANNO. *A National Survey of General Hospital Psychiatric Units.* Washington: Joint Information Service of the American Psychiatric Association and the National Association for Mental Health, 1965.

20. HARROW, M., B. M. ASTRACHAN, R. E. BECKER et al. "An Investigation into the Nature of the Patient–Family Therapy Group," *Am. J. Orthopsychiatry*, 37 (1967), 888–889.

21. JOINT COMMISSION ON MENTAL ILLNESS AND HEALTH. *Action for Mental Health; Final Report, 1961.* New York: Basic Books, 1961.

22. KORANYI, E. K. "Physical Health and Illness in a Psychiatric Outpatient Department Population," *Can. Psychiatr. Assoc. J.*, 17, Suppl. 2 (1972), SS109–SS116.

23. LAMB, H. R. and V. GOERTZEL. "The Demise of the State Hospital—A Premature Obituary?" *Arch. Gen. Psychiatry*, 26 (1972), 489–495.

24. LIPOWSKI, Z. J., R. A. RAMSAY, and H. P. VILLARD. "Psychiatric Consultations in Medical and Surgical Outpatient Clinics," *Can. Psychiatr. Assoc. J.*, 14 (1969), 239–245.

25. McKERRACHER, D. G. and C. SMITH. "A Survey of Psychiatric Units in General Hospitals in Canada," *Can. Med. Assoc. J.*, 90 (1964), 1032–1033.

26. MEASEY, L. G. and H. SMITH. "Patterns of New Chronicity in a Mental Hospital,"

Br. J. Psychiatry, 123 (1973), 349–351.

27. NATIONAL INSTITUTE OF MENTAL HEALTH. Biometry Branch, Survey and Reports Section. *Length of Stay of Discharges from General Hospital Psychiatric Inpatient Units, United States 1970–1971*, Statistical Note 70. Washington: U.S. Govt. Print. Off., 1973.

28. NEWTON, H. J. "Therapeutic Community in a County General Hospital," *Calif. Med.*, 98 (1963), 243–248.

29. REDING, G. R. and B. MAGUIRE. "Nonsegregated Acute Psychiatric Admissions to General Hospitals—Continuity of Care within the Community Hospital," *N. Engl. J. Med.*, 289 (1973), 185–189.

30. ROSENBAUM, M. "Role of the General Hospital in the Care of Special Medical Problems," *N.Y. State J. Med.*, 60 (1960), 376–381.

31. SASLOW, G. and J. MATARAZZO. "A Psychiatric Service in a General Hospital: A Setting for Social Learning," *Ment. Hosp.*, 13 (1962), 217–226.

32. SOSKIS, D. A., M. HARROW, and T. P. DETRE. "Long-term Follow-up of Schizophrenics Admitted to a General Hospital Psychiatric Ward," *Psychiatr. Q.*, 43 (1969), 525–543.

33. STRAKER, M. "Institutional Psychiatry Revisited," *Dis. Nerv. Syst.*, 35 (1974), 123–127.

34. STRAKER, M., C. YUNG, and L. WEISS. "A Comprehensive Emergency Psychiatric Service in a General Hospital," *Can. Psychiatr. Assoc. J.*, 16 (1971), 137–139.

35. TUCKER, G. J. and J. S. MAXMEN. "The Practice of Hospital Psychiatry: A Formulation," *Am. J. Psychiatry*, 130 (1973), 887–891.

36. WEISMAN, G., A. FEIRSTEIN, and C. THOMAS. "Three-day Hospitalizations: Model for Intensive Intervention," *Arch. Gen. Psychiatry*, 21 (1969), 620–629.

37. WING, J. K. and A. M. HAILEY, eds. *Evaluating a Community Psychiatric Service; The Camberwell Register 1964–1971.* London: Oxford University Press, 1972.

38. YTREHUS, A. "The Development of a Comprehensive Treatment Programme; Experiences from the Aftercare Service of a Mental Hospital," *Acta Psychiatr. Scand. Suppl.*, 245 (1973), 1–60.

CHAPTER 32

THE PRIVATE HOSPITAL

Dexter M. Bullard, Jr.

Choose your apothecary and I will prescribe. [The next day,] they blooded him largely, confined him to a dark room and put a strong blister in each of his arms with another all over his head. But he still was as 'mad' as before, praying or singing, or giving thanks continually; of which having laboured to cure him for six weeks in vain, though he was now so weak he could not stand alone, his mother dismissed the apothecary and let him be 'beside' himself in peace. [p. 423]

> James Monroe (1740),
> physician to the Bethlehem Hospital,
> as quoted by Hunter and Macalpine [27]

⟨ History

DURING the seventeenth and eighteenth centuries, the American colonies shared with Europe a poverty of understanding and a systematic neglect of the insane. Both professional and lay people conceived of mental illness as beyond man's comprehension and a manifestation of the spiritual world, within the province of theology. A "mad person" was believed to be possessed by the devil and represented a threat to society. If confession and penitence were unavailing, the only recourse was imprisonment or execution.[18,53] The few physicians who attempted to treat the insane invoked Cullen's prevailing humoral theory of disease, prescribing the most stringent and inhumane treatments.[43]

During this period, the American people lived in rural colonies and mental illness was as scattered as the population. Families had to assume the responsibility for their own mentally ill members, and, when the care of the insane did fall on the community, the afflicted were placed with paupers in almshouses or with criminals in jails. On occasion, they were auctioned off for a small fee to work as farm laborers or "sent away," secretly taken by night to a distant village and left there, thus passing the responsibility on to another community. For the few who were treated, if that term may be used, the treatment was usually limited to confinement with chains and fetters, purges, cathartics, and blood-letting.[28,45]

This was the pitiable condition of the insane in America before the nineteenth century. Then, in a period of one hundred years, society's relationship to the mentally ill was transformed. Reason and scientific inquiry replaced demonology and witchcraft; secular concern replaced theological condemnation, and new theories of mental illness followed the medical discoveries of the age. For example, Benjamin Rush, a Philadelphian, and the foremost physician of his era in America, devised an elaborate system of medical psychology based on William Harvey's discovery of the circulation of the blood. While his speculations proved insubstantial, mental illness was placed irrevocably in the field of medical concern.[44,50]

The eighteenth century witnessed the rise of cities in America and this concentration of population led to the formation of various learned groups, among them medical societies, important supporters of our early asylums. The sick and infirm, and the poor became visible in the growing cities, and communities began to construct facilities, including hospitals, to care for them. To these developments in American society must be added more specific agents for change. Pinel's dramatic and well-publicized work was closely followed in America and his *Traité Mèdico-Philosophique sur l'Aliénation Mentale ou la Manie*, had a profound influence.[38] His concept of "moral treatment" was equally persuasive to the English Quakers and, stimulated by William Tuke, they established the Retreat near York, the most advanced institution for the mentally ill in the English-speaking world, where "the superior efficacy of a mild system of treatment was demonstrated beyond all contradiction," (as quoted by his son Samuel).[51]

Philadelphia, with a population of more than 50,000 was the sophisticated leader of American cities. Its citizens were in close touch with European men of science and the social changes of that turbulent period. At the newly founded Pennsylvania Hospital, the first in the American colonies, Benjamin Rush had sought to establish a free-standing institution for the insane and his efforts eventually led to the move of all mentally ill patients from their basement quarters to the West Wing constructed in 1796.[8] Paralleling this move in Philadelphia, Governors at the New York Hospital began similar efforts to move the insane into quarters of their own. Aided by the legislature, a separate greystone building, initially housing 107 patients, was erected and opened in 1808, and the attending physician, Archibald Bruce, was required to visit it three times weekly.[30]

The difficulties in managing the mentally ill, which beset the newly established general hospitals, were not lost on community leaders. The Quaker community in Philadelphia observed the problems at the Pennsylvania Hospital and one of its most prominent laymen, Thomas Scattergood, visited the Retreat near York. In 1813, Samuel Tuke published *Description of the Retreat Near York*, and a shortened version was circulated through the Philadelphia community.[1] The response was enthusiastic enough to support the construction in 1817 of the Friends Asylum at Frankford, Pennsylvania, the first private mental hospital in America.[1] At this point, other American physicians and laymen moved decisively to establish institutions for the mentally ill, and between 1795 and 1825 nine hospitals were erected, seven of these under private auspices.

The Quaker influence was also felt in New York. The Lunatic Asylum of the New York Hospital came under pressure to provide a more humane environment for its increasing number of patients.[35] Thomas Eddy, President of the New York Hospital, a Quaker and well-known social reformer, acquainted with Samuel Tuke's publications, urged the construction of a separate institution for the insane.[21] His enlightened program called for the routine keeping of case histories, a departure from the prevailing custodial philosophy. After four years of construction, the Bloomingdale Asylum was opened in 1821, a freestanding institution and a department of the New York Hospital containing space for 100 patients.[30]

In Boston, a similar development took place after the establishment of the Massachusetts General Hospital in 1811. The State Charter called for two departments, one for general disease and one for the insane. After a fundraising campaign, the institution for the insane was constructed, across the Charles River from Boston, and opened in 1818 under the direction of Angus Wyman, the first physician superintendent appointed in this country.[49] He was particularly concerned about the nursing care and specified that the attendants should possess "amiable dispositions and soundness and maturity of judgment."[33] A small institution housing less than fifty patients in its early years, the asylum received a generous donation from John McLean in 1821, and was later named after its benefactor.[9]

Baltimore followed the same course, erecting a general hospital in 1798, "for the Relief of Indigent Sick Persons and for the Reception and Care of Lunatics." Under both public and private auspices, it was finally chartered exclusively as a mental hospital in 1839.[29]

The York Retreat became the model for another early American hospital, the Hartford Retreat. Sponsored by the newly formed Connecticut State Medical Society in 1821, the General Assembly was petitioned by Thomas Hubbard to provide an asylum or retreat for the more than 1000 insane persons in the state to "mitigate their suffering and restore their reason."[2] Following Pinel and Tuke, medical records were required and an attending committee was appointed to review the medical and moral practice of the institution and to report abuses. It was chartered in 1822 and opened in 1824 under Eli Todd, a prominent Connecticut physician whose interest in mental illness was spurred by the recurrent depressions and eventual suicide of his sister.[11]

The description of early private hospitals would not be complete without noting further developments at the Pennsylvania Hospital. Though the West Wing was a decided improvement, Rush later advocated the erection of entirely separate buildings for the insane but, at his death in 1813, Philadelphia had no physician who supported this view. Cholera epidemics preempted other medical interests until the 1830s when the numbers of mentally ill from Philadelphia's expanding population prompted the Board of Managers to secure 110 acres outside the city and construct a new hospital which received its first patients January 9, 1841, under the direction of a Quaker, Thomas Kirkbride.[9]

Other private hospitals established before the mid-nineteenth century included the Hudson Lunatic Asylum (1830), Brattleboro Retreat (1836), the Mount Hope Retreat (1840), and the Butler Hospital (1847).[4,41] These institutions, because of their small size, could provide individualized care and flexible treatment programs. They played a central role in the development of American psychiatry, their medical superintendents forming the nucleus of the Association of Medical Superintendents, founded in 1844, forerunner of the American Psychiatric Association.[36]

Nineteenth-Century Private Hospital Treatment

A maniac had made several attempts to set fire to the hospital; upon being remonstrated he said, 'I am a salamander;' 'But recollect,' said my friend Coates, 'all the patients in the house are not salamanders.' 'That is true,' said the maniac, and never afterwards attempted to set fire to the hospital.

> Reported by Thomas Eddy
> of his friend Samuel Coates,
> President of the Pennsylvania Hospital[21]

Treatment between 1800 and 1850 was profoundly influenced by Pinel's writings, by Tuke and the York Retreat, and by John Conolly, the English advocate of nonrestraint.[14] The Quaker community was a vehicle for bringing this treatment philosophy to the United States and it found a ready acceptance in the newly constructed "Retreats," freed from their parent hospital practices and with no traditions to uphold.

The death of Benjamin Rush in 1813 signalled a turning away from the medical therapies which he advocated to "moral" treatment, which arose from a humanistic and psychological interpretation of mental disorder. Purges, emetics, Rush's mechanical contrivances, the "gyrator" and the "tranquilizers," and the induction of fear, gave way to less violent medications, such as the opium derivatives, stramonium, quinine, iron tonics, and continuous baths.[3,39] Punishment, confinement, and shackles and chains were replaced by policies of nonrestraint. Moral treatment returned humanity and reason to the insane. In the words of the Governors of the New York Hospital on the opening of the Bloomingdale Asylum, "This institution has been established with the express design to carry into effect that system of management of the insane, happily termed moral management, the superior efficacy of which has been demonstrated in several of the hospitals of Europe, and especially that admired establishment of the Society of Friends, called The Retreat, near York, in England."[34]

The Committee of the Connecticut State Medical Society planning the Hartford Retreat recommended: "Such an asylum should be the reverse of everything that enters into our conceptions of a madhouse. It should not be a jail, in which for individual and public security the unfortunate maniacs are confined. Nor should it merely be a hospital where they may have the benefits of medical treatment— for without moral management the most judicious course of medical management is rarely successful. . . ." as quoted by Braceland.[10]

Wyman, in his report to the board of governors of the Massachusetts General Hospital in 1822,[33] sounded a similar note, writing: "Living under a system of rules and regulations for everything has a powerful effect in tranquilizing the mind, breaking up wrong associations of thinking and inducing correct habits of thinking as well as acting; and finally . . . lunatics are not insensible to kind treatment, that whips and chains are forever banished from every well-regulated asylum for the insane and that kindness and humanity have succeeded to severity and cruelty." It was best stated by Amariah Brigham in 1847,[12] shortly after leaving his post at the Hartford Retreat: "The removal of the insane from home and former associations, with respectful and kind treatment under all circumstances, and in most cases manual labor, attendance at religious worship on Sunday, the establishment of regular habits and of self control, diversion of the mind from morbid trains of thought are now generally considered as essential in the moral treatment of the insane."

At mid-century, Thomas Kirkbride, by then the foremost institutional psychiatrist in America, developed a plan for the organization and construction of mental hospitals that was successful at the Pennsylvania Hospital and served as a model for thirty-one states during the next half-century. At a time when there were no standards of privacy, comfort or safety, the Kirkbride Plan was an enlightened and humane advance in the care of the mentally ill.[32] A colleague of Kirkbride's in his later years and superintendent of the Butler Hospital in Providence, R.I., for two decades, Isaac Ray, became a national authority on legal aspects of mental disorder. In a volume published in 1863,[42] Ray examined the principles of mental hygiene defined as "the art of preserving the health of the mind against all the incidents and influences calculated to deteriorate its qualities, impair its energies or derange its movements." Another hospital superintendent, George Cook of Brigham Hall, had published the first two papers on mental hygiene in 1859.[15] These principles were later put into practice in the earliest outpatient psychiatric clinic in America established at the Pennsylvania Hospital by John Chapin in 1885.

The study of treatment results first appeared in annual hospital reports, many of which exaggerated their successes. The founding of the *American Journal of Insanity* in 1844 encouraged more dispassionate research in mental hospitals, particularly concerning the natural history of the mental disorders.[16] Pliny Earle of the Bloomingdale Asylum, brought new vigor into the evaluation of treatment in his studies over a twenty-year period.[20] In 1882, Edward Cowles established at McLean Hospital in Waverley, Mass., the first permanent training school for nurses and took the then daring step of introducing women nurses to male wards, against widespread condemnation.[17,50] By the end of the century, occupational therapy, which had long been a mainstay of moral treatment, was dignified by a formulation of its principles and practices, opening a new career choice in mental health largely through the efforts of William Rush Dunton at the recently opened Sheppard and Enoch Pratt Hospital[22] in Towson, Md.

([Psychodynamic Theory and the Private Hospital

For a considerable time I have harboured a suspicion that paranoia, too—or classes of cases which fall under the heading of paranoia, is a psychosis of defense; that is to say, like hysteria and obsessions, it proceeds directly from the repression of distressing memories and that its symptoms are determined in their form by the content of what has been repressed. [p. 174][24]

> Sigmund Freud (1896),
> "Further Remarks on the
> Neuro-Psychosis of Defense"

Although Freud did not concern himself with hospitalized patients or form a completed theory of the psychoses, he established through his case histories and theoretical papers the central importance of the genetic and unconscious determinants of the major psychiatric disorders.[23,25,37] Subsequent workers, most notably Harry Stack Sullivan, formulated further psychodynamic concepts which applied directly to the treatment of the hospitalized patient.[47,48] The development of ego psychology with its many contributors, added to the understanding of these disorders and defined the psychodynamics of the treatment process.

The impact of these theories on the conduct of private hospitals was substantial. Psychodynamic considerations became a part of every hospital's diagnostic assessment and treatment program. The psychology of human development and behavior became a basic element in hospital curriculums for medical and nonmedical staff. The functioning of groups in the hospital setting and the importance of group process to the outcome of treatment became evident to hospital clinicians and treatment in groups became standard practice. Administrative procedures and the organizational structures of many private hospitals reflected the advances in knowledge of the dynamics of human interactions. Sociologists, social psychologists, and social anthropologists now consider the hospital itself as a social entity from which much can be learned about human interactions.

([Modern Private Psychiatric Hospitals

It is hard to keep in mind what it means subjectively to be a mental patient; to be so fearful that each aspect of the environment represents a threat to one's existence; to experience the world as unreal and to see the 'outside' as just a flimsy structure with no substance; to live with a feeling of restraint and being closed in, or suffocated, and to feel rebellion and resentment at this and be unable to express it in any effective way; to experience utter, desperate, and unrelieved loneliness, with no hope of change; to feel that in the entire universe there is no person that will ever understand one; to believe that one's actions have no effect and that one is not affected by the actions of others. [p. 68][46]

> A. Stanton and M. S. Schwartz (1954),
> *The Mental Hospital*

Developments in the past seventy years have radically altered private psychiatric hospitals and their role in the treatment of the mentally ill. Today, diversity is their most notable characteristic and they range from small and specialized hospitals to comprehensive mental-health facilities that meet the entire mental-health needs of a defined geographical or population area. Some private hospitals have little or no relationship to governmental facilities; others are closely affiliated with governmental institutions. Some private hospitals are one part of a larger body containing both governmental and nongovernmental components; others carry out mental-health services by grant or contract arrangements with states or municipalities. Still others have major commitments to teaching and research. A private hospital distinguishes itself from other types of hospitals by placing its highest priority on the excellence of patient care. Though it may engage in many other activities including teaching, research, and mental-health related social programs, its first responsibility is to the individual, mentally ill person who seeks its help.

Two criteria define the character of the private hospital: the scope of its services and the population it serves. The range of services reflects the many and diverse needs of patients suffering from mental illness. In the nineteenth century, hospital treatment was largely confined to inpatient care. The past seventy years has seen a gradual expansion of services. At the present time, the range of service is extensive and the hospital has become a locus or starting point for these varied programs. The decision to place a patient in the hospital or in any other treatment program rests on the nature of the disorder and its symptomatic expression. Inpatient care, while remaining a vital concern and activity of most hospitals, is no longer the sole method of treatment and is but one of a number of treatment programs which a hospital may offer. The increase in hospital services has allowed a more exact fit between the needs generated by the patient's illness and the specific treatment plan.

A partial listing of services includes:
    psychiatric diagnostic evaluation
    individual psychotherapy
    group psychotherapy
    family therapy
    social casework
    milieu therapy
    psychiatric nursing care
    behavioral modification therapy
    activity therapy
    art therapy
    music therapy
    recreational therapy
    occupational therapy
    psychological testing
    educational testing
    vocational testing
    rehabilitation training
    counselling
    special educational services
    drug treatment
    physical therapies
    medical and dental services
    inpatient hospital services
    day hospital services
    night hospital services
    outpatient services
    crisis intervention

All of these elements of the treatment program share the basic emphasis on the psychiatric care of the individual patient. Services are integrated and a comprehensive range of appropriate services is available for each patient. Established patterns of responsibility set the priorities of treatment and care so that the patient's condition is regularly reviewed and the therapy reassessed to meet the current needs of the patient and his life situation. One physician is identified as responsible for the planning and implementation of treatment and, while he may seek consultation, responsibility for the patient's care is his and is not dispersed among the members of a group. Integrated rehabilitative services extend beyond the hospital itself and arrangements with other institutions make further services available to the patient and his family.

The size of the patient population has an important impact on the organization of services and the delivery of quality care. Large institutions, by necessity, sacrifice the individuality of patients and personnel because their policies and procedures must be standardized, and a uniformity of approach is required.

Private hospitals have traditionally been smaller than their public hospital counterparts; ideally small enough so that each patient and staff person is a recognized member of the hospital community. As a consequence, the entire hospital embodies the therapeutic program. The flexibility of the program is a direct outgrowth of the size of the hospital and large programs cannot quickly meet the changing needs of each patient and the demands of a continually changing patient group. A small, flexible hospital program permits the fullest utilization of the principles of milieu therapy, for a hospital is not merely a place where patients are treated but a community in which the major activity is patient care.

Certain groups of patients, such as the elderly, and those with alcoholism, drug addiction or chronic psychotic disorders require specialized services. Many hospital programs and some institutions specialize in particular patient subgroups or disease categories. In addition, they take into account the age of the patient and the severity of his disorder. This requires adaptation of the therapeutic modalities to the particular patient group and direct collaboration with other facilities and organizations such as Alcoholics Anonymous, schools, programs within the criminal justice system, rehabilitation programs, and community services for the aged.

The physical surroundings must also reflect concern about the individuality of each patient and contribute to the patient's sense of familiarity and safety. A simplified living situation should support the patient's sense of privacy and self-respect, and promote the natural interactions between the patients and staff. Overcrowding, which is detrimental to both patients and staff, must be avoided to allow the successful functioning of the therapeutic milieu.

Continuity of care forms an indispensable link between the patient and his hopes for a resolution of his illness and requires an exact knowledge of the patient, the origins of his illness and its progress, his current status and his family, and social circumstances. The dependability of the treatment program will rest on long-term experience with the treatment and the situation in which it is given. A familiarity with the patient's responses to treatment is a prerequisite for further additions to the treatment program. Changing personnel disrupt the treatment to the detriment of the patient.

The entire hospital community participates in the therapeutic endeavor. This includes not only the traditional nursing services but also the "nonclinical" departments such as dietary and housekeeping personnel who have daily contact with patients. To the extent that the patient's disorder permits, he engages fully in the community life of the hospital. Therapeutic patient activities include not only expressive modalities, such as occupational and recreational therapy, but also task-oriented activities, such as patient work programs or group projects. The essence of the patient's involvement in the hospital community is the preservation and strengthening of those capacities and capabilities which have not been compromised by the patient's disorder. The prevention of the "atrophy of disuse" is as central to the hospital program as the direct treatment of the patient's disorder.

Skilled nursing staff are basic to a successful treatment program and the staff of the private hospital should be selected for their personal aptitudes and skills in treating mental illness. A high staff–patient ratio provides a flexible staffing pattern that maximizes attention to the particular needs of each patient. Staff members should have a full knowledge of the patient, his disorder, and his current family situation. Inservice educational programs are essential to teach the basic elements of mental disorder and the subtleties of interpersonal relationships. Only then can the staff see the patient as a troubled human being with interests, talents, and capabilities, despite the limitations imposed by his illness.

The relationship between individual staff members and patients forms an essential and integral part of the treatment program and should be encouraged. Such relationships form the human context for the therapeutic experience of the interest of another person and the development of mutual respect. They also provide an environment for the expression of the patient's habitual modes of relating to others and allow for repeated examination of his pathological adaptations. For the modification of unconscious mental functioning, the establishment of transferential relationships is essential and infantile derivatives, thus elicited and expressed, form the matrix of the therapeutic interactions with the hospital staff. In this instance, the constant environment of the hospital program is a necessary backdrop for the expression of unconscious conflicts and their resolution.

The hospital maintains the continuity of relationship between the patient and his physician for as long as psychiatric treatment is indicated, often over a period of several years. In this respect, the psychiatrist resembles the family doctor whose knowledge and availability to the patient and his family grow more valuable and effective as time passes.

The psychotherapeutic relationship is the optimal means through which the patient brings his disturbance of adaptive functioning under rational scrutiny. Individual psychotherapy is of prime importance for the improvement of interpersonal relatedness and the alteration of the emotional factors that underlie mental disorders. Group techniques have proved essential to most hospital treatment programs. The budgetary requirements of many public institutions require the use of group techniques as a primary modality of treatment. The private hospital has the responsibility of providing each patient with a program suited to his own needs, which includes both individual and group treatment.

Sedatives and tranquilizing medication, judiciously employed, is of substantial benefit to many patients. The availability of a range of major and minor tranquilizing and antidepressive agents has led to their use in all hospitals. The prescription of these drugs must be aimed at target symptoms and the improvement of adaptive and integrative functions enabling the patient to expand the range of his activities and participate more fully in the therapeutic and rehabilitative effort.

Medical and dental services are an essential constituent of all psychiatric hospital programs. The contributory role of nonpsychiatric medical conditions to the mental illness is established during the hospital diagnostic study and appropriate treatment instituted. For all patients under the continuing care of the hospital, medical and dental services are provided directly or through arrangement with another resource.

Hospital Treatment

All psychiatric hospitals attempt to provide comprehensive treatment for the disturbed patient while protecting him from his destructive and self-destructive impulses. Hospital treatment should interrupt the process of isolation and destructiveness that the patient's illness has provoked in himself, his family and others, and allow the family to reestablish its integrity usually strained under the impact of the patient's disorder.

Prior to treatment, the patient and his family are advised of the need for treatment and the nature of the services the hospital offers. During hospital treatment further diagnostic study, including psychiatric evaluation and additional special studies, are carried out. Following discharge from the program, a period of follow-up contact is essential if recurrences are to be prevented.

Treatment programs must take into account that psychiatric disorder may be acute or chronic and relapsing. Hospital treatment subsequently may be categorized as short-term or long-term. The selection of the appropriate treatment program rests on the diagnosis, the factors that have contributed to the disorder and the immediate problem that confronts the patient.

Disorders which develop acutely, for example, those associated with some disruption of the life situation, that occur in response to an external trauma or the loss of a loved one, or result from a clearly defined and circumscribed intrapsychic conflict, are most suitable for short-term treatment.

Long-term treatment may be required for disorders which have an insidious onset, those having a pervasive and unrelenting downward course, those not resulting directly from a defined trauma or loss, or associated with a developmental arrest. Because it is difficult to predict the course of psychiatric disorder, most patients are treated initially within a short-term program. For those who do not respond, transfer to a long-term facility should be made. Hospital programs should clearly define the goals of their programs and whether they are short-term or long-term as the modalities of treatments differ markedly.

SHORT-TERM TREATMENT

The goals of the short-term treatment program are to reestablish a successful adaptation of the patient to the world around him, especially to those people closest to him, and to help the patient regain an equilibrium between the inner and outer forces that govern his functioning, thus freeing him to further pursue his life interests. This often means helping a patient through a life crisis whose elements have been elicited and related to each other during the diagnostic study. Occasionally, the process of clarification itself during the diagnostic process is sufficient to resolve the immediate difficulty. Usually, a combination of changes must take place in the patient and treatment procedures will vary accordingly. Depending on the patient's internal pathology, a reduction in anxiety is helpful. Often, assistance in establishing controls over certain behaviors is necessary. The patient can be helped to consider and develop alternative pathways for action. Healthy elements of family support may be mobilized and a return to ordinary life routines is usually indicated. At times, it is necessary for the patient to remove himself from a pathological family or social situation. During the course of treatment, the patient is helped to develop his capacity for self-observation.

The variety of treatment modalities provided by hospitals has already been noted, but their application within the framework of short-term intervention reflects the special goals of this procedure.

The private hospital may offer short-term treatment in a program of brief hospitalization followed by day care. Brief hospitalization offers temporary protection of the patient from outside stress with which he cannot cope and from his own impulsiveness or destructive inclinations. The move into a day-care program, in addition to its diagnostic usefulness, offers a daily respite to the patient and an opportunity to examine his current methods of dealing with his life circumstances free from the unbearably stressful home situation. Supportive psychotherapy deals with those aspects of the patient's difficulty that are susceptible to conscious scrutiny and directly supports the patient's own autonomous problem-solving efforts. Group meetings and/ or short-term group psychotherapy emphasize current relationships and life situations. They encourage group members to compare experiences and share their understanding and their patterns of coping. Milieu treatment for either the day treatment or hospitalized patient provides a structure of daily routine and a reliable and consistent group of professional people with whom the patient interacts.

From the outset, attention is focused on the circumscribed nature of the hospitalization and the goal of an immediate return to the home or a move to a suitable living situation. Somatic therapies, including drug treatment, are utilized with these same goals in mind.

Occupational and recreational therapies provide a structured relationship around a task or activity. These and other activities reestablish the reality of the patient's capabilities, personal interests, and competence. Modulated expression of feelings and awareness of personal concerns may take place through the medium of music, drama, art, and dance therapy under the guidance of a person experienced in these modes of treatment.

Casework with the family is central to the treatment program and reflects the importance of the current life situation. Emphasis is placed on the family's understanding of the patient's immediate difficulty and the ways in which they can be supportive to his effort to deal with it. Family members are helped to restructure the home situation to better meet the needs of the patient and of themselves.

Planning for discharge and for appropriate care after discharge from the hospital or hospital program is an important part of the treatment endeavor. All illnesses severe enough to require hospitalization also require this type of aftercare planning and patient contact, and the success or failure of short-term hospitalization will rest on this aspect of the therapeutic program. Thus, the continuation of appropriate treatment measures and the continuing assessment of the living situation ensures that outside circumstances contributing to the illness are eliminated or modified.

LONG-TERM TREATMENT

The criteria for patient selection for long-term treatment are: (1) the previous failure of short-term measures; (2) the presence of a chronic or recurring disorder; and (3) the need for a stable and therapeutic environment that will support the treatment process as long as is required.

Patients who require long-term hospital treatment have usually been hospitalized briefly without success and a variety of measures, including drug treatment, have failed to prevent the progress of the disorder. Though this situation is often desperate and their families hopeless, they are not in an acutely conflicted situation.

These patients show a gross inability to cope with normal living situations and their histories reveal arrests in psychic development and long-standing disorder. The resolution of the disorder requires a resumption of development beyond the point of arrest.

The goals of long-term treatment are to rid the patient of the disabling symptoms and behavior which result from his disorder, and to remove developmental arrests allowing further emotional growth. For the more severely disordered patient, this will require a significant alteration in the level of his personality functioning and the intervention of a skilled psychotherapist. Changes in intrapsychic processes and the modification of the personality affect the patient's view of himself, his ability to contain his impulses, his relationships to other people, and his capacity to lead a more autonomous life. Over the period of treatment, the patient should gain an understanding of the forces that contributed to his disorder so that compromised or undeveloped capabilities can be explored and utilized. Rehabilitation plays an important role in the treatment procedure and should develop the maximal use of partial functions and establish the optimal circumstance for a range of self-supporting activities.

Comprehensive long-term hospital treatment programs include motivational, psychological, interpersonal, educational, and environmental methods. All aspects of the patient's adaptation to the world, both pathological and healthy, are incorporated in the therapeutic endeavor.

Environmental structure is basic to any long-term treatment program. A common cause for failure of short-term therapy is the failure of the patient to maintain a stable living situation. The living experience of many patients prior to hospitalization is chaotic, dangerous, and destructive to their families and themselves. Hospitalization establishes a safe, reliable, consistent environment. The daily routine of sleeping and eating, and the activities of self-care are reestablished. The expectations of the environment are unambiguous and predictable. Behaviors that are detrimental to the patient and others are limited. An essential constituent of any long-term environmental structure is the interaction between the hospital staff and patients. These interperonal relationships and the direct experience of the patient with other human beings interested in his welfare and skilled in dealing with the distortions of human relationships imposed by the patient's illness, are powerful tools in modifying the patient's pathological adaptations. These interactions take place formally, informally, individually, and in groups. They may be concerned with a task having to do with personal hygiene or eating, or they may be spontaneous and without a task orientation. These relationships can only develop gradually as the patient gains a feeling of worth and acceptance by another person and comes to value their interest and attention. In groups, the interactions and the feelings of each of the members are identified and brought to the attention of the group. The stability and continuity of key figures of the hospital staff are essential to the development of these individual and group relationships.

Psychological study begins with the initial psychiatric interview and the formal psychological testing procedures. The identification of the conscious and unconscious conflicts within the personality of the patient determines the nature and role of subsequent psychological investigation. Intensive individual psychotherapy, utilizing the intense relationship between the therapist and patient to study the patient's external and intrapsychic life, is essential to help the patient become aware of the forces that shape his relationships with the world and the impediments that underlie his disability. While psychotherapeutic technique varies as widely as surgical procedures, the basic goal is the remission of symptoms and relief from paralyzing internal psychic conflict. Such basic changes in personality functioning require a relationship that with time will allow the full development of pathological patterns of behavior that then can be consciously experienced, clarified and resolved. These often hidden attitudes and beliefs that the patient holds about himself and the world are reenacted toward the therapist and the environment, often in negative and self-destructive ways. Hence, the collaboration of therapist and those responsible for the environmental structure is essential.

In addition, the therapeutic program addresses the healthy, progressive, and nonpathological aspects of the patient's functioning. A range of planned activities is provided which reflect the wide diversity of human capacities still available to the patient. For the most severely disturbed patient, they may be limited to the basic human functions of self-care. For the less disturbed patient, a greater variety of activities may be effectively mobilized.

A partial list includes the following:
    occupational,
    recreational,
    music,
    art, and
    dance therapy
    exercise and sports
    patient work programs
    educational classes
    patient government
    psychodrama

Some of these activities have specified therapeutic aims and utilize specialized techniques and materials. This may involve the production of an object or artistic creation. It may involve the recognition of feelings through rhythmic movement or musical or dramatic expression. These therapeutic procedures may be applied individually or in small groups. Other activities have a more general purpose, to expand the healthy or nonpathological functioning capacities of the patient. Exercise and team sports provide a constructive avenue for physical expression of feeling and conflicts. Supervised teamwork and competition allows an expression of aggression, and feelings of jealousy and envy within a secure and structured situation. Classes geared to the patient's capabilities and interests teach skills such as self-care, cooking, and mechanics, and enlarge the patient's awareness of his own capabilities and cultivate healthy interests hitherto dormant.

Patients who are able to work derive con-siderable benefit from hospital employment. For many, it is a renewal of a satisfaction which had been given up at the onset of the illness. For others, it is the first evidence that they are needed, useful and valued for what they can do. Work situations must reflect as careful an understanding of the patient's needs and capabilities as other therapeutic activities. The responsibilities of a job are an excellent indicator of the readiness for responsibilities in the community.

Rehabilitation may be considered the joining together of these activities in a planned sequence and their further elaboration in a community setting. The rehabilitation effort goes beyond the patient, however, and includes structures within and without the hospital. These structures include administrative arrangements to continue contact with the patient as he moves toward more community responsibility and involvement, a continuing assessment of the patient's functional capacities and limitations, and provisions for appropriate living situations, work opportunities, social activities, and sources of financial support, medical care, and psychiatric and social services. While the hospital may not provide all of these services itself, it has arrangements with other community facilities which, together, provide a coordinated and integrated program.

Hospitals vary considerably in their emphasis on particular elements of the long-term treatment program, depending on the factors which maintain the illness, the type of limitation suffered by the patient, and other characteristics of their patient population. Each hospital program aims for the maximal development of the patient's capacities to function in society and the reduction or elimination of the disabilities arising from the patient's disorder.

The Treatment of Children and Adolescents

While children and adolescents have been admitted to mental hospitals for more than a hundred years, the modern development of institutional programs devoted specifically to youth began with the founding of the Juvenile Psychopathic Institute in Chicago in 1909. This was followed by the establishment of the Judge Baker Foundation in Boston in 1917 and, after World War I, the first Child Guidance Clinics in Norfolk, Va., and St. Louis, Mo., sponsored by the Common Wealth Foundation.[26] Since that time, many mental hospitals have established departments for children and adolescents, and in the past decade the proportion of patients admitted to the hospital under twenty-one years of age has risen dramatically.

Accumulated experience has revealed marked differences between mental disorders in children and adults, differences affecting their diagnosis and treatment. Mental illness in children not only compromises psychic structure and function but limits and distorts development. The child, still immature, remains dependent on his parents and other adult figures not only for his nourishment and protection but also for the transmission of their culture and values which the child must have to meet the responsibilities of adulthood. The child will have different needs, depending on his chronological age, and his level of maturation and development. The impact of the environment with all its psychological and social complexities is much greater in childhood and group relationships have a special significance in this period of life as the child seeks to establish a durable autonomy from his parents. The vital role of education in every child's life cannot be overemphasized. These principles and others related to the mentally disordered child have been carefully described in the Standards for Psychiatric Facilities for Children.[7]

The consequence of these differences, between child and adult, on the care and treatment of children is substantial. The indications for hospital treatment, particularly for inpatient care, must fully take into account the patient's dependence on his family. Removal from the family may be indicated by the patient's disorder, the family disorder around the child patient, or pathological relationships between the child and his family. However, the severity of the illness must be weighed carefully to assure that the benefits of hospitalization outweigh the harmful effects of disrupting the child's life and home situation.

Psychiatric facilities for children are organized to meet the needs of children as well as to treat their psychiatric disorder. Space is an essential ingredient; both the private space allotted to each child as his own, and the open, out-of-doors space which the child can use and explore. Provision must be made for the child's safety, physical health, and for appropriate supervision. The staff who serve *in loco parentis* must be trained in child development as well as child psychopathology and be able to distinguish symptoms of illness from temporary regressions or normal age-related variations in behavior.

Therapeutic programs for children and adolescents cover the same range of modalities as their adult counterparts with the exception of the physical therapies. Treatment is carried out within the context of the child's chronological age, maturation, and developmental level. Education forms an essential part of every therapeutic program and the educational component is designed to meet developmental needs within the limits set by the mental disorder. The provisions for peer-group and social relationships, recreational and athletic activities, special interests and appropriate job training must be included in each child's and adolescent's program. The treatment of children requires a more extensive program, a more defined and explicit treatment structure, and a larger therapeutic staff. As the child improves, the ongoing therapeutic work prepares also the family for his return home. Postdischarge treatment planning for the child and his family is essential to maintain the gains of treatment.

Education and Research

Though not primary goals of the private psychiatric hospital, significant educational and research endeavors have marked the development of private hospitals during the past century.

EDUCATION

Since Kirkbride's early lectures to his nursing attendants, education of hospital personnel has played a vital role in the patterns of patient care. Although many colleges now offer courses in mental-health practice, the special skills required for the care of psychiatric patients must be taught through direct experience in an inservice educational program. The curriculum includes the observation of patient–staff interactions, the delineation of characteristic patterns of patient behavior, self-observation by staff of their responses to the varied types of patient behavior, the study of group processes in both patients and staff, the awareness of each patient's unique qualities, and many other topics. This type of curriculum is most meaningful in conjunction with daily contact with patients.

All members of the hospital staff are included in educational programs appropriate to their role and function. Orientation, continuing education, and training for increased responsibilities are also part of the hospital curriculum. Instruction may also be provided for a variety of professionals at both undergraduate and graduate levels. A partial list includes:

> physicians
> nurses
> psychologists
> social workers
> mental health workers
> teachers
> counselors
> occupational,
> recreational,
> art,
> music,
> dance, and
> activities therapists

Affiliation with universities, medical and nursing schools is the rule, and teaching by the hospital staff may be in either the hospital or university setting.

The hospital provides a natural setting for the study of human, psychological, and social processes. Training in the recognition of symptoms of mental illness leads inevitably to the study of psychological functioning and those biological, developmental, and environmental factors that affect it. The milieu treatment program provides a natural laboratory for the study of social and group processes as well as the impact of administrative structure on patient and staff behavior. Here the student may experience at first-hand the process of group formation, the establishment of group goals, the influence of psychopathology on group process, and the importance of group functioning to changes in patient and staff behavior. Thus, beyond the training for a specific professional task, education in the private hospital examines the complexities of man's feelings and behavior as they are experienced within himself and in relation to others.

RESEARCH

In the early nineteenth century, research in psychiatry began in psychiatric hospitals, the first opportunity for physicians to study mental illness in groups of patients in one setting. Of necessity, the early studies of Rush and others described and classified the natural history and phenomena of disease. Studies of moral treatment and its efficacy, accounts of hospital organization, construction, and management preoccupied the early superintendents, as their annual reports document. The two most important works published at this time were Benjamin Rush's *Medical Inquiries and Observations Upon the Diseases of the Mind* (1812), and Isaac Ray's *A Treatise on the Medical Jurisprudence of Insanity* (1838).[40] The new *moral theory* of treating insanity was discussed by Amariah Brigham (*Remarks on the Influence of Mental Cultivation and Mental Excitement, upon Health,* 1832), Thomas Upham (*Outlines of Imperfect and Disordered Mental Action,* 1838), and William Sweetser (*Mental Hygiene,* 1843), as cited by Bunker.[13]

The *American Journal of Insanity,* the first periodical in English solely concerned with mental disorder, was founded in 1844 by Amariah Brigham, changing the course of psychiatric research in this country. For the next fifty years, articles, notes, and commentary were contributed by hospital superintendents and other physicians, leading to important independent works[13] by Kirkbride, Earle, and Cowles, and the establishment of hospital-research laboratories.[6,31]

Today, research in private hospitals extends to all aspects of mental disorders and their treatment. In the area of clinical research, private hospitals are in a unique position to make contributions to our knowledge of mental illness, as the pioneering studies of Stanton and Schwartz have demonstrated.[46] The primacy of patient care leads inevitably to the examination of psychological, social, family, and group processes that contribute to or maintain illness. The evaluation of specific therapies, such as the psychotherapies, drug therapies, and milieu treatment, in their short- or long-term effectiveness, is readily accomplished in the hospital setting.

Program evaluation utilizing research methodology is an essential component of clinical investigation and measures the effectiveness of existing services. Other valuable research endeavors include outcome studies, assessment of community's needs, the comparison of alternative methods of treating different segments of the population, and studies of administrative organization.

Biochemical, physiological, psychological, and sociological studies are carried out by a number of hospital research departments, usually affiliated with a medical school or university. Formal research programs are carried out through the support of federal and state governments, private institutions and foundations, churches, individuals, and the hospitals themselves. A variety of institutional settings conduct research in biochemical, physiological, psychological, anthropological, and sociological factors in mental disorders. More extensive research programs and those removed from clinical practice operate more effectively in a separate affiliated research institute or foundation.

([Conclusions

The private hospital, a wellspring of modern psychiatry, today has a broadened role in the delivery of mental-health services in the United States. Its treatment programs have extended to children and adolescents, and include all forms of mental disorder. Its programs go far beyond in-hospital care and provide both curative and preventive services. Through affiliations, jointly sponsored endeavors, and formal ties, the private hospital fulfills a necessary role in the community health system, sponsored by both public and private resources. Its educational and research programs are extensive and support its primary goal of excellence in patient care. From the establishment of the earliest institutions, the private hospital has remained a basic part of mental-health care in the United States.

([Bibliography

1. *Account of the Rise and Progress of the Asylum*, with an Abridged Account of the Retreat near New York, by S. Tuke. Philadelphia: Kimber & Conrad, 1814.
2. *An Act of Incorporation*, Establishing a Retreat for the Insane at a General Assembly of the State of Connecticut, 1822.
3. AMERICAN JOURNAL OF INSANITY. "Medical Treatment of Insanity," 3 (1846), 353–358.
4. ———. "Institutions for the Insane in the United States," 5 (1848), 53.
5. ———. "Editorial Correspondence," 5 (1848), 66.
6. ———. "The Progress and Promise of Psychiatry in America," 54 (1898), 638–641.
7. AMERICAN PSYCHIATRIC ASSOCIATION. *Standard for Psychiatric Facilities Serving Children and Adolescents*. Washington: American Psychiatric Association, 1971.
8. BINGER, C. *Revolutionary Doctor, Benjamin Rush*, p. 2. New York: Norton, 1966.
9. BOND, E. D. *Dr. Kirkbride and His Mental Hospital*. Philadelphia: Lippincott, 1947.
10. BRACELAND, F. J. *The Institute of Living,*

1822–1972, p. 8. Hartford: Institute of Living, 1972.

11. ———. "The Hartford Retreat," in F. Braceland, *The Institute of Living, 1822–1972*, pp. 25–26. Hartford: Institute of Living, 1972.

12. BRIGHAM, A. "The Moral Treatment of Insanity," *Am. J. Insanity*, 4 (1847), 1–13.

13. BUNKER, H. A. "American Psychiatric Literature during the Past 100 Years," in Am. Psychiatr. Assoc., *100 Years of American Psychiatry*, p. 199. New York: Columbia University Press, 1944.

14. CONOLLY, J. (1847) *The Construction and Government of Lunatic Asylums*. London: Dawsons, 1916.

15. COOK, G. "Mental Hygiene," *Am. J. Insanity*, 15 (1859), 272–282, 353–365.

16. COWLES, E. "Memoirs of Dr. Amariah Brigham," *Am. J. Insanity*, 14 (1858), 1–29.

17. ———. "Notes and Comments," *Am. J. Insanity*, 51(1895), 108–110.

18. DEUTSCH, A. *The Mentally Ill in America*, p. 29. New York: Columbia University Press, 1949.

19. ———. *The Mentally Ill in America*, pp. 104–105. New York: Columbia University Press, 1949.

20. EARLE, P. *The Curability of Insanity; a Series of Studies*. Philadelphia: Lippincott, 1887.

21. EDDY, T. *Hints for Introducing an Improved Method of Treating the Insane in the Asylum*. New York: Samuel Wood, 1815.

22. FORBUSH, B. *The Sheppard and Enoch Pratt Hospital*, p. 66. Philadelphia: Lippincott, 1971.

23. FREUD, S. (1911) "Psycho-Analytical Notes of an Autobiographical Account of a Case of Paranoia (Dementia Paranoides)," in J. Strachey, ed., *Standard Edition*, Vol. 3, pp. 1–82. London: Hogarth, 1955.

24. ———. (1896) "Further Remarks on the Neuro-Psychosis of Defense," in J. Strachey, ed., *Standard Edition*, Vol. 3, p. 174. London: Hogarth, 1955.

25. ———. (1914) "On Narcissism," in J. Strachey, ed., *Standard Edition*, Vol. 14, pp. 73–102. London: Hogarth, 1957.

26. GARDNER, G. E. "William Healy, 1869–1963," *J. Am. Acad. Child Psychiatry*, 3 (1972), 1–29.

27. HUNTER, R. and I. MACALPINE. *Three Hundred Years of Psychiatry*, p. 423. New York: Oxford University Press, 1963.

28. HURD, H. M. *The Institutional Care of the Insane in the United States and Canada*, Vol. 1, pp. 84, 140. Baltimore: Johns Hopkins, 1916.

29. ———. *The Institutional Care of the Insane in the United States and Canada*, Vol. 2, pp. 510–513. Baltimore: Johns Hopkins, 1916.

30. ———. *The Institutional Care of the Insane in the United States and Canada*, Vol. 3, pp. 134–136. Baltimore: Johns Hopkins, 1916.

31. ———. *The Institutional Care of the Insane in the United States and Canada*, Vol. 3, pp. 622–625. Baltimore: Johns Hopkins, 1916.

32. KIRKBRIDE, T. S. *On the Construction, Organization and General Arrangements for Hospitals for the Insane*, 2nd ed. Philadelphia, Lippincott, 1880.

33. MASSACHUSETTS GENERAL HOSPITAL. *Addresses to the Public*. Boston: Belcher, 1814; Tileston and Weld, 1816, 1822.

34. NEW YORK HOSPITAL. *Governors Address to the Public*. New York, 1821.

35. NEW YORK LUNATIC ASYLUM. *Report of the Physician of the New York Lunatic Asylum*. New York: Samuel Wood, 1818.

36. OVERHOLSER, W. "The Founding and Founders of the Association," in Am. Psychiatr. Assoc., *100 Years of American Psychiatry*, pp. 45–72. New York: Columbia University Press, 1944.

37. PAO, PING-NEI. "Notes on Freud's Theory of Schizophrenia," *Int. J. Psychoanal.*, 54 (1973), 469–476.

38. PINEL, P. *Traité Médico-philosophique sur l'aliénation mentale ou la manie*. Paris: Richard Panes, 1801.

39. RANNEY, M. H. "The Medical Treatment of Insanity," *Am. J. Insanity*, 14 (1862), 64–68.

40. RAY, I. *A Treatise on the Medical Jurisprudence of Insanity*. Boston: Little, Brown, 1838.

41. ———. "The Butler Hospital for the Insane," *Am. J. Insanity*, 14 (1862), 64–68.

42. ———. *Mental Hygiene*. Boston: Tickner and Fields, 1863.

43. RUSH, B. *An Eulogium in Honor of the Late Dr. William Cullen*, p. 9. Philadelphia: Dobson, 1790.

44. ———. *Medical Inquiries and Observations upon the Diseases of the Mind*, p. 26.

Philadelphia: Kimber and Richardson, 1812.

45. SHRYOCK, R. H. "The Beginnings: From Colonial Days to the Foundation of the American Psychiatric Association," in Am. Psychiatr. Assoc., *100 Years of American Psychiatry*, pp. 1–28. New York: Columbia University Press, 1944.

46. STANTON, A. and M. S. SCHWARTZ. *The Mental Hospital*, p. 68. New York: Basic Books, 1954.

47. SULLIVAN, H. S. *Conceptions of Modern Psychiatry*. Washington: White Foundation, 1940.

48. ———. *Schizophrenia as a Human Process*. New York: Norton, 1962.

49. SULLIVAN, R. *Address Delivered before the Governour and the Council at King's Chapel*. Boston: Wells & Lilly, 1819.

50. TUKE, D. H. *The Insane in the United States and Canada*, p. 7. London: Lewis, 1885.

51. TUKE, S. *Description of the Retreat*. London: Dawsons, 1964.

52. WISE, P. M. "Training School for Nurses in Hospitals for the Insane," *Am. J. Insanity*, 54 (1898), 81–91.

53. ZILBOORG, G. *A History of Medical Psychology*, p. 245. New York: Norton, 1941.

CHAPTER 33

RESIDENTIAL TREATMENT OF EMOTIONALLY DISTURBED CHILDREN

Joseph D. Noshpitz

RESIDENTIAL TREATMENT is a form of therapy that involves the total life of a disturbed child in a planful organization that is built upon a defined theory of treatment. It requires the child to live in a special setting, where he is cared for by trained personnel who mold their everyday interactions and relationships with him toward therapeutic ends. Characteristically, within a residential treatment center (RTC), a host of specific therapies are present that are organized around a common strategy of treatment. It is this quality of integrating the details of everyday living with a wide variety of therapies that gives residential treatment its unique character. In particular, this pattern of treatment usually includes the child's family, either as individuals or as a family unit.

On the whole, residential treatment tends to be a long-term rather than short-term approach, and it is typically directed toward children who are not severely retarded or extremely regressed. It is to be distinguished from the services delivered by those special schools, hospital wards, or other settings where education or other forms of treatment are provided but no conception of an intensive, totally structured, and integrated therapeutic life prevails.

◖ Types of Residential Settings

It is evident that the number of variables that have to be meshed to create a residential treatment center is very large. Hence it is not surprising that these settings vary in organization to the extent that almost each center is unique. There are, after all, a great many ways of combining so many treatment details. The number and variability of the patterns that can ensue are enormous, and actual descriptions of individual settings show a predictable lack of uniformity. Moreover, these settings have emerged from many different backgrounds, which in turn has resulted in further degrees of variety and differentiation.

Without trying to be complete, a few characteristic types of settings can be mentioned to illustrate something of the richness of character of the existing patterns. It is obvious that many new permutations and combinations will appear as time goes on.

1. *The school-centered program.* Here the name of the agency often identifies it as a school, and the program is built largely around an academic core. However, classes are often as small as one or two youngsters per teacher, and teachers may act as child-care personnel after the school hours are over. Psychiatric and psychological consultants are usually part of the environment and may be on the staff. The children are considered pupils rather than patients, even though each one is in psychotherapy and/or group therapy and/or drug therapy (all of which are part of the total treatment plan of the setting). Characteristically, there is a central emphasis on the milieu as therapeutic.
2. *The casework program.* Typically, the agency is administered by a social worker who gives direction to a staff of caseworkers or group workers. Psychiatric consultants or resident psychiatrists may be part of the scene, but the children are viewed as clients rather than patients. The actual child care work may be done by live-in house parents, social workers, or trained child care workers who rotate through shifts. Again, however, milieu therapy is central.
3. *The hospital or ward setting.* Here the basic pattern is that of a small mental hospital largely staffed by nurses and nurses' aides. But where the unit functions as an RTC, the nurses usually do not wear uni-

forms and they work much as the child care workers do in other settings. The doctors write orders, but they may play a role not dissimilar to that of the psychiatrist in the casework agency. Often enough a psychologist or social worker is ward administrator, and the actual details of hospital organization are looked upon as irrelevant or as minor irritants that get in the way of delivering the basic service: a wide spectrum of specific therapies integrated into a therapeutically oriented pattern of living. The quality of staff interaction and the emphasis on developing a therapeutic, child-oriented life style give the setting its basic flavor.

◖ Administrative Structure

As is evident from this account of models, no single pattern or even philosophy of administration governs all residential settings. There are a few pervasive concepts that need to be noted, but even these are protean in form and dimension as one passes from center to center.

1. *Team-oriented administration.* The most common style of bringing together a group of therapists around a single case is to structure a team of professionals for each child or each small group of children, and to consider this team as the essential deliverer of treatment services. The team would have to include all the people actively involved in the child's life. Typically this would involve the child-care worker, the parent worker, the individual and/or group therapist, and the teacher. In a hospital-type center three to five disciplines might well be represented at each team meeting, whereas in a casework center social workers and a teacher might form the whole treatment group. In any case, the keynote of their work is collaboration. The exchange of information, opinions, and ideas among the various team members, and the formulation of a common concept of what the child's behavior means and how to cope with it are the essence of the treat-

ment. Whatever service impinges on the child is a function of this kind of mutual interaction. The team leader may be any member or a consultant or someone non-designated who emerges from the group interaction.

2. *Authority-oriented administration.* In such settings a single dominant leader deals with the team members. He meets with each team, tells them what the patient's behavior means, interprets to them the nature of their countertransference, and formulates the treatment plan that they are to follow. He may address the team as a group, or he may work with each member individually, sharing information and explaining what needs to be done in a one-to-one context. In such settings, the discipline of origin becomes particularly unimportant and the psychiatrist may work as child care worker under the direction of the psychologist leader, or both psychologist and psychiatrist may take direction from a social worker.

3. *Therapist-dominated administration.* Here the accent is on the work of the individual therapist. While a unit administrator actually cares for the details of everyday organization, the team takes its direction from the child's therapist. He formulates the picture of the child's needs at the time, and the way in which the team can answer them. He sets the tone for the child-care work and indicates the atmosphere that he thinks should prevail at school. He weighs programmatic details and decides whether or not a visit is indicated, a restriction is called for, or a special conference needs to be held. However, he works closely with the other team members and considers it his responsibility to see that they understand the patient's dynamics.

❲ History of Residential Treatment for Children

A number of different agencies that sought to meet the needs of different groups of children have gradually converged on the patient population they selected, and they have developed parallel means of coming to grips with the problems the youngsters presented. One major source of such centers was the old-style orphanages of the nineteenth century. These settings gradually woke up to the fact that they were handling fewer orphans and more and more children who were dependent, neglected, and disturbed. They began to call in consultants and hire specialized staff people and, finally, to change their charter altogether. Many of today's residential treatment centers began in this way.

A second source of such agencies was the hospital units created for brain-injured children. With the accumulation of experience and the passage of time, such units began to devote themselves to youngsters with primary emotional difficulties.

A third source of residential care came from schools for retarded youngsters. Many such schools continue to exist today; but here and there, what had started out as a special or remedial educational institution altered its character and began to focus on the troubled child who was not retarded. Curiously, there has been a tendency in recent years for centers that had previously excluded children with low IQ's to begin to accept and to treat them in greater numbers than ever before (when appropriate emotional disturbances were present).

A fourth channel for the creation of residential treatment flowed from settings for delinquents. The old-time reform school with its tradition of strict discipline and total obedience has in at least a few instances given way to a more therapeutically oriented, group-life program in which regular casework and consultations attempt to integrate milieu principles and psychotherapy into a treatment pattern. Such "conversions" have been less frequent than the transformations of schools and orphanages, but they have occurred.

In recent years a number of settings have come into being de novo, designed as residential centers from the very beginning. Some of these are being constructed today in connection with community mental health centers, while others have been established as autonomous units or in connection with a variety of other settings.

Inevitably, such a movement as residential treatment has developed its core of shared principles, practices, and methods. At the same time it stands in equilibrium with a series of alternative methods and approaches that share with it some common principles but differ from it in significant ways. One major difference in method has been to challenge the reliance on psychotherapeutic or casework principles as the central core of values in the approach to treatment. In recent years a series of settings have appeared that avoid this element. They instead seek to build their methods around a common-sense, didactic model in which behavior is considered as something to be taught, rather than interpreted, and modeling takes the place of interviewing as a vehicle for change. Some of these settings, taking their cue from the French *educateur* experience, are called "RE-ED." (The educateur is the basic staff person in the French welfare and delinquency settings.) Others, working along similar lines, have been part of the American scene for a long time as homes for homeless children (e.g. Boys' Town) in which an atmosphere of repair and rehabilitation prevails, based on common sense or on religious principles. The essence of such experiences as RE-ED and others is that they offer the child a break in the continuity with the home environment, an alternative encounter with a "healthy-minded" staff, a great deal of focused attention on behavior that disturbs the environment, and a relatively rapid return (after three or four months) to the home setting. The major differences between such approaches and residential treatment are the former's strong de-emphasis on therapy, the lack of an integrated therapeutic milieu, the reliance on identification, modeling, and behavioral instruction as the primary agents for change, and the brevity of the experience. In a sense, these approaches are both less intensive and less extensive.

In contrast, there are a number of treatment styles now emerging in which the intensity is as great as and possibly even greater than the residential approach, but in which the extent of treatment is less. This is seen in many of the day-hospital settings that are now appearing. The essence of these programs is to provide an active therapy approach, which may include therapeutic school, occupational therapy, an individual therapy hour, a group therapy session, and a family therapy encounter all in the same day. The youngster spends a good part of his weekday in an intensive, integrated, therapeutic milieu five days a week. He goes home each afternoon and stays there all night to return to the program the next morning, then stays home for the weekend and re-enters treatment on Monday morning. Or the full residential program may continue on a live-in basis five days a week, with the child going home each weekend.

Thus many variations of the basic pattern have been established by now, and more are being experimented with. Some settings have abandoned individual therapy and instead focus exclusively on group tactics and methods for regulating the daily life in the setting and exploring each individual's personal history and character. Such an approach is often seen in the group homes and halfway houses that so often help youngsters to make the transition from penal or therapeutic placements to total responsibility for their own care and therapy in the open life of the community. This kind of group-oriented living takes on some of the character of the therapeutic community, in which the essence of the approach is to have regular and frequent group involvement in issues of care and in decision making.

(Intake of Children

Selection

The traditional age group referred to RTC's has been the latency-puberty group, roughly from the ages of six to fourteen. Many settings have limited the upper intake age to twelve or thirteen and then kept the youngsters to fourteen or fifteen. Others have preferred to deal with smaller children who are physically easier to handle and do not present the complications of puberty.

Every setting expects children to be action-prone to some extent and has to think and plan in terms of how to manage acting-out. As a result, relatively few centers attempt to care for older adolescents, with whom such problems can become grave and, not infrequently, overwhelming. However, there are a fair number of RTC's that concentrate on the middle adolescent group, with an upper age limit of sixteen or seventeen. Curiously enough, a movement has begun toward extending the age of residence downward and accepting preschoolers for such care. This is parallel to and perhaps in equilibrium with the concepts of day care emerging in the United States. In any case, there are now some voices speaking for the acceptance of younger children.

Many RTC's accept only boys. There are two reasons for this. (1) There are perhaps three to five times as many boys referred for such care as there are girls. This is true of the pattern of referral of children for psychiatric treatment in general: boys form the largest porportion of the applicants for service to outpatient clinics, to private practitioners and indeed to all mental health facilities. In this respect it is also important to remember that most RTCs are small; their census runs in the tens, not in the hundreds. In the face of the scarcity of female referrals, the needs for appropriate facilities, different staff, and a whole additional set of concerns pose a very considerable burden. (2) Many professionals have observed that the girls who are referred for care are typically much sicker than the boys who tend to apply. Since an important criterion for program planning is the level of pathology that a particular setting accepts, this has automatically ruled out many girls from such possible placements. On the other hand, quite a few centers, especially the large ones, keep an active girls' unit as part of their range of treatment facilities and welcome the opportunity to work with this group. This is perhaps more likely to be the case where puberty-age and adolescent youngsters are accepted, because at this age the level of referral of females picks up sharply.

Reasons for Referral

The reasons for referral to such treatment are manifold. The placement of a child in residence involves his total removal from home and is at best a major disruption of his life. It may be a major relief in certain situations, but by and large one must view it as a traumatic event and initiate such a pattern only in the face of clear-cut need. Optimally, no youngster would be accepted who has not had a previous attempt at outpatient treatment or day care.

In any given case, the character of the need for placement requires careful weighing. Generally speaking, referral is indicated when the youngster's horizons for successful adaptation have shrunk to a very narrow band or have disappeared altogether. Thus if withdrawal is the dominant issue, the child would have been too shut in to profit from school or from neighborhood and community activities, and might now be starting to remove himself even from family life. Attempts at therapy have been fruitless. Now residential treatment is the next appropriate recourse. Again, when issues of depression or of phobic or obsessional symptomatology are in the forefront, the degree of incapacity should be considerable before resorting to such care. Indeed, where neurotic configurations predominate, the indication for alternative forms of treatment is particularly strong. Only when both the emotional crippling and the failure of outpatient therapy are marked should such a referral ensue.

By and large, borderline children with various behavioral and neurotic-like symptoms form the largest group in residence. Their failures in adaptation are of sufficient severity to keep them in a turbulent and troubled state of interaction with their human environment. Their need for relationships (and for coping with the aching void of separation emptiness that is so characteristic of their syndrome) makes them appealing, needy people who, often enough, turn out to be good treatment cases. It is true that frankly psychotic children are often taken in as well. Nonetheless, more overtly bizarre and uncommunicative children are frequently not accepted or are referred to a few hospital or hospital-like settings that have a larger tolerance for such regressive symptoms. Fortunately, however, there are a relatively few highly specialized RTC's that accept primarily autistic or severely psychotic children.

One major grouping of children often referred for treatment in residence is the one gathered under the term "behavior disorders." This rather diverse diagnostic category includes a wide variety of dynamic conditions. They range all the way from true sociopathy, in which the child will act out his impulses quite naturally, without anxiety, and with no sense of personal discomfort unless he gets caught, to the criminal-from-a-sense-of-guilt type of masked depression, in which the youngster tries to provoke the environment into punishing him in order to avoid the far more horrid threats of his cruel and implacable superego. Many children are referred to residential care because of bad behavior. It takes careful diagnostic screening to sort out those who need interpretive and ego-supportive therapy from those who need limits, education, structure, and patterning. Not all residences can do all kinds of treatment, and it takes a very special orientation to cope with the severely psychotic or the inflexibily antisocial character disorder.

There are also instances in which it is best *not* to refer a youngster for residential treatment. One, obviously, is when he needs a different kind of care but no other type of service is convenient. To place in residence a child who could be treated at home is simply bad medical practice. It is like a surgeon operating when conservative medical treatment is indicated—it may indeed be a way to obtain relief, but it still isn't right. Another instance is when the youngster's difficulties created by separation from his family would be more catastrophic than continuing to live with the symptoms. This type of situation ensues where a youngster has had a number of serious losses and is clinging to his current relationships in a way that is as desperate as it is destructive. When admission is contemplated at all in such

a case, the optimum approach is to enter into a prolonged process of trying to work the child into the setting gradually. Thus, he might visit the setting once a week or even once a month for several months, and then spend a night or a weekend, bit by bit overcoming the separation panic as he begins to use the residential facilities. Indeed, as we shall presently see, placement in general is best done as part of a process of engagement, with a period of anticipatory planning and (where possible) a more or less gradual working through of the actual admission.

❰ Steps in the Intake Process

When we talk of picking children out of one setting and moving them to another, we always need to keep before us the reality of the stress such moves pose for the immature ego. This is true even when an intact family moves as a unit to a new neighborhood or a new city. Many a child suffers no small sense of wrenching loss and real depression under such circumstances, despite the support of his parents and siblings. The practice of sending children off to camp for the summer also has its quota of failures and of unfortunate adjustments, even though the accent is on fun and pleasure and even though it is self-limited and only for a few weeks or a couple of months. This is not to say that most children cannot handle such stress and come out of it better than they went in. They can and do. But the important point is that it *is* a stress. It takes a good deal of coping and mastery, and the hurt child may find this especially hard to manage.

The Preliminary Study

When we swing away from these everyday situations and face our current concern, the matter of taking a child out of his home and putting him into residential care, we have to weigh a number of additional elements. The child has already been in big trouble. He typically feels himself—and often enough is—the family reject, the troublemaker, the scapegoat. His leaving home has about it something of the feeling of failure become catastrophe: he wonders if he is really being sent away as punishment; he wonders if he will ever be accepted back. His parents tend to feel a mixture of guilt, relief, and shame as they simultaneously admit defeat, seek succor, and rid themselves of what has become an intolerable burden. Clearly, such a congeries of disturbing feelings needs the most careful and sensitive sorting out for diagnostic understanding, and a planful and supportive approach in order to try to make the intake experience as therapeutic as possible. Typically, residences require at least a visit or two by the child and family to allow for study and, in turn, to allow the prospective client his chance to spend time in the setting and to get a feeling for its atmosphere and its ways. All of this is of primary importance in making the transfer from home to residence. When there are many reservations about entering treatment, every effort should be made to extend the period of evaluation and preparation for admission. Even if it takes a year to move a child into residence, the ensuing year will be infinitely more therapeutic than if the youngster is forced despite his terrified opposition and thus started off in a totally negative way.

The nature of the preliminary study is similar to that of the conventional pattern for mental health diagnosis, with special extentions along some additional dimensions. The child is usually seen in a playroom interview, psychological tests are administered, the parents are seen in one or more sessions, not uncommonly the whole family (including the candidate for admission) is seen as a unit, a physical exam (sometimes with a routine neurological evaluation) is carried out, and previous school and therapy records are reviewed. The special work done for residence study involves having the child attend school for a day, putting him in (perhaps for an afternoon) with the living group he would be joining, showing him where he would sleep, and, if possible, having him and perhaps his family eat with the children in residence at one or more of the regular daily meals.

The observations gleaned by the staff during this series of interactions are made part of the record and of the ensuing intake conference. This conference is the site where all the clinical material and the current observations are reviewed and a decision is reached. The issues to be considered include whether or not the child should be admitted; if he should be, how the process should be carried out; once carried out, what kind of program he would need in the residence; while he is in, what sort of support and communication structure his family would require; and once inhouse treatment is at an end, where he would go. It is only when such a clinical review has been accomplished that one can say that admission is indicated. No residence does itself or its patient a favor by accepting someone it cannot treat effectively.

In actual practice it might take several years and a host of trying experiences before a given center becomes sure and clear of its therapeutic identity, before it knows what it can do and cannot do and admits patients accordingly. Typically, when a new agency of this sort opens its doors, it initially tends to receive a spate of referrals of children who have gone from agency to agency and setting to setting in that community, always failing and ever and again being transferred, discharged, or simply dropped. Often enough, if a number of patients of a certain kind—for example, suicidal children, youngsters with severe sexual acting-out, runaways, or whatever—are accepted at the outset, the agency becomes known as the proper site for that kind of referral, and that's what it will tend to get for some time. Hence it behooves the staff to be especially circumspect at the outset in order to avoid accepting cases they cannot help and to prevent themselves from being "type-cast."

The Matter of "Fit"

The evaluation of patients for admission to residence is an art form of considerable sophistication. The criteria of admission are both general and specific. They are general in the sense of a given age range, a given sex, a given IQ, a given set of inclusive or exclusive diagnostic categories, and the like. They are specific in the sense of "We will only accept patients whom we feel we can help" or "We will only accept patients who have an adequate family group to work with who will accept responsibility at the time of discharge," or "We evaluate new patients in terms of how they would fit into our existing treatment groups." In effect, this means that from the array of possible candidates who meet the general criteria, a given child might be accepted or rejected at a certain moment because the setting is adjudged to "need" a more withdrawn case to balance an overabundance of acting-out children. A youngster with more behavioral problems might be indicated because there are too many quiet schizophrenics in residence. A girl might be preferred rather than a boy because there are too few girls. Or the setting might be trying to achieve a certain racial balance, and so on. Since the matter of group composition is a vital factor in the success or failure of a treatment venture, these specific determinants are fully as important as the more general characteristics; indeed, they may be more important.

What concerns the intake staff members is the general matter of "fit." They seek to determine if they have the proper therapeutic "mix." (The repeated resort to quotation marks around these words indicates the intensely subjective character of some of the decisions that have to be made.) One sizes up a group, one sizes up a treatment staff, one sizes up a child; and the question becomes—given the existing group, the available staff team, and the particular make-up of the new applicant—what are the chances of the child doing all right if they are all put together? What will the new group be like, and how will the current staff group interact with this changed group composition as well as with the new child? There are obviously a great many unknowns in all this, and the fundamental importance of highly trained, highly experienced, clinical know-how can scarcely be overestimated.

Planning for Disposition

The matter of disposition is a critical factor for treatment; it is standard practice to begin planning for discharge at the time of intake. This usually implies a careful evaluation of the family and the preparation of the family for the eventual discharge of their child. Obviously not all children return home, so this possibility sometimes needs to be considered from a very early moment in the management of the case as well. Many centers will not accept a child whose home is just breaking up or a child who is being separated from the last of a series of unsuccessful foster placements. The child is refused because the staff insists on having a secure home base for the youngster outside the setting. They view this as part of the treatment. They look ahead to Christmas and Easter and summer holidays, when so many children can at least visit home, and they know that sooner or later placement plans will have to be faced. This can be a major stress for an agency—to have a child who is ready to move on, but for whom there is no setting available to move on to. Thus, as a condition of intake, disposition patterns must also be clear.

Many would-be treatment centers are supported by the state or county and are required to take all admissions as long as they have beds. Thus, the Juvenile Court judge or the Department of Welfare or the mayor has the authority to require that a child be admitted. This requirement is enough to differentiate between a treatment setting and a would-be treatment agency—in the parlance of the residential treatment professionals, ". . . if you cannot control intake, you're dead." And indeed they speak from long-range and intensive experience: the composition of a treatment group and the proper fit of each new patient represent the difference between a true therapeutic situation and a holding, warehousing, or survival effort. If the setting is to be a valid treatment environment, the treatment team, and only the treatment team, must control intake.

⟦ Methods of Treatment

The essence of residential treatment is the reality of the setting itself. If properly put together, it is a dynamic organization of many elements to express a central theme. The theme is likely to vary from agency to agency, but it will be implicit in everything: the choice of wallpaper or paint colors, the layout of the day hall, the choice of rugs and furniture, the quality and timbre of voices in which people speak, the way staff dress and walk, the posture and facial expressions of the secretary and the director and the social worker and everybody else, the kinds of play equipment available, the average level of order and cleanliness in the setting, the degree to which groundskeepers and kitchen help and laundry personnel and all the rest know and feel themselves to be part of a treatment project, and on and on. Such details give a setting its character and atmosphere. Not only are they the context in which treatment takes place, they are in themselves primary elements of the therapeutic process; they are part of and state the theme. The theme may be a very simple one: "Here you can relax and be yourself and we will take care of you." Or it can be: "Our people won't let you get hurt, they won't let you get away with things, but they will help you understand yourself." Or perhaps: "Here we take kids who've been in lots of trouble and we have to hold onto them pretty tightly. But we also care about them and we always find a way to help."

Sometimes a particular therapeutic style can dominate the atmosphere. Thus, some residences build their treatment program around work with families. They see the role of the residence primarily as one of protecting child from family and family from child while it brings both of these warring parties together in varying contexts and at regular intervals, in an attempt to detoxify and restructure the internal life of that family group. Another therapeutic setting may regard the individual psychotherapy as central and the residential life as a sort of sanitary environment that holds the troubled child and meets his needs more adequately than the family could, in order to allow the therapist to do his work. Or a group orientation can prevail in which the emphasis falls on various patterns of group interaction —day hall meetings, cottage meetings, school assemblies, classroom groups, therapy groups, whole unit meetings, whole families as units, and groups of families as therapy units—all of them concerning themselves both with the issues of everyday living and with the details of individual psychopathology. Still another style of structure emphasizes the behavior model approach. Such behavior techniques are finding an ever-increasing role within residential treatment, and there are some settings in which the basic strategy of engagement involves schedules of reward and of patterning behavior.

Each such "method"-dominated environment will of course emphasize its particular technique as its central theme, and the organization of the life it creates will speak for this theme. But in the long run, most settings are far more eclectic and their themes are far more complex. They utilize all these treatment modalities and more; indeed, many take pride in the richness of their treatment resources and the number of possibilities they can invoke for any given case. Their theme then becomes one of living in an open, communicative, and engaged way as the essential stepping stone toward health, while finding the specific treatment equation needed by the particular child within the total context of the residential life.

Much of what these settings are is a reflection of the character and the values of the director. Residential treatment is not run according to democratic principles, or even very much by consensus. The director sets the tone as well as the limits of what the setting will do, and his interactions with his staff will provide the model for much that will presently be transmitted to the children.

The Milieu as Treatment

In keeping with the notion that the overall setting is a basic treatment modality, a great deal of careful thought has gone into what Redl called "the ingredients of the milieu."[12] What has emerged is a major emphasis on programming and an even greater commitment to the tailoring of the interpersonal life of staff and patients toward the goals of treatment.

PROGRAMMING

The use of programming is one of the most neglected therapeutic skills.[8] It deals with the structuring of time and the prescribing of activity for the individual's life and for the group's life, and it depends on an accurate reading of individual and group dynamics in terms of needs and potentialities.

Time is framed for patients in a variety of ways. There are the time relations of holidays and special events. There is the rhythm of visits, both from parents and to them. There is the structure of a given week, with its weekday work-school quality and its weekend relaxation-recreation atmosphere. There is the time frame of the individual day, with its many possibilities of alternating educational and large muscle sports, and fine-muscle focused crafts, social interactive, solo contemplative, adult-oriented, and peer-group-structured moments. There are the choices of therapies: individual, group, family, behavioral, occupational, remedial, speech, music, art, recreational, work, and so forth. And there are the contrapuntal cadences of sublimatory play-expressive experience; the hike; the party; the game; the museum tour; the boat trip; the spectator-sport or participant-sport event; the police-station or fire-house or garbage-disposal-plant visit; the magician, the clown, the TV star, or the disc jockey, come to the unit to perform . . . One could go on at great length detailing the myriad experiences that creative and imaginative programmers build into children's lives as part of the flow of therapeutic matrix elements that is milieu therapy. For the residential therapist, time is a supple, plastic stuff that he molds and shapes into the countless irregular forms that fit within the administrative limits, the logistical and financial possibilities, and the peculiar temperament of each patient–staff group, and the individual needs of particular persons within the group. Good programming can serve as a powerful instrument for healing a sick child. Nothing is more expressive of the essence of residential treatment than the program that the environment develops.

INTERACTIONS

Along with time, the second great therapeutic instrument in this work is the "other person." Children are already enormously vulnerable and needy and reactive to adults, and sick children are reactive to a degree that far transcends conventional social experience. Their every interaction holds within it the potential for remediation or for trauma. It was the recognition of the power of human interaction—even of the most banal variety, around the most pedestrian subjects, during the most humdrum and everyday exchanges, at the most inconspicuous and workaday level —in other words, the recognition of the extraordinary force of the ordinary in children's lives that led residential therapists to the formulation of these basic principles. In brief: in the ideal RTC, every human interaction between staff and patients would be a therapeutic one. To the extent that the work with the children approaches this ideal, the therapy will be optimal.[4,5,11,12]

In practical terms, this means that each person in such an environment knows something about the needs of the child and what it will take to meet those needs. There is a careful formulation of the meaning of the youngster's behavior. What is he warding off? Where does he feel weak or afraid? How does he act to protect himself? Why does he attack a given person, at a certain time, and in a certain way? And there is an equally thoughtful attempt to decide what is the best response to make to each of these aspects of the child's behavior. Here is a shut-in child who is beginning to be aggressive. Does one make a joke about it, or does one set limits, or does one congratulate him, or does one ignore the behavior? Is there an interpretation that should be made? This thinking-through of the everyday behavior in the child's living space constitutes much of the work of such treatment. To the extent that adequate responses are found, the work will have a good outcome.

In this connection, a special kind of interviewing skill has developed. Its originator, Fritz Redl, called it "life space interviewing." In brief, it seeks to utilize the moments of stress in everyday living as primary sites for therapeutic interaction. If a child gets an upsetting letter, or hits another child and runs and hides, or is the victim of such an attack, or gets upset for any reason, or acts in some inappropriate way, the event becomes (within this particular framework) a signal for an interview. The interview will be conducted by whatever staff person happens to be present and part of the experience. It takes place there and then, at the site of the happening (or reasonably close by); and as close in time as possible. Sometimes, with a very upset child, two people have to share the interview while they contain him. Indeed, the interview might take the form of dialogue between these people about what the child is going through as he struggles or cries or hides; they talk to each other about what it all might mean.

These interviews are therapeutic, but they are not psychotherapy.[12] Often enough they will seek to define certain behavior or feelings as problems that should be taken to the therapist or brought up in the group. Or they may strive to strengthen the child's ego, to bring the youngster back to reality, to restore a sense of structure and limits, to provide a bridge of acceptable and accepting human interaction and human warmth and interest, to divert the child from obsessive brooding and self-recriminations, to put salve on the teased youngster's deep narcissistic wound by finding something to praise, to dispel a sense of loneliness and emptiness that may have suddenly become overwhelming, and so on, for the many necessary bits of healing experience that will presently form the mosaic of treatment. Or they may try to set bounds on impulses, to limit the scope of action patterns, to draw the fangs of revenge fantasies, to define structure, and to speak to the realities of order and the limits of social tolerance.

Generally speaking, "life space" interviews

try to convert everyday issues into therapeutic experience and to provide a form of skilled crisis intervention that makes each point of stress in the child's life a site for potential mastery and progress. Like other crisis interactions, they are not easy to conduct. It takes a great deal of training and group interaction to develop the consensual values and the appropriate level of skill that will allow a staff to use this instrument effectively.

Such interactions are not limited to one child. There are many moments in residential work when group "life space" interviews are necessary, when one or more staff members sit down with youngsters involved in a particular escapade or mass reaction of some sort and deal with the issue of how the group functioned. Indeed, in settings with a primary or a major group focus, much individual problematic behavior is seen as a group responsibility, and the group is restricted or deprived when the individual child acts out. With such an approach, powerful group pressures can be brought to bear on each child in the service of maintaining the integrity of unit life.

In many instances, a given child needs certain freedoms or limits or other programmatic structures that are unique for him. He may have a talent that should be specially developed or an interest that can be exploited to further his education and/or his treatment, or else some programmatic variation is possible that will make him feel specially cared for at some moment of unusual need. Such variation is essential. It is a vital dimension of treatment, and it requires the staff to be able to say to each patient something to the effect of: "Johnny gets something exceptional when he needs it, and when you need it we will do something very special for you, too." There is, however, an endless balancing act that is necessary between the needs of the group and the needs of the individual. The important thing is to preserve enough degrees of freedom to allow a unit to function in either realm.

Psychotherapy

Various residential settings have included all kinds of therapies, from psychoanalysis (or intensive psychoanalytically-oriented psychotherapy) through the whole range of individual interview therapies.[7,13] At the other extreme of the spectrum is the group of behavioral therapies—the system of approaches that arise from theories of conditioning, both operant and classical. Behavioral therapies are currently being tried, sometimes in an experimental way and sometimes as the established treatment of choice. Since, in fact, residential treatment tends to be eclectic in its values and methods, behavioral therapies will in fact find an appropriate place in time among the roster of available methods. The implications of suppressing specific behaviors are not yet thoroughly understood, but the value of doing so in certain instances is self-evident. However, the problem for the residence, again and again, is how to use the relationship with the therapist—that is, how to integrate the therapist's understanding of the child into the total program. Hence, it is impossible to discuss the role of psychotherapy (be it group, individual, or family) without commenting on the problem of collaboration.

Psychotherapy in residential treatment is inherently less confidential than it is in outpatient situations. Since the whole staff and the entire milieu structure strive to be therapeutic, one cannot so easily draw a distinction between the therapist and the nontherapists in the situation. Treatment is everybody's business, and it is a two-way street. Sometimes the patient will select as the object for his confidences someone who is a member of the kitchen staff or who serves as unit handyman. Indeed, the youngster may tell very little of what he thinks to the actual designated therapist. Therefore, to conduct the individual work in a serious way, the therapist needs constant input from whoever is receiving the child's communications. To keep that person, (and indeed the whole team around the child) functioning well, the therapist must constantly feed back to his teammates a sense of what is going on in the youngster's mind, what his behavior means or might mean, what he is hiding and revealing, and what he needs and what he seeks to avoid. The other team

members, in turn, each have their areas of expertise and special access to the patient, and each will have a contribution to make. Indeed, often enough, the key to what a complicated behavioral pattern or difficult attitudinal set is all about may come from the teacher's observations in school or what the caseworker learned on a home visit.[14] In any case, it takes an active and mutually respecting exchange to make the therapist's input useful and functional within the residential life.

All residential work is directed toward groups of patients, although many settings do not include formal group therapy sessions. However, there is always some sort of ward meeting or cottage meeting or unit assembly that brings together child-care workers and patients for a review of the current status of unit life. These meetings may occur every day or several times a week. Sometimes the focus is on the notes of the day before, sometimes on the program for the day or for the week to come, sometimes on issues of problem behavior as they have been coming up and on what is to be done about them, and sometimes on projects that everyone is involved in (Christmas decorating, an Easter pageant, a unit toy-making project for poor kids, and so forth).

Certain settings seek to minimize group interaction among patients by binding the youngster so tightly to the staff members on his therapeutic team that these persons become far more important to him than his peers. Other centers take the opposite tack and carefully structure milieu groups that are addressed as such and that become vital elements in the management of behavioral difficulties. Thus, in the extreme case, all responsibility for acting-up is viewed as a group responsibility, and the group is restricted if one youngster acts out. As a result, the grouping tendency is brought into the service of the therapeutic enterprise and becomes an important factor in the creation of the treatment milieu. Indeed, one way of conceptualizing residential treatment is to view it as the long-range interaction of a staff group and a patient group within a common life space.

⟨ Administration

There are three facets to the actual running of residential treatment that need special emphasis. These are: role clarity, collaboration, and accountability.

Role Clarity

Role clarity means that everyone in the setting has a pretty good idea of what his job is and how it fits into the overall mission of the setting. Role clarity begins with a written job description, but it scarcely ends there. The role of chief child-care worker may be written down ever so precisely, but it still says very little about the fact that the particular incumbent sees himself as the primary therapist and may feel that he and his child-care group should keep certain aspects of unit life secret and not tell the psychiatrists or caseworkers about them. Thus there are official roles and then a universe of emergent, unrecorded, but functionally crucial conceptions about what people do that crystallize out of the interactions of ongoing therapeutic life. Authority may be formally assigned one way, but power may lie very much elsewhere. The matter of role is thus not an assigned and stable function alone; it is a dynamic entity that ebbs and flows and that must forever be worked at.

Nonetheless it is important to have clear initial formulations, so that there are no built-in structural impediments that would tend to make role clarity impossible. For example, questions of who can formally impose a restriction on a child and who cannot, who can conduct a group meeting and who cannot, who has access to petty cash for incidental purchases and who does not, whose responsibility it is to see that patients get to needed services or to recreational activities and who is not responsible for this, and so on—such questions often become sticking points and need definition.

Collaboration

But it is also clear that no amount of effort can or indeed should define everything, and we thus arrive at the next major administrative element: collaboration.[2,11,14] This is the heart of residential work. It is the process by which people from different backgrounds, bearing different responsibilities, and working out of different orientations get together and interact cooperatively to accomplish a common mission—to help the children. It sounds complicated, and it is; but it is also indispensable. It is important enough to require respect as a modality all of its own. Residential settings have to plan precious staff time on a regular basis for team collaboration. They must set aside and protect the occasions when the parent worker, the child care worker, the individual and/or group therapist, and the teacher all get together to do the critical task of communicating, exchanging, sharing, and planning for their patient and/or group. Their work is to pool their observations in order to arrive at a better understanding of the child, and to regulate their activities and build further programs on the basis of this shared insight. It can safely be predicted that there will be times when collaborators will disagree or will resent and criticize one another, to the point that collaboration breaks down and people stop working together. This in turn becomes a treatment crisis. It means that a consultant or a referee of some sort must sit down with this team and work with them, not on the problems of the child but on the issues in their collaboration. For unless these are resolved or at least partially detoxified, there will be a series of mixed messages and double binds that get through to the child and the family, and treatment will fail. It is at the point of collaboration that the integrative, interactive process that is residential treatment finds its purest expression. The facilitation or the inhibition of treatment that follows is a specific function of how well this process is handled. It is here, in fact, that the covert roles referred to above find their fullest realization, and the informal power structure of the entire setting will appear here in specially pure form.

Accountability

The third administrative element that is becoming ever more important is the matter of accountability. This usually takes the form of requiring that a treatment plan with specific goals be formulated for each patient. Then a series of regular reviews can be undertaken to see whether these goals have been achieved or are being achieved, and if not, to ask why not.

This seems like a simple and common-sense course of action, but in fact it is a hotly debated and highly uncertain procedure. For many professionals the nature of clinical work is to be open-ended and to deal with what the patient brings up, rather than what we wish him to bring up. A given youngster may be shy, withdrawn, and encopretic. The goals may take the form of making him more outgoing and getting him to stop soiling. In fact, however, as the work with the child gets under way, he may develop new symptoms that weren't visible before. For example, he may start to play with fire and matches, he may develop some patterns of aggressive behavior toward staff or peers, or homosexual activity may come into view that wasn't previously described. In short, a whole new set of concerns may arise, so that goals may need to be reset. Meanwhile the child might continue the encopresis, refusing either to discuss or to change this. At this point he may look like he's gotten worse rather than better, but in fact the staff is simply getting to know him better and obtaining a fuller view of his problem. In one case the encopresis may be the first thing to clear up; in another it may be the last, and it may persist long after other symptomatic behavior has disappeared. In any case, one has to work with what is now workable.

With so uncertain, shifting, and changing an object for professional attention, the formulation of concrete goals and the assessment of where one is are by no means straightforward matters. Even to measure whether or not a child is more withdrawn or less withdrawn can be a subjective and variable issue with many degrees of imprecision. The tendency to avoid long-term or over-all goals and to concentrate on the immediate issues of defense and relationship, to let the work come as it must, and to take it step by step as it unfolds, is by no means an evasive or unfortunate attitude on the part of many settings. It has its profound justification within the nature of the clinical situation, just as the notion of clearly defined goals and measures finds its rationale in the everyday commonsense world of making and doing. One must make choices, and either choice is fraught with dangers. To impose goals can distort the nature of clinical work and make the therapist work for the goal rather than for the patient's needs of the moment, while to fail to set goals allows for loose, amorphous, unselfcritical work whose value and validity cannot be examined. It seems clear that some compromise needs to emerge. A way will have to be found to formulate the degrees of possibility for particular children and to specify how best to realize these possibilities, and then to look at the situation periodically and see how well one has read the situation and how well the methods used have accomplished what was defined as necessary. At the same time, this formulation will need enough flexibility so that it does not inappropriately constrict or deform the emerging clinical pattern as one works with a child.

It is hard to accept and understand that much work with very sick children takes a long time, that a fair number of such youngsters may need to be in some kind of treatment all of their lives, and that a few of them will even need to be in institutions all of their lives.[3,5,13] Where one deals with such problems, goal-setting and evaluation have a different quality than they do with less severe forms of pathology. There is a considerable difference between altering a life style and removing a symptom.

(Parent Work

The usual parent worker is a psychiatric social worker. One of the commonplaces of residential treatment is that patients are sent to such settings in part because they can't tolerate home or in turn be endured there. Once in the center, however, the connection with home often becomes a critical reality that might form the focus of treatment for many months. The parents, for their part, often need more intensive clinical work around the fact of the placement than they would if the child lived at home and were treated as an outpatient. The phenomenon of having a child institutionalized is a radical confrontation for any family. It has profound repercussions in the areas of parental guilt ("It's me who is to blame and my child is paying the price"), narcissism ("I've failed as a parent, but so miserably!"), jealousy ("How can these strangers think they are as important to my child as I am"), rage ("Look at the kind of people my suffering sick child is being subjected to"), and shame ("All the world knows now that my child had to be put away"). As a result, dealing with the parents of these youngsters requires immense amounts of time, skill, and support. In many settings, the question of the "workability" of the parents is one of the critical factors in deciding for or against admission; in others, regular parental attendance at casework or treatment sessions is a requirement for accepting a child.[11] Some agencies see the resident child and his family together at the time of the parental visits, while others have casework for the parents quite apart from the treatment of the children. A number of settings view groups of families as treatment units. Sometimes these multifamily groups parallel the group structures for the children in the milieu.

Settings that take children from far away often have to dispense with close direct parent work, but they might recommend or require that the parents obtain help in their local community. A few centers—a very few—prefer to take over the child's life completely, discourage much contact between child and parent, and ask the parent simply to keep out of the picture as much as possible.[4] The other extreme is to throw the major emphasis of treatment life on family therapy and to use the center as a catalyst and enabler for such therapy. In general it seems fair to say that residential treatment requires and must be prepared to cope with active family participation in the therapeutic process at some level.

⟪ School

One of the major differences between the life of the child and that of the adult is our culture's absolute emphasis on the centrality of school in the child's life. An adult may attend school; a child must. Moreover, the child has a range of developmental needs and areas for ego growth that are specifically addressed by the realities of school. These include such elements as sublimation, mastery, cognitive unfolding, and refining of methods of impulse control; the widening of his range of identification possibilities; authority encounters with nonparent figures; peer relationships away from the enmeshments with siblings; and a chance to try his wings outside the home in a variety of ways that make for growth. When children have problems, these may take the form of school failure in any of many realms. The child may fail to learn in one particular area or in all areas. He may be unable to cope with peers and may either withdraw, stay in chronic trouble, or run away. He may have a variety of reactions to teachers, from ungovernable erotic wishes to equally intense, angry, provocative engagements. All sorts of blends of such problems may appear, or one area of difficulty may in turn beget others. Thus, a child with a learning problem may feel so different from and inadequate in comparison to his peers that his behavior may alter. He may be unwilling to go to school, daydream all the time he is there, or divert himself from the pain of failure by whispering, joking, or clowning or by teasing, annoying, or attacking other children.

Hence, when a child becomes sufficiently disturbed and is referred for residential care, a major means for achieving a good treatment result must be to try to find out how to help him succeed as a student. In the service of this goal, a host of special techniques have been evolved for specific learning problems, generalized learning inhibition, coping with behavioral difficulties in the classroom, working out teacher–student interactions, and addressing the entire issue of the child as problem student. So central are such concerns to child mental health that, as we saw before, many settings direct the main thrust of their treatment along this axis. They call themselves schools, their patients are officially pupils, and the whole therapeutic structure is built around a central core of academic and scholastic services. Other settings emphasize the milieu and consider the school as a major component, but still as only one factor among many within the structure of the child's daily life. In a few settings school is viewed as relatively peripheral to the more immediate goal of delivering various forms of therapy. Indeed, these are settings that have no special school of their own and send their children to the adjacent public schools. (Needless to say, they can accept only those children who can fit into such a pattern; and in any case, the residence staff has to work quite intensively with the public school personnel.) On the other hand, quite a few residences arrange with the local public school system to approve the residence school as a special branch within the larger system. This helps both with finances and with scholastic credits. In general, it is safe to say that some form of special schooling is offered within most residential treatment centers and forms a vital sector for help, therapy, and the furtherance of growth.

Typically, such schooling is conducted with classes that may be as small as two and seldom larger than eight. Many children will need some special one-to-one tutoring as well. The school group often is a vital area for work with peer interactions and can be used as one way to structure a therapy group. When a child no longer needs full residential care, he may often continue to attend the residence school after discharge. Contrariwise, a major advance while still in residence may be to start attending an outside public school every day. In the common situation where a day hospital or day care program exists side by side with residential treatment, the children in residence attend the same in-house school and sit in the same classrooms with the day students. It goes without saying, that the teacher is a vital link in the treatment chain and needs

to be included as a full-fledged collaborator in the team that serves that child.

❪ Personnel

There are a great variety of professionals and paraprofessionals who work in the area of residential treatment. Occupational therapists, recreation therapists, speech therapists, art and dance therapists, and many others may be found practicing their discipline within or serving as consultants with a given setting. However, five core disciplines that are the most consistently present need special enumeration: social work, psychology, psychiatry, education, and child care work. The last group is the newest on the scene and merits separate recognition.

With the development of residential care, there has been an increasing emphasis on the life space experience as a vital dimension of treatment. As a result, the need for skilled people to live with the youngsters and bear this therapeutic responsibility has increased proportionately. The child care practitioner has been the object of a great deal of thought, study, and debate in the field. A profile is emerging that tends to look something like this: by and large, some post-high school education is considered essential. In some settings the requirement for employment is junior college preparation that lasts two years and that is tailored specifically for child care work. Other settings accept a baccalaureate as a minimum preparation and do most of their training on the job.

In general, the child care workers need to understand something about normal development, the meaning of disturbed behavior, and how to intervene in crisis situations. They have to master a variety of programming skills, and they require a good deal of back-up and support in order to cope with many emotional challenges and confrontations that are their daily fare with the disturbed children. Optimally, the senior mental health professionals on the staff should supervise the worker's life space interviews and, on occasion, join with him in conducting such exchanges with children in order to serve as a model and guide. One of the most difficult tasks facing the members of the group of life space practitioners is to grasp the nature of the work done by the other mental health professionals and to recognize both the limits and the extent of their own work in relation to that of their colleagues. When an adequate sense of role has been achieved and sureness and skill have been developed in the management of the children, the experienced child care worker emerges as a professional of considerable accomplishment and a vital member of the residential team.

(Discharge

The work involved in the discharge of a child reflects the general task of the residential treatment center. The time spent in residence is only one phase of the total therapeutic experience of a disturbed youngster. Typically, the child coming into residence will have had some outpatient care before admission. It is because he needs more than outpatient experience can give him or than he can obtain from day care that he enters residence. Presently, if things go well, he will show improvement. The residential phase of the therapy is not aimed at cure. It is instead intended to effect enough improvement so that the further therapy does not have to be performed in residence. As soon as this degree of positive change has taken place, the child's treatment can be continued in day care or with clinic visits. Hence the discharge process is designed to effect the continuation of therapy under different circumstances.

It is often difficult to know when a child is ready to return home, or when he is ready to leave so long as he does not have to return home. Sometimes an extended visit (a three- or six-week stay) at home can be tried in order to test whether both child and home are prepared for the changes in each other and whether they can now establish a way of life

with one another that will work. Often it is clear that the child cannot return to that home, and foster placement is attempted. If the foster home can be assigned months before the time of actual discharge, the youngster can begin to visit there, spend holidays with the foster parents, and develop a meaningful connection. In this way, he will be moving to a familiar setting when his time comes to leave. Some agencies have established halfway houses, or group homes run by professional staff, to help bridge the gap between residence and community. Many children can well profit from such an intermediate, semiprotected setting.

Like intake, discharge is not an act: it is a process. As we saw, it implies moving to another level of treatment rather than to termination. Dealing as it does with very sick children and very sick families, residential care is at best demanding and hazardous: a properly designed, fully worked through termination is as vital to its successful outcome as is every other stage of its approach to the needy child.

(Concluding Remarks

The need for residential treatment is difficult to determine. It is often remarked that in any given population of children, such as a school system, somewhere between one child in ten and one child in twenty will need psychiatric care. Of this troubled group, it may be conservatively estimated that one out of every ten children who need care would benefit by residential treatment. On the basis of this reasoning, a rule of thumb in projecting need would be: of any given body of children, one child in one hundred to two hundred needs some time in residence. Thus if we estimate that the current population of children and adolescents is something like one third of the nation's people (one third of 210 million, or 70 million), then our need for residential beds is in the neighborhood of 350,000 to 700,000. Currently we probably have less than 10,000 in all fifty states.

Such figures are soft at best. The criteria for

admission to residential care are not sufficiently precise to allow for exact estimates, nor do we know how many residential treatment centers there are, or how many beds they represent. In a way, it scarcely matters. The disparity between available services and even a wildly different estimate of need (say one tenth of these figures) still leaves an enormous gulf between what is necessary and what is available. In this connection it is important to recall that buildings can be provided quickly, but a pool of skills grows only slowly.

(Bibliography

1. AICHORN, A. *Wayward Youth*. New York: Viking, 1935.
2. ALT, H. *Residential Treatment for the Disturbed Child*. New York: International Universities Press, 1960.
3. BALBERNIE, R. *Residential Work with Children*. Oxford: Pergamon, 1966.
4. BETTELHEIM, B. *Love Is Not Enough*. New York: Free Press, 1950.
5. ———. *The Empty Fortress*. New York: Free Press, 1967.
6. EASSON, W. M. *The Severely Disturbed Adolescent*. New York: International Universities Press, 1969.
7. EKSTEIN, R. *Children of Time and Space, of Action and Impulse*. New York: Appleton-Century-Crofts, 1966.
8. FOSTER, G. W., K. D. VANDER VEN, E. R. KROMER et al. *Child Care Work with Emotionally Disturbed Children*. Pittsburgh: University of Pittsburgh Press, 1972.
9. HOLMES, D. J. *The Adolescent Psychotherapy*. Boston: Little, Brown, 1964.
10. KONOPKA, G. *The Adolescent Girl in Conflict*. Englewood Cliffs, N.J.: Prentice-Hall, 1966.
11. MAYER, M. F. and A. BLUM. *Healing through Living*. Springfield, Ill.: Charles C. Thomas, 1971.
12. REDL, F. and D. WINEMAN. *The Aggressive Child*. Glencoe, Ill.: Free Press, 1957.
13. ROBINSON, J. F., ed. *Psychiatric Inpatient Treatment of Children*. Washington: Am. Psychiatric Assoc., 1957.
14. TRIESCHMAN, A. E., J. K. WHITAKER, and C. K. BRENDTRO. *The Other Twenty-Three Hours*. Chicago: Aldine, 1969.

CHAPTER 34

PSYCHIATRIC MENTAL HEALTH NURSING

Marguerite J. Holmes

Psychiatric mental health nursing is an integral aspect of all nursing as well as an area of clinical specialization. It has been variously defined by leaders in the profession. It is generally agreed, however, that psychiatric nursing is an interpersonal process and that it is concerned with the promotion of mental health and the prevention of mental illness as well as with the assessment of and intervention with people who are evidencing problems in living and in relating with other people. Volume 2 of the first edition of this *Handbook* includes a chapter by H. Peplau, "Principles of Psychiatric Nursing," which very adequately describes the field of psychiatric nursing up to 1959.[59] This present chapter is intended to be supplemental to that work.

In this paper the term "generalist" refers to a nurse with basic preparation. The terms "specialist" and "psychiatric nurse" refer to nurses with a master's degree in the clinical specialty area of psychiatric mental health nursing.

❨ Trends and Issues in Psychiatric Nursing

Many developments since World War II led to modifications in the practice of psychiatric nursing. Such events include social legislation, particularly the legislation that led to the community mental-health movement; the development of new technologies in psychology and psychiatry; and changes within the health care delivery system and the profession of nursing. Some implications of these events are discussed below. Changes in the practice of psychiatric mental health nursing include those made in the settings for practice; the addition of new roles, skills, and techniques; and the increase in responsibility and accountability for one's own practice.

Impact of the Community Mental-Health Movement

Psychiatric care has moved from the narrow focus of hospital psychiatry to the more inclusive concept of community mental health services. This major shift in emphasis, which has affected all the mental health professions, was ushered in by the report of the Joint Commission on Mental Illness and Health. Congress, through the Mental Health Study Act of 1955, had directed the commission (as chosen by the National Institute of Mental Health) to analyze and evaluate the needs and resources of the mentally ill in the United States and to make recommendations for a mental health program. The report, after being submitted to Congress, the Surgeon General of the Public Health Service, and the governors of the fifty states, was published in 1961 under the title *Action for Mental Health.*[38]

This landmark report on the history of mental health in the United States noted that progress depends on the solution of problems in three areas: (1) manpower, (2) facilities, and (3) cost. While recognizing that certain kinds of medical, psychiatric, and neurological examinations and treatments must be carried out under the immediate direction of physicians specifically trained in these procedures, the report stated that nonmedical mental health workers with aptitude, sound training, practical experience, and demonstrable competence should be permitted to do general short-term psychotherapy. This helped pave the way for nurses to become primary therapists, taking full responsibility for their therapeutic work with clients. The report also recommended the establishment of additional clinics, psychiatric units in general hospitals; the development of regional state hospitals of not more than 1000 beds; the creation of aftercare and rehabilitation services; and a public education program.

President Kennedy, in a message to Congress in 1963, had stated: "We need a new type of health facility, one which will return mental health care to the mainstream of American medicine and at the same time upgrade mental health services." Congress enacted the "Mental Retardation Facilities and Community Mental Health Centers Construction Act" in October of that year. This legislation authorized federal funds for use by the states in constructing comprehensive community mental health centers. The 1963 act covered only the construction of community mental health centers, but in 1965 the measure was considerably strengthened by legislation that provided substantial funding for staffing of the centers for the next five years.[2]

The Narcotic Addicts Rehabilitation Act of 1966 took a major step in revising society's attitude toward addiction by establishing the narcotics addict, within federal law, as a sick person to be treated rather than punished. Through its administration of this act and of the Narcotic Addict Rehabilitation Amendment to the Community Mental Health Centers Act, the National Institute of Mental Health actively carried out the congressional mandate to treat and rehabilitate drug addicts. Nurses have become more involved in dealing with drug abuse and the management of drug-dependent individuals since this legislation was enacted. Subsequent legislation defining public drunkenness as an evidence of sickness rather than as a crime is also altering treatment methods for alcoholics, which will probably produce further changes in the practice of psychiatric nursing.

By the mid-1960s the community mental health movement was well under way. Since that time it has drastically influenced the practice of psychiatric nursing, which might now more appropriately be called community mental health–psychiatric nursing. The changes that have occurred largely as a result of this movement include the following:

1. A shift from hospital-based to community-based practice.
2. A shift from an individual-patient focus to a family orientation.
3. An emphasis on the competencies and coping abilities of people as well as on their problems and psychopathology.
4. An emphasis on prevention as well as on treatment and rehabilitation.
5. A greater number and diversity of settings of practice.
6. A greater number and diversity of roles for psychiatric nursing.

7. An increased involvement of generalist-level nurses (particularly public health nurses) in mental health work.
8. An increase in the responsibility and accountability of nurses for their own practice.
9. A greater use of group leadership skills and techniques.
10. A greater awareness and conscious use of social systems and human relationship systems.

Innovations in the Treatment of Psychiatric Patients

Changes in the hospital practice of psychiatry have also had an impact on psychiatric nursing practice. In settings where the prevailing philosophy of treatment has been the traditional one-to-one psychotherapy or psychoanalysis, the role of nursing tended in the past to be custodial—the "other twenty-three hours." Within this framework in the mid-twentieth century, nurses struggled to be recognized as more than just caretakers. They tried to do this by becoming more or less traditional one-to-one therapists, following the medical model.

"Milieu therapy" also had its beginnings within the framework of psychoanalytically-oriented inpatient psychiatry. The importance of the interaction with the nursing staff became obvious in treatment programs that recognized the importance of the impact of the total milieu on the individual patient. Nursing personnel are the conveyors of the culture; in very large part, they constitute the milieu of the patients. In milieu-conscious programs, nursing came to be recognized for the significant roles it plays in providing therapeutic care.

The "therapeutic community" concept[39] opened further doors to the development and recognition of therapeutic nursing roles in hospital psychiatric treatment. The development of psychiatric nursing in therapeutic communities was described by Holmes and Werner.[37] Concerning psychiatric nursing in a therapeutic community, they said that it is "an exciting adventure, marked by loss of tradi-

tional nursing roles, blurring of roles of all disciplines, increased responsibility for therapy on the part of both patients and staff, more intense staff–patient relationships, and a whole complex of problems for nursing that we are just beginning to explore." [p. iii][37]

The development of the therapeutic community concept did a great deal for the development of psychiatric nursing, by providing a framework in which nurses could participate more actively and utilize their skills in many more ways. The distinctive features of the therapeutic community are: (1) patients are included in practically all information-sharing processes on the ward; (2) patients' opinions are included in decisions about other patients' readiness for such things as passes and discharges; and (3) such inclusion of patients in a democratic community process is considered treatment.[37] One can readily see that such a framework fosters open communication and responsibility. In such a setting nurses as well as patients become more responsible members of the society. Psychiatric nursing, while still interpersonally oriented and concerned primarily with relationships, is extended beyond the one-to-one or formal group setting to the total milieu. The therapeutic-community framework applies to part-time treatment situations such as day or evening care programs as well as to full-time inpatient units. In many situations where the concept has been implemented, such as therapeutic communities for drug addicts and alcoholics, nurses are involved and are active contributors to the total treatment program.

The application of social learning theory has had a considerable influence on psychiatric nursing. Although it may have been most influential in hospital settings, the use of behavior-modification techniques, like the use of therapeutic-community concepts, has also received wide application in outpatient settings. Social learning programs have perhaps been most widely used for chronic schizophrenic patients, mentally retarded people, and children. When behavior modification is utilized in hospital settings, nurses are generally involved in implementing the program; in some instances they are the initiators.[21,13,71]

Psychiatric nurses (prepared at the masters' level) generally are familiar with social learning theory and its clinical application. Some, indeed, are expert in the use of behavior-modification techniques. The graduate preparation is not uniform in this regard. Generalist nurses, while they may have some familiarity with theory and techniques, usually need in-service education to supplement their knowledge and enable them to implement behavior-modification programs effectively.

The incorporation of approaches based on learning theory was evident in the papers presented at a 1969 conference called "The New Hospital Psychiatry." This conference brought together a large group of professionals engaged in the hospital treatment of psychiatric patients. The papers at this conference "reflect the newly vitalized eclectic spirit of modern hospital psychiatry. They document the shift from the narrowness of the exclusively medical model to ths more inclusive "education and social learning" points of view, which make possible both a theoretical and a technical pluralism in approaching mental disorder." [p. ix][1] A great many new techniques for and approaches to the treatment of patients were described in relation to a variety of treatment programs. These include: action group processes, including psychodrama; group-treatment situations of many kinds; family approaches; a great many behavioral approaches, including token-economy systems; special sessions using role playing; and sessions using mirrors, tape recorders, and video tape for feedback. Also described were special sessions designed to help the patient with particular kinds of behaviors (expressing anger, being assertive, and so forth), representing opportunities for the patient to practice behaving in certain ways and to assume roles that are foreign to him or difficult for him. The treatment program worked out with and for each patient presented an impressive variety of therapeutic activities. And in many if not most of these activities, nurses were key personnel.

The paper presented on psychiatric nursing at the 1969 conference analyzed the influences of these myriad new techniques on the practice of psychiatric nursing. The functions of

the psychiatric nurse were described as follows. She does all the ordinary things such as observing the patient and becoming aware of all the things that are affecting his life: how he is eating and sleeping, what is happening between him and his family, how he is feeling and behaving, how he is getting along in the unit, and what he is doing in his treatment program. The nurse is responsible for learning all these things every day about every patient, recording the information and reporting it to the appropriate people, and participating in making and revising the program for each patient. Other than that, "all" she does is work with the patients, get to know them, eat with them, play with them, and participate with them in all the activities that are part of the patients' treatment programs. [p. 90][36]

Psychiatric nursing consists of the experiential aspects of living with the patients—observing, caring, sharing, nurturing, sustaining, and communicating for the simple purpose of understanding a patient's meaning as opposed to changing his thinking or behavior. But it also consists of strategic maneuvers —carefully thought out and planned ways of responding to a patient that are designed to have an impact on a particular aspect of his behavior. There is more to nursing than the use of verbal skills. If nursing is unique in anything, it is in the totality of the view of the patient and in the experiential aspects of living with the patient. In nursing there is an opportunity for genuine encounters between human beings. [p. 90][36]

Psychiatric Nursing in the General Hospital

An increasingly important role for psychiatric nurses exists in the general hospital setting. Bulbulyan[16] has described the development of the role of the psychiatric nurse as a member of the psychiatric consultation service, within a general hospital, that provided emergency consultation to the entire hospital. Gradually the nurse assumed the task of evaluating the status of patients referred for psychiatric consultation and preparing the patients for that consultation. The psychiatric nurse also set up her own mental health consultation program with the nursing personnel in the general hospital. These were weekly conferences in which patients and patient situations were discussed with the nursing personnel of the units. The main focus was on nursing care. In these conferences, every attempt was made to integrate mental health concepts with the physical care and social needs of patients.

Progressive hospitals throughout the country seek the services of such clinical specialists to function in the general hospital setting. In some situations a psychiatric nurse is employed full-time to work as a clinical specialist in the general hospital. She may not be attached to any particular nursing unit but may develop a consulting relationship with the nursing staff on any or all of the units in the hospital. In other situations the psychiatric nurse is a member of the psychiatric consultation service within the general hospital. In still other instances the psychiatric nurse is employed as a consultant by the department of nursing to provide consultation to nursing services.

The functions of the psychiatric nurse fall into two main areas: (1) directly intervening with patients and families, and (2) teaching and consulting with the nursing staff. The kinds of patients with whom psychiatric nursing intervention is useful include: (1) patients who are experiencing acute psychological disturbances while in the hospital; (2) certain high-risk groups of patients; and (3) patients who cause the nurses acute psychological distress (the well-known problem patients). But although the psychiatric nurse in a general hospital setting does do crisis intervention with patients who become acutely upset by some aspect of their illness or experience with hospitalization, her work might best be considered primarily as preventive mental health work. Much of it deals with patients and families who, because of the physical health problems they have, are very prone to emotional problems. (Some examples are discussed below.) Working with children and their families in regard to surgery, serious disease, or hospitalization can do a great deal to prevent

later serious emotional disturbances. Patients undergoing extreme kinds of surgery (particularly life-and-death operations such as open-heart surgery and mutilating operations such as amputations of breasts, legs, or other body parts) are a high-risk population. Patients who go on chronic kidney dialysis are also prime candidates for mental health consultation. These patients have to live from day to day depending on a machine to sustain their life; generally, too, they suffer from chronically poor health and a lack of vitality. Thus the psychological and social problems of kidney dialysis patients are very great, but in many instances they can be worked with effectively through psychiatric nursing intervention.

Patients and families of patients with long-term, progressively debilitating, or fatal diseases or with crippling injuries can also be helped by psychiatric nursing intervention. The time of diagnosis of such a disease is likely to be a time of crisis for the patient and his immediate family. A psychiatric nurse who understands loss and the processes of grief can often be helpful to the family in facing this situation. These are but some of the high-risk patients and families in the general hospital setting who might profit from mental health consultation provided by a psychiatric nurse. As previously stated, this consultation includes both working directly with the patient and his family, and consulting with the nursing staff to help them develop attitudes and behaviors which will be useful in sustaining these patients and families through their experience.

An example of nursing intervention with a dying patient illustrates the potential usefulness of a psychiatric nursing consultant to a medical–surgical nursing unit.[35] The problem concerned a newly admitted patient with near-terminal cancer. She was extremely anxious, extremely demanding, and never satisfied by anything that was done for her. The staff members were very upset with this patient, refusing to work with her, and some were even requesting transfer to other units. The coordinator, being sensitive to the experiences of both the patient and the staff, recognized that this situation could easily develop into a disaster for all concerned. She requested a consultation from the psychiatric nurse, who in this situation worked directly with the patient and with the nurse who was coordinator of the unit in which the patient was hospitalized. The coordinator, then, worked with the nursing staff on the unit and with members of the patient's family. The consultation began with an interview with the patient, in which the coordinator participated. The interview was introduced by asking the patient to let the two nurses know her better, so that together they might plan the best possible nursing care. The patient responded well to this invitation and began to discuss more and more openly and with less denial the progression of her cancer, her despair, her concern for her family, and the wall of silence that separated her from them. Following this interview, the coordinator was able to talk with the nursing staff from a different orientation. She was able to help them change their perspective on the patient, no longer seeing her as a demanding, irritable, and irritating patient but as a needful, dying person who was experiencing the greatest difficulty of her life. The remainder of the consultation consisted of brief weekly interviews with the patient and discussions with the coordinator about the nursing care.

In this situation (and in many like it), a relatively brief intervention with the patient and with key members of the nursing staff was helpful in enabling the patient to face her own death and take care of the unfinished business between her and her family. It also helped the nursing staff to appreciate the struggle the patient was having and to sustain her throughout the experience.

The psychiatric nurse may or may not elect to work with the patient directly. If she does choose to do so, it is often useful for her to do it in a manner that makes her intervention directly available to at least some members of the nursing staff. In the above case the interview with the patient was done in conjunction with the coordinator, so that the coordinator might learn more directly how such an interview can be helpful to a patient. The coordinator could then use this information in helping the nursing staff to understand the patient and her experience better, to understand

something about their own reactions to the patient and their participation in the problem, and to refocus their efforts so that they could work effectively with the patient and gain satisfaction in doing so. The psychiatric nurse is likely to be better able to provide this kind of consultation to nursing personnel than are other mental health professionals. She has been down this route herself, and she knows very well the frustrations and trials of attempting to provide good nursing care on a busy, hectic unit. She knows the strains nurses bear when they work daily with patients who are in pain, grieving, or dying. She understands the kinds of defenses that nurses inevitably erect aganst these experiences. And because she understands so well what the nurses might be going through, she can often help them set their own needs aside in order to respond to the patient in terms of his needs and his experiences.

Psychiatric Aides and Mental Health Technicians

In 1953 the American Nurses Association–National League for Nursing Coordinating Council accepted the recommendation that, in meeting the need of the mentally ill, the nursing profession should assume the leadership and the responsibility for the training of all those nursing personnel who take care of psychiatric patients. This was to include registered nurses, licensed practical nurses, and psychiatric aides.

The nursing profession stated the principle that all who give nursing care to psychiatric patients are in fact nursing personnel. In an effort to improve the care given by nonprofessional nursing personnel, the National League for Nursing, in conjunction with the American Psychiatric Association, cosponsored the Seminar Project for Teachers of Psychiatric Aides. This was a demonstration project conducted in four southern states between the years of 1958 and 1960. The project was supported by a grant from the National Institute of Mental Health. It developed a method of upgrading psychiatric care by improving the teaching and supervision of psychiatric aides. This was accomplished by providing an intensive learning experience for the nurses—primarily head nurses and supervisors—who in effect were the teachers of aides. It is not known how far-reaching the effects were of this demonstration project, but several states subsequently set up similar programs aimed at improving the teaching and supervision of aides.[47]

The career mental-health worker has lately come into his own. Florida was the first state to develop a two-year mental-health technician training program within a junior college setting.[8] Now there are a variety of training programs for mental-health workers and technicians (the terminology varies). In some instances nurses have set up and operated these programs, but the mental health workers who are the products of the program are not necessarily considered part of the nursing discipline. The preparation may be at several academic levels. In some instances these workers are employed by the nursing staff and considered to be nursing personnel; in other instances they form their own discipline. Workers employed in mental health centers, where departmental ties are generally considered obsolete, usually constitute their own discipline and generally are not considered subprofessional members of the nursing staff.

Thus this is a changing scene, with both conceptual and political implications. The political aspects have to do with such issues as power, money, status, and recognition. The conceptual aspects have to do with the fact that roles are emerging rather than static. Perhaps in hospital situations, nursing care is a sufficiently clear entity for all to agree on what constitutes nursing care and who gives it (although even there the situation may get cloudy at times). In mental health centers the situation is less clear. There are large areas of overlap in the functions of all the mental health disciplines. In many instances, people from different disciplines do very much the same thing. Probably roles will stabilize and solidify as it becomes clearer what each discipline can best contribute in the field of mental health. In the meantime, roles are not rigidly defined in this fluid, emerging field.

Some Changes within the Nursing Profession

Nursing is unusual among the health professions because of the wide range of levels of preparation found there. This variety is both a problem and a source of continuing change and development. Increasing numbers of nurses have achieved doctorates, for the most part in the sciences related to nursing. Nurses with doctorates in nursing and related sciences are prepared to do independent research, to teach others research methods, to contribute directly and indirectly to the development of theory in nursing, and to provide leadership for the further development of nursing practice and nursing education.

Certification is an area in which several developments have occurred simultaneously, which results in considerable confusion. Some states established certification of nurses as a requirement for licensure, which usually means that the nurse must give evidence of continuing education in order to renew her license to practice. On the national level, the American Nurses Association (ANA) provides certification of practitioners at the general-nursing level in recognition of excellence of practice in the clinical area of psychiatric mental-health nursing. In addition, there is a movement among clinical specialists in psychiatric nursing (prepared at the master's level or above) to obtain board certification as specialists in their field; this certification would be a formal recognition of advanced preparation, experience, and excellence in practice. The term "certification" is used to indicate all three of these movements, which are quite different from one another. But when the issues and problems involved are all resolved, "certification" in nursing should have a consensual meaning.

One additional development of considerable general importance is the expanding role of nurses. A plethora of terms is being utilized to describe the changing roles of nurses, including "expanded role," "extended role," "primary care agent," and many others.[8] Nursing practice has been defined as including acute care, long-term care, and primary care, with nurses having extended responsibility in any of these areas. There is an increased emphasis on having nurses function in areas of health assessment, health maintenance, health promotion, and the prevention of illness and disability. The general trend is for qualified nursing specialists to participate actively in health care programs that reach out into the communities.

⟅ The Generalist in Psychiatric Nursing

Preparation: Settings for Practice

Psychiatric nursing is an integral aspect of all nursing. The generalist in psychiatric nursing is any nurse with basic (as opposed to graduate) preparation who works in a psychiatric setting. The settings for psychiatric nursing services vary widely. They include hospitals (both general and psychiatric), public health agencies, clinics, day- and night-care centers, offices, homes, schools, camps, industrial centers, and probably others as well. Insofar as psychiatric nursing is an aspect of all nursing, in fact, any setting in which nursing is practiced might be considered a setting for the practice of psychiatric nursing. Community agencies such as public health agencies, schools, and mental health centers have become increasingly important settings for practice.

The basic preparation for nurses is gained through any one of three routes: (1) an associate degree from a two-year junior college program; (2) a diploma from a three-year hospital program; and (3) a baccalaureate degree from a college or university. Graduates from all three kinds of programs are eligible to take state board examinations to become registered nurses, which gives them the legal authority to practice. Nurses graduating from all these programs have had basic psychiatric –mental health nursing, which usually includes an emphasis on communication skills and on relating therapeutically with psychiatric patients. Some programs also include the study of family relationships and group dy-

namics. The nurses study theories and methods of treatment of psychiatric illness, the expected effects of treatment on patient behavior, and patient care. The theoretical approach varies from school to school, but it is often based on psychoanalytic or interpersonal theories.

Graduates from baccalaureate programs generally have more theoretical preparation, which may include some familiarity with learning-theory-based approaches as well as more traditional psychiatric orientations. The course of study in the baccalaureate programs combines special education in the theory and the practice of nursing with general education in the humanities and the behavioral, biological, and physical sciences.

Graduates of collegiate programs in professional nursing accredited by the National League for Nursing (NLN)—the national accrediting agency for nursing education, recognized by the National Commission on Accrediting and by the nursing professon itself—are prepared to give high-quality nursing care to patients and their families and to direct the nursing care given by other nursing team members working with them. They are qualified for employment in general nursing practice in any setting where professional nursing care is given: hospitals, public health agencies of all kinds, the military and other federal nursing services, nursing homes, and so forth. These nurses have the educational background necessary for graduate study in nursing at the master's degree level.[56]

In the mid-1970s there were more than 200 baccalaureate programs accredited by the NLN. These programs all included theory and practice in both public health and psychiatric mental health nursing. In some of the newer programs (or those with revised curricula) the mental health concepts were integrated throughout the curriculum. Such programs also stress independent study, mastery of content, and self-determined rate of progress.

Roles and Functions

Some aspects of the practice of the generalist in psychiatric nursing are described below.

They are summarized from the ANA *Statement on Psychiatric Nursing Practice*.[5]

1. *Clinical nursing care*. Such care includes a variety of activities designed to obtain data for the formulation and implementation of the clinical nursing care plan. The nurse observes and assesses patient behavior (including group behavior), interprets and implements physicians orders, reviews information from other disciplines, holds individual and group conferences with nursing and non-nursing personnel, and participates in investigative activities.

2. *Providing a therapeutic milieu*. The nurse makes use of such concepts as authority, power, dependence, independence, responsibility, and decision-making in the development and maintenance of a sociopsychological milieu conducive to recovery. The patient's strengths and potential for helping others are utilized as active forces in the therapeutic milieu.

3. *Counseling*. The nurse is concerned with helping the patient understand what is happening to him in the present situation, so that he can integrate this knowledge with his other experiences in life. The focus is on experiential learning. The aim of counseling is to work specifically on the problem or behavior pattern that is presenting difficulties. Counseling by the nurse can include regularly scheduled interviews (as well as unscheduled sessions) with patients, their families, and others.

4. *Being a symbolic parent*. Experiences of daily living form the basis for nursing interventions that aim at encouraging constructive changes in a patient's behavior. Nursing care activities that are utilized for this purpose include bathing, feeding, and dressing. By suggesting and persuading, comforting, guiding, and setting limits, the nurse supplies supportive, emotional-care elements of "parent-like" supervision.

5. *Teaching health*. The teaching of proper health practices is a responsibility of all nurses. Subjects include the usual good personal practices, but the nurse is also concerned with behavioral patterns such as aggression, personal problems such as anxiety, and group problems such as adolescent drug addiction. Such teaching involves serving as a good model of health, and it requires the formal or informal teaching of patients, families, and community groups.

6. *Serving as a social agent*. Nurses provide leadership in individual and group activities designed to assist patients in gaining the social skills that are basic to improved relationships with others and good adaptation to cultural norms. Nurses promote and help to improve the patients' recreational, social, and occupational competence.

7. *Providing clinical assistance to personnel*. Nurses provide leadership and support for one another through formal and informal conferences with nursing personnel. Nursing conferences are used to discuss, review, and evaluate nursing-care planning and intervention.

8. *Technical activities*. The technical aspects of nursing in psychiatric settings are essentially the same technical activities involved in nursing in any setting. Included are preparing and dispensing medications, observing effects and complications, collecting data for clinical trials of new drugs, preparing patients for specific therapies, and preparing for and supervising varied treatments and procedures. Nurses performing such nursing procedures have an essential concern for the quality and purposiveness of their interactions with patients.

9. *Joint planning*. Joint planning with other professional workers is essential to providing total patient care. In interdisciplinary conferences, nurses discuss the nature of and rationale for nursing care and coordinate it with the approaches taken by other professional workers.

Writings on the development of nursing in community mental health indicate some new emphases in psychiatric nursing by the generalist nurse. One important aspect of the community mental health movement is the increasing use of public health nurses to work with psychiatric patients. This is particularly true in programs for follow-up of patients—especially chronic schizophrenic patients—who have been hospitalized. There are numerous community care programs for the mentally ill in which public health nurses play the principal roles. Many of these programs came into being when mental hospitals joined forces with public health nursing agencies in an endeavor to provide continuity in total service to the mentally ill and their families. The public health nurse plays a key role in these operations and may function as liaison between the public health agencies and hospitals.[4,65]

The role of public health nurses in community mental health nursing is of increasing significance. One important contribution that nurses with public health preparation bring to the mental health team is their community orientation. Public health nurses have found themselves in many places. They have traditionally been welcomed by families as persons who have something to offer and who care. They are interested in the prevention of disease and chronic illness and therefore consider not only the individual but the family as well. Home visiting by a public health nurse is a valuable tool in dealing with crisis situations. In any home visit the nurse assesses the kind of neighborhood and house in which the family lives, the family's interactions, their strengths as well as their weaknesses, and their material and emotional needs. Thus the orientation of public health nurses leads them to consider the total health needs of the entire family.[25]

In inpatient treatment settings, nurses are usually involved in and may carry major responsibilities for a host of treatment modalities. Staff nurses often carry responsibilities for patient–staff meetings and are active in all programs for hospitalized patients. They may be leaders or co-leaders of patient activity groups and therapy groups. They are involved in such community activities as visiting patients and their families in conjunction with the patients' therapy.

Nurses are also working in methadone maintenance centers, in halfway houses for drug addicts, and with drug-dependent individuals in general community mental health centers. School nurses are increasingly involved with drug abusers. By virtue of their professional preparation and interest in the health and welfare of children, school nurses can work effectively in the areas of drug abuse prevention and the rehabilitation of addicts.[27]

In community mental health centers, nurses are moving into many additional roles. Generally they spend most of their time seeing clients. Among the activities of nurses in mental health centers are individual, family, and marital crisis therapy; evaluation and disposition of patients; and short-term and longer-term work with clients in many different ways, including specialized kinds of group therapies. Nurses are also used in medication follow-up. They are particularly apt to work well with patients and families who have a combination of physical, psychological, and social problems. They make home visits, often working with the whole family as well as the identified patient. In addition, the role of liaison between nursing staffs in hospitals (or in community agencies such as the visiting nurse services) and the mental health center seems to be carried out best by nurses. Those nurses with a background in mental health bring to consultation with other nurses not only their knowledge of the mental health problems involved but also an understanding of ward management problems that may influence a staff's reaction to a particular patient.[14]

(The Specialist in Psychiatric Nursing

Preparation: Settings for Practice

Clinical specialization in psychiatric nursing is based upon the knowledge and skills obtained through completion of a program of graduate study in a university with clinical specialization in psychiatric–mental health nursing. The master's degree is currently the basis of clinical specialization. Theoretical bases, concepts, and principles from which therapeutic skills are developed are acquired through academically supervised study and clinical practice. The skills developed during this educational experience are further refined to a high degree of expertness through continuing education, clinical practice, and competent supervision. It is recognized that additional education at the graduate level is required to provide for competent practice in subspecialties such as child psychiatric nursing. [p. 14][5]

Graduate education in nursing prepares for specialization. Most graduate study is offered at the master's level, although graduate education in nursing also increasingly includes doctoral programs. The masters program builds on the foundation of an undergraduate college education with a nursing major. The purpose of this program is to prepare professional nursing leaders. It is distinguished by a concentrated study of a specific area of nursing (such as psychiatric mental health nursing), an introduction to research methods, and an independent study of a nursing problem using research techniques. Many NLN-accredited master's programs combine study of a clinical area, such as psychiatric nursing, with study of a functional activity, such as teaching, supervision, administration, or consultation. Although nursing is the major focus of the program, a master's education also includes advanced courses in the natural and social sciences relevant to the area of specialization. Other subjects appropriate to graduate education may also be required.[56]

In the mid-1970s there were over seventy NLN-accredited master's degree programs in psychiatric mental health nursing. This number included programs in all areas of psychiatric mental health nursing: adult and child programs; community programs; and programs related to teaching, administration, supervision, and clinical specialization in psychiatric mental health nursing. Within this number were more than forty master's programs (in nearly as many universities) that specifically prepared nurses to function as clinical specialists in psychiatric mental health nursing.

The term "clinical specialist" in psychiatric nursing has come to be accepted as indicating the nurse with a master's-level preparation in the clinical specialty area of psychiatric nursing. Other terms such as "nurse clinician," "nurse practitioner," and "psychiatric nurse" are also sometimes used to mean approximately the same thing. Because of existing variations in the use of these terms, it is well to clarify what meaning is intended.

The clinical content of the various psychiatric nursing master's programs varies somewhat, although all include both theory and supervised practice in psychiatric mental health nursing. Theoretical approaches to the study of psychopathology and treatment include psychoanalytic, interpersonal, family-systems, biophysical, behavioral, and phenomenological approaches. Some programs include an overview of all of these; others are more limited in scope. Most programs emphasize interpersonal approaches because of their usefulness in psychiatric nursing intervention. Clinical practice emphasizes community settings as well as hospitals. Group and family interaction processes are studied, and master's students generally have some clinical experience in both these areas. Preventive aspects of mental-health consultation are receiving greater emphasis in many programs.

Leininger defined some of the content that should be included in the new psychiatric nursing instruction. She urged that this content be integrated with the older content, particularly that related to individual, group, and family therapy. (Some programs do encompass much of this content, and others can be expected to move in this direction.) The newer content she identified includes:

theoretical concepts about the nature and definitions of a community; community and social organization theories; ecology and mental health; demographic aspects of mental illness; culture and mental illness; social systems theory and its application in both institutional and community social systems; social structure concepts; the dynamics of family social structure; role theory (sick and well role behavior); the culture of poverty and mental health; ethnological aspects of cultural groups; psychocultural and sociological research findings about 'normal' and 'abnormal' mental behavior; cross-cultural viewpoints about mental illness; human and physical community resources supporting optimal mental health; preventive aspects of mental illness; and criteria for the assessment of mental illness in different communities. [p. 19][42]

The settings for practice for the clinical specialist in psychiatric nursing are many and varied. Hospitals, both general and psychiatric, are the traditional arenas for practice. Community agencies of many kinds are becoming more important as settings, however, particularly comprehensive community mental health centers. All the settings previously listed are available to the psychiatric nurse. In addition, some nurses are going into the private practice of counseling and therapy, generally with other mental health professionals.

Roles and Functions

The primary role of the clinical specialist is that of the expert practitioner giving direct care to patients who present the most complex nursing problems. Today's clinical specialist in nursing may also function in such roles as teacher, consultant, director, or coordinator. The ANA *Statement*[5] categorizes these as *direct-* and *indirect*-care functions. The direct-care functions are inherent in the therapy of psychiatric patients. The scope of the functions of these clinical nursing specialists depends upon a variety of factors, including educational preparation and clinical experience, personal aptitude and preference, opportunities for clinical practice in specific psychiatric settings, and the availability of competent supervision.

The direct-care functions, as defined by the ANA, are summarized below.

1. *Individual psychotherapy.* The clinical specialist in psychiatric nursing is prepared to practice individual psychotherapy under supervision. The purpose of individual psychotherapy is to develop and assess the meaning of the experience with the patient so that he is increasingly able to use these insights in further problem-solving and in improving his relationships with others.

2. *Group psychotherapy.* The psychiatric nurse is qualified to conduct group psychotherapy, either as therapist or as cotherapist, with supervision. Some psychiatric nurses have adequate training and experience to function as teacher, supervisor, and consultant to other mental health professionals who are learning to conduct group therapy.

3. *Family therapy.* The psychiatric nurse may assume the role of a family therapist directly involved in attempting to influence family groups in the maintenance of mental health and the resolution of their mental health problems. The nurse may function either alone or as cotherapist with other mental health professionals.

4. *Sociotherapy.* The key concept of sociotherapy is the provision of a therapeutic environment that promotes mental health through corrective or remedial experiences, fosters healthy coping abilities, and corrects maladaptive coping patterns. Sociotherapy encourages the development of interpersonal skills that help people to manage their environment and strengthen or correct their coping abilities. The psychiatric nurse practicing sociotherapy is responsible for providing a therapeutic environment and coordinating the collaborative efforts of others who are involved in the treatment and care of the individual. In the practice of sociotherapy, the psychiatric nurse has the opportunity to contribute to the development of community programs and the solution of community mental health problems.

The indirect nursing care roles described in the ANA *Statement* include: administrator, clinical supervisor, director of staff development and training, consultant or resource person, and researcher.

COMMUNITY MENTAL HEALTH WORK

These are the more or less well-established roles of the psychiatric nurse. In addition, primarily under the impact of the community mental health movement, psychiatric nursing is extending out into the community. In making this move, nurses have pioneered new roles. Some of these roles are already becoming stabilized, but many are still very much in the developmental stages.

The roles and activities performed by an individual nurse are influenced by many variables unique to the individual center and the individual nurse. These variables include the interest and talents of the nurse, her academic preparation, and her prior experience in community mental health and other kinds of nursing. They also include the requirements and interests of the larger social system of which she is a part—namely, the staff of the community mental health center in which she works, and the community that the center serves. "Among the variables that influence the role of the nurse are the type of services performed by the center in which she is working, the composition, preparation, and organization of the staff rendering the services, the population served, the community's needs as viewed by the community and as viewed by the center, and finally the nurse's own beliefs as to what her role or roles can be within that setting." [p. 645][69]

Another variable that influences the way in which nurses (as well as other professionals) function in community mental health centers is the model under which the center operates. These models, as identified and described by Schulberg and Baker,[66] are as follows.

1. *The medical model.* Here the doctor–patient relationship is important. The patient is considered sick, and community resources are mobilized by the doctor for his patient. The focus is on the individual. Under this model one can predict that the services that are offered tend to focus on the provision of therapy.

2. *The public health practice model.* This model is concerned primarily with the community population as a whole. The focus is on the prevention of mental disorders. Here one can predict that there will be more interaction between the community and the center.

3. *The ecological systems model.* Here the individual is viewed as functioning within a succession of open systems, and mental disorder is considered a manifestation of intolerable strain in some or all of the systems. Here again, one can predict considerable interaction between the center and the community, and therapy would probably focus primarily on groups rather than on individuals.

Several studies in the 1960s and 1970s described the role, functions, and activities of nurses in various community mental health centers.[26,33,70,78] The results of some of these studies are presented to show the range and diversity of activities of the psychiatric nurse in the mental health centers.

Zahourek[78] studied the activities of twenty-one nurses in the mental health center of the Denver General Hospital. This included generalist nurses as well as clinical specialists. In the emergency service (with on-call psychiatric back-up) they evaluated and made disposition of all psychiatric patients seen in the emergency room. As members of the generic outpatient teams, they received cases on a random basis from the neighborhood served by the teams, evaluating these patients and developing and implementing treatment plans for them. They also provided indirect services to patients through consultation with and education of other providers of community care. Nurses held both top and middle management positions within the center, including those of outpatient team leader and director of psychiatric nursing. These nurses had diversified functions, serving as therapists, educators, administrators, community liaison, consultants, and research assistants. Nurses working in the emergency room and outpatient situations had many contacts with the community. These included community health nursing agencies; police; juvenile and adult legal agencies; hospitals; schools; churches, welfare, vocational and rehabilitation services; educational programs in nursing and other health care disciplines; community action centers; charities; specialized agencies caring for alcoholics and drug addicts; and businesses. The nurses provided consultation to other emergency room personnel, medical–surgical unit personnel, schools, psychiatric hospitals, local visiting nurse services, and welfare agencies.

Hess[33] studied a group of ten nurses at a community mental health center in Illinois. These nurses saw their roles as follows: therapists, in-take workers (assessing, evaluating, and assigning patients to teams), and workers in a variety of informal situations such as the home.

Over a five-year period, Stokes[70] and three colleagues participated in the activities of a newly developed mental health center. They developed an outline of their roles, functions, and activities within the framework of a model of primary, secondary, and tertiary prevention. The roles that Stokes and her colleagues considered a psychiatric nurse to be able to perform included the following:

psychotherapist, with individuals and families; cotherapist, with families or groups; consultant to other professionals and community groups; teacher; liaison to general hospital departments; and collaborator—for instance, between professional and community groups.

Bulbulyan[17] felt that the main goal of the mental health center in relation to the community at large was to develop a collaborative relationship with members of the community in order to accomplish the gigantic task of maintaining and promoting mental health. This involves working with groups and organizing coordinating committees of agencies in the community, which means working with people in the neighborhoods and schools, churches, and social and civic agencies. It involves organization of self-help movements among the client population, aimed at changing the factors and social stresses that tend to influence mental health. Bulbulyan stated that she did not believe that the therapist role is the most important role for the psychiatric nurse. Other nursing roles are equally important, particularly those that involve the sum total of the nurse's unique background *as* a nurse, and her ability to integrate mental health concepts in other areas and to assist all members of the team to function effectively.

Nurses, by virtue of their medical and social science background, are well prepared to function in community psychiatry. It is the particular combination of skills that nurses have that makes them unique and valuable members of the team. Because they are rooted in the biological and sociological disciplines, they are in an unique position to assess a client's problems, to interpret them to the appropriate specialist, and to intervene constructively themselves.[75]

⟨[Concluding Remarks

It is evident that, in a few short years, nurses have established their usefulness in community mental health work. As members of the health professions, nurses are interested primarily in fostering the physical and emotional welfare of individuals. The generality of their orientation is useful. They are oriented toward the whole person, in the context of his family and community. Because of their generally pragmatic approach, they are able to help people deal more effectively with some of the realistic problems of life, such as poverty, illness, child-rearing problems, and family-life problems. They are comfortable in making home visits, and are usually well accepted into the clients' homes. Because they are skilled at working collaboratively with other health professionals in the community, such as public health nurses, they make excellent liaison people and mental health consultants.

Nurses have been active in defining the theoretical basis for practice. In crisis intervention and suicide prevention programs, nurses have delineated the theoretical framework on which crisis intervention is based.[3]

The additional concepts and skills needed by psychiatric nurses to enable them to move into community mental health work are being identified and integrated into graduate programs. These include such things as knowledge of community organization techniques, of mental health consultation, of social systems, of group processes, and of the epidemiology of mental illness. Among the trends that are most obvious in the practice of psychiatric nursing are broadened scope of practice, greater diversity of roles, greater responsibility, and greater extension into the community. One prediction I can safely make for the future is that there will be even more change.

⟨[Bibliography

1. ABROMS, G. M. and N. S. GREENFIELD, eds. *The New Hospital Psychiatry*. New York: Academic, 1971.
2. ADELSON, D. "Community Mental Health: A New Frontier," in M. E. Kalkman, ed., *Psychiatric Nursing*, 3rd ed., pp. 279–293. New York: McGraw-Hill, 1967.
3. AGUILERA, D. C., J. M. MESSICK, and M. S. FARRELL. *Crisis Intervention: Theory and Methodology*. St. Louis: C. V. Mosby, 1970.

4. AMENDT, J. A. and R. O. WHITE. "Continued Care for Mental Patients," *Nurs. Outlook*, 13 (1965), 56–60.

5. AMERICAN NURSES ASSOCIATION, Division on Psychiatric-Mental Health Nursing. *Statement on Psychiatric Nursing Practice.* New York: Am. Nurses Assoc., 1967.

6. ANDERSON, D. B. "Nursing Therapy with Families," *Perspect. Psychiatr. Care*, 7 (1968), 21–27.

7. ARAFEH, M., E. K. FUMIATTI, M. E. GREGORY et al. "Linking Hospital and Community Care for Psychiatric Patients," *Am. J. Nurs.*, 68 (1968), 1050–1056.

8. ATTY, L. M. "A New Technician in the Mental Health Field," *Perspect. Psychiatr. Care*, 10 (1972), 13–18.

9. BARTEN, H. H. and L. BELLAK, eds. *Progress in Community Mental Health*, Vol. 2. New York: Grune & Stratton, 1972.

10. BELLAK, L. and H. H. BARTEN, eds. *Progress in Community Mental Health*, Vol. 1. New York: Grune & Stratton, 1969.

11. BINDMAN, A. J. and A. SPIEGEL, eds. *Perspectives in Community Mental Health.* Chicago: Aldine, 1969.

12. BLACK, K. M. "An Existential Model for Psychiatric Nursing," *Perspect. Psychiatr. Care*, 6 (1968), 178–184.

13. BOURGEOIS, T. L. "Reinforcement Theory in Teaching the Mentally Retarded," *Perspect. Psychiatr. Care*, 6 (1968), 116–136.

14. BROCKMEIER, M. J. "Nursing in Two Community Health Settings," *Nurs. Outlook*, 16 (1968), 55–58.

15. BULBULYAN, A. A. "The Psychiatric Nurse as Family Therapist," *Perspect. Psychiatr. Care*, 7 (1969), 58–68.

16. ———. "The Extended Roles of the Prepared Professional Psychiatric–Mental Health Nurse in Primary Prevention," in G. Stokes, ed., *The Roles of Psychiatric Nurses in Community Mental Health Practice: A Giant Step*, pp. 103–120. Brooklyn, N.Y.: Faculty Press, 1969.

17. BULBULYAN, A. A., R. M. DAVIDITES, and F. WILLIAMS. "Nurses in a Community Mental Health Center," *Am. J. Nurs.*, 69 (1969), 328–331.

18. CAPLAN, G. *Principles of Preventive Psychiatry.* New York: Basic Books, 1964.

19. ———. *The Theory and Practice of Mental Health Consultation.* New York: Basic Books, 1970.

20. CASKEY, K. R., E. V. BLAYLOCK, B. M. WAUSON. "The School Nurse and Drug Abusers," *Nurs. Outlook*, 18 (1970), 27–30.

21. COCKRILL, V. K. and M. E. BERNAL. "Operant Conditioning of Verbal Behavior in a Withdrawn Patient by a Patient Peer," *Perspect. Psychiatr. Care*, 6 (1968), 230–237.

22. DAVIDITES, R. M. "The Extended Roles of the Prepared Professional Psychiatric–Mental Health Nurse in the General Hospital Setting," in G. Stokes, ed., *The Roles of Psychiatric Nurses in Community Mental Health Practice: A Giant Step*, pp. 75–102. Brooklyn, N.Y.: Faculty Press, 1969.

23. DELOUGHERY, G. W., K. M. GEBBIE, and B. M. NEUMAN. *Consultation and Community Organization in Community Mental Health Nursing.* Baltimore: Williams & Wilkins, 1971.

24. DEPAUL, A. O. "The Nurse as a Central Figure in a Mental Health Center," *Perspect. Psychiatr. Care*, 6 (1968), 17–24.

25. DEYOUNG, C. D. "Nursing's Contribution to Family Crisis Treatment," *Nurs. Outlook*, 16 (1968), 60–62.

26. DEYOUNG, C. D. and M. TOWER. *Out of Uniform and Into Trouble.* St. Louis: C. V. Mosby, 1971.

27. FOREMAN, N. J. and J. V. ZERWEKH. "Drug Crisis Intervention," *Am. J. Nurs.*, 71 (1971), 1736–1739.

28. GEBBIE, K. M., G. DELOUGHERY, and B. M. NEUMAN. "Levels of Utilization: Nursing Specialists in Community Mental Health," *J. Psychiatr. Nurs. Ment. Health Serv.*, 8 (1970), 37–39.

29. GLASSCOTE, M. A., J. N. SUSSEX, E. CUMMING et al. *The Community Mental Health Center: An Interim Appraisal.* Joint Information Service of the Am. Psychiatric Assoc. and the Natl. Assoc. Ment. Health. Baltimore: Garamond/Pridemark, 1969.

30. GLASSCOTE, R. M. and J. E. GUDEMAN. *The Staff of the Mental Health Center: A Field Study.* Joint Information Service of the Am. Psychiatric Assoc. and the Natl. Assoc. Ment. Health. Washington: U.S. Govt. Print. Off., 1969.

31. GOLDMAN, E., ed. *Community Mental Health Nursing: The Practitioner's Point of View.* New York: Appleton-Century-Crofts, 1972.

32. GRIER, A. M. and C. K. ALDRICH. "The Growth of a Crisis Intervention Unit under the Direction of a Clinical Nursing Specialist in Psychiatric Nursing," *Perspect. Psychiatr. Care*, 10 (1972), 73–83.

33. HESS, G. "Perception of Nursing Role in a Developing Mental Health Center," *J. Psychiatr. Nurs. Ment. Health Serv.*, 7 (1969), 77–81.

34. HICKS, C., G. L. DELOUGHERY, and K. M. GEBBIE. "Progress in Community Mental Health Nursing: Is Role Diffusion Ending?" *J. Psychiatr. Nurs. Ment. Health Ser.*, 9 (1971), 28–29.

35. HOLMES, M. J. "Nursing Intervention with a Dying Patient," in M. Duffey, E. H. Anderson, B. S. Bergerson et al., eds., *Current Concepts in Clinical Nursing*, Vol. 3, pp. 37–47. St. Louis: Mosby, 1971.

36. ———. "Influences of the New Hospital Psychiatry on Nursing," in G. Abroms and N. Greenfield, eds., *The New Hospital Psychiatry*, pp. 83–100. New York: Academic, 1971.

37. HOLMES, M. J. and J. A. WERNER. *Psychiatric Nursing in a Therapeutic Community*. New York: Macmillan, 1966.

38. JOINT COMMISSIONS ON MENTAL ILLNESS AND HEALTH. *Action for Mental Health*. New York: Basic Books, 1961.

39. JONES, M. *The Therapeutic Community*. New York: Basic Books, 1953.

40. KALKMAN, M. E. *Psychiatric Nursing*, 3rd ed. New York: McGraw-Hill, 1967.

41. KNEISL, C. R. "Increasing Interpersonal Understanding through Sociodrama," *Perspect. Psychiatr. Care*, 6 (1968), 104–109.

42. LEININGER, M. M. "Community Psychiatric Nursing: Trends, Issues, and Problems," *Perspect. Psychiatr. Care*, 7 (1969), 10–20.

43. LESSLER, K. and J. BRIDGET. "The Psychiatric Nurse in a Mental Health Clinic," in A. J. Bindman and A. Spiegel, eds., *Perspectives in Community Mental Health*, pp. 585–592. Chicago: Aldine, 1969.

44. LEWIS, E. P., ed. *The Clinical Nurse Specialist*. New York: American Journal of Nurs. Co., 1970.

45. ———. *Changing Patterns in Nursing Practice*. New York: American Journal of Nurs. Co., 1971.

46. LEWIS, E. P. and M. H. BROWNING, eds. *The Nurse in Community Mental Health*.

New York: American Journal Nurs. Co., 1972.

47. LEWIS, G. K., M. J. HOLMES, and F. KATZ. *An Approach to the Education of Psychiatric Nursing Personnel*. New York: Natl. League for Nurs., 1961.

48. MacCALLUM, R. G. "A Study of the Activities of Nurses Working in Community Mental Health Centers in the State of Arizona." Master's thesis, College of Nursing, Arizona State University, 1973. Unpublished.

49. MELLOW, J. "The Experiental Order of Nursing Therapy in Acute Schizophrenia," *Perspect. Psychiatr. Care*, 6 (1968), 245–255.

50. MERENESS, D. A. "Family Therapy: An Evolving Role for the Psychiatric Nurse," *Perspect. Psychiatr. Care*, 6 (1968), 256–259.

51. MERTZ, H. "How the Nurse Helps the Patient in His Experience with Psychiatric Care," *Perspect. Psychiatr. Care*, 6 (1968), 260–263.

52. MESSICK, J. M. and D. C. AGUILERA. "Realistic Utilization: Levels of Preparation," *J. Psychiatr. Nurs. Ment. Health Ser.*, 6 (1968), 133–137.

53. MISHEL, M. H. "Crisis Theory and Crisis Therapy Applied in a Nurse–Patient Situation," in *Exploring Progress in Psychiatric Nursing Practice*. New York: Am. Nurses Assoc., 1966.

54. MISTR, V. R. "Community Nursing Service for Psychiatric Patients," *Perspect. Psychiatr. Care*, 6 (1968), 36–41.

55. MURPHY, J. F., ed. *Theoretical Issues in Professional Nursing*. New York: Appleton-Century-Crofts, 1971.

56. NATIONAL LEAGUE FOR NURSING, Department of Baccalaureate and Higher Degree Programs. *Brochure on Masters Education*. New York: Natl. League Nurs., 1972.

57. PEARSON, B. A. "Methadone Maintenance in Heroin Addiction," *Am. J. Nurs.*, 70 (1970), 2571–2574.

58. PEPLAU, H. E. *Interpersonal Relations in Nursing*. New York: Putnam, 1952.

59. ———. "Principles of Psychiatric Nursing," in S. Arieti, ed. *American Handbook of Psychiatry*, Vol. 2, 1st ed., pp. 1840–1856. New York: Basic Books, 1959.

60. ———. "Interpersonal Techniques: The

Crisis of Psychiatric Nursing," *Am. J. Nurs.*, 62 (1962), 50–54.

61. ———. "The Nurse in the Community Mental Health Program," *Nurs. Outlook*, 13 (1965), 68–70.

62. ———. "Psychotherapeutic Strategies," *Perspect. Psychiatr. Care*, 6 (1968), 264–270.

63. POPKIN, D. R. "Resurrection City, U.S.A.: Social Action and Mental Health," *Perspect. Psychiatr. Care*, 6 (1968), 198–204.

64. ROBINSON, L. "Liaison Psychiatric Nursing," *Perspect. Psychiatr. Care*, 6 (1968), 87–91.

65. SCARPITTI, F. R., J. ALBINI, E. BAKER et al. "Public Health Nurses in a Community Care Program for the Mentally Ill," *Am. J. Nurs.*, 65 (1965), 89–95.

66. SCHULBERG, H. C. and F. BAKER. "Interprofessional Relationships," in H. Grunebaum, ed., *The Practice of Community Mental Health*, pp. 645–662. Boston: Little, Brown, 1970.

67. SHELDON, A. and P. K. HOPE. "The Developing Role of the Nurse in a Community Mental Health Program," *Perspect. Psychiatr. Care*, 6 (1968), 36–41.

68. SINKLER, G. H. "Identity and Role," *Nurs. Outlook*, 18 (1970), 22–24.

69. STOKES, G. A. "Extending the Roles of the Psychiatric–Mental Health Nurse in Community Mental Health," *Nurs. Clin. North Am.*, 5 (1970), 638–645.

70. STOKES, G. A., ed. *The Roles of Psychiatric Nurses in Community Mental Health*

Practice: A Giant Step. Brooklyn: Faculty Press, 1969.

71. SWANSON, M. G. and A. M. WOOLSON. "A New Approach to the Use of Learning Theory with Psychiatric Patients," *Perspect. Psychiatr. Care*, 10 (1972), 55–68.

72. TRAVELBEE, J. *Intervention in Psychiatric Nursing: Process in the One-to-One Relationship.* Philadelphia: Davis, 1969.

73. TUDOR, G. "A Sociopsychiatric Nursing Approach to Intervention in a Problem of Mutual Withdrawal on a Mental Hospital Ward," *Psychiatry*, 15 (1952), 193–217.

74. UJHELY, G. B. *Determinants of the Nurse Patient Relationship.* New York: Springer, 1968.

75. ———. "The Nurse in Community Psychiatry," *Am. J. Nurs.*, 69 (1969), 1001–1005.

76. WILLIAMS, F. S. "The Extended Roles of the Prepared Professional Psychiatric–Mental Health Nurse in Secondary and Tertiary Prevention," in G. Stokes, ed., *The Roles of Psychiatric Nurses in Community Mental Health Practice: A Giant Step*, pp. 53–74. Brooklyn: Faculty Press, 1969.

77. YOLLES, S. F. "The Drug Scene," *Nurs. Outlook*, 18 (1970), 24–26.

78. ZAHOUREK, R. "Nurses in a Community Mental Health Center: Functions, Competencies and Satisfactions," *Nurs. Outlook*, 19 (1971), 592–595.

79. ZAHOUREK, R. and M. TOWER. "Therapeutic Abortion: The Psychiatric Nurse as Therapist, Liaison, and Consultant," *Perspect. Psychiatr. Care*, 10 (1971), 64–71.

CHAPTER 35

SOCIAL WORK IN PSYCHIATRIC SETTINGS

Helen Harris Perlman

PROBABLY at no time has it been more difficult to define and describe the helping process called "psychiatric social work." Since the 1950s it has been, (along with all other "mental-health professions") subject to upheavals in social thought and structures, to shifts in values, and to questions and challenges about causes and cures and instruments and methods of help. Thus psychiatric social work has been pushed and pulled by swift and often radical social and professional movements. The only certainty one can presume to set down in describing what is or what may be, with respect to this field—is that nothing is certain. What follows is an effort to catch and for a brief time hold steady a complex of purposes, forms, and processes that moves even as one tries to pin the subject down. The first step in this chapter is to define the subject's boundaries and nature; the second, to describe its development; and the third, to describe its present operations and directions—which are all in flux.

⟨ Social Work in Psychiatric Settings

"Psychiatric social work" is social work within a psychiatric hospital, department, or clinic. It embraces a range of services that stem from the idea that the patient, like all other persons, is affected by (and in turn affects) current and potent transactions between himself, the "significant others," and significant circumstances in his social environment. Those services include: (1) direct problem-solving guidance, counseling, and psychotherapy for the patients themselves (usually in outpatient clinics); (2) the gathering and transmission to the treatment team of information about the patient's dynamic social milieu (formerly in terms of "background history," currently in transactional terms); (3) direct efforts to influence those persons and situations assumed to be vital to the patient's ill- or well-being; and (4) direct efforts to find and arrange those material aids or services needed by the patient and/or his family to facilitate their adequate social functioning (whether within the hospital or on the outside). Which of these services are most characteristically or frequently in use is determined by a number of factors: the treatment beliefs and bents of the leader psychiatrists in any given setting; and, of course, the beliefs, bents, and skills of the psychiatric social worker herself. (The feminine pronoun is used here not out of female chauvinism but because clinical social workers in psychiatric settings are predominantly women.)

The professionally prepared psychiatric social worker today is more appropriately called a "clinical social worker," "clinical" being used here in its etymological sense of being *with* the patient as observer and helper. This is in contrast with the social worker whose unit of attention is a community or a "catchment area," or one whose activities are focused not on the individual patient or client but on supervising, teaching, consulting with direct service personnel, administering or organizing services, working with community members towards the development of good mental health conditions on a wider scale, and so forth. These kinds of social work activities have proliferated with the community mental-health movement. Sometimes they are carried along with clinical functions, but often they require the social worker's full time and energies. No identifying title has been given to the combination of these varied functions. Certainly the older term "psychiatric social work" does not convey their nature, even though they are performed under the aegis of a psychiatric setting.

Thus, for the purposes of this account the direct-service functions of social workers in psychiatric settings will be the focus of discussion. Clinical social work was once all but synonymous with casework. Today it often combines case- and groupwork. "The case" is seen not only as the patient/client himself but as a unit of transaction involving family members or "significant others," as well as significant social circumstances. Such "others" may be dealt with as a group (as a family), and sometimes patients themselves may be drawn into group rather than individual interview

sessions, in order to increase their socialization capacities or because the patient has problems in common with others, such as preparing for discharge from the hospital, rejoining families, and so forth. The choice of treatment mode, whether by social worker, psychiatrist or others is often a matter of expedience or personal style. Criteria for such choice have yet to be developed.

The clinical social worker is called a "psychiatric social worker" when she is employed in a psychiatric setting. She may previously have worked in a family counseling agency, where she would have been a "family caseworker." Tomorrow she may elect to work in a child welfare agency, where she would become a "child therapist" or "adoption worker" or, more generally, a "child welfare caseworker." In brief, the major function of the employing agency determines the major area of the clinical social worker's specialization. As will be discussed in detail later, the basic training in schools of social work for direct work with clients/patients is generic, essentially the same for all. Specialization and expertise in any one of the many problem fields in which social workers practice are learned, it is assumed, from various postgraduate sources and from the actual experience that psychiatric (or other) settings offer.

Theoretically—and increasingly in actuality —the special arena for professional clinical social work, whether in the psychiatric setting or elsewhere, is the field of transactions involving the patient/client and his tasks or other persons. It is generally agreed that casework–groupwork processes have as their goal the restoration or enhancement of the individual's social functioning in its twofold aspect of personal gratification and social effectiveness.[2] The part of the person's global "social functioning" selected out and concentrated upon at one time, the decisions made about the "treatment of choice," the emphasis given to direct client/patient therapeutic interviewing (rather than, say, the attempt to influence the attitude and behavior of teachers or spouse or to making arrangements for job training, boarding care, relief grants, and so forth)— the determination of all these variables is (or should be) the consequence of diagnostic assessments and treatment planning by the psychiatric team.

The special stance which differentiates the social worker from her clinical teammates (psychologist, psychiatrist, nurse, etc.) is her consistent focus upon the interchange between the psycho- and socio-dynamics in the patient/client's problem. The range of the social worker's treatment targets, then, extends from the disturbed individual himself to those persons and conditions in his proximal environment with which he is in vital transaction. Thus when external relationships or conditions tend to lead to stress and strain, their modification or amelioration becomes the focus of work. In social work this has been called "environmental modification" or "manipulation." When the feelings, thought processes, or actions of the client/patient are the sources of malfunctioning, they become the focus of treatment attention. But even then they are dealt with chiefly as they play themselves out in the person's social situation, bringing him rewards or (more frequently) forms of social punishment or hurt. In varying degree, most cases call for efforts both to increase the patient's coping capacities and to diminish the external obstacles to this end.

Some problems are inherent in the social worker's special focus. Often—and this is more true in psychiatric hospitals than in clinics—the psychiatric staff views the social-work staff simply as "arrangers" of socially necessary circumstances or as "linkers" between patient and the outside.[1] While these are no mean services, and while they may require considerable skill, they are often "handed down from above" by psychiatric authority, with the result that environmental modification services have frequently been denigrated by social workers themselves.

This denigration of the importance of the special skills involved in influencing the patient's social situation has until recently been due to the lack of clear understanding among social workers themselves of just how potent social experience is as it shapes and colors psychological dysfunction. Even today in community health centers and other psychi-

atric settings, "environmental modification" tends to be assigned to the untrained personnel, on the tacit assumption that it requires more footwork than headwork. But a number of emerging notions and practices have begun to highlight the necessity for professional knowledge and skill in dealing with the persons and happenings in the current life of the psychiatric patient. Among these are: (1) the rise of family treatment as a therapeutic mode, based on recognition of the powerful dynamics in family roles and interrelationships; (2) concepts from systems theory and concepts of social roles that link the personality to social expectations and inputs; (3) the heightened awareness of the effects of economic-sociocultural forces upon personal development and behavior; and (4) the fresh recognition of the complexities in urban and bureaucratized life that make it difficult for even the fully capable person to find and connect with problem-solving resources. These and other enlightened views of the second half of that long-used hyphenated term "psychosocial" are bringing fresh impetus to the social worker's interest in the current living environment of the client/patient.

When, as is frequent, the psychiatric social worker carries responsibility for direct treatment of the patient's mental-emotional-behavioral disorder, it may be all but impossible—and perhaps not even useful—to differentiate her psychotherapeutic process from that of the psychiatrist. The reasons for this are not hard to see. Many principles of treatment skill and direction are "common property" of all helping professions;[11] many psychiatrists, like social workers, are breaking out from old molds and experimenting with new treatment methods; increasingly psychiatrists are sensitive to economic-sociocultural factors in their patient's life (though they may not directly deal with them in treatment); when they operate well team members teach and learn from one another; and so on. Especially for inexperienced social workers "psychotherapy" has both an allure, for its implications of status and helping power, and also a forbidding aspect because of its ambiguity of definition and its frequent misuse as a synonym for psychoanalysis. The adequately schooled and experienced psychiatric social worker tends to be steady in her recognition of the common knowledge and skills she shares with her collaborators along with the area of special expertise of each.

Whether in the psychiatric setting of clinic or hospital, or in schools, medical centers, family and children's agencies, clinical social work represents a continuum of services. At one extreme is the work of finding and providing resources necessary to physical subsistence and adequate social functioning. At the other is the work of psychological influence upon a person's feelings, thought, and behavior so that he can carry his social relationships and tasks with (for him) minimal cost and maximal satisfaction and effectiveness. In-between lies that broad range of personal social interchanges which requires continuous attention to the interface between people's inner and outer realities. The patient/client may need a job and be unable to find one—and have no means of subsistence. He may want a job and be unable to find one—and feels he is slipping back into his apathy again. He has a job but is unable to bear it. He likes his job, but cannot seem to please his boss. He does alright on his job—but things at home are so bad he cannot keep his mind on it. The psycho-social variations on just this one theme suggest the range of social and psychological services that may be involved in the activities of a psychiatric social worker among many cases and, often, within a single case.

Within the broad margins of agreement on their functions and purposes, today's clinical social workers use a diversity of treatment methods. Once they adhered to outlines of treatment derived from the psychoanalytic model. Today's modes of treatment are varied, however, reflecting many new perspectives on and notions about the cause and course of mental illness. For reasons to be discussed later, all clinical personnel and not only social workers are trying out a number of new methods in the push to be more effective and to help more people. Short-term, crisis-oriented, task-centered forms of individualized treatment; group therapies such as sensitivity,

encounter, and transactional family therapy—all these and others are to be found as the preferred or dominant treatment mode at different places and times. It is not always possible to establish whether the "treatment of choice" derives from the personal style of the helper, from some leap out of frustration onto the bandwagon of a fad, or from some persuasive theory that has been carefully translated into action principles.

The treatment mode that seems currently to be gaining most interest and adherents in psychiatric settings, among all staff members, is operant conditioning. Its specificity, its controls, the measurability of its outcomes—these among other factors offer the attraction of security and limits in settings that are characteristically stressful because of the overload of patients and the complexities of the problems encountered. But many psychiatric social workers are uneasy about this treatment mode, fearing that the humanism that underlies more traditional treatment methods may wither under actual or pseudo-scientism.

For the most part, however, a few long-practiced modes of clinical social work still seem to be predominant.[12,17,19,23] Currently they are the most widely taught in schools of social work. While there are differences of emphasis among them, certain convictions and principles governing skill are basic to them all.

Underlying all of clinical social work is a belief in the worth of the individual man, and therefore a commitment to provide the necessary means, social and psychological, by which he can realize his worth. There is the belief that the person is more than his illness or failure, and that, therefore, his motivation, capacities and opportunities to realize that "more" must be ascertained and developed. The belief in the interpenetration between man's psychological and social experience, already explicated, suggests focus and goal.[20]

Among the skills learned and practiced by most clinical social workers are: the development and management of relationship with the client for the many powers of nurture and safety that this human bond proffers; the lowering of excess stress through environmental changes as well as empathic sharing of emotion and ventilation of conflict; the identification, clarification, and selection or division of the problem to be placed in the center of attention at any given time; the exploration of conflict and ambivalences; the consideration of the connections between the person's feelings, thought, actions, and between these and their effects upon others; consideration of action choices and decisions, in the light of their probable consequences; the facilitation of connections between the primary client and such persons and/or things as he may need. In capsule, the skills of the competent clinical social worker, used differentially in line with her ongoing assessments, are fashioned by present-day understanding of the means by which ego capacities are strengthened and exercised in coping.

⟮ Professional Education for Clinical Social Work

The professionally prepared social worker has earned a master's degree from an accredited school of social work in a university. Until the mid-1950s many such schools had a carefully prescribed curriculum of courses for the preparation of "psychiatric social workers," just as there was a specialized curriculum in other fields such as child welfare, medical social work, family casework, and so forth. Since that time however, such specializations have been abandoned.

Several major factors supported the movement towards "generic" casework and, later, group work. One was the fact that social workers were highly mobile, moving often from one setting to another and apparently able to adapt their basic knowledge and skills to the particular requirements of the new field. More important was the growing conviction (and actual evidence) that whatever the problem area that differentiated one setting from another, all work with individuals and small groups required a basic understanding of normal and deviant behavior, of personality development, of psychosocial forces in people's daily lives, and of the means by which people could be influenced to cope with their

recognized problems. Indeed, in family and children's agencies, in school social work, in general hospitals, and elsewhere, social caseworkers were dealing with as many problems of psychological disturbance and social malfunctioning as were to be found in psychiatric clinics. Therefore schools of social work moved to infuse all courses concerning direct work with people with the theoretical perspectives and the ensuing treatment principles that had previously been the special content of the psychiatric sequence.

The social work student who wants to do "social treatment," as differentiated from the student interested in "social development,"* now undertakes approximately the following course of study:

1. Courses in personality development and socialization, combining psychodynamic theory with theories and findings on ethnic, class, and cultural dynamics; courses in deviant development and behavior, as found both in adults and children.

2. Courses in social welfare policies, programs, and problems (in order to attain a basic orientation toward income maintenance and social insurance programs, health care provisions, and so forth).

3. Courses in "methods", that is, instruction in the processes by which people's emotions, attitudes, thought, and behavior may be influenced towards more satisfying and adequate social functioning. Such courses may concentrate on casework or on group work; increasingly, there are combinations of both. The problems such methods deal with are identified and studied both in their objective forms (marital conflicts, child neglect, school dropout, and so forth) and in their subjective and individualized forms with consequent implications for treatment.

* The terms, "social treatment" and "social development," are taken from curriculm statements of the University of Chicago's School of Social Service Administration. Other schools may use these or synonymous terms. "Social treatment" embraces helping services and processes used in direct work with individuals and/or small groups. "Social development" encompasses community organization and planning, administration, research and other processes aimed at macro-system influence.

4. Increasingly, as research studies and experiments have yielded knowledge not only of the nature of psychological and social problems but of outcomes of social and psychological interventions such studies have been incorporated into relevant courses and/or studied as research. Research courses at the master's-degree level attempt chiefly to teach the rudiments of statistical and measurement concepts, so that clinical (and other) social workers may be intelligent and critical readers of published studies and cogent participants in agency research projects.

5. A practicum, or "field work"—the counterpart of classroom theory on treatment. Concurrent with class work, cases in psychiatric, medical, or social agencies are carried under the tutelage of experienced, professionally qualified supervisors or field teachers. This is done two to three days a week or in block placements of several months at a time, following and preceding class sessions. The student whose interest lies in working with emotionally disturbed adults or children may opt for a field placement in a psychiatric clinic or hospital. In that sense she may establish her specialization. The fact is, however, that many family and children's agencies also offer experience in dealing with people suffering emotional disturbances and have close collaborative or consultative relationships with psychiatrists.

Doctoral study in schools of social work has been developing rapidly over the past decade. Most doctoral programs have concentrated on preparing experienced social workers to become teachers, researchers, or social development planners. Few as yet offer clinical doctorates, but the need for ongoing, higher-level clinical knowledge, skill, and critical analysis is increasingly recognized. A number of other urgent pressures in the 1960s—among them, the pressure to use money and brain-power resources for dealing with massive social problems—forced attention away from individualized treatment. In the meantime, many clinical social workers take advanced courses in problems or processes in treatment where they can find them—in extension courses, in

psychotherapy institutes, in private group seminars with psychiatrists, and so on.

At the other end of educational preparation for social work, there has been a recent burgeoning of undergraduate "social welfare" courses in bachelor's programs and in junior colleges. Casework and/or group work, often accompanied by field experience, take a prominent place in these undergraduate programs. Widespread manpower needs within mental health programs have brought many young and only partially prepared persons into positions as aides, subprofessionals, and paraprofessionals; as a result, there has been a frequent blurring of the boundaries of skill and responsibilities between such persons and the professional clinical worker.

([Background and Development of Psychiatric Social Work

"Social treatment" in conjunction with psychiatry was instituted by several outstanding psychiatrists who, early in the 20th century, had come to understand the relationship between people's mental and emotional health or sickness and their social circumstances. In 1904, Adolph Meyer of the Manhattan State Hospital encouraged his wife to visit the families of his patients for the purposes of helping to broaden the clinical understanding of social forces affecting the patients' lives and "reaching out to the sources of sickness . . ." Not long thereafter, social services began to be part of the treatment in a number of neurological and psychiatric hospitals in Boston and New York. Best known was the development at Boston Psychopathic Hospital under E. E. Southard, because its social worker director, Mary Jarrett, gave impetus and direction to the growth of psychiatric social work. The purposes and operations of the psychiatric social worker—a title coined by Jarrett—in collaborative work with the psychiatrist were first clearly set forth there. Treatment was "construed in its broadest sense to mean restoration of capacity for normal living or provision of the greatest possible comfort."[p. 521][24] To this end the social worker, in addition to taking a social history, dealt with the patient's family in relation to his needs and acted as a linker between the patient and such community resources and agencies as were necessary to his social and emotional adaptations.

In 1914 Southard, Jarrett, and others began apprentice training for social workers at the hospital, and courses were given at the Simmons College School of Social Work. Adolph Meyer, having become director of the Phipps Clinic of Johns Hopkins Hospital, hired a social worker who, along with her clinical responsibilities, took part in the training of students of social work in the School of Economics at Johns Hopkins. By 1918 social workers had been drawn into leading psychiatric clinics and hospitals not only in the large eastern cities but as far west as Chicago. Schools preparing social workers in New York, Boston, Philadelphia, and Chicago all offered courses in aspects of psychopathology. In 1918 Smith College put forward the first curriculum for the preparation of psychiatric social workers. World War I, with its aftermath of mentally and emotionally disturbed veterans, had given impetus to the public recognition of mental disturbance and the need for social as well as psychiatric treatment.

Concurrent with the growth of psychiatric social work were several other developments that required the services and the special training of psychiatrically oriented caseworkers. One was the "visiting teacher" movement (later called "school social work"), which came into being as behavior problems of children began to concern school personnel and as the concept of prevention became widespread. Another was the study (particularly by William Healy at Chicago's Juvenile Psychopathic Institute) of the "feeble-minded" and the "psychopaths" and the noxious social conditions of which these cases were held to be both cause and effect. A third development was the "mental hygiene movement," with its intent to disseminate conceptions of mental health that would contribute toward goals both of reform and of prevention. Psychiatric social workers were drawn into each of these developments. Beyond their direct service to individual cases,

they were extensively involved as interpreters and educators in mental health concepts, as consultants to social agencies dealing with families and children, and as co-planners and administrators of programs aimed at increasing community understanding and support of mental health efforts.

Because of the psychiatric social worker's identification with dynamic psychiatry, because her training (based on the medical model) was probably the most disciplined in form and content, and because she was visible within the "social psychiatry" movement as a leader outside clinical and hospital walls, the psychiatric social worker came to be regarded by her fellow social workers as one of an "elite" group. When in 1926 the American Association of Psychiatric Social Workers was formed, its purpose was twofold: to develop the specialization of social work in relation to psychiatry, and to contribute to other fields of social-work practice the "mental hygiene" knowledge and insights essential to working with people. This dual commitment—to people needing psychiatric help and to the dissemination of psychodynamic knowledge for use by all social workers—was articulated in 1919 by Jarrett.[13] It was a position broadened and strengthened in 1929 by two outstanding leaders of social psychiatry, Porter Lee, a social worker, and Marion Kenworthy,[15] a psychiatrist.

As far as expertise in social work treatment was involved, the psychiatric social worker remained a leader for the next decade, especially the worker in child guidance clinics. Established and founded in the early 1920s by the Commonwealth Fund, eight outstanding "demonstration" child guidance clinics flourished into the 1930s. In a number of planned (and also unforeseen) ways, the clinics heavily influenced the direction and quality of all social casework. They were innovative by design and attracted clearly superior personnel from the several collaborating professions. The psychiatric social worker in these clinics was able to develop her clinical skills in diagnosis and treatment most fully.[7] Typically, she probed the social-environment factors with which the problem child was in transaction.

But more than this: while the psychiatrist took the child as his patient, the caseworker took the mother as client, in treatment collaboration. Not infrequently the mother was more disturbed than the child, and often she was the more difficult client. Under the tutelage of such talented psychiatrists as David Levy, Lawson Lowrey, and Marion Kenworthy, the psychiatric social worker learned and then articulated and taught the principles governing treatment that emerged from a growing grasp of psychodynamics. The therapeutic powers of relationship, long experienced by social workers, now began to be understood and put to conscious use. The effect of scarcely conscious attitudes and motivations upon behavior turned social workers to eliciting feelings and ambivalences. By these and many other insights applied to treatment, and by her observations and assessments of the active social components involved in cause and cure, the child guidance caseworker found herself a valued and vital member of the clinical team. Whether because of the "halo effect" of demonstration clinics or because of the happy combinations of secure and competent personnel, the team relationships in these clinics seem to have achieved a high level of collaborative respect and effectiveness. For the psychiatric social worker, it was an experience that secured her professional identity and proficiency.

The dissemination of the insights and skills of psychiatric social work came largely as a result of the depression in the 1930s. Child guidance clinics and demonstration projects in school social work were all but choked off by the constriction of supporting funds and by the sudden shift of attention from preventive mental hygiene to the harsh realities of the economic collapse and its resultant crises. Many psychiatrically knowledgeable and skillful caseworkers moved into the newly established public welfare agencies, concerned to build a system that not only provided "relief" but also considered the "common human needs" of relief clients. Many others, pushed by the contraction of psychiatric services and pulled by their interest in the problems of families and children being dealt with under

social work's own auspices, joined the staffs of family and children's agencies. Often they served as consultants and teachers of psychodynamic theories to staff members who had not as yet been educated in this area. Often they taught, full or part-time, in schools of social work.

Small though their number was, their influence was powerful in the development of treatment of psychosocial problems, partly because of the implicit promise and hope that psychiatric knowledge might unlock the mysteries of human motivation and influence, and partly because the psychiatrically trained social worker of the 1930s was probably the most systematically trained and clinically sophisticated of caseworkers. From the social agency the psychiatric social worker in turn drew sustenance and added knowledge and stature. Beyond the immediate patient or client and his family, she came to see more broadly the environmental factors that affect emotional well-being as well as the psychological import inherent in such humdrum things as money, housing, and jobs.* Added to this was the psychiatric social worker's new experience within the social agency of both the responsibilities and rewards of autonomy. Though she frequently used psychiatrists as guides and consultants on her cases, her accountability was to a social rather than to a medical agency, and her sense of identification with social work (rather than with psychiatry) was enhanced. Under these conditions, psychiatric casework and generic casework began to fuse.

In 1955 the American Association of Psychiatric Social Workers, along with several other specialist organizations of social workers, merged with social work's over-all membership organization, the National Association of Social Workers. The assumption was that all good direct service to clients and patients should be psychodynamically informed. "Psy-

* For perspectives of one outstanding psychiatric social worker and teacher see Charlotte Towle's comments in articles published in 1936 and 1939.[21] [Pp. 54, 61–65, 220–226, 228–234] See also her 1945 work.[25] Still read as a small classic it is an interpretation to new public assistance workers of the psychodynamics of everyday functioning of everyday people.

chiatric social work" came specifically to mean social work under psychiatric auspices.

(Trends and Problems

The years since World War II have brought social upheavals of many sorts. Expectably, the mental health professions—social work among them—have undergone shifts and upheavals of perspectives, beliefs, and modes of work. Along with other professions, clinical social work has made many adaptations of its practices to cope with new problems or with old ones freshly perceived and more fully understood. Two (among other) salient forces have affected social work in psychiatric settings: one, the rapprochement between psychodynamic and social science theories and research; and the other, the reorganization and expansion of hospital and clinical services resulting from the community mental health movement. These are intertwined factors, scarcely separable in reality; but each will be given separate comment.

Rapprochement of Theories

Hospitable to and informed in recent years by psychodynamic theories and perspectives, the research and constructs of several of the social sciences have been shaped by and have become more relevant to mental health concerns. Simultaneously, both dynamic psychiatry and social work began in the 1950s to look out from their long concentration upon intrapsychic and narrow interpersonal dynamics to identify the factors in the patient's or client's wider social experience that seemed to be potent determinants of his attitudes and behaviors. The social group to which the person was attached, the family as a transactional system, the "milieu" or environmental systems with which the person was in interaction— these social determinants, among others, came increasingly to be recognized and taken account of in the diagnosis and treatment of mental disturbance.

Among the earliest essays that affected social-work thought and practice was *Men Under Stress* (1945),[9] a study of soldiers whose breakdown under combat and subsequent course of recovery seemed signally related to current group morale and leadership. The author of a later work, *Social Science and Psychotherapy for Children* (1952),[22] was hired by the Jewish Board of Guardians, a psychoanalytically oriented social agency for the treatment of children, to identify social factors operating in emotional and behavioral disturbance. Today's clinical thinking— certainly that in schools of social work preparing case and group workers—is literally awash with concepts and notions from social science: systems theory as it bears on the therapeutic milieu, concepts of role, status, class, and ethnicity as they bear upon internalized and externally expressed attitudes and behavior; ideas from communications theory related to interpersonal and family group transactions; learning-theory propositions and their implications for conditioning of behavior; and so on.

Along with the spillover into social work of these newly formulated ways of viewing social forces in the lives of people, there has been the heightened concern of the total society over the persistence of poverty, the existence of racism, and the increase of crime—in short, over the prevalence and visibility of social "evils" and problems that both create and are created by mental/emotional disturbances. This concern has been experienced with particular intensity within social work.

The effects of these intensified concerns and new (or revived) perspectives upon the training and practice of social work have been manifold, unsettling, and as yet difficult to assess. In barest outline: in addition to explanations of psychodynamics social work students are increasingly exposed to considerations of sociodynamic factors in the lives of their clients and to the behavior-shaping forces inherent in social systems, whether in the dyad of a marital pair or in the staff groupings within an institution. Practice has shifted from exclusive use of the individual interview as the desired and status-giving mode of treatment to include family interviewing and often family treatment; group interviews (of persons with common concerns); "reaching out" by home visits and persistent efforts to engage the "hard-to-reach" or unmotivated patient or client; attempts to modify traditional "middleclass" treatment approaches in line with the differences of expectation and perception created by the client/patient's educational-sociocultural background; and efforts, as yet more trial-and-error than systematized, to deal with the "significant others" and the significant circumstances that constitute the individual's psychosocial life-space. Perhaps "ecosystem," a less static and more up-to-date term now given to "environment," will further social work's willing involvement in "social diagnosis" and in dealing with environmental forces.[8,10]

Reorganization of Services

The community mental-health movement, responsive to the vision of a group of "social psychiatrists,"[14] has been a second major force in the reshaping of psychiatric hospitals and clinics and of social work practice within them. Interchanges between the intent to provide accessible, swift, and comprehensive mental-health services to total communities and the impact of burgeoning knowledge about both social deficits and desiderata have resulted not only in a tremendous expansion and variation in services but also in changed methods of direct service.

The combination of chemotherapy with convictions about the undesirability of prolonged hospitalization and the psychological values of the patient's remaining in his natural community has led to recurring waves of discharged patients from (and of repeated readmissions to) hospitals. Yet the resumption of social functioning outside the hospital (whether with family, job or job training, a boarding home, or with sources of recreation) and the carrying of essential social tasks and roles is often a staggering prospect for the discharged patient. The necessity that he have an "enabler"—a linker between his needs and resources, a supporter, an advocate, a supplier of information and material aids—is obvious.

Social workers offer these services, which require many psychological skills of intervention with and influence upon the people who make up the patient's environment, in addition to those needed for dealing with the expatient himself. But the need for such services has far outstripped supply. Thus large numbers of untrained or partially trained personnel have been added to hospital and clinical staffs. Variously called "caseworkers," "social workers," "paraprofessionals," "social work aides," and so forth, they are often oriented, supervised, and taught by professional social workers whose own direct clinical work with patients and their families has diminished as their teaching–supervisory and administrative functions have increased. A recent study shows that on "casework therapy" for after-care patients, nonprofessional social workers gave far more time than did the professionals, as they did also in providing concrete services to patients and their families. They spent more than twice as much of their time "interviewing patients" as did the trained social workers. [p.108][1]

In part as a counteraction to the blurring of the social worker's professional identity and standards by this influx into clinical practice of large numbers of untrained personnel, a National Federation of Societies for Clinical Social Workers has been formed. While concerned with such problems as "third party payments" and licensing, another objective seems to be the protection and solidification of the values, knowledge and competences considered to be the benchmarks of professional clinical social work.

Necessity, sometimes happily and sometimes uneasily combined with theory, has forced many other changes in the direct diagnostic and treatment services at the community health center outpatient clinics. Staff shortages, increased patient applications, and some evidence of success in experiments with forms of short-term treatment have combined to make limited, brief help the typical treatment mode in the community clinic. Crisis treatment focused on a current crucial need or event, task-centered treatment focused on one selected aspect of a problem, operant condi-

tioning focused on the elimination of an identified symptom, group interviews wherein several persons with like problems are engaged in
problem-solving—these are among the common methods in use today by clinical social
workers, trained and untrained. It is evident
that many treatment values are to be found in
these new modes. It is quite possible, too,
that they are a healthy antidote to former slav-
ish adherence to interminable psychotherapy.
Yet among social workers (as among their
colleagues in psychiatry, psychology, and psychiatric nursing) there is some emerging and
uneasy awareness that the "treatment of
choice" seems to be determined more by expedience and the lure of the new than by
diagnostic considerations. But the press of
service demands has thus far not allowed for
critical examination of this possibility.[6]

Upon the fully trained social worker has
been placed many of the essential tasks of
disseminating mental health ideas to lay persons and also to other professionals in the
community, of consulting with other human
welfare institutions, and of collaborating with
others to develop social resources to fill the
deficit needs of ex-patients. These duties,
along with supervising subprofessional workers, teaching and learning in staff/team sessions, and carrying some or most administrative responsibilities, have considerably
enlarged the scope but often fragmented the
work of the present day psychiatric social
worker.

One further and differently directioned
trend in clinical social work must be noted:
the widespread growth of private practice by
professionally trained and clinically experienced social workers. The service provided is
usually psychotherapy. Its responsible practitioners attempt to maintain their social-work
identification, calling themselves "social psychotherapists," "psychiatric social workers," or
the like. Their required qualifications (set in
1964 by the National Association of Social
Workers) are a master's degree in social work,
followed by five years of fulltime practice
under the supervision of a professionally qualified supervisor. Beyond these basic requirements, many private social-work practitioners

have had personal psychotherapy and have
taken postgraduate courses in psychopathology, psychotherapeutic treatment, and so
forth. Furthermore, 95 percent of all private
practitioners maintain some practice connection with a social or psychiatric agency as a
source of both professional stimulation and
anchorage.[17]

That rapid social changes and new notions
and institutional rearrangements should bring
new problems in their wake is axiomatic. The
problems faced today in clinical social work
cluster mainly about considerations of its
functions in psychiatric settings and about the
educational preparation of its practitioners.

The growth and proliferation of community
mental-health centers occurred on a high
wave of both responsible concern for the mental health of the population and of optimism
about the available means by which it could
be secured and reinforced. Along with other
psychiatric personnel, social workers were literally scooped up into what took on the aspect
of a "movement." Their ranks were supplemented by numbers of paraprofessionals
(often also called "social workers"). As is inevitable, the visibility of resources raises the
awareness of need. Applications for help grew
geometrically, not only for problems of psychological dysfunction but for their social
accompaniments, namely, need for boarding
arrangements, recreational or affiliative possibilities, rearrangements in family responsibilities and understandings, income provision,
and so on.

Psychiatric social workers were thrust, thus,
into carrying a number of highly varied functions: (1) direct work with patient/clients
and their "significant others"; (2) efforts to
locate and connect the isolated patient with
significant others; (3) efforts to influence
community leaders and agencies to develop
and support provisions for adequate housing,
boarding and half-way houses, and financial
aid; and (4) the supervision and direction of
nonprofessional staff. In brief, in the burgeoning "mental-health business" the psychiatric
social worker has been thrust into being all
things to all men. As a result many of them
have felt a fragmentation and diffusion of

their work activity. Furthermore, it has taken an energy toll, and has operated against the development of mastery and skill that depends in part, at least, on concentration and specialization.

As the study by Berg et al.[3] has shown, the sense of role diffusion and role stress is high among social workers in community-health centers. In part this is due to carrying too many diverse roles, in part due to the fact that the social worker has often not been prepared by professional training for many of the activities into which she has been thrust. Most social workers who have chosen to be clinicians have "majored" in one-to-one or one-to-small-group processes aimed at psychotherapy. Then they find themselves in community organization or development work, or teaching and training others, sometimes before they themselves have had time to digest their learning, and usually more ready to give directions than to educate. As in the other clinical professions there are among these social workers, of course, the "naturals"—those whose talents make them adaptable to shifting roles and responsibilities. But schools of social work are facing the need to reassess the nature of the preparation of social work clinicians.

The role problem experienced by psychiatric social workers in any hospital or clinic setting, namely that of her likeness to and difference from other psychiatric personnel, has already been alluded to. But now, with the widespread use, not only in community mental-health clinics but in hospital settings too, of "aides," "social-work associates," paraprofessionals—most of whom come to be grouped loosely under "social work," there is another boundary that blurs out the psychiatric social worker's identity and area of specialization. In 1968[1] most of the direct work with patients and their families in psychiatric hospitals was performed by the untrained workers. In short, who does what, and why, are frequent unspoken but present questions in psychiatric settings.

All mental-health professions face the problem of how collaboration may be maximized and competition and communication gaps minimized among often equally competent team members. Few of them in their formal professional education have had the instruction or guidance that would help them to tackle and solve these on-going issues. Social workers are perhaps best schooled in the desirability of "collaboration" and "cooperation." But the principles governing teamwork have yet to be articulated if they are to be operationalized beyond "good human relations."

Graduate schools of social work characteristically stand with one foot in a university and one in the field of practice, with one eye upon what has intellectual, theoretical, empirical validity and integrity, and the other upon what the field of practice seems to need. The 1970s have for many reasons brought a number of upheavals and imbalances into social work education, many of which have been problematic to the development of clinical social work and to the preparation of psychiatric social workers. Specifically to the latter is the development of undergraduate social-work curricula and courses, in bachelor degree programs and in community colleges that have spread across the country in great numbers. At least until the economic recession of the mid-1970s graduates of these programs have found jobs in mental hospitals and community mental-health clinics as well as in other tax-supported health and welfare agencies.

Questions are facing graduate schools on the necessary changes they must make in the preparation of their students. What, for instance, is the nature of an advanced degree? Does it lie in a higher degree of clinical sophistication towards direct work with clients who have psychological problems? And is this what psychiatric settings want and need? Does it lie in a more variegated, generalized kind of educational experience, where, say, all students are required to take courses and get some actual experience in community work, administration, supervision, and teaching? Is this what psychiatric settings need and want? Can mastery be achieved without specialization? And if specialization in consultation, administration or community organization is chosen, for instance, is it possible to consult or administer processes in which one's experience has been minimal? Of course, similar questions plague almost all professional schools today.

The literature of social-work education and of clinical social work is rife with self-questioning and self-criticism. Not only are the above-noted issues in scrutiny, but there is widespread concern to predict the future of the several helping professions, predictions of some hoped for steady state from a position of disequilibrium. There is, furthermore, serious concern over what most research has revealed about outcomes of clinical efforts, the apparent ineffectiveness of one-to-one or one-to-group services in a "sick society."[5] These have roused considerable malaise among psychiatric social workers as among others. At the same time they have served to firm up considerations of accountability, of reasonable goals, of valid research hypotheses and methods, of treatment choice.

Meantime, back at the hospitals and clinics, psychiatric patients still seem to need the help toward "restoration of capacity for normal living or provision of the greatest possible comfort." [p. 521][24] Still proffered by psychiatric social workers and their colleagues, it is that same modest but irreducible goal articulated by a social psychiatrist and his social worker collaborator fifty years ago.

([Bibliography

1. BARKER, R. L. and T. L. BRIGGS. *Differential Use of Social Work Manpower.* New York: Natl. Assoc. Social Workers, 1968.
2. BARTLETT, H. *The Common Base of Social Work Practice.* New York: Natl. Assoc. Social Workers, 1970.
3. BERG, L., W. REID, and S. COHEN. *Social Workers in Community Mental Health.* Chicago: School of Social Service Admin., 1972.
4. BERKMAN, T. *Practice of Social Workers in Psychiatric Hospitals and Clinics.* New York: Am. Assoc. Psychiatric Social Workers, 1953.
5. BRIAR, S. and H. MILLER. *Problems and Issues in Social Casework.* New York: Columbia University Press, 1971.
6. COOPER, S. "The Swing to Community Mental Health," *Soc. Casework,* 49 (1968), 275–380.
7. FRENCH, L. *Psychiatric Social Work.* New York: Commonwealth Fund, 1940.
8. GERMAIN, C. "An Ecological Perspective in Casework Practice," *Soc. Casework,* 54 (1973), 323–330.
9. GRINKER, R. R. and J. SPIEGEL. *Men under Stress.* Philadelphia: Blakiston, 1945.
10. GRINNELL, R. M., JR. "Environmental Modification: Casework's Concern or Casework's Neglect?" *Soc. Serv. Rev.,* 47 (1973), 208–220.
11. HENRY, W. R., J. SIMS, and S. L. SPRAY. *The Fifth Profession.* San Francisco: Jossey-Bass, 1971.
12. HOLLIS, F. *Casework: A Psychosocial Therapy,* 2nd ed. New York: Random House, 1972.
13. JARRETT, M. "The Psychiatric Thread Running through All Casework," *Proc. Natl. Conf. Social Work,* Chicago, 1919, pp. 587–593.
14. JOINT COMMISSION ON MENTAL ILLNESS AND HEALTH: *Action for Mental Health.* New York: Basic Books, 1961.
15. LEE, P. R. and M. E. KENWORTHY. *Mental Hygiene and Social Work.* New York: Commonwealth Fund, 1929.
16. NATIONAL ASSOCIATION OF SOCIAL WORKERS. *Use of Groups in the Psychiatric Setting.* New York: Natl. Assoc. Social Workers, 1960.
17. ———. *Encyclopedia of Social Work,* pp. 1195–1225, 1246–1273. New York: Natl. Assoc. Social Workers, 1971.
18. NORTHEN, H. *Social Work with Groups.* New York: Columbia University Press, 1969.
19. PERLMAN, H. H. *Social Casework: A Problem-Solving Process.* Chicago: University of Chicago Press, 1957.
20. ———. *Persona: Social Role and Personality.* Chicago: University of Chicago Press, 1969.
21. PERLMAN, H. H., ed. *Helping: Charlotte Towle on Social Work and Social Casework.* Chicago: University of Chicago Press, 1969.
22. POLLAK, O. *Social Science and Psychotherapy*

for *Children*. New York: Russell Sage Foundation, 1952.

23. ROBERTS, R. W. and R. H. NEE. *Theories of Social Casework*. Chicago: University of Chicago Press, 1970.

24. SOUTHARD, E. E. and M. C. JARRETT. *The Kingdom of Evils*. New York: Macmillan, 1922.

25. TOWLE, C. *Common Human Needs*. New York: Natl. Assoc. Social Workers, 1945.

CHAPTER 36

REHABILITATION

Francis J. Braceland

The task of medicine is to promote health, to prevent disease, to treat the sick when prevention has broken down, and to rehabilitate the people after they have been cured. These are highly social functions and we must look at medicine as basically a social science. [p. 241][33]

Henry E. Sigerist

"To rehabilitate the people after they have been cured" is indeed, as Sigerist says, a highly social function, but it is more than that—it is an essential part of treatment and it has a quality of genuine altruistic concern about it. There are differences of opinion as to the best definition of rehabilitation. Everyone seems to know what it is, yet it is difficult to define. Its underlying philosophy is clear, however, and we defined it earlier as: Based upon humanitarian and practical considerations it is the inherent right of each individual to participate in society to the fullest extent of his capabilities and the advantage to society of his being as self-reliant as possible.

Of itself, the word means to clothe again, and by extension, it means to invest again

with some right authority and proper regard for oneself. The semantic meaning is also inherent in the philosophy of rehabilitation, which in essence holds the human being to be entitled to the privilege of his humanness. If disabled, he has the right to be a complete person again and to be restored as much as possible to usefulness and dignity in the world of his fellows.

Thus the form of rehabilitation considered here deals essentially with the restoration of a handicapped individual to a higher level of personal, social, and occupational functioning. Modern psychiatry has a vital role to play in bringing this about. It can give physicians, nurses, and rehabilitation workers the tools to understand the person and to learn the meaning of his presenting symptoms and their emotional overtones. Thus prepared, no physician is likely to neglect the human aspects of the patient or slight his dignity or his human wants and needs.

Howard Rusk,[32] one of the prime movers in the rehabilitation field, expressed a basic rehabilitation principle when he said of persons handicapped by physical disability:

A man with a broken back has not been rehabilitated if we spend four months teaching him to walk but leave him with such anxiety that he will not go out of the house. And if we meet this objective and then send him home to a fourth floor walk up apartment where he is a prisoner in his own room the rest of his life, we have done him no great service. Until we have found him a job which he can do we have not fulfilled our responsibility.

By the same token, when a patient is discharged from a mental hospital today he frequently is not entirely recovered. He is referred to community facilities with the expectation that he will be helped through his posthospital problems and set on the path to employment and independence. This expectation is not always met. Lonely, anxious, fearful, and ashamed, someone will have to see that he gets to the community center, assuming that one is operative. Someone, also, will have to see that he takes his medication and that he does not withdraw and isolate himself, particularly if he has no home or has worn out his welcome in it.

The patient's return to the community, therefore, is fraught with danger. Not uncommonly, he is fearful of relapse. Unless we in psychiatry keep all of these factors in mind and make provisions for follow-up and rehabilitative care, we have done him no great service and have not fulfilled our responsibilities either. Hence the need for inpatient and outpatient rehabilitative care of many descriptions.

(History

The history of efforts to rehabilitate the mentally ill and to restore them to a higher level of personal, social, and occupational functioning goes well back into the ages. Various methods were tried—some worthwhile, some unless, some humane, some inhumane—but modern psychiatry began with *moral treatment*, which was, in essence, rehabilitation. It was practiced by those who had compassion on the mentally ill and saw them as members of the human family, victims of illness and misfortune, rather than the prey of demons.

By means of moral treatment, attempts were made to bring those of the patients' faculties which remained sound to bear upon those which were diseased. It emphasized the value of occupation, education, and social influences, and operated in an atmosphere of high expectation. Early, the moral therapists reported excellent results in cases of recent illness, and though less optimistic about chronic illness they occasionally could announce a restoration to health.

It is interesting that in the past, when the patients were discharged to their homes after hospitalization, stress was laid upon the saving grace of work as a rehabilitative measure. Eli Todd, in 1830, wrote[34] in terms quaint and poignant to a family of a patient about to be discharged from his Hartford Retreat:

. . . I cannot too strenuously urge the advantage and even the necessity of his being engaged in some regular employment which shall hold out the promise of moderate but fair compensation to his industry and prudence.

Freud, at a much later date, voiced the same sentiments in his *Civilization and Its Discontents*:[13] "Laying stress upon the importance of work has a greater effect than any other technique of living on binding the individual more closely to reality."

Work is equally important in rehabilitative efforts today, and though the so-called "Protestant work ethic" is at the moment under a cloud according to the avant garde and the young radicals, it nonetheless remains as an important rehabilitative measure. In our civilization, work is what men live by. Man works to earn the necessities of life, to secure its comforts, and to provide for his family. Work helps still the feelings of inferiority that unconsciously beset us. It gains us parity with our fellow men and the acceptance of the community; thus its importance to everyone, well and sick men alike. No matter how humble the task, it dignifies our daily lives. By means of it man may work off his aggressive impulses and ward off his profound feelings of insecurity and helplessness. With work man earns more than a stipend—he earns his self-respect.

We are interested in work here because of its rehabilitative potential. Glasscote and his colleagues would say, however, that while this emphasis on employment is fine, some people are not able to work, they are too old or frail, or too disordered mentally; but they state that this in itself does not necessarily mean that they must be hospitalized. "With some help they can meet the day to day demands of community living without harm to self or others."[15] Olshansky thinks the role of worker is the easiest one for expatients to fill, it is the most structured. Also, he thinks, even some of the sickest exmental patients are able to work. Olshanky asks: Why do expatients work? (1) To acquire self-esteem in their identification as workers and in functioning in an approved adult role (becoming self-supporting is important in our culture); (2) work is a way of shedding patienthood; (3) work provides a means of denying illness and avoiding the threat of hospitalization—"it proves wellness;" and (4) work provides an opportunity to have something to do.[28]

Moral Treatment

In our country it was the advent of private mental hospitals in the first few decades of the nineteenth century that showed the way to improve the lot of the badly treated and poorly understood mentally ill patients. The method practiced was known as *moral treatment*. Moral treatment had never been defined, because—as Bockoven, an authority on the subject, stated—its meaning was self-evident, i.e., "compassionate understanding treatment, even for those whose illness was thought to be due to willful and excessive indulgence in the passions."[7] Unfortunately, the fine balance which permitted moral treatment to flourish in those early decades was later to be disturbed as large numbers of impoverished mental patients arrived from foreign lands and inundated the hospitals. Moral treatment perished in that flood. It raised its head cautiously again in new guises, in recent times in the form of "milieu therapy;" but the

excitement it created in the early nineteenth century has never been recaptured. The cult of incurability gradually made its appearance and for a long time the public forgot about its sick citizens incarcerated in large monolithic institutions.

As mental hospitals grew larger, more numerous, and more crowded with chronic cases, moral treatment had to be abandoned. Beyond protecting itself against acts of the insane, society took little but a remotely horrified interest in the mentally ill. It was believed that once the doors of the asylum closed upon a patient, he would never emerge again. This belief was well founded because the patient's illness was usually chronic by the time he was committed.

There were cautious modifications of this outlook early in this century as dynamic psychiatry was making its way upon the scene, but even then little could be done about overcrowded, understaffed, and isolated institutions. It was not until the 1940s that any real hope was kindled. This was the time that insulin shock and convulsive therapies appeared upon the scene. Like all new therapies, they brought with them exaggerated hopes which, while never quite completely realized, did encourage physicians and roused psychiatrists from their discouraged attitude.

World War II Developments

The holocaust of World War II brought new insights into the treatment of the physically and mentally ill. New rehabilitative efforts arose perforce. Men with spinal and head injuries, heretofore given up as lost, were brought under treatment, achieved a modicum of recovery, and the modern science of rehabilitation of the sick and injured was initiated. Psychiatry benefited by the fact that for the first time large numbers of clinicians were in the field and in bases throughout the world accompanying the fighting men. The value of drug-facilitated abreaction was learned at the time, as was the value of immediate first-aid treatment for emotional disorders administered close to the front lines. This proved later to be of great value in the Korean War episode, and it greatly reduced the number of psychiatric casualties who returned as invalids. Group therapy, necessary because of the large number of patients requiring treatment, began to prove its value.

Several other events in World War II indicated that the mentally and emotionally disordered could under necessity respond well to the stresses of their environment. When the German army invaded France, a substantial number of patients at Charite-sur-Loire left the hospital without permission and were able to find lodging and employment for themselves. In England at Croyden Hospital[22] bombs demolished the structure and material to repair it was not to be found. The patients were adrift, but there were none of the dramatic consequences that might have been anticipated. These and other incidents led British psychiatrists to embrace the concept of the open-door hospital and to play a leading role in the therapeutic community movement.

The concept of "therapeutic community" soon found wide acceptance and was featured in the Third Report of the Expert Committee on Mental Health of the World Health Organization, published in 1953.[41] Its implementation was already apparent in the statistics of some hospitals before the tranquilizing drugs came into general use in 1955, which is usually cited as the year of revolution in patterns of psychiatric care. It was also the year which marked the real beginning of the declining annual statistics for the mental hospital population, as it did for the greatly diminished incidence of disturbed and regressive behavior. In that same year, the United States Congress passed a Mental Health Study Act directing a Joint Commission to make recommendations for a national mental health program. The final report of the Joint Commission on Mental Illness and Health in 1961 then inspired the new movement toward Comprehensive Community Mental Health Centers advocated by President Kennedy in his message of February 1963.

In England, meanwhile, continuity of care, community-care, and aftercare programs also received official endorsement in the Mental Health Act of 1959. For the notion of chronic mental patients, which is ambiguous and which lifts responsibility from society, was substituted the notion of the mentally handicapped which implies a positive factor in the person invalided by a mental illness.

Thus, the philosophy of treatment of psychiatric patients has changed. There is increased emphasis on community care as compared to hospital care, a leaning toward social definitions of mental disturbances, as well as intrapsychic definitions on the strengthening of the continuity of care and the rewarding of innovative as opposed to traditional programs. The development of social rehabilitation programs for exmental patients is one of the outcomes of this changing philosophy.

Mental health leaders today also teach the philosophy that mental illness is an episode in life, rather than a person's manifest destiny, and hospitalization is, therefore, also an episode and one which should be kept to a minimum. The patients' rehabilitation is, or should be, a continuous process in, as well as out, of the hospital, and the patients should move in graded steps from one transitional setting to the next until recovery.

All too often the mental hospital presents a highly abnormal social structure. The view is prevalent that it is improper to rely primarily on diagnostic labels in treating and releasing patients; nor is it always proper to keep the patient in the hospital until he has lost all his symptoms. As soon as the florid symptoms are suppressed or under control, it may be advisable to return him to the community, provided, of course, that aftercare services are available. Patients who can be saved should not be overlooked in the chronic population of the hospital either. A goodly number of these patients no longer belong in the hospital; if possible, they should be weaned from their dependent way of life and made self-supporting. An underlying assumption seems to be that society soon will have to raise its threshold of tolerance for deviant behavior, like it or not. These are the present-day trends; whether they will prove to be wise or otherwise remains to be seen.

Rehabilitation in psychiatry, therefore, has broad connotations unfortunately, often somewhat vague. The various definitions given generally reflect the doctrines of their proponents. Commenting upon the diversity of definitions, Freeman and Simmons were able to find one basic agreement, namely, that the successfully rehabilitated patient is one who is able to live in a nonmedical setting at a level of occupational and social performance comparable with that of other adults in the community.[11]

Rehabilitation further implies that there is a need to remove or reduce a handicap. It is only when the individual retains vestiges of his illness that care needs be taken, lest he find security only in his return to the hospital. Not only must he cope with the end product of his illness, but his family and friends must be able to tolerate his foibles. It is upon this that his tenure in the community depends. Failure to adjust satisfactorily only too often means the beginning of the "revolving-door" readmissions to the hospital.

◖ Treatment versus Rehabilitation

It is difficult to draw a sharp line between treatment and rehabilitation in mental disorder. Treatment is directed toward the symptoms leading to distressing or socially upsetting behavior, while rehabilitation emphasizes those social and vocational skills that diminish the liabilities and obscure the handicap. Treatment aims at correcting the illness, whereas rehabilitation aims at restoring the patient to his social and employment roles.

Greenblatt views rehabilitation from the standpoint of total treatment, and under psychological rehabilitation he includes measures that reduce or remove disruptive anxieties and neutralize intrapsychic conflicts.[18] Walter Barton finds no sharp line between treatment and rehabilitation since they proceed simultaneously from the beginning; but he does make the distinction that treatment is directed toward the primary problems, whereas rehabilitation emphasizes readjustment and the development of social and vocational skills that diminish the liabilities and overcome the handicap.[2]

Barton is critical of the activities program of many public hospitals and believes that preparation for real life is not made possible through a program of handicrafts and games. The fact that unskilled laborers and working class men predominate among state hospitalized patients makes it necessary that a more practical type of program be instituted. "The change to a useful work program and to a leisure time schedule likely to be practical later on," he notes, "should come as early in the program of therapy as the patient can manage it."[2]

As the patient prepares to leave the protection of the mental hospital for the uncertainty of a sometimes rejecting and hostile world, he must be well prepared for the difficulties he will encounter. This is why the program should start early and continue throughout his hospital stay. Failure brings risk of isolation and loneliness, and perhaps accelerates his early return to the secure but unnatural protection of institutional life.

Maxwell Jones says that rehabilitation is the attempt to provide the best community role which will enable the patient to achieve the maximum range of activities compatible with his personality and interests and of which he is capable.[24] Bellak and his associates submit that the major task of rehabilitation is the reconstruction of the patient's ego strength so that he can be made mentally fit and ready for work and able to cope with the emotional and interpersonal factors in starting and continuing the job.[5] One of the major purposes of rehabilitation is to restructure object relationships to help the patient adapt more realistic and objective ways of thinking and acting and to acquire useful social and occupational skills.

In-Hospital Rehabilitation

Necessarily, the prime purpose of mental hospitals and the main reason for their existence is the treatment of patients who are mentally ill. Were it not for this, there would be little reason for their being. There is no reason to list here the illnesses treated in these hospitals, nor the methods of treatment involved. Suffice it to say that the overall efficacy of treatment plans depends to a large extent on the atmosphere of the individual hospital and the interpersonal and intergroup transactions which take place within. Studies of mental hospitals have revealed the crucial roles which leadership and individual workers play.

Russell Barton has identified a syndrome among hospitalized patients characterized by apathy, withdrawal, resignation, and loss of individuality. Contributing factors to this *institutional neurosis* are loss of contact with the outside world, enforced idleness, authoritarian staff, loss of personal possessions, oversedation, depressing surroundings, and loss of prospects for the future. A therapeutic atmosphere can only be created by what Barton calls "people concepts" (happiness and comfort of patients, morale and efficacy of staff and personnel); these should be as important as "object concepts" (number of beds, number of doctors, etc.).[1]

In a conference in 1970 on rehabilitation of the mentally handicapped, Donald Miles[21] presented evidence for and against basing rehabilitative efforts in hospitals rather than in the community. In favor of hospital-based rehabilitation programs are (1) space available as the census lowers; (2) the population of the hospitals is homogenous and the program can be tailored to fit; and (3) adequate clinical and support facilities are readily available. Against hospital-based rehabilitation programs are (1) the patient's behavior in the community cannot be predicted from his hospital behavior since coping behavior does not transfer readily to the community; (2) patients' stay in hospitals is usually not long enough to learn adaptive behavior; and (3) Miles believes that not all patients are helped by certain rehabilitation programs. Others agree with him and opt for more workshops and incentive programs in the community. Whatever opinions may be expressed, one thing is certain, namely, due to the inexorable march of time, and hopefully progress, *the scene has changed markedly since the late 1960s and rehabilitative efforts on a large scale have shifted and still are shifting to programs based in the community.*

The Therapeutic Community

The therapeutic community concept is an important factor in the treatment of in-hospital patients. Its importance is lessened only by the above mentioned present-day rapid discharge from hospitals to community programs. In other words, the present-day trend seems to be more toward short-term crisis oriented therapy in the hospital, rather than to long-term rehabilitative efforts. The value of the short-term hospital stay, if that is all that is required, is obvious.

The therapeutic milieu* is based upon a number of interacting factors and made essential by the fact that in the old hospital regimes patients lost their identities and their individuality, and thus were reduced to anonymity. The first necessary step to correct this was to establish a good relationship among people, beginning with the hospital director and filtering down through the staff and the various hospital employees. The possibilities of rehabilitation are lessened by inadequate liaison between different members of the treatment team, particularly between the professional staff and the employees who are on the wards with the patients most of the hospital day. The therapeutic possibilities of the nursing staff are only now being recognized fully. Their potentialities were always known, but generally too little use was made of their skills. Each encounter between nurses, aides, and patients, like those of the physician, can be either psychonoxious or psychotherapeutic.

The possibilities inherent in these various forms of social therapy received their greatest impetus in and following World War II. They rested upon the observation that certain types of emotional ills were the result of disturbed interpersonal relations and operated upon the belief that the culture of a hospital or a ward could be used deliberately to assist the individual by group experiences and social influ-

---

* Terms such as milieu therapy or administrative therapy are occasionally used interchangeably with that of therapeutic community. There is no one ideal pattern and a number of forms are permissible, provided the general principle of patient participation in the therapeutic process is honored.

ence. The medium used is frequent group meetings, made up of ward doctors, nurses, social workers, occupational therapists, the patients themselves, and everyone involved in their care. The group meets daily in open discussion to informally consider ward happenings, personal grievances, personal relationships, tensions, and misunderstandings. The preservation of the patient's dignity is thus bolstered. He is given to understand that he is important and responsible, and that he can be trusted. Personal problems and misbehavior are treated as communal responsibilities and are analyzed and interpreted, usually in psychodynamic terms. A consensus then is sought so that difficulties can be resolved by group influences and pressures. The way the ward operates is influenced greatly by these group meetings and they constitute the main area for the interchange between patients, physicians, and caretaking personnel.

Necessarily, the staff must meet on its own and a certain amount of unity of approach is required. Physicians and nurses are expected to assign rehabilitative measures and duties to the various categories of helpers and the staff should be taught to deal with its own anxieties. Though the physician is usually in charge at staff meetings, reliance must be placed on the nursing staff for transmission of the culture or group climate of the unit.

The preservation of the patient's individuality is thus an extremely important characteristic of the therapeutic community. The day is past when idle, neglected, uncared for patients may be confined in locked wards. This is intolerable. To deprive patients of their small personal possessions and reduce them to nonpersons is to alienate them further from society. All too often in the past the only thing the patient was left with was his delusional system. The patient must be recognized as a person, not a case, and his self-esteem must be cultivated if he is not to withdraw.

It stands to reason that in a well-run hospital most patients can handle themselves properly and that only a few require to be behind locked doors. Symbols of incarceration, high walls, iron bars, and keys jangling have done more harm than good in the past.

The rehabilitation process depends upon sustained living experiences with people who are mature, kind, and understanding, and who do not reject the patient. Overpermissiveness is as destructive as overprotectionism, however, not only because of its malign influence on morale but also because it is not proper preparation for what the patient will encounter when he leaves the hospital.

Thus, the therapeutic community is a reasonable situation in which activities abound and where diversification is sufficient to interest persons of different bent. Helpfulness and understanding are the watchwords, responsibility and initiative are expected and respected. It is necessary to present most patients with simple steps en route to more complicated ones, with a reliable work program as the ultimate goal.

Other In-Hospital Activities

Upon admission to the hospital, the patient's interests and potentialities should be assessed. The change to a useful work program and to the constructive use of leisure time likely to be helpful in the future should come as early as possible. All too often the patient has no avocation and, perhaps just as frequently, he is not interested in his daily work either. To encourage him to develop a new interest or to take new interest in old skills is an early and important step in the rehabilitation process.

The continuing education of young patients who are hospitalized is of the greatest importance to prevent further widening of the distance between them and their peers outside the hospital walls. Toward this end, several first-class hospitals have opened regularly established high schools in which the patients are enrolled as bona fide students, attend classes, receive grades, and are granted credit toward a high school diploma and college admission. This is a remarkable step forward. The patients learn while being helped with their emotional problems, and education becomes a valuable part of their therapy.

Correspondence courses for adults, some leading to college or industrial-school credits, are also in vogue. State and municipal education authorities are usually anxious to help. These courses are in addition to programs of music, art, handicrafts, theatre, and reading which have long proven their value, as every mental hospital director can attest. Some patients discover that they have hidden talents or skills and developing them improves their personal image and advances their recovery.

Patients who exhibit special skills are often enlisted to help teach others, and thus may acquire a new status which in itself is therapeutic. Volunteers can help in the teaching of dramatic arts, music, shop work, and in conducting discussion groups; their particular value often lies in the fact that patients see them as people from outside the hospital, not part of the paid establishment, who think enough of them to come in and give of their service.

It has long been recognized that idleness is demoralizing, but earlier forms of occupational therapy were often dull and stultifying. Patients either tired of them soon or did them mechanically, simply passing time without therapeutic benefit. All of this is now seen in a different light. Interesting work therapy, which relieves tension and anxiety, serves, in addition, to increase socialization and fulfills certain instinctive drives. It caters to the needs for activity and has the possibility of bringing recognition and approval.

More and more, as the length of hospital stay in the acute admissions group is shortened, patients progress rapidly from the ward and occupational therapy shop into real situations. En route, they should learn proper attitudes toward authority, turn their attention to personal appearance, and, under the acceptance and approval of their teachers, acquire new respect for themselves. The chronically ill require much longer periods before a satisfactory work level is reached.

In many hospitals work programs are instituted in conjunction with industrial firms. The patient is put on employee status and held to acceptable standards of performance. The patients thus employed in English hospitals receive rates of pay comparable to those outside of the hospital. In our own country the rates are lower, but are sufficient for the patient to pay something for his "board and keep" and even retain some earnings. The prestige that accrues to these patient employees is ego building and eventually the skills learned may help secure employment when the patient leaves the hospital.

Landy and Griffith, in a study of employer receptivity toward psychiatric patients, observed that when the patient does not have to find his own job and it is secured for him, he either fails to get the job or to hold it.[26] Readiness to hold a job, therefore, may be judged by the degree of initiative the patient shows in looking for work. One department store manager in a New England town informed a hospital staff member that he "would not know what to do without the help of the hospital patients at Christmas time." Interestingly, some of these patients never worked for wages before.

❲ Rehabilitation in the Community

Let us consider the following statement from the report of the Joint Commission,[23] published in 1961:

. . . aftercare and rehabilitation [are] essential parts of all services to mental patients and various methods of achieving rehabilitation should be integrated in all forms of services. Among these services should be day hospitals, night hospitals, aftercare clinics, public health nursing services, foster family care, convalescent nursing homes, rehabilitation centers, work services, and ex-patient groups. . . . It is important that rehabilitation be regarded as a part of a comprehensive program of patient services in which each and every member of the mental health team has a part to play. [pp. 270–271, 272]

Transitional Stages

In the present progressive climate in psychiatry, the prospects for the patient's recovery from mental illness are viewed with much greater optimism than ever before. As patients leave the protective environment of the hospital there is frequently a need for an intermediate, or transitional stage in the form of partial hospitalization. Night and day hospitals were instituted for this purpose.

We have already considered the night hospital in relation to the patient's extra-mural employment while still an inpatient. The day hospital is one step further on the recovery path. In addition to its role as an alternative to full hospitalization, the day hospital is an excellent aftercare rehabilitation facility. In it the patient can reap the benefits of continued psychiatric care and at the same time maintain ties with family and the community. These adjunctive rehabilitation units have grown in popularity since the 1960s. Most good hospitals have such facilities, and, in addition, independent day hospitals, not linked to a mother institution, have appeared on the scene. Such installations also seem to fit naturally into the general hospital and psychopathic institute picture.

One important stimulus to the growth in numbers of these facilities is the fact that in order to qualify for federal funds granted by the Department of Health, Education and Welfare under the Community Mental Health Centers Act of 1963, each center must include provisions for a day-care facility. This provision understandably has caused a noteworthy increase in the number of such facilities. Day care has by now become firmly established in various countries throughout the world as a significant psychiatric service, and in several countries, beside our own, provision for them has been written into the law.

The first modern psychiatric day hospital is said to have been organized by M. A. Dzhagarov in Moscow in 1933. Most of the Western World heard about the concept, however, through the establishment of a facility in Montreal by Ewen Cameron in 1947, and by Joshua Bierer in England in 1948 at the Institute of Social Psychiatry.

Glasscote[17] notes that British clinicians wished that the professions in the United States ". . . would adopt the English practice of delineating day programs as either day hospitals or day care." He quotes the British psychiatrist, Douglas H. Bennett, who states that "a day hospital is a program in which every form of treatment that could be provided in a psychiatric hospital is available, while a day center is independent of a hospital and provides social and occupational services plus limited medical supervision."

Bierer, who launched the day-hospital movement in England, had different ideas. He would limit the term "day hospital" to independent structures which were hospitals in their own right—not a part of another institution—and which would admit every kind of patient. It would replace the mental hospital in his scheme and provide every kind of treatment available to modern psychiatry. These definitions and requirements did not meet with wide support either in England or in the United States.

No matter what the connection with other institutions or lack of them might be in this country, Kramer[25] sees certain issues of universal concern in their operation, albeit to varying degrees. These, he states, "include short-term versus long-term care; the degree of administrative control over admissions; staff initiative versus patient initiative; and finally the collaboration between the staff of the day care center unit and the psychiatric inpatient service in the hospital to which it is affiliated. . . . The unit's approach to these issues will give shape to its program and determine its function in the community." He sees a critical requirement for the successful operation of these units to be a quick and easy access to an inpatient bed when the need for it arises.

As to treatment procedures in day-care facilities, they differ markedly in accordance with the governing philosophy, the size, and the location of the units. All provide, in some fashion, medical treatment, psychiatric care, occupational therapy of some sort, socializing activity, and various other routines. Whatever their particular approach may be, the primary task of the unit is to create a therapeutic milieu so that the environment of itself may be of benefit to all the patients concerned.

As to the results of treatment in these centers, there is no doubt that they provide an easy transition to life in the outside world for some patients. The general belief is that this is one of their primary functions. The value to the patient in maintaining community ties as a rehabilitative measure is definite. The answer to the question whether partial hospitalization is better than full hospitalization depends upon the patient, the illness, and the availability of first-class centers and hospitals.

In a controlled study concerned with day versus inpatient hospitalization, Herz and his colleagues report that for those patients for whom both treatments are equally feasible clinically, newly admitted patients from the catchment area were randomly assigned to either day or inpatient facilities. In the evaluation, including measures of psychopathology and role function seen at follow-up intervals, the authors found clear evidence of superiority of day treatment on virtually every measure used to evaluate the outcome.[20] Glasscote and his associates warn that it is "important to recognize that day treatment may denote either a service unit or element, or merely a patient status." The latter is the case, he says, when day patients come into the inpatient service and join the program taking place there.[17]

Halfway Houses

As the rehabilitative efforts for patients with emotional disorders have reached further into the community since World War II, there has been an impressive increase in the number of community residences known as halfway houses. These transitory residential centers serve to meet the needs of patients discharged from mental hospitals for a temporary residence in which to make a readjustment to social life and employment in the community. They attempt to maintain a climate of health rather than illness and to develop and strengthen normal capacities and responsibilities.

Though the British began with their "hostels" in the last century, there were only about ten halfway houses in the United States in 1960. When Raush and Raush made their survey in 1963, there were approximately forty.[30] When Glasscote, Gudeman, and Elpers made their survey in 1969, 128 were located, more than half of them having been established from 1966 to 1969 [p. 1].[16] They believed

that this new locus for serving the mentally ill, "considered little more than a curiosity a decade ago, carries the promise of becoming a major consideration in the continued redirection of mental illness services during the years immediately ahead."

While there have been a number of definitions of halfway houses in the past decade, Glasscote and his colleagues propose one of their own:

A halfway house for the mentally ill is a nonmedical residential facility specifically intended to enhance the capabilities of people who are mentally ill, or who are impaired by residuals of or deficits from mental illness, to remain in the community, participating to the fullest possible extent in community life. [p. 1][16]

(They say "nonmedical residential facility" meaning that the medical involvement "should be only of consultative and backup nature" in the venture.)

Halfway houses are not always welcomed with enthusiasm by the residents of various communities. Local officials and citizens do not quite know how to regard them. Their initial reaction is frequently unfavorable. Town meetings, zoning laws, and citizens' groups have been called into play to keep out these "unwarranted intrusions on neighborhoods" which, the residents are sure, would lessen the value of their property or even endanger their personal safety and that of their children. Much depends, of course, upon the way in which the concept of these houses is presented to the neighboring citizens. With diplomacy and tact, the citizens can be brought to see that the centers will be community assets and opportunities to help restore sick fellow citizens to health at less cost and with less human suffering than if they would be consigned to large state hospitals. The ideal situation, of course, would be to have a nonprofit house or hostel with a board made up of interested citizens. The patients' stay in halfway houses varies from a few months to a year or more and depends upon many factors. Most see them as way stations in which residents are gradually prepared to live in the community independently.

It used to be necessary to keep patients in state hospitals, even after their symptoms had abated, because there was no other place for them to go. Now a number of these individuals can be treated in day centers while they live in halfway houses. This should be a slow and painless way of returning to a full life in the community. Some centers, under lay auspices, include ranches and farms in rural settings where work projects, outdoor living, and planned recreational programs are offered. Glasscote and his group believe that these centers could also offer a more or less permanent placement for people who no longer need be in hospitals yet have no potential to live in the community or be employed without special supports. As a good example, they mention Cobble Hill Center in Brooklyn [p. 22].[16]

The typical community halfway house, however, is either a large, old house donated for the purpose, or even a boarding house already in operation. Generally, it will be staffed by employees, some acting as house parents, or even an interested and altruistic owner. Ordinarily the house is operated on a nonprofit basis, the staff is relatively constant, and decisions regarding policy and changes in policy are made within the group. For the most part there are no written laws but consensual rules are in force. Any infractions of the rule are usually handled by group pressure, but if necessary a staff member intervenes. Most of the halfway houses place a time limit of a few months up to a year upon their residents but this is not strictly enforced. Hopefully within the time mentioned, the residents will have made strides toward establishing some form of independent living.

The unfortunate aspect of the halfway house concept is the small number of patients that they can accommodate. Even if all of the more than 200 halfway houses accepted only mental patients, and if each one accommodated fifteen patients (many accommodate fewer), there still would be only a small fraction of the more than half-million patients still in psychiatric facilities who could be accepted, when ready, for a trial outside the hospital. The big contradiction in this statement is to be found in the fact that not all of the large

number of patients in the hospitals would be capable of living in these community houses and another large number would not need this transitional facility.

As to the programs followed, there are no set standards and each differs according to its purpose, its census, and its staff personnel. Some are high expectation centers[37] where the residents must work or attend a class; others are of intermediate expectation with residents enrolled in a day program or in some way active in the community. The objection to laissez-faire centers with no program lies in the fact that they are in danger of becoming "mini state hospitals."

A variant of the halfway house is the use of subsidized apartments for recently discharged psychiatric patients. The best known and the first psychosocial rehabilitation center to be established in the United States is Fountain House in New York City.[10] It is one of the largest installations of its kind; another is Horizon House in Philadelphia. Both offer comprehensive programs. From its attractive six-story headquarters in mid-Manhattan, Fountain House provides an impressive array of social, vocational, and residential services to many hundreds of persons with a history of mental illness, in a program that operates every day of the year.[15]

Begun modestly by expatients in the early 1940s due to their mutual needs, Fountain House soon attracted the attention of altruistic individuals and the center has grown apace. Eventually, after a successful fund-raising campaign, the present headquarters were constructed at a cost of approximately two million dollars. Its various units are supervised by social workers and visited by volunteers. There is a day center and a program of transitional paid employment, and it has helped its residents by reaffirming a sense of belonging and of being needed. Staff members participate side by side with the residents in all of the daily happenings and events which are comparable to those which take place in the household of a normal family. The staff is not interested in the patient's pathology or in their background, but rather "in teaching them what they need to know and giving them the supports they need to work with, to live in the community and to have a decent kind of life."[15]

In Philadelphia, Horizon House is a combination residence and day center. Council House in Pittsburgh is a unique facility in that it does not have a residence of its own but rather it utilizes a variety of community facilities. It began modestly in 1957 as an expatient club and it has grown substantially ever since. Its purpose has remained the same, however— namely, to provide educative and membership experiences to patients who have had serious mental illnesses. There are a variety of other residential houses and clubs for discharged patients where professional workers give supportive counseling and assist residents in finding employment. There are also residences in which expatients live with those who have not had mental illnesses; for example, a house in Cambridge, Massachusetts, which accommodates expatients and volunteer Harvard and Radcliffe students.

Not all observers are sure of the usefulness of halfway houses, and admonitory voices have been raised by some knowledgeable individuals. Walter Barton is among those who wonder whether these way stations are really worth the expense entailed. Data so far available does not show a significant difference between the rehabilitative successes of the halfway houses and the programs associated with direct placement in the community.[2] Admittedly, however, this situation is hard to evaluate. In the balance, at the present moment, the houses seem to the casual observer to be worthwhile.

Russell Barton warns of the danger of developing chronic hostel patients and wonders whether the size of the hostel is apt to become a compromise between what is clinically desirable and what is economically expedient, with the hostels eventually proving to be "white elephants."[1] Cooper and Early warn that the patients, unless care is taken, may simply exchange one institution for another. They believe the stop should be only one of *transition* en route to a normal life.[8] It does seem, however, that the hostels are on the way to accomplish the purpose for which they

were organized. It seems likely, also, that halfway houses will continue to grow in number, not only because of the help, the protection, and the transitional steps which they offer, but also because of the fact that at the moment state and mental hospitals in general are in disfavor.

Occupational Rehabilitation

Community programs for occupational rehabilitation are provided for in the United States under the federal–state rehabilitation system, job placement agencies of various sponsorship, and the sheltered workshop programs. In 1971 the National Association of Sheltered Workshops estimated that of the 1300 workshops in the United States, one thousand accept people with a mental-illness diagnosis, but that relatively few are for mental patients exclusively. Unfortunately, there is even evidence that a number of workshops have resisted the acceptance of mental patients for a variety of reasons.

Exclusionary activities in sheltered workshops, as far as mental patients are concerned, are unfortunate, for many patients might do well to participate in all activities. They offer an orientation to work, and with work as we have seen comes the acceptance of an individual which he needs badly. The earning of money and the example of others laboring under difficulty seem to help patients who have been confined to mental hospitals; it is estimated that approximately one-third of them can eventually become self-supporting. Ideally the workshop should be structured to approximate the work set-up in the normal world in work hours and in at least partial reward of the workers.

Altro workshops in New York, a part of the Rehabilitation Center for Chronic Relapsing Illnesses, began admitting psychiatric patients nearly a decade ago. There the mental patients are mixed with the physically handicapped and a cadre of normal employees, including supervisors and instructors. Host to approximately fifty psychiatric patients, on any given day, the workshops are in close collaboration with Rockland State Hospital, the

New York Departments of Mental Hygiene and State Education, along with the Office of Vocational Rehabilitation.

The largest of the workshops appears to be the one connected with the Brockton Massachusetts Veterans Administration, which was started in 1961. Called Chirp (Community Hospital Industry Rehabilitation Program), it offers a diversified program of sheltered work and educational and manual arts therapies. It is based on the principle of most such endeavors and its purpose is also to make transition to autonomous community life easier for the patients. The patients are paid and a diversified group with varying diagnoses takes part in the program. The concept has spread to other veterans hospitals and the working conditions are similar to those in factories in normal life. In the first four years, 1400 patients went through the program; only 115 had to be readmitted to hospitals.[40]

Special workshops are also run by the Goodwill Industries. First established in 1902, this is probably the largest national network of such endeavors. All 141 workshops of the national programs now accept people who have a history of mental illness. Although in 1969 the Goodwill Industries estimated its workshops were servicing about 24,000 people per day and restoring 7000 of them to the competitive labor market, they were unable to estimate the portion of those serviced and restored who were mental patients.

It is a special advantage of the sheltered workshop, according to Russell Barton, that it tests work capacity without estranging the employer who is, of necessity, concerned primarily with production and profit rather than with public and social welfare.

Expatients Clubs

Expatients clubs, which have come into prominence since 1937, also serve as a transitional rehabilitation resource between the hospital and life at home and in the community. Originally formed by the patients themselves, some hospitals followed suit and organized comparable clubs as part of their rehabilitation programs. It is difficult to even estimate the number of such clubs or the numbers formed by hospitals, citizen groups, or the patients themselves. Most of the clubs are supported by the members dues and whatever outside assistance they can muster.

The largest and perhaps the oldest of these organizations is Recovery, Inc., which was organized by Abraham Low of Chicago in 1937. It has perhaps 5000 members in various categories and exists in approximately twenty-five states. These groups are intensely loyal to the precepts laid down by their founder and to one another. Undoubtedly this form of socialization and group spirit does a great deal of good for the club members.

Bierer in London inaugurated a therapeutic social club in 1938 and believed it to be an important step in the direction of the therapeutic community. Run by a committee elected by the patients, the club is an integral part of the treatment program of London's Marlborough Day Hospital, with the psychiatrists serving as advisors. A number of similar clubs sprang up in small towns, and subsequently comparable therapeutic social clubs for outpatients were opened in the London area.

The same situation obtains in the United States. Many expatients clubs are based in small cities. All seem to have the same function, but some are directed toward the purpose of particularly helping schizophrenics, while others are for older age groups. It is impossible to estimate the number of these clubs. One famous club was Club 103, attached to the Massachusetts Mental Health Center, which has now given way to Wellmet Houses, run by students and other interested parties with a minimum of supervision.

Much depends upon the leadership and the orientation of these clubs. Well directed, they are potentially helpful in overcoming the isolation and the loneliness of the members and in preparing them to meet the stresses of everyday life. Should they fall into the hands of paranoid leaders or under the control of a "hard-core" group of expatients, however, there is bound to be trouble. Such groups lose their usefulness by quarreling with authorities and with one another.

Foster Family Care

The practice of placing mental patients in selected foster homes is an ancient rehabilitation practice that remains valid in the twentieth century. The philosophy of family care is based upon humanitarian, economic, and rehabilitative considerations. It is assumed that chronically ill patients may live a more normal life in a foster home than in a mental hospital, that foster family care serves as a bridge to eventual community placement, and that it is less costly than hospital care and reduces the overcrowding in mental hospitals.

Foster family care started in Gheel, Belgium, centuries ago, and today a large segment of Gheel's inhabitants are mental patients. Some work and show little evidence of illness; others are obviously ill. These patients are visited regularly by a nurse and are returned to an inpatient center when treatment of some kind becomes necessary. Germany and France use the foster home plan on a limited basis; Norway uses it extensively. In the Netherlands a program of foster care centered around an active treatment program in a day hospital, which also serves as an inpatient 100-bed unit, is conducted in the rural community of Beilen.[3]

Foster family care in the United States goes back very far; in colonial times some communities auctioned off distracted persons to the lowest bidder to be "boarded" and put to work. Flagrant abuses emerged from this practice and it had to be given up. In many cases it amounted to bondage. In recent times the foster home plan has been used to some extent, especially in the state of New York, but only since the 1960s has its growth been noticeable.

The selection of a foster home depends on the presence of a desirable domestic atmosphere, with benevolent parent figures, harmonious and cooperative relationships, and the apparent tranquility and cheerfulness of a home which can withstand emergencies. A patient should not be placed above his social level or in a home with standards of order and neatness much different from his own. Unsuit-able for foster home care are problem patients, such as the aggressive and potentially violent, the suicidal, the sexually deviant or alcoholic, and others with nuisance characteristics. According to Walter Barton,[3] one social worker can carry about forty patients in family care. Home visits may be made by the psychiatric nurse, in which case the social worker may specialize in selecting homes, training the caretakers, and placing patients ready to move from foster family care elsewhere. Patients remain under the medical supervision of the hospital. In some programs the services of a local physician are engaged for routine medical attention.

The results of foster family care are encouraging. Although many patients have to be returned to the hospital, many are able to remain in the community, with a substantial proportion moving on to full independence. Unfortunately there are a number of barriers to the expansion of these programs, such as a shortage of space in the modern family home, an economy in which taking in boarders no longer has much appeal, and a scarcity of professional workers to develop the program.

Family Care

In the present climate of administrative psychiatry patients are returned to the community whenever and as fast as possible. As soon as florid symptoms are suppressed or under control, the discharge apparatus is set in motion. Even among the chronic cases, candidates for release are found by enthusiastic rehabilitators. The justification for discharge is often based upon social grounds but it is often done without much foresight. Hospitals presently seem to be vying with one another for the record of the shortest patient stay possible.

Symptoms have improved (with or without) treatment, to the degree that patient behavior is, more or less, socially accepted. In many cases, however, the original illness is still present and unless conditions after discharge are favorable, the patient is likely to relapse. A major problem in rehabilitation is the fact that most patients return to the environment in which they broke down in the first place. In other words, most patients go back to families, frequently before either patient or family are ready or properly prepared.

That the family of the patient should be involved in certain aspects of the treatment process is an opinion that has wide support, but until recently little implementation. Ideally, a family diagnosis should be made at the time of admission of the patient so that an effort can be made to deal with troublesome conflicts and attitudes. Experience shows the value of group therapy in this area.

Earlier it was generally agreed that work with groups of mothers and sons or daughters was usually successful, but work with husbands and wives was found to be somewhat more difficult. The better hospitals have changed markedly. When family or marital difficulties are the problem the social worker sees the spouse or parent regularly while the physician treats the patient. This is particularly efficacious for it prepares the other family members for the return of the patient involved.

Heretofore it was the duty of the social worker to maintain contact with families while a member was hospitalized in order to make early release feasible and successful. Patients should be referred to the appropriate community and other health and welfare resources even before release. Patients on maintenance chemotherapy are in need of medical follow-up. This brings the family doctor or the local psychiatrist into the picture if they are available; if not, some form of outpatient mental health facility is indispensable.

These facts bring to light several changes in recent years which are not always to the benefit of the patients and one or two which might be helpful. First, many social workers have changed their orientation and are now practicing psychotherapists. Secondly, in England[35] and in the United States, hospitals are being emptied too rapidly. In both countries patients are being discharged quickly and told to apply to their local community mental-health services. Unfortunately many of these centers are not quite prepared for a large in-

flux of patients who are only partially recovered.

In both countries psychiatrists in general favor community care but are of the opinion that the mental hospitals should not be phased out until these centers are properly prepared to take care of the patients who will accrue to them.

Aftercare community mental health resources, although rapidly increasing, are still inadequate to take care of the problems arising out of the transformation of patterns of psychiatric care. The family care emphasis is moving some observers to the conservative position.

According to Wing, it is far from true that schizophrenic patients, after a long stay in a hospital, can be easily resettled in the community even when extensive social services are available.[39] Short-term patients also present serious problems. Investigation of a series of schizophrenic patients released from London mental hospitals after four months, showed that only 27 percent were free of symptoms at the time of their discharge, while 34 percent were actively deluded. A year later 56 percent of the discharged patients showed clinical deterioration and 43 percent were readmitted to the hospital usually after a sudden emergency involving police, firemen, neighbors, and the general public. Half of the patients for whom drugs were prescribed failed to take them, and half of those who found work were dismissed or left after a short time. These facts were reported in the 1960s but there is no reason to believe that the situation has changed. In fact, it is compounded by the population explosion.

The British Tripartite Report in 1972,[35] notes that "Community care has been a popular slogan for the past decade. Indeed, the operation of a system of community care is seen by some enthusiasts as a penacea, even as a cure for chronic schizophrenia. . . . The subsequent development has been uneven and decisions have been taken based more upon intuition than on knowledge, research, and experience."

This is not only an important mental health problem but it is one with ethical and moral connotations. Families will do what they can do to put up with a disturbed patient, but when that patient is the mother of small children the situation assumes serious proportions.

These same problems exist in the United States. The mental hospital census *is* declining and this is to be applauded, but where are the patients going? Is this simply the transfer or concealment of a serious problem? Every thinking person will agree that hospitalization in a mental institution is not an ideal situation and that community care is highly desirable, but the fact that many discharged patients often will neither take their medication nor seek out community care is not considered. To rehabilitate patients, someone must be responsible to see that they receive proper attention. As one instance of this problem, George H. Wolkon, the resident director of Hill House in Cleveland, states that "two-thirds of the patients referred from psychiatric hospitals to a post-hospital rehabilitation center did not follow through on the referral" (204 patients chose not to follow through on a referral total of 312).[36]

Rapid or premature discharge of patients without adequate provision for aftercare or without regard to facilities for resettlement is irresponsible and likely to damage the whole policy of the open door in mental hospitals. A follow-up of discharged patients shows that altogether too large a percentage of them is rehospitalized within a year.

One cannot help but bring to mind that before mental hospitals were established the mentally ill were the responsibility of the community and sick people wandered through the towns and ended up in jails, garrets, and poorhouses. It was for this reason that state hospitals were built, and to give patients better care. Now it does seem as though these institutions are failing in their duty as they are being pressured to rapidly discharge the patients. Mayer-Gross warned a generation ago that incautious discharge of the mentally ill can have tragic repercussions on the family.[27]

Without doubt the community mental-health program has opened new vistas of hope for the mentally ill, but we must be mindful of the hazards of wishful thinking. The good mental hospital will be the backbone of the cure and the rehabilitation effort for a long time to come, for there will always be patients whose recovery will take longer than they, their doctors, the family, or even Blue Cross find convenient.

⟨ Addendum

It is written that he who neglects the lessons of history will be fated to repeat its errors. As this report is being written, the rehabilitation efforts for mentally ill patients is deteriorating in a number of states, both large and small. The same may be said of the situation in England[35] where a crusade is underway to denigrate the mental hospitals with the intent of phasing them out. Presently their plans call for the extremely low ratio of mental illness beds of 0.5 per thousand population. In the United States the same situation is found though not as dramatically. These aims would be admirable were all the community centers properly prepared and staffed to receive the mentally ill, but unfortunately very few are thus prepared and some others are in a sorry state.

Originally the community centers were conceived to furnish mental health service to a segment of the population which was unable to afford private care and for whom psychiatric service was generally not available. That some of the centers have deviated from their original purpose is of no concern to us here. The fact remains that these centers have the potentiality for being excellent treatment and rehabilitative agencies, and a number of them are already accomplishing that purpose. Since their inception these centers have been heavily dependent upon the Federal Government for financial support, especially for staffing. The outlook for future Federal support is bleak and should this support be withdrawn altogether, it is impossible to conjecture what will happen to community centers. Some will undoubtedly weather the storm but others will just as surely disappear. Undoubtedly the general and the private hospitals will in some way move into the breech and our advances in treatment and rehabilitative methods will not be lost no matter under whose auspices they will be given.

It is clear that delivery systems for all health services will undergo major reorganization in the near future. Robert Gibson states: "The needs are of such magnitude that all health resources must be drawn in if we are to meet them. Excellence will have to remain the watchword if they are to be viable components of the reorganized system."[14]

With this statement all can agree, since an emotionally ill person has the right to be rehabilitated and restored as much as possible to usefulness and dignity in the world of his fellows.

⟪ Bibliography

1. BARTON, R. "The Psychiatric Hospital," in H. Freeman and J. Farndale, eds., *Trends in the Mental Health Services*, pp. 156–163. New York: Macmillan, 1963.
2. BARTON, W. E. *Administration in Psychiatry*. Springfield, Ill.: Charles C. Thomas, 1962.
3. BARTON, W. E. and W. T. ST. JOHN. "Family Care and Out Patient Psychiatry," *Am. J. Psychiatry*, 117 (1961), 644–647.
4. BELLAK, L., ed., *Handbook of Community Psychiatry and Community Mental Health*. New York: Grune & Stratton, 1964.
5. BELLAK, L., B. J. BLACK, A. LURIE et al. "Rehabilitation of the Mentally Ill through Controlled Transitional Employment," *Am. J. Orthopsychiatry*, 26 (1956), 285–296.
6. BLACK, B. J. *Guides to Psychiatric Rehabilitation*. New York: Altro Health and Rehabilitation Services, 1963.
7. BOCKOVEN, J. S. "Moral Treatment in American Psychiatry," *J. Nerv. Ment. Dis.*, 124 (1956), 167–194, 292–321.
8. COOPER, A. B. and D. F. EARLY. "Evolution in the Mental Hospital," in H. Freeman and J. Farndale, eds., *Trends in the Mental Health Services*, pp. 79–86. New York: Macmillan, 1963.
9. FISHER, S. H. "The Recovered Patient Returns to the Community," *Ment. Hyg.*, 42 (1958), 463–473.
10. FISHER, S. H., J. H. BEARD, and V. GOERTZEL. "Rehabilitation of the Mental Hospital Patient: The Fountain House Program," *Int. J. Soc. Psychiatry*, 5 (1960), 295–298.
11. FREEMAN, H. E. and O. G. SIMMONS. *The Mental Patient Goes Home*. New York: Wiley, 1963.
12. FREEMAN, H. and J. FARNDALE, eds., *Trends in the Mental Health Services*. New York: Macmillan, 1963.
13. FREUD, S. *Civilization and Its Discontents*. New York: Cape and Smith, 1930.
14. GIBSON, R. W. "The Private Psychiatric Profile 1971," *Am. J. Psychiatry*, 127 (1971), 1395–1397.
15. GLASSCOTE, R. M. *Rehabilitating the Mentally Ill in the Community: A Study of Psychosocial Rehabilitation Centers*. Washington: The Joint Information Service of the American Psychiatric Association and the National Association for Mental Health, 1971.
16. GLASSCOTE, R. M., J. E. GUDEMAN, and R. ELPERS. *Halfway Houses for the Mentally Ill*, p. 1, 22. Washington: The Joint Information Service of the American Psychiatric Association and the National Association for Mental Health, 1971.
17. GLASSCOTE, R. M., A. M. KRAFT, S. M. GLASSMAN et al. *Partial Hospitalization for the Mentally Ill: A Study of Programs and Problems*. Washington: The Joint Information Service of the American Psychiatric Association and the National Association for Mental Health, 1969.
18. GREENBLATT, M. "Rehabilitation of the Mentally Ill," in A. Deutsch and H. Fishman, eds., *Encyclopedia of Mental Health*, Vol. 5, pp. 1737–1747. New York: Watts, 1963.
19. GREENBLATT, M., D. J. LEVINSON, and G. L. KLERMAN. *Mental Patents in Transition*. Springfield, Ill.: Charles C. Thomas, 1961.
20. HERZ, M., J. ENDICOTT, R. L. SPITZER et al. "Day versus Inpatient Hospitalization—A Controlled Study," *Am. J. Psychiatry*, 127 (1971), 1371–1382.
21. HOSPITAL AND COMMUNITY PSYCHIATRY. "Conference Report: Conference on Rehabilitation of the Mentally Handicapped, Sept. 24–25, 1970, Philadelphia," 22 (1971), (4)–(6).

22. JAEGGI, F. "Aspects sociologiques de l'hospitalisation et de l'evolution des psychoses chroniques," *Encephale*, 52 (1963), 97–166.

23. JOINT COMMISSION ON MENTAL ILLNESS AND HEALTH. *Action for Mental Health.* New York: Basic Books, 1961.

24. JONES, M. *Social Psychiatry, a Study of Therapeutic Communities.* London: Tavistock, 1952.

25. KRAMER, B. "Day Care: A Phase of Partial Hospitalization," in A. M. Freedman and H. I. Kaplan, eds., *Comprehensive Textbook of Psychiatry*, pp. 1300–1302. Baltimore: Williams & Wilkins, 1967.

26. LANDY, D. and W. D. GRIFFITH. "Employer Receptivity toward Hiring Psychiatric Patients," *Ment. Hyg.*, 42 (1958), 383–390.

27. MAYER-GROSS, W., J. A. HARRINGTON, and A. A. BAKER. "Breaking up the Mental Hospital," *Lancet*, 2 (1958), 697–698.

28. OLSHANSKY, S. "The Vocational Rehabilitation of Ex-psychiatric Patients," *Ment. Hyg.*, 52 (1968), 556–561.

29. OVERHOLSER, W. "The Volunteer in Psychiatric Rehabilitation," *Ment. Hyg.*, 45 (1961), 163–166.

30. RAUSH, H. L. and C. L. RAUSH. *The Halfway House Movement: A Search for Family.* New York: Appleton-Century-Crofts, 1968.

31. RENNIE, T. A., T. BURLING, and L. E. WOODWARD. *Vocational Rehabilitation of Psychiatric Patients.* New York: Commonwealth Fund, 1960.

32. RUSK, H. "Rehabilitation," *Abbott Tempo* (Publication of Abbott Laboratories), 3 (1963), 3.

33. SIGERIST, H. E. *Civilization and Disease*, pp. 229–244. Ithaca, N.Y.: Cornell University Press, 1943.

34. TODD, E. Unpublished Letter 1830, at the Institute of Living Archives, Hartford, Conn.

35. TRIPARTITE COMMITTEE. *The Mental Health Service after Unification, Mental Health in a Unified National Health Service.* Report with the authorization of the Royal College of Psychiatrists, the Society of Medical Officers of Health, and the British Medical Association, p. 8. London: Tripartite Committee, 1972.

36. WOLKON, G. H. "Characteristics of Clients and Continuity of Care into the Community," *Comm. Ment. Health J.*, 6 (1970), 215–221.

37. WILER, J. F., M. KESSEL, and S. C. CAUFIELD. "Follow up of a High Expectation Halfway House," *Am. J. Psychiatry*, 124 (1968), 1085–1091.

38. WING, J. K. "Rehabilitation of Psychiatric Patients," *Br. J. Psychiatry*, 109 (1963), 635–641.

39. WING, J. K., E. MONCK, G. W. BROWN et al. "Morbidity in the Community of Schizophrenic Patients Discharged from London Mental Hospitals in 1959," *Br. J. Psychiatry*, 110 (1964), 10–21.

40. WINICK, W. *Industry in the Hospital, Mental Rehabilitation through Work.* Springfield, Ill.: Charles C. Thomas, 1967.

41. WORLD HEALTH ORGANIZATION, Expert Committee on Mental Health. *World Health Organization Technical Report Series no. 73.* Geneva: World Health Organization, 1953.

CHAPTER 37

DANCE THERAPY

Sharon Chaiklin

DANCE THERAPY is a form of psychotherapy that focuses on the use of movement as the medium of change. While the complex relationships between mind and body have long been recognized and studied, there has been limited exploration in modern western cultures on using the body as a healing force for emotional distress. Eastern cultures have more extensively examined this relationship. Many movement forms such as T'ai Chi are meant for meditation and self-growth. The mind-body is seen as a system that must function in ease and harmony. Disruptions of the flow and unity may indicate the presence of psychological and physical stress and conflict. Dance therapy is based upon such assumptions, built upon psychological and physiological concepts with the strong belief in the psychic-physical relationship.

❨ Historical Development

Dance has long been fundamental to man's existence as an expression of life itself. To be alive is to move, to function harmoniously with the rhythms of one's own body and the surrounding universe. In all cultures, man's earliest attempts at communication, historically and developmentally, occurred on the preverbal level. Gesture and body expression were clearly the vehicle to any attempt to share experience. As language and tribal structures developed, religion gave shape to life, and dance was inextricably part of the worship and prayer that attempted to both structure and explain life. It was a powerful and unifying expression of the solemn movements of man's life: birth, puberty, marriage, and death. Dance was part of the means to control life by propitiating the forces which controlled the rain, the sun, and the fertility of earth and man. The rhythms and movements of tribal members provided group strength and unity during war, and solace during mourning. Its structures provided a means to pass tribal learning on to younger members. Dance is a language which uses the totality of body–mind–spirit to relate to the most profound experiences, painful and joyous, to those who would observe or share in the experience. Its deeply primitive aspects foster empathic understanding.

⟨ Dance Therapy as a Profession

The impetus for professionalizing dance as a therapeutic modality occurred after World War II, as the need for new therapeutic forms arose to meet the demands of the many psychological sufferers. Various group modalities were used experimentally and evolved as valid techniques. At this time, Marian Chace was teaching and performing in Washington, D.C. She was a member of the Denishawn dance group that experimented with new forms and had alliance to Eastern spiritualism and religious expression. She observed in her teaching that students who had no intention of becoming professional dancers, kept returning for dance classes. She carefully took note of their individual movement communications and began to heed their separate motivations and psychological needs. It led to further understanding of why dance was a fullfillment of some of these needs. With her focus shifting to individual needs through movement, or client-centered dance rather than technique oriented, several psychiatrists became aware of her skills and began to send patients. With the recognition of her special skills, she was invited to work at St. Elizabeth's Hospital in Washington, D.C., using dance as therapy. Similarly during these same years, other individuals developed their art to use in a new and meaningful way to aid in the reintegration of body and mind. Trudi Schoop, working in California, developed her own techniques for working with psychotics.[130] Mary Whitehouse, Blanche Evan, Liljan Espenak, and others specialized in the relationship of movement to the neurotic process. Each came to the field after a rich background of performance and teaching in dance. They took what was basic to their art and purposefully made use of movement concepts to aid others in finding new ways of understanding and coping with emotions. Dance therapy now has several hundred practitioners in a great variety of settings. The power of dance itself was the force that drew each of them toward the realization of the therapeutic possibilities of dance therapy as a profession.

Presently there are two terms, "dance" and "movement" therapy, to describe the profession. *Dance* was modified to *movement* by those who wished to detach themselves from dance as a performing art. The word "dance" in our culture has a narrow definition. The term is often misunderstood when used within therapy because of such stereotyping. There is also variation by dance therapists in the use of music in treatment. Those who make little use of music but rather rely on the internal rhythms developed by the patient more frequently use the term "movement." However, the rhythmic quality of movement, particularly as related to groups, and concepts of space, time, force, and balance have roots in dance itself. Many believe it important to maintain identification with dance as an art form, for it is that balance between art and science that makes the creative and therapeutic use of dance so valid and successful. There have been other attempts to find a descriptive term, such as Schoop and Salkin's "body-ego technique." However, all lead back to dance and movement therapy as generic terms. As in all disciplines, understanding the concepts proves more helpful than depending upon the name.

⟨ Psychiatric Theory and Dance Therapy

Because the use of movement in therapy has to do with the most basic and primitive concepts of human behavior and expression, it is possible to use it within the theoretical structure of existing psychiatric theories. All systems take cognizance of preverbal levels of development, of primary processes and of the many causes and difficulties leading to blockage of verbal communication, and yet the tools of psychiatry for direct intervention on these levels have been very limited. The work of Wilhelm Reich[110,111] is very useful as a base of understanding. He did extensive work to show that physiological behavior is functionally identical with psychic behavior; "character armor" appears not only as psychological defenses, but also as muscular defenses. Reich analyzed the muscular patterns and rigidities of his patients and believed them to be essential to the inhibition of primitive feelings. He therefore worked simultaneously to dissolve resistance in both the somatic and psychic realms. Lowen[91–94] continued to develop Reich's theories into a system of "bioenergetics." A useful concept he developed is the relationship of improper breathing to the blockage of feeling. He states, "Moving with feeling is only possible when the respiratory movements are harmonized with the expressive movement."[93] When crying is inhibited, the muscles related to eyes, jaw, and throat control and prohibit deep breathing. In dance therapy, many of the bioenergetic theories are useful in aiding in the release of body tension related to emotion. The application should be in the context of on-going therapy rather than merely offering exercises to deliberately elicit emotion.

In psychomotor therapy, Pesso[108] makes use of Freudian analytic concepts. He realizes it is not only the emotion that is repressed, but the movement behavior it calls forth. He carefully structures therapy to allow for the impulses and resultant movement behavior after helping patients to not accede to inhibiting movement defenses. Pesso develops an interactional model to permit the patient to follow through with appropriate movement behavior.

It is possible through dance therapy methodology to work on those basic levels that psychiatric theory has long taken account of but which has not been available. The framework that the dance therapist works within may differ. Chace primarily was conceptually Freudian and Sullivanian while Whitehouse was trained in the Jungian tradition. Differences in theoretical conceptualization may alter the style or technique, but the underlying movement theories are inclusive. Dance therapy offers an alternative method for working within the context of any systematized theory of human behavior.

Psychological and Physiological Concepts

The body itself is a source of memory, response, and learning. Learning about the self is closely allied with the understanding of how our body responds to the many conflicts and stresses in daily life. Dance therapy provides a structure which allows development of a sense of the body and through movement, makes use of the muscular and visceral responses related to emotion and emotional memory. This process allows an opportunity for cathartic release and expression of feelings which perhaps have been blocked or disguised. Lowen states:

Every emotional illness is characterized by a degree of paralysis of body movement, specifically those movements of the body that express feeling. These movements which come from within as opposed to voluntary movements directed by the conscious mind are summed up in the expression, the motility of the body. The reduction of body motility is a measure of the severity of emotional illness. You only have to see a person in a catatonic state to realize the significance of this relationship between motility and health. There are also sick people who are hyperkinetic, hyperactive or hysterical. In these cases the motility is not so much reduced as it is fragmented, chaotic, frenzied or frantic. [p. 3][93]

Movement change and psychological change are integrally connected. Cognition and intellectual awareness are of course necessary for change. In dance therapy, the body and its movement are the prime tools that work toward that awareness and the unity of self.

Dance and movement therapists are clarifying the importance of the body, not only in its relationship to emotions and learning, but also its accuracy as a communicative force. To unravel the myriad of movement patterns of an individual becomes an intriguing and therapeutically rewarding task. Movement style is a language which speaks of how an individual has adapted to the life forces around him and his system of coping with those forces. By recognizing the language of movement, the dance therapist enables an individual to reach the source of emotional constriction and explore new and more satisfying systems of behavior.

Theories delineating the connections between emotions, the body and the mind are most important to dance therapy but would require a separate treatise to do the subject justice. However, it is appropriate to briefly discuss a few of these hypotheses and their implications for dance therapy.

All life is made up of movement. Our very existence is made up of both voluntary and involuntary sensory-motor responses to inner sensations and the environment without. We are continually acting upon these impressions. Even when we are "still," experimental evidence suggests that muscular tension can be localized to particular muscle groups so that energy is released in sufficient amounts to be measured, even in the thinking processes.

Life initially is represented by tactile, thermal, and pain impressions which are acted upon by motor activity. Movement begins as random and uncoordinated. As a child matures, he is better able to control his gross motor activities. Adults heed and respond to the body communications of the infant. With the development of language as communication, less significance is placed upon his physical responses. The intellectual processes receive the recognition for learning and communication. Language is a translation of primary processes.

Very relevant to dance therapy theory, are learning theories, defining the physiological changes of the body in relation to emotion, the development of the kinesthetic sense and empathic muscular response, and concepts related to the development of body-image. Theories of emotion examine the relationship between physiological and muscular change, awareness and response. To experience an emotion such as anger, is a physical experience. Darwin's[31] work 100 years ago described the innate nature of facial and bodily expressions in emotion. More recently, Ekman and Friesen,[46] in their cross-cultural studies support the hypothesis that certain facial expressions are universally associated with the same emotions. Similar muscular tensions and impulses in emotion are experienced by all; it is the translation to expressive movement which can be controlled, inhibited, censored, or diversely communicated according to the cultural and personality dynamics of the indi-

vidual. Various theories of the origin of emotion and thought (Carl Lange, William James, Nina Bull) point to the experience of bodily sensations and movements which are the immediate response to perceptions of stimuli. Since dance is body movement, the emotions as expressed and communicated can be experienced and used directly in therapy. There is no need to translate those emotional experiences into the symbolism of words.

The central nervous system is organized into *movement patterns*. It is believed by kinesiologists that certain patterns are innate in our biological heritage, such as throwing and locomotive patterns. Others must be learned and perhaps modified for specific situations. Kinesthetic perception and memory are the base of the learning of voluntary movement. Such memory enables the performer to initiate a whole pattern of movement or to modify a part of the whole. Only through experience and experimentation with movement are such patterns firmly established. In most sports activities, one is concerned only with specific skills and the body's relation to these. Little effort, except in dance and theater, has been made to consciously develop kinesthetic memory of the entire body and its parts.

Our relationships to the world around us are dependent upon our sense of body image. If knowledge of the body is incomplete or faulty, all actions for which this particular knowledge is necessary will be faulty too. Directional concepts such as *up, backwards*, and *sideways*, all relate to an internal sense of self. Spatial relationships develop by first using our own bodies as a point of reference. Many children have difficulty with this learning process and thus their learning is incomplete. They are not sufficiently aware of body parts, how to move them, or what they can do. As Schilder explains:

. . . movement leads to a better orientation in relation to our own body. We do not know very much about our body unless we move it. Movement is a great uniting factor between the different parts of our body. By movement we come into a definite relation to the outside world and to objects, and only in contact with this outside world are we able to correlate the diverse impressions concerning our own body. The knowledge of our own body is to a great extent dependent upon our action . . . The postural model of the body has to be built up. It is a creation and a construction and not a gift. [p. 112–113][126]

Posture is one aspect of body image. A dynamically changing posture is the core out of which motor behavior flows. Controlled by the cerebellum, it is maintained by nerves and muscles in reaction to the shifting location of the body's center of gravity. It is through posture that we are able to maintain an orientation to the earth's gravitational force and the environment around us. All learned movement patterns and learned responses result from the elaboration and reorganization of the basic posturing adjustments. The gravitational axis of the body is the zero point from which we establish direction and concepts of space. The implications for dance therapy would suggest that as an individual is able to increase his range of movement and develop a more flexible posture, he is more likely to have increased choices of behavioral responses.

While a kinesthetic sense aids in the muscular rememberance of coordination, weight, shape, and spatial factors, it also is an element in the empathic emotional perception of the muscular tensions of another person. Berger states:

Kinesthesis, then, is important not only in the perception and control of the movement, position and balance of the body, but in the emotional experience and expression of the entire individual. Proprioceptive impulses arising from within our musculature enable us to regulate the force and coordination of all the motor activity required of us in the function of living and contribute to our experience of our own postural and emotional condition. And proprioceptive impulses which are activated by the external stimulation of the movement of others enables us to understand their emotional condition in terms of our own experience, and to receive cues which are important in our total reaction to those around us. [p. 210][11]

Dance therapy works to heighten kinesthetic experiences and thereby aids in expressive movement. Body posture, as a dynamic

element, and gesture relate to emotional states. These become a form of communication as movements become expressions of feeling. Particular physical activities may carry with them specific feelings, such as the rocking of a baby, or shaking a stick. Schilder's treatise[126] relates the concept of body-image to movement, kinesthesis, and postural reactions within a psychoanalytic framework. He states:

Motion [thus] influences the body-image and leads from a change in the body-image to a change in the psychic attitude . . . Tension and relaxation are the elementary components in the dynamic sequence. There is so close an interrelation between the muscular sequence and the psychic attitude that not only does the psychic attitude connect up with the muscular states but also every sequence of tensions and relaxations provokes a specific attitude . . . every emotion expresses itself in the postural model of the body, and (that) every expressive attitude is connected with characteristic changes in the postural model of the body . . . The body contracts when we hate . . . this is connected with the beginning of actions in the voluntary muscles . . . We expand the body when we feel friendly and loving. We open our arms . . . We expand, and the borderlines of the body-image lose their distinct character. [pp. 208–210][126]

Dance therapy makes use of this interwoven relationship between emotions, the body and muscular patterning. Individuals express sorrow, joy, anger, and other strong feelings in their body movements. These are universal experiences in response to external stimuli. However, as a reverse process, by working with the muscular patternings related to an emotion, the feeling itself can be experienced cognitively merely from the muscular memory of such relationships. By developing strong, sharp, quick movements in the arms and legs, involving the torso and quickened breathing, the sensation of anger can begin to be felt because of the movement itself. The process builds upon itself in that as one begins to experience such a sensation there is a further muscular discharge of energy that reflects awareness of this expressive quality. Ritualized movement, as used by various cultures, is based on this phenomena. In early tribal war dances, the rhythmic use of strong movements as a group experience helped develop for each individual a sense of strength, power, unity, and indestructibility. Similarly, the development of whirling dances, because of vestibular stimulation, were experienced ecstatically as losing a sense of the body and experiencing only the spiritual self. By structuring movement experiences and understanding the connections between muscular impulses and emotion, a dance therapist can help a patient comprehend and work through blocked emotions, or structure those emotions which are overwhelming.

Other studies are equally important to the understanding of movement. Condon,[28] a psychologist, has studied the synchrony of movement based on a film analysis of human interactions. He defined "self-synchrony" as movement in relation to one's own speech articulations, and "interactional synchrony" where the movement of a listener is synchronous with the speech and movements of the speaker.

. . . there is a basic, dance-like sharing of movement on the part of the interactants during communication. This seems to be a general characteristic of normal interaction. Over 100 films of human interaction have been studied frame by frame (this included films of Kung Bushmen, Eskimos and Mayan Indians), and the phenomenon of interactional synchrony was found to occur consistently. [p. 33][28]

Relating the concept of synchrony to dance therapy, Condon states: "Moving together in harmony is communication. It is a relationship which is the message, 'I am with you.' Indeed, it resembles *heightened* interactional synchrony which . . . states closeness."[28] This element of synchrony can be analyzed in dance terms. The rhythmic and empathic kinesthetic sense that brings about similar movement patterns in space and time is very meaningful to people. There seems to be a reaffirmation of self, and self in relation to another being. Synchrony of movement is normal in daily interactions. It can be dys-

synchronous if people are not in harmony, or when an individual is not in harmony with himself. Synchrony with the therapist and with others is therefore a moment of awareness and closeness. This might evolve in a variety of therapeutic situations.

While dance therapy is primarily concerned with individual and personal experience, it is essential for us to maintain awareness of the larger scope of cultural learning that we each absorb. For instance, how individuals use touch and space may differ, due to their cultural heritage and not to their psychic problems. Scheflen[123–125] and Birdwhistell[13,14] among others, study movement within a cultural context. They maintain that body language is related to speech patterns, group processes, and the social order as a whole. "Kinesics," a term devised by Birdwhistell, denotes the behavior of touch, gesture, posture, eye contact, facial expression, and spatial territory in relation to social processes. If a dance therapist works in a multiethnic urban setting, it is vital for her to be sensitive to diversity in the use of body language and respect those differences.

Related to these concepts, Bartenieff and Paulay[7,8] did a study of cross-cultural differences of dance styles called "choreometrics." They found that "styles of movement were learned, like other communication systems in culture, and that they varied by culture; that there were important categories of movement shaping all behavior in a culture and serving to identify the individual as a member of his group." Furthermore, dance style is the crystallization of that culture's everyday movement style which is socially, economically, and culturally determined.

⟮ Basic Goals and Structure

The basic goals of dance therapy are both similar and yet different from any other psychotherapy. Self-awareness, comfort with the self, clearer perceptions of others, development of satisfying relationships and an ability to acknowledge and develop choices for oneself are basically a result of the therapeutic process. Simultaneously, the dance therapist works with her client toward achieving a "healthy" body; a body not frozen with conflicts, tensions, distortions, and unable to act as an openly expressive part of the self. The body should be free to work out those stresses and strong emotions which are part of man's existence, to acknowledge the moment and then restore itself to a relaxed balance and underlying unity of flow to perceive and radiate life. Therefore, recognizing that the mind and body are part of the same expression, dance therapy focuses upon movement change. Change is better understanding of the body and its messages, enabling an individual to extend the range of his movement so that there is opportunity to make choices and have options in how he copes with life. One should appropriately perceive and respond to one's own feelings and to others, enabling a person the freedom to spontaneously use the body and its movement as an expressive medium clearly related to ongoing thoughts and feelings.

Although one seeks to allow people to find their own movement and develop spontaneous responses, the dance therapist must provide the structure. This structure is similar in any psychotherapeutic modality. There must be defined limits of expected behavior, wide enough to allow narrow boundaries to broaden but clearly present should control be needed. The structure established in a dance therapy session should be primarily nonthreatening and supportive. Movement is seen as a joyful experience; there is even joy in experiencing sorrow and anger if these have been too tightly contained. Movement is never seen as right or wrong. At times it may be inappropriate or limited, but it is always an individual's expression of how he must respond at that time. Whitehouse says:

It is the *feeling* of dancing that counts: not the discovery of what their bodies cannot do but of what they *can* do, of what is naturally available to them, of the joy and rhythm and energy that is their rightful heritage . . . I saw that the deeper I could get into the sensation of how movement felt *to the person doing it* the more expressive it became and the more clarity emerged. [p. 63][142]

The individual is the focus, and movement or dance is the tool. The therapist works with the existing patterns of the individual rather than using a stylized form of dance such as ballet or social dance (although sometimes special forms are used purposefully). Techniques may vary but there are underlying goals which are similar to all dance therapists. The dance therapist uses her skills, creativity, and spontaneity to enable others to experience themselves on the level of body sensations and impulses and allow communication through body action. Not only must a therapist have a rich vocabulary of movement but she must also be aware of her own responses and the messages she relates through her own body. Communication must be direct and simple, for movement is an honest reflection of the self, one that cannot be hidden by words. Appropriate and sensitively responsive to any communication, the therapist must be prepared to confront anger and hostility as well as withdrawal or apathy. While one's role is often active, there is need to take care that it arises from the needs of the group or individual rather than from those of the therapist. The experience becomes one of co-workers making discoveries about the patient, their relationship to each other, and to their surroundings.

There is a range of techniques that makes one therapist's style different from another's. Some therapists work using pure dance and others work on a continuum that ends close to psychodrama and encounter techniques. Some work only with individuals, while others are more attuned to group processes. Those who stress the dance aspects tend to use much synchrony of movement and fluid movement transitions, and participate on a more equal basis. The amount of verbalization and interpretation will vary. There are times a therapist will not participate but will rather be an observer. Movement then often becomes a vehicle to make a conflict more immediate and at that time the therapist may be more directive. The use of music will also vary. Those working with groups, particularly institutionalized groups, tend to make greater use of structured rhythms. There are many levels of directed movement experiences. These are dependent upon the goals, age, handicap, or disability of a patient and the setting of treatment.

❲ Description of Dance-Therapy Group Session

The following is a generalized description of a dance therapy session with a small group. The dance therapist might have a large room to work in so that patients come to her area, or in the case of large institutions, she may at times go directly to a day room on a ward and work with those present. After greetings and a quick preliminary assessment by the therapist as to the overall tenor of the group, there generally is a warm-up period, both of bodies and relationships. The beginning of a session might look very much like a dance class with stretching, shaking out of limbs, exploring the use of isolated body parts, changing rhythms, and priming energy levels. The therapist initiates contact with each patient by responding qualitatively to his movement patterns, adapting her own movement style to that of the patient. The beginning simple rhythmic movement of hands, feet, the head or a shoulder, works not only on coordination but toward the direct expression of emotion. Whether it is shame, defeat, anger, or fear that a person experiences, related muscular tensions are reflected in the posture and the gestures. The therapist uses the warm-up to carefully observe and pick up cues as to the communications and needs of individuals and the group as a whole.

Using movement as the focus, themes can be developed which literally parallel any psychological or psychiatric concept. By relating to and responding to constantly changing patterns, expanding the use of the involved musculature and verbalizing about these body representations, foremost concerns begin to evolve. Our language descriptively amalgamates these feelings in body terms. We have feelings of falling apart, being out of step, not being able to stand on one's own feet, needing a shoulder to lean on, keeping someone at arm's length, wanting to curl up, maintaining a stiff upper lip, and so it goes. Picking up movements and verbal signals, themes can be explored, developed, and expanded using the dynamics of movement. For example, the dynamics of foot-tapping might begin to change by moving with more energy, strength, and quickness. Shouts may be added and pushing-pulling sequences may be devised, or a gentle touch may lead to a shared slow-rocking movement.

Movement, because of its association with feeling, tends to draw people together. The sharing of an expression of anger communicates that *all* people feel anger at some time and that it can be expressed without being totally destructive to others or self. According to Freud,[51] there is an emotional contagion in a group that brings it together. ". . . men's emotions are stirred in a group to a pitch that they seldom or never attain under other conditions; and it is a pleasurable experience for those who are concerned, to surrender themselves so unreservedly to their passions and thus to become merged in the group and to lose the sense of the limits of their individuality." Just as early tribal dances used rhythmic action for cohesion, so the group can provide the same support. The use of the group releases the isolation of emotional feeling and one is able to go beyond usual individual limitations.

The flow of the session develops intensity as the leader connects one spontaneous expression to another. The ideas for the movement actions flow from those participating in the group, whether from the direct leadership of one of the group members, or through the observational skills of the therapist. Each derives private meanings from the same moment in time and the experience comes from the movement.

A time for closure, a pulling together, a lowering of intensity serves the function of clarifying boundaries, sensing the integrity of one's own body, and recognizing the warmth and support of a shared experience.

(Dance Therapy for the Mentally Ill

The Psychotic Patient

Perhaps most work in dance therapy has been with the institutionalized psychotic patient. These people have many needs which are symbolized through their movement expression. When using dance therapy within a psychiatric facility, it is important to be open to the unique communications of each individual and to respond to these directly. Yet, we can also make some basic assumptions.

One of the most striking characteristics of the hospitalized patient are the many differences in the quality and quantity of movement. Movement behavior clearly indicates those patients who have been there for long periods, those most acutely disturbed, and those who are closest to leaving. The more disturbed an individual, the more dyssynchronous and fragmented are his movement patterns. There is a lack of connection between mind and body, an irregular and sporadic flow of effort, a lack of gestural or postural change or unity, or gestures which are random, ritualized or distorted. Davis shows:

1. That there are movement characteristics which are unique to schizophrenia, and more specifically, that there are movement patterns which correspond to various behavior—disorganization, stereotyping, regression and so on—in the illness.

2. That these movement features increase (i.e., appear or develop from less pathological characteristics) as the patient becomes seriously ill and decrease as he improves. [p. 26][34]

A prime goal of a dance therapist working with hospitalized patients is, therefore, to aid in body integration and awareness, strengthen a realistic sense of body-image and either enlarge the vocabulary of movement or help control impulsive, random behavior. Bernstein[12] outlines five levels of body-image organization and specific techniques for aiding these and various other "developmental constellations." She divides body-image levels into (1) investment of positive affect, or the capacity to perceive and accept the body and its functions; (2) differentiation of the body from the environment; (3) recognition of body parts and their interrelationships; (4) movement of the body through space; and (5) sexual identity. There perhaps should be another level before sexual identity pertaining to the body in relation to others.

In schizophrenia, there seems to be a need to relearn developmental patterns associated with body organization. Dance therapists work directly on elements related to gravitational pull, the growing or shrinking related to breathing, the flow of energy, the isolated movements of body parts using varied efforts and spatial concepts as well as total body movement, small and gross locomotive patterns, spatial patterns relating to others in space, and various tactile, kinesthetic, optic, and vestibular stimulations to aid in physical integration. One must first have a perception of oneself, some sense of control and choice before one is able to perceive clearly and relate to others. Fears and other strong feelings lead to a profound sense of isolation. Words are used as barriers rather than as attempts to communicate. The depth and scope of feeling is too intense to speak about easily and therefore creates further loneliness. Basic movement and dance is an effective way to cut through this isolation.

In psychosis, internal stimuli determine most behavior; there is a lessened relationship to the reality of the environment. Because it is so difficult for psychotic patients to interact with others, group rhythmic movement becomes a way of responding, first to the structure of the music, then to the therapist and to each other. Music is useful in initiating and focusing on rhythmic action. The circular structure of a movement group is supportive to building relationships and the movement becomes a satisfying experience in itself.

Chace[25] wrote:

A positive quality of aliveness is present in the group of dancers which is in strong contrast to the patients who are sitting listlessly absorbed in no activity, withdrawn from all others in loneliness. It is exciting to see one of these passively still people rise as though drawn by a magnet and move toward this living group. One must subscribe to the belief that rhythm and a shared emotional experience is important to a feeling of well being. Basic dance is the externalization of these inner feelings which cannot be expressed in rational speech but can only be shared in rhythmic symbolic action.

Activation of the withdrawn and depressed is an important function of dance therapy. It is particularly advantageous with the catatonic. Movement, no matter how small or subtle, is the one useable form of communication for those so withdrawn. There is great sensitivity to the movement communications of the therapist on the part of a catatonic patient. Hence, a relationship can be established that requires no use of speech on the patient's part. One begins on whatever level the patient is functioning. With catatonics, it is possible to start with what *can* be done, which may be to focus on breathing rhythms. To *take* a breath becomes an active role.

For those who exhibit ritualized movement patterns, perhaps associated with anxiety or compulsiveness, the opportunity to change the use of muscular patterns eases tension, at least temporarily. This is more difficult for the manic patient as his strong, quick gestures seem to afford little relaxation. The therapist must meet the patient's movement on his own level, which says to the patient, "I understand what you are saying," and gives the therapist an opportunity to modify and restructure patterns. Symbolic movement battles tend to be shared experiences that may lead into the beginning of mutual understanding while verbal exchanges may tend to further isolate. Chace describes a scene:[20]

An assaultive patient, when moving forward with threatening gestures, will invoke fright in the therapist, no matter how transient. This fright usually provokes aggressive, retaliative action. If, however, the fright is put into dance movement, such as shrinking to the floor, and then quickly developed into a very broad welcoming, friendly gesture, the expected retaliation is forestalled. If the patient continues to come toward the therapist with a threatening movement, the next response is usually one of steadfastness, carried out by wide, firmly placed feet and erectness of the torso . . . again developed into a friendly movement. I often suggest putting hands on each other's shoulders and pushing back and forth, setting up a swing-

ing motion . . . this action is in essence, a substitute or sublimation of the assaultive action, which for some reason had seemed necessary to the patient. [p. 222][20]

There are times when an individual session may be more appropriate than a group experience for a psychotic patient. An individual may be too anxious to work in a group. At times there is a need for more prolonged personal exploration in creative movement. Those who are more acutely disturbed may make good use of such sessions to focus on immediate intense feelings.

With a group that has been institutionalized, the therapist must fight against the passiveness and dependency which often pervades a group. As in all therapy, the development of spontaneous movement is a goal to be achieved. Lowen writes:

Spontaneity is an expression of the unconscious. Coordination is a function of consciousness. When the unconscious and the conscious are integrated in any person you have grace, the physical expression of emotional health. Spontaneity is a manifestation of the aliveness of the so-called id, the feeling aspect of the person. Coordination reflects the strength of the ego. In a unified personality id and ego, or body and mind are fused with the result that every movement of the body is graceful. Movements that are coordinated but not spontaneous are mechanical. Movements that are spontaneous but uncoordinated are infantile or impulsive. [p. 8][93]

According to J. L. Moreno, spontaneity is the vital element related to catharsis. It is through spontaneous interaction that doors are opened to new behaviors.

While movement is the prime tool, verbalization should not be ignored. There is a need to develop cognitive and thought processes in relation to movement in order to maximize its potential. Imagery and verbalization in response to movement patterns involve individuals further. The depth of discussion is dependent upon the abilities of the group to deal with insight and language.

The changes that occur in a movement group can be clearly observed during a session. The feeling tone will have changed from one of silence and fear to a more open awareness of each other shown by relaxed laughter and conversation, comfortable touching and spatial closeness.

The Neurotic Patient

With neurotic groups, basic goals are similar to those followed when working with the psychotic, in that body awareness, extension and integration of movement, and spontaneous expression and interaction are fundamental. Techniques to achieve these vary somewhat. The emphasis shifts to better awareness of inner sensations and being free to respond to these, rather than structuring the experience to be more in touch with external reality as needed for psychotic patients. In neuroses, there are frequently many inhibitors and censors so that the body is restricted, composed of "dead" areas, and tension ridden.

Dance therapists work to develop awareness of tension areas, breathing patterns, and expressive movement. Relaxation techniques, improvisational movement built upon specific themes, shared group improvisation and task-solving exercises are some techniques which may be used. By analyzing and linking these patterns to one's experiences, related cognitive and emotional experiences occur. Such experiences may lead to new understanding and possible alternatives in behavior. In describing her experiences with Whitehouse, Cheney writes:

These experiences are not only deeply meaningful . . . but provide increased sensitivity, insight, perspective and material . . . 'Movement in depth' is considered primarily as therapy. Therapy in the concept of Whitehouse is cathartic and creative; resolving the past while constructing a new present, getting rid of excess tension while realizing new uses for energy. It has phases of unconscious and conscious work, occurring in movement and then brought into conscious awareness. One not only gets rid of symptoms but makes an effort to understand the causes. [p. 67][27]

Such work is done individually or through group experiences where interactional opportunities add an additional dimension.

The Autistic Child

Dance therapy with autistic children is proving to be a particularly rewarding use of this therapeutic modality. As Kalish notes in her description of working with an autistic child:

The initial aim of movement therapy is to reach the autistic child at the level where he seems to be functioning—a primitive sensory-motor level; and to explore with him rhythms, vocalizations and body actions, in an attempt first to gain his attention and hopefully lead to an emotional relationship, and second, and equally important, to help him form a body image. This is the ingredient I sensed was missing in these children. While the schizophrenic may have a distorted image or lost what he once had, the autistic child has never formed an intrapsychic representation of his own body. Therefore the therapist must keep this in mind, as she works to help the child build new psychic structures and concepts. [p. 51][69]

Janet Adler depicts her techniques in working with autistic children most movingly in her film *Looking For Me*. She begins by entering into the child's world of movement. There is first a period where she will ". . . speak her language by moving with her as she moves in space. In the beginning there is much direct imitation, which by definition means delayed responses on my part. However, as she permits my presence and as the trust develops, I find the one-sidedness falls away and a more mutual dialogue begins to creep into being; we become synchronous."[1] There seems to develop two main concepts in the work of both of these therapists, influenced somewhat by different perspectives. Kalish focuses more on a developmental view of autism, relating it to a movement scale based on a system of movement observation. Adler is more descriptive of the interactional processes leading to communication. Yet, both of them are concerned with body image and a therapeutic relationship. Both describe the child's initial lack of a sense of self and the reenactment of developmental stages that had never been completed satisfactorily. The first stage seems to be a fusion or symbiotic relationship between therapist and child; then evolves a thorough exploration of the therapist's body and finally the child's discovery of himself as a separate being, relating to another. It is at this stage that synchronous movement may develop.

Dance therapy is being used with children and adolescents in many settings. The concepts are essentially the same and again the structure is altered to provide the controls and limitations within which a child is free to grow. Special education schools make good use of dance therapists, for dance provides many sources of learning simultaneously. In addition to emotional problems, movement aids the developmental processes that serve as an aid to learning because of increased abilities in sensory-motor development and perception. Use of a great variety of props becomes particularly useful with children in order to organize movement more efficiently. The use of images helps in kinesthetic learning. Dance makes use of a child's natural interest in play and movement. When the activity is one of joy rather than ritual, when spontaneity is encouraged, motivation is not a problem in learning.

Varied Settings

There are several other areas where dance therapy is supportive of rehabilitation. Many therapists work with the retarded in order to give positive structure to emotions and develop improved body awareness and coordination. People with limitations such as blindness, deafness, and speech disorder always exhibit additional physical manifestations in the use of the body in space and as a form of communication. Dance-therapy concepts are most valid in working in any area where there is stress upon normal communication or where there are body-image difficulties.

With the development of gerontology as a mental-health field, dance therapy can also serve a very important function. Aside from the assistance it provides in maintaining physical health through use of the physiological and muscular systems, it is particularly helpful in developing and maintaining self-esteem and

social interaction. Loneliness is dispelled as people move rhythmically together, no matter how limited they are in physical movement due to illness or age. The goals most probably would be more supportive rather than seeking basic personality change.

Dance therapists also work in the field of corrections as the problems related to self and others are basically the same. Half-way houses, community mental-health centers, and referred private practice are all settings for dance therapy. Within a multidisciplined agency, a dance therapist functions as a team member contributing her skills as a clinician to the treatment plan set forth by the staff.

Contraindications

At present there seems to be no condition when dance therapy is contraindicated. The structure changes to serve the purpose. If someone is brittle, has superficial controls, and the intensity of feeling may be too frightening, movement should be closely structured to nonemotional patterns such as working with ballet technique. In a group, where at some point in time an expressive display of anger would be too frightening for that particular group to handle, it is possible to structure energetic movement that has the same muscular release but eliminates conscious emotional overtones. One such group used a small foam ball to throw and kick in a wild and exuberant "soccer game." When necessary to the development of physical and psychic controls, creative forms give way to formal patterns and safe structure.

⟨ Research and Movement Observation

In the process of developing a profession, we have need to establish typologies of diagnoses and methods used in dance therapy. There is a need to examine for whom dance therapy is most useful, at what stages, if there are contraindications, and varied methods within the scope of dance therapy. No diagnostic system is perfect or considered definitive. We can only use the level of knowledge on which it is based. If we can facilitate the examination of the information we have and create the possibility of communication, we can then advance our knowledge. Because dance therapists are just beginning to be involved in writing and research, theoretical concepts are generalized and described in global terms rather than in terms specific to diagnostic categories. There are some beginning attempts to become specific. As a new profession, there is need for research to establish and validate theoretical structures.

A troublesome problem in the use of movement has been the difficulty in accurately observing, analyzing, and describing what is seen other than in subjective language descriptions. Also, it is so ephemeral, lasting briefly, and then gone. While the use of video and films have been a useful device, movement description must be a language equally shared by the observer. One person's stylized walk might be simultaneously described as "sloppy, carefree, strolling, sassy, not caring, or sexy," depending upon the eye and the interpretation of the various observers. The development of a system of observation founded upon movement terms is invaluable for dance therapy. It allows for an objective description of movement behavior. The context and theoretical foundations of the therapist can lead to interpretation of that behavior.

While it is not part of dance therapy procedure, one such system of observation is *Labananalysis*, or "effort-shape," as it is still more commonly called. It provides a theoretical structure from which movement can be observed objectively and analytically. Rudolf Laban,[81-85] a multifaceted and talented dancer and choreographer, developed a system of observation based upon the natural affinities of movement. Later elaborated upon by Lamb,[86,87] a replicable system was devised which could be used for describing, measuring, and classifying movement. Every individual has patterns of movement which are fairly constant for himself. An analysis of these patterns suggests observable behavior related to neurophysiological and psychological pro-

cesses within a cultural framework. How he adapts to inward strivings and copes with outer stimuli is accurately reflected by his movement behavior.

Bartenieff and Davis[6] state:

Ultimately behavior must be understood in relation to neurophysiology and total organic functioning. The effort-shape theory of movement is based on an organic model of behavior. The major hypothesis of this presentation is that neural processes, adaptation and expression are integrated in movement. Every movement in any part of the body is at once adaptive and expressive; it functions as a coping mechanism while at the same time it reflects something about the individual. The alpha-gamma system and the reticular formation, as the major integrative mechanisms of sensorimotor activity, are considered the physiological basis of this unity of expression and function. Movement perceived through effort-shape appears to reflect the functioning of the alpha-gamma system itself, from the stirs of effort flow in the newborn to the mature movement repertoires of the adult. There is a great deal of evidence that effort-shape can be used to trace each stage of development and contribute significantly to the understanding of mature functioning. [p. 51][6]

Effort-shape is a system which requires much study and practice in observation. The meanings and implications of its terms cannot be presented here in detail. However, a few words will be defined and used with the context of describing its use in dance therapy. Basic concepts include: (1) the use of the body's flow of muscular tension between bound and free (effort-flow); (2) movement that flows toward or away from the body (shape-flow); (3) the use of body planes (horizontal for widening and narrowing, vertical for rising and sinking, sagittal for advancing and retreating); (4) exertions related to an active attitude toward space (direct vs. indirect), time (quickness vs. sustained), and force (strength vs. lightness) called *efforts*; (5) moving into space (directional, shaping qualities); and (6) the relationship between gesture (use of an isolated body part) and posture (activation of many parts in relation to each other).

The myriad of reciprocal relationships, combinations, proportions of frequency, range of use, phrasing, body parts used, and spatial relationships are some of the aspects related to the immense variety and complexity of human movement. Because this system of observation is applicable to all human movement it is, at present, being used in psychology, anthropology, cross-cultural and child development studies, dance education, business personnel assessments, and, of course, dance therapy.

Labananalysis, as a technique of observation, provides a tool for research in dance therapy. As Bartenieff, the leading proponent and teacher of effort-shape wrote:

Those of us in the dance therapy field using Effort-Shape see in it not a method of therapy but a tool of increasing sensitivity to movement responses and direct communication. Its usage has convinced us that we do not yet fully understand the entire range of nonverbal behavior; nor could we claim that Effort Shape is the panacea in specialized methods of therapy. But a theory of movement that is not merely a borrowing from the verbally oriented psychological and psychiatric vocabulary seems a vital factor in establishing methods and in enabling the therapist to make specific contributions to research, while maintaining his intermediate position between the arts and science. [p. 15][5]

With a standard nomenclature to describe movement in addition to a theoretical model based on movement itself, dance therapists have the means to diagnose through movement and to develop treatment plans. Since one can fairly accurately notate the movement patterns of an individual at varied periods, it becomes possible to assess movement change both in quantity and quality, keeping in mind that movement change is synonymous with psychological change. For example, an effort-shape analysis is made of a patient within a psychiatric hospital. The therapist observes that there is reduced mobility, range of tension-flow is minimal, the torso is set, head and shoulders are still, flow is bound, movement is somewhat fragmented in that weight shifts are disorganized, movement is limited to the vertical plane, there is no use of gesture or shaping of space and effort qualities are not observable, i.e., no use of strength *or* lightness. For clarity, not all possible variables are de-

scribed. In psychiatric terms the diagnosis might be schizophrenic, catatonic reaction. This movement is fairly clear and simple to observe. It is possible to assess much more complex movement behavior where individuals are active but show conflicting use of the body or are limited in specific areas of the body in effort and/or shape and space qualities. The dance therapist very clearly has specific movement goals based upon the movement analysis. The underlying assumption is that the larger the movement repertoire a person has to choose from, and the better integrated these patterns are, the better able he will be to cope with the environment and with his own emotions in a flexible and more satisfying manner. Davis[34] developed a Movement Diagnostic Scale describing the movement characteristics of hospitalized patients. She was able to establish those characteristics which were indices of change. The grouping of patients by movement profile also indicated the possible relationship of movement characteristics to clinical diagnoses.

The use of movement observation is also of real value in child development studies. Kestenberg,[74-79] a child analyst, sees dance therapy as an aid to her own work. She has done several studies using movement assessment to observe infants and children. Her findings are correlated with a classification of diagnostic criteria devised by Anna Freud. The rhythms and attributes of tension flow, "a basic alteration of free and bound discharge of changing levels of intensity, high and low, building up steeply or gradually, held on even keel or modulated,"[77] are distinguishable and correlate with the psychosexual development of the child. Rhythmic tension-flow patterns reflect the oral, anal, urethal, inner genital, and phallic stages. Kestenberg also concludes that rhythms in infants are congenitally determined. While there may be changes in the complexity of movements, because of maturity and interaction with the environment, preferences for certain rhythms influence character formation and drive discharge. Her theories have led her to examine the movement patterns of infants and those of mothers to determine possible conflicting rhythmic patterns and to help mothers adjust their own rhythms to those of her child. Her assessments give indications of the areas needed to be experienced and enlarged upon by a child so that the dance therapist can extend and retrain movement to complement the psychotherapy.

Similarly, Kalish,[70] a dance therapist who has done much work with autistic children, has devised a movement scale for observation that she hopes will prove useful in early assessment of dysfunctional movement patterns of children and thereby serve as a means for early preventative treatment.

(Training

Partly due to new interest in nonverbal techniques by other disciplines, there has been a rapid growth in the use of dance and movement therapy. There are differences in the use of the nonverbal. Dance therapists view movement behavior as the prime area for change while other disciplines often see it as a preliminary to verbal interaction. While other professional disciplines add to the understanding of movement and human behavior, it is above all the theoretical concepts of dance itself and the experience of movement which have meaning and satisfaction of their own. It is hoped that other disciplines will make use of movement within their methodology; however, because of the patient's need for the profound understanding and comfort when using movement, a dance therapist must be well trained in her art. The American Dance Therapy Association, formed in 1966, is continually working to define the meanings of dance therapy and thereby clarify the kind of education and training needed to practice. An intensive and extensive dance background is basic, as well as the understanding of human growth and behavior and the structures of the body. These can then be woven into a theoretical base useful to understanding the unique concepts of dance therapy. The application of these concepts into treatment must be carefully supervised before a trainee is ready to practice.

(Conclusion

Dance therapy is a new profession that is still in the process of defining itself. Research and study will further establish it as a distinct therapeutic discipline. The significance of dance therapy is that it uses and develops the strengths of people by starting with what they *can* do and working toward the total integration of the body and the mind. It is a creative experience and often a joyful one. Movement is the gift we all share.

(Bibliography

1. ADLER, J. "The Study of an Autistic Child," Proc. Am. Dance Ther. Assoc. 3rd Annu. Conf., Madison, Wis., 1968, pp. 43–48.
2. ALLPORT, G. W. and P. E. VERNON. *Studies in Expressive Movement.* New York: Macmillan, 1933.
3. ARDREY, R. *The Territorial Imperative: A Personal Inquiry into the Animal Origins of Property and Nations.* New York: Atheneum, 1966.
4. AUBERT, C. (1927) *The Art of Pantomine.* Translated by E. Sears. New York: Benjamin Blom, 1970.
5. BARTENIEFF, I. "Dance Therapy: A New Profession or a Rediscovery of an Ancient Role of the Dance?" *Dance Scope*, 7, Fall-Winter (1972–1973), 6–18.
6. BARTENIEFF, I. and M. DAVIS. *Effort-Shape Analysis of Movement: The Unity of Expression and Function.* New York: Albert Einstein College of Medicine, 1965. Unpublished monograph.
7. BARTENIEFF, I., M. DAVIS, and F. PAULAY. *Four Adaptations of Effort Theory in Research and Teaching.* New York: Dance Notation Bureau, 1970.
8. BARTENIEFF, I. and F. PAULAY. "Choreometrics Profiles," in Alan Lomax ed., *Folk Song Style and Culture*, AAAS Publ. no. 88, pp. 248–261. Washington: Am. Assoc. Adv. Sci., 1968.
9. BENDER, L. and F. BOAS. "Creative Dance in Therapy," *Am. J. Orthopsychiatry*, 11 (1941), 235–244.
10. BERGER, M. M. "Nonverbal Communica-

tions in Group Psychotherapy," *Int. J. Group Psychother.*, 8 (1958), 161–178.

11. BERGER, M. R. *Bodily Experience and Expression of Emotion.* Monogr. no. 2, pp. 191–230. Columbia, Md.: Am. Dance Ther. Assoc., 1972.

12. BERNSTEIN, P. L. *Theory and Methods in Dance-Movement Therapy.* Dubuque, Iowa: Kendall-Hunt Publ., 1972.

13. BIRDWHISTELL, R. L. *Introduction to Kinesics.* Louisville: University of Louisville Press, 1952.

14. ———. *Kinesics and Context.* Philadelphia: University of Pennsylvania Press, 1970.

15. BOAS, F. "Origins of Dance," Proc. Am. Dance Ther. Assoc. 6th Annu. Conf., Washington: 1971.

16. BULL, N. *The Attitude Theory of Emotion.* Nerv. Ment. Dis. Monogr. no. 81. Baltimore: Williams & Wilkins, 1951.

17. CAMPBELL, D. G. "Posture: A Gesture Toward Life," in *Impulse* (1951), 25–30.

18. CANNER, N. . . . *And a Time to Dance.* Boston: Beacon, 1968.

19. ———. *Stimulating Sounds and Vocalization Through Body Movement and Rhythm with Hospitalized Children.* Monogr. no. 2, pp. 1–12. Columbia, Md.: Am. Dance Ther. Assoc., 1972.

20. CHACE, M. "Dance as an Adjunctive Therapy with Hospitalized Mental Patients," *Bull. Menninger Clin.*, 17 (1953), 219–225.

21. ———. "Common Principles in Music Therapy," *Music Ther.*, 4 (1954), 87–90.

22. ———. "Development of Group Interaction through Dance," in J. H. Masserman and J. L. Moreno, eds., *Progress in Psychotherapy*, Vol. 3. Technique of Psychotherapy, pp. 143–153. New York: Grune & Stratton, 1958.

23. ———. "Dance Alone Is Not Enough," *Dance Mag.*, 38 (1964), 46–47, 58.

24. ———. "The Power of Movement with Others," *Dance Mag.*, 38 (1964), 42–45, 68–69.

25. ———. "Dance Therapy for Adults," Paper presented at the Natl. Educ. Assoc. Conf., Atlantic City, N.J.

26. CHAIKLIN, S. "Dance Therapy," Proc. Am. Dance Ther. Assoc. 4th Annu. Conf., Philadelphia, 1969, pp. 25–31.

27. CHENEY, G. "It Is a Gift," *Impulse* (1969–1970) 65–68.

28. CONDON, W. S. "Linguistic-Kinesic Research and Dance Therapy," Proc. Am. Dance Ther. Assoc. 3rd Annu. Conf., Madison, Wis., 1968, pp. 21–42.

29. CORNYETZ, P. "Movement Therapy and Total Health," Proc. Am. Dance Ther. Assoc. 6th Annu. Conf., Washington, 1971, pp. 1–12.

30. CRATTY, B. J. *Movement, Perception and Thought.* Palo Alto: Peek Publ., 1969.

31. DARWIN, C. *The Expression of the Emotions in Man and Animals.* New York: Philosophical Library, 1955.

32. DAVIS, F. *Beyond Words: The Science of Nonverbal Communication.* New York: McGraw-Hill, forthcoming.

33. DAVIS, M. "An Effort-Shape Movement Analysis of a Family Therapy Session." Yeshiva University, 1966. Unpublished paper.

34. ———. "Movement Characteristics of Hospitalized Psychiatric Patients," Proc. Am. Dance Ther. Assoc. 5th Annu. Conf., New York, 1970, pp. 25–45.

35. ———. *Understanding Movement Behavior: An Annotated Bibliography.* New York: Arno, 1972.

36. DELL, C. *A Primer for Movement Description: Using Effort-Shape and Supplementary Concepts.* New York: Dance Notation Bureau, 1970.

37. DE MILLE, A. *The Book of the Dance.* New York: Golden, 1963.

38. DENBY, E. (1949) *Looking at the Dance.* New York: Horizon, 1968.

39. DEUTSCH, F. "Some Principles of Correlating Verbal and Non-verbal Communication," in L. A. Gottschalk and H. A. Auerbach, eds., *Methods of Research in Psychotherapy*, pp. 166–184. New York: Appleton-Century-Crofts, 1966.

40. DRATMAN, M. L. "Reorganization of Psychic Structures in Autism: A Study Using Body Movement Therapy," in Proc. Am. Dance Ther. Assoc. 2nd Annu. Conf. Washington, 1967, pp. 39–45.

41. DUNBAR, F. "Interpretation of Body Behavior during Psychotherapy," in J. H. Masserman, ed., *Science and Psychoanalysis*, Vol. 3. Psychoanalysis and Human Values, pp. 223–230. New York: Grune & Stratton, 1960.

42. DYER-BENNETT, M. "Some Thoughts about Change—Our Most Deceptive Thera-

peutic Goal," Proc. Am. Dance Ther. Assoc. 5th Annu. Conf., New York, 1970, pp. 51–57.

43. DYRUD, J. and M. CHACE. "Movement and Personality," Proc. Am. Dance Ther. Assoc. 3rd Annu. Conf., Madison, Wis., 1968, pp. 16–20.

44. EKMAN, P. "Communication through Nonverbal Behavior: A Source of Information about an Interpersonal Relationship," in S. S. Tomkins and C. E. Izard, eds., *Affect, Cognition, and Personality*, pp. 390–442. New York: Springer, 1965.

45. EKMAN, P. and W. V. FRIESEN. "The Repertoire of Nonverbal Behavior: Categories, Origins, Usage and Coding." *Semiotica*, 1 (1969), 49–98.

46. ———. "Constants across Cultures in the Face and Emotion," *J. Pers. Soc. Psychol.*, 17 (1971), 124–129.

47. ELLIS, H. (1923) "The Art of Dancing." in *The Dance of Life*, pp. 34–63. New York: Modern Library, 1929.

48. ESCALONA, S. and G. M. HEIDER. *Prediction and Outcome: A Study in Child Development*. New York: Basic Books, 1959.

49. ESPENAK, L. *Body Dynamics and Dance in Individual Psychotherapy*. Monogr. no. 2, pp. 111–127. Columbia, Md.: Am. Dance Ther. Assoc. 1972.

50. FISHER, S. and S. E. CLEVELAND. (1958) *Body Image and Personality*. New York: Dover, 1968.

51. FREUD, S. (1921) "Group Psychology and the Analysis of the Ego," in J. Strachey, ed., *Standard Edition*, Vol. 18, pp. 69–143. London: Hogarth, 1955.

52. GATES, A. *A New Look at Movement: A Dancer's View*. Minneapolis: Burgess Publ., 1968.

53. GESELL, A. and C. S. AMATRUDA. *Developmental Diagnosis: Normal and Abnormal Child Development Clinical Methods and Pediatric Applications*, 2nd rev. ed. New York: Hoeber, 1947.

54. GOFFMAN, E. *The Presentation of Self in Everyday Life*. Garden City, N.Y.: Doubleday, 1959.

55. ———. *Encounters: Two Studies in the Sociology of Interaction*. Indianapolis: Bobbs-Merrill, 1961.

56. ———. *Behavior in Public Places: Notes on the Social Organization of Gatherings*. New York: Free Press, 1963.

57. GOODENOUGH, F. L. "Expression of the Emotions in a Blind-Deaf Child," *J. Abnorm. Soc. Psychol.*, 27 (1932), 328–333.

58. GOVINE, B. *The Use of Movement as Adjunctive Therapy in the Rehabilitation of Psychiatric Day Patients*. Monogr. no. 1, pp. 12–15. Columbia, Md.: Am. Dance Ther. Assoc., 1971.

59. HALL, E. T. *The Silent Language*. Garden City, N.Y.: Doubleday, 1959.

60. ———. *The Hidden Dimension*. Garden City, N.Y.: 1966.

61. H'DOUBLER, M. A. *Dance: A Creative Art Experience*. New York: Appleton-Century-Crofts, 1940.

62. HORST, L. *Modern Dance Forms in Relation to the Other Modern Arts*. New York: Dance Horizons (not dated).

63. HUANG, A. C.-L. *Embrace Tiger, Return to Mountain—The Essence of T'ai Chi*. Lafayette, Calif.: Real People Press, 1973.

64. HUNT, V. "The Biological Organization of Man to Move," in *Impulse* (1968), 51–62.

65. ———. "Neuromuscular Structuring of Human Energy." Paper presented at the 45th Conf. Progr. and in the Annu. Rep. of the Western Society for Physical Education of College Women, 1970. Unpublished.

66. IRWIN, K. *Dance as Prevention of, Therapy for, and Recreation from the Crisis of Old Age*. Monogr. no. 2, pp. 151–190. Columbia, Md.: Am. Dance Ther. Assoc. 1972.

67. JACOBSON, E. *Progressive Relaxation: A Physiological and Clinical Investigation of Muscular States and Their Significance in Psychology and Medical Practice*, 2nd rev. ed. Chicago: University of Chicago Press, 1938.

68. ———. *Biology of Emotions: New understanding Derived from Biological Multidisciplinary Investigation: First Electrophysiological Measurements*. Springfield, Ill.: Charles C. Thomas, 1967.

69. KALISH, B. "Body Movement Therapy for Autistic Children," Proc. Am. Dance Ther. Assoc. 3rd Annu. Conf., Madison, Wis., 1968, pp. 49–59.

70. ———. *A Study of Nonverbal Interaction in the Classroom*, Monogr. no. 1, pp. 16–37. Columbia, Md.: Am. Dance Ther. Assoc., 1971.

71. KAMIN, D. *Thoughts on Therapy*. Monogr.

no. 1, pp. 50–68. Columbia, Md.: Am. Dance Ther. Assoc., 1971.

72. KENDON, A. "Movement Coordination in Social Interaction: Some Examples Described," *Acta Psychol. (Amst.)*, 32 (1970), 100–125.

73. KEPHART, N. C. *The Slow Learner in the Classroom.* Columbus, Ohio: Merrill, 1960.

74. KESTENBERG, J. S. "The Role of Movement Patterns in Development: I. Rhythms of Movement," *Psychoanal. Q.*, 34 (1965), 1–36.

75. ———. "The Role of Movement Patterns in Development: II. Flow of Tension and Effort," *Psychoanal. Q.*, 34 (1965), 517–563.

76. ———. "Rhythm and Organization in Obsessive-Compulsive Development," *Int. J. Psycho-Anal.*, 47 (1966), 151–159.

77. ———. "Suggestions for Diagnostic and Therapeutic Procedures in Movement Therapy," Proc. Am. Dance Ther. Assoc. 2nd Annu. Conf., Washington, 1967, pp. 5–16.

78. ———. "The Role of Movement Patterns in Development: III. The Control of Shape," *Psychoanal. Q.*, 36 (1967), 356–409.

79. KESTENBERG, J. S., H. MARCUS, E. ROBBINS et al. "Development of the Young Child as Expressed through Bodily Movement: 1," *J. Am. Psychoanal. Assoc.*, in press.

80. KUBIE, L. S. "Body Symbolization and the Development of Language," *Psychoanal. Q.*, 3, 1934.

81. LABAN, R. *Principles of Dance and Movement Notation.* London: MacDonald & Evans, 1956.

82. ———. *The Mastery of Movement*, 2nd rev. ed., L. Ullmann, ed. London: MacDonald & Evans, 1960.

83. ———. *Modern Educational Dance*, 2nd rev. ed., revised by L. Ullmann. London: MacDonald & Evans, 1963.

84. ———. *Choreutics.* Annotated and edited by L. Ullman. London: MacDonald & Evans, 1966.

85. LABAN, R. and F. C. LAWRENCE. *Effort.* London: MacDonald & Evans, 1947.

86. LAMB, W. *Posture and Gesture: An Introduction to the Study of Physical Behaviour.* London: Gerald Duckworth, 1965.

87. LAMB, W. and D. TURNER. *Management*

Behaviour. New York: International Universities Press, 1969.

88. LANGAR, S. K. *Feeling and Form: A Theory of Art.* New York: Scribners, 1953.

89. LEFCO, H. *Dance Therapy: Narrative Case Histories of Therapy with Six Patients.* Chicago: Nelson-Hall, 1974.

90. LOMAX, A., I. BARTENIEFF, and F. PAULAY. "Dance Style and Culture," in A. Lomax, ed., *Folk Song Style and Culture*, AAAS Publ. no. 88, pp. 222–247. Washington: Am. Assoc. Adv. Sci., 1968.

91. LOWEN, A. (1965) *Love and Orgasm.* New York: New American Library, 1967.

92. ———. *Betrayal of the Body.* New York: Macmillan, 1967.

93. ———. "The Body in Therapy," Proc. Am. Dance Ther. Assoc. 5th Annu. Conf., New York: 1970, pp. 1–9.

94. ———. (1958) *The Language of the Body.* New York: Macmillan, 1971.

95. LUCE, G. G. *Biological Rhythms in Psychiatry and Medicine*, Public Health Service Pub. no. 2088. Washington: U.S. Govt. Print. Off., 1970.

96. LURIA, A. R. *The Nature of Human Conflicts: An Objective Study of Disorganization and Control of Human Behaviour.* Translated and edited by W. H. Gantt. New York: Liveright Publ., 1932.

97. MASON, K., ed. *Focus on Dance. 7: Dance Therapy.* Washington: Am. Assoc. Health, Physical Education, and Recreation, 1974.

98. MAY, P. R. A., M. WEXLER, J. SALKIN et al. "Non-verbal Techniques in the Re-establishment of Body Image and Self Identity: A Preliminary Report." *Psychiatr. Res. Rep.*, 16 (1963), 68–82.

99. MEERLOO, J. A. M. *Dance Craze and Sacred Dance.* London: Peter Owen, 1961.

100. ———. "Rhythm in Babies and Adults: Its Implications for Mental Contagion," *Arch. Gen. Psychiatry*, 5 (1961), 169–175.

101. ———. *Unobtrusive Communication: Essays in Psycholinguistics.* Assen, The Netherlands: Van Gorcum, 1964.

102. MEHRABIAN, A. "Methods and Designs: Some Referents and Measures of Nonverbal Behavior." *Behav. Res. Meth. Instrument.*, 1 (1969), 203–207.

103. MONTAGU, A. *Touching: The Human Significance of the Skin.* New York: Columbia University Press, 1971.

104. NADEL, M. H. and C. G. NADEL. *The*

Dance Experience: Readings in Dance Appreciation. New York: Praeger, 1970.

105. NORTH, M. *Personality Assessment through Movement*. London: Macdonald & Evans, 1972.

106. OSTRANDER, S. and L. SCHROEDER. *Psychic Discoveries Behind the Iron Curtain*. Englewood Cliffs, N.J.: Prentice-Hall, 1970.

107. PENNINGTON, J. *The Importance of Being Rhythmic*. New York: Putnam, 1925.

108. PESSO, A. *Movement in Psychotherapy: Psychomotor Techniques and Training*. New York: New York University Press, 1969.

109. PRESTON, V. *A Handbook for Modern Educational Dance*. London: MacDonald & Evans, 1963.

110. REICH, W. *The Function of the Orgasm*. Translated by T. P. Wolfe. New York: Noonday, 1942.

111. ———. *Character-Analysis*, 3rd ed. Translated by T. P. Wolfe. New York: Noonday, 1949.

112. ROBINS, F. and J. ROBINS. *Educational Rhythmics for Mentally and Physically Handicapped Children*. New York: Association Press, 1968.

113. ROLF, I. P. "Structural Integration: Gravity, an Unexplored Factor in a More Human Use of Human Beings," *Systematics*, 1 (1963), 66–83.

114. ROSEN, E. *Dance in Psychotherapy*. New York: Teachers College Press, Columbia University, 1957.

115. ROWEN, B. *Learning through Movement*. New York: Teachers College Press, Columbia University, 1963.

116. RUESCH, J. *Disturbed Communication: The Clinical Assessment of Normal and Pathological Communicative Behavior*. New York: Norton, 1957.

117. ———. *Therapeutic Communication*. New York: Norton, 1961.

118. RUESCH, J. and W. KEES. *Nonverbal Communication: Notes on the Visual Perception of Human Relations*. Berkeley: University of California Press, 1956.

119. RUSSELL, R. W. "The Wisconsin Dance Idea–Tribute from a Movement Therapist," *Impulse* (1969–70).

120. SACHS, C. *World History of the Dance*. Translated by B. Schonberg. New York: Crown Publ., 1937.

121. SAMUELS, A. *Movement Change through Dance Therapy–A Study*. Monogr. no. 2, pp. 50–70. Columbia, Md.: Am. Dance Ther. Assoc., 1972.

122. SCHACHTEL, E. G. *Metamorphosis: On the Development of Affect Perception, Attention and Memory*, 4th ed. New York: Basic Books, 1959.

123. SCHEFLEN, A. E. "The Significance of Posture in Communication Systems," *Psychiatry*, 27 (1964), 316–331.

124. ———. *Body Language and the Social Order*. Englewood Cliffs, N.J.: Prentice-Hall, 1972.

125. ———. *How Behavior Means*. Garden City, N.Y.: Doubleday Anchor, 1974.

126. SCHILDER, P. *The Image and Appearance of the Human Body*. New York: International Universities Press, 1950.

127. SCHLICHTER, J. "Movement Therapy," in O. Pursglove, ed., *Recognitions in Gestalt Therapy*. New York: Funk & Wagnalls, 1968.

128. SCHMAIS, C. and E. WHITE. "Introduction to Dance Therapy, Workshop in Dance Therapy: Its Research Potentials," pp. 1–6. Proc. Joint Conf. Am. Dance Ther. Assoc., C.O.R.D., and Postgraduate Center for Mental Health, New York, 1968.

129. ———. "Movement Analysis: A Must for Dance Therapists," Proc. Am. Dance Ther. Assoc. 4th Annu. Conf., New York, 1969, pp. 52–59.

130. SCHOOP, T. *Won't You Join the Dance? A Dancer's Essay into the Treatment of Psychosis*. Palo Alto: National Press Book, 1974.

131. SELVER, C. "Sensory Awareness and Total Functioning," *Gen. Semant. Bull.*, 20–21 (1957), 5–16.

132. SHEETS, M. *The Phenomenology of Dance*. Madison, Wis.: University of Wisconsin Press, 1966.

133. SMALLWOOD, J. C. "Dance-Movement Therapy," in J. H. Masserman, ed., *Current Psychiatric Therapies*, Vol. 14, pp. 115–121. New York: Grune & Stratton, 1974.

134. SORELL, W. *The Dance through the Ages*. New York: Grosset & Dunlap, 1967.

135. SPITZ, R. A. *No and Yes: On the Genesis of Human Communication*. New York: International Universities Press, 1957.

136. STANISLAVSKI, C. *An Actor Prepares*. Trans-

lated by E. R. Hapgood. New York: Theatre Arts Books, 1936.

137. STERN, E. M. "She Breaks through Invisible Walls," *Ment. Hyg.*, 41 (1957), 361–371.

138. SIEGEL, E. V. *The Phantasy Life of a Mongoloid; Movement Therapy as a Developmental Tool.* Monogr. no. 2. Columbia, Md.: Am. Dance Ther. Assoc., 1972.

139. TODD, M. E. (1937) *The Thinking Body: A Study of the Balancing Forces of Dynamic Man.* New York: Dance Horizons, 1968.

140. WACHTEL, P. L. "An Approach to the Study of Body Language in Psychother-

apy," *Psychother. Theory, Res. Pract.*, 4 (1967), 97–100.

141. WHITE, E. Q. "Child Development Movement Studies (Part 1)," unpublished paper, Goddard College, Plainfield, Vt., 1968.

142. WHITEHOUSE, M. "Reflections on a Metamorphosis," *Impulse* (1969–70).

143. WIGMAN, M. *The Language of Dance.* Translated by W. Sorell. Middletown, Conn.: Wesleyan University Press, 1966.

144. WOLFF, W. *The Expression of Personality: Experimental Depth Psychology.* New York: Harper & Brothers, 1943.

CHAPTER 38

AFTERCARE SYSTEMS

Israel Zwerling

⟨ Introduction

THE PRINCIPAL LOCUS of treatment for the psychotic patient in the United States has, since 1955, been shifting from inpatient to outpatient facilities. This may be documented in terms of the briefer median duration of inpatient stay, the declining average daily census of mental hospitals, or the increasing numbers of outpatients on the rolls of hospital outpatient services. Over the same period, admissions to mental hospitals have increased, largely because of the high rate of readmissions. Table 38–1 shows the relevant data for the mental hospitals operated by the New York State Department of Mental Hygiene as an example.

The modal career of patienthood has been altered, in parallel with these changes, from extended or life-long institutionalization punctuated by brief stays in the community, to extended residence in the community punctuated by brief periods of hospitalization. It is not directly in the province of this chapter to attempt an analysis of the sources of this change; it seems clear that effective psycho-

active drugs, the altered organization of the service-delivery structures of the hospitals, and the burgeoning of community psychiatry programs, all inextricably interrelated, have been central to this shift in focus from inpatient to outpatient treatment.[63] It is by no means suggested that no further problems confront a hospital staff faced with an acutely psychotic patient, but the more pressing challenge now in the treatment of this patient is the stabilization of his recovery and his maintenance in the community after discharge.

There is no dearth of reports of aftercare efforts, but only few substantive conclusions may be drawn, because of the inadequate data reported. To begin with, the greatest number of studies by far are either cross-sectional or cover a brief period of follow-up time; quite clearly, the need in dealing with chronic disability is for long-term longitudinal research. Second, most reports use rehospitalization as the sole criterion for the success or failure of the effort described. This is questionable, for one reason, because hospitalization is so highly dependent upon extraneous factors (e.g., the availability of beds and of

TABLE 38–1.   Admissions and Readmissions in New York State Mental Hospitals, 1955–1972

	YEAR			
	1955	1960	1965	1972
Average daily census	92,165	89,334	85,172	53,598
Median duration of stay	211	not available	75	43
Total admissions	21,931	27,152	35,254	31,258
Percent readmissions	27.2	32.8	35.5	60.6
Readmission index*	180.3	213.1	198.7	161.8

* Number of readmissions per 1000 discharges

alternative treatment facilities, and the tolerance of the family and community for deviant behavior). For another, they fail to differentiate a fully functioning, socially active expatient from a totally dependent recluse in the back room of the home of a tolerant family; both would be equally tabulated as "not rehospitalized." Third, the number of factors which may be presumed, or have been demonstrated, to play significant roles in determining posthospitalization adaptation is quite large. Few studies have been able to control variables adequately and/or study a sufficiently large sample so as to provide compelling correlational data between one particular treatment variable and outcome. It is therefore not surprising that, with a few exceptions which will be noted, for virtually every study demonstrating a significant advantage to the inclusion of a particular component of an aftercare system, other studies report that the same component offers no significant advantage, or may even be a disadvantage.

(General Issues

Central to an analysis of aftercare systems is a formulation of the goals of aftercare. This, in turn, requires some conceptualization of the disability which led to the hospitalization. If psychosis is perceived as essentially an intraorganismic organic process, rather different expectations of the posthospital course and different treatment concerns would prevail

than if it is seen as the consequence of an imbalance of intrapsychic forces and counterforces, or as a product of intrafamilial or sociocultural disequilibria. Confronted with the need to account for the grossly deranged behavior of a psychotic patient, one can take any position along a broad range between two extremes. At one end of the range of explanations, one can assume that the behavior is the product of a disordered organism, neurochemically or psychologically incapable of satisfactory adaptation to any expectable environment. Alternatively, at the other extreme, one can assume that the behavior is the response of an essentially normal organism to a noxious environment, much as one would expect a *normal* liver bathed in a high-alcohol, low-protein, low-vitamin environment, sooner or later, to undergo fatty degeneration and ultimately to become cirrhotic. The implications of these polar positions for the appropriate scope of the work of a psychiatrist are quite different. While nobody would expect an internist, e.g., to attempt to treat a patient with cirrhosis while the diseased liver continued to be bathed in the same noxious environment, one still is challenged occasionally about the appropriateness of a psychiatrist in a program concerned with jobs, schooling, housing, welfare, recreation, and the like. It is quite evident that these polar views are not mutually preclusive, that both diathesis and stress (both psychological and socio-cultural determinants) may be expected to be implicated in the occurrence of psychotic behavior, and that a psychiatrist undertaking the operation of an aftercare program must be prepared to direct therapeutic efforts to whatever system level appears critically disordered and amenable to intervention.

There is a considerable body of evidence which indicates that aftercare programs can indeed be effective in reducing the incidence of rehospitalization in a population of discharged patients.[2,18,36] A handful of studies report, separate from or in addition to this criterion, a more desirable level of social activity and a generally improved quality of life as correlates of successful aftercare programs. Cassell et al.,[13] in a two-year follow-up study of 458 patients discharged after a minimum of two years of continuous hospitalization, point out that the financial cost to the community of maintaining these patients out of the hospital is less than half the cost of hospital care. Whatever the criteria employed, there is consistency in the finding of greater success in an experimental program than in no program, or in a minimal program. Some general observations may be extracted from these studies, before attempting to describe and assess some of the specific tactics of aftercare systems.

1. A number of studies report an initial period of high success, with a subsequent decrease in improvement rate and a narrowing of the gap between experimental and control subjects.[18,19,43] This would seem to suggest a kind of Hawthorne effect to be operative, and underscores the importance of such factors as the enthusiasm of the providers of service and their attentiveness and dedication to their patients, as well as perhaps the awareness of the patients that they are in a special program.

2. Perhaps related to the above observation is the consistency of the report of success when high expectations of patients' performance are built into the design of the aftercare program. Darley and Kenny[16] have coined the term "the Queequeg syndrome" to describe the self-fulfilling character of the prophecy of the family and community that the discharged patient is chronically ill and cannot be held responsible for himself. This is not, of course, to suggest that unrealistic demands for performance are likely to be helpful to chronic patients; Schooler et al.,[57] indeed,

in describing the composite picture of their successful one-year post discharge patient, state: ". . . his functioning is not at the level expected of members of the community. He appears to satisfy the expectations of his own family and himself by virtue of their realistically low level."

3. There is substantial agreement that extended hospitalization, generally defined as more than two uninterrupted years in an institution, is associated with a poor prognosis in aftercare programs.[33,49,51] Since the long-term patients tend to be disconnected from family and community even before hospitalization and may be assumed to suffer from a more severe degree of mental illness, it is simplistic to account for this finding solely on the basis of the social breakdown syndrome.[31] It is likely that the desocializing process of a total institution, the alienation from family and community, and the greater severity of illness all are implicated in the difficulty of effecting a stable equilibrium in the community for patients discharged after long periods of hospitalization. It should be emphasized that the observed relationship, while it applies to duration of hospitalization, does not appear to apply, within parallel time units, to alternative modes of treatment; Lamb and Goertzel[39] observe ". . . growing evidence that whatever treatment is given or not given during 24-hour hospitalization is not related with post-hospital community tenure or level of instrumental functioning."

4. There is a generally expressed sensitivity to the problem of whether a discharged patient is really *in the community*, as well as to the converse problem of *the burden on the family and community*. Lamb and Goertzel[38] caution against the assumption that a patient discharged to a boarding home is in the community; many family-care homes are in effect small satellite wards of the hospitals from which the patients were discharged. The seemingly self-evident criterion of contact with nonpatients and participation in nonpatient activities, while useful, must in turn be applied with caution since, as will be reviewed below, there are reports of successful aftercare programs built around the tactic of forming a

small patient group while in the hospital and discharging the group as a unit into a house or apartment; contacts and activities may then remain limited to intragroup relationships for some time. An assessment of the effects of all the component elements of a total prescription for aftercare upon the process of normalization, i.e., of rejecting the identity of patienthood and acquiring a primary identity as a citizen without stigmatization, must be a central consideration in the design of an aftercare program.

5. There is considerable disagreement concerning the optimal locus of aftercare services. Jansen[35] cautions against mental hospitals operating halfway houses on their premises; Black and Benney[9] and Keil[36] similarly argue for rehabilitation centers to be separated from hospitals. At the same time Hott[34] reports strikingly good results from establishing an aftercare clinic on the ward at Bellevue Hospital in New York City from which patients were discharged; his rationale, directly contrary to the fears of the above cited contributors that in-hospital aftercare services tend to keep patients seeing themselves as patients, is precisely that "Return to the original ward as a visitor to the Follow-Up Program lets the patient enjoy the prestige of his new status, increases his self-esteem, and helps to establish his self-image of health." [p. 225][34] Crary and Kirts[14] report a similar program in Los Angeles. Pechan[52] describes a successful halfway house on his ward, while Lamb and Goertzel[39] report a study in which patients discharged to a transitional day hospital improved significantly when they were scheduled so as not to mix with the inpatient population. Silverstein[58] comments that the mental hospitals in Pennsylvania provide half of all aftercare services themselves; he cautions that "It should be kept in mind that no research has established that community-based services are more effective than hospital-based services for the seriously mentally ill." [p. 53][58] It may of course be that the locus of the aftercare effort is of minor significance in determining its effectiveness, compared with other qualities of the effort; it may, indeed, be help-ful to some patients to have a graded range of services extending from the hospital itself to full participation in community life.

6. A review of the literature leads compellingly to the conclusion that, even with the most effective programs devised, considerable disability may be expected in the greatest number of patients. Anthony et al.,[2] after reviewing an extensive body of the literature, suggest as a baseline against which experimental programs may be tested, that standard programs show 40 to 50 percent of discharged patients returning to the hospital within a year of discharge, and 20 to 30 percent working at that time. The data reported by Schooler et al.[57] are representative of the better studies: of 299 patients discharged from an initial, larger cohort of newly admitted schizophrenic patients, and in the community one year following discharge, 41 percent had been rehospitalized during the year (the number not discharged at all, and the number discharged, rehospitalized and back in the community at the time of the one-year follow-up, are not given; the percentage of the *original* cohort of patients discharged and out of the hospital a year after discharge is certainly below 50 percent). Of this population of 299 *successful* patients, only 11 percent were described functionally "as good as the average person in the community," and only 58 percent were employed. It should be emphasized that these data concern an acutely ill patient population continuing to reside in the community a year after discharge; Paul,[51] citing five studies of chronic patients, offers the disheartening summary that ". . . the probability of release and community stay after two years continuous hospitalization is reported to be about 6 percent, without change in this century."

These observations suggest the critical importance of defining the goal of an aftercare system. If mental illness is perceived exclusively in the simplistic and absolute model of infectious disease, the likelihood is that unrealistic goals of total cure will be set, and inappropriate and ultimately destructive efforts will be made to force patients to perform at levels of functioning far above their capabilities. More will be said to this point after a review of the factors of significant relevance to the effectiveness of aftercare systems.

⦅ Residence

There is wide agreement that the most compelling determinant of success or failure in the posthospital adaptation of a patient is the nature of the residence to which he is discharged. Schooler et al.[57] suggest that this factor actually precedes the hospitalization; they write: "The single fact about the patient which contributed the most to the evaluation of his present [i.e., one year postdischarge] functioning was his prehospitalization family type . . . Patients who lived in conjugal settings were more likely to be performing successfully in the work role on all four measures of work performance. Over-all functioning was also higher for these patients." Freeman and Simmons,[23] initially exploring the hypothesis that the family's tolerance for deviance was the critical factor in the posthospitalization course of a patient, found four interrelated variables significantly related to whether the patient was rehospitalized or still in the community a year after discharge: work, social participation, instances of bizarre behavior, and the extent to which the patient represented a management problem to his family. Brown et al.[11] demonstrated that patients who were discharged to relatives with whom they were involved in highly emotional relationships, most particularly to the homes of their parents, were most likely to suffer a relapse of florid symptoms and require rehospitalization. In a recent, more careful study, Brown et al.[10] employed a parameter they term "expressed emotion," composed essentially of a combination of the number of critical comments made about the patient, the presence or absence of expressions of hostility to the patient, and expressions of dissatisfaction about the patient. Not surprisingly, a significant relationship was demonstrated between families with *high expressed emotion*

and the relapse of patients discharged from hospitals to these families; conversely, marked warmth expressed to patients without *emotional over-involvement* was associated with a very low rate of relapse. Miller[48] has similarly demonstrated that, while in general patients returning to a conjugal home show a lower rate of rehospitalization than those returning to a parental home, there is a significantly better outcome when there is an absence of marital conflict than when conflict is present.

A number of alternative hypotheses at rather different systems levels have been proposed to account for these findings. Brown et al.[10] suggest that the high physiological arousal potential of schizophrenic patients make a socially and emotionally intrusive environment a double-edged risk: the patient may overreact and become floridly psychotic, or may attempt to defend against psychotic disorganization by social withdrawal, a process he cannot control and which may therefore proceed to a state of psychotic isolation. Sanders[56] suggests a more complex social process in which the labeling of a patient as "mentally ill" changes his status from that of a sick patient to that of a chronic patient, with the inevitable expectations of recurrence; the rejecting family, which emphasizes disability, is then an alternative less desirable than the hospital, in which his role as chronic patient provides acceptance and even status. Whatever the nature of the forces at work, it is abundantly clear that no aftercare system can ignore the matter of the residence to which the patient is discharged. Some approaches to this issue have included family therapy, halfway houses, hostels and family care programs, and Fairweather lodges (see below).

Family Therapy

There is burgeoning literature on family therapy, but few studies are immediately relevant to aftercare programs. A thoughtful summary of the outcome of family therapy of schizophrenia has recently been contributed by Massie and Beels.[45] Langsley et al.[41] demonstrated the resounding advantage of intensive family-crisis therapy in lieu of hospitalization; six months after the initial episode, only half the number of patients in the group treated intially by family-crisis therapy had been hospitalized, as compared with the number of patients treated initially by hospitalization who were rehospitalized. In a later study, Langsley et al.,[42] reporting on the same patient population, found that after eighteen months there were no differences in hospitalization rates between the two groups. Friedman et al.[25] describe, in detail, family therapy in four cases, two of which were quite successful. Lurie and Ron[44] report success with an aftercare program for young adults in which the patient met with a patient group and the parents with a separate couples group for three months before patients and parents began meeting together in activity groups and, after a year, in a joint camping experience. Esterson, Cooper, and Laing[21] describe a program in which forty-two schizophrenic patients were treated exclusively by family therapy while in the hospital and in three family sessions during the year following discharge; only 17 percent required rehospitalization.

Weiner et al.,[60] on the other hand, suggest caution concerning the effectiveness of family therapy as a treatment modality for a population of chronic mental patients. Their book describes in detail the development of the Home Treatment Service at Boston State Hospital as an effort which . . . "kept the patient in his natural habitat where his allies in the community could contribute to his support, prevented the disruption of family, community or occupational ties, and obviated the stigma of referral to a hospital." [p. xv][60] However, they go on to note, . . . "when home services were first started, there was a growing interest in family dynamics and family treatment. Home-service personnel undertook some family treatment, wherein the entire family was seen regularly, usually once a week. Although much could be learned by the therapist about family dynamics, results did not justify the enormous amount of time spent in this kind of therapy. Motivation among family members varied greatly, and it was

quite easy for a member to avoid a treatment session by being out of the house, by being asleep, by drinking too much beer, etc. Some families claimed that the topics which came up were disturbing enough to upset family life for the rest of the week." In later phases, this type of family treatment was discontinued. Actually, in these later phases, the home services became a triage and crisis intervention unit; they comment, concerning their shift from "home treatment" to "community management" that ". . . long-term or intensive home treatment has the same drawbacks as long-term outpatient psychotherapy, namely, an enormous expenditure of professional time and energy." [p. 22][60]

It must be kept in mind that *treatment of the family* is not as definitive a process as, say, *treatment with phenothiazines*. The range of therapeutic tactics in, and of conceptual approaches to, family therapy is extremely extensive,[29] and outcome studies of this modality are as unsatisfactory as are evaluations of individual psychotherapy. It appears, however, that the capability of intervention at the level of the family system is a vital component of an aftercare system. The data concerning the impact of family behavior and family attitudes on recurrence of symptoms are quite compelling. A measure of face validity to focusing on such family behaviors and attitudes in treatment is lent by the fact that virtually every report of a comprehensive aftercare system includes family therapy as part of the treatment armamentarium.

Halfway Houses

Since the family so frequently represents an emotionally disturbing setting for a newly discharged patient, and since the gap between the dependent role of cared-for patient and a fully independent community role is for many patients unmanageably wide, a kind of in-between facility inevitably suggests itself. It thus seems surprising that halfway houses have been so slow in developing in the United States; there were only two in 1950, and ten in 1960.[27] The number has been increasing rapidly, as has the literature describing their role in aftercare programs. Two excellent and informative surveys of halfway-house practices have been published.[27,53]

Glasscote[27] offers the following definition: "A halfway house for the mentally ill is a nonmedical facility specifically intended to enhance the capabilities of people who are mentally ill, or who are impaired by residuals of or deficits from mental illness, to remain in the community, participating to the fullest possible extent in community life." [p. 11][27]

Typically, a halfway house has a capacity of between twenty and twenty-five residents, though they range from four to 200. Most limit their services to the mentally ill, often to the exclusion of patients with alcoholism, drug addiction, and sex deviations. Most are intended to function only as transitional facilities, and impose a restriction on the length of stay; the average appears to be from four to six months. They may, however, also serve as a long-term or even a permanent placement for patients incapable of more independent community living. In some instances—data are lacking, but the impression of this writer is that almost all halfway houses are used in this way to a minor degree—they serve also as an alternative to hospitalization. As transitional facilities, halfway houses have been significantly instrumental in shortening the duration of hospitalization for patients no longer in need of hospitalization, while waiting for a suitable residence to be located, or for the resolution of intrafamilial conflicts too severe to permit discharge to the parental or conjugal home. A hoped-for side effect is the role a halfway house can play in educating a community to accept former mental patients.[35]

A number of issues and problems are related to the use of halfway houses. Walter Barton's caution of a decade ago, as quoted by Glasscote, unfortunately remains true today: "No proof appears to be on record from past experience that the halfway house is worth the expense . . . Tentative findings suggest that the number of patients who succeed and fail in the community after release from the mental hospital is not very much different if they go to a halfway house or to board in the community."[27] Studies of halfway houses tend to report only the outcome of the patients admitted, and do not offer outcome data for alternative, matched populations not afforded a halfway-house placement. Patently, a very cautious and conservative selection process, limiting intake to patients with the best prognosis, would yield quite different outcome data from a study of a randomly selected group of discharged patients, or from a group deliberately chosen to test the applicability of a halfway house for patients with a poor prognosis.

As was noted above, there is a generally expressed preference for the sponsorship of a halfway house by other than a hospital, to avoid creating a facility which is nothing more than a community-based annex of the hospital. Closely related is the problem of staffing; there is general support for a nonpsychiatric, and even a nonprofessional, staff, again, to avoid creating an extension of the hospital. Debates on this issue seem really to miss the critical point about halfway houses; it is as though a halfway house was located by a mathematical determination at precisely a point half-way—(in distance? in dependent status? in proportion of time spent with non-patients as against patients?)—between the hospital and the community, and the issue was to define the properties of that specific point. The halfway house as a *concept* is better seen as a *range* than as a *point*. At the Bronx State Hospital, for example, many patients begin their return to the community through a brief predischarge stay on a *hotel ward*, a virtually unstaffed ward on which the patients are almost completely responsible for their own daily programs; one might see this as a one-eighth-way house. Two of the hospital units utilize a traditional halfway house. Many patients subsequently move to apartments leased and furnished indirectly by the hospital; one might see this as a three-quarter-way house. The degree of contact with hospital staff appropriate for one point along the range from hospital to community would be quite inappropriate for another point in this range, and to debate the merits of a total spectrum of available residential facilities with a single set of criteria is really without purpose.

Perhaps the most critical variable in the functioning of a halfway house in an aftercare system is the ambience established with regard to the expected competence of the residents. Jansen[35] has described the alternative sets of attitudes, i.e., the *low-expectation* halfway house, where staff may underestimate the capabilities of patients, take responsibility for their care, and assume a parental role to patients, and a *high-expectation* halfway house, where each patient is expected to make the maximal contribution to his own and to other patients' recovery. Apte[3] has described the failure of low-expectation halfway houses to rehabilitate and return patients to the community. Wilder et al.[61] have described a high-expectation halfway house, with moderately favorable outcomes for patients. Baganz et al.,[6] demonstrated the effectiveness of a halfway house established in a community YMCA, with minimal staffing; the exceptionally favorable outcome may simply reflect the prerequisite for admission, namely, that the patient have a job in the community.

Relatively little has been written about family-care and foster-home placements for discharged patients, though a considerable number of such dispositions are made by mental hospitals. Lamb and Goertzel[38] raise the concern that patients in such settings are frequently not truly in the community at all, but occupy what is in effect a one-room back-ward annex of the hospital. Anthony et al.[2] point out that such placements tend in actuality to be transitional; only 20 to 30 percent of patients placed in foster homes are still there after a year. Campbell[12] found a group of patients discharged to hostels to show greater ability in self-care and independent functioning than a group remaining in the hospital; however, on retesting a year later, the hospital group showed significant progress, while the hostel patients showed none at all. Unless there is continued involvement of patients in a program of follow-up care and treatment, there is little reason to expect emotional growth, or even the sustained capacity to cope with the pressures of community life, in the setting of a foster-home placement.

Fairweather Lodges

In the view of this writer, the most promising addition to the resources available to an aftercare system with regard to the residence of discharged patients is the practice, first, of the establishment of small patient groups in the course of hospital treatment, and second, the discharge of these patients, *as a unit*, to a house, apartment, or other residence in the community. The most thorough study reported to date of this kind of effort is that of Fairweather et al.,[22] at the Palo Alto VA Hospital. They studied a group of seventy-five chronic patients who were moved into a motel (the "Lodge") after a four-week planning period in the hospital, devoted to discussing the potential problems they would face in the community and the possible solutions to these problems. Except for an occasional visit by a staff member on a specific mission, the lodge was completely organized and operated by the patients. Jobs as janitors and gardeners in the community were taken by lodge units, rather than by individual patients; the work responsibilities of a patient indisposed and incapable of working for a brief period could then be assumed by other lodge members, so that the job would not be lost. The living and working arrangements, such as who would do the marketing, the cooking, the bookkeeping, etc., essential for maintaining the lodge, and who would cover which outside jobs, were established by group meetings of lodge residents. The results were extremely impressive: in the first six months, 65 percent of the lodge group remained out of the hospital and 50 percent were employed full-time during this period; in contrast, in a carefully matched control group, 24 percent remained out of the hospital and only 3 percent worked for the full six-month period. The differences between the two groups remained strikingly significant over the thirty-month follow-up period. What is of greatest interest is that there were no significant differences in psychopathological symptoms between the two groups when the patients were studied individually; the symptoms ceased to be disabling in the setting of the lodge. The social structure of the lodge permitted the evolution of an extremely effective system of mutual supports, in which the disability of any one patient, which might have rendered him incapable of coping in the community if he were living alone, could be made up for by others in the group.

Variants of this approach abound, with differing numbers of patients, different patterns of heterogeneity or homogeneity with regard to age, sex and diagnosis, and with different types of residential settings. Reference was made above to the pattern used at the Bronx State Hospital since 1966. Because of the concern of many patients that they may suffer recurrences, they are reluctant to undertake long-term leases on apartments and to purchase furniture. A nonprofit philanthropic corporation, the *Pibly Fund*, undertook to actually lease the residences, pay for the furniture, and collect the rent. Groups of three to six patients, recovered from acute psychotic episodes and disconnected from their families and communities, are brought together on a section of a minimally staffed "hotel ward;" patients are usually, but not always, of one sex and of a narrow age range. When the group is felt ready for discharge they, along with a representative of the Pibly Fund, search out an apartment, purchase furniture, and move out of the hospital. Initially there are daily staff visits to the apartment, but these are rapidly reduced until the new pseudo-family is completely on its own. A total of 106 patients were discharged from the hospital in this fashion to eleven apartments from 1968 to 1972.

⟦ Vocational and Social Rehabilitation

Black and Benny[9] define rehabilitation as ". . . an all-out, concerted, dynamic process involving the use of a variety of professional and technical skills and a variety of community resources to help handicapped people achieve the maximum functioning of which they are capable." [p. 735][9] Glasscote et al.[28] differen-

tiate rehabilitation from treatment on the basis that the latter represents a direct attack on the disabilities of a patient, while the former represents an effort to identify and exploit the patient's assets to the end of providing the best possible community role; they note: ". . . such facilities as halfway houses to live in, sheltered workshops on special job placements to work in, and social clubs to socialize in are in essence rehabilitating, while after-care clinics and day hospitals are in essence treating." [p. 15.][28] The matter of a residence *to live in* has been reviewed in the preceding section; the two remaining areas—places *to work in* and *to socialize in*—constitute the principal remaining components of rehabilitation programs in aftercare systems.

In a culture in which, as in the American middle class, a *doing* rather than a *being* value orientation is so dominant,[37] the role of work is preeminently determining of both the way an individual is perceived socially and, pari passu, the way in which he values and identifies himself. It is therefore not surprising that work and training for work have played a prominent role, starting from the earliest programs for the care of the mentally ill. Work for patients was a fundamental component of *moral therapy*, and work status has continued to be a criterion for assessing outcome in all studies of aftercare systems which go beyond the simple tabulation of rehospitalizations. Formal programs of *occupational therapy* for the mentally ill were first introduced after World War I; initially limited to diversionary craft training, they began in the early 1930s in England to approximate normal working conditions, and the term "industrial therapy" began to replace "occupational therapy."[9] *Work-for-pay* units and sheltered workshops are now a standard component of comprehensive rehabilitation programs, both for inpatients and in aftercare systems. They serve a range of functions, including prevocational screening, vocational training and evaluation, and ego-strength assessment; in addition, for those patients whose disabilities render them incapable of securing and maintaining work in the competitive labor market, they may serve to provide permanent employment. The settings vary; they may be located in a hospital or clinic, or they may be independent. They range from simple bench-type assembly jobs to complex industrial operations which provide training and supervision for a number of semiskilled occupations. A detailed description of a large-scale program, including a stepwise summary of its development and implementation has been contributed by Winick.[62]

Just as was noted above to be the case with halfway houses, the widest and firmest conviction prevails concerning the positive value of vocational rehabilitation, despite the total lack of evidence demonstrating the advantages of such programs in a hospital or an aftercare system. Silverstein,[58] reporting on a sample of the 10,500 patients discharged annually from Pennsylvania state mental hospitals, modified his prestudy hypothesis about the need for a network of vocational training centers and sheltered workshops when he found that ". . . less than 20 percent of the total patients released might have unmet needs in the vocational field." Crisswell,[15] in a summary of projects supported by the U.S. Vocational Rehabilitation Administration, reported that regardless of the retraining procedures used, from 60 to 80 percent of discharged mental patients return to the hospital; of those who remained in the community, 67 percent required continued professional contact. Anthony et al.[2] reviewed a half-dozen studies of work therapy programs and similarly concluded that: ". . . work therapy alone does not increase the patient's probability of remaining in the community or obtaining employment." [p. 450][2] Nevertheless, a number of principles enjoy a near unanimous consensus among writers,[9,28] e.g., that vocational rehabilitation efforts should begin as early in the hospitalization as possible; that the work provided should be real work, in a real work atmosphere and at real wage levels; and that a widely varied range of jobs should be available in order to provide channels for the diverse talents and interests expectable in a random group of patients.

The situation with regard to social rehabilitation is, again, that without substantive sup-

porting evidence, the widest consensus accepts firmly the value of programs which attempt ". . . to teach the clients in a variety of ways such things as how to groom themselves appropriately, how to ride on buses, how to get to events on time, how to shop for food, how to plan and cook a meal . . . even if he is still persuaded that his head is full of wires or that his body is full of microphones."[23] A growing network of freestanding socialization centers has developed, which include, among those best known in the United States, Fountain House in New York City, Thresholds in Chicago, Council House in Pittsburgh, Portals in Los Angeles, Horizon House in Philadelphia, and Hill House in Cleveland. Landy,[40] in an early article, predictive of the concern with social learning and role modeling which was to increase almost explosively during the ensuing decade, called attention to the ways in which the acculturation process of the already socialized patient differs from the socialization of the child: "No matter how deprived he might have been, no matter how asocial a warped socialization may have rendered him, he is not simply facing life de novo." Social rehabilitation, in his view, is then a process through which a range of role models serve to provide for the *relearning* of socially appropriate adult-role behaviors. The staffing and activity patterns of socialization centers and patient social clubs depend upon the particular resocialization goals of the program. For example, attitudes of hopefulness, respect, approval, patience, and lack of censure are more important than traditional professional skills if the goal of a center is to develop in patients the capacity for establishing friendships and to provide opportunities for feeling accepted. Hansell and Benson[33] provide a detailed description of a highly structured aftercare program designed to restore social skills to very long-term hospitalized patients. Bill[8] reports success with a social club for discharged patients run by volunteers, and David,[17] and Allodi et al.[1] describe socialization programs organized entirely by coordinating existing community agencies.

A study of an innovative rehabilitation program operated as a school, in which 106 patients attended as full-time students for three months, was conducted by Bauman.[7] The formal curriculum included remedial education (reading, arithmetic, and English), vocational counseling, homemaking skills, familiarization with public transportation and points of interest around the city, and local and national political issues. The faculty was entirely nonprofessional. A careful review of the extensive body of data indicates that both at graduation and at a six-month follow-up review there were significant improvements in social and vocational skills; although no clinical services were offered, there was also a decrease in symptomatology. In the nine-month study period following discharge, 23.4 percent of the students were rehospitalized. At the time of graduation, 22 percent were considered ready for employment, and virtually all of these patients did find jobs, but six months later only half of these patients were working. The data are even more sobering when it is recognized that the 106 patients represented those of the 198 discharged patients who were referred to the program; thirty-four were rejected as too severely ill, and fifty-eight who were accepted either refused to participate or dropped out immediately after beginning.

⟨ Specific Treatment Modalities

Studies of the effectiveness of alternative treatment approaches tend not to differentiate between results obtained with an inpatient population and results obtained in an aftercare program. The assumption implicitly made is that a treatment plan which is effective in equilibrating an acutely psychotic inpatient is equally effective in maintaining this equilibrium after the patient is discharged. This is a rather shaky assumption; the degree of control of the total environment of the patient in the hospital is of a totally different order from that in the community, and it is risky to predict the impact upon patients of drugs, individual psychotherapy, vocational and social counseling, and family and group therapy in the context of community life on the basis of their effectiveness in the hospital.

It is abundantly clear that antipsychotic drugs must play a central role in the hospital treatment of chronic psychotic patients.[47] Particularly impressive evidence, because their study was not directed primarily at demonstrating the value of the drugs, was supplied by Pasamanick et al.[50] who reported that 77 percent of the patients in a drug-plus-home-care program remained in the community throughout the two-and-one-half years of their study, as against 34 percent in the placebo-plus-home-care program. However, there are disquieting findings which raise doubts about automatic and universal prescription of drugs to all aftercare patients. Brown et al.[10] report that "Drug taking does relate to outcome, but only modestly, and just fails to reach statistical significance . . . drugs appear to have no effect on patients living with relatives rated low on EE, suggesting that medication might serve mainly to protect patients who live with relatives showing a high EE." [p. 25][10] While the greater value of drugs in the setting of a hostile family may appear reasonable enough, it is difficult to understand this finding in relation to the demonstration of the effectiveness of drugs in the presumably nonhostile, low "EE" (expressed emotion) environment of a hospital.[46] It is even more difficult to account for the finding by Schooler et al.,[57] in a careful one-year follow-up study of a cohort of 299 discharged schizophrenic patients, that "Patients who received placebo treatment in the drug study [i.e., during hospitalization] were less likely to be rehospitalized than those who received any of the three active phenothiazines." [p. 991][57] The same investigators, reporting about the same patients, also note that "Patients who received phenothiazines and/or psychotherapy after discharge to the community were less likely to be rehospitalized than those who did not." Their efforts to account for the former finding lack conviction, i.e., they suggest that the additional six weeks in the average duration of hospital stay of placebo-treated patients, resulting from the fact that they improved less than the drug-treated patients, led to some "special quality in care, treatment or concern" on the part of the staff. It has not been this writer's experience that patients who fail to respond to treatment evoke special care from the ward staff.

The role of psychotherapy in aftercare is even more problematic than that of drugs. May, who makes short shrift of any applicability of psychotherapy at all to the hospital treatment of schizophrenia,[46] nevertheless urges all efforts to support the patient and his family at the time of discharge and immediately afterwards.[47] Safirstein[55] describes an aftercare clinic in which psychotherapy is clearly the principal treatment modality, and while no study known to this writer proposes psychotherapy alone as an effective treatment approach to chronic psychotic patients, there have been a number of reports of psychotherapy in combination with pharmacotherapy. The most carefully controlled of these studies was reported by Grinspoon et al;[30] they demonstrated that, over a two-year period, psychotherapy alone, although conducted by experienced therapists, was without any salutary effect, whereas psychotherapy in combination with phenothiazines was effective in reducing psychotic symptomatology. These authors make the observation that, with only one exception in the placebo population, patients not receiving drugs gave no indication of having established any meaningful relationship with their therapist, whereas patients receiving drugs gave clear evidence that their therapist was important to them. It would appear, contrary to the concerns of some that drugs result in a *chemical strait-jacketing* of patients and their inaccessibility to psychotherapy,[59] that in fact appropriate chemotherapy renders patients who are otherwise unreachable, accessible to psychotherapy.

A crucial difficulty in the evaluation of a program of psychotherapy is the lack of specificity in the variable being evaluated, and this is even more problematic in assessing milieu therapy. May,[46] in a study which demonstrated that milieu therapy was the least effective and, next to psychotherapy alone, the most expensive way to treat hospitalized schizophrenic patients, reports the number of visitors, the number and changes of ward staff

and patient population, the number of staff meetings, and a monthly rating of the ward climate (noise level, patient demands on staff, destructive and constructive behavior, interstaff conflict, and the adequacy of the physical surroundings). The contrast between this simplistic assessment of a milieu and, e.g., that of Edelson[20] could hardly be overstated. May argues that his concern was to provide a milieu which could realistically be replicated in most public mental hospitals; perhaps he is then comparing a fully adequate, sophisticated drug program with a naive and grossly inadequate milieu program. There are, in any event, few studies of milieu therapy in aftercare programs. Guy et al.[32] report a study of 137 patients discharged randomly into a drug-therapy program or into a day hospital in which patients were afforded both drugs and a carefully devised milieu. In two global judgments, on "severity of illness" and on "degree of improvement," there was a significant advantage to the milieu-plus-drugs program, particularly in the population of schizophrenic patients. However, the rehospitalization rate over the year of the study was the same for the two groups; the drugs-alone group showed a significantly shorter duration of treatment, and, perhaps not really baffling, the drugs-plus milieu group showed a *worsening* of sexual problems (which one might expect to have been brought into focus in discussions at the day hospital).

A particularly significant recent innovation in the treatment of hospitalized mental patients has been the application of learning theory to the clinical alteration of behavior. A growing literature[4,5] reports the effectiveness of a token economy pattern of reinforcing desired responses and punishing undesirable behaviors in reducing bizarre acts and increasing adaptive role performance. There are, however, obvious problems in organizing such programs in community settings; Paul,[51] after summarizing the impressive results in inpatient studies, observes about social-learning therapies that, "Like milieu therapy, the greatest weakness to date has been the failure to include provision for community support and follow-up." [p. 89][51]

Criteria for determining which patients will respond to drugs and/or individual, family, or group psychotherapy do not exist; indeed, some writers[43] underscore the unreliability of predictors of success or failure in alternative treatment approaches. Given the complexity of the interaction among the biological, psychological, familial, and sociocultural determinants of well-being and illness, it is unlikely that firm and dependable criteria for prescribing a treatment regimen for a patient in an aftercare program will emerge in the foreseeable future. It would appear more reasonable to expect that an aftercare system with a broad range of available treatment approaches would be more effective than one with limited therapeutic options.

⟦ A Perspective on Aftercare Services

Reference was made earlier to the importance of defining the goals of an aftercare system in a manner consistent with a conceptual approach to mental illness as a manifestation of disturbance at some one or several particular system levels, such as biological, psychological, interpersonal, familial, or sociocultural. Intertwined with but separable from these essentially etiological alternatives is a spectrum of service models, ranging from those— especially medical—models which aspire to *cure* the *illness*, to those—especially educational—models which aspire to *teach* more gratifying adaptational techniques. Patently, the service model, as well as its goals, must be consistent with the conceptualization of the illness of the patients being served, and it is in this context that the issue of models and goals requires explication. What is here proposed is an etiological approach at multiple systems levels, a service model which makes provision for intervention at each level, and the goal of achieving the optimal adaptation for each patient.

The establishment of a service-delivery system, which provides for intervention at several systems levels in the interest of securing optimal functioning of a patient, is hardly strange

to medicine. Indeed, a cardiologist would likely be subject to malpractice charges if he did not combine drug, diet, exercise, and lifestyle prescriptions for his patients. Yet, somehow, there appears to persist in the approach of the traditional psychiatrist the expectation that, given only the proper kind and dosage of drugs and/or psychotherapy, all patients should be capable of being cured. One reflection of this is the series of dichotomies noted throughout this report and about which debates continue, namely, an in-hospital versus a community base for an aftercare clinic, high-expectation versus low-expectation programs, a medical model versus a social competence model. All these are not seen as equally necessary options in a broad range of resources for the mentally disabled or handicapped, but as mutually exclusive alternatives. It is a tragic miscarriage of an unrealistic drive to make everyone as functional and independent as we are. A more realistic and humane perspective starts with a view of human behavior as the product of a complex interaction between a biological organism and its psychological apparatus, in the matrix of a family system, within a hierarchy of sociocultural forces and counterforces. When the product of this interaction is of a specified order of deviancy and/or disability, it constitutes *mental illness,* and the goal of treatment may then be more realistically defined in terms of readjusting those elements of the complex interaction which are available to intervention in such fashion as to diminish the degree of deviancy and disability. This view acknowledges the existence of a range of levels of ability and of disability along the spectrum of mental illness, much as we acknowledge a range of levels in other spectra of human variability, and suggests the necessity for a corresponding range of social modalities to provide for the broad spectrum of abilities and disabilities.

There are inescapable consequences to this perspective, perhaps more profound than are immediately apparent. If we accept the likelihood that every instance of psychosis has biological, psychological, and sociocultural determinants, and if we accord equally to the psychotic patient as we do to those of us who are not identified as mad the right to solve his problems as best he can, we are committed to an aftercare system which provides (1) the full range of biological, psychological, and social therapies; (2) the full range of levels of vocational, residential, social, and recreational opportunities, through which a patient may move towards greater autonomy and independence, *or at any of which a patient may rest as optimal for him for whatever length of time*; and (3) the fullest coordination of all component elements of the aftercare system, to insure the availability of all to each patient, and to provide continuity of care as a patient moves through the different available levels in the system. Glasscote[28] states the issue in terms of ". . . what we believe to have become a commitment to the mentally ill: not just the privilege but the right to live in the community, and to have as good a life there as possible." [p. 28][28] Freeman[24] spells out these implications more concretely: "Posthospital service must be dynamic, supervised, and affiliated with other health units without restrictions to the flow of people. Posthospital care means the availability of care as long as needs exist, to the full measure of services, available for the full duration of life." [p. 128][24] We can continue to evaluate aftercare programs against a set of arbitrary and demonstrably unrealistic criteria of *success* and *failure*, at an awesome cost in human suffering, or we can utilize our experience as a guide to the establishment of a range of residential, vocational, treatment, and socialization resources adequate to provide for the identified needs of perhaps the most oppressed of all our minority groups, the chronically mentally ill.

❡ Bibliography

1. ALLODI, F., M. BELYEA, S. SNIDERMAN, and S. FREEMAN. "The Community Group Program: Evaluation of a Multi-Agency Therapeutic Social Club," *Can. Psychiatr. Assoc. J.*, 17 (1972), 45–50.

2. ANTHONY, W., G. BUELL, S. SHARRATT et al.

3. APTE, R. Z. "The Transitional Hostel in the Rehabilitation of the Mentally Ill," in G. McLachan, ed., *Problems and Progress in Medical Care*, pp. 155–187. London: Oxford University Press, 1966.

4. ATTHAVE, J. N. and L. A. KRASSNER. "A Preliminary Report on the Application of Contingent Reinforcement Procedures (Token Economy) on a 'Chronic' Psychiatric Ward," *J. Abnorm. Psychol.*, 73 (1968), 37–43.

5. AYLLON, T. and N. AZRIN. *The Token Economy.* New York: Appleton-Century-Crofts, 1969.

6. BAGANZ, P., A. SMITH, R. GOLDSTEIN et al. "The YMCA as a Halfway Facility," *Hosp. Community Psychiatry*, 22 (1971), 156–159.

7. BAUMAN, G. and N. R. GRUNES. *Psychiatric Rehabilitation in the Ghetto.* Boston: Lexington Books, 1974.

8. BILL, A. "Social Clubs Help Prevent Readmission," *Hosp. Community Psychiatry*, 21 (1970), 161–162.

9. BLACK, B., and C. BENNEY. "Rehabilitation," in L. Bellak and L. Loeb, eds. *The Schizophrenic Syndrome*, pp. 735–756. New York: Grune & Stratton, 1969.

10. BROWN, G. W., J. L. BIRLEY, and J. K. WING. "Influence of Family Life on the Course of Schizophrenic Disorders: A Replication," *Br. J. Psychiatry*, 121 (1972), 241–258.

11. BROWN, G. W., E. M. MONCK, G. M. CARSTAIRS et al. "The Influence of Family Life on the Course of Schizophrenic Illness," *Br. J. Prev. Soc. Med.*, 16 (1962), 55.

12. CAMPBELL, A. "Aspects of Personal Independence of Mentally Subnormal and Severely Subnormal Adults in Hospital and in Local Authority Hostels," *Int. J. Soc. Psychiatry*, 17 (1971), 305–310.

13. CASSELL, W., C. SMITH, F. GRUNBERG et al. "Comparing Costs of Hospital and Community Care," *Hosp. Community Psychiatry*, 23 (1972), 197–200.

14. CRARY, W. and S. KIRTS. "Brief Aftercare on an Inpatient Ward," *Hosp. Community Psychiatry*, 22 (1971), 244–245.

15. CRISSWELL, J. H. "Considerations on the Permanence of Rehabilitation." Paper presented at Annu. Meet. Am. Psychol. Assoc., Washington, 1967.

16. DARLEY, P. J. and W. T. KENNY. "Commun-

2. "Efficacy of Psychiatric Rehabilitation," *Psychol. Bull.*, 78 (1972), 447–456.

ity Care and the 'Queequeg Syndrome': A Phenomenological Evaluation of Methods of Rehabilitation for Psychotic Patients," *Am. J. Psychiatry*, 127 (1971), 69–74.

17. DAVID, A. "Effective Low Cost Aftercare," *Ment. Hyg.*, 55 (1971), 351–357.

18. DAVIS, A., S. DINITZ, and B. PASAMANICK. "The Prevention of Hospitalization in Schizophrenia: Five Years after an Experimental Program," *Am. J. Orthopsychiatry*, 42 (1972), 375–388.

19. DAVIS, D., S. RUBIN, and T. SONNE. "Evaluation of a Hospital Activity Program for Released Psychiatric Patients," *Psychiatr. Q.*, 43 (1969), 666–674.

20. EDELSON, M. *The Practice of Sociotherapy.* New Haven: Yale University Press, 1970.

21. ESTERSON, A., D. COOPER, and R. LAING. "Results of Family Oriented Therapy with Hospitalized Schizophrenics," *Br. Med. J.*, 2 (1965), 1462–1465.

22. FAIRWEATHER, G. W., D. H. SANDERS, D. L. CRESSLER et al. *Community Life for the Mentally Ill: An Alternative to Institutional Care.* Chicago: Aldine, 1969.

23. FREEMAN, H. E. and O. G. SIMMONS. *The Mental Patient Comes Home.* New York: Wiley, 1963.

24. FREEMAN, J. T. "Posthospital Care of the Patient Past 65," *Geriatrics*, 26 (1971), 121–128.

25. FRIEDMAN, A., I. BOSZORMENYI-NAGY, J. JUNGREIS et al. *Psychotherapy for the Whole Family.* New York: Springer, 1965.

26. FUNKHOUSER, J. and E. LANTZ. "A Progress Report on Aftercare," *Ment. Health*, 96 (1969), 625–626.

27. GLASSCOTE, R. *Halfway Houses for the Mentally Ill.* Washington: Joint Information Service of the American Psychiatric Association and the National Association for Mental Health, 1971.

28. GLASSCOTE, R., E. CUMMING, I. RUTMAN et al. *Rehabilitating the Mentally Ill in the Community.* Washington: Joint Information Service of the American Psychiatric Association and the National Association for Mental Health, 1971.

29. GROUP FOR THE ADVANCEMENT OF PSYCHIATRY. *The Field of Family Therapy.* New York: Group for the Advancement of Psychiatry, 1970.

30. GRINSPOON, L., J. EWALT, and R. SHADER. "Psychotherapy and Pharmacotherapy in Chronic Schizophrenia," *Am. J. Psychiatry*, 124 (1968), 67–74.

31. GRUENBERG, E. "The Social Breakdown Syndrome—Some Origins," *Am. J. Psychiatry*, 123 (1967), 12–20.

32. GUY, W., M. GROSS, G. HOGARTY et al. "A Controlled Evaluation of Day Hospital Effectiveness," *Arch. Gen. Psychiatry*, 20 (1969), 329–338.

33. HANSELL, N. and M. BENSON. "Interrupting Long-Term Patienthood: A Cohort Study," *Arch. Gen. Psychiatry*, 24 (1971), 238–243.

34. HOTT, L. "An On-Ward Follow-Up Program," *Psychiatr. Q.*, 45 (1971), 221–226.

35. JANSEN, E. "The Role of the Halfway House in Community Mental Health Programs in the United Kingdom and America," *Am. J. Psychiatry*, 126 (1970), 1498–1504.

36. KEIL, E. "Follow-Up Programs for Emotionally Restored Patients: Some Issues and Considerations," *J. Rehabil.*, 36 (1970), 32–33.

37. KLUCKHOHN, and F. STRODTBECK. *Variations in Value Orientation.* Evanston, Ill.: Row, Peterson, 1961.

38. LAMB, H. R., and V. GOERTZEL. "Discharged Mental Patients—Are They Really in the Community?" *Arch. Gen. Psychiatry*, 24 (1971), 29–34.

39. ———. "Evaluating Aftercare for Former Day Treatment Centre Patients," *Int. J. Soc. Psychiatry*, 18 (1972), 67–78.

40. LANDY, D. "Rehabilitation as a Sociocultural Process," *J. Soc. Issues*, 16 (1960), 3–7.

41. LANGSLEY, D., K. FLOMENHAFT, and P. MACHOTKA. "Follow-up Evaluation of Family Crisis Therapy," *Am. J. Orthopsychiatry*, 39 (1969), 753–759.

42. LANGSLEY, D., P. MATCHOTKA, and K. FLOMENHAFT. "Avoiding Mental Hospital Admission: A Follow-up Study," *Am. J. Psychiatry*, 127 (1971), 1391–1394.

43. LEVENSTEIN, S., D. KLEIN, and M. POLLACK. "Follow-up Study of Formerly Hospitalized Voluntary Psychiatric Patients: The First Two Years," *Am. J. Psychiatry*, 122 (1966), 1102–1109.

44. LURIE, A., and H. RON. "Family-Centered Aftercare for Young Adults," *Hosp. Community Psychiatry*, 21 (1970), 258–260.

45. MASSIE, H. N., and C. C. BEELS. "The Outcome of Family Treatment of Schizophrenia," *Schizophr. Bull.*, 6 (1972), 24–36.

46. MAY, P. *Treatment of Schizophrenia*. New York: Science House, 1968.

47. ———. "Modifying Health-Care Services for Schizophrenic Patients," *Hosp. Community Psychiatry*, 20 (1969), 363–368.

48. MILLER, D. "Retrospective Analysis of Post-hospital Mental Patients' Worlds," *J. Health Soc. Behav.*, 8 (1967), 136–140.

49. PAERREGAARD, G. "The Significance of Follow-up Treatment for the Hospital Requirements of Schizophrenic Women," *Acta Psychiatr. Scand.*, 47 (1971), 217–222.

50. PASAMANICK, B., F. SCARPITTI, and S. DINITZ. *Schizophrenics in the Community*. New York: Appleton-Century-Crofts, 1967.

51. PAUL, G. "Chronic Mental Patient: Current Status-Future Directions," *Psychol. Bull.*, 71 (1969), 81–94.

52. PECHAN, B. W. "A State Hospital Halfway House," *Hosp. Community Psychiatry*, 22 (1971), 344–345.

53. RAPPAPORT, J., J. M. CHINSKY, and E. L. CAVEN. *Innovations in Helping Chronic Patients*. New York: Academic, 1971.

54. RAUSH, H. L. and C. L. RAUSH. *The Halfway House Movement: A Search for Sanity*. New York: Appleton-Century-Crofts, 1968.

55. SAFIRSTEIN, S. "Psychiatric Aftercare Including Home Visits," *N.Y. State J. Med.*, 71 (1971), 2441–2445.

56. SANDERS, D. H. "Innovative Environments in the Community: A Life for the Chronic Patient," *Schizophr. Bull.*, 6 (1972), 49–59.

57. SCHOOLER, N., S. GOLDBERG, H. BOOTHE et al. "One Year after Discharge: Community Adjustment of Schizophrenic Patients," *Am. J. Psychiatry*, 123 (1967), 986–995.

58. SILVERSTEIN, M. *Psychiatric Aftercare*. Philadelphia: University of Pennsylvania Press, 1968.

59. SZASZ, T. "Some Observations on the Use of Tranquilizing Drugs," *Arch. Neurol. Psychiatry*, 77 (1957), 86–92.

60. WEINER, L., A. BECKER, and T. FRIEDMAN. *Home Treatment*. Pittsburgh: University of Pittsburgh Press, 1967.

61. WILDER, J., M. KESSEL, and S. CAULFIELD. "Follow-up of a 'High-Expectations' Halfway House," *Am. J. Psychiatry*, 124 (1968), 103–109.

62. WINICK, W. *Industry in the Hospital: Mental Rehabilitation through Work*. Springfield, Ill.: Charles C. Thomas, 1967.

63. ZWERLING, I. *Some Implications of Social Psychiatry for Psychiatric Treatment and Patient Care*. Institute of Pennsylvania Hospital Strecker Monograph Series, No. 2. Nutley, N.J.: Roche Laboratories, 1965.

PART FIVE

*Psychiatry and
General Medicine*

CHAPTER 39

OFFICE PSYCHOTHERAPY FOR THE PRIMARY CARE PHYSICIAN

C. Knight Aldrich

⟮ The Primary Care Physician's Contribution to Mental Health Care

ACCORDING TO the Joint Commission on Mental Illness and Health,[18] three out of ten mentally troubled persons turn first for help to their family doctors. Not everyone has a family doctor, however, and so many people turn instead to internists or pediatricians, or else bring their problems to the hospital emergency room. In this chapter, all these medical sources of help for emotional problems will be identified as "primary care physicians," or PCPs.

The PCP undertakes the treatment of most of these patients in his office, and by doing so relieves a great deal of the pressure on overburdened psychiatrists and other mental health resources. But even if there were no lack of mental health professionals, the PCP would be important in mental health care since he is in a particularly strategic position to treat mild and relatively uncomplicated mental health problems. If he recognizes their early symptoms and institutes appropriate treatment, he may be able to prevent these problems from becoming chronic. For example, if he identifies a patient's anxiety and focusses in his medical care on the anxiety rather than on its symptomatic manifestations, he may forestall the development of an entrenched hypochrondriacal displacement.

The PCP, particularly if he is a family physician, is naturally involved with his patients during normal life developmental crises as well as during crises of separation, mourning, and disability. He is therefore well situated to carry out secondary prevention, and to note the subtle personality changes that often are the first signs of psychiatric illness. He has another advantage in that he usually knows the patient's family background. He is selected by his patient, who thus demonstrates confidence in him, and therefore he does not have to work through resistances to referral. He provides continuity of general medical care, and thus has a natural opportunity for follow-up care after a course of psychiatric treatment has ended. Finally he is usually more accessible than the mental health professional.

All these considerations contribute to making him the key "firing-line professional"[19] in the nation's mental health efforts. However, the PCP needs encouragement to carry out this aspect of care and to use his potential more effectively. In the past, psychiatric theory and practice as taught to physicians have tended to discourage them from undertaking such care; psychiatrists have implied, if not actually stated, that the management of mental health problems routinely requires such detailed patient histories and such extensive exploration of unconscious forces that no PCP would have the time or the skill to get involved. Although this viewpoint appeared to limit mental health care to mental health professionals, recent work has indicated that less time-consuming and less intensive exploration carried out early in the course of emotional disturbance may often be more effective than longer and more intensive treatment undertaken at a later point.[6,22] Treatment by the PCP may therefore be the treatment of choice in many cases.

As Zabarenko[23] reports, most PCPs develop a psychological awareness in managing the psychological aspects of illness, often using it spontaneously without recognizing its nature, value, or implications. In some cases this awareness may be enough for satisfactory care, but more often the PCP needs help in understanding psychiatric principles and practice, how they relate to his patients, and how he can adapt them to his own patient care milieu. Psychiatrists who provide this kind of help are not only applying their skills indirectly to many more patients than they can themselves treat, but also are encouraging the referral of more suitable and better prepared patients.

Epidemiology

How much of the PCP's practice is "psychiatric"? The answer to this question depends on one's criteria for identifying a psychiatric case. Greco,[16] in a careful review of his own family practice, states that the majority of his patients suffered from what Balint[3] calls "unorganized illness," as contrasted to well-defined, identified illness, with the implication that the psychiatric component was significant in the majority.

About 5–10 percent of the PCP's practice fits into such standard psychiatric categories as anxiety neurosis, schizophrenia, or phobia. The remaining 90–95 percent may be divided roughly into three groups. The first group consists of patients for whose conditions psychosocial elements represent the major contributing factors. These include, among others, patients with psychophysiological disorders, hypochrondriacs, and a number of depressed patients whose depression is masked by physical symptoms. The second group consists of conditions for which psychological factors play definite although secondary contributing roles. An example might be a patient recovering from a coronary thrombosis who is overweight and cannot seem to curb his appetite.

The final group comprises organic conditions which are, nevertheless, of some psychiatric interest because of their psychological impact. Thus an organic illness may be accompanied by irritability in some patients and overly compliant behavior in others. It may produce denial and counterphobic responses in some and exaggeration of symptoms in others. Finally, it may result in depression or in paranoid projections. Any of these emotional concomitants may affect the course of treatment of the organic illness, and so should be recognized and properly managed by the physician.

Although the PCP needs to recognize the psychological factors in most of his patients, he should not feel constrained to undertake formal treatment with all of them. In most cases in which the psychiatric factor is not of major significance, he can incorporate a concern for the psychological component into his conventional medical care.

The emphasis in this chapter will be on the PCP's psychotherapeutic care of relatively acute conditions in which the psychiatric factor is primary, and on the consulting, teaching, and referral relationships between the psychiatrist and the PCP. The care of psychosomatic conditions is discussed in Volume 4 of this *Handbook* and the care of chronic psychiatric conditions is discussed in other chapters of this volume and in Volume 3.

Differences Between the Psychiatrist's and the PCP's Psychotherapies

The PCP's psychotherapeutic care of patients with relatively short-term psychiatric problems resembles, in many ways, the directive-supportive techniques described in other chapters of this volume. Inevitably, however, there are differences between the psychotherapy carried out by mental health professionals and that carried out by the PCP. Since World War II the type of psychotherapy usually taught and practiced in the United States has had as its stated or unstated goal the uncovering of unconscious processes, with the expectation that once these thoughts and feelings are out in the open the patient will be able to cope with them in a more realistic way. However, the nature of a primary care physician's practice and the amount of training in psychotherapy which he can be expected to undertake make it impractical, except under unusual circumstances, for him to attempt to undertake uncovering psychotherapeutic procedures. There is also a question whether such an attempt is even desirable, considering his volume of patients and the time required for uncovering. He therefore should concentrate on short-term treatment, emphasizing conscious rather than unconscious processes and aiming at symptomatic relief rather than personality change.

Another difference between the two kinds of practice arises out of the relatively open and busy nature of the PCP's office which may promote an atmosphere which appears incompatible with confidentiality. The PCP needs to counteract this appearance by making it completely clear that what the patient tells him in confidence will be kept in confidence.

Furthermore, there are significant differences between the psychiatrist's and the PCP's clienteles. One consists only of patients with acknowledged psychiatric problems; the other consists of patients with all kinds of medical problems, including some acknowledged and some unacknowledged psychiatric conditions. These differences may lead the PCP to resist the idea of practicing psychotherapy. He cannot afford to antagonize too many of his patients, and he may believe that he should avoid psychotherapeutic involvement lest his patients be insulted. Such avoidance, however, often reinforces a patient's feeling of shame because of his inability to cope with his problems, and thus increases his resistance to exposing them. Eventually some of those patients must be referred, and they are more likely to perceive such referral as rejection if it comes without warning. On the other hand, routine investigation of emotional as well as organic components during diagnosis sets the stage for the PCP to make the best possible use of himself as a treatment agent, reduces resistance to a possible psychiatric diagnosis, and can facilitate later referral if necessary.

⟨ The PCP's Diagnostic Process

The diagnosis of a psychiatric condition or component should not be made solely by exclusion of organic disease. Instead, it should be made, whenever possible, primarily on the basis of its signs and symptoms, as in any other medical condition.

However, diagnosis is often complicated by the simultaneous occurrence of both organic and psychiatric components. For many of the PCP's office patients, moreover, and particularly those with the "unorganized illness" described by Balint,[3] a final diagnosis only emerges gradually and piecemeal, if at all, as treatment proceeds. The model of medical care taught in most medical school and post-graduate training, which emphasizes hospital-ized patients and requires the physician to look for a single cause and to develop a single, clear-cut definitive diagnosis before undertak-ing treatment, is thus often not adaptable to office patients.

The presence of either an emotional illness or a significant emotional component is usu-ally apparent to the reasonably experienced PCP after the first few minutes of history-taking.[7] To diagnose the nature of the emo-tional component requires, however, a more detailed history and occasionally interviews with family members. To evaluate possible contributing or concurrent organic compo-nents requires a physical examination and, perhaps, laboratory tests.

The History

The nature and quality of the psychiatric component should be determined through the history. The history of any illness in which there is a possible psychiatric component should include: (1) an account in the patient's words of the nature of the symptoms; (2) the time of onset of symptoms and a review of the patient's life situation at that time; (3) the course of the illness, including events or changes in the patient's life situation which occurred at the time of or prior to changes in the illness; (4) previous treatment efforts and their effects; and (5) the reason why the pa-tient is seeking help from the PCP at this par-ticular time. The events around the time of onset give the PCP clues to the *precipitating factors*; the discussion of the course and previ-ous treatment gives the PCP clues both to the *perpetuating factors* of the illness and to his treatment regime; and the immediate reason for seeking help may indicate significant re-cent changes, usually for the worse, in the pa-tient's symptoms or life situation.

History-taking should be carried out to the extent possible through open-ended inter-views, in which the PCP gives the patient the responsibility for continuity.[12] The PCP facili-tates communication by nonspecific, catalyz-ing comments ("yes . . . I see . . . mmm . . ."), and encourages the patient to keep on the track by repeating key words or phrases or by open-ended questions ("Would you tell me more about . . . ?"). He defers direct questions as much as possible to the end of the inter-view, focussing them on essential material that has not emerged spontaneously.

Thus the PCP does most of the listening and the patient does most of the talking as the story gradually unfolds. As Greco says, "In-sightful listening time spent on (exploring) the actual reasons for coming results in less time spent in (later) non-productive visits . . . when I am talking, I am not listening, and when I am not listening I don't hear the real reason why the patient is calling for help at this juncture." [p. 73][16]

Throughout the history, the PCP should be alert to the patient's emotional response to his interest in the psychological side. With some patients, who resist associating psychological factors with their symptoms, the PCP may need to go more slowly in exploring these fac-tors than with other patients.

The past and family histories form the basis for understanding the *predisposing factors* of a psychiatric disorder. The PCP, however, does not need as comprehensive an understanding of these factors as does the psychiatrist, and for the most part can afford to defer collecting the details of the past and family histories until they come up naturally during treatment in a context that has relevance to the patient. There are even some parts of the past history which are initially better not revealed, particu-larly episodes which the patient may be too ashamed even to tell a trusted PCP until he has tested the response to less disturbing as-pects. The PCP should not feel that he must ferret out all the gory details before he can start being helpful, nor should he feel person-ally affronted if the patient withholds certain information.

The Tentative Diagnostic Statement

Patients often resist acceptance of a psycho-logical basis for symptoms, because of pride, shame, or the need to avoid facing their conflicts, and they may either reject the PCP's arguments and authoritative statements or simulate acceptance for the sake of keeping the peace. If the possibility has been explored during the history-taking, however, the physician can naturally discuss psychological factors before he undertakes his laboratory workup and perhaps even before he carries out his physical examination. The resistant patient usually believes that the tests will prove the physician wrong, and so he may be less hesitant to discuss a possible psychological factor before the diagnosis has been made than he would be if it were already established and he had no possible escape. If the laboratory reports are negative, they can be presented as confirmatory evidence of the physician's positive diagnosis rather than as the bases for establishing a diagnosis by exclusion. In this way the patient's confidence in the physician, essential for effective treatment, is strengthened by the work-up, and his resistance to discussing psychological factors is reduced.[1]

For example, a patient with a palpitating heart can usually accept the significance of a normal EKG when it confirms the doctor's earlier statement—the statement that he believes that the tension the patient has discussed is sufficient to account for the palpitation, but that he has ordered an EKG to make doubly sure there is no additional organic factor. The same patient would be harder to convince if the doctor had not discussed the relationship of tension to palpitation until he had the negative EKG to prove that the symptoms must be functional. Thus, by waiting until the physical and laboratory examinations have been completed and then attempting to use their negative results to persuade the patient that his symptoms are psychological, the PCP relies too much on the laboratory, and dilutes the impact of his own diagnostic skill. In this situation, the patient often simply suggests that more tests should be carried out.

Even if the physical and laboratory examinations result in the diagnosis of an associated organic disease, treatment is made easier by an early diagnosis of an emotional factor. Both factors will require treatment, and the PCP, having made positive diagnoses of both, can engage his patient in the simultaneous treatment of both.

Communication with Family Members

Diagnostic information from external sources may be of considerable help, but the physician should be sure that his patient's confidential communications are respected. Only in emergency situations should he communicate with the relatives against the patient's wish, and under these circumstances he should so inform the patient, indicating that he realizes he is taking matters into his own hands and explaining why he is doing so. There are relatively few occasions when a physician must get information from relatives simply to check on the veracity of his patient's story. Much of the importance of communication with relatives lies in providing the PCP with an opportunity to enlist their help in future treatment, as well as in giving him a broader view of the setting in which the problem has developed.

([Psychotherapeutic Procedures

Introductory Explanation

Once the diagnosis of a psychiatric condition is reasonably clear, the physician and patient should agree on the goals of treatment and plan for their attainment. It is important for the PCP to make a distinction between the illness and the personality; if he sets his sights on personality change, he is undertaking a much more ambitious goal than he will have time or training to accomplish. In the case of a compulsive personality suffering from superimposed depression, for example, his goal should be the relief of the depression, but there should be no explicit or implicit promise that treatment will continue until the compulsivity no longer exists. The psychotherapeutic model is not the infectious disease/antibiotic model in which the goal is the total elimination of illness, but the cardiac decompensation model in which the goal is restoration of function within the limitations of an impaired heart. However, there is an important difference. Psychotherapy which effectively counteracts the episode can leave the patient free to continue his personal development through his life experience, whereas the compensated but damaged heart tends to become more damaged as time goes on. Moreover, psychotherapy for the crisis situation may indirectly result in improvement of the patient's basic personality problems: the compulsive patient who has overcome his depression may, as a side effect, become less compulsive.

In any event, the patient should know what the PCP hopes to accomplish, and how he plans to accomplish it. Most patients expect that their PCPs will give them advice, medication, and definite answers to their questions. Since the patient's role in psychotherapy requires more activity on his part and less from the PCP, enough time should be spent in an introductory session on explaining the new procedure so that the patient is not confused or disappointed when formal treatment begins.

This explanation is particularly important when the PCP is simultaneously treating psychological and organic components. The depressed cardiac patient may need to play a dual role, namely, to accept advice and medication about his heart but to talk about his depressed feelings, and he should understand when and why a shift in role is required in the course of a visit to his PCP.

Duration of Treatment

Such mundane concerns as duration and frequency of interviews, and their cost, should also be discussed before treatment begins. Psychotherapy conventionally is carried out by mental health professionals in forty-five to fifty-minute sessions, once a week or more often, usually over a period of months. This pattern is appropriate when personality change rather than symptom relief is the goal of treatment, but it should not be assumed to be appropriate for psychotherapy carried out by the PCP. It encourages the emergence of

unconscious material with which he is not prepared to cope, and it requires more time and more predictability of scheduling than he can provide.

Shorter sessions are better adapted both to the PCP's treatment goals and to his schedule. With respect to the length of sessions, Castelnuovo-Tedesco[9] recommends a "twenty-minute hour," based on observations that the total time spent by the physician in all aspects of an average visit is twenty minutes; others report an average time of fifteen minutes. But whether the physician decides on fifteen, twenty, or thirty minutes, he should stick to his plan and give the patient all of the time he has decided on and all of his attention. The patient feels short-changed if the PCP terminates early, but on the other hand the patient often delays getting down to business if limits are not rather firmly set.

Therefore, sessions should be ended on time, firmly and without apology. Consistency in terminating sessions also lets the patient wait until the end of a session to bring up a subject which he fears may shock or alienate the PCP, secure in the knowledge that he will not have to pursue it past a predetermined point. When he finds that the PCP is neither shocked nor alienated, he can risk bringing up the uncomfortable subject earlier in a later session. Preplanned termination also provides a structured stopping place for the PCP; in most contacts the PCP terminates with a decision and a prescription, but in psychotherapy there is no analogous point of closure.

Psychotherapeutic efforts are best contained within regular appointments, usually once a week. More frequent sessions risk getting the PCP too deeply involved, and less frequent sessions impair continuity. Additional contacts (office, home visit, or telephone) may be necessary in the course of the doctor's medical care of the patient, but if these contacts include psychotherapy, the patient will be tempted unconsciously to seek more and more of them. Along with his other problems, virtually every patient enters treatment with many unfulfilled dependency needs deeply embedded in his personality structure.[11] If the PCP does not set consistent limits to the amount of time he provides in the context of psychotherapy, the patient's attention can easily be diverted, without his realizing it, from a potentially productive effort to overcome his symptoms to a futile attempt to fulfill his dependency needs. For this reason, psychotherapy is best kept within structured limits. It is also best not undertaken during night calls; although they are usually accompanied by a substantial amount of patient anxiety, and are often useful in diagnosing emotional problems, the psychotherapeutic treatment is best carried out in the office.[10]

The PCP often hesitates to start psychotherapy because he assumes—and often has been taught—that it must go on indefinitely. In recent years, however, many advantages of therapy with termination planned in advance have been recognized, advantages to the doctor and to the patient, who both benefit from knowing more clearly just what they are letting themselves in for.[2,14] Although once in treatment, patients may unconsciously seek to prolong it to fulfill their dependency needs, they initially tend to fear an indefinitely prolonged period of psychological dependency, and may be more likely to enter treatment if they see a definite end to it.[20] There are also more mundane but nevertheless important financial barriers to entering a type of treatment whose total cost cannot be predicted; although the cost of prolonged treatment can be used as psychological resistance to entering treatment, it is more often than not a realistic consideration.

Treatment, therefore, in the PCP's usual case should be set up for a definite number of sessions—perhaps eight or ten for most relatively acute conditions—with a planned recapitulation at the end. For the most part, psychotherapy of the type discussed in this paper will be effective within eight to ten sessions; if it is not, it is doubtful whether it will be effective in a longer period and the PCP should then consider referral for a more intensive or different type of treatment.

Time-limited, regularly scheduled psychotherapy is not the appropriate treatment for all the PCP's psychiatric clientele. He needs to be more flexible with certain patients— chronic ambulatory schizophrenics, for example,—and arrange to see them at variable intervals according to their current needs. There are also dependent personalities with long-standing hypochondriacal symptoms who do best when the PCP does not plan termination in advance, but instead accepts their need for a stable, protective, not too intense relationship. Once these patients find that their PCP is not trying to get rid of them, that he welcomes them for brief—perhaps ten-minute—regular visits even without symptoms as tickets of entry, and that he evidences more interest in their life situations than in their physical complaints, they often begin to show marked improvement.

Scheduling and Privacy

Although the PCP cannot insure the same kind of privacy, confidentiality, and predictable scheduling as the psychiatrist, he can often make enough of an adaptation to approximate the ideal. Some PCPs have found that scheduling their psychotherapeutic work on one afternoon or one morning a week is possible; others schedule these patients at the end of the work day, although there is some question whether fatigue limits their effectiveness at this time. In any case, privacy is essential, and an assurance of confidentiality is particularly important since the PCP usually also cares for other members of the patient's family as well as for friends and acquaintances.

In other types of medical care, distractions and interruptions, while not welcome, can be tolerated. However, because psychotherapeutic success depends so much on continuity of attention, the physician is best advised to arrange for all interruptions, telephone or otherwise, to be deferred until the session is over, except for extreme emergencies. Interviewing requires not only attention but the appearance of attention to be effective. The PCP who says, "Go ahead, I am listening," while he looks through papers on his desk lets the patient know that he is not receiving full attention.

Basic Principles of Psychotherapy

Psychotherapy is in many ways an extension of history-taking with a slightly different emphasis. Although the PCP takes a history in order to understand the patient and his illness, the patient often finds that he too understands better as he relates his history, and that he can use this understanding to find new and more effective ways of coping with his stresses and conflicts. In the same way, psychotherapeutic interviews often have as a by-product an enrichment of the patient's history with consequent increased understanding by both patient and therapist.

Although some of the technical aspects and goals of the PCP's psychotherapy differ from those of the mental health professional's, the basic principles are the same. The patient is helped to use the therapist as a sounding board to express thoughts and feelings which have frightened him or confused him or made him feel ashamed or guilty. The therapist listens to these thoughts and feelings empathically and without passing judgment, and through various types of intervention helps the patient sort them out and reevaluate them more realistically. He does not try to superimpose his solutions on the patient, but instead helps the patient develop confidence in his own capacity to cope with the stresses and complexities of his life.

That is about all there is to it, and it sounds deceptively simple. Its success depends, however, not on a learned routine, but on a rather complex and intangible kind of interpersonal communication. This kind of communication differs in many ways from the PCP's usual communication with patients who are having medical problems, and it differs among PCPs, because it depends to a considerable extent on each individual's communication style. Thus the PCP whose style is bluff and hearty will be inclined to intervene more frequently and will have to be more careful about giving too much advice than the PCP whose style is more taciturn. There are, however, some basic requisites for effective psychotherapeutic communication that apply no matter what the individual's communication style.

The PCP's Attitudes

The first requirement for effective psychotherapy is to take the patient seriously. If the PCP considers his nervous patients to be less sick than his other patients, or if he assumes they are imagining or are capable of consciously controlling their symptoms, or if he thinks they are consciously exploiting him by wasting his time, it will be hard for him to communicate the kind of understanding the patient needs to benefit from his treatment.

Failure to take psychiatric patients seriously may be due in part to lack of experience. Most PCPs simply have not had an adequate exposure to this kind of patient during their training. They have not learned how to go about approaching psychiatric problems; they are not sure that any "talking" treatment they provide can be effective; they are not confident of their ability to set limits to the amount of time they spend with such patients; and they question whether they are justified in expecting equivalent compensation for this kind of treatment. Many of them look to psychiatrists for help in managing these problems. Through his participation in continuing education programs, the psychiatrist can provide information which, if tailored realistically to the PCP's needs, will give him the understanding that can overcome many of the barriers to his acceptance and effective treatment of psychiatric patients.[4,5,23]

Transference

Some of the barriers stem from the PCP's unfamiliarity with the concept of unconscious transference of emotional attitudes from people in the past to people in the present. The PCP is confronted with transferred feelings to some extent in all aspects of his practice.

Transference is usually intensified during times of stress, when the individual tends to regress to a more childlike type of relationship. Most patients regress to some extent during illness, and tend to transfer attitudes characteristic of their childhood relationships with their parents to the medical personnel on whom they are now dependent. The PCP, therefore, is a frequent target for his patients' unprovoked or exaggerated anger, fear, affection, or sexual feelings. Unless the physician recognizes the manifestations of transference, he may be surprised or angered or he may have his feelings hurt by the unjustified anger or distrust expressed by his patients.

Patients with emotional disturbances seem to be more prone than other patients to transfer earlier attitudes to their therapists. Interpretation of transference, while important in deeper types of psychotherapy, is usually not necessary or advisable in therapy carried out by the PCP. On the other hand, awareness and understanding of the patient's transferred feelings can be helpful to the PCP in maintaining his objectivity while encouraging the patient to talk and to express his feelings.

Transference distorts most relationships, especially dependent relationships, to some extent, and PCPs themselves are not immune. Thus, a PCP without realizing it may carry over some of his own parents' attitudes toward himself and his siblings to his patients, and in that way overreact to his patients' realistic feelings, as well as to their transferred feelings. Even though these countertransference attitudes are usually not conscious, awareness that they may occur can help the physician correct for possible distortions in his response to his patients' transferred attitudes.

The phenomena of transference are more familiar and more acceptable to psychiatrists than they are to other physicians, who may interpret as criticism the intimation by psychiatrists during continuing education courses, for example, that they are not being objective about their patients. Material about transference can be presented tactfully, however, so that it becomes acceptable and helpful to the PCP in his concern for his own or his patients' feelings.[15]

Empathy

A basic requirement for carrying out effective psychotherapy is *empathy*. In this context, empathy is the capacity to look at a patient's problem from the patient's point of view. Empathy does not mean that the PCP necessarily agrees with that point of view; after all, treatment often involves a change in the patient's outlook, and if the therapist identifies with his patient so much that he agrees with everything the patient believes or feels, he will find it hard to encourage the patient to change. He also needs to be tolerant and realistically uncritical of the patient, "realistically" in the sense that he cannot very well condone antisocial *behavior*, although he can understand the *feelings*, usually angry or sexual feelings, that make the patient think of or wish to carry out antisocial behavior. Furthermore, since depressions often result from unrealistic self-criticism, the PCP cannot identify to the point of sharing the patient's self-criticism.

Empathy is somewhat different from sympathy, when sympathy implies feeling sorry for the patient and agreeing with the patient's perception of his problems. A sympathetic ear is traditionally helpful to the person in trouble; it is useful when the patient simply wants to share his troubles, and when no change in his way of looking at his troubles is indicated. Too much sympathy, however, may make a later effort at attitude change seem like a betrayal, e.g., if a PCP's sympathy has implied agreement that a woman's troubles are all her husband's fault, she feels betrayed when he tries to help her look at her own role.

Furthermore, too much sympathy with its implied agreement often makes it harder for the patient to reverse himself; if he has persuaded the PCP that he is completely in the right, he hesitates to acknowledge later that he is not really so sure. Finally, it is hard to be angry at a sympathetic listener, and patients often need to blow off steam at their PCPs.

Listening

A good deal of the PCP's participation in psychotherapy consists of encouraging the patient to talk about whatever is bothering him. But since what is bothering him is often concealed beneath symptoms or other screens, it is often difficult for the PCP to know when to encourage the patient's exploration of a given subject and when to discourage it.

If the PCP gives signals, subtle or otherwise, to the patient which indicate what he does not wish to hear, the patient will tend to respond accordingly. The patient may detect —or assume through past experience—that the PCP is primarily interested in symptoms, and since talking about symptoms serves the double purpose of interesting the PCP and avoiding discussion of painful conflicts, treatment may quickly turn into a fruitless repetition of a catalogue of symptoms. Talking about symptoms is familiar ground to the PCP and he may without realizing it encourage his patients to continue in this vein. Moreover, talking about life problems may make the PCP uncomfortable, if he believes that he is supposed to have answers to all of them. Once he recognizes that he does not have to have the answers, that psychotherapy is a process of sharing problems and a mutual search for ways to resolve them instead of the provision of ready-made solutions, he can be more comfortable in gently encouraging the patient to talk about his life situation.

Gentle encouragement or discouragement is not so much active as passive; it is usually conveyed by the PCP's show of interest—by nonverbal signs and by requests for further details, etc.—in the subjects he considers significant, and by the absence of such signs and requests in response to a recital of symptoms. The PCP keeps his own participation to a minimum; he keeps the patient talking or communicating feeling by an attitude of interest and concern and by nonspecific comments, or he modifies the direction of the communication by comments that emphasize or focus on one particular aspect.

The PCP finds listening to patients talk about what is important to them less familiar than does the mental health professional. The PCP is accustomed, perhaps more than he should be, to carrying most of the responsibility for the direction of his medical inter-

views and to being the one who gives information in his treatment. Changing his set to become a receiver of information and to encourage the patient to explore areas whose relevance may not be immediately apparent is difficult and may require a persistent effort as well as a conviction on the PCP's part that the results will be worth the effort.

Intervention

Although the patient does most of the talking and the PCP most of the listening, there are times when it is appropriate for the PCP to intervene. There is no exact formula for deciding on the nature and timing of interventions, and their choice should be determined by the goals of the interview.

Establishing goals for each interview is seldom undertaken when therapy has no planned termination and is expected to require a long period of time. Psychotherapy with a planned termination date, however, usually requires more guidance from the therapist. In order to guide, the therapist must know the destination and the path, both of which should be derived from the diagnostic understanding of the problem.[1]

This process is illustrated in the following case example. Mrs. C. came to the office of Dr. F., her PCP, complaining of headaches of a few weeks' duration. In the course of his history-taking, he noted that she was mildly but definitely depressed, and he diagnosed the headaches as symptoms of her depression and found no evidence of organic illness. The depression seemed to have been set off, at least in part, during an incident when a neighbor had called in some distress to ask Mrs. C. to stay with her children because she had to take her husband to the hospital. Mrs. C. knew the neighbor very slightly, but was happy to comply; the day passed uneventfully and the neighbor's husband soon got well. Mrs. C.'s depression seemed out of proportion to the event, but since it was the only out-of-the-ordinary event in her life situation about the time her symptoms began, Dr. F. suspected that it had a special symbolic meaning to her.

In the course of taking the history, Dr. F. found that going to or even talking about hospitals made Mrs. C. uncomfortable, that her father had died—in a hospital—when she was nine, and that she had had to give up some plans for the day she helped out her neighbor. When asked to talk more about these aspects of her history, she protested that no one liked hospitals, that she was too little when her father died to know much about it, and that her plans were really not very important—her neighbor would have done as much for her.

Dr. F. listened noncommitally, but thought to himself that her antipathy to hospitals was more than one might expect, and that she seemed to be protesting a little too much about the inconsequentiality of her abandoned plans. He also kept in mind that children at nine are both aware of death and concerned about it. Recognizing that unresolved grief, shame, guilt, or a combination thereof are usually involved in the causes of depression, he speculated that a delayed reaction to the loss of her father and/or shame at her unwillingness to help her neighbor might be contributing factors. The source of guilt, if any was involved at all, was certainly less evident and probably would be less accessible to his treatment.

He decided to explore psychotherapeutically the shame and unresolved grief possibilities. He decided to hold off the guilt possibility until he had heard what emerged during the discussion of the first two, and tentatively planned to refer her to a psychiatrist if guilt appeared to be the major factor. He explained the treatment conditions and procedure to Mrs. C., and she agreed to a ten-session course of psychotherapy. He told her that they would be discussing at greater length some of the matters that she had spoken of during the history-taking, and perhaps some other matters; he did not state explicitly the sequence he intended to follow, in part because he thought he might decide to change the sequence, and in part because she had not shown much enthusiasm about either possibility when he had suggested them during history-taking, and he did not want unnecessarily to stir up more resistance to them.

In the course of Mrs. C.'s treatment, Dr. F. interspersed his listening with various types of intervention. Depending on the situation, he made *catalytic* comments to encourage her to proceed, *empathic* comments to communicate his understanding and to elicit expression of feeling, *focusing or directive* comments to start an interview or to keep her on the track, *questioning* comments to elicit more information, *confronting* comments to encourage her to reconsider a position, and *summarizing* comments to terminate a session or a phase of treatment.[13]

Dr. F. started the first session with a focusing comment: "Mrs. C., I'd like to hear a few more details of that day you were asked to baby-sit with your neighbor's children, about the time your depression began."

Mrs. C. talked for a while, but the details that she produced did not seem significant, even with Dr. F.'s catalytic comments. (Dr. F.'s personal way of encouraging someone to continue talking was to say "Yes" when that person showed signs of slowing down. Most people have their own styles in this kind of catalytic communication, whether in social or professional situations. Dr. F. said "Yes;" another doctor would have said "Unh-hunh," repeated a word or phrase said by the patient, or given whatever other signal he was accustomed to use.)

Dr. F. discerned no evidence of shame or resentment over her baby-sitting task, and so he decided to focus a little more definitely on the loss possibility with a questioning comment. He asked an open-ended question, one that could not easily be answered in a word or two, and that gave Mrs. C. a range of choices for her answer. He asked, "How did the children feel about what had gone on that day?" Mrs. C. gave some details, more about what the children did than how they felt. Dr. F. tried again, gently, to focus: "Yes, but how did they feel?" Mrs. C. claimed that she did not think they seemed particularly upset. Dr. F., sensing that his rapport with Mrs. C. was good enough so that he could risk a mildly confronting intervention, said, "Even with their father gone to the hospital?" Mrs. C. responded, with some sharpness, "I suppose you are trying to get me to say that all this re-minded me of when my father was sick."

Dr. F. at this point momentarily considered an empathic, or mirror intervention, such as "You seem a bit upset by that idea," but hesi-tated to say it. Later, in reviewing the session, he wasn't sure why he had hesitated—perhaps because it seemed too obvious, or possibly be-cause it might have added unnecessarily to her annoyance. Instead, he said nothing. Silence may seem to be a nonintervention rather than an intervention; paradoxically, however, it has the effect of an intervention when the situa-tion would ordinarily call for a comment. Si-lence in such situations is not easy to main-tain, and often requires a therapist to restrain his tendency to do something to keep the conversation going. Too long a silence, how-ever, may be perceived as anger or boredom. In this case, Mrs. C. soon broke the silence: "Well, all right, I can see how they have some-thing in common, but I don't see what they have to do with what's wrong with me now."

Dr. F.'s next comment was conditioned by the fact that the interview time was up. It was in part summarizing, and in part could be classified as directive, although he carefully phrased it in a nonauthoritarian way: "I'm not sure what relationship they have, but I think there's enough chance of a connection so that we should talk some more next time about your father's death and your reaction at the time."

Dr. F. opened the second interview with a focusing statement: "We were going to talk this time about your father's death." Mrs. C., helped by some catalytic responses, gave a good many details of the events leading up to her father's death. She told Dr. F. about say-ing good-bye to him before going to school on the day he went to the hospital. The following is transcribed, with minor editing, from the interview, which was tape recorded with Mrs. C.'s permission.

DR. F.: "And when you came back . . ." (cata-lytic)

MRS. C.: "Well, we went up to see him in a hospital . . . My brother came over . . . we were playing outside . . . the four younger kids with the neighbor kids. We were sort of dirty, didn't

look very nice, but he just picked us up off the street and said 'Come on with me.' "

DR. F.: "Um . . . yes." (catalytic)

MRS. C.: "And he took us in this building—it was the first time I had ever been in a hospital. Oh, do I have to talk?"

DR. F.: "It's really upsetting to remember it." (Although this comment did not answer her ques-tion directly, it implied that she should continue. It was an empathic intervention, and gave sanc-tion to her expression of emotion. She began to cry, and Dr. F., realizing that it was important for her to express her feelings, did not attempt to con-sole or reassure her. He remained silent; Mrs. C. gradually stopped crying.)

MRS. C.: "It's silly to be crying now."

Dr. F. might well have responded with an-other empathic intervention, which probably would have precipitated more tears. He de-cided instead that she had cried enough, at least for this session, and moved on with a question to encourage her to continue her story. Either response would have sufficed; as in most situations, there is no one correct in-tervention.

DR. F.: "Did you cry then?"

MRS. C.: "No. I was too . . . I don't know. I felt bad, but I couldn't cry . . . Everybody else was crying, but I didn't cry. He looked so . . . he looked so changed." (pause)

DR. F.: "Changed?" (catalytic)

Mrs. C. continued to describe these events, with some more tears, while Dr. F. listened empathically. At the end of the session, he summarized: "I know it's been painful to talk about your feelings about your father's death; it sounds, however, as if you've needed to have more of a chance to share them with someone. Next time I think we had better con-tinue on in this direction."

In the next six sessions they continued to discuss the events surrounding her father's death, until Mrs. C. felt sufficiently relieved of her depression and headaches to terminate treatment.

The case excerpt illustrates the use of fo-cussing, catalytic, empathic, directive, con-fronting, questioning, and summarizing inter-ventions in helping a patient to express feelings and to maintain progress toward the goal of therapy. Another type of intervention is clarification, which may be used in helping a patient understand attitudes. Thus, when later in the series of interviews Mrs. C. expressed a great deal of anger at her mother's lack of understanding of Mrs. C.'s feelings about her father's death, Dr. F. observed that her mother might have been so preoccupied with her own grief that she had nothing left over to give her children, but that this would have been hard for a nine-year-old to understand. The clarification of feeling—in this case, clarification of the mother's, not the patient's—was made tentatively, not dogmatically, and with care not to make Mrs. C. feel ashamed of not having understood her mother.

Clarification of alternatives is used to help a patient make a decision or take action. In most instances it is better for the therapist to clarify alternatives and help the patient make his own decision than to give advice and, in effect, make the decision for the patient. Clarification does not come naturally to the PCP, whose spontaneous impulse, based on his routine with other types of patients and his concept of a physician's proper role, is to respond to questions or indecision with advice. "The most significant outgrowth of the medical orientation is the inner conviction that unless one gives the patient something (medication, a rest, a diet, an incision, an appliance, advice, or directions), one is not treating him adequately." [p. 332][17]

The trouble with advice that can be followed is that it encourages the patient to rely on the PCP rather than on himself for decision-making and thus reinforces the patient's feeling that he is not competent to make his own decisions. Advice that cannot be followed— "Stop worrying," for example—is useless and indicates a lack of empathy; if the patient could have stopped worrying on his own, he would not be seeking help.

Except when the patient does not have the background to judge, as in medication problems, the PCP can usually be more helpful if instead of giving answers he attempts to clarify the problem. Thus if the patient says, "I feel terribly tired and I am sick of my job.

Do you think I should quit?" the PCP should not feel obligated to give advice. On the other hand he should not simply say, "Well, it's your decision," which gives no help at all. Instead he might ask, "What do you think might happen if you changed jobs?" leading to a discussion of the relative merits of the alternatives. In this way the patient can be helped to come to a decision, and while he has received the help of the physician, he also has the satisfaction of having ultimately made his own choice.

Reassurance is a response many PCPs almost automatically make to patients' fears about organic illness. But reassurance is only reassuring when it is based on valid data, and a premature attempt at reassurance which promises relief of symptoms before the PCP knows enough about them is often perceived as indicating lack of empathy. "How can he be so sure I will be all right when he doesn't really know what is wrong?" thinks the patient, although he may not say so for fear of offending the doctor on whom he is dependent. Reassurance needs to be couched in realistic terms. A comment such as "I suspect you will be able to carry on in spite of your symptoms," appears at first glance to be less reassuring than "Your symptoms will all go away," but if it is based on adequate information it is likely to be borne out by experience and therefore in the long run perceived as evidence of the doctor's understanding and competence.

Reassurance is frequently used prematurely to abort the expression of feeling. But since, as in the case of Mrs. C.'s tears described above, the expression of sadness, anger, discouragement, or other strong feeling more often than not hastens the progress of treatment, it usually should be sanctioned, not restrained, by the therapist. To indicate by quick reassurance that the expression of feeling is unacceptable to the therapist may repeat the sequence of events that caused its expression to be inhibited in the first place, and so perpetuate the problem instead of relieving it. When a patient is experiencing but attempting to conceal strong feeling, an empathic intervention often helps him to acknowledge it, express it, and learn to be less afraid of it.

Modification of the Environment

Modification of the environment can be helpful, but it is generally overused. When the doctor sends the depressed patient on a vacation for a change of scene because he wants to remove environmental irritants, he is also removing the patient from sources of support, including himself. Since most depressions as well as most other psychiatric disorders are primarily related to internal problems, which the patients carry on vacation with them, they may become worse instead of better away from home and doctor.

Another example of overused environmental modification is the case of the adult child who, in response to his doctor's recommendation, prematurely banishes a cranky parent to an institutional setting and then suffers more from guilt at the parent's absence than from annoyance at his presence. This does not mean that elderly relatives should never be institutionalized, but that all factors should be taken into account before the recommendation is made. As in the case of advice, clarification of the alternatives which helps the patient make his own decision is better than prescribed environmental change in most instances.

Medication

In most of his practice, the PCP tends to rely primarily on medication and secondarily on his personal interaction with the patient. He therefore may be inclined to put too much confidence in the use of medication for his psychiatric patients. He also is often tempted to use medications as placebos for illnesses without organic causes. Indeed, the initial apparent effectiveness of placebos may lead him to have more confidence in them than a longer view justifies.[21] The problem with placebos is that their duration of effectiveness is usually brief, and if the PCP's contact with his patient is at all prolonged, he will find that the patient will soon look for a more effective drug. The efficacy of the new drug will in turn be short-lived, and the PCP will then find himself in a fruitless search for the ideal placebo, while the patient becomes dissatisfied, overmedicated, addicted, or all three.

The PCP, therefore, should if anything play down the effectiveness of his medication in conditions likely to be of long duration, even though playing it down reduces the component of suggestion and the placebo effect. He should emphasize instead the search for psychological solutions. He may say, "I know you are having a good deal of discomfort (insomnia, etc.) and I want to prescribe this medicine which I believe will relieve your symptoms to some extent. Meanwhile it is important that we get down to business and look for what is causing the symptoms." In this way the patient can judge the effect of the medication more realistically, will not expect too much of it, and will be less inclined to become overly dependent on it.

When medication is definitely indicated, it should be used in adequate quantities rather than in homeopathic doses. It is best in the long run for the physician to know well the indications, dosages, expected action, and side effects of one or two tranquillizers, one or two antidepressants, and one or two hypnotics rather than to try for a superficial knowledge of all the myriad psychoactive drugs that have been developed. He should substitute new drugs on his list only after a clear superiority in pharmacological action has been demonstrated. If he adopts each new drug that the detail man recommends, he can easily get pharmacological and placebo effects mixed up, and in the long run may substitute less effective for more effective drugs in his armamentarium.

Family Problems and Joint Interviews

Emotional problems tend to cluster in families, and problems in family relationships are often brought to the PCP. Even when the primary complaint may appear at first to be limited to one member of the family, treatment may be facilitated if the marital couple or other members of the family are treated as a unit.

Marital and family therapies are somewhat more complicated than individual therapy, but may still be within the competence of the PCP. As Browne and Freeling observe, "There is no doubt that the joint interview has its pitfalls, and as with all medical techniques, requires experience to obtain the best results, but for the general practitioner it is probably the most neglected and yet one of the most powerful therapeutic tools at his disposal." [p. 37][7]

In family treatment, it is important for the PCP to avoid taking sides or attempting to act as a referee. His goal instead is to act as a catalyst in improving communication within the family and in helping members of the family to modify their attitudes to one another. Many of the techniques described in Chapter 18 can be effectively used by the PCP.

Psychiatric Consultation and Referral

Not all patients with emotional problems can be effectively treated by the PCP. Suicidal and acute psychotic conditions are among those for which referral is appropriate, although the PCP often has an advantage in the follow-up care of such patients after they have been discharged from psychiatric hospital care. These patients may be less likely to neglect follow-up treatment if they are referred back to a PCP whom they know and whose office is more accessible and more familiar than a follow-up clinic.

In anticipation of his possible follow-up care of any of his patients who have been in a psychiatric hospital, the PCP should maintain communication with the relevant psychiatric services. This type of communication can best be established at the time of referral, or early in the patient's hospital stay if the PCP has not been the original referring agent. Through such communication, treatment regimens can be coordinated, and the PCP may also act as a bridge between hospital personnel and the patient's family, helping to clarify the patient's clinical condition and his needs to the family, and helping to maintain the family's linkage to the patient.

The decision to refer a patient to a psychiatrist or to a mental health facility depends on the nature, severity, and treatability of the condition. The effectiveness of the referral depends to a considerable extent on the PCP's personality and skill in engineering the transition from his care to psychiatric care. If the patient takes the referral to mean that he is being rejected by the PCP, or that his illness is imaginary or hopeless, he is likely to resist acceptance of the referral or of subsequent psychiatric care. On the other hand, the patient should not be oversold in an effort to persuade him to accept the referral. Overselling that promises a cure within an unrealistically brief period can result in the patient's becoming discouraged when magical results are not forthcoming. The referring PCP also should not be vague or misleading about the nature of the referral; the patient feels betrayed if he is led to believe that he is going to see someone other than a mental health professional. Finally the PCP should be aware of alternative community resources such as family service agencies which may be equally or more appropriate sources of help.

Open lines of communication between the PCP and the psychiatrist are essential for successful consultation and referral, but require an effort on the part of each participant to understand the other's special circumstances. The PCP is used to receiving a written, definitive diagnosis after a relatively brief period of evaluation from specialists to whom he has referred patients; the psychiatrist's diagnosis tends to develop gradually over a relatively long period of time and to overlap treatment. There is often no clear-cut point, therefore, at which the psychiatrist can give a final summary of his diagnosis and recommendations, and consequently he often delays any communication back to the referral source. Furthermore, psychiatric evaluation tends to be rather long-winded, and it is not always clear how much information the PCP finds useful.

Many psychiatrists and PCPs, therefore, find that telephone communication is more productive. Telephone communication, when scheduled to fit into the idiosyncratic practices of each party, makes it possible for each to answer the other's questions, and to develop the kind of collaboration which is in the best interests of the particular patient or family. With easy access to a psychiatrist's telephone consultation, the PCP can feel secure in undertaking a more substantial share of the mental health problems in his community, and the psychiatrist can expedite appropriate referrals.

The PCP should know his referral psychiatrist well. However, since psychiatrists have particular interests—hospital psychiatry, child psychiatry, intensive psychotherapy, adolescent psychotherapy, addictions, etc.—it also may be advantageous for the PCP to get to know more than one referral psychiatrist, so that when possible his patient can be directed to someone with a special interest in his particular type of problem.

Even when referral is not indicated, the PCP who has established a relationship with a psychiatrist feels that he has someone to turn to if he needs guidance or reassurance in the management of some of his patients. The kind of consultation Caplan[8] has called "consultee-oriented," can be useful to the PCP; the patient is not seen by the consultant and the focus is on the PCP's problems in management of the patient rather than directly on the patient's diagnosis and treatment recommendations. The psychiatrist who makes himself available for this kind of consultation as well as the more conventional kind to the PCPs in his community will render service far beyond the limits of his practice. He will thus strengthen the collaboration between PCPs and mental health professionals which is essential for optimal prevention and treatment of the range of psychiatric problems in his community.

❲ Bibliography

1. ALDRICH C. K. *An Introduction to Dynamic Psychiatry.* New York: McGraw-Hill, 1966.
2. ——. "Brief Psychotherapy: A Reappraisal of Some Theoretical Assumptions," *Am. J. Psychiatry,* 125 (1968), 585–592.
3. BALINT, M. *The Doctor, His Patient and the Illness.* London: Pitman Medical, 1957.
4. BALINT, M., E. BALINT, R. GOSLING et al. *A Study of Doctors.* Philadelphia: Lippincott, 1966.
5. BECKER, A., ed., *The General Practitioner's Role in the Treatment of Emotional Illness.* Springfield, Ill.: Charles C. Thomas, 1968.
6. BELLAK, L. and L. SMALL. *Emergency Psychotherapy and Brief Psychotherapy.* New York: Grune & Stratton, 1965.
7. BROWNE, K. and P. FREELING. *The Doctor-Patient Relationship.* London: Livingstone, 1967.
8. CAPLAN, G. *Theory and Practice of Mental Health Consultation.* New York: Basic Books, 1970.
9. CASTELNUOVO-TEDESCO, P. *The Twenty-Minute Hour.* Boston: Little, Brown, 1965.
10. CLYNE, M. B. *Night Calls.* London: Tavistock, 1963.
11. COLEMAN, J. V. "The Initial Phase of Psychotherapy," *Bull. Menninger Clin.,* 13 (1949), 189–197.
12. ENELOW, A. J. and S. N. SWISHER. *Interviewing and Patient Care.* New York: Oxford University Press, 1972.
13. ENELOW, A. J. and M. WEXLER. *Psychiatry in the Practice of Medicine.* New York: Oxford University Press, 1966.
14. FRANK, J. D. "The Role of Hope in Psychotherapy," *Int. J. Psychiatry,* 5 (1968), 383–395.
15. GASKILL, H. S. "The Physician-Patient Relationship," *J. Med. Educ.* 36, II (1961), 133–140.
16. GRECO, R. S. and R. A. PITTENGER. *One Man's Practice.* New York: Lippincott, 1966.
17. GROUP FOR THE ADVANCEMENT OF PSYCHIATRY. *Medical Practice and Psychiatry: The Impact of Changing Demands,* p. 332. New York: Group for the Advancement of Psychiatry, 1964.
18. JOINT COMMISSION ON MENTAL ILLNESS AND HEALTH. *Action for Mental Health,* p. 148. New York: Basic Books, 1961.
19. KIESLER, F. "Is This Psychiatry?" in S. E. Goldstein, ed., *Concepts of Community Psychiatry,* pp. 147–157. Bethesda: National Institutes of Health, 1965.
20. REID, W. J. and A. W. SHYNE. *Brief and Extended Casework.* New York: Columbia University Press, 1969.

21. SHAPIRO, A. K. "The Placebo Effect in the History of Medical Treatment (Implications for Psychiatry)," *Am. J. Psychiatry,* 116 (1959), 298–304.

22. WOLBERG, L. R., ed., *Short-Term Psychother-* *apy.* New York: Grune & Stratton, 1965.

23. ZABARENKO, L., R. A. PITTENGER, and R. N. ZABARENKO. *Primary Medical Practice: A Psychiatric Evaluation.* St. Louis: Warren H. Green, 1968.

CHAPTER 40

CHILD PSYCHIATRY FOR THE GENERAL PSYCHIATRIST

Laurence A. Cove and Reginald S. Lourie

THE PROFESSIONAL ACTIVITIES of general psychiatrists will touch upon the lives of children to variable degrees and by different routes. Some may have regular clinical contacts with young patients. The usual work of other practitioners will affect them only indirectly. In this chapter, we shall present some points of view about meeting children's psychiatric needs under the following broad headings:

1. Direct work with children and adolescents in the general psychiatrist's practice.

2. Implications in care of adult patients of the two-way interaction between them and their children, especially with regard to the impact upon the children of psychopathological reactions or states in their families.

3. Opportunities for application of knowledge about growth and development in consultative and collaborative roles.

Though the problems to be solved differ within and among these areas, some basic principles are common to all. (1) The importance of constitution: it is increasingly recognized that the individual traits and potentials which the child brings into the world significantly influence the outcome of particular experiences with it. (2) The dimension of development: the child's responses to his internal and external environment are a function of where he is in his development; the form of response reflects what is important and available during a certain phase; clinical thinking must attend not only to the current situation but also to effects in the future. (3) The central position of the family: the child is dependent on family members not only physically but emotionally; his attachments to them are of a different order than those of adults; actions on one side of the parent–child relationship have reciprocal effects on the other.

⟮ The Child as the Patient

Child psychiatry, as a specialized field with a distinct body of theoretical knowledge and clinical approaches, has gained increasing recognition since the beginning of formal training in the 1920s. In the 1970s about 6 percent of the psychiatrists in the United States are also recognized as specialists in the problems of children. By virtue of variations in distribution, local referral practices, individual interests and public resistance to recognizing emotional disturbance in children until it becomes acute, a large proportion of young children with psychiatric difficulties are first brought to the attention of the general psychiatrist. In addition, adolescents form a "no-man's land" between the areas of expertise and activity of the general psychiatrist and the child psychiatrist. Technical information about diagnostic procedures and therapeutic modalities for children and adolescents can be found in Vol. 2. Here, we shall touch on certain problems which may confront the practitioner who is consulted about a child in circumstances which make it advisable or even mandatory that he respond himself.

Psychiatric Emergencies

As in other aspects of medicine, first attention is due to whether the child's immediate condition, usually meaning his behavior, poses an imminent threat to himself or others.

Acute conditions which account for the bulk of emergencies in adults are less common in children. Before puberty one rarely sees the acute onset of florid psychotic syndromes with hallucinations or delusions.[36] Psychosis in children is more likely to be noted, often after symptoms have been present for some time, in disturbed relationships, social withdrawal, school failure or bizarre habit patterns. Instead of overt depressive reactions attended by suicidal risk, children are more likely to show *depressive equivalents* in the form of eating or habit disturbances, being *naughty* or running away. Acute brain syndromes related to drug ingestion or withdrawal are apt to be by-products of curiosity, shows of bravado, imitation of parents, or competition with siblings for oral supplies. A careful physical examination should always be performed, with neurological consultation if indicated, since a number of infectious, neoplastic, and metabolic disorders can initially present in behavioral changes.

A child will usually have given clues to mounting anxiety in conduct disorders, nonspecific emotional upsets and/or adaptive difficulties before an external event puts him in the spotlight. This often entails the parents being faced with a crisis, as when the child exceeds academic or disciplinary tolerance in school, becomes an object of community concern or presents a major obstacle to important family plans or aspirations. Demands upon the psychiatrist for dramatic intervention will then be quite insistent and he should bear in mind the need to understand who is feeling the distress at the moment. This is another way of saying that a symptom's *value* can be measured on a number of scales. The child, too, will be aware, at least on some level, of this fact.

Approach to the child's medical situation must take into account the critical role and participation of parents or their surrogates. The child is not a free agent. His environment has a greater impact upon him than upon most adults. On the positive side, the psychiatrist may thus be able to effect influences upon his patient's behavior which would be impossible with adults, who may have to be hospitalized to achieve the same effects. On the negative side, the child's dependence upon people with whom he lives renders him more vulnerable to them. He is more helpless in the face of physical actions by parents or other caretakers. Also, their great importance to him for survival in combination with his own immature defenses and coping abilities make him more likely to react in action modes to what they do to him psychologically. An emergency evaluation of a child, therefore, is incomplete without assessment of the likelihood of his milieu's influencing him to bring his behaviors under control or contributing to their persistence and even escalation.

Finally, two key principles which define an emergency are relatively unique to childhood and adolescence. The first is that there will be normal developmental crises.[18] Their symptomatic manifestations may be more spectacular and arouse more concern in parents than those of truly fixed psychopathology. At times these upheavals of the status quo may even resolve existing conflicts, though complacency on this score is unwarranted. The second principle also derives from the fact of children's rapid growth and evolution. Any situation which creates a significant hiatus in essential experiences may be disastrous to orderly development. The risk of such a hiatus occurring, irrespective of cause, constitutes a very real emergency and may deserve overriding priority for intervention. For examples, severe understimulation and emotional deprivation in the early years; chronic inaccessibility to basic education as a result of learning disabilities or hyperactivity; atypical or absent models for identification and superego formation; and use of consciousness-altering drugs which keep an adolescent from acquiring academic, vocational, or social skills.

SUICIDE

Youthful suicides have been recorded in almost every culture and have aroused medical comment for more than a century. Incidence has been rising since the 1930s. While rare in the years before adolescence, attempts have been noted by children as young as three years old. There is a peak around age ten and another in the fifteen- to nineteen-year age group, where it ranks among the two or three leading causes of death. Attempts by boys outnumber those by girls until adolescence. The ratio of attempts to successful suicide ranges from 5:1 to 100:1 and may be even higher when covert efforts are taken into account. Parents and authorities tend to conceal or discount its occurrence. A number of children making overt attempts, let alone those with repetitive *accidental* self-injuries, may thus miss receiving needed attention. The general guideline to take all suicidal overtures seriously applies to children as well as to adults. Criteria for assessing *genuineness* of

frank attempts are comparable to those used in adults.

Child suicide is characterized by impulsivity, apparently trivial precipitants, and little, if any, planning or premeditation. Since the concept of death undergoes evolution during development, individual children's attempts stem from varying admixtures of magical thinking, efforts at control, and manipulation and direction of hostile impulses against the self.[48] Generally, there will already have been disturbances in fusion of libidinal and aggressive drives with failures of neutralization, inhibition or dilution of the latter. Problems with impulse control, often culturally determined, are thus a significant precondition. While suicidal thoughts and fantasies are almost ubiquitous during childhood and adolescence and can be pleasurable, acting on them is usually rejected as an adaptive device. When the step is taken, the most frequent psychodynamic issues are aggression and escape from an intolerable intrapsychic or external situation. The aggression is most often directed towards a parent or the whole family, though self-punishment for hostile thoughts or forbidden acts such as masturbation is not an uncommon motive. Most children tend to regress under overwhelming or extremely painful circumstances. When the heightened dependency needs go unmet, escape from discouragement, helplessness, or severe threat may then be sought through suicide. Other important dynamic elements include identification with a beloved relative, delusional thinking, and suggestion.

Chronic depression and superego conflicts become a prime factor only after early adolescence, usually in those who are having trouble functioning comfortably in new sexual and social roles because they have not resolved earlier developmental issues. Difficulties in making the transition from home to community can be based on discrepant values, constitutional inadaptability, or defensive rigidity. In turn, they can bring on the helplessness, hopelessness, and guilt which the suicide seeks to escape. At times there may be "external compliance" through reinforcement by parents of a teenager's fantasies of worthlessness and dangerousness. He may come to consider himself *expendable* and see dispensing with himself as a favor to others, whom he yet wishes to please.

Hospitalization is usually indicated, though in some unusual circumstances the necessary medical care and observation may be feasible elsewhere. The patient should be reassured and supported as a child in trouble. If agitation or drug effects indicate restraint, they should be applied for control rather than punishment. Such a protective atmosphere should allow for the beginning of a deeper understanding of the patient's symptomatic distress and the family situation. To be appropriate, psychotherapy should address the immediate emergency, the need for prevention against recurrence, and the patient's long-term needs. Environmental changes, such as reassignment from an excessively stressful academic placement, may be helpful. Involvement of the whole family should be considered, first via crisis intervention techniques and teamwork, and then in an ongoing manner as indicated by their dynamics and ability to come for help after the current crisis passes. An appreciation of the special style and needs of impulsive families[35] might increase the chances of rendering more definitive treatment.

School Phobia

This relatively common syndrome of early childhood merits attention as an acute psychiatric emergency because of its frank interruption of progress along a number of developmental fronts and because prognosis is so dependent on appropriate early management. Should it become chronic, the phobic pattern of avoidance and regression may be almost irreversible and continue into later life.[12] Patients with *work phobia* seen by the general psychiatrist often have genetic and dynamic features in common with school-phobic children.

The point at which psychiatric attention is sought depends on the child's initial symptomatology and the attitudes of physician, parents, and school authorities. Frequently the syndrome begins with complaints during school hours of gastrointestinal upset or malaise for which no organic basis can be found. Trials of indulgence, encouragement, or coercion prove fruitless. Fears related to the classroom, teacher, or playground may be expressed, especially if there has been a frightening or dangerous *real* event. Response through environmental manipulation is rarely successful, however. Even in the absence of overt fears, it becomes evident that the child dreads leaving home and that the family is somehow unable to induce his return to school. Differentiation from truancy is fairly easy: the impulsive or antisocial child dislikes school; he avoids or leaves it in order to pursue pleasures elsewhere; he returns home because of convenience or fear, not anxiety; and he will try to keep his truancy a secret from parents. The phobic child, on the other hand, is usually motivated to learn, sticks close to home, draws family attention to his problem, and is ashamed to have others know about it.

The significance of this syndrome varies with the child's stage of development and the degree to which it stems from fixed internalized processes. For the otherwise healthy young child confronting the stress of a new situation, it may be due only to expectable and transient separation anxiety. In the adolescent, it may be premonitory of more severe personality disturbances, including psychosis. In the latency child (where incidence in girls is at least as high as in boys), persistent partial or total inability to go to school associated with irrational dread often represents a serious individual and family problem around dependency and aggression. When the psychodynamics of the situation come to be understood, the characteristic picture is of a preexisting, excessively close, child–mother relationship rooted in hostile dependency; an event which threatens the security of both and increases their mutual dependency; a vicious circle of mounting demands, anger, expiatory giving-in, and undoing; and an atmosphere of contradictory verbal and action messages, projection and displacement. The father's role in the dynamic processes, while perhaps indirect, is also important. Parental behavior may clearly foster the child's remaining close, but he himself also cannot leave home because of anxiety about what he might lose or what his unconscious hostility might cause in his absence. Parental violence or a younger sibling's presence adds reality weight to such concerns.

Definitive treatment obviously must address the child and family pathology, which often involves intensive and lengthy psychotherapy. Early return to school must nevertheless take high priority. This step is essential to the child's continued development and for prevention of increasing academic and social handicaps. It also should serve long-term treatment goals by helping to make the unconscious determinants on all sides more accessible. From the outset, management should be a joint physician–family–school undertaking. Detailed step-by-step plans may be needed. The psychotherapeutic approach offers exceptional indications and opportunities for collaboration with the specialist in child psychiatry. The work with the parents, or perhaps mother alone, should be undertaken with the same point of view as the treatment of severely neurotic or borderline adults.

FIRE SETTING

The emergency nature of this dramatic symptom varies greatly. At one end of the spectrum, it may derive exclusively from the intense concern it understandably generates in the community. At the other end, it may be the signal of significant psychopathology, such as psychosis, antisocial personality disorder, or acute anxiety states. Preschool children, mostly boys, often are impelled by curiosity, imitation, or phallic exhibitionism to set fires which then get out of control. In this age group, but more so in latency, pathological fire setting is usually associated with other manifestations of poor impulse control, such as rage reactions, hyperactivity, eneuresis, cruelty, truancy, or stealing. Severe anxiety and/or learning disabilities may have contributed to poor social adjustment in some children. The fires which preadolescent children tend to set in or near their homes commonly have a psychodynamic meaning related

to love, such as revenge on rivals, punishment of ungiving parents, or attention-seeking. In adolescents fire setting has a more ominous import, both in terms of the underlying psychopathology and the danger to others. These patients are more likely to be schizophrenic, mentally retarded, or psychoneurotic with sexual perversions. However, some adolescents without severe personality distortion may resort to this type of behavior as a cry for help with situational or intrapsychic conflicts.

Whatever the age of the child involved, direct management is dictated for his own and the community's welfare. As a rule, the behavior may be expected to be repeated. With some younger children, parents may be able to assume the necessary responsibility for their supervision. Where this is not so, and in the case of adolescents, removal from the home to an institution may be necessary. The choice between an open or closed setting will depend on individual factors, such as the meaning of the symptom, overall reliability of impulse controls, history of premeditation, planning, and seriousness of the incendiarism. A long-term psychotherapeutic approach, attuned to the child's basic condition, will usually be needed. Family participation in conjoint or collaborative therapy is, of course, essential.

ANOREXIA NERVOSA

Anorexia nervosa, which occurs predominantly in pre- and early adolescent girls, is a symptom constellation centering about severe weight loss, failure of appetite, and unusual attitudes towards food.[24] It may begin with bulimia and/or deliberate dieting. Early relationship conflicts, especially about feeding, and body-image problems are generally found. The overall clinical picture may be of a personality disorder of predominantly obsessive-compulsive, hysterical, or schizoid type. This syndrome occurs in psychotic patients as well. The suicidal potential in self-starvation also fits in with the dynamics of children who have suffered losses of important people or self-esteem.

Though long-term psychiatric attention is often necessary, response on an emergency basis is dictated during the first phases of management of the acutely anorectic child and his environment. Here the psychiatrist would function most usefully as a member of the medical treatment team. As the immediate need is to deal with the life-endangering starvation, efforts to manage the patient's nutrition will likely already be underway. The psychiatrist can contribute through a preliminary assessment of whether the particular child–family interaction is conducive to implementing the medical regimen at home. This will quite often not be likely and, perhaps after a further trial, transfer to hospital will occur. Initial efforts to establish a psychotherapeutic relationship with the patient and family should take place within the context of the team approach. Confident psychiatric diagnosis and prognosis will probably be obscured in the midst of the crises created by the precarious physical situation and the importance of day-to-day management. At this point, an ongoing consultative role for the psychiatrist will help with the intense emotional impact which anorectics have upon those concerned with their care. Their defense of starvation, negativism, and ingenious manipulativeness may arouse in the professional staff anxiety, guilt, and hostility comparable to those which paralyzed the parents. Sustained application of psychiatric insights and skills to the minute details of the patient's dealings with those in his milieu is often required to maintain the team's consistency in being firm and understanding, reestablishing regular eating patterns and limiting destructive interactions with the family.

Direct psychotherapeutic work with the child and parents should begin promptly. It may be enhanced by having them see different therapists who should have regular collaborative meetings. These keep lines of communication open, obviate being manipulated into opposition with other staff, and dilute the potentially interfering countertransferences created by the pressure of their patients' demands.[37] In the first phase of work with the child patient, the therapist aims at providing a positive relationship, accepting disturbing feelings of hostility and oral greed, helping with controls and giving a sense of protection

from an environment viewed as malign. As the need for self-starvation abates and the anxiety level drops, the therapist's focus can enlarge to understanding and working with the underlying psychopathology.

ASSAULTS ON CHILDREN

The psychiatrist may be called upon to participate in cases of abused, assaulted, or grossly neglected children in his role as a hospital staff member, consultant to social and legal agencies, or private practitioner. His skills in interviewing and knowledge of development and individual and family psychopathology remain the basic tools in making evaluations and decisions about disposition. The special quality of these situations may provide opportunities to help all those involved by also bringing to bear consultative skills, awareness of the complexities of child-family interactions, and appreciation of the long-term sequelae of these emergencies.

THE BATTERED CHILD

Social and medical alertness to the prevalence (estimated at 10–20 percent of those seen in emergency rooms) of physical abuse or gross neglect of children has risen significantly in recent years.[32] Physicians have learned to include parent-inflicted trauma as an etiological possibility in the diagnosis of a range of childhood injuries and illnesses. An increasing number of jurisdictions have made reporting of suspected cases mandatory. All those present in an emergency room may be thus operating under crisis conditions. The onus of legal responsibilities upon the professional staff and their identification with the child victim may skew their approach to examining and interviewing. Parents sensing accusation and danger may conceal medical data, become angrily defensive, be incapacitated by anxiety, or attempt to flee, thereby interfering with the child's care and building up the case against themselves. Later, mandatory legal and social investigations may be carried out in a way which alienates them from sources of help or imperils the family's community standing or financial security. The child may react to the battle he sees (or fantasizes) raging about him with agitation, regression, withdrawal or picking sides. Information he gives should be weighed as well in the light of his expectable cognitive capacities, reality-testing, and attitude toward the truth. Removal of the parents for police interrogation, his own hospitalization for treatment of injuries and psychosocial workup, sometimes with enforced isolation from the family, or even institutional placement pending legal action, will usually be a significant trauma in its own right. The reactions to separation or to the uncertainty of his future may be erroneously ascribed to the original abuse and go inadequately attended.

In fortunate instances, the suspected battered child and family are offered from the outset the services of an interdisciplinary medical-mental health-social service team. Police and legal involvement is provided in a collaborative spirit by units, e.g., the juvenile squad or the Children's Court clinical staff, trained to reconcile the requirements of justice with those of family rehabilitation and individual emotional needs. Ancillary services, such as day-care centers and innovative psychotherapeutic approaches, are mobilized. Emphasis is on following through with meeting the specific needs of parents and child as they reciprocally influence each other.

The considerable body of descriptive and research studies which has evolved in this field has tended to focus upon the parental side of the interaction. Such data can be useful to the psychiatrist in direct work with parents. While a consistent diagnostic picture has not been found, there is ample evidence of ego and superego distortions and instinctual drive disturbance in the battering parent as well as the silent spouse. Examination of child-rearing patterns reveals not only a frequent repetition of violence experienced in the abuser's own childhood, but a deeper conviction that the child should be punished even during infancy for failing to meet parental needs through proper behavior and gratifying achievement. Sensitive interplay and warm, empathic motherliness outside the mechanical aspects of child care are often significantly lacking. The child may be misperceived as bad, spoiled,

sickly, out of control, or a problem in some other way. He may be a disappointment to conscious or unconscious wishes. Specific dynamic constellations have been described in parents centering on fear of the child's helplessness, seductiveness, or punitiveness. In certain cases it is possible to identify a gross distortion in which a child in a particular stage of development is perceived as a hostile persecutory adult; the assault is thus provoked by such a circumscribed psychotic transference.

The perspective of child psychiatry can add to this category of data a respect for the child's possible contribution to the disturbed relationships which result in his being attacked. Physical abnormalities, conditions of conception, sex, and impact of his birth upon the family's living situation could be obvious factors which feed into existing parental difficulties. A part may also be played by more subtle constitutional qualities, whether the overtaxing of a marginally coping mother by a mentally retarded or hyperthymic infant or the anxiety about intactness raised by one who is quite passive. Characteristics of the infant secondary to maternal deprivation, notably in the area of ego defects, may perpetuate a vicious circle. So could the child's retaliatory behavior, learned during earlier episodes of being attacked or stemming from identification with behavior of family members towards each other.

SEXUAL ASSAULTS

These include not only forcible rape but also a variety of overstimulating activities which exceed the child's ability to cope with them. Their impact, therefore, is independent of the degree of willingness or seduction on the child's own part. Effects will depend not only on the circumstances of the act but also on the child's current phase-specific fantasies, ego capacities, and means of handling anxiety.[28] Immediate symptoms will not be pathognomonic of sexual assault. Rather, they will reflect the involvement by anxiety of the period's major developmental issues. Thus, infants may show disturbed feeding, excretory, or speech functions. Insistent craving for stimulation may appear. In early childhood, there will be habit and conduct disorders, phobic symptoms, sexual idiosyncrasies, or interference with learning. Older children may react with transient neurotic or psychosocial problems.

Psychiatric concern centers about the effects upon the child of a trauma which does not get worked through. The general principle applies that he will attempt to defend against externally caused anxiety by "doing unto others," i.e., becoming the aggressor in repeating the action in which he was originally the passive party. Frank sexual deviation is a possibility in later years.

Acute management should respect the importance of environmental reaction. The child will pick up messages of anxiety, guilt, or accusation from parents and authorities, who should be helped to see his needs objectively. Opportunities should be provided for the child to ventilate and abreact guilt, anxiety, and feelings of responsibility and to be supported and reassured. Techniques will depend on age and specific conditions. The victim of actual rape will often be in a state of acute fear or even panic. Hysterical symptoms may be present. Medical and other inquiries should be handled so as not to aggravate the problem. Handling at home is desirable, with hospitalization only if the child is a clear suicidal risk or if the parents' inability to manage their own feelings would add further major trauma. The initial phase of "talking things out" is often best done with a friendly, objective person other than a relative. The whole family should also be helped to discuss the assault together to obviate the child's assuming that (s)he is considered bad or to blame. The psychiatrist may find it most useful to act in a consultant role during these steps rather than offering therapy directly to the child and family.

Sexual assaults by close relatives, especially parents, signify disturbed object relationships somewhere in the family. Further follow-up is indicated, including attention to possible compliance or encouragement by the "noninvolved" parent. In cases of assault by others, the best preventive psychiatry may be more careful selection of babysitters.[30]

OTHER ACUTE SITUATIONS

Anxiety attacks may follow external catastrophes, life stresses, or family upsets. Great fear, crying, mutism, perseverative speech, or sleep disorders may be seen. Concomitant parental anxiety may contribute to a vicious circle and make the child uncontrollable. Observing him in isolation from the family temporarily may bring relief and help to identify the origins of anxiety-provoking stimuli. It may emerge that the child has been chronically anxious in company with his parents. Appropriate treatment for all should follow.

Children may also react acutely to deaths of parents or other close relatives, though a slower time table is more typical. The precipitant is often panic or decompensation in those around them. Such situations are special because of the excessive guilt often involved. Initial management should therefore stress adequate opportunities for ventilation with an objective professional.

Other children will be overcome by shame or guilt following the injury (or death) of a relative or pet for which they hold their own fantasies responsible. Confusional states, hallucinations, and withdrawal may follow. Admission to a hospital or similar setting may be necessary to protect the child from his own acting-out. When the crisis abates, he should be evaluated for underlying psychopathology, which frequently will have gone unrecognized.

Definitive Diagnosis and Treatment

The child's receiving adequate psychiatric care is based on a complete and useful diagnostic and prognostic evaluation. The timing of this step will vary with individual circumstances. Sometimes the clinician will first see the child in an emergency and have to respond to his presenting behavior and its immediate consequences. At other times, he will be furnished some descriptive data about the child and asked if they indicate a possible psychiatric problem. In either event, the psychiatrist will eventually have to recommend not only whether and when a further workup should be done but also what his own part in it should be. The choice of alternatives may be: following the child's course at second-hand for a while; doing the whole evaluation himself; enlisting other professionals to examine the child while he studies the parents and community; or referral of the whole case to a specialist colleague or clinic. Relationship to the original referral source, personal expertise, and availability of other resources will all be factors in the decision.

The diagnostic process is considered in detail in Volume 2, Chapter 1. It aims at a formulation of the child's status in terms of his endowment, the genetic and dynamic elements in his illness, his overall healthy and maladaptive potentials, and the assets and weaknesses in the family and the larger environment. It should culminate in a clear treatment plan which takes into account the child's "treatability" under different conditions.

Such answers cannot necessarily be expressed in terms from a nosology based on symptoms or one of reaction types. Symptoms in the child will generally be nonspecific and phase-related whatever the etiology of his problem, while any disturbance involving predominantly psychological components is a reaction type.[22] Therefore, the conceptual steps in diagnosis would be to identify the determinants of symptomatic behavior, to spell out the goals of change in the child's existence, and to select the intervention methods to achieve them. The following categories can provide some guidelines for such an approach.

1. *Reactions to current crises* or external events include situations which are largely responses to important happenings in the child's milieu, to expectable growth processes within him or, in early stages, to frustrations or blocks to continued development as a result of inappropriate handling and stimulation.[18] In this category, the child might have distortions to solutions in developmental stages, or in habit or adjustment patterns, such as expectations from relationships or the environment. Initial goals would include environmental modification and provision of new opportuni-

ties for the child to use his abilities to master his situation. Tactics might be brief support through parents, temporary help across adjustment hurdles with peers or in school, or changes in family activity patterns.

2. *Surface conflicts* entail disordered functioning as a manifestation of a clash, primarily at the conscious level, between the child's drives and feelings and his environment. These might be around academic demands, social pressures, sexual impulses, or the advent of siblings. There would be a greater contribution from the child's side in terms of the particular meanings to him of events about him; the nature of his adaptive resources would also have played into the problem's arising. A greater degree of intervention would be required to achieve goals involving the environment, the child's ways of responding, or both. Changes in intrafamilial functioning might be sought through family or couple therapy, in peer-group interaction through structured experiences or the support of additional figures for identification, in school by class reassignment or organized tutoring, and in the child through counseling or focused psychotherapy.

About 80 percent of children's mental-health problems fall into the two groups above and often respond to surface approaches. These conditions are not static and may go on to have a longer-term distorting effect on personality.

3. The group of *internalized conflicts*, into which the others may evolve, covers a broad range of stable maladaptations, resulting from and perpetuated by largely unconscious intrapsychic conflicts, whether inter- or intrastructural. While the environment continues to influence functioning and is important in recovery, effective treatment for this group of children has to include the psychotherapeutic opportunity to deal with conflicts on the level where they are occurring. Ancillary to this may be measures to help correct deficiencies secondary to the internalized problem or to channel developmental forces freed up during treatment, e.g., remedial education, a therapeutic milieu, or treatment for parents.

Implicit in the approach so far is the recognition that psychotherapy is not the only good treatment and that manipulation of the child's environment is not necessarily fruitless. Individualized planning goes on to take into account the question of "treatability."[23] The answers should be free of distortions due to the diagnostic team's personal backgrounds, experience, therapeutic optimism, or sociocultural stereotypes. Valid ones will be built up from knowledge of the child's characteristics and potential, family variables and the community setting. Children's therapeutic potential cannot be inferred from diagnosis. It differs according to their capacity for conceptualization and communication, psychological mindedness, object relationships, frustration tolerance, and the degree of secondary gain of their illness. The family's likely participation in treatment will reflect their cooperation, solidarity, emotional health, general outlook on life, ties with the community, and dependence on the child's illness for maintenance of its own homeostasis. Inputs utilizing the extended family and its resources may be important even in this modern society. The value of community facilities and supports will depend not only on their existence but availability.

The plan will specify whether psychotherapy is needed and how it fits in with other efforts to help the child resolve his problems and to potentiate his healthy development. The most appropriate setting for this total program will be identified: (1) Treatment as an outpatient while living at home is best if it is workable. This will depend in general on the child's motivation and ability to cope during treatment, as well as the family's adequacy in meeting his needs and their willingness for him to be treated. Removal from the home may be necessary because of the stresses the family brings to bear on the child. Sending the child elsewhere only because outpatient resources are not available is highly regrettable but may sometimes be the least of the evils. (2) Specialized day-care facilities are a useful alternative for children needing a more controlled environment than the home setting can provide, especially if they also require ameliorative educational, occupational, recrea-

tional, and/or group experiences. (3) Out-of-home placement, as in residential treatment centers or foster care, is essential in some cases. Children may have to be separated from a pathological family situation to give psychotherapy a chance to operate. Others may be unable to tolerate the closeness of or distortions in interactions in a family unit and will engage in severe provocation or acting out. More familiar are those who act out and need the limits and behavioral controls which only a specialized milieu can provide.

The diagnosticians' efforts and the family's investment in the process become meaningful only when the results of the work are interpreted in a useful way. At this point, the parents (and often the older child) are entitled to have presented to them a dynamic formulation, diagnosis, and treatment plan. The ultimate aim is to establish a common understanding and purpose among all concerned. This step is as technically difficult as it is important. Care is in order to avoid factual misunderstanding, to recognize resistances, and to assure that the consensus reached is based on what is really right for the child rather than on political or expedient compromises.

The general psychiatrist's role vis-à-vis the child's further treatment should be decided according to individual needs rather than any set model. The comments below apply to possible participation other than as the child's therapist, i.e., in some role involving work with the parents as an aspect of treatment of the child. Philosophy and format of this approach have changed over the years. Throughout, however, it has been a basic tenet that parents' participation is important to the success of any treatment plan for the child.

Indirect treatment of children through their parents has a long and honorable history. Some years ago the assumption became prevalent that children's disturbances originated in those of their parents, who were therefore made the principal therapeutic targets. Children are nowadays understood to make unique contributions to their problems and parents have become partners in the therapeutic effort. It may nevertheless be decided that the child not be seen himself, but be treated indirectly, either throughout or in the opening stages.

When a child is to be seen directly, many psychiatrists and clinics follow a *collaborative model*. In this approach parents see someone else and it is understood that information will be exchanged between the therapists. Sometimes there are indications to avoid such a split, though not to do family therapy, so both child and parents have separate sessions with the same person. The general psychiatrist may have been treating one or both parents before the child himself came to diagnostic attention. Changing the therapeutic contract to one of collaboration with the child's therapy will usually be contraindicated.

Age of the patient and nature of the treatment are important factors. In the case of a younger child in psychotherapy, parents may have to go beyond making his sessions possible to being the carriers and implementers of critical environmental factors. Their involvement will therefore have to be greater. Parents may be seen less frequently if the patient is an adolescent, depending on the degree of his independent functioning and the need to have the treatment be his own. The relative importance of advice-giving, ego-supportive techniques, focusing on the marital relationships, or the depth of inquiry into parents' personality functioning differ from therapeutic approaches not oriented to a child.

Whatever format is found to be best adapted to the individual situation, some problems are typically encountered as parents go through treatment with their children. At the outset, parents will often feel to blame for their child's difficulties, intellectual knowledge and reassurance to the contrary notwithstanding. Having to bring their child to someone else for help can be a blow to their self-esteem, especially when the help is perceived as personal or competitive with parents rather than truly professional or scientific. Such feelings are often reflected in questions about what the psychiatrist does with the child or how he helps him. Rivalrous impulses may be

stimulated, and be similarly expressed. When such questions come up in their own sessions, they can be put into context and used to advantage. However, parents may act out their feelings by quizzing the child about what went on, coaching him in what to say, or even joining him in the treatment room. Such behaviors will increase the child's concerns about confidentiality, precipitate further conflicts of loyalty, or even convince him that the therapist is the parents' agent.

Narcissistic issues also enter into initial treatment planning and arrangements. From the child's side, it should be recognized that a therapeutic alliance may begin to form during the diagnostic sequence. If the psychiatrist ends up working with the parents, feelings of loss or rejection can be carried over into the child's first contacts with his own therapist. Parents already in treatment may ask for and get a referral for a child who is arousing warranted concern. They may then experience it as disapproval of themselves or preference for the child. Psychiatrists are familiar with the phenomenon of children being brought as tickets of admission by parents who really want help for themselves. From the opposite end, others will find the child's needing treatment a means of getting out of their own. This is even more likely when the person dealing with them around the child can be seen as more tolerant, giving of advice or approving of self-sacrifice for the child's sake.

During treatment parents may feel disadvantaged versus the child, who comes and plays during his sessions, while they confront painful issues in their own counseling or therapy. Guilt may prevent them from spontaneously ventilating their resentment of the inequality or cause them to deny their real difficulties with treatment arrangements until it is too late to relieve them. A parent's neurotic need to fail may show up in their work here as elsewhere.

As the child gets further into the psychotherapeutic process, his regressive shifts may discourage or infuriate those around him. Parents also need help in the face of the aggressive and erotic energies which are freed but not yet directed appropriately. Particularly stressful is a child's questioning of family norms and adults' self-destructive behaviors, or his insistence that they be consistent, often with threats to report them to the therapist. The child's new behaviors in this area touch upon the chance of his upsetting the family homeostasis by getting better, and alertness to this danger can help to meet it in time and work it through before it leads to premature termination.

⟮ The Impact of Family Illness

Children are inevitably influenced by what goes on with other family members, whether these are healthy or have a medical problem. The psychiatric nature of a relative's illness or its severity do not automatically augur more damaging consequences. Its impact will be determined by the vectors pertinent to the meeting of the child's basic needs, his opportunities for growth, and the intrapsychic events that result. Somatic diseases, neuroses, and personality disorders in those around him may lead to more profound dysfunction in a child than psychoses or severe depressions in the family. It is more likely, however, that concern about children is generated when their parents fall into the latter group. The following discussion therefore centers on such cases of illness in the family. Some reference will be made to other situations, including normal ones, by way of illustrating the considerations which apply.

When his seriously ill patient is a parent, the psychiatrist faces the complicated task of deciding which (if any) steps are in order to minimize adverse effects upon children. A number of perspectives can be employed: (1) the child will participate in changes or distortions of general family functioning resulting from a member being or becoming ill; (2) direct effects upon the child will depend on his specific relationship with the ill member and what both bring to it; (3) interventions to aid the individual child should not only meet his needs but those of the whole family from which he will then profit indirectly.

General Family Response

A family's way of coping with the stress of a member's illness depends on its existing strengths in organization, integration, social affiliation, interpersonal ties, and material resources. While the member is unable to function, such variables influence the degree of overall family disorganization, deprivation of other individuals, anxiety, and acting out. They underlie the way the family returns to previous patterns as the member recovers, or the way it makes a long-term adaptation if the disability is chronic. Some shifts are probably inescapable in the areas of status and role evaluations (especially dominance),[1] the direction and intensity of interpersonal transactions, affection, discipline, and daily operations. Social isolation may result from preoccupation with the member's illness and the family's difficulties. In fact, the absence of at least some reorientation of interest and concern might raise questions about earlier family relationships and/or their current adaptive efforts and intrapsychic defenses.

The child's experience depends upon: his age, sex, and ordinal position, his role allocation within the family, and his habitual style of functioning within its socioeconomic and cultural context. The range of possibilities is almost infinite and includes those in which illness (as also in cases of actual absence) of a parent or sibling results in the family's being better off. An urban, two-parent model can be used to illustrate the effects of incapacity of different family members assuming that no one else fills in for them. It is recognized that none of the roles is fixed or exclusive in real families, especially with regard to the meeting of emotional needs and, increasingly, activity outside the home.

Illness of the *father* would thus theoretically be expected to mean the endangering or loss of the source of material support and status, the deprivation of a key model for extra-family socialization, and a threat to an object of libidinal and aggressive drives involved in the processes of identification and superego formation. The child, as a result, would experience increased adaptive and social problems outside the home, sacrifice of maternal care and attention to the father with increased wishes and/or competition for it, and added obstacles to the resolution of psychosexual conflicts.

Serious illness in the *mother* would usually be more disruptive, as it would lead to withdrawal of the often predominant source of emotional security, dependency gratification, and maintenance of intrafamilial homeostasis. In addition to the loss of the specific functions the mother may have served in supporting social interaction and appropriate identification, the child would experience ubiquitous emotional deprivation which other family members would not be in a position to make up, leading to consequences at all psychosexual levels.

Illness of a *sibling* might mean massive diversion of parental attention, the rearousal and accentuation of dependency strivings, regression and interference with the resolution of conflicts involving the parental figures. Even without this, there would be loss of a coparticipant in the mastery of tension on the way toward social maturity and functional autonomy.

Thus general family disruption, secondary to a member's serious illness, can be translated into the essential functions and inputs of which the child would be deprived. The ultimate impact upon the child would thus be a function of the duration and degree of the deprivation. This, in turn, would depend on the outcome of the individual's illness, on the pace and effectiveness of the whole family's coping efforts and, most critically, on the moving in by others to meet the various needs of the child. These do not necessarily operate in the same direction, though a better prognosis for the patient will certainly ease the load upon the rest of the family. Nevertheless, physical attention, training in self-care, stimulation, maintenance of household routines, and encouragement socially and academically may go by the board or be filled in for the child irrespective of a parent's psychiatric course.

Seen as a whole, the response of some families is marked by growth of collective effectiveness and healthy development of the children. Here, the clinician may find it advisable to defer recommending shifts in their living situation. Some indices for making such an estimate are drawn from or comparable to those used in prognosis of an individual patient's recovery from a severe illness. From the side of the healthy parent(s), these could include: a history of satisfactory childhood; good marital relationships; stable and mature friendships; successful school and work performance; demonstrated ability to cope with previous life challenges and everyday problems. Comparable criteria for the children in such a holistic approach to the family would be: evidence of timely and successful meeting of developmental challenges (achieving a sense of basic security, autonomy, initiative, industriousness, etc.);[8] degree of resistance to pathological regression in the face of the current stress; sustained satisfactory school work and peer relationships; ability to openly and willingly collaborate with other family members to keep the home running. Another favorable sign would be the observation that the child is able to tolerate his ambivalence towards the ill family member, especially a parent. This might be seen in a child's recognition of the fact of the illness and of its arousing feelings within him, accompanied by an approach of tolerance and love, rather than one of denial with consistent rage or withdrawal.

The overall picture in other families will not be consistent with a favorable expectation. Application of the indices noted above may give a negative answer for some or all members. There may be frank psychopathology, a tendency towards disintegration of mutual activities, marked constriction of interests with excessive anxiety about security and/or progressive alienation of individuals from each other. With their greater dependence on other people and on the structure of the family unit, children in such situations could be expected to suffer more intensely from its breakdown.

Separations and Losses

Even if it remains together in the long run, the family with intrinsic weaknesses may also be more prone to transient breakups. Experiences of separation and loss can be a repetitive theme in the lives of children with severely ill parents. Moves in and out of hospitals are more frequent now that maintenance in the community is easier and has become official policy. Community rejection, due to disturbed behavior or fearful steroetypes, can cause frequent changes of address. Parental discord and violence, material insecurity and broken marriages, often secondary effects themselves, add to concerns about separation. The clinician would then have to consider the relative merits of the children continuing to remain within the family life-pattern, allowing for the possible effects of ameliorative maneuvers, against the long-term risks of chronic exposure to such events. He may also be in a better position to provide helpful intervention for children when such traumata have occurred but are still fresh and reversible.

The understanding of the nature and effects of separations raises questions of definition. Do children mourn and how is this related to adult mourning of a permanently lost object? Is attachment a form of instinctive behavior or associated with gratification of other instinctual drives? What are the roles of both parents? These questions are being actively worked on. For present purposes, we shall suffice with describing the sequence of observable reactions of a young child to the loss of an important (*the* important may be more apt) figure. Following Bowlby,[7] four phases can be described: (1) *numbness,* lasting a few hours to a week, perhaps interrupted by outbursts of intense distress and/or anger; (2) *protest,* with yearning and searching for the lost figure, lasting months to years; and (3) greater or less degree of *detachment* from the old object; and, (4) hopefully, *reorganization.*

Such a sequence may have a profound effect on the child's affective life and ability to form relationships. It is accompanied by intense and disturbing fears of abandonment,

yearning for the lost object, and anger at his absence. The urge for the lost figure may lead to direct action or take the form of withdrawal into fantasy. Some adolescents, even many years after a loss, embark on a search for their origins reflecting the continued pressure of this urge.[6] The child angrily reproaches anyone who seems to be responsible for his loss or standing in the way of reunion. The major part of his psychic energy can become bound up in these repetitive activities and thus impede his growth. One such experience, let alone repeated ones, may compromise a child's ability to feel secure with and trust other people, with far-reaching consequences for superego development, learning or identity formation, or the major task of the stage he is at.

The intensity and duration of reactions to separation should serve to highlight the importance of intervention to help the child through them with minimal long-term personality damage. To do this, application may be made of the psychotherapeutic principle that facing reality and being freed from the struggle with the past require appropriate understanding, support, and opportunities for expression of feelings about the lost person. This may be especially critical if the rest of the family are attempting to deal with their loss and ambivalence through denial, displacement, or avoidance.

Direct Effects of the Parent–Child Relationship

Examination of this area is of necessity a highly individualized matter. Children usually show different responses to parental illness, even when it is florid. This is to be expected from their being of different ages and at different points in their cognitive growth and progress along the developmental line from the mother–child dyad through the family unit into the outside world. Effects also depend on the extent to which they become enmeshed in the parental psychopathology.

Determinants of direct effects upon children can come from the following areas:

CONSTITUTIONAL DIFFERENCES

As with other life experiences, a child's interactions with members of his family will be influenced by his unique endowment. Children with perceptual difficulties, physical handicaps or intellectual limitations will be readily thought of as more vulnerable to failures or disruptions in progressive growth. Under the best conditions of care, they can be expected to encounter problems around relationship, body-image, socialization and eventual independent functioning.[17]

Even in the absence of marked disability, premonitory evidence of vulnerability may be gathered from examination of the child's "temperamental qualities."[44] These variables in individual endowment affect the functioning of children in any environment. Here we shall cite some possible implications of this general fact in families with an ill parent, to show that what is important to the child in the relationship is the kind of response, not the diagnosis.

1. *Activity level.* As a result of his normal high level (i.e., not the hyperactivity associated with neurological abnormality or psychopathology) a child may move about so rapidly and energetically as to repeatedly damage himself or household objects. Such a child may pose a threat to a parent who is struggling with his own aggressive impulses, slowed down by depression or psychotropic drugs, busy ministering to another family member who is ill, overburdened by having to do the jobs of both parents or especially irritable during withdrawal. The feedback to this child may well have as its major theme his "badness" and include demands for self-restraint which he cannot meet. After a while, he may become depressed—if previous experience has laid the groundwork—or habitually disobedient—if he gives up on trying to please. On the opposite end of the spectrum, a very slow-moving child may be unable to mobilize himself fast enough to benefit from the few opportunities for pleasurable interaction or outside stimulation which an intermittently available parent can offer.

2. *Rhythmicity.* Individual differences in this area may prove an obstacle to anxiety-free functioning during a parent's illness. One child's diurnal cycles (hunger–feeding, sleeping–waking, elimination) may be so regular that "you could set your watch by him," while another's may be highly erratic and unpredictable. The former may experience as highly disruptive and anxiety-provoking the shifts and adjustments which the family must make to cope with illness. On the other hand, a parent whose illness or recovery process makes her very needful of structure and regularity herself may find the second kind of child beyond her ability to respond to, leaving him either uncared for, the object of frustrated attack or a believer in the basic inadequacy of his bodily processes.

3. *Adaptability.* Children who can change a previous behavior pattern to one which works in a new situation only after repeated, consistent exposure with a maximum of anxiety may be unable to adapt to the changes in behavior of an ill parent, even when these in themselves are not extreme. Rather than making the necessary shifts, they may withdraw and thus deprive themselves of the benefit of the parent's being in fact available to them on an at least minimally adequate level.

4. *Other temperamental qualities,* such as the ability to react to the environment, perseverance at tasks in the face of distractions and frustrations or typical mood, could be similarly discussed. It is difficult except in anterospective research with quite young subjects to pick out one or another discrete "quality" in pure culture. Application of the constitutional point of view can be made, however, in history taking. Practically, it is most likely to be called for in the case of children whose behavioral style demonstrates the effects of typical constellations ("clusters") of traits. Their clinical picture will of course also show the blurring of temperamental characteristics by the kind of responses the environment has previously made.

a. The most obvious group about whom there may be concern on this basis are those who are "difficult" to raise because of their irregular biological functions, predominantly negative responses to new stimuli, slow adaptability, intense reactivity, and frequently negative moods. Such children present any parent with special challenges for consistent and tolerant handling based on an objective recognition of their patterns of reaction. If such essentially unusual parenting is forthcoming, these children can master in a stepwise manner the requirements of socialization. With parenting that is "good enough" for most children, however, this group face greater odds of developing behavior problems and engender in their parents feelings of resentment, guilt or helplessness. Their difficulties would be compounded if the parenting available to them was by someone already beset by her own problems in being consistent, tolerant, and objective while struggling with the internal issues raised by her own psychopathology.

b. The child who is "slow to warm up" because of slow adaptability and initial negative responses to new situations may withdraw in the face of situations where getting his needs met requires rapid and effective moving in. With fortunate parental and school handling, such a child can become interested and involved. A mother who is apathetic, especially needy of approving feedback, or driven to succeed may neglect a child without the sending power to engage her interest or contribute to his withdrawing by actively turning him off. Similarly, having a teacher who is unable to meet him where he is may deprive him of potential opportunities for satisfying achievement and introduction into a supportive peer group, with further adverse consequences for his sense of security and self-esteem.

c. Surprisingly, even the "easy" child whose positive moods and approach, regularity and easy adaptability endow him with the ability to evoke approval from others may become a casualty of his own strengths. Such a child may accommodate easily to the idiosyncratic qualities of an ill parent and to deviations from conventional roles and procedures which the family made in order to be able to function together. Having adapted well to the ground rules at home, he may be thrown into conflict when introduced into a school or peer group setting with differing ones. He may thus find himself confused, overwhelmed, inept,

criticized, punished, or ridiculed. Through efforts to defend against this new stress, such as withdrawal, avoidance, counterattack, or overcompensation, he may come to present problems in the form of aggressive outbursts, academic underachievement, "bossiness," or nonparticipation.

In this last case, we are not referring to children whose problems stem from deep-seated personality distortions they have suffered in adapting to parental illness and family change. They result rather from the conflict between these home expectations and those of the world outside, becoming manifest at times when they try to make the shift.

Age

In general the younger the child, the more vulnerable he will be to both the acute and long-term effects of growing up in relationship to a disturbed parent.[9]

1. *Infancy.* Spitz's[42] classification of psychogenic diseases in infancy illustrates the possible damaging effects of "psychotoxic" maternal behavior patterns. Thus, "primary overt rejection" of the "passive" type may be associated with coma in the newborn (infants with mothers who globally reject them in an active manner, if they live, usually are not kept by them and thus cannot be studied in this way). "Primary anxious overpermissiveness" has in many cases been associated with three-month colic; "hostility in the guise of anxiety" has been a factor in some infantile eczemas; "oscillation between pampering and hostility" is implicated in hypermotility (rocking); "cyclical mood swings" with fecal play; "hostility consciously compensated" with aggressive hyperactivity. Various combinations of tendencies to somatization, pathology of object relationships, depressive constellations, and personality disorders may follow later in life.

If there is quantitative (as opposed to the "qualitative" types above) inadequacy of care, the infant is at risk of experiencing varying degrees of home-based maternal deprivation. Children cared for by psychotic mothers on their own, especially if there is associated depression, may be somber in mood, irritable, unspontaneous, hypoactive and retarded in motor activities. Early adverse effects may be growth retardation, nutritional deficiency, disorder of basic biological functions, pica and habit disturbances, to name a few. The correlation of maternal deprivation with later psychopathology, especially delinquency, is by now widely recognized.[12]

2. *Later stages.* The parent's diminished functional capacity due to illness and the re-arousal of his own conflicts may also handicap him in meeting the phase-specific challenges posed by the child's later development.[1] These are outlined briefly below and mentioned in more detail elsewhere in this chapter and in others in this *Handbook.*

a. Separation-individuation. Giving up the "symbiotic" child; relating to him on a new level; supporting his nascent autonomy and new abilities.

b. Struggles over mastery and control of bodily functions; sadism; libidinal-aggressive balances.

c. Sexual interests and seductiveness; family roles.

d. Acceptance by the community; new identifications; sharing the child; moral and ethical standards; intellectual abilities.

e. Adolescent sexuality; new forms of aggression; adolescent "upset"; changing loyalties.

DIFFERENCES IN INVOLVEMENT OF THE CHILD BY ANOTHER'S PSYCHOPATHOLOGY

The effects upon children of overt, severe mental illness in the family have as yet not been systematically explored. Available information does at least point up the dangers of making facile assumptions in this area.[38]

1. The incidence of neurotic disorders is not higher in the children of psychotic than of nonpsychotic adults. However, conduct disorders are more frequent, with differential effects according to sex. Boys are more susceptible to developing antisocial disorders. Child-rearing philosophy and methods of discipline have less bearing on such an outcome than family stability and the quality of relationships.

Precise work in this field is made difficult by its dependence on how study populations become available. This, in turn, is influenced by social attitudes towards the definition of delinquency in boys and girls and the two sexes' different means of expression—aggression versus sexual acting out and pregnancy.

2. Further uncertainty is introduced by the discontinuity between the clinical manifestations of emotional disturbance in the same individual in early and later life. The possibility of a worse long-term prognosis for some of these children is raised by follow-up studies which show a high incidence of teenage or early adult schizophrenia after an earlier antisocial picture.

3. When clear psychopathology does become evident in the offspring of psychotic people, neither its form nor its severity correlates with that of the parents. Such a similarity is probably more common in the ill children of adults with neurotic or affective disorders.

4. A woman's psychosis does not automatically render her incapable of mothering adequately. Her ability to do so seems more related to her general capacity to relate to others.

5. There is more danger to a child if he is directly involved in the parent's current illness:

a. He may be a figure in the delusional system; an object in the depressive constellation; a target of intense hostility and ambivalence by virtue of sex, ordinal position, parentage or physical characteristics, and resemblances; the "cause" of a family or personal misfortune which precipitated the other member's falling ill.

b. A psychotic mother might maintain a state of emotional symbiosis with her child far beyond the time of his normal psychophysiological need for such a relationship. Thereby, he will tend to identify only with her and be isolated from peers and other adults. Among the possible additional sequelae can be crippling dependency, interference with cognitive development, sharing the maternal delusional beliefs and/or frank folie a deux.

c. Imitative sharing of someone else's defense mechanisms can leave a child poorly equipped to handle the pressures of his own life. Comparable processes may be involved in the frequently cited "contagion" of neurotic traits in a family.

6. Even when direct interactions are benign for the child, illness may have a meaning for him in reference to his own drives, leading to a sense of responsibility and feelings of anxiety and guilt. This can occur independent of the actions or suggestions of others. It can be stimulated by the "healthy" parent turning excessively to the child for emotional and physical support or making him a confidante in place of the ill spouse.[10]

7. While not specific to the family with known psychiatric disturbance, child abuse may be more likely in one whose members are already under stress, having problems with impulse control and susceptible to rapid displacements of blame.

Intervention

Looking out for children in the family adds another complex dimension to the already difficult task of delivering optimum care to the individual parent. While incomplete, the range of information available can aid in identifying more clearly the elements which can be helpful as well as hazardous to a patient's offspring or siblings. The conclusion that can be most confidently drawn at this time is that the key factor will be whether relationship experiences are consistent and developmentally appropriate.

Using this criterion, evaluations can be made of the impact of interpersonal contacts, the family's coping style, the community pattern of care and supportive services as well as of the direct parent–child relationship. Choice and timing of interventions for the sake of the child on a number of possible levels will be a matter of clinical judgment. We would suggest the overriding importance of helping efforts being coordinated and synergistic.

Treatment of individual patients should thus be oriented toward providing continuity of care, maintaining regard for the family's emotional needs and preventing its disruption by social and economic by-products of the one member's psychological decompensation.[33]

In large mental-health programs, these goals should not be obscured as patients go back and forth from hospital to outpatient status. Different social agencies move in and out of contact with the family to deal with concrete reality problems. Efforts to assure adequate regard for the psychic realities may be especially valuable at such times. Homemaker services should be geared to furnishing consistent maternal surrogates who have been educated to provide the kind and intensity of relationships children need.

The scope of psychotherapeutic efforts might be usefully extended to supportive work with the healthy parent or the family group. Children may need to be seen individually, particularly during unusual changes in parental functioning and at times of separation. The psychiatrist can sometimes be more effective by serving as consultant and preceptor to people with an existing natural connection with the family, such as empathic relatives, ministers, pediatricians, school counselors, or visiting nurses. He should be responsible for integrating information fed back to him into an evolving picture of the nature of the child's progress.

If this picture turns out to be one of continued regression or developmental arrest despite the multiple channels through which help is being offered, the question of environmental change has to be answered. Brief placements with appropriate relatives, a specially trained foster family or even a children's shelter may give all concerned a breather and allow better functioning after reunion. By and large, such measures often prove less helpful than hoped for because of the chronicity of the family dysfunctioning and the effects of the separations in themselves. Should the prospects be that placement will have to be long-term, it is highly desirable to plan it so as to obviate interim shifts. The setting chosen should be able to provide the child with emotional experiences which will make up the deficiencies he has suffered in the past. A good residential treatment center may be necessary if the children themselves show significant internalized psychopathology. If they do not, it should not be assumed that such a specially oriented and expensive milieu will be the best one for them. Special foster homes with built-in ongoing parent education, counseling, and psychotherapy for the child have demonstrated their value in this regard.[15] Boarding schools, though academically and physically adequate, often emphasize peer relations and social skills at a level beyond that of the child's basic needs.

❰ Consultation and Collaboration

Children are often involved at second hand in the general psychiatrist's other diagnostic, therapeutic, or consultative activities. The extent to which children's interests can be taken into account depends on the nature of the work.

At times, there are technical contraindications in the psychotherapy of an adult to raising or responding to questions about the impact on the patient's children of contemplated life decisions such as initiating a pregnancy, having an abortion, making a move, or separations. Factual information for the patient may then have to come from other sources or be provided by arranging a consultation. How these facts are perceived and dealt with can, of course, be used in psychotherapy as can any other material. For example, they may illuminate unconscious processes originating in the adult's own childhood. In the treatment of parents, the psychotherapist's sensitivity to what his patient is experiencing may be heightened by a knowledge of the phase-specific instinctual pressures, superego conflicts, and problems in socialization which children face and carry over into what they do with and to their parents.

At other times, such as in work with social agencies, the psychiatrist may be asked to evaluate adults as part of decisions specifically related to children's welfare, e.g., placement in adoption or foster care, child custody, or employment. Other professionals usually have screened such adults and refer only those about whom there is concern. The psychiatric evaluation would rely in the customary way on examination of the individual's life history, current adaptation, and whatever can be anticipated from these for future functioning. Here, additional useful dimensions may be drawn from knowledge of the expectable problems in children's development and how they would be reacted to.

Adoption and Foster Care

Adoptive and foster parents share many motivations with those who become (and remain) biological parents. Among these common motivations may be forces aiming at compensation or restitution for their own early life experiences. Such variables could include abandonment, other separations, parents who devoted themselves to others, unusual roles vis-à-vis siblings, positions of esteem in the family, distorting conflicts about discipline or sexuality, frustration of vocational goals, frank psychopathology, etc. Other influences can be traced to events during adult life and in the marriage. A couple may want children to complete the family picture, to solve problems they are having individually or between them, or as an alternative to a currently ungratifying work or social life. The problems these couples have do not differ in number or severity from those of people raising their own offspring. On the other hand, there are psychological features of special importance for nonbiological parents. These, and the fact that their becoming parents entails successive decisions on their part and by social agencies, offer some unique opportunities for preventive psychiatry.

The emphasis here is on factors potentially conducive to maladaptive responses. Those evident in advance of placement should by no means be seen as a priori disqualifying, but rather should be taken into account prognostically. Ideally and ethically, they will be shared in a tactful and professional manner with consultees. In fortunate cases this will help the prospective adoptive or foster parents to clarify their motivations and make the best decision for all concerned. An awareness of such factors may assist in dealing with problems brought to psychiatric attention in the years following placement.

When a couple have become prospective adoptors due to infertility, they will have been confronted by the need for major intrapsychic changes involving self-concept and body-image not infrequently built up in early childhood identifications and fantasies.[40] They miss the months of pregnancy which serve to initiate attitudinal, attachment, and role shifts in biological parents.[5] A comparable period may be provided by the usually lengthy pre-adoption screening and waiting for the baby, if this is not excessive. Questions about successful outcome can be raised during this period by faltering of initial motivation or the decrease of the desire for a child. Taking in someone else's child can be a powerful stimulant to rescue fantasies. Rage at disappointment of these fantasies may be overt; defenses against the rage may lead to inconsistent limit setting. Receiving the baby immediately after birth provides the best opportunity for the mother to engage with it in the emotional symbiosis which is the foundation of close relationships. The father's sharing in this effects the assimilation of the child into the family unity. If the adoption was for the sake of one parent, the way is open for interferences with this process. Some parents may be unable to allow separation-individuation out of fear of losing the child to others. When aggressive and sexual drives become manifest they may be ascribed to the "bad" biological parents, especially if conception was out of wedlock. Social encounters over the years may lead to a need for help with the parent's or child's sense of being different. The defense of denial such experiences can mobilize may set a pattern for handling other family stresses and conflicts, including the fact of adoption itself. In contrast, some parents respond to the continuing narcissistic pain of barrenness and "defectiveness," which may be projected onto the child as well, with a persistent proclaiming of adoptive status. The not uncommon birth of a "natural" child following an adoption may set into motion mechanisms of scapegoating, rejection, or overcompensation of the adopted child which show up in his behavior. Parents may not experience successive reactivation of the earlier periods in their own lives as the child passes through the stages of psychosexual development and continue to relate to him on inappropriate earlier levels. Persistent infantilization may also be resorted to in the service of the wish to stave off adolescence. This period may be exceptionally threatening on a number of counts. Parents may envy the child's (especially the girl's) ability to conceive, at the same time fearing that (s)he will imitate the biological parents by doing so. The weaker incest taboo may bring normal sexual rivalries closer to the surface and repression may fail altogether. A basic threat to parents during adolescence is the chance of the child's putting into action his wishes to find the biological parents. If the child is adopted later, especially after age two, the images of previous parents or surrogates he is carrying around and reacting to intrapsychically may cause him to feel and act like a stranger in his new home.

These same issues affect foster families. Here, however, reality factors create important additional complications.[43] Couples may become foster parents once, or as a career. The mother is generally the dominant figure in recruitment of homes, consideration of children, and dealings with the legally responsible parties. There are usually continuing financial transactions around the children's care. Entry into foster care is on an essentially pragmatic basis. The children are a highly diverse group in age, history, and functional capacity. Many show the signs of neglect, abuse, or family deterioration which led to their separation from their biological parents or relatives. There will often have been other intervening moves or periods of institutionalization in their lives, with the added effects thereof. Placement may be designated as emergency or temporary. Even when it is planned to be permanent, chronic themes of uncertainty and tentativeness may pervade the relationship. These may derive from the constant presence of the monitoring outside agency and/or legal requirements for periodic review and court appearances. The latter, often intended to assure the children's welfare and preserve biological parents' rights, can repetitively stimulate anxious fantasies and clashes of loyalties.

The foster role is socially more painful than the adoptive for both children and parent. Change to the more comfortable relationship may be resisted within the foster family because of the long-term emotional commitment involved. More often it is obviated by the natural parents' wishes and fluctuating status. The children, or what they represent, are important to them. They are not easily given up for adoption even in the face of reality. The natural parents may engage the children in their maneuvers to deal with their own ambivalence, deny loss, and protect their self-concepts. Their intermittent appearances and mixed messages are probably the most potent barriers to the children's being able to work through their own mourning, resolve relationship conflicts, and become able to respond to new opportunities for psychosocial progress.

Such problems have led to serious doubts about the effectiveness of foster care and to calls for its abandonment in favor of professionally staffed residential facilities, especially for children already showing stigmata of disturbed development.[46] Any population of children contains some who do need such settings. Often, however, foster families cope well. An understanding of their specific problems and the needs of a given foster child may be put to surprisingly good use. Data collected during the problem child's often checkered preplacement career can yield insights into his individual makeup, the likely kinds of adjustment difficulties and the frustrations and gratifications parents can expect from him.

Longitudinal observations of couples functioning as foster parents are often at hand to help in identifying their strengths and vulnerabilities. Some may be known to agency professionals as preferring and doing well with children up to age three and then losing interest. Others tolerate aggression well but sexuality poorly or vice versa. Adolescents are fun for some, intolerable for others. Intellectual standards or attitudes toward physical deformity may be highly significant. In certain homes children of any age do well, but each transfer out can be exceptionally painful to all, with depression for the parents and deterioration of behavior for the children. Opportunities thus exist for informed prediction and more precise matching of placements.[34] The phenomenon of foster parents "wearing out" as children grow older, even in the absence of obvious adolescent problems or stress, may direct efforts to make the children's progress toward independence a source of continuing satisfaction rather than the harbinger of eventual aloneness. The psychiatrist's awareness of unconscious meanings and fantasies may contribute to management procedures which better reconcile parents' aims while establishing an emotional kinship with new children with the ongoing responsibilities of social agencies for them. Needs for focused educational or supportive measures may become evident in the light of knowledge about how children mourn and how their idealization of and intent search for old objects may threaten new ones who are offering themselves. In programs with built-in psychotherapeutic resources, such insights may specifically determine when, how, and with whom even the obviously disturbed child begins treatment.

Child Custody

Psychiatric status of family members at times enters importantly into court decisions in cases of family breakup and dispute over custody of the children. This consideration may become more common as legal philosophy and codes evolve in response to new knowledge and social change. The prevailing view has been that mother is indispensable until at least preadolescence. This meant that custody by her was presumed to be in the child's best interests unless proven otherwise, a process often fraught with severe psychic distress to all. There is now a movement toward more flexible definition of the child's "best interests," using meaningful criteria which include the mental health of the competing parents.[4] The psychiatrist's participation in this area can have high preventive and educative value.

The actual assessments of family members might best be as part of a team including specialists in clinical psychology and child development. The work's purpose would be best served by orienting it toward the nature of the parent–child relationships rather than toward static nosologic labeling. The aim would be an understanding of the dynamic interplay between parental functioning and children's individual characteristics and needs, and the probable developmental consequences in the phases ahead. As described elsewhere, the fact that a specific diagnostic finding has or has not been made in a parent is in itself no guarantee of pathological or benign influence on his or her child. The consultant should communicate to the court the result of such an individualized evaluation in a way which demonstrates its rationale, teaches the relevance of the variables, and translates the observations into a conclusion which can be put to use judicially.

Much has been said about the effects of separation from mothers. A word might be in order here about the meaning of father absence, which has been of concern particularly around male children's development. Some approaches to this question have concentrated on sexual preferences in adult life. Employing permutations of masculine-feminine, active-passive, and present-absent factors yields a set of expected outcomes, such as varieties of homosexuality. Other studies have looked at the effects upon boys of father absence in fantasy and behavioral traits during later childhood. The general impression is of increased passivity, feminine identification, and decreased masculine interests. Correlations of teenage delinquency with father absence have received repeated attention. Consequences have also been found in overall academic performance, discrete cognitive deficits, impulse control, and many other areas.

Some caveats should be kept in mind if one is considering application of these many theories and findings to clinical decisions and recommendations. From the research standpoint, the reliability of inferences from a study depends on its methodology and the level it addresses. There are differences in practical terms among: *sex-role orientation* (identification), which taps conscious/unconscious perceptions of male-femaleness; *sex-role preference*, reflecting preferential set toward culturally defined representations of sex-role;

and *sex-role adoption*, which deals with observed social, sexual, and other behaviors. First of all, for many families father absence is in a sense normative. These include not only one-parent households but a number of occupational groups. Secondly, modern family life even in "intact" cases is increasingly matricentric due to home–job distances, female-dominated school systems, reliance on the mother-driven automobile, etc. Finally, the effects on personality development of father's presence or absence cannot be determined in isolation from other factors such as timing and length, the sociocultural milieu, surrogate models, maternal behavior and messages, let alone the quality of his own mental functioning and relationship with the child.

An illustration from the authors' ongoing study of time-limited father absence in the military[3] may serve to point up the complexities in this field. Looking only at masculine identification, it seems that late oedipal-early latency boys proceed along this dimension while the father is away if the relationship with him has been good, the family keeps him idealized, involved in decision making, *and* the mother does not change her preseparation coping style. His return is marked by interference with progressive identification probably due to rearoused rivalries. However, if mother becomes newly active and assertive during the separation, the boy's masculine identification can come to a halt though movement in the feminine direction does not replace it.[11] Father's return is then attended by masculine identification starting up again if he rescues the boy from confusion about the sex-role meanings of the active-passive parameter.

Schools

The school is often the most consistent and sustained extra-familial social setting in a child's life. Especially in mobile or isolated families, other group and community experiences may be tentative or unavailable. School can be where the child has key successes or failures in emotional and social growth. It thus has naturally attracted the interest of professions whose primary areas of concern are other than academic. In addition to their use in specialized psychoeducational facilities, there have been efforts to systematically integrate psychodynamic principles into general education. From time to time, nursery and elementary school programs have been oriented around psychoanalytic theory. Other workers have studied the psychological impacts of teaching styles, family–school interactions, the prediction of academic failure from emotional indices, cultural conflicts, and the value of counseling for academic staff.

Many of the general psychiatrist's basic tools can be used productively in consulting with individual schools or a local system. These include his developmental perspective, ability to tune in to the dynamics of institutional relationships and orientation towards providing children with a network of collaborative supports. The value of these skills is not contingent on a background of full training in clinical work with children. The general psychiatrist can also perform preliminary triage of cases of suspected emotional disturbance, with a back-up specialist for referral when indicated.

The consultant's approach to establishing a relationship with school personnel should respect their special knowledge and experience. The insights he contributes from his own field of expertise are intended to help them use theirs best, rather than as magical pedagogical solutions. It is useful to begin with the working assumption that the school is able to solve most of the problems which its students present. It can also be expected that some children do, in fact, need outside professional attention. However, identifying and referring these individuals should be a step in an orderly, mutual process which begins with making the most of the potentials within the school itself.

The psychiatrist first coming into a school as a consultant is often met by requests to solve its long-standing problems with certain "hyperactive" or otherwise "unreachable" students. This group may contain a number of children who need full-scale diagnostic evaluations. As their problems are discussed, it may

be possible to ask how they have responded to the educators' usual methods for providing learning and social stimulation. Such genuine requests for information by the consultant might in themselves serve to dispel teachers' unwarranted doubts about the validity of their observations and hesitations at making referrals. In other cases, looking at problems afresh can resolve blind spots about a child, clarify how to work with home-based interferences with his school adjustment and remind teachers of ways to reach him. If an outside workup is needed, its findings and recommendations might be "walked back" to the school (with appropriate attention to ethical safeguards). Recommendations can then be mutually and flexibly considered in the light of the resources available and a final academic decision made which resolves impasses on both the child's and the teacher's sides.

As trust evolves from working together around the most difficult cases, the consultant may be presented with less obviously dysfunctional children or asked about general issues in child development and school–home interaction. Such questions may come closer to the school staff's concerns about their own professional adequacy and personal reactions. Again, the consultant's focus should be on problems inherent in the work situation, not in the teacher or pupil personnel worker.

Success in being accepted more fully by a school carries with it the need to be more aware of potential hazards to the ongoing collaborative structure. The consultant is most effective if he continues to be careful to observe the system's ground rules, to work within its communication channels and to use customary professional tact. In time, he may be turned to for guidance about the kinds of teaching programs and relationships which would be most profitable to children of different ages, sexes, and socioeconomic backgrounds. Advice may even be sought about assignment of students to specific teachers the consultant has come to know. Such requests should be met with an eye to his appropriate professional identity and role. Oft-times flattering individual inquiries about direct psychotherapeutic help should be responded to on a similar basis.

❪ Bibliography

1. ANTHONY, E. J. and T. BENEDEK. *Parenthood: Its Psychology and Psychopathology.* Boston: Little, Brown, 1970.

2. ANTHONY, E. J. and C. KOUPERNIK, eds. *The Child in His Family.* New York: Wiley, 1970.

3. BAKER, S. L., L. A. COVE, S. FAGEN et al. "Impact of Father Absence: III. Problems of Family Reintegration following Prolonged Father Absence," (Abstract), *Am. J. Orthopsychiatry,* 38 (1968), 347.

4. BENEDEK, E. P. and R. S. BENEDEK. "New Child Custody Laws," *Am. J. Orthopsychiatry,* 42 (1972), 825–834.

5. BENEDEK, T. "Parenthood as a Developmental Phase: A Contribution to the Libido Theory," *J. Am. Psychoanal. Assoc.,* 7 (1959), 389–417.

6. BLOS, P. *On Adolescence: A Psychoanalytic Interpretation.* New York: Free Press, 1962.

7. BOWLBY, J. *Attachment and Loss:* Vol. 1, *Attachment;* Vol. 2, *Separation.* New York: Basic Books, 1969 and 1973.

8. CAPLAN, G. *Principles of Preventive Psychiatry.* New York: Basic Books, 1964.

9. CHANDLER, C. A., R. S. LOURIE, and A. D. PETERS. *Early Child Care: The New Perspectives.* New York: Atherton, 1968.

10. CLAUSEN, J. A. and M. R. YARROW, eds. "The Impact of Mental Illness on the Family," *J. Soc. Issues,* 11 (4) (1955), entire issue.

11. COVE, L. A., S. FAGEN, and S. BAKER, "Military Families in Crisis: Father Goes to War." Paper presented 46th Annu. Meet. Am. Orthopsychiatr. Assoc., New York, April 1969.

12. EISENBERG, L. "School Phobia," *Pediatr. Clin. North Am.,* 5 (1958), 645–666.

13. ERIKSON, E. H. *Childhood and Society,* 2nd ed., New York: Norton, 1963.

14. ESMAN, A. H., ed. *New Frontiers in Child Guidance.* New York: International Universities Press, 1958.

15. FINE, R. "Moving Emotionally Disturbed Children from Institution to Foster Family," *Children,* 13 (1966), 221–226.

16. FRAIBERG, S. *The Magic Years.* New York: Scribners, 1959.

17. FREUD, A. "The Role of Bodily Illness in the Mental Life of Children," in *The Psychoanalytic Study of the Child,* Vol. 7, pp. 69–80. New York: International Universities Press, 1952.

18. ———. "Assessment of Childhood Disturbances," in *The Psychoanalytic Study of the Child,* Vol. 17, pp. 149–158. New York: International Universities Press, 1962.

19. ———. *Normality and Pathology in Childhood: Assessments of Development.* New York: International Universities Press, 1965.

20. ———. "Indications and Contraindications for Child Analysis," in *The Psychoanalytic Study of the Child,* Vol. 23, pp. 37–46. New York: International Universities Press, 1968.

21. GOLDFARB, W. "An Investigation of Childhood Schizophrenia: A Retrospective View," *Arch. Gen. Psychiatry,* 11 (1964), 620–634.

22. GROUP FOR THE ADVANCEMENT OF PSYCHIATRY, Committee on Child Psychiatry. *Psychopathological Disorders in Childhood,* GAP Report no. 62. New York: GAP, 1966.

23. ———, Committee on Child Psychiatry. *From Diagnosis to Treatment: An Approach to Treatment Planning for the Emotionally Disturbed Child,* GAP Report no. 87, New York: GAP, 1973.

24. GULL, W. W. "Anorexia Nervosa," *Trans. Clin. Soc. London,* 7 (1874), 22–27.

25. HARRISON, S. I. and J. F. McDERMOTT, eds. *Childhood Psychopathology.* New York: International Universities Press, 1972.

26. JOINT COMMISSION ON MENTAL HEALTH OF CHILDREN. *Crisis in Child Mental Health: Challenge for the 1970's.* New York: Harper & Row, 1970.

27. KEMPE, C. H. and R. E. HELFER, eds. *Helping the Battered Child and His Family.* Philadelphia: Lippincott, 1972.

28. LEWIS, M. and P. SARRELL. "Some Psychological Aspects of Seduction, Incest and Rape in Childhood," *J. Am. Acad. Child Psychiatry,* 8 (1969), 606–619.

29. LOURIE, R. S. "The First Three Years of Life," *Am. J. Psychiatry,* 127 (1971), 1457–1463.

30. ———. "The Expectable Problems which

Adolescent Personality Development Faces: Its Tasks and Hazards," *Aust. N. Z. J. Psychiatry*, 7 (1973), 241–248.

31. MORRISON, G. C. and J. G. COLLIER. "Family Treatment Approaches to Suicidal Children and Adolescents," *J. Am. Acad. Child Psychiatry*, 8 (1969), 140–153.

32. NATIONAL CONFERENCE ON CHILD ABUSE, Proceedings. *Clin. Proc. Child. Hosp. Natl. Med. Centr.*, 30 (1974), 35–58.

33. PAVENSTEDT, E. and V. W. BERNARD, eds., *Crises of Family Disorganization*. New York: Behavioral Publications, 1971.

34. PRATT, C. and L. COVE. "The Assembled Foster Family: A Practical Experiment," (Abstract), *Am. J. Orthopsychiatry*, 41 (1971), 269.

35. REXFORD, E., ed. *A Developmental Approach to Problems of Acting Out: A Symposium*. New York: International Universities Press, 1966.

36. ROBINSON, J. F. "The Psychoses of Early Childhood," *Am. J. Orthopsychiatry*, 31 (1961), 536–550.

37. ROLLINS, N. and A. BLACKWELL. "The Treatment of Anorexia Nervosa in Children and Adolescents: Stage 1," *J. Child Psychol. Psychiatry*, 9 (1968), 81–91.

38. RUTTER, M. *Children of Sick Parents*. London: Oxford University Press, 1966.

39. SABBATH, J. C. "The Suicidal Adolescent— The Expendable Child," *J. Am. Acad. Child Psychiatry*, 8 (1969), 272–289.

40. SCHECHTER, M. D. "Psychoanalytic Theory as It Relates to Adoption (Panel Report)," *J. Am. Psychoanal. Assoc.*, 15 (1967), 695–708.

41. SENN, M. J. E. and A. J. SOLNIT. *Problems in Child Behavior and Development*. Philadelphia: Lea & Febiger, 1968.

42. SPITZ, R. A. *The First Year of Life*. New York: International Universities Press, 1965.

43. TAYLOR, D. and P. STARR. "Foster Parenting: An Integrative Review of the Literature," *Child Welfare*, 46 (1967), 371.

44. THOMAS, A., S. CHESS, and H. G. BIRCH. *Temperament and Behavior Disorders in Children*. New York: New York University Press, 1968.

45. WINNICOTT, D. W. *The Family and Individual Development*. London: Tavistock Publications, 1965.

46. WOLINS, M. and I. PILIAVIN. *Institution or Foster Family: A Century of Debate*. New York: Child Welfare League of America, 1964.

47. WORLD HEALTH ORGANIZATION. *Deprivation of Maternal Care: A Reassessment of Its Effects*. Public Health Papers No. 14. Geneva: World Health Organization, 1962.

48. YACOUBIAN, J. H. and R. S. LOURIE. "Suicide and Attempted Suicide in Children and Adolescents," in S. L. Copel, ed., *Behavior Pathology of Childhood and Adolescence*, pp. 149–165. New York: Basic Books, 1973.

CHAPTER 41

MEDICAL PSYCHOTHERAPY: A GENERAL SYSTEMS APPROACH

Chase Patterson Kimball

MEDICAL PSYCHOTHERAPY is the application of psychotherapeutic principles and techniques to the emotional and behavioral responses of individuals who are catastrophically and/or chronically ill.[5] It includes all of the traditional approaches to problems of behavior that fall under the broad label of psychotherapy: psychoanalytically oriented psychotherapy,[71] behavioral therapy,[77] client-centered psychotherapy,[68] psychopharmacology,[52] family therapy,[1] group therapy,[58] and sociotherapy.[20] In short, any interaction between a physician and a patient —frequently without the conscious awareness of either party—carries the potential for a psychotherapeutic relationship.

In this chapter a deliberate effort is made to focus on the general rather than the specific problems encountered by such patients. All of them experience an upheaval in their total psychophysiological equilibrium, requiring adjustments on their part in the spheres of self-concept, family, and community. During the past several decades, investigators have studied a number of disease processes that have long been identified as having major psychological aspects. Franz Alexander's "Holy Seven"[3]—bronchial asthma, hypertension, peptic ulcer,[45,46] neurodermatitis, thyrotoxicosis, ulcerative colitis, and rheumatoid arthritis—still dominate the scene as *the* psychosomatic diseases. Other investigators have demonstrated that diseases such as myocardial infarction,[34] diabetes,[39] and cancer[56,63,64] also have major psychological correlates.

Recently, attention has been focused on the reactions of patients to specific procedures and environments and the experience of illness itself. These studies focus on hemodialysis,[16,17] intensive care units,[53] cardiovascular surgery,[48,51] transplantation,[21] cataract surgery,[74] plastic surgery,[36] burns[4] and chronic pulmonary disease.[2] The reader is referred to the specific sections in Vol. 4 of this *Handbook* for an overview of the literature referable to these conditions.

(The Role of the Psychiatrist in Liaison-Consultation Activities

The subject of liaison psychiatry is discussed in Volume 4, Chapter 36 of this *Handbook*. Since it is difficult to mark the precise division between evaluation and therapy, it is important to reexamine briefly the role of the psychiatrist in the nonpsychiatric inpatient and outpatient services of a general hospital.

Psychiatry is emerging as a collection of several languages through which behavioral problems may be approached. These languages are developing at a prodigious rate, and they extend far beyond the confines of psychiatry to the social and behavioral sciences. The student of psychiatry who is training in a modern academic center needs to learn several of these conceptual approaches if he is to adequately evaluate and identify appropriate therapeutic measures for a variety of behavioral situations. While these approaches are not mutually exclusive, each represents an attempt to view behavior in a logical framework of reference that involves hypotheses, methods, observations, and conclusions. The psychiatrist who uses several conceptual approaches to behavior functions to a large extent as a general systems analyst, selecting one or several models for formulating the diagnostic and therapeutic approach to a specific problem.[6,38]

Among the currently useful models available to the psychiatrist are (1) dynamic psychiatry; (2) behavioral psychiatry (learning); (3) biological psychiatry; and (4) social psychiatry.[55] The model identified here is largely based on dynamic psychiatry. However, it is important to emphasize that these principles

have been applied to patients sustaining catastrophic and chronic illness on the basis of detailed examination of patients with many different illness problems. The therapy of such individuals must always remain particular for the case involved. The therapist must become intimately familiar with the facts of the underlying disease, its treatment, and the relationship between the patient and his physician, as well as with the patient's life situation, personality, and reaction to illness. A general approach is never a substitute for precise attention to the details of a patient's experience.

Compatible with such an approach is the use of pharmacological agents, sedative–hypnotics, analgesics, major and minor tranquilizers, antidepressants, conditioning therapies,[18] hypnosis,[35,76] relaxation therapy,[42] or electroconvulsive therapy. These methods facilitate improvement in certain defined conditions, but they are not alternatives to the psychotherapeutic relationship between the patient and his doctor. Similarly, group and family processes that attempt to define both the commonality and the uniqueness of similar illness experiences are adjuncts rather than alternatives to the one-to-one doctor–patient relationship.

(The Medical–Psychiatric Interview

The interview is the *sine qua non* of the diagnostic and therapeutic approach to the patient.[49] It is the vehicle through which physician and patient establish a relationship which in turn influences the on-going data collecting and therapeutic aspects of the interview. The interview is not restricted to a verbal interchange but is based also on nonverbal communications.[7] Awareness by the physician not only of the patient's facial expressions, hand movements, and changing bodily positions but also of the physician's own nonverbal expressions are essential to understanding what is going on in the interview process. The senses of touch and smell are also useful in collecting data from patients and relating with them.

Together, the verbal and nonverbal processes assist the physician in the essential task of accumulating the data needed to formulate a diagnosis and therapeutic plan. In the process of accumulating the data, he communicates a sense of competency and self-confidence that reassures the patient that the strange and disturbing symptoms and signs of his complaint may be understood and approached. The physician, through listening, allows the patient to express his feelings about these symptoms. He assists the patient in clarifying the chronology and patterns of the illness, which leads the patient toward a more objective observational approach. At the same time, through the explanations of the physician, the patient learns something of the meaning of his complaints.

Determinants of the Interview Process

The medical psychiatrist's work is facilitated by an awareness of what his patient brings to the interview situation. He becomes familiar with his patient's biological predisposition to physical and emotional stress, his life cycle status, and his defensive style. The physician also adds his own determinants to the interview situation. Having this data in mind allows the physician to make more rational decisions about the medical and psychological management of the patient.

THE ILLNESS-ONSET SITUATION

Before considering the medical-psychiatric interview as such, it is of interest to look into some of the hypotheses as to why illness occurs at a given time. Many of these hypotheses will remain touchstones for the physician as he collects the raw data of the interview. Recently, the attention of investigators has turned toward an examination of the multiple factors associated with the onset of illness. Repeated studies emphasize the high correlation between stressful environmental and social situations, psychological reactions, and physiological symptoms and signs.[41,65,66]

Real or symbolic social situations representing *loss* are seen as contributing to changes in psychological status. Engel and Schmale iden-

tify the situation of loss as precipitating the "giving-up—given-up" complex.[26] This is described as: (1) an affect of helplessness or hopelessness; (2) a sense of inadequacy in the ability to cope; (3) a feeling of being trapped; (4) a diminished sense of the future; and (5) a preoccupation with past misfortunes and tragedies. They suggest that in this state the individual exists at greater risk and is more vulnerable to physiological and psychological decompensation. At times of stress, individuals showing this psychological reaction are liable to pathophysiological decompensation of vulnerable organ systems because of concurrent physiological changes. For instance, the individual with structural heart disease, leading to a psychological state associated with an altered state of metabolism, at times of stress, is more likely to develop congestive heart failure than an individual without structural disease.[12] The enlisted soldier with a high serum pepsinogen and significant psychological vulnerability, when exposed to the stress of basic training, is more likely to develop peptic ulcer disease than an enlistee with a low serum pepsinogen and less psychological vulnerability.[73]

The relationship between stress and onset of illness is not only manifest at the time of first occurrence but is also present for exacerbations of the same condition.[67] In the latter situations, it behooves the clinician to attend to possible stimulus–response patterns. An identification of recurrent patterns may lead either to a modification in the social system or to altered responses to similar stimuli. These responses may be learned either through traditional psychotherapeutic techniques, in which the patient becomes aware of relationships and consciously alters them once the conflict behind the bodily response has been uncovered, or through various behavioral techniques. The setting of each recurrent exacerbation of illness needs to be identified in terms of environmental events and psychological reactions that may be associated with the process. In addition to the reaction of the patient to illness, on-going social stresses and his psychological reaction to them may need to be identified, investigated, and therapeutically dealt with by social services as well as by the clinician–therapist.

THE PATIENT AND THE LIFE CYCLE

Another major touchstone in the physician's orientation to the patient is his perception of the patient's place in life.[57] Age, sex, ethnic background, religion, and profession are among the major orienting variables around which the physician develops a picture of the patient (which may or may not be correct). Much of the interview process involves substantiating or deleting the physician's biases that have been based on this picture. Age, for example, immediately elicits a list of possible disease processes that are more or less age-specific. Sex, race, profession, and socioeconomic status increase or decrease the possibility of a specific disease factor, as well as modifying its presentation and the patient's reaction to it. The physician needs to make himself aware of conscious and unconscious prejudices based upon these variables. To the extent that he is able to do this, it will augment his diagnostic acumen and also help to sensitize him to his own reactions to patients.

A knowledge of the life cycle, in such terms as Erikson's[29] "eight ages of man," is helpful to the physician in identifying where the patient is in his negotiations with life. For example, if the physician can recognize that an adolescent with diabetes mellitus may inappropriately use the illness in attempting to cope with those tasks of adolescence identified by Blos[8] (sexual identity, separation from parents, and career projections), this then becomes an essential and frequently the major focus of treatment. Again, it depends upon a physician's knowledge of life cycles as to whether he recognizes that a middle-aged woman experiencing an organ-referable complaint may have a covert depression reflecting an involutional situation (with fears of the consequences of her changing physiology, the "loss" of her children, increasing distance from her husband, and an indeterminate sense of the future).

The coping processes of individuals in relation to catastrophic and chronic illnesses are different at different times in the life cycle, depending also on their previous experiences with sickness. The young person with a congenital heart problem may view himself as having been cheated by his parents and feel that life owes him something.[47] The middle-aged man confronted with debilitating and progressive illness may work out his depressive reactions, with his physician, by identifying the objective tasks he must perform: putting his affairs in order; and providing for the continued well-being of his wife and children.[9]

THE PATIENT AND PERSONALITY FACTORS

Early in the course of the interview, the therapist becomes aware of psychological processes in his patient through which the latter attempts to control and monitor emotion. The emotions and the defenses that serve to regulate the expression of emotion, together with conitive aspects of behavior, suggest patterns that are identified as personality styles. A consideration of such styles is useful for the physician who models his diagnostic and therapeutic evaluation on their early identification.[19]

Personality styles may be regarded as the result of an exaggeration of one or several normal defense patterns, patterns that have become fixed and stereotyped responses to external or internal processes that make an individual feel anxious or otherwise unpleasant. (More recently, the displeasure associated with a depressive reaction has also been conceived as a basic affect state against which the organism defends.[25]) These responses to anxiety and depression serve to bind experiences in such ways as to maintain a relatively stable state, helping to keep in check the unpleasant emotions generated around conscious or unconscious conflicts. When these conflicts come too close to the conscious life of the patient and cause feelings of displeasure, or the displeasure generated by actual experience in conscious life becomes too great, the individual utilizes the defensive patterns that have been useful in the past. These patterns, for our purposes, may be viewed as deriving from both the genetic predispositions and the learned experiences of the individual. The patterns may be considered pathological when they are over-determined in response to the initiating stimulus, resulting in behavior that is maladaptive for the biological and/or social adjustment of the individual.

An individual who reacts to any consciously or unconsciously determined affect of displeasure with a stereotyped, nonselective, rigid set of defenses may be considered to demonstrate a psychoneurosis. The characteristic defenses used by the individual on a repetitive basis in response to stress will serve to identify his neurotic style. All individuals may be considered as having life styles characteristic of and polarizing more closely toward one neurosis rather than another. However, so long as these are effective in maintaining a stable state that is not maladaptive for the individual in most of his life experiences, they are not considered pathological. It is when they are employed inappropriately, at unsuitable times, that they no longer serve adaptively for the individual. Rather, they lead toward disharmony with life, in terms of the individual's inner tranquility and his interaction with the environment. At the same time, it is pertinent to recognize that these styles may serve as a protection against a less adaptive state and further disintegration of the ego.

The Basic Defenses. These are characteristic verbal means whereby an individual attempts to allay or modify the experience of anxiety or depression that occurs in response to conscious external and unconscious internal processes. Of the large number of defenses, the following are presented and grouped for identification and definition.[28]

1. Denial, suppression, and repression are processes used by an individual in attempting to eliminate feelings or thoughts from conscious life that usually give rise to unpleasant affect. The processes may be thought of as being somewhat on a continuum, varying from a deliberate conscious effort to an effort of which the individual is not consciously aware. These terms should necessarily require an identification of what affect or conflict is so being handled. For example, an individual may deny an event such as illness by a flat statement that he is well, or by a failure to acknowledge either to himself or others that he experiences any affect relating to that event. Suppression is a more or less conscious effort to keep from thought an incident that causes the experience of discomfort, whereas repression is a process whereby the conflict that could give rise to a feeling of displeasure is neither consciously identified nor accepted.

2. Intellectualization and rationalization are specific maneuvers that an individual uses in order to avoid experiencing the affect associated with uncomfortable events or the thought of them. The individual binds the event in so many verbal explanations that he is often able to convince himself (auto-suggestion) that there is no need for further concern about this event.

3. Displacement and projection are means by which an individual attempts to rid himself of the affect associated with a conflict, or of the conflict itself, by attributing it to another event or identifying it as actually existing in another individual.

4. Reversal of affect occurs when an individual attempts to deny the real affect experienced in relation to a conflict, and to demonstrate or suggest that he is instead feeling the opposite emotion.

5. Introjection is considered a primitive means of coping with a conflict and with emotion. The individual fails to identify the objective existence of the conflict as only one part of his life. Instead, he incorporates it and elevates it as the central concern of his life, to which all of his actions are related. In other words, the individual comes to represent, or *be*, the actual conflict or situation that has caused discomfort. In doing so, he may be said to become the affect by acting it out, and by so doing he loses his own autonomous ego functioning.

6. Sublimation, in contrast, is a highly sophisticated process whereby the libidinal energies associated with (usually) sexual and aggressive conflicts or events are directed or channeled toward activities and concerns that are adaptive for the individual's security and welfare.

7. Obsessive and compulsive mechanisms

are those defenses whereby the organism attempts to deny or repress conflicts by means of involved, worrisome thought processes or complex, ritualistic physical activity. The obsession or ritual is only symbolic of the repressed conflict.

8. Regression is a kind of mental withdrawal and retreat from the use of more sophisticated defense processes to more primitive ones. The term is essentially an ambiguous one, inasmuch as it refers to both psychological and behavioral processes that do not necessarily correlate with one another.

Many other terms could be listed that identify defense processes and/or the behavior exemplifying these processes. To a large extent, any such activity of an individual may be interpreted as representing a psychological mechanism serving to bind the affect associated with an unconscious conflict and/or as a means of keeping the conflict from the conscious life of the individual. When these activities fail, the individual may be so flooded with the affect associated with the conflict that he can no longer pursue life-facilitating activity. Instead he must seek refuge in an increasing distortion of reality in order to escape from the tortures of uncomfortable affect.

Neurotic Personality Styles. When characterized by increasing rigidity of thought and action, these represent combinations of defense mechanisms that have become so formalized and stereotyped and so pervasive in the life of the individual that they no longer serve the specific defense purpose for which they were originally intended. Instead they are employed indiscriminately by the individual in his interaction in life, thereby becoming inefficient and maladaptive. It is possible to hypothesize an almost infinite number of more or less specific neurotic patterns based upon the various combinations and permutations of basic defenses. However, several investigators[30,43,69,70] have identified personality styles that appear more basic than others and that are pragmatically useful for the clinician, both from the standpoint of diagnosis and therapy. These are: (1) the obsessive-compulsive; (2) the paranoid; (3) the hysterical; (4) the im-

pulsive; (5) the depressive; and (6) the infantile.

Obsessive-Compulsive. The individual with an obsessive-compulsive personality is frequently hard-working, conscientious, industrious, and perfectionistic. His habits are marked by orderliness and stereotypy, his work by rigidity and inflexibility. He cannot accept change, which may in fact cause his behavior to become even more rigid and stereotyped. Things have to be just so. There needs to be a place for everything and everything needs to be in its place. Until this state is achieved the obsessive cannot sit back and rest, and since things are never just right he is always busy, always thinking about something that needs doing. Even when he is sitting still, he needs to somehow be doing two things at once. If he is looking at television, he is also doing something with his hands. While he listens to music his thoughts are far afield, turning to something that he is planning or needs doing. In all that he does there is a sense of urgency, a need to get things done and over with, while at the same time his perfectionism may drive him to exact repetition until things are the way they should be.

There is only one way, one method, one perfection. This one way is dictated not so much by the individual as by his conscience, or superego, which seems to have moved in, dominating and directing his every action. Such emphasis on an idealized perfection frequently interferes with productivity. The inability to deviate prevents innovation. On the other hand, the individual may do extremely well performing technical tasks requiring unswerving attention to detail and rigid adherence to procedure. As long as there is work to be done, a task—anything that will provide a structure for him to organize and direct his activities—he is able to bind his underlying anxieties by compulsive activity. His style of thinking is stimulus-bound, dogmatic, opinionated, and appears unresponsive to anything anyone else may say. This is not necessarily because the other person is disagreed with, but more likely because the obsessive-compulsive is unable to countenance or hear anything that will distract from the thought sequence already in motion. Such an interference would upset everything, resulting in chaos and anxiety.

When not in absolute control of his environment—i,e., when not at home or in a familiar and secure work situation—the obsessive-compulsive experiences a pervasive sense of uneasiness that leads to a stilted social manner and posture, lacking in spontaneity and burdened with perfunctoriness that is made only more acute by the individual's self-awareness. While often opinionated and dogmatic in responding to peripheral issues, the individual, when confronted by a problem central to his own life, is plagued by doubts, reservations, and deliberateness. This leads to indecisiveness, failure to act, frustration, and, finally, anxiety or depression and an awareness of inadequacy, missed opportunites, and resulting loss. The lack of a sense of self is everywhere apparent as the individual attempts—always unsuccessfully—to adopt one role and then another, which, in his continual search for absolute perfection, he disregards in turn because of the failure of each to satisfy his superego demands. He never does anything exactly because he wants to, but rather because he should. This style serves to weave a web in which the individual is eternally entrapped and which prevents him from ever doing anything of his own in his own right, hence assuring that he will never achieve any real satisfaction or gratification.

The more entrenched and formidable these patterns become, the more maladaptive they are, tending to result in increasing purposeless and goal-less activity. The importance of recognizing these styles lies in their prevalence among patients. At a time of illness and of resulting increased anxiety, such patterns usually become exaggerated. The physician who realizes this can help his patient to overcome this anxiety by working with the patient in structuring his illness experience in ways that reinforce the patient's need for control. This is frequently accomplished with a precise outline of what is wrong, what needs to be done, and when it will be done, with gratifying results for both patient and physician. When the neurotic patterns become so formidable as to interfere seriously with the social and domestic functioning of the individual, there is generally a need for further exploration and treatment by a psychiatrist. At times of increased stress, these patients may exaggerate latent phobias that may respond to conditioning therapies if treated early.

Paranoid. The paranoid individual is best characterized by a single word: suspiciousness. He is at every moment on the watch for the overt or covert insult, slight, or potential threat to himself and the world that he has built around him. Such a style attempts to protect him from his sense of vulnerability and penetration. His fear of violation demands that he be ever on guard against all manner of attacks on all sides at all times. To this end he scans word and picture, deed and talk, the slightest movements or sounds in his perceptual sphere, for the personal message they may have for him. The fear (and its underlying wish that he might be slighted or otherwise selected for vulnerability or honor) is projected outward onto the environment, which is always viewed as menacing and hostile.

At the same time as he experiences an omnipresent fear of external control, the paranoid individual exercises intense internal control. There is a lack of spontaneity in his behavior that leads to a loss of affective expression. Constant preoccupation with autonomy leads to a narrowing of behavior. Rigidity and intentionality characterize his external behavior, which is always calculated and frequently gives the impression of being feigned or imitative. Whether the individual gives an external appearance of furtiveness and constriction and suspicious apprehensiveness, of aggressive edginess and arrogance bordering on the megalomaniacal, or of rigid preoccupation, the quality of hypervigilance is ever present. Beneath these facades, almost always hidden from public view, are extreme hypersensitivity and feelings of shame and inadequacy that the externalized projections have been erected to shield.

The paranoid position is both a psychological and a physical one. The individual is in a continuous state of mobilization in preparation for an emergency. In this defensive vigilance there is continual muscular tension. In situations in which the predisposed individual is threatened with real or fantasized injury, these usual modes of perception are exaggerated, leading to a loss of a sense of proportion and to behavior out of context with the social situation. Delusions may occur that dramatize the internal fears of the individual. At the same time there is a frightening intactness and internal logic to the delusion that may escape the unsuspecting physician and may only be detected after talking with the patient's relatives and family.

When threatened with physical injury or discomfort, the paranoid patient exhibits high-level anxieties and defenses. At these times he will view the environment with even more than his usual suspicion and will need very simple, direct explanations from all those working with him to account for what is wrong, what is to be done, and how it will be done. Even then, the physician and staff should be prepared for constant criticism and antagonism from the patient. Understanding that an acutely anxious and sensitive individual exists beneath this facade will tend to alleviate the negative reactions of the staff in response to these projections.

Hysterical. The basic mechanism of the hysterical personality is the repression of underlying conflicts, resulting in emotions that are often out of context and always out of proportion to the environmental or social stimulus. The hysteric lives his life by reacting to stimuli with affect, projecting theatrical, seductive, and exhibitionistic presentations of himself. A single affect, however, is rarely sustained, and the general mood is one of fleetingness and changeability. At times, especially around issues or incidences likely to give rise to affects of displeasure, the hysteric appears unconcerned. This style—the lack of sustained presentation—has caused investigators to note the apparent shallowness of the hysteric's behavior and to suggest an underlying sense of inadequacy and core of depression or emptiness.

The affectual style is matched by an equally superficial cognitive style characterized by a global approach to events—that is, grasping events in their totality by visual impressions rather than by careful and detailed analysis. There is an incapacity for intense or persistent intellectual activity, but rather an exaggerated tendency toward distraction, vagueness, and suggestibility. The hysteric shows an obliviousness to factual detail and an inability to describe things with sharp definition and precision, contributing to an impression of naivete, incredulity, and deficient intelligence. Ideas are not developed but are seemingly pulled out of the air, or they materialize as hunches and are presented in their initial form as accomplished fact. There appears to be a failure in the ability of the hysteric to work through any thought or problem according to traditional logic.

It is suggested that the purpose of this mode of behavior and cognition is to deliberately prevent the individual from taking a look at himself, thus shielding himself from an awareness of the underlying emptiness and uncertainty that he vaguely feels. Such an individual, confronted with catastrophic environmental situations or physical difficulties, reacts in characteristic dramatic ways that are often marked by exhibitionism or indifference. The hysteric may not be able to summon the necessary attitudes for the remediation of problems and may need the reassuring guidance of the physician. This is best provided in a matter-of-fact manner that suggests certainty and allows for the dramatic, though medically irrelevant, productions of the patient. Hysteric patients do not require precise and detailed descriptions of their illness. In fact, they may often become extremely uncomfortable when such descriptions are attempted. The denial utilized by such a patient in regard to his illness (which may interfere with diagnostic procedures or therapy) may require ingenious efforts on the part of the physician to convince the patient, through processes that defy logical explication.

Impulsive. In the impulsive personality, there is an impairment of normal feelings of deliberateness and intention. Individuals with this handicap seem to act on impulse, whim, or urge. Action is unplanned and instantaneous, abrupt and discontinuous. It is as though there were a short circuit between stimulus and response, whether arising internally or externally. Impulsive activity is not limited to small and inconsequential acts. It may also be involved in monumental and frequently catastrophic ones, such as robbing a bank. The incriminated individual may offer the seemingly shallow but matter-of-fact explanation, "I just felt like it," without any show of affect. However, on closer scrutiny, it would seem as though the act itself is a way of handling an affect that is only dimly perceived, never documented. It would also appear that such persons have a low tolerance for frustration or tension.

It may be hypothesized that impulsive personalities lack a discriminatory perception of a range of emotions. Rather, at the time of feeling a vague discomfort, they strike out in a way that often appears antisocial. This has led many to view impulsive individuals as lacking in the development of a superego, or conscience, but on closer scrutiny one is struck with their rigid conformity to the prevailing moral and social code, even in the face of contradictory behavior. This pattern is also reflected in the concrete and passive thinking that is manifested. Odd behavior is explained in terms of having been made to do the inappropriate act by the simple mechanism of projection. That is, because an urge to do something has been felt, this is offered as the complete explanation for the act. The individual's concern rarely extends beyond the immediate boundary of his own existence. There appears to be either an absence of or intolerance for imagination or speculation. Thought is devalued and sacrificed for the physical act, in which there appears to be more compulsion than pleasure.

Because of this, the impulsive person appears to be lacking in the ability to have meaningful and empathic relationships with others. Other people are viewed in terms of their use or compliance in some immediate action at hand. The impulsive person's inability to see himself objectively assures that reflectiveness and revision are not part of his style. Individuals with impulsive disorders may become sociopaths, alcoholics, and drug addicts, because their perceptual and cognitive styles lead to indiscriminatory behavior and dependency on objects outside of themselves. When such an individual is confronted by physical difficulties, both of these results may be exaggerated in the face of rising anxiety and frustration. The physician aware of the predilection of his patient to such actions may allay some untoward precipitous and catastrophic behavior by attempting to anticipate the anxiety. This may be done by simple formulations of what the difficulty is, how it will be investigated and treated, and what the prognosis is, with the physician setting matter-of-fact limits in terms of his own or the hospital's authority. Longer-term care may require frequent, brief reinforcement of the terms of the initial contract between patient and physician.

Depressive. A case may be made for a basic depressive style of life. It is characterized by reacting to internal or external events less with anxiety than depression and less with an active response than with one of withdrawal. It is a style marked by passivity, and one that is easily and readily vulnerable to environmental manipulation. While it contains characteristics also found among the hysteric and impulsive styles, it is less ritualized, less structured, and in many ways more primitive. While many individuals may react with a giving-up—given-up state in the face of insurmountable catastrophes, the depressive is always so predisposed. The precipitating stimulus is frequently mild and sometimes merely imagined. A psychological and physical withdrawal immediately ensues. The psychological stance includes ideations of inadequacy and emptiness, sometimes proceeding to more aggressive self-condemnation. More often, expression is given to fears of being left, abandoned, or ignored, and to attitudes of helplessness or hopelessness.

Depressive individuals are inordinately dependent on external supplies coming from others in the environment and seem to have an omnipresent fear that these will be denied them for one reason or another, usually because they feel undeserving. Their whole life style appears to be one of assuring an ever-present supply, and their behavior is a manipulative attempt to achieve this. Their behavior is marked by a passive aggression that defies the environment to deny them their just but undeserved due. Since they are always fearful that external resources will be withdrawn and that they will come face to face with their own emptiness, much of their cognitive style is aimed at achieving involved and symbiotic relationships with others. When there are no others around with whom to make these involvements, the search for refuge from internal feelings of displeasure may lead to dependence on drugs or alcohol. When there is a sense of total abandonment, the characteristic posture is one of helplessness; and when this is not effective in securing the attention and help of others, a hopelessness may ensue that defies help.

The passivity of this state is not without aggressive manipulation, which is directed both at the self and others. The individual entrapped in it is vulnerable to his own destructive acts as well as prey to persons who would take advantage of him for their own purposes. It is more than likely that the depressive state itself has correlative biological aspects that make the individual more vulnerable to the environment. At times of physical illness, the patient with this predilection gives up and becomes entirely dependent on the environment. He may do this even while maintaining the semblance of independence through defiance. The depressive state thus calls for a reassuring, sympathetic, nurturing attitude on the part of the physician and nursing staff, who may also have to decide to what extent regression is to be allowed. The description presented here should not suggest that these individuals lack perception or even great capability at times when they are not faced with the threat of diminished external supplies.

Infantile. The infantile personality described by Ruesch[69] is mentioned here because it contains characteristics that have been given for the preceding five. Thus the infantile personality is more amorphous and results in less rigid, formalized, and consistent patterns of cognition and behavior. Ruesch identified it as the core problem in psychosomatic medicine, listing its characteristics: (1) arrested or faulty social learning; (2) impaired self-expression channeled through either direct physical action or organ expression; (3) a persistence of childhood patterns of thinking and ideation; (4) dependency and passivity; (5) a rigid and punitive conscience; (6) overextended ideals; and (7) an absence of the ability to integrate experience. Ruesch, less concerned with specificity factors, did not offer an explanation as to why one organ system rather than another was chosen for the expression of conflict. Rather, he outlined a therapeutic approach—rare in the history of psychosomatic medicine—for physicians working with patients having infantile or immature personalities. This included: (1) reeducation through benevolent firmness; (2) instruction of the patient as to the manipulative and implicit content of his complaint; (3) reduction of long verbal productions to single words or sentences concerning problems; (4) externalization of feelings and emotions as objectifications in their own right, rather than resorting to organ expressions and complaints; (5) acceptance of the patient himself as a psychological and biological entity distinct from others; and (6) the model of the physician as a consistent, accepting, available, and self-expressive person.

PHYSICIAN-RELATED DETERMINANTS

The physician also introduces his person into the interview situation, in terms of both his physical presence and his personality. An awareness of the effect his physical presence, its appearance, and his personality may have on a patient will help him to understand the various forms that the relationship takes. He may in time learn to use these in a facilitative way in relating with his patient.

The physician also comes to the interview with various feelings that may determine its course. He may be rushed, preoccupied with other problems, hungry, or fatigued. As far as possible, he needs to attend to these feelings in order to be comfortable and relaxed during the ensuing interview. At times it may be appropriate to communicate some awareness of these pressures to the patient.

The physician likewise comes to the interview with prejudices and biases related to his stage in life, sex, social position, religion, ethics, and politics. Each one of them consciously or unconsciously intrudes upon his relationship with the patient. An identification of these biases as they affect his relationship with the patient is a necessary part of the physician's task. Added to this are the biases generated in the physician by the patient's own sex, social position, and so forth. The latter biases will need to be identified and objectified as fact or nonfact during the course of the interview.

Generally and specifically, the physician–therapist, in the course of his relationship with patients, will identify with a patient in a number of ways. The identification may be in terms of life stage, problems, sexual attraction, and/or the patient's reaction to illness. Becoming aware of and acknowledging the identification is the first step in evaluating its adaptive or compromising effect on the patient–physician relationship. Once aware of the feelings and secondary defenses generated by this identification, and with the conflicts involved, the therapist is in a better position to be objective. The awareness by the physician of identification or of other defenses will lead him to an assessment of their applicability in a constructive patient–physician relationship. In some physician–patient relationships, the identification itself may be utilized in a positive way, especially if it leads to empathy.

There are many patients, illness processes, and procedures that are anathema to a physician. An analysis of these reactions by the therapist will be required if a relationship is to evolve. Physicians react with the same basic emotions and defend against these feelings with the same defenses as their patients do. Attitudes towards chronicity, debilitation, and death are also present in physicians, although

usually rigidly defended against, and they may need help in coming to a recognition of these feelings and reactions. A psychiatrist who works with physicians caring for patients with catastrophic and chronic illnesses will assist them in this process of awareness. In turn, the psychiatrist participating with his colleagues in such a process will need assistance in working through his own feelings and defenses in regard to many of the problems on which he is asked to consult.

The Extended Interview as Medical Psychotherapy

Medical psychotherapy commences with the initial medical interview, which is the vehicle for the therapeutic process.[49] Crucial to the success of the relationship and accumulation of data that are the objectives of the interview are: (1) making sure that the patient is as comfortable as possible; and (2) assuring an environment that is a quiet one in which distractions are minimal and confidentiality is assured. The interview begins with the contract, which is both implicit and explicit. Both physician and patient have implicit expectations about each other. The patient has a complaint and sees the physician as someone who can diagnose and subsequently alleviate suffering. The physician sees the suffering patient as someone who seeks him out in the anticipation that suffering will be alleviated, based on the former's application of knowledge and skill.

The psychiatric physician referred to a nonpsychiatric patient may come to the initial interview with extensive information about the patient's condition and the referring physician's reason for the consultation request, but he needs to view his relationship with the patient as commencing in the here and now. The consultant's first task is to make himself aware of and attentive to the patient's comfort before beginning the formal interview. It is also important that he make the situation as acceptable as possible to his own needs. Bedpans may need to be removed from under patients and emptied, television turned off, doors closed, beds raised, and so forth. The consultant must try to understand what is going on at this moment with the patient in his attempt to adjust to his altered state of health. He may open the dialogue with a simple question such as "How are you feeling?" or "Can you tell me about your illness?"

From this point on, the physician's task is to stay with the patient, following his lead in focusing on the seemingly random and spontaneous subject matter brought into the interview. Whatever the patient introduces into the conversation is data for the physician in his effort to understand what is going on. Not only is it the physician's task to accumulate verbal data, he must also consider the manner in which this material is discussed, and with what emotion; when it is presented in the course of the interview; and whether or not the verbal identification reflects the actual circumstance. In listening to the words, he needs to listen also to their possible other meanings.[37] He must always observe the patient's facial expression, his posture, the attitude of the body, and the use of hands and feet. Do the emotional expressions of affect match up with what is being said? At the same time, the physician has the opportunity to observe the general environment of his patient, the disarray of the bed clothes, the orderliness of the bedside table, the reading material scattered on the floor, the carefully aligned slippers next to the bed.

The dialogue frequently begins with the patient's immediate illness problems. This is what the patient is feeling and what he is most interested in talking about. Allowing the patient to speak freely about his illness accomplishes several therapeutic objectives: it suggests the patient's ability to cope with his feelings about catastrophic illness; and it provides the physician with important facts about the illness, its onset, its course, and the negotiations that have already taken place in the patient's acceptance and partial resolution of this event. At this stage of the interview, the psychiatrist may facilitate this process by helping the patient focus on: (1) the symptoms and signs of illness; (2) the setting in which the illness occurred in terms of the environment; (3) who was present at the time of illness; (4) the steps taken by the patient to remedy his discomfort and secure assistance; and (5) what the patient thought was happening. A precise description by the patient of these aspects of the illness assists the physician in gaining an understanding of the illness. Simultaneously, through this process of clarification, as the patient orders his experience into objectified awareness, he can stand at some distance from it and join with his therapist in the slow process of making the necessary adaptations.

THE GRIEVING PROCESS AS A THERAPEUTIC MODEL

Catastrophic illness comes as a shock, especially for the individual with little illness experience. It brings in its wake the slow realization of vulnerability and mortality. Illness represents a loss. It is responded to by the patient in ways partially predictable from his defensive style and partially determined by the more or less predictable process that begins with any such loss, or threatened loss. The psychological reaction to loss may be conceptualized as a bereavement, or grieving, process. Assisting the patient through the grieving process in terms of the extended interview is the core of medical psychotherapy. The process[24,59] is conceptualized as having four phases: (1) denial; (2) ventilation of affect; (3) defensiveness; and (4) reconstitution. Although these may be seen as sequential, they overlap and recur with diminishing intensity over a period of time with the patient's gradual acceptance of and resignation and adaptation to the losses and limitations incurred by the illness. Specific techniques, useful in assisting the patient to work through this process, are identified.[11,13]

Denial. During the early phase of illness, the patient may often deny his illness or deny the feelings that he has about illness. Denials of illness, or of the affects associated with illness, often involve delay by the patient in obtaining assistance or his refusal in accepting appropriate medical intervention.[10] Until this denial is confronted, life-saving efforts by physicians may be thwarted, resulting in deterioration in the patient's condition and engendering frustration and hostility, at first, on the part of the attending physician. Such patients need to be directly confronted with their condition in matter-of-fact terms, at the same time allowing for and giving permission for the ventilation of anxiety, sadness, and anger. It is not until the denial is confronted and broken through that the patient will begin to accept his condition and engage in the treatment process.

Ventilation. In Western society, particularly in the hospital environment, the process of ventilating unpleasant affects such as anxiety, sadness, and anger is difficult for patient and professional staff alike. Patients (men more frequently than women) attempt to repress or displace emotions attendant to catastrophic illness and the dislocations that such illness brings about in their lives. Similarly, physicians and nurses, in an attempt to maintain distance and objectivity as well as to preserve their own equanimity, all too frequently attempt to suppress the expression of emotion by patients. It is often necessary to give permission to the patient to express his feelings. This may be done by asking the patient how he feels or suggesting that he does not look very comfortable. Once the patient has begun to express his feelings, the physician needs to resist his own inclinations to intervene with reassurances, the proffering of a tissue, or a defense against the anger that the patient may be directing toward him. Rather, whatever techniques the physician has learned that can help him to facilitate expression by the patient will enhance his therapeutic prowess at this stage. Silence at such times is often of great value, especially when facial expressions communicate "It is all right" or "I understand." Ventilation of emotion may need to be a daily process until the patient has begun to find adequate coping processes for coming to grips with his condition.

As the physician follows the patient's lead in eliciting an account of the present illness, he will note frequent reference by the patient to other illnesses, other life events, other persons. That these facts and feelings are introduced at a specific time in the interview is always pertinent and should be further identified at that point by simple repetition, such as "Your father . . ." or "You say you were seven when you had your appendix out". . . . In this way the therapist is assisted in extending back in time his knowledge of his patient as a person, while noting the past associations that the patient makes to his present circumstance. An interview conducted in this manner does not regiment a patient's presentation of himself along a stereotyped history form. It allows for the easy backward and forward movement of the individual along the life continuum. If the physician finds it useful to structure the content of the interview either on the basis of chronology or in some other way, he may do this periodically during the interview or at the end of it by a succinct summary. Summarization allows the physician to order his own thoughts, with the patient in attendance to make appropriate addenda and corrections. It also serves to communicate to the patient that he has been heard and that some ordering and sense has been made out of his complaint.

Subsequent interviews with the patient may begin by asking how the patient is feeling and frequently may progress through sequences similar to but more abbreviated than earlier ones, with particular points explored in greater detail. Again, emotional correlations with verbal presentations are compared, and the ventilating process is facilitated. As the relationship between physician and patient develops through identification of the personality traits and the particular life history of the patient, increasing attention may be directed toward the defensive patterns used by the patient in handling his feelings about his illness. The initial denial and anxiety characterizing the early phases of catastrophic illness are always present, but they become less marked. They are replaced by a second phase characterized by sadness (and sometimes other aspects of depression) and by defenses characteristic of the patient's personality prior to illness.

It is during this phase, when anxiety and sadness may be overwhelming—especially for patients also afflicted with an impairment of cognitive processes and in the unfamiliar environment of an intensive care unit—that psychotic-like delirium may be precipitated. The psychological significance of this behavioral state may be that it represents the last defense the individual has against the multiple insults of the illness and the environment. Patients demonstrating such behavior frequently are seen to emerge from the interlude with ventilation of affect still to be accomplished.

The sadness of the second phase of self-grieving is frequently difficult to assess. It may be characterized by many of the phenomena associated with grieving subsequent to loss, which is appropriate for catastrophic illness. The patient is indeed now grieving for a loss of a part of self in terms of function and role. The symptoms and signs of this stage of grieving include many of those associated with depressive syndromes: vegetative signs comprising disturbances in appetite, sleep, libido, and body symptoms; and mental feelings of inadequacy, inability to cope, despair, hopelessness or helplessness, inability to project a future, and, sometimes, suicidal preoccupation. These features have been variously conceptualized as reactive depression, the giving-up—given-up state,[26] depression–withdrawal,[25] and reactive withdrawal. The degree and intensity of the symptoms and signs are perhaps the clearest guides for the clinician as he evaluates the significance of this stage in the patient's illness. This is best done by the frequent and close observation of the patient, and especially by attending to his verbal behavior.

Following major surgery, during the second week, it is not unusual to observe a patient who turns away from family, friends, and the physician, sleeps long hours, eats minimally, and reacts to solicitations with irritability and annoyance. This behavior is especially ungratifying to clinicians who have, in their own minds, triumphantly attended the patient through the critical period, and is viewed as both undesirable and possibly pathological. Many of these patients are in fact communicating that they are aware of their behavior, that they are worn out, that they feel that they have "made it," and that all they want to do is to be left alone. They feel a need to withdraw (lick their wounds) and can do so quite well

in private. This response, viewed as a form of conservation–withdrawal,[25] appears both psychologically and perhaps even physiologically appropriate to acute exhaustion and trauma. Such a phase is self-limited and may cease more or less abruptly during the third week of convalescence.

When more depressive elements are present, the possibility of a reactive depression and/or the giving-up—given-up syndrome must be considered. The intervention of the clinician in this state is appropriate. Depression may suggest that the patient has not moved through the second phase of grieving (ventilation of affect), and is attempting to repress these feelings by inappropriate defenses such as anger turned inward, guilt, and projection, which lead to maladaptive behavior interfering with recovery. The therapist may need to reopen the wounded ego, allowing once again for the outpouring of anxiety, anger, and sadness before he can assist the patient into the third stage of grieving, that of ascending the scale of defenses.

Defensiveness. In the third stage, the reaction of the patient to catastrophic illness and loss is seen as having progressed from denial through ventilation of emotion to the use of increasingly sophisticated defenses in the control of affect. This defensive stage is viewed as one in which the patient ascends from denial, shame, guilt, projection, displacement, identification, rationalization, intellectualization, and other defenses to attain sublimation. Again, this is an approximate process, with as many regressions as forward steps. It is rarely accomplished during the acute hospitalization period, and much remains to be done at the time of discharge to the continuing care unit, the convalescent or nursing home, and, even later, upon return to social and community roles. Coincident with the more sophisticated psychological processes involved in handling the emotion generated by reaction to illness are the actual coping steps taken by the patient in facilitating his own rehabilitation and adaptation. The clinician's task during this phase of therapy is to work with the patient in sorting out the adaptive and maladaptive defenses and coping styles. Inappropriate defenses may need to be met by directly confronting the patient with their maladaptiveness or, indirectly, by giving him an opportunity to examine examples of his behavior or that of other patients with similar conditions. Confrontations may lead the clinician to the identification of new or old unconscious conflicts that have been brought nearer to consciousness because of illness. Some of these may be identified by listening for the patient's reports of dreams, whose manifest or near-manifest content is frequently profuse and vivid during this period. Depending on the seriousness of these conflicts and their nearness to the patient's present life-field they may deserve immediate attention or may be deferred until a later time for definitive investigation and treatment. During this phase of the therapeutic process the therapist helps the patient gain self-reassurance by exploring with him the positive assets of self, in terms of previous accomplishments, family, and social relationships.

Since many of the problems confronted by patients during the convalescent stage of illness are realistic ones, didactic approaches are of considerable value. Often these approaches have been used with groups of patients with similar disease processes.[75] Groups serve to assist the patient in identifying with other individuals in a similar situation and to begin to exchange confidences as well as sometimes useful methods of coping with a disability. Therapists working with these groups can introduce didactic instruction regarding the dos and don'ts of treatment, some common problems met by patients with a particular handicap, problems encountered by spouses, sexual counseling, and reintegration problems at home and work. Individual family counseling has also been useful. It provides an opportunity for the therapist to work with a family in exploring the emotions and attitudes experienced by individual members in reaction to the patient, the shifts that have occurred in the home as a result of an absence, and the readjustments and problems that are and might be anticipated on the return home. Follow-up visits by the therapist in the home help the family and clinician to monitor the

reintegration process. For many patients with chronic and extraordinary illness processes, the formation of special groups such as Mended Hearts, Ileostomy Clubs, Prosthesis Clubs, and so forth, proves helpful in continuing this process of identification and sublimation by providing consultation services to other patients undergoing similar procedures.

Reconstitution. The final stage of grieving, that of reconstitution, rarely occurs in the hospital or during the immediate hospital period. It may never occur, or it may develop slowly through long and frequently painful months of rehabilitation. It is perhaps best epitomized by that individual who actively and constructively utilizes his handicap in helping others with a similar condition to pull through. Such an individual may continue to require therapy from time to time, but frequently he has learned to provide some of this himself through his ability to empathize with the experiences of others and to hear their problems without resurrecting his own resolved ones.

Throughout this process, the usual unspoken but omnipresent stance of the therapist is one of hope, of affording the suggestion of working together with the patient toward improvement in the patterns of coping.[32,33]

(Specific Psychiatric Problems on Medical Floors

Conversion

Conversion processes are among the most challenging and interesting problems confronting consulting psychiatrists on the medical, surgical, and obstetrical floors. These frequently show themselves as pain.[23] They are often unsuspected and undetected by physicians until after elaborate and sometimes traumatic investigative and operative procedures have failed to identify a pathophysiological basis for the illness. It is at this point that a psychiatric consultation is requested. In his interview with the patient the consulting physician may first be struck by the somewhat bizarre language with which the patient de-

scribes his symptoms. For example, a headache may be described as "seven little men
inside my head hammering away." Subsequently the therapist may identify that the
pattern of the symptom is atypical in terms of
the usual physioanatomical presentation. In
one patient, there may be glovelike anesthesia
of the hand and wrist (*i.e.*, loss of feeling
which defies neurophysiological explanation).
In another, the therapist may note an affect of
relative indifference to a paralysis, known as
"la belle indifference." In yet another, he may
be impressed by a dramatic affect discordant
with what would seem a relatively minor
symptom. As the illness-onset situation is explored, the clinician may discover a time correspondence with a major social stress or a
circumstance whose significance or even occurrence may have been and may still be
denied by the patient. For example, after several interviews, the patient may suddenly recall that he had totally wrecked his automobile
the day before the onset of symptoms. The
identification of the illness-onset situation,
once again, reveals an event of actual or symbolized loss and vulnerability. The loss may be
reacted to with the same grieving response
described above, in which denial is subsequently replaced by more sophisticated defenses. During the third stage of grieving the
process of *identification* occurs, a process
sometimes manifested by a conversion reaction in which the bereaved attempts to "hold
onto" the lost person by adopting one or more
of his traits, including symptoms of illness.
Conversion reactions are also quite frequent
during depressive states, especially those accompanying involutional periods. A woman
experiencing difficulty at menopause may develop itching or pain in the perineal area,
which on further investigation is found to
symbolize her concern over loss of reproduc-
tive functions.

The interpretation of the symptom is crucial
to therapy involving a patient with a conversion process. A model almost always exists for
this symptom. The model may be the dead
person or another key individual in the individual's past or present life, a person about
whom unresolved conflicts persist. Sometimes

the patient himself serves as the model, in
terms of utilizing a previously elaborated
symptom for which there is no identifiable
pathophysiology—much like the dog who,
having at some time in the past injured his leg,
now feigns an injured leg when scolded. Often
patients with chronic disease patterns associated with symptoms such as angina pectoris or
dyspnea, superimpose conversion reactions
modeled after these symptoms. For example,
the patient with a classic history of angina
pectoris may develop a conversion pattern
based on this, with pain over the left nipple.
The reactions, however, are rarely identical,
although it takes a precise description in order
to differentiate one from the other.

Secondary gains relating to conversion processes are examined last, only because it is all
too easy to identify manipulative aspects related to illness. The best example of a secondary gain is probably that of the school child
who awakens with a stomach ache and is kept
home from school, and upon recovering has a
perfectly great day at home with mother. The
stomach ache may then begin to recur with
increasing frequency, resulting in both a
shorter period of resolution and more days
spent at home.

In considering pain, the physician needs to
be simultaneously aware of both the universal
and the idiosyncratic, or private, experience of
pain for the individual.[72] Universal pain may
direct both the physician's and the patient's
attention to a physioanatomical conceptualization. Private pain is endowed with subjective
characteristics that are based upon the individual's unique ways of responding to pain,
the memories he has of other pains, and the
expectations that he has of others in responding to pain.

SYMPTOM FORMATION

Symptom formation in conversion processes
is theoretically as well as pragmatically interesting, as investigators attempt to obtain a
clearer understanding of how mental conflicts
come to be manifested in physical symptoms
or processes. One way of viewing conversion
processes is to see them as the physical symptoms of psychological illness. From the above

examples one might speculate that at some time in a patient's past, a memory trace related to a traumatic event has been established that is recalled or reinvoked when a new stress occurs in which the old trauma, or conflicts about that trauma, are resurrected. A possible mechanism for the sensitization of nerve-possessing structures that are secondary to psychological conflict is the antidromic phenomenon. That is, when the distal end of a sectioned afferent nerve is stimulated, an antidromic impulse occurs, resulting in the peripheral release of substance P, kinins, and histamines at the nerve ending. In this situation, in which a definitive physiological change may be observed, there is at least a model for possible psychophysiological mechanisms. Accordingly, it is possible to hypothesize that neurophysiological processes secondary to psychological activity in the frontal lobes could bring about such an antidromic response along afferent (and other) nerves innervating organ systems.

An extension of the conversion hypothesis to include the autonomic as well as the voluntary nervous system suggests that conversion processes and psychophysiological reactions may be similar processes.[27] In each, the end organ selected is based upon a sensitized or vulnerable organ system that is used for the expression of an unconscious conflict. The reaction attempts to resolve an unconscious conflict— symbolizing simultaneously the wish for and the defense against its actualization and ultimate resolution—by channeling it through a body process and thereby keeping it from consciousness. For example, a 33-year-old Catholic speech therapist and father of six changed jobs in order to increase his income, and for the first time he drastically altered his marital relations in order to preclude the possibility of another child. Shortly thereafter he developed paralysis of the left upper extremity. As the history unfolded, it was noted that the man had previously worked with hemiparetic patients. Shortly after assuming private practice, he enrolled a 19-year-old woman in therapy. He saw her at her home in the early evening. Arriving at the home, he would be greeted by the woman's mother and

escorted into the parlor, where he would place his tape recorder on a coffee table in front of the couch, sitting to the right of the patient. As speech therapy progressed, he began to arrive earlier and earlier and, as his wife later noted, began wearing his best suit. Presented to a neurologist, he was finally diagnosed as having multiple sclerosis. The above information was obtained through six interviews, during which time the patient's symptoms gradually diminished as he became increasingly conscious and accepting of the conflict situation and of the underlying emotions.

When a majority of these criteria are fulfilled, the diagnosis of a conversion reaction can be entertained on positive grounds, rather than by the exclusion of pathophysiological processes after elaborate and oftentimes traumatic diagnostic and therapeutic approaches.

In many ways, the phenomenon of hyperventilation (often accompanied by aerophagia) may be conceptualized as a conversion process, fulfilling the criteria suggested above. In hyperventilation, the model is often the individual. There would seem to be a learned element in the development of this process, possibly extending back to the early difficulty in coordinating the complex acts of breathing and sucking-swallowing during nursing. In any event, an environmental situation symbolizing an internal repressed conflict triggers this common response, precipitating the symptoms of hyperventilation described by the patient: light-headedness; dizziness; wooziness; tremulousness; shortness of breath; tightness in the chest; "pins and needles" in the extremities; and muscle cramps. Signs of the condition include fainting, muscular spasms, rapid shallow respirations, yawning, sighing, and occasionally coughing. Hyperventilation is sometimes also seen in individuals complaining of *globus hystericus*, the symptoms of which are: a lump and tightness in the throat; an inability to swallow; and signs of gagging, regurgitation, and spitting. The latter condition still is seen most commonly among individuals who have conflicts over participating in fellatio,[31] although in some individuals it would seem to relate more to an attempt to repress crying and even the production of tears. Although several traumatic situations may serve as models for the hyperventilation syndrome, a frequent one appears to be the first sexual experience. Situations that stir unconscious associations with this experience and its unresolved conflicts precipitate the symptoms (and, secondarily, the signs) related to physiological changes induced by hyperventilation. A careful exploration, first of the symptoms and then of the situation, leads the therapist and his patient to a diagnosis. Frequently, over a few sessions, they reach an understanding of the dynamics of the process, including the secondary gains.

Hyperventilation is only one of several conversion processes in which symptoms that lead to physiological reactions re-enact the drama of an original situation that produced conflict around sexual situations. Many of the symptoms experienced among middle-aged men and women, when further investigated, reflect unresolved sexual conflicts. These include frigidity, impotency, infertility, dyspareunia, premature ejaculation, inability to achieve orgasm, and other complaints referable directly or indirectly to the genital apparatus.[14,15,60] The specific nature of the unconscious conflicts is varied. The conflict may have been satisfactorily handled for years with acceptable sexual practices until some disequilibrium becomes introduced into the marital situation, not the least of which may be aging or the pressure of adult responsibilities and obligations. Many parents of adolescents find increasing anxiety about their own sexuality as they witness the development of sexuality in their children and the vicarious identifications that are projected. Symptoms of sexual dysfunction in this age group may be part of a greater decompensation of ego functions, such as depression or the increasing use of alcohol or other addicting drugs for whatever reason. Rarely can single determinants be identified as the *raison d'être* of these "middle-aged syndromes." The relationships are complex and cyclical, reflecting one or more disbalances in the current life cycle that resurrects conflicts previously held in check by adaptive mechanisms. Attention by the therapist to the total life field will assist him in determining which

of the problems requires priority in treatment. Frequently, this will be depression, which, once diagnosed, can be approached by a variety of therapeutic routes—frequently a combined pharmacological and psychotherapeutic one.

THERAPY OF CONVERSION

As suggested above, the therapy of conversion begins in the interview process of listening to the patient's account of his illness, and taking note of the atypicalness of the symptom, the bizarre language with which it is described, the dramatic or unconcerned affect, the identification of recent loss, the presence of a model, the underlying psychopathology such as grief or depression, and secondary gains. As the therapist explores these aspects in detail over six to twelve sessions, the patient frequently begins to develop some insight into the relationship of the onset of the symptom with significant contemporary stresses in his life field. Not infrequently in this process he will experience an *abreaction*; that is, the repressed conflict suddenly comes into consciousness along with the outpouring of intense emotion, anger, sadness, or anxiety. The therapist often first gains a handle on this process by helping the patient to become aware of the repressed grief experience or of an underlying depression. By focusing the attention of the patient on his grief or depression and working with this over several sessions, the therapist assists the patient in expressing these feelings.

With this expression of affect, the underlying conflict is brought to consciousness. The therapist is then in a position to help the patient work through the four stages of grief described above. When a depression is uncovered, the therapist can address his attention to it by using psychopharmacological agents such as the tricyclic antidepressants, or electroconvulsive therapy, while continuing the psychotherapeutic process. Frequently the dramatic abreaction does not occur, and insight by the patient into the conversion process is more slowly attained. Rather, the therapist gains remediation of the symptom complex through the use of suggestion and by helping the patient to gradually translate the symptom representing body language into an appropriate psychological concept such as depression or grief.

Cognitive Impairment

Early in the course of an interview, a patient may appear a bit slow in responding to the morning greeting, show some confusion when asked questions about events occurring on the previous day, have trouble following the physician's explanations, yawn, and answer slightly irrelevantly in a slow speech. The patient may be showing signs of mild confusion, inattention, and memory deficits. A review of the nurses' notes may turn up greater confusion, with disorientation in terms of time, place, and person—especially during the evening, which is suggestive of the so-called "sun-downer" syndrome in older patients. The patient is, in fact, suffering from delirium.[22] One way of viewing delirium is as the psychological symptom of a physical process. Two of its essential characteristics are: (1) fluctuations and reversibility; and (2) a characteristic EEG pattern, with slowing and decreased amplitude of the alpha rhythm. In contradistinction, chronic organic brain syndromes (usually related to permanent morphological changes in the brain) are irreversible, and they present varying EEG patterns (including normal ones).

Signs

A brief examination at the bedside may help the physician uncover (1) *disorientation* in one of three areas—person, place, or time; (2) *memory impairment*—more often in the areas of recent and immediate recall (as in giving back numbers backward and forward) and less often in relation to the distant past. For immediate recall it is important to choose the numbers randomly and to space them equally in a monotone without identifying the ending. (Incidentally, it is helpful to have the numbers written down so that the examiner remembers them.) Another test for immediate recall is to ask the patient to count from one to twenty-two; then, after a three-minute wait to

ask him to continue counting for three more numbers. For a test of recent memory, having the patient identify some of the events of the previous day will do. (3) *Attentiveness* and *concentration* may be tested by asking the patient to subtract seven from 100 and then seven from this answer and to continue doing so in the same pattern. If seven from 100 seems too difficult, three from 100 will do; even less difficult is the test of counting backward from twenty by twos. The significance of this test is that once the patient has started, he provides his own cues and does not rely on the stimulus of the examiner. Impairments in attention and concentration are frequently difficult to pick up unless tested for specifically. And (4) *Impairment in abstractive ability* may be spotted in the form of faulty reasoning in a patient's judgment concerning his daily activity. It may also be tested for by asking the patient to complete standard proverbs such as "A rolling stone . . ." or by asking him to find similarities, working from rather simple ones such as "How are an apple and an orange the same?" to difficult ones such as "How are a tree and a fish the same?"

On the basis of this brief examination the clinician may satisfy himself as to the presence and quality of intellectual impairment in the areas of orientation, memory, concentration, and abstraction. When required, more formal and extensive testing is available, such as the Wechsler Adult Intelligence Scale (WAIS) Block Design Test, the Bender Test, and other tests. A convenient test is to ask the ten questions of Kahn and Goldfarb,[44] which may be used daily to identify changes in the mental status: (1) Where are you now? (2) Where is that? (3) What are today's date and day? (4) Month? (5) Year? (6) How old are you? (7) When were you born? Month? (8) Year? (9) Who is the President of the United States? (10) Who was President before him? A checklist of symptoms frequently associated with delirium has also been found useful in intensive care units.[51] On a five-point scale, nurses rate the status of eleven items: orientation, alertness, sleep, activity, appropriateness, anxiety, complaints, agitation, delusions or hallucinations, confusion, and mood. With ratings from the three nursing shifts, time fluctuations for the various factors can be identified easily.

The changes observed in mild states of delirium have been described. Moderate and severe states are characterized by more severe disruptions in each of the cognitive areas, with the development of illusions, hallucinations, and delusions, accompanied by increasing anxiety and agitation in reaction to these. At the extreme end are diminished levels of responsivity and coma. In contrast, the earliest phase of delirium may be characterized by hyperalertness and hypervigilance. The patient may observe that perceptions are a bit sharper, colors brighter, and thought processes faster.

CAUSES

The causes of delirium are frequently specific, iatrogenic, and identifiable. The most frequent offenders are drugs. Of these, the most often incriminated in the hospital are barbiturates, which are hypnotic as well as sedative. Older people and children are most vulnerable to the effects of barbiturates and, paradoxically, frequently show irritability rather than sedation. For this reason, antihistamines such as diphenhydramine hydrochloride (Benadryl) have gained favor as nighttime sedatives in many hospitals. Other drugs frequently associated with delirium are analgesics—pentazocine (Talwin) is a frequent offender—and drugs used for the treatment of the underlying illness. The latter would include almost any medication.

Factors associated with the underlying illness and affecting the circulation to the brain constitute another cause of delirium. Circulatory factors may include not only a diminished supply of essential nutrients to the brain but also the accumulation of toxic products as a result of an impairment of venous return from the brain. In short, any disease process, and almost any medication used in sufficient quantities, can contribute to the development of delirium.

A third cause of delirium, frequently overlooked among surgical patients, is that associated with withdrawal and the use of unauthorized medications. Frequently a patient enters the hospital the day prior to surgery. Two to

five days later, after an uneventful recovery, the patient may demonstrate increasing confusion and agitation. He is, in fact, suffering from alcoholic withdrawal. He may not match everyone's definition of an alcoholic. He may have reported only three or four highballs a night when queried about drinking habits. Nevertheless he has become physiologically dependent. A preoperative evaluation had ignored, or more frequently the patient has denied, a history of high alcoholic intake. Identification is the key to prevention and treatment. The patient may be in incipient delirium tremens. The mortality rate is high (15 to 30 percent) in this kind of medical emergency. Immediate and energetic intervention is essential, in terms of measures to support vital functions and calm the extreme agitation. Methods differ. Usually it is best to use the methods with which one is most familiar or those in vogue at a particular hospital. They include the administration of chlordiazepoxide (Librium), sodium amytal, or phenothiazines. Chlordiazide (50–100 mg.) may be given orally or parenterally every thirty to sixty minutes until the insomnia and agitation are controlled. The cumulative dose required to control these symptoms is subsequently given every six to eight hours, depending on the condition of the patient.

With narcotic addiction, withdrawal symptoms develop after twenty-four to forty-eight hours. Withdrawal can be accomplished with methadone. The amount will depend on the dose and purity of the narcotics the patient is on. It is most important to monitor the physiological and psychological signs and symptoms: agitation; lacrimation; rhinorrhea; nausea and vomiting; sweating; and diarrhea. Five to fifteen mg three times a day in decreasing doses over three days is usually effective to overcome physiological signs of withdrawal. Other patients may demonstrate alterations of consciousness in the hospital unexplained by either the authorized medications or the underlying disease process. These patients may have their own drugs or may be given drugs by visitors. This occurs even on well-supervised psychiatric services. Above all, a thorough examination of the patient is necessary. This may include laboratory examinations for the suspected drug. Depending upon the endogenous or exogenous chemical and its predilection for particular areas of the central nervous system (CNS) the picture of delirium may vary, with one or another of the stages heightened and of greater duration.

TREATMENT

The treatment of organic brain syndromes includes: (1) diagnosis; (2) identification of cause; (3) removal or remediation of cause; and (4) symptomatic support. Diagnosis, as suggested above, requires a high index of suspicion. It also requires paying attention to the patient's appearance, how he looks, how he speaks, and his motor behavior, as well as his verbal content. Does he appear drowsy and lethargic? Is he hypervigilant? Does he slur his speech? What are his pupils like? Does he make sense? Does he understand you? What have nurses, aides, and relatives observed in the past twenty-four hours? Is he a lonely old man without relatives who is quietly hallucinating unbeknown to the staff? Several of the causes of organic brain syndromes are obvious. Oxygen may help some patients with organic brain syndromes. For a patient with congestive heart failure, raising the bed to a more upright position may dramatically change his symptoms and identify the cause. The physician should ask what medication and treatment, including the corticosteroids, are being used. Can a suspect medication be changed, removed, substituted for? Different individuals respond differently from one analgesic, antihistamine, or sedative to another.

Supportive measures include the recognition that disorientation and confusion themselves generate anxiety and agitation. Calendars and clocks, radios and music may be useful. Lights may help prevent the development of illusions, which sometimes contribute to delusions and hallucinations. Contacts should be with a few, fully identified individuals. Simple and repeated reassurances by all who attend the patients are the order of the day. Of greater value is the attendance by a limited number of staff who reassure and reorient. "You are in this place." "It is one o'clock." "This is what happened." "We are doing this in order to take care of you." "Tomorrow this will happen." Brevity and conciseness are important, but more important, are the patience, slowness, and repetition with which communications are made. When agitation is great and associated with delusions and hallucinations, the need for reassurance is equally great. The patient should not be left unattended. An aide is a good companion. She should not talk too much or enter into a discussion of the delusions. Relatives often are not good at this because they get too involved. Simple and concise reassurance and repetition are the best medicine.

Small doses of phenothiazines are usually successful in treating extremely agitated patients suffering from delirium. The objective is to calm the patient by suppressing his hallucinations and delusions without adding another medication that may have untoward effects of its own or interact adversely with other medications. Phenothiazines are cardiotoxic in terms of arrhythmias and may cause orthostatic hypertension, but in small amounts neither of these side effects is of great danger to bedridden patients. A small amount is defined as under twenty-five mg of perphenazine (Trilafon) a day, given orally if possible but otherwise intramuscularly. If given orally, the dosage should be 2 mg hourly or every two hours 3 or 4 times until the patient is quieter. Supervision and attention to vital signs is imperative prior to each new dose. Usually after six to eight mgs the symptoms are controlled. A maintenance dose of the minimal cumulative dose that has been effective should be given every eight hours thereafter. If effective and tolerated, this should be maintained for a week to ten days following the delirium. One reason for this dosage and duration is that frequently it is this long before the contributing factors to the delirium are controlled. Another reason is that delusional and hallucinatory phenomena tend to remain with the patient, continuing to frighten him and possibly causing cardiac arrhythmias or other aspects of anxiety.

Patients experiencing delirium are and remain fearful that they are "going crazy."

Frequently they are aware that the unconscious material that has been dredged to the surface tells them something about themselves and their conflicts, and this is rarely pleasant. A very few of these patients will need to review this development with a psychiatrist. Most, however, will be able to handle it as they would a bad dream or nightmare. When they have recovered, it is helpful to talk and laugh with them about it. Understanding how it occurs may help—that it is the brain reacting as an end organ to unsatisfactory chemicals in the same way that a heart goes "wacky" with too much coffee or adrenalin or digitoxin. In this way anxiety may be reduced, leaving the individual to accept his natural boundaries again.

Delirium continues to be the most frequent adverse behavioral phenomenon that the consulting psychiatrist sees on the inpatient medical and surgical floors, accounting for up to 40 percent of consultation requests.

Death and Dying

The liaison consultant, in his or her work with physicians and nurses, is frequently called upon to help with the patient whose illness is rapidly progressive and terminal. To some extent, the concept of the dying patient is an arbitrary and relative one.[40] Most patients who come to the hospital for serious illness as well as for suspicious symptoms and signs have a naturally increased fear of vulnerability and death. In a sense, most adults have a sense of the possibility of death at any time.[50] We defend against this, appropriately or inappropriately, by a number of different psychological processes. As physicians, our defenses have developed early and have been constantly reinforced on the basis of our experience with patients during our training and work. In our work with other professionals around the dying patient, we need to begin with how we and they think about our own deaths, inasmuch as these attitudes determine our interaction or lack of interaction with patients. Sessions that explore these feelings and attitudes assist professional groups who are continually working with dying patients to help them communicate their feelings.

In working with the dying patient, it is essential to stay with what the patient feels, what he knows, what his thoughts are. By staying with these, the psychiatrist augments and facilitates his patient's expression, allowing for the development of empathy. Most physicians find this role difficult, embued as they are with an unconscious if not conscious fantasy of their superhuman ability to prevent death. The dying patient usually knows that death is inevitable and that he is dying, and no longer needs his physician's defenses to deny this fact. However, the patient does frequently need permission to ventilate his feelings to a neutral individual—the physician. This communication in and of itself is a vital life process, the expression of personal thoughts and feelings rarely shared with another individual. It is private, confidential and often confessional. In these communications, the physician permits and encourages the ventilation of affect, anxiety, shame, anger, and sadness. He assists the patient in examining appropriate and inappropriate defenses against these affects, depending upon the physical and psychological state of the person.

The level of the cognitive functions in the dying patient requires evaluation. The extent to which orientation, memory, concentration, and abstraction are compromised will determine the affectual and cognitive level at which the communication of the physician with the patient will take place. Many dying and terminally ill patients are thus compromised because of the underlying disease process and/or sedative and analgesic medications. Patients with organic brain syndromes demonstrate emotional changeability and cognitive disorientation, which prohibit abstract discussions and rational decision-making processes. These individuals require an attention on the part of the physician that allows for regression and supportive therapy. Supportive therapy includes reassurance, which frequently can be ministered through relatives who may understand from the physician what is going on with the patient. Keeping the patient tied in with close family relationships frequently maintains orientation in the present.

PSYCHOTHERAPY OF THE DYING PATIENT

The principle psychotherapeutic maneuvers that the therapist uses with dying patients are: (1) facilitating a self-grieving process; and (2) allowing a regressive process.[62] In the first instance, the patient is permitted to grieve for his lost functions, physical and psychological: his diminishing control over life processes in terms of his physical functions, and the implications that this has for his participation in family, social, and professional life. These are real losses for the patient. By helping him and his family to acknowledge them, both can communicate the real emotions that such losses evoke. With this ventilation of affect, the therapist is in a position to help the patient objectify adaptive defenses from maladaptive ones. Appropriate defenses will assist the patient in coping with the life processes still in his control. These will vary, depending upon the life stage of the patient and the tasks peculiar to his life situation. For the mother of children not yet grown, her task may be to plan for the care of the children after her death.[61] In this way, the dying patient gains some projection of herself into the future, and thus some assurance that she is continuing to fulfill her role as a responsible mother.

As death becomes more imminent with continual and rapid decrease of physical and often mental functions, the therapist assists the patient in delegating (to family members and others) increasing responsibility for tasks he formerly undertook. The patient is given permission to regress to a more dependent state in which he can accept the assistance of others, without the burden of guilt and ambivalence toward those on whom he depends. Examples of the regressive process include not only the permission for ventilation of affect but also the support of less sophisticated defense mechanisms such as identification, minimalization, and symbiosis.[54] The therapeutic art involved in regressive therapy is to stay with the patient's physical and mental state and to allow for fluctuations in this state. At one time the patient will be capable of functioning at a more sophisticated psychological state than at another. Throughout the course of regression, most patients will carry on with greatest facility if they have the close attention of immediate relatives. The therapist's task during the later stages of regression will often become increasingly directed toward the relatives, who are absorbing an increasing role in facilitating the process. As the patient's cognitive functions become increasingly diminished, the interaction between therapist, family, and others needs to become simpler and more direct. It should be largely aimed at the life events most meaningful to the patient, which usually include family and business affairs. By focusing attention on these, relatives and therapist often successfully maintain the patient's orientation to the environment.

⟦ Concluding Remarks

The extended interview is seen as the vehicle of medical psychotherapy. It is based upon an ever-widening acquaintance with the patient, starting with his present illness stage, the gradual unraveling of that illness, the life situation of the patient at the time the illness occurred, the patient's previous experiences with life and illness catastrophes, and the patient's personality prior to illness. As this information gradually develops, patient and physician form a therapeutic alliance that is directed toward the facilitation of a grieving process: the patient grieves for his lost health and the functions also lost thereby. The therapist's role in the patient's reaction to illness is to assist him through the four stages of grief: denial; ventilation of affect; the defensive stage; and restitution. During these stages, the therapist uses such maneuvers as confrontation, clarification, interpretation, educational remarks, review of patient assets, and reassurance. Specific attention is paid to the therapy of patients with conversion processes, acute organic brain syndromes or delirium, and terminal illness.

The liaison role of the psychiatrist in the general hospital is discussed in terms of his relationship to the nonpsychiatric physician, nurses, and the patient's family. Adjunct therapeutic processes include pharmacological agents, group and family therapy, and behavior therapy.

(Bibliography

1. ACKERMAN, N. W., J. LIEB, and J. K. PEARCE, eds. *Family Therapy in Transition.* Boston: Little, Brown, 1970.

2. AGLE, D. P., G. M. BAUM, and E. H. CHESTER. "Multidiscipline Treatment of Chronic Pulmonary Insufficiency: I. Psychologic Aspects of Rehabilitation," *Psychosom. Med.,* 35 (1973), 41–49.

3. ALEXANDER, F. and T. M. FRENCH. *Studies in Psychosomatic Medicine.* New York: Ronald, 1948.

4. ANDREASEN, N. J. C., R. NOYES, and C. E. HARTFORD. "Factors Influencing Adjustment of Burn Patients during Hospitalization," *Psychosom. Med.,* 34 (1972), 517–525.

5. BALINT, M. *Psychotherapeutic Techniques in Medicine.* London: Tavistock, 1961.

6. BERTALANFFY, L. VON. "An Outline of General Systems Theory," *Br. J. Phil. Sci.,* 1 (1950), 134–165.

7. BIRDWHISTELL, R. L. "Kinesics and Communication," in E. Carpenter and M. McLuhan, eds., *Exploration in Communication.* Boston: Beacon, 1960.

8. BLOS, P. *On Adolescence: A Psychoanalytic Interpretation.* New York: Free Press, 1960.

9. BOWERS, M. K., E. N. JACKSON, J. A. KNIGHT et al. *Counselling the Dying Patient.* New York: Thomas Nelson, 1964.

10. CASSEM, N. H. and T. P. HACKETT. "Psychiatric Consultation in a Coronary Care Unit," *Ann. Intern. Med.,* 75 (1971), 9–14.

11. CASTELNUOVO-TEDESCO, P. *The Twenty-Minute Hour: A Guide to Brief Psychotherapy for the Physician.* Boston: Little, Brown, 1965.

12. CHAMBERS, W. N. and M. F. REISER. "Emotional Stress in the Precipitation of Congestive Heart Failure," *Psychosom. Med.,* 15 (1953), 38–60.

13. COLBY, K. M. *A Primer for Psychotherapists.* New York: Ronald, 1951.

14. COURTENAY, M. *Sexual Discord in Marriage: A Field for Brief Psychotherapy.* Philadelphia: Lippincott, 1968.

15. DALTI, Z. "Psychogenic Male Infertility," *Psychosom. Med.,* 21 (1969), 326–330.

16. DE-NOUR, A. K. "Psychotherapy with Patients on Chronic Haemodialysis," *Br. J. Psychiatry,* 116 (1970), 207–215.

17. DE-NOUR, A. K. and J. W. CZACZKES. "Personality Factors in Chronic Hemodialysis Patients Causing Non-Compliance with Medical Regimen," *Psychosom. Med.,* 34 (1972), 333–344.

18. DICARA, L. V. and N. E. MILLER. "Instrumental Learning of Systolic Blood Pressure Responses by Curarized Rats: Dissociation of Cardiac and Vascular Changes," *Psychosom. Med.,* 30 (1968), 489–494.

19. DOLLARD, J. and N. MILLER. *Personality and Psychotherapy.* New York: McGraw-Hill, 1950.

20. EDELSON, M. *Sociotherapy and Psychotherapy.* Chicago: University of Chicago Press, 1970.

21. EISENDRATH, R. M. "The Role of Grief and Fear in the Death of Kidney Transplant Patients," *Am. J. Psychiatry,* 126 (1969), 381–387.

22. ENGEL, G. L. "Delirium, A Syndrome of Cerebral Insufficiency," *J. Chronic Dis.,* 9 (1959), 260–277.

23. ———. "Psychogenic Pain and the Pain-Prone Patient," *Am. J. Med.,* 26 (1959), 899–918.

24. ———. "Is Grief a Disease? A Challenge for Medical Research," *Psychosom. Med.,* 23 (1961), 18–22.

25. ———. *Psychological Development in Health and Disease.* Philadelphia: Saunders, 1962.

26. ———. "A Life Setting Conducive to Illness: The Giving-Up—Given-Up Complex," *Bull. Menninger Clin.,* 32 (1968), 355–365.

27. ———. "A Reconsideration of the Role of Conversion in Somatic Disease," *Compr. Psychiatry,* 9 (1968), 316–326.

28. ENGLISH, O. S. and S. M. FINCH. *Introduction to Psychiatry,* 3rd ed. New York: Norton, 1964.

29. ERIKSON, E. H. *Childhood and Society,* 2nd ed. New York: Norton, 1963.

30. FAIRBAIRN, W. R. *Psychoanalytic Studies of*

the Personality. London: Tavistock, 1952.

31. FENICHEL, O. H. *The Psychoanalytic Theory of Neurosis.* New York: Norton, 1945.

32. FRANK, J. D. *Persuasion and Healing: A Comparative Study of Psychotherapy.* Baltimore: The Johns Hopkins Press, 1961.

33. ———. "The Role of Hope in Psychotherapy," *Int. J. Psychiatry,* 5 (1968), 383–412.

34. FRIEDMAN, M. and R. H. ROSENMAN. "Association of Specific Overt Behavior Pattern with Blood and Cardiovascular Findings," *JAMA,* 169 (1959), 1286–1296.

35. GILL, M. and M. BRENMAN. *Hypnosis and Related States.* New York: International Universities Press, 1959.

36. GOLDWYN, R. "Operating for the Aging Face," *Psychiatry Med.,* 3 (1972), 187–195.

37. GRAHAM, D. T., R. M. LUNDY, L. S. BENJAMIN et al. "Specific Attitudes in Initial Interviews with Patients Having Different Psychosomatic Diseases," *Psychosom. Med.,* 24 (1962), 257–266.

38. GRINKER, R. R. *Toward a Unified Theory of Human Behavior.* New York: Basic Books, 1967.

39. HINKLE, L. E. and S. WOLF. "A Summary of Experimental Evidence Relating Life Stress to Diabetes Mellitus," *J. Mt. Sinai Hosp.,* 19 (1952), 537–570.

40. HINTON, J. *Dying.* Baltimore: Penguin, 1967.

41. HOLMES, T. H. and R. H. RAHE. "The Social Readjustment Rating Scale," *J. Psychosom. Res.,* 11 (1967), 213–218.

42. JACOBSEN, E. *Progressive Relaxation.* Chicago: University of Chicago Press, 1938.

43. KAHANA, R. and G. BIBRING. "Personality Types in Medical Management," in N. E. Zinberg, ed., *Psychiatry and Medical Practice in a General Hospital,* pp. 108–123. New York: International Universities Press, 1964.

44. KAHN, R. L., A. I. GOLDFARB, M. POLLACK et al. "Brief Objective Measures for Determination of Mental Status in the Aged," *Am. J. Psychiatry,* 117 (1960), 326–328.

45. KARUSH, A., G. E. DANIELS, J. F. O'CONNOR et al. "The Response to Psychotherapy in Chronic Ulcerative Colitis: I. Pretreatment Factors," *Psychosom. Med.,* 30 (1968), 255–276.

46. ———. "The Response to Psychotherapy in Chronic Ulcerative Colitis: II. Factors Arising from the Therapeutic Situation," *Psychosom. Med.,* 31 (1969), 201–226.

47. KENNEDY, J. A. and H. BAKST. "The Influence of Emotions on the Outcome of Cardiac Surgery: A Predictive Study," *Bull. N.Y. Acad. Med.,* 42 (1966), 811–849.

48. KIMBALL, C. P. "Psychological Responses to the Experience of Open-Heart Surgery (I)," *Am. J. Psychiatry,* 125 (1969), 348–359.

49. ———. "Techniques of Interviewing: I. Interviewing and the Meaning of the Symptom," *Ann. Intern. Med.,* 71 (1969), 147–153.

50. ———. "Death and Dying: A Chronological Discussion," *J. Thanatol.,* 1 (1971), 42–52.

51. ———. "The Experience of Open-Heart Surgery: III. Toward a Definition and Understanding of Post-Cardiotomy Delirium," *Arch. Gen. Psychiatry,* 27 (1972), 57–63.

52. KLEIN, D. F. and J. M. DAVIS. *Diagnosis and Drug Treatment of Psychiatric Disorders.* Baltimore: Williams & Wilkins, 1969.

53. KORNFELD, D. S., S. ZINBERG, and J. R. MALM. "Psychiatric Complications of Open-Heart Surgery," *N. Engl. J. Med.,* 273 (1965), 287–292.

54. KUBLER-ROSS, E. *On Death and Dying.* London: Macmillan, 1969.

55. LAZARE, A. "Hidden Conceptual Models in Clinical Psychiatry," *N. Engl. J. Med.,* 288 (1973), 345–351.

56. LESHAN, L. L. and M. L. GASSMAN. "Some Observations on Psychotherapy with Patients Suffering from Neoplastic Disease," *Am. J. Psychotherapy,* 12 (1958), 723–734.

57. LIDZ, T. *The Person: His Development Throughout the Life Cycle.* New York: Basic Books, 1968.

58. LIEBERMAN, M. A., I. D. YALOM, and M. B. MILES. *Encounter Groups: First Facts.* New York: Basic Books, 1973.

59. LINDEMANN, E. "Symptomatology and Management of Acute Grief," *Am. J. Psychiatry,* 101 (1944), 141–148.

60. MASTERS, W. H. and V. E. JOHNSON. *Sexual Inadequacy.* Boston: Little, Brown, 1970.

61. NORTON, J. "Treatment of a Dying Patient," in *The Psychoanalytic Study of the Child,* Vol. 18, pp. 541–560. New York: International Universities Press, 1963.

62. PAYNE, E. C., JR. "Teaching Medical Psycho-

therapy in Special Clinical Settings," in N. E. Zinberg, ed., *Psychiatry and Medical Practice in a General Hospital*, pp. 135–168. New York: International Universities Press, 1964.

63. PECK, A. "Emotional Reactions to Having Cancer," *Am. J. Roentgenol. Radium Ther. Nucl. Med.*, 114 (1972), 591–599.

64. PILOWSKY, I. and M. R. BOND. "Pain and Its Management in Malignant Disease: Elucidation of Staff-Patient Transactions," *Psychosom. Med.*, 31 (1969), 400–404.

65. RAHE, R. H. and T. H. HOLMES. "Life Crisis and Disease Onset. I. Qualitative and Quantitative Definition of the Life Crisis in Association with Health Change," in preparation.

66. ———. "Life Crisis and Disease Onset. II. A Prospective Study of Life Crisis and Health Changes," in preparation.

67. REISER, M. F., M. ROSENBAUM, and E. B. FERRIS. "Psychologic Mechanisms in Malignant Hypertension," *Psychosom. Med.*, 13 (1951), 147–159.

68. ROGERS, C. R. and R. DYMOND. *Psychotherapy and Personality Change*. Chicago: University of Chicago Press, 1954.

69. RUESCH, J. "The Infantile Personality," *Psychosom. Med.*, 10 (1948), 134–144.

70. SHAPIRO, D. *Neurotic Styles*. New York: Basic Books, 1965.

71. SIFNEOS, P. E. *Short-Term Psychotherapy and Emotional Crisis*. Cambridge: Harvard University Press, 1972.

72. SZASZ, T. *Pain and Pleasure*. New York: Basic Books, 1957.

73. WEINER, H., M. THALER, M. F. REISER et al. "Etiology of Duodenal Ulcer," *Psychosom. Med.*, 19 (1957), 1–10.

74. WEISMAN, A. D. and T. P. HACKETT. "Psychosis after Eye Surgery: Establishment of a Specific Doctor–Patient Relation in the Prevention and Treatment of "Black-Patch Delirium," *N. Engl. J. Med.*, 258 (1958), 1284–1289.

75. WILLIAMS, R. B., E. M. OVERLAN, J. H. RYZEWSKI et al. "The Use of a Therapeutic Milieu on a Continuing Care Unit in a General Hospital," *Ann. Intern. Med.*, 73 (1970), 957–962.

76. WOLBERG, L. R. *Medical Hypnosis*, Vol. 1. New York: Grune & Stratton, 1948.

77. WOLPE, J. *Psychotherapy by Reciprocal Inhibition*. Stanford, Calif.: Stanford University Press, 1958.

CHAPTER 42

PSYCHOTHERAPY IN OLD AGE

Robert N. Butler

THERE ARE POSSIBILITIES for growth and change throughout life, including old age.* Therefore psychotherapy is useful with older people, although it is less commonly practiced than would be appropriate. It is also a valuable part of the general treatment program for a variety of emotional and mental conditions among the elderly, not excluding those with varying degrees of organic brain disorder. Unfortunately, many psychotherapists resist undertaking psychotherapy with older people, and many older people themselves look upon their situation as futile. Consequently, in this chapter, these obstacles to treatment must be considered in addition to general therapeutic principles and common themes.

* Old age is arbitrarily defined in contemporary society through custom, social security benefits, and other entitlements and retirement rules. The most commonly used dividing age is 65. Biologically, of course, aging begins with conception.

(Is There a Psychotherapy of Old Age?

Is there justification for a psychotherapy directed specifically to older people? (Psychotherapy is here distinguished from environmental manipulation, behavioral modification, reality orientation, or other techniques *applied to* the person.) Should there be a geriatric or gerontological psychiatry?[21] Are the circumstances of old age so unique that special forms of psychotherapeutic treatment are necessitated? Do emotional and mental reactions occur in old age with sufficient frequency or intensity to warrant special consideration? Should not therapists be willing to undertake psychotherapy for patients of all ages and diagnostic categories—with, of course, the proper training? In short, should not therapists operate from the perspective of the life cycle† as a whole?

† See references 2, 5, 6, 19, and 31.

The number of actively practicing psychotherapists with respect to older people of the
United States is extremely small. In 1959 a
study[12] showed that less than one percent of
American psychiatrists spent any substantial
amount of their time working with older people, in terms of any method of treatment.
Studies of public clinics[4] and individual private practice[24] showed that the amount of
contact between psychiatrists and persons
over 65 approximated two percent of the total,
although older people make up ten percent of
the American population and perhaps as much
as twenty-five percent of the psychopathology.
Studies made in 1971 of community mental
health centers[28] revealed that only approximately five percent of those using the centers
were older people. Nor are they seen in any
greater frequency in research and training
centers. Despite the introduction of limited
Medicare coverage for emotional and mental
disorders in 1965, the utilization of psychotherapy with older patients has remained
about the same.

Crude estimates suggest that some three
million of the approximately 19 million older
people residing in the community (as of the
mid-1970s) have varying degrees of emotional
and mental disorders, most of which go untreated. Another one million older people—
five percent of the rough total of 20 million—
reside in nursing homes, mental hospitals,
chronic disease hospitals, and a variety of
other care facilities where they customarily receive custodial care and very little active psychiatric support. Indeed, they seldom receive
a comprehensive diagnostic evaluation, let
alone a trial of treatment.

Psychiatrists, psychologists, social workers,
and other mental health workers should receive adequate training with respect to those
features that are particular to old age. (See
the author's chapter on "Old Age" in Vol. 1 of
the 2nd edition of this *Handbook.*) They must
have sufficient experience with older patients
to be prepared to work effectively with them.
Therapists should have personal empirical
validation of the effectiveness of therapy with
older people. They should observe the reversibility of such emotional and mental states

as depression and paranoia and the amelioration of organic brain disease.

Private mental hospitals, in particular, demonstrate a correlation between financial capacity and reversibility of illness. In studies done
in private institutions, Gibson,[35] Myers, and
others have stressed the reversibility of the
psychiatric conditions of old age: 54 to 75 percent of the patients over 65 were able to be
discharged to their own homes in two months.
Thus if one can afford private care, the
chances are much greater for improvement
and eventual discharge to home. At any rate,
it is possible to bring comfort and support to
the elderly who must grieve the loss of loved
ones, and to those who, because of extreme
brain damage, may not have the capacity to
change.

With positive clinical experience, therapists
are willing to work with older people. The
intellectual stimulation of the work derives
partly from the unexpectedly high success
rates, indicating that old people are particularly susceptible to change. Moreover, the opportunity to study "lived" lives and to follow the course and observe the denouement of
various aspects and kinds of human character
is most rewarding. Such an opportunity provides a kind of "control" group against which
to measure one's work with other, younger
patients.

There is the further value of unraveling
long lives in depth. As Proust said in *Remem-
brance of Things Past*:

People foolishly imagine that the vast dimensions of social phenomena afford excellent opportunities to penetrate farther into the human soul;
they ought, on the contrary, to realize that it is
by plumbing in depths of a single personality that
they might have the chance of understanding
those phenomena.

The same general principles of psychotherapy apply to old age as to other age groups:
the importance of listening; of observing and
interpreting reactions of the patient to the
therapist; of uncovering and exploring motivation; of understanding dreams and language;
of working through dependency. The traditional routes of intellectual insight and emo-

tional working-through can be effectively reinforced by helping the older person to initiate actions. These actions can range from restitution to atonement, from finding replacements to finding redemption. Old age is framed by the reality of death. Loss and grief are frequent companions of old age. Time is both the ally and the antagonist of the therapist. It is the motor of rapid change: it is the limit of further fulfillment.

Freud—whom we would not remember, it may be pointed out, had he died before forty —was despairing about old age. Abraham[1] was the first of the classic psychoanalysts to observe improvements in analytic work with what, in the 1920s, Abraham regarded as older patients (they were in their fifties). Jelliffe,[50] in the United States, noted that the age of the neurosis was more important than the age of the patient. While Freud emphasized youth and sexuality, Jung was more oriented to the life cycle as a whole.[51] Of Jung's patients, two-thirds are said to have been middle-aged and older, which may in part account for some of his theoretical differences with Freud. Jung emphasized "individuation"—that is, the development of the individual personality—and other psychological processes more commonly observed in the postmeridian period of life.

Only since 1950 have there been psychiatrists who have devoted substantial amounts of time to work with older people. Grotjahn,[44] Gitelson,[36] Goldfarb,[40] Meerloo,[66] Weinberg,[91] Linden,[60] Greenleigh,[43] Busse,[16] Thompson, and Berezin,[8] among others, have written about psychotherapy with older people. Martin,[64] Lawton,[56] and Oberleder[72] are among the psychologists who have worked with older patients. In family agencies as well as in community and multipurpose senior centers, social workers* have provided both individual counseling and group work. In fact, more older persons probably have been aided through forms of group psychotherapy rather than through individual treatment.

Rechtschaffen[78] wrote the last comprehensive review of psychotherapy with older patients in 1959. What he observed then still

* See references 15, 54, 76, 81, 87, and 89.

applies: there have been no systematically controlled studies of the effectiveness of various psychotherapeutic procedures with older people. (This is the case with other age groups as well.)

If there is any validity at all to a "geriatric psychotherapy" it may be a transitory one, lasting only until a body of knowledge is acquired that will then be available for all therapists who will be in contact with the elderly.

(**Obstacles to Treatment**

In Western civilization, and in the United States in particular, there has been a broad, pervasive and negative view toward older people. This has been the institutionalized expression of the culture's defense against aging and disability. In an effort to dramatize the impact of the cultural devaluation of older people, the author has used the word "ageism."[20] Ageism is the systematized stereotyping of and discrimination against people because they are old, just as racism and sexism stereotype skin color and gender. Old people are categorized as senile, rigid in thought and manner, and old-fashioned in morality and skills. They are described pejoratively as "old fogies" and as "over the hill." Ageism allows us to see old people as "different" from those of us who are younger. We cease to identify with them as humans, and when we do this we can feel more comfortable about their poor social, personal, and economic plight.

The personal risk in ageism is different from that in racism and sexism. Racists and sexists need never fear becoming black or female, but all people potentially have the possibility of ending up old—and thereby becoming the object of their own prejudice. The traditional buffers of religious beliefs have been in the process of challenge and change. No general ethical or philosophical system has evolved as yet to deal with the whole of human life, including aging and death.[42] Since the mid 1950s, increasing attention has been paid to helping the dying patient confront death and its psychological impact.[29,55] But aging, often the prelude to death, has yet to be given equivalent consideration.

Psychotherapists reflect their culture.[17] We have already seen how research, training, and service facilities have been neglectful of older patients. Underlying institutional negativism towards old age is the primitive fear and distaste of one's own aging, the reality of one's own eventual death. Despite therapists' awareness of this effect of countertransference, relatively little attention has been paid to its obstructiveness in work with older people. One ingredient, of course, is one's relations with one's own parents. The degree to which conflict, anger, and disappointment exists or existed with parents and grandparents may be decisive. Again, if distaste with working with older people is based on a dislike of ugliness, then visual esthetics—a fine sensibility in itself—becomes inhumane. It should be superseded by a moral esthetic derived from a vision of the human condition that inevitably must incorporate the fact of decline and reckon with mental and physical destruction.

Another element in countertransference is that the patient may die while in treatment, challenging the therapist's sense of importance. (Death, paradoxically, can also bring relief to the therapist when the treatment is not going well.) And another element, noted by Greenleigh, is the anger and resentment younger people feel toward their parents for taming them, for domesticating their impulses and instincts. Similarly, older people are also held responsible for contemporary problems—"the mess we are all in"—such as pollution, war, and the like.

Therapists in American culture have been brought up to feel that they need to have instant gratification from a demonstration of their effectiveness. Their need for such cures must be counterbalanced by the realities of life and by the fact that one of the goals of therapy is amelioration and comfort as well as definitive change. Moreover, old people are part of a laboratory of lives-as-lived that provides knowledge for the therapist that is transferable to work with other age groups. One of the unfortunate consequences of infrequent contact with older persons in research and treatment is the denial of this important source of data about the nature of man.

The extent to which therapists work with the "young, attractive, verbal, intelligent, and successful" led Schofield to write of the "YAVIS" syndrome.[82] Often therapists believe they are wasting their skills on those who are so near death. (Yet on what other occasion could a person need more humane and compassionate attention?) Therapists who do work with older people are sometimes met with the contempt of their colleagues who think of them as having a morbid preoccupation in the elderly.

The elderly themselves may resist psychotherapy for a variety of reasons. They may fear the unknown. They may be very distrustful of the possibility of losing their independence and fear that the therapist may "put them away." They may previously have had bad experiences with therapists and counselors who gave them short shrift. Because of institutional ageism old people may, in effect, be prejudiced against themselves, just as we see self-hate in a variety of disadvantaged groups. In studies at the National Institute of Mental Health, Margaret Singer Thaler[9] found that the Rorschach case records of some older people who accepted the negative attitudes of the culture against old age were similar to those of collaborating prisoners of war in the 1950–53 Korean conflict. (On the other hand, some older people's tests were like those of POWs who did not collaborate with their captors.)

Older people may actively collaborate with the cultural stereotype, even vehemently exploit it as a defense.[17] They may call attention to their impairments and invoke their age to curry favor and assistance. The degree to which they may exploit their age may be excessive, leading to overnursing, the loss of autonomy, rapid deterioration, lowered morale, dissatisfaction, and earlier death. It is difficult for the older person and his family and therapist to walk the tightrope between the maintenance of basic dignity and independence on the one hand and the appropriate meeting of needs on the other.

One must also note the extent to which "aging graciously," "civilized behavior," "dignity," and "respect" may be used against older people—for example, by their children or by doctors—forcing them to cover up their feelings of grief, pain, discomfiture, and anger over their lot. Nor can "tranquility" or "serenity" be accepted by the therapist as a defense of the older person against examination of the painful possibilities of old age.

Cultural attitudes and personal or countertransference reactions are not the only obstacles to treatment. Lack of knowledge as a result of inadequate research and training poses serious impediments. Poverty, so common and extreme in old age, is a major financial block. For example, Medicare has discriminatory provisions with respect to mental health care compared to physical health care: in general, an older person can afford perhaps eight psychotherapeutic visits a year under Medicare's annual outpatient limit of $250 a year. Also, older people are most numerous in inner city and rural areas where health services and psychotherapy are least available. Transportation may make care inaccessible. Moreover, fear of violent street crime in cities may lock old people in.

General Treatment Considerations

Older people are major survivalists. They have lived a long time and have survived many crises. Therefore the extent to which they are patronized or infantilized is quite inappropriate. Older people in crisis—whether enduring grief over the death of loved ones, fearing spiraling inflation, or dreading an impending operation—may be anxious, dismayed, and confused, but they must not be written off as being in their "second childhood." They are reacting precisely as one would expect: with trauma-cum-anxiety, grief, and/or depression. Because the patients are old and have survived, it is important that partnership be the cornerstone of the psychotherapeutic collaboration. There should be a coming together in a joint venture to help work through the episode

that has brought the patient to the therapist. The word "patient" literally means "to suffer;" the word "client" comes from a word meaning "to depend." Thus equality is more in order. The therapist and the older person must share responsibility in the resolution of the issue at hand. They must join in decision making. The older person must not be denied choices. It is a powerful beneficence when the older person feels he can teach a therapist some things—which, indeed, he can; therapists can, if they will, learn a great deal about life from older people.

It is difficult to estimate treatability. When in doubt, treat.[23] It is very easy to decide that an older person is "a poor candidate" for psychotherapy. Some clearcut functional depressive reactions may prove extraordinarily refractory to psychotherapeutic efforts. Some older persons with definitive organic brain disease may nonetheless profit enormously from psychotherapeutuc work, including the gaining of insights into their historic and contemporary conflicts.

It is very painful for a person to be written off as hopeless. One must at times undertake therapy not only for its positive value but to avoid the negative impact of nihilism. Goethe said, "If you treat an individual as he is, he will stay as he is, but if you treat him as though he were what he ought to be and could be, he will become what he ought to be and could be." Therapists cannot permit themselves excessive private preferences but must work instead with various patients they may not prefer to work with, as part of a fundamental professional responsibility to consumers rather than to their special needs as providers.

The therapist's emotional commitment to work with older people must be explored. One may want to work with dependent, damaged older people because it is comfortable to be master in a situation that can offer the counterpart, in psychiatry, to the surgeon "burying his mistakes." It has been the author's impression, however, that therapists who work most effectively with older people are those who like to work with a variety of patients of various age groups and diagnostic categories. In general, therapists (hopefully) are open, flexible personalities interested in a range of life styles and with a sense of personal and cultural history. Nonverbal signs often give away the depth of this commitment to work with persons of different ages, including the older person. Facial expressions of revulsion and discomfort, movements of the body and manners of touch count among such evidences.

The use of "listening" as a form of therapy is crucial. Older people are often regarded as garrulous and their reminiscences as valueless. But loquacity and the expression of memories are due to loneliness and a tenacious reaching out for human contact, and to the occurrence of a basic process that the author has called the "life review."[18] The author conceived the life review as a naturally occurring, universal mental process characterized by the progressive return to consciousness of past experiences and, particularly, the resurgence of unresolved conflicts. Simultaneously, and normally, these revived experiences and conflicts can be surveyed and reintegrated. One may put these concepts to work as life review therapy.

One may encourage the older person to use a tape recorder to record his life. One may ask him to bring in photograph albums, motion pictures that may be available, mementos, family records, and old letters to help conduct the review. Self-confrontation through the use of the mirror may also help the older person in formulating and resolving his life course. Pilgrimages to the homes of one's childhood and searching for knowledge of one's family and forebears are important avenues to establishing meaning and continuity. The fact of listening *per se* can be therapeutic, particularly to the isolated, lonely older person who is trying to give some sense and meaning to his life as he faces the prospect of death. Aiding the older person to develop a relationship with a companion—an intimate[62]—is of great value to the patient and may make termination of professional psychotherapy possible.

However, termination need not be a goal in psychotherapy with an older person. This may be true for a variety of reasons. A fatal illness may be at hand; one may work with the older person until death. Even when a fatal illness may not be immediately present, changes are frequent, multiple, and rapidly occurring in old age. Restitution, growth and development, and resolution of issues are continuing tasks. Active reconciliation with siblings and friends with whom the person may have lost contact or been alienated is one direction in treatment. The moment that one part of the work may have been accomplished, such as making restitution for one loss, another may confront the patient. The therapist may simply need to be continuously available to the patient to aid him on the occasion of crises, or to have regularly scheduled and periodic sessions, or both. Moreover, as Jung wrote, "Serious problems in life are never fully solved. If ever they should appear to be so, it is a sure sign that something has been lost. The meaning and purpose of a problem seems to lie not in its solution but in our working at it incessantly."[51]

Whether the traditional separation between supportive and insight therapy is always appropriate among the elderly (or any age group), and whether the dichotomy is as sharp as the terminology would imply, is questionable. The social status of the patient, the presence or absence of brain damage, and other circumstances such as poverty and the quality of housing all contribute to the person's present mental status, outward behavior, inner experience, and level of adaptation. Moreover, these factors are constantly changing, so that giving the patient insight may be appropriate at one moment, giving him support at another, and both may be appropriate on still another occasion. Most writers argue that full-scale classic psychoanalysis is rarely applicable to the older person. This has never been adequately tested. Major reconstruction of character may be neither desirable nor desired, but the patient should share in that decision. It should not arbitrarily and covertly be made for him.

Goldfarb[37,38,40] takes the view that the older person needs a parent surrogate, requiring someone over whom he can develop an illusion of mastery, whom he can control for his own good. Goldfarb's "brief therapy"[40] was originally developed in the institutional setting and probably reflects some of the qualities of total institutions in which passivity is expected if not demanded. From the study of Perlin,[73] persons with life-long passive personalities adjusted more effectively than the independent personality in the old age home. The independent person becomes the "problem patient"; he needs a powerful ally such as the doctor to provide him brief but effective contact. The passive person needs to control and, by nature, does so. Goldfarb's elaboration of his theory depends upon his definition of the older person as someone who is frail and dependent rather than upon a definition by chronological age. Other writers use chronological age as the initial basis for evaluation and recognize that discrepancies exist between physiological, social, psychological, medical, and chronological aging.

Goldstein[41] observed the occurrence of a catastrophic reaction among World War I soldiers, a massive behavioral response of irritability and anxiety when the person was confronted with a task he could not handle. This reaction, as might be expected, is seen from time to time among the elderly. A skilled therapist must monitor his work with the brain-damaged older person. He must neither overstimulate nor understimulate, he must not permit withdrawal and yet must not be excessively intrusive. He must use the range of nonverbal as well as verbal communications, including holding and touching, to maintain psychotherapeutic progress.

Effects of Various Settings

The older person's inability to come to the office regularly or at all cannot be hastily interpreted as "resistance." It may be a function of physical limitations, transportation problems and expenses, illness, and the like. Therapists should choose to respond to the needs of the older person rather than their own convenience. They may see the older person at home and must therefore take into account the meaning of seeing the older person on his home ground. Therapists may see older patients who are residents of a home for the aged, or convalescent or permanent patients in a nursing home. Therapists may conduct psychotherapy in mental hospitals, particularly private mental hospitals—but rarely, and unfortunately, state institutions.

The therapist may see older people under favorable circumstances in their homes. But one may also sometimes encounter "battlefield" conditions.[23] One may see the person in roach- and rat-infested homes in dangerous neighborhoods. There may be the smell of urine and feces. There may be the visual image of sickness and squalor in nursing homes, old age homes, and hospitals. It becomes essential to work through one's distaste and discomfiture. It is important, too, to try to establish a decent private setting within the most crowded surroundings, so that the older person can speak in confidence about himself.

Sometimes one will interview persons who are chronically chairfast or bedfast. It is important to remember that for these people the structure of their lives revolves wholly around the confines of their chair or bed, and that psychotherapy must be viewed in this context.

Communication Problems

A skilled therapist must learn nonverbal communication. Lip reading is necessary when working with the deaf, with those who are too weak to talk, and with those who are unable to talk. One develops one's intuition, making hypotheses concerning what the person might be thinking and feeling. Signals may be established so that the therapist speaks "for" the patient and the patient nods in assent or disagreement. The use of touch and physical affection, so valuable to the old, must be mentioned again. In working with the deaf, clarify whether there is one "good" ear. In relating with a stroke victim, it is useful to maintain eye contact.

When called upon to work with older persons who do not speak English, one should either find therapists who speak the language or interpreters who can translate. One may even need help with ethnic dialects and slang. If one cannot find a therapist with the same cultural and linguistic background, one should at least have consultative advice from a representative of that culture and language.

Some six million older people do not have a telephone. Those that do find it very reassuring to have phone contact. Old people may understandably be quite anxious and fearful when isolated from the larger world, so the use of the telephone for therapeutic sessions is appropriate with the older person.

Respect for the more formal communication styles of the elderly is important, such as Mr., Mrs., and Miss, rather than what the therapist might prefer, such as first names. The presumptuous use of first names or nicknames implies careless, thoughtless, and even contemptuous attitudes toward the feelings of older people who grew up at a time when this was demeaning and disrespectful. Epithets used behind the backs of older people are also expressive of disdainful attitudes. For example, "old granny," "gramps," "old biddy," "old fogey," "crock," and other such terms all indicate negativity. The style of the language of older people must be noted as well. A woman might refer to a "delicate condition" rather than pregnancy, for instance. One must be most respectful of the life styles of different people.

Psychoanalytic Theory

Psychoanalytic theory is a valuable means of viewing old age. Ego, id, superego, and ego ideal are useful constructs. In the presence of brain damage, impulses may overrun inhibitions. That is, executive functions having been damaged, the id may overpower the superego and the ego. Awareness of incomplete fulfillment of ego ideal occupies an important part of the content of the life review in both brain-damaged and unaffected patients. With the latter, considerations pertinent to ego psychology indicate the continuing capacity of the elderly ego to grow and the superego to become more flexible. The notion of the weakening of the id or libido with age is unestablished. A full range of transference possibilities can be seen in the elderly as in any other age group. Thus one may see the older person taking the role of parent to the therapist, in

which case dominating or patronizing behavior may supervene. Older people may also manifest helplessness, trying to imbue the therapist with magical powers. The notion of regression in relationship to age has been much misunderstood. Second childhood and regression—fundamentally a Darwinian concept by way of Herbert Spencer and a neurological concept by way of Hughlings Jackson—occurs in relationship to loss and trauma, not in relationship to chronological aging per se.[68]

The author[23] has used the term "average expectable life cycle" as a counterpart to Heinz Hartman's concept of "averge expectable environment"[46] to bring focus to the notion that there are average normative experiences against which to measure individual patterns. In clinical work the author[23] has also referred to the development of an individual inner sense of the life cycle. This is not the same as the average expectable life cycle or as the personal sense of identity, though it is certainly related to both. It is a subjective feeling about the life cycle as a whole, its rhythm and variability, and the relation of this to the individual's sense of himself.

Much has been made in the psychoanalytic literature of the relationship of the fear of death to the fear of castration and to the fear of impotence in old age. While each fear certainly reinforces the other, the fear of death per se is a legitimate, authentic concern, independent of the fear of castration.

◖ Forms of Psychotherapy

The decision as to the form that psychotherapy should take with the old is similar to that with any other age group, once it has been decided that psychotherapy itself would be desirable and desired. It is first essential to conduct comprehensive medical, psychiatric, and social testing in this age group.[23,80] Thus comprehensive psychological testing may be of some value in determining the presence of organic brain disease; in its presence, psychotherapy may be useful and indeed the more necessary.

With respect to group therapy, groups may be set up that are age-segregated, that deal with specific themes such as grieving widowhood, or that are age-integrated.[39] The latter may be balanced for age, sex, and personality dynamics. The membership of such a group might display a range of near-normal to pathological reactions to adolescence and might include representatives of married and single life, divorce, parenthood, employment and retirement, widowhood, illness, and impending death. Most groups tend to meet weekly. Sometimes there are cotherapists and, if so, usually one is male and one female.

In age-integrated group therapy[22] it has been noted that older people and younger people may be mascoted by the middle-aged who pre-empt leadership. Eventually, however, the unique contributions of the elderly come out. These include models for growing older, solutions for loss and grief, creative uses of reminiscence, and an historic empathy and a sense of life. From the point of view of the elderly, membership in a group helps counterbalance the prejudices and segregation that they may feel in American culture.

Group therapy utilizes principles and techniques from individual psychotherapy as well as those related specifically to the group process itself. Group therapy has been widely used in work with the elderly, in and out of institutions.* (In the past it was often used because it was economical.) Volunteers have been trained to conduct group therapy. So too have been administrators, aides, nurses, social workers, psychologists, and psychiatrists. Sociability and emotional catharsis have been objectives. In institutional settings, "management" of behavior is emphasized. Where group therapy endeavors to understand and not simply control, it can be most valuable in and out of institutions. Irwin D. Yalom has noted a range of possible contributions and certainly does not regard group therapy as of secondary value to individual therapy. Indeed, it may complement individual therapy. Combined individual and group therapy can be very useful. The corrective recapitulation of

the primary family group, one of the features that Yalom emphasized, is particularly helpful in work with the older person. Altruism—a sense of giving to others—is another of the ten factors listed by Yalom[92] that is pertinent to the older person. Yalom's list includes: (1) Imparting of information; (2) installation of hope; (3) universality; (4) altruism; (5) corrective recapitulation of the primary family group; (6) development of socializing techniques; (7) imitative behavior; (8) inner personal behavior; (9) group cohesiveness; and (10) catharsis. [p. 5][92]

As in group therapy in general, the role of the therapist may be active or passive. It may involve various activities, embracing the passive one of listening and the active ones of questioning, explaining, teaching, protecting, reassuring, and confronting. In some cases therapists lose older patients because the therapist has inadequately prepared them and failed to intervene appropriately in group sessions.

A case illustration of this failure follows:

Mr. John M. was pressured to enter group psychotherapy because of the therapist's concern for his profound sense of meaninglessness, alienation between himself and his son, and his depression, which appeared likely to become potentially severe. At his second meeting with an open group (one that had existed for some time) he in effect committed social suicide. He demanded that the group tell him exactly what they thought of him. He interdigitated this demand with severely critical, self-righteous remarks about members of the group, name-dropping, and statements about his past accomplishments. The therapists were unable to intervene successfully in protecting him against his all too effective masochistic demand for personal attack. Neither he nor the group had been well prepared for his participation. He was unable to deal with the anxiety generated by the group experience and dropped out.

Group therapy can be very useful to families of older persons and should be used more frequently for that purpose. For example, families need help in working through the admission of the older person into nursing and old age homes. Indeed, families should frequently be involved in work with older people, al-

* See references 39, 53, 54, 60, and 61.

though it must always be clear as to who constitutes the "patient." Sometimes the older person is "brought in" by a son or daughter, and it is quickly apparent that it is the adult child that needs help. Issues in family therapy include the need for decisions about the older person, feelings of guilt and abandonment, and old family conflicts. It may be necessary to see the entire family together. Older couples may also need aid in the working out of marital and sexual conflicts, the handling of serious illnesses and approaching death, and worries about children and grandchildren.

Sometimes one interview, one consultation, with an older patient or a spouse or an extended family may set the tone for months of reasonably effective living for both patient and family. An older person, stricken by guilt, may need one explosive session to reveal, confess, and resolve.

It is essential that the therapist deal with the environment of the patient and be conscious of the realities—social, economic, and otherwise—that constitute the day-to-day experience of older people. First of all, the patient must survive, requiring adequate food and nutrition—which, indeed, may also affect mental and emotional health. In some measure the therapist may need to become an advocate on behalf of his patient, persuading him to gain public housing to which he might be entitled, or to assist him in securing any legal assistance that he might need.

Drugs should be used judiciously and wisely in the course of treatment,[80] particularly when anxiety may be disruptive or depression overwhelming. Indeed, drugs should never be used alone but should be a component of a broad therapeutic program that includes psychotherapy or counseling (ranging from support to insight psychotherapy) and, possibly, the use of environmental resources. Drugs must be weighed as to their ultimate impact: no drug brings penitence, replaces memory, or resolves grief. It may be essential that the older person work through his grief; if the antidepressant or the tranquilizer suppresses the opportunity to ventilate that grief, it may create further problems later. Heavy tranquilization may feed into the older person's

fears about his waning abilities. Many of the tranquilizers, for instance, create impotence. Similarly, care must be taken with sleeping medications. A simple bedtime regimen may be much more effective and safer than strong hypnotics. There is less of a morning-after hangover that can interfere with an active life, so contributory to mental well-being.

⟮ Common Themes in Psychotherapy

Psychotherapy in old age must certainly deal with grief, the losses of loved ones, and the dysfunctioning of one's own body and its parts. Efforts at restitution are required; one cannot deal in a negative context only, discussing what one has lost, but not what can be done to make up.

One great theme in psychotherapy with older people is related to guilt and atonement. "We have left undone those things which we ought to have done; and we have done those things which we ought not to have done," says the Anglican Book of Prayer. (There is also a guilt of survival[26] as well as a pride in survival.) The therapist, of course, has no power to grant mercy or to bring full alleviation to distress. But he can truly listen and bear witness. It is crucial that he not regard expressions of guilt as irrational but take them seriously as Martin Buber has stressed.[14] And Camus has said, "We cannot assert the innocence of anyone, whereas we can state with certainty the guilt of all." The confrontation of genuine guilt makes it possible for the person truly to become free of it and move on. For the truth is that older people are capable of guilt-producing acts in the *here and now* as well as in the past.

Acknowledgement, then, is the first step in dealing with guilt. Denial by the older person, or a person of any age, obviously cannot be dealt with. But talk alone may not be adequate to expunge guilt. Acts of atonement, expiatory behavior, may be necessary.

A case illustration follows:

A seventy-three-year-old woman spoke in a childish voice in a high pitch. She spoke constantly and was filled with excessive and compulsive symptoms to which she continually returned. Her main complaints were pain within her mouth and an itchy skin. She was clearly agitated and depressed and yet there was a disarticulation between the degree of seriousness which she presumed her symptoms entailed and the quality of her concern about them, suggesting the *la belle indifférence* of the hysterical patient. She was self-degrading and spoke of her hatred of herself in looking in her mirror at herself. She thought of aging as a punishment. She distrusted people, including the therapist and all her doctors, from dermatologists to internists. In the course of the psychotherapeutic work her dependency and self-centeredness became increasingly clear to her. After ten or fifteen minutes of high-pressure, explosive speech she would begin to calm down and could deal at first with possible concrete solutions to her living situation (whether to live in her apartment or to move in with a daughter). The therapist took a comprehensive approach including coordination with the dermatologist for treatment of her dry skin and its consequent pruritus. The therapeutic work itself dealt most largely with guilt and atonement. She had been cold and withholding in her marriage, for which she was experiencing great regret and pain, which had slowly evolved over the ten years since her husband's death. It was necessary for her to actively contribute to others as well as talk out her feelings.

Another great theme is that of independence or autonomy, which at times gets admixed in some minds with identity. In old age most healthy people find themselves essentially the same as they have always been.[30,74] With emerging medical problems (for example, changes in the body scheme or image) and emotional problems (for example, depression), the sense of the self may go through continuing re-evaluation. The problem is not simply self-sameness over time; the issue is often autonomy. "Can I survive independently without being a burden?" It is true, of course, that if one's identity is closely bound to autonomy, the two merge together, as it were. For instance, the patient whose identity has been that of a dependent person may find it easier to accept illness and institutionalization than would an independent person.[73] Also, many older people deeply wish to escape their identities.[23] (But Erikson[30,31] has proposed a rather fatalistic acceptance "of one's own and

only life cycle" in the last of his program of man's life stages. In his view, resolving "ego integrity versus despair," is the central task. Others have not found his conception universal.)

Another theme relates to the illusions or myths that have been built up or maintained over a lifetime. Obviously one cannot handle these with a frontal attack. The same principle applies in working with persons of all ages. One must work compassionately and carefully to understand and encourage a realistic lowering of defenses, rather than assaulting them overtly. *Primum non nocere*, first do no harm. Philosophic views and religious beliefs such as "suffering makes sense," and "I'm going to heaven," and idiosyncratic notions such as "I'm not that old" (the Peter Pan attitude) are quite common and must not be directly and negatively confronted.

Still another element concerns time. One may see older people who develop "time panics," who are fearful and frightened at the speed with which time moves. Others complain of the dullness and monotony of the rituals and patterns of their lives: "The salt has lost its savor." The therapist should help the older person to develop a sense of the immediacy of the here and now, of presentness, which may make simple enjoyment possible and bring the tranquility and serenity of which ancient writers spoke. The author has referred to "elementality" in the context of this effort, indicating the importance of shapes and sizes, of geometry and color, of plants and growth, and of the stripping away of the conventions and encrustations of a lifetime.[19]

Another theme not uncommon in psychotherapy with older patients relates to attitudes toward the young. Older people may feel hope and excitement over the possibilities of the future with respect to their children and grandchildren, or they may feel despair and anger over the behavior of the younger generation. The Anglo-Saxon etymology of the word "envy" gives away its ambivalence: it means both "admiration" and "hate." When the therapist is younger than the older person, as he is statistically apt to be, the issue of the relations between old and young must be dealt with. This is partly true because the older person may use the age difference as a defense. He may say to the younger therapist, "You are too young, you've had too little experience, you cannot possibly understand." In some measure this should be acknowledged. There is much that one cannot understand without the older person's active collaboration and teaching. In some measure this must be overcome through developing a sense of the history of the times in which the older person has lived, in order to enhance one's empathic relationship to older people. However, the defense of age difference must not be fully accepted. One must avoid falling into a trap. It is not only the old who do this; patients of all ages and diagnostic categories often assert that someone outside of themselves "cannot possibly understand."

Of course almost everything can be grist for the defensive mill. The older person may say he cannot properly speak about a dead relative or marriage partner, that it would not be appropriate to admit anger. This protectiveness of the dead elicits unease in the therapist, who may be made to feel that it is immoral and reprehensible to question relationships that presumably one can no longer do anything about. However, it is not simply events (about which, indeed, one can do little) that are at issue in psychotherapy. Also at issue are the interpretation, reconstruction, and consequences of these events that are continuing to have a psychological impact that must be dealt with. This must be qualified, of course, by the humane and compassionate understanding of the defensive illusions already referred to.

Among the fears of old age are loneliness and poverty. About the latter much could be done through progressive social policy. That is also true of loneliness, in some measure. However, it is the way that life has been led that contributes most to the issue of loneliness. A person who has developed a balanced portfolio—different skills, activities, and roles; and not simply idle hobbies, but highly grossing activities—is better protected from loneliness. He is also better able to deal with the sense of

uselessness expressed in such statements as "I am finished" and "It's all over."

A sense of uselessness also results from defective social policy. There is no constitutional basis for arbitrary, mandatory retirement, and court cases on behalf of older people may lead to increasing implementation of their right to work as a function of their desire and competence. Until the millennium of an ideal social policy, however, any sense of uselessness and loneliness can be alleviated, in part, through psychotherapeutic work. There is no shortage, really, of things that need to be done on behalf of oneself and on behalf of society, and these can often be brought into natural alliance. The feeling of being able to be constructive and resourceful is of great therapeutic influence. To teach and to be heard are very important. The sheer fact of surviving per se is emotionally significant to the sense of uselessness. The day-by-day struggles to maintain one's house, create order, keep one's books, manicure one's lawn, and get to the store despite painfully arthritic knees are all important elements of one's mental well-being. It is paradoxical that the struggle for survival itself is important to mental health. (One must not be carried away with this notion, however, for boundary conditions are obviously important. There comes a point beyond which one cannot survive against overwhelming odds.) There are also the wealthy and powerful who have no need to struggle for brute survival but who nonetheless carry on internal intellectual and emotional struggles that may make them creditable, confident, and satisfied human beings. Thomas Mann, for example, writing of the genesis of his novel, *Dr. Faustus*, described his own capacity to survive serious chest surgery.*

Related to the theme of uselessness is the more general abstraction that life itself is meaningless: "It is miserable to be old;" or, "There is nothing to look back on." Usually when older people are asked if they would live their lives over they tend to say "no." But they do not say "no" for the same reasons. One

* Mann, T. *The Story of a Novel* (New York: Knopf, 1961).

basis for saying no relates to existential despair. Existential psychotherapists might have been expected to have made contributions to working with older people but have not done so directly.[33] Considering existentialism as one philosophy in the general humanistic tradition, it may be argued that a humanistically-oriented psychotherapy would be appropriate for all age groups, including—and perhaps especially—old age. For old age is surely the period in which one must wrestle hardest with the fundaments of life: its meanings; the fact of death; inner resources and solitude; grief and restitution; guilt and atonement; autonomy and identity; power and powerlessness; intimacy and distance; compassion and indifference; and, following Camus, suicide—which he regarded as the great philosophical problem.*

Another theme that often emerges pertains to pain. We know that pain thresholds vary with culture, social grouping, and ethnic background, as well as with individual differences. How one lives with the pain of angina pectoris or osteoarthritis or lingering malignancy is a legitimate task for psychotherapy. The conquest or alleviation of pain should not be left to analgesics alone. Psychotherapy and hypnosis can aid in the reduction of pain. Its impact on spouse and family must also be treated.

Older people frequently express a sense of being a burden to others and indicate their desire not to be one. This may in part be legitimate. Calculated suicides are sometimes undertaken, particularly by men, to avoid leaving a family bereft of finances. Subtle, nonflamboyant forms of suicide may also be observed, including a failure to obtain medical care, not eating, and wandering in the streets. But the statement, "I am a burden," may also be a cry for help in which the older person is saying, "I need to be a burden and to be dependent, and there is no one on whom I can depend." It may also be an expression of hostility, reflecting family conflict and anger and a desire to embarrass the family. These

* Camus, A. *The Myth of Sisyphus* (New York: Vintage Books, 1959; originally published in 1942).

various possible bases for the sense of burden form part of the controversy over euthanasia (which means "good death"). Passive euthanasia is increasingly accepted; Pope Pius XII and leaders of other Judeo-Christian religious faiths have declared that there is no need to use heroic means to perpetuate life. It is possible to sign a "living will" months and years prior to possibly being in the helpless position of a "living death." The problem of active euthanasia, however, goes beyond the purview of this chapter—and, in the author's view, of medicine in general. Active euthanasia is a problem of social policy to which medicine and psychiatry may make a contribution, but decisions on active euthanasia should not be left—certainly not exclusively—to medical or therapeutic disciplines.

The sense of life is an important psychological description of the preparation for old age. Many people are unprepared for it and even psychologically deny its reality. Some pretend that they remain young, thus deceiving themselves but not others. This futile effort may be seen in many forms: frenetic efforts to maintain a youthful appearance, dying one's hair, seeking cosmetological surgery. It may be observed in counterphobia,[74] in which the older person endeavors to prove his prowess to himself and others despite aging, disability, and the prospect of death. One may see Peter Pans who petulantly refuse to grow up *and* old, who ignore birthdays and anniversaries, and who are literally shocked one day to find that they have attained old age. However, the sense of process, of being part of interlocking generations (which appears to be a common aspect of Eastern culture), can be effectively developed in a psychotherapeutic context. Developing a sense of life is, in fact, an integrative therapeutic goal, which relates all of the themes or issues discussed up to this point. Of course it almost goes without saying that a therapist cannot deal in vacuo with any of the themes that have been mentioned. Although the therapist and patient may jointly take up various issues one by one, they must ultimately be integrated.

Old people give the impression that they

know certain secrets that young people don't know. One of the most morbid and despairing thoughts would be that the secret is that life is essentially not worth living, or that all is futile and vain when one conceives the larger cosmos. Camus, on the other hand, refers to the "benign indifference of the universe." The universe and life, in its ebb and flow, is not per se a malignant or malevolently-engineered process but a neutral one. There is no punishment for being either young or old; there is no superiority concerning what life is about, real or imagined, in the wisdom of older people or the innocence of the young.

One basis for the notion of older persons that they have great secrets is that this is a means of defending powerlessness. For in fact, old age is a socially acculturated weakness, an invalidity. That is one reason why equality in the therapist–patient relationship is highly desirable so long as it is not patently contrived. A partnership of this sort may then be generalized to a larger social field where the older person may regain a sense of control over his own destiny.

⟮ Special Treatment Problems

To begin with, one problem that frequently arises between the patient, the therapist, and the staff, particularly in institutional settings, concerns racial relations. In some geographic areas old people are taken care of by minority-group personnel. Older black and other minority patients are the least likely to receive psychotherapy and decent psychiatric care, in many parts of the United States.[25] On the other hand, older white persons' racial attitudes may boomerang against them, affecting their care.

Sexual Problems

In the United States there are over 11 million women among those 65 or older, compared to some eight million men, and some six million of them are widowed. Destitute, lonely older women form one of the most disadvan-

taged groups in American society. They also bear the heritage of unequal opportunities against women, having limited financial, intellectual, and other resources to face old age. The difference in life expectancy between men and women often means that the older woman has nursed her husband but has no one to nurse her. Unlike the older man, the older woman is denied sexual outlets. Because of the unavailability of men, women may become involved in difficult situations. One illustration may serve:

Jenny Simmons, sixty-seven-years old, had continuing sexual needs and interests. She established what appeared to be a warm and sincere relationship with a forty-nine-year-old man who had recently been divorced. He confessed to her his confused feelings about her as an older woman and his interest in a young man. Unfortunately the older woman had always been vulnerable to men who had yet to resolve their relationships with mothers.

"From a psychosexual point of view, the male over age fifty has to contend with one of the great fallacies of our culture. Every man in this group is arbitrarily identified by both public and professional alike as sexually impaired." So state Masters and Johnson.[65] For a variety of causes associated with chronological aging there are age-related sexual changes, but these are not necessarily a function of age per se. Sexual disability may be a function of drugs (especially tranquilizers), alcohol, and a variety of organic conditions. The older man ordinarily does take longer to obtain an erection, but as Masters and Johnson pointed out, "One of the advantages of the aging process in specific reference to sexual functioning is that, generally speaking, control of the ejaculatory demand in the 50-to-75 year age group is far better than in the 20-to-40 year age group." Most data show that older men are usually able to continue an active sexual life well into the 80s and even beyond.

Biologically, the older woman experiences little sexual impairment as she ages. If she is in reasonably good health she can expect to continue sexual activity until late in life, assuming she has maintained a frame of mind that encourages this and has a sexual partner with whom to enjoy it. The biological impact of the change of life has been questioned by recent studies, which show that the physiological changes are not of as great significance as psychological ingredients associated with the middle years.[70] However, steroid insufficiency does cause a thinning of vaginal walls; at times cracking, bleeding, and pain (dyspareunia) can result during sexual intercourse. Natural estrogen treatment can overcome this.

Sexual therapy has been undertaken successfully—for example, by Masters and Johnson. They have reported a 50 percent success rate in their older patients, even when the problem has existed for over twenty-five years. The psychotherapist may also be able to help provide sexual education of older persons, to help them face the guilt that may be associated with masturbatory and other variations in sexual activity that might be required because of physical illnesses. Psychological preparation is indicated prior to any surgery that may affect sexual capacity. This is particularly true when a man must have the perineal type of prostatectomy which may lead to sexual impotence.

Retirement

Another major problem of a special kind in late life is retirement.[85] There is no question but that everyone "reacts" to retirement, but not everyone goes through a "retirement crisis." Retirement means different things to different people. Those who have been strongly identified with their jobs (sometimes called "workaholics") may find retirement extremely difficult. Others may see retirement as a relief from hard, bone-breaking work, or from boring assembly line employment. Attitudes and reactions to retirement, of course, also depend upon other possibilities: alternatives for new careers and roles; the state of one's personal relationships; one's health; the variety of one's intellectual and skill resources; and so forth.

Pre-retirement preparation programs are still not frequent, and when they do occur—for example, within the federal government—they often neglect the ingredient of mental health in favor of considerations relating to finances, housing, and the like. Moreover, a retired person may not be in a position to know the real problems of retirement—of his specific individual retirement—until he is in it. What is it like for a husband and wife to be together for twenty-four hours a day? What does it mean not to have a time structure in one's life?[32] How does a man's retirement compare to the situation for a woman who in effect has no retirement but continues to work at home? Psychotherapeutic work with respect to retirement therefore deals with a range of subjects that essentially includes the themes already described.

Alcoholism

Alcoholism is surprisingly common in late life.[34] Today more people who have had long histories of alcoholism live longer than did so in the past. In addition, many older people develop alcoholism for the first time in late life, in response to grief, depression, loneliness, boredom, or pain. Therapists have found working with alcoholism difficult at any age group and no more so with the old. One should call upon Alcoholics Anonymous and other forms of group therapy as well as individual psychotherapy. Because late-life alcoholism is more frequent than is recognized, and imbibing is a way of warding off feelings of loneliness and grief, the therapist must be careful about suggesting the use of alcohol. The world's oldest tranquilizer may bring relief and increase sociability, but it creates dangerous muscular incoordination and adds to the risk of falls. It may also lead to alcoholism and its devastating effects.

Brain Syndromes

Psychotherapy is one component in the overall management of a patient suffering with an organic brain syndrome. An individual may have counted heavily upon his memory: for example, a writer may have a massive depression associated with organically based brain disease. Through counseling, families may be helped in maintaining at home the older family relative with an organic brain syndrome. There is no doubt but that patients with definitive organic brain disease have been maintained in the community through an overall treatment program of which psychotherapy may be one part, even though the condition itself will not be reversed. Goldfarb's brief therapy[40] may be of special value in this group, whose members need a sense of mastery.

Depression

It is dismaying at times, how refractory the depressions of later life can be.[18,52] The milder depressions associated with a sense of insignificance[16] may be helped by therapists assisting the older person in finding an authentic interest, role, and place in society. With the more serious depressions related to the death of loved ones, serious illness, and other losses, the psychotherapeutic approach may not always be oriented toward insight, because insight may be unbearable. Instead, the relief of anger, grief, and guilt can be particularly valuable even if the overall therapeutic treatment and management context includes drugs—and, if they fail, electroconvulsive therapy.

A case illustration follows:

The sixty-six-year-old patient had been in reasonably good health until five years before entering psychotherapy when he developed emphysema. Because of progressive disability he became depressed and socially withdrawn. His depression became severely immobilizing, and he sought and received early retirement. He regarded that retirement as forced and quickly became almost totally dependent on his wife; his demands became most burdensome. After intensive diagnostic interviews the patient was referred to residential treatment including psychotherapy. Upon hospitalization he was quite obviously depressed and very uninterested in his surroundings. His appetite was poor and he was an insomniac. He was demanding. He was seen in a program that included individual psychotherapy, group activities, and one of the tricyclic antidepressants. After three months he was visibly less depressed, his appetite picked up and his ability to tolerate physical exertion improved. He developed other interests and became

much more understanding of his burdensome impact upon his wife. He was discharged and was continuing to make good progress according to the one-year follow-up.

Anger

Anger is usually considered to be a crucial element in depression, but it has not been designated as a diagnostic entity in Western culture. It is so regarded in some societies, however, and perhaps it should be so regarded in our own. There are many manifestations of anger: violence; cold hostility; sarcasm; defiance; tantalizing and teasing; sneering; passive obstructiveness (either dependent or aggressive); gossip; withdrawal; and, of course, self-destructive behavior to the point of suicide. Anger must be confronted and expressed but its expression is not enough, contrary to popular belief. Anger may be a cover for deeper problems—for instance, relating to the need for intimacy. It is shocking to sense the extent to which lifetime grudges and events of decades past may psychologically be very much alive. Hate may outlive love.

Anger can be a useful force when it is put to work in the favor of personally and socially constructive ends. Sometimes, however, one sees an older person or older people in torrents of rage. It is as though the aging flesh fell away and angry children came out fighting.

Resistance against reconciliation, as between divorced spouses or between parents and children, may be intense. Thus anger, resentment, and related feelings are a common problem in work with older people. Anger may relate to paranoid reactions, wih the projection of one's anger on others. Anger and paranoid feelings may complicate depressions, involving, as they may, issues relating to dying and to mourning for others as well as for oneself and for the loss of one's own body parts and functions.

Death-Related Problems

Elizabeth Kübler-Ross's work[55] has delineated five stages in the psychology of dying, and she has developed a therapeutic approach. The elements include: denial; then anger; then negotiation, as with God; then depression; and finally, acceptance. There are many small deaths along the course of life; these are intimations of mortality. When they occur, essentially the same stages are seen as are described by Kubler-Ross, and the same efforts must be made to deal effectively in counseling and psychotherapy with each evidence of mortality.

Work with older people, with disability, and with dying can be extremely difficult. The therapist needs ongoing consultation to help his patient and himself. It is important to reaffirm that the fundamental issues of life and consequently of psychotherapy—love, guilt and atonement, separation, and integration—can be dealt with to the very end of life. It must not be thought, as is often said, that nothing can be done because there is no future for the older person, and that he only has an existence in the present. After all, we all live only in the present. And the great fundaments of life are always subject to change.

Memorial societies can offer a valid form of psychotherapy for survivors, where the center of concern in the service is the personality of the individual. Memorial societies also provide low-cost funerals, which are less destructive to the financial situation of low-income survivors.

The Uniform Anatomical Gift Act or its equivalent now exists in every state and in most Canadian provinces. It provides Uniform Donor Cards, which may be filled out and signed by the donor and two witnesses; these then constitute a legal document. The person has final say of the disposition of his body and its parts. This makes possible the bequeathal of one's body or body parts to medical schools, to the eye banks, or other facilities. This is a material expression of the natural sense of legacy that is found as part of the psychology of late life.[19] It is pertinent to the process of psychotherapy itself to aid the older person in providing appropriately for others.

It is also essential to be wary of those older people who, out of their fear of desolation, illness and poverty, hoard excessive money and property. It is important to explore the extent to which the older person may use his income and property as a weapon of control against his heirs. Fear of loss of money may also relate to a fear of death itself. The older person may in effect be saying, "I want to outlive my resources and live forever." From one angle the therapist may help the older person to focus on leaving a zero estate—that is, to utilize his resources in the here and now for his own edification and pleasure, rather than feeling obligated to provide for those who follow. But when he does provide for those who follow, he should be helped to do so in a way that is authentically constructive for his heirs and for society at large. Spendthrift and skip-generation trusts may superficially seem attractive to the older person, but they may really reflect their deep sense of failure as a parent. The therapist may do much to help relieve the older person of any sense of parental failure and, in effect, also really help the heir by throwing him on his own, requiring an independence that a large inheritance would not permit.

The emotional help needed by a widow differs from the needs of a widower. The latter, if he has been a typical husband, may be totally unprepared to cook for himself, sew on buttons, and the like. He may need concrete assistance in learning how to do these things for himself. The therapist must help him do this rather than simply finding someone else upon whom to become dependent. For widows, the grief associated with their state is a process that often requires a year's emotional journey as one moves through fresh and painful memories, various anniversaries and holidays. This may be complicated by an anger which the therapist can help the survivor to express. The Widow to Widow Program established in Boston and staffed by widows as an experimental mental health program of preventive intervention could well be extended nationally. Like Alcoholics Anonymous, it would be a useful adjunct to the therapist in his work.

Paranoia

It is an absolute that one must be scrupulously honest with paranoid patients. (One should be so with all patients. A paranoid patient, however, cannot accept even the most usual and unintentional lapses.) The therapist must be attentive, make reasonable suggestions, and be firm, combining warmth with detachment. The therapist must *not* be "nice," giving out reassurances or accepting everything that is said. Nothing can anger paranoid patients more than to think that they are being "buttered up" or exploited. At various points, of course, there must be frank disagreements; for if there were none, that would also spell trouble. The therapist has to take issue with a patient or else the latter ceases to believe in him. The therapist must have self-confidence and know what he is talking about. The fact is it is most difficult to establish and sustain a therapeutic relationship of trust with paranoid patients. Rapport may be slow in building, and the work may be long-term. On the other hand, the paranoid person has been profoundly deprived emotionally, yearns for closeness, and will not easily spurn it, although superficially he may show hostility and withdrawal. Irony and humor—referring to the universalities of the human condition—are valuable. Any work with the family must be done only with the full knowledge of the paranoid patient and usually only in his presence.

One case illustration will serve:

Miss Anne Warner is an unmarried eighty-two-year-old woman living alone on a small governmental pension. She is both hostile and suspicious toward anyone who enters her life. She called the office of a therapist in the community mental health center to ask for help with symptoms of "dizziness and forgetfulness." However after several home visits were made she became more and more suspicious, finally cutting off contact after she intimated the therapist was trying to "cheat" her.

Six months later she called and asked if the therapist would come again to see her. When the therapist arrived she was greeted warmly by Miss Warner who then spent a full hour telling her things she had stored up because, as she said, "I don't talk to another living soul. When I thought of who I could talk to I always think of you." She first admitted to paranoid thoughts concerning the therapist after seeing a similar name in the news-paper. After satisfying herself that the therapist was not that person she went on to discuss a frightening dream she had had which reminded her of her own death—she wondered if such dreams were natural or pertinent to imminent demise. She concluded by deciding she should be more realistic about her age and do those things she had always wanted to do. She had been thinking about buying a bus ticket for an extended trip around the United States, stating cheerfully there was no longer need to save for the future. "I will indulge the gypsy in myself." Miss Warner asked the therapist if she could count on her to help dispose of her belongings "in case I don't come back."

Narcissism

Narcissism—self-centeredness—is one of the problems seen in old age, but it is not new per se in old age; it is the outcome of a life. Camus put the following into the mouth of his character in *The Fall*, "It is not true, after all, that I never loved. I conceived at least one great love in my life, of which I was always the object."

Ingmar Bergman's motion picture *Wild Strawberries* centers on the life of a seventy-six-year-old physician. His "punishment" for his life of indifference, intellectualism, emotional withholding, and egotism is describable in part as "loneliness" and/or "deadliness." The protagonist says, "The last few months I have had the most peculiar dreams. . . . It's as if I'm trying to say something to myself which I don't want to hear when I'm awake, that I am dead, although I live." His daughter-in-law tells him, "You are an egoist, father. You are completely inconsiderate. You have never listened to anyone but yourself. All this is well hidden behind your mask of old fashioned charm and your friendliness, but you are as hard as nails even though everyone depicts you as the great humanitarian." As the film unfolds, even in his closeness to death, the protagonist undergoes major positive psychological changes.

Insomnia

Insomnia can be a most serious, regrettable symptom in late life. Early morning awakening is more common among the inactive who retire early and take catnaps throughout the day. This may be a step toward serious daytime sleep reversal, which should be avoided. Despite mythology, old people often need more and not less sleep, because of illnesses and degenerative diseases that create fatigue, headache, aches, and pains. People with insomnia may fear sleep itself, for with sleep their defenses are down; the defenses may be against anxiety, anger, and other emotions. Psychotherapy can help the individual to understand his particular brand of insomnia. It is important to establish simple rituals— warm tubs, well-made beds, bed boards for support, back massages, and white wine or warm sake (Japanese rice beer) before trying hypnotic drugs. Barbiturates may prove excitatory to older patients. When sleeping medications are used, nonbarbiturates or chloral hydrate may be the more desirable.

Nutrition

Another special problem to the psychotherapist may be nutrition. Older people, particularly those living alone, may eat little and poorly, and develop organic symptoms as a result. Referral to the internist and nutritionist is necessary.

❨ Cooperating with Other Professions

Old age is a period characterized by multiple changes involving multiple symptoms. They may occur rapidly, or they may be sustained in a long plateau. Clearly a comprehensive approach is required. Philosophically the older person is dealing with the essence of existence during the closing chapter of life, but at the same time he is affected by a myriad of physiological, psychological, and social changes. It is therefore imperative that the therapist be willing to function within the team approach, and to reduce problems of hierarchy and status in order to work effectively with others, including medical specialists, nurses, social workers, and paraprofessionals. Sometimes

psychotherapists may get clues to medical problems and environmental problems, necessitating proper referral to others. It may also be hoped that medical specialists and others will increasingly recognize the rewards that come from effective psychotherapy and will refer older people to therapists to bring relief to loneliness, pain, and despair—conditions all too common in later life.

❨ Bibliography

1. ABRAHAM, K. "The Applicability of Psychoanalytic Treatment to Patients of Advanced Age," in *Selected Papers*, pp. 312–317. New York: Basic Books, 1953.

2. ARIES, P. *Centuries of Childhood: A Social History of Family Life*, translated by R. Baldick, New York: Knopf, 1962.

3. ATKIN, S. "Discussion of Old Age and Aging: The Psychoanalytic Point of View," *Am. J. Orthopsychiatry*, 10 (1940), 79.

4. BAHN, A. K. *Outpatient Population of Psychiatric Clinics: Maryland 1958–59.* U.S. Public Health Service Monogr. no. 65. Washington: U.S. Govt. Print. Off., 1965.

5. BENEDEK, T. "Climacterium: A Developmental Phase," *Psychoanal. Q.*, 19 (1950), 1–27.

6. ————. "Parenthood as a Developmental Phase: A Contribution to Libido-Theory," *J. Am. Psycho. Assoc.*, 7 (1959), 389–417.

7. BERENSON, B. *Sunset and Twilight: Diaries of 1947–58.* New York: Harcourt, Brace and World, 1963.

8. BEREZIN, M. A. "Some Intrapsychic Aspects of Aging," in N. E. Zinberg and I. Kaufman, eds., *Normal Psychology of the Aging Process*, pp. 93–117. New York: International Universities Press, 1963.

9. BIRREN, J. E., R. N. BUTLER, S. W. GREENHOUSE et al. *Human Aging: A Biological and Behavioral Study.* U.S. Public Health Service Monogr. no. 986. Washington: U.S. Govt. Print. Off., 1963. (Paperback reprint, 1971.)

10. BLANK, M. C. "Utilization of Psychotherapy with Aged Persons." Paper presented at Ann. Meet. of the Gerontol. Soc., San Juan, 1972.

11. BLAUNER, R. "Death and the Social Structure," *Psychiatry*, 29 (1966), 378–394.

12. BOWMAN, K. M. "Geriatrics, Review of Psychiatric Progress, 1958," *Am. J. Psychiatry*, 115 (1959), 621–623.

13. BRENMAN, M. and R. P. KNIGHT. "Hypnotherapy for Mental Illness in the Aged: Case Report of Hysterical Psychosis in a Seventy-one Year Old Woman," *Bull. Menninger Clin.*, 7 (1943), 188–198.

14. BUBER, M. "Guilt and Guilt Feelings," *Psychiatry*, 20 (1957), 114–129.

15. BURNSIDE, I. M. "Group Work with the Aged: Selected Literature," *Gerontologist*, 10 (1970), 241–246.

16. BUSSE, E. W. *Therapeutic Implications of Basic Research with the Aged*. Strecker Monogr. Ser. no. 4. Philadelphia: The Institute of the Pennsylvania Hospital, 1967.

17. BUTLER, R. N. "Intensive Psychotherapy for the Hospitalized Aged," *Geriatrics*, 15 (1960), 644–653.

18. ———. "The Life Review: An Interpretation of Reminiscence in the Aged," *Psychiatry*, 26 (1963), 65–76.

19. ———. "Toward a Psychiatry of the Life Cycle: Implications of Socio-psychologic Studies of the Aging Process for the Psychotherapeutic Situation," in A. Simon and L. J. Epstein, eds., *Aging in Modern Society*, pp. 233–248. Washington: Am. Psychiatric Assoc., 1968.

20. ———. "Ageism: Another Form of Bigotry," *Gerontologist*, 9 (1969), 243–246.

21. ———. "Should There Be a Geriatric Psychiatry?" *Psychiatr. Opin.*, 7 (1970), 27–32.

22. BUTLER, R. N. and M. I. LEWIS. "The Role of the Elderly in a New Treatment Form: Age-Integrated Life-Crisis Group Therapy" (Abstract), Int. Congr. Gerontol., Kiev, 1972.

23. ———. *Aging and Mental Health: Positive Psycho-social Approaches*. St. Louis: Mosby, 1973.

24. BUTLER, R. N. and L. G. SULLIMAN. "Psychiatric Contact with the Community-Resident, Emotionally-disturbed Elderly," *J. Nerv. Ment. Dis.*, 137 (1963), 180–186.

25. CARTER, J. H. "'Differential' Treatment of the Elderly Black Victims of Stereotyping," *Postgrad. Med.*, 52 (1972), 211–214.

26. CHODOFF, P. C. "Late Effects of the Concentration Camp Syndrome," *Arch. Gen. Psychiatry*, 9 (1963), 323–333.

27. DASILVA, G. "The Loneliness and Death of an Old Man," *J. Geriatr. Psychiatry*, 1 (1967), 5–27.

28. DOVENMUEHLE, R. H. "A Review of the Impact of the Community Mental Health Center Movement on Psychiatric Services to Senior Citizens," in *Mental Health Care and the Elderly: Shortcomings in Public Policy*, pp. 177–179. A Report of the U.S. Senate Special Committee on Aging. Washington: U.S. Govt. Print. Off., 1971.

29. EISSLER, K. *The Psychiatrist and the Dying Patient*. New York: International Universities Press, 1955.

30. ERIKSON, ERIK H. "Growth and Crises of the Healthy Personality," *Psychol. Issues*, 1 (1959), 50–100.

31. ———. *Childhood and Society*, 2nd ed. New York: Norton, 1963.

32. FERENCZI, S. (1919) "Sunday Neuroses," in J. Rickman, ed. *Theory and Techniques of Psychoanalysis*, Vol. 2, pp. 174–176. New York: Basic Books, 1952.

33. FRANKL, V. (1959) *Man's Search for Meaning*. New York: Washington Square, 1963.

34. GAITZ, C. M. "Characteristics of Elderly Patients with Alcoholism," *Arch. Gen. Psychiatry*, 24 (1971), 372–378.

35. GIBSON, R. W. "Medicare and the Psychiatric Patient," *Psychiatr. Opin.*, 7 (1970), 17–22.

36. GITELSON, M. "The Emotional Problems of Elderly People," *Geriatrics*, 3 (1948), 135–150.

37. GOLDFARB, A. I. "Psychotherapy of Aged Persons: IV. One Aspect of the Therapeutic Situation with Aged Patients," *Psychoanal. Rev.*, 42 (1955), 180–186.

38. ———. "Psychotherapy of the Aged: The Use and Value of an Adaptational Frame of Reference," *Psychoanal. Rev.*, 43 (1956), 68–81.

39. ———. "Group Therapy with the Old and Aged," in H. I. Kaplan and B. J. Sadock, eds., *Comprehensive Group Psychotherapy*, pp. 623–642. Baltimore: Williams & Wilkins, 1971.

40. GOLDFARB, A. I. and H. TURNER. "Psychotherapy of Aged Persons: II. Utilization and Effectiveness of 'Brief' Therapy," *Am. J. Psychiatry*, 109 (1953), 916–921.

41. GOLDSTEIN, K. and M. SCHERER. "Abstract and Concrete Behavior," *Psychol. Monogr.*, 53 (1941), 239–287.

42. GORER, G. *Death, Grief and Mourning in Contemporary Britain*. London: Grosset, 1965.

43. GREENLEIGH, L. "Some Psychological Aspects of Aging," *Social Casework*, 36 (1955), 99–106.

44. GROTJAHN, M. "Psychoanalytic Investigation of a Seventy-One-Year Old Man with Senile Dementia," *Psychoanal. Q.*, 9 (1940), 80–97.

45. ———. "Some Analytic Observations about the Process of Growing Old," in G. Roheim, ed., *Psychoanalysis and Social Science*, Vol. 3, pp. 301–321. New York: International Universities Press, 1951.

46. HARTMANN, H. *Ego Psychology and the Problem of Adaptation*. New York: International Universities Press, 1958.

47. HAUSER, S. T. "The Psychotherapy of a Depressed Aged Woman," *J. Geriatr. Psychiatry*, 2 (1968), 62–87.

48. HERKIMER, J. and J. A. M. MEERLOO. "Treatment of Mental Disturbances in Elderly Women," *Social Casework*, 32 (1951), 419–425.

49. JACKSON, J. J. "The Blacklands of Gerontology," *Aging Hum. Devel.*, 2 (1971), 156–172.

50. JELLIFFE, S. E. "The Old Age Factor in Psychoanalytic Therapy," *Med. J. Record*, 121 (1925), 7–12.

51. JUNG, C. G. "The Stages of Life," in *Modern Man in Search of a Soul*. New York: Harcourt, Brace, 1933.

52. KAUFMAN, M. "Psychoanalysis in Late Life Depressions," *Psychoanal. Q.*, 6 (1937), 308–335.

53. KLEIN, W. H., E. J. LE SHAN, and S. S. FURMAN. *Promoting Mental Health of Older People through Group Methods: A Practical Guide*. New York: Mental Health Materials Center, 1965.

54. KUBIE, S. and G. LANDAU. *Group Work with the Aged*. New York: International Universities Press, 1953.

55. KÜBLER-ROSS, E. *On Death and Dying*. New York: Macmillan, 1969.

56. LAWTON, G. "Psychotherapy with Older Persons," *Psychoanalysis*, 1 (1952), 27.

57. LEWIS, M. I. and R. N. BUTLER. "Why Is Women's Lib Ignoring Old Women?" *Aging Hum. Devel.*, 3 (1972), 223–231.

58. LIEDERMAN, P. C. and V. R. LIEDERMAN. "Group Therapy: An Approach to Problems of Geriatric Patients," *Current Psychiatr. Ther.*, 7 (1967), 179–185.

59. LINDEMANN, E. "Symptomatology and Management of Acute Grief," *Am. J. Psychiatry*, 101 (1944), 141–148.

60. LINDEN, M. E. "The Significance of Dual Leadership on Gerontologic Group Psychotherapy: Studies in Gerontologic Human Relations, III," *Int. J. Group Psychother.*, 4 (1954), 262–273.

61. ———. "Transference in Gerontologic Group Psycho-Therapy: Studies in Gerontologic Human Relations, IV," *Int. J. Group Psychother.*, 5 (1955), 61–79.

62. LOWENTHAL, M. F. "Antecedents of Isolation and Mental Illness in Old Age," *Arch. Gen. Psychiatry*, 12 (1965), 245–254.

63. MADDOX, G. L. "Disengagement Theory. A Critical Evaluation," *Gerontologist*, 4 (1964), 80–82, 103.

64. MARTIN, L. J. *A Handbook for Old Age Counselors*. San Francisco: Geertz, 1944.

65. MASTERS, W. H. and V. E. JOHNSON. *Human Sexual Inadequacy*. London: Churchill, 1970.

66. MEERLOO, J. A. M. "Psychotherapy with Elderly People," *Geriatrics*, 10 (1955), 583–587.

67. ———. "Transference and Resistance in Geriatric Psychotherapy." *Psychoanal. Rev.*, 42 (1955), 72–82.

68. MODELL, A. "Aging and Psychoanalytic Theories of Regression," *J. Geriatr. Psychiatry*, 3 (1960), 139–146.

69. NEUGARTEN, B. L., R. J. HAVIGHURST, and S. S. TOBIN. "The Measurement of Life Satisfaction," *J. Gerontol.*, 16 (1961), 134–143.

70. NEUGARTEN, B. L. and R. J. KRAINES. "Menopausal Symptoms in Women of Various Ages," *Psychosom. Med.*, 27 (1965), 266–273.

71. NEWMAN, G. and C. B. NICHOLS. "Sexual Activities and Attitudes in Older Persons," *JAMA*, 173 (1960), 33–34.

72. OBERLEDER, M. "Crisis Therapy in Mental Breakdown of the Aging," *Gerontologist*, 10 (1970), 111–114.

73. PERLIN, S. "Psychiatric Screening in a Home for the Aged: I. A Follow-up Study," *Geriatrics*, 13 (1958), 747–751.

74. PERLIN, S. and R. N. BUTLER. (1963) "Psychiatric Aspects of Adaptation of the Aging Experience," in *Human Aging: A*

Biological and Behavioral Study, pp. 159–191. Washington: U.S. Govt. Print. Off., 1971.

75. PFEIFFER, E. "Geriatric Sex Behavior," *Med. Aspects Human Sexual.*, 3 (1969), 19–29.

76. PINCUS, A. "Reminiscence in Aging and Its Implications for Social Work Practice," *Social Work*, 15 (1970), 47–53.

77. PINDERHUGHES, C. A. "The Universal Resolution of Ambivalence by Paranoia with an Example in Black and White," *Am. J. Psychother.*, 24 (1970), 597–610.

78. RECHTSCHAFFEN, A. "Psychotherapy with Geriatric Patients: A Review of the Literature," *J. Gerontol.*, 14 (1959), 73–84.

79. ROCKWELL, F. V. "Psychotherapy in the Older Individual," in O. J. Kaplan, ed., *Mental Disorders in Late Life*, 2nd ed., pp. 423–445. Stanford Calif.: Stanford University Press, 1956.

80. ROSSMAN, I. *Clinical Geriatrics*. Philadelphia: Lippincott, 1971.

81. RYDER, M. B. "Case Work with the Aged Parent and His Adult Children," *Family*, 26 (1945), 243–250.

82. SCHOFIELD, W. *Psychotherapy: The Purchase of Friendship*. Englewood Cliffs, N.J.: Prentice-Hall, 1964.

83. SILVER, A. "Group Psychotherapy with Senile Psychotic Patients," *Geriatrics*, 5 (1950), 147–150.

84. STERN, K. "Problems Encountered in an Old Age Counseling Center." *Trans. Conf. on Problem of Aging*, pp. 30–38. New York: Josiah Macy Foundation, 1950.

85. STREIB, G. F. and C. S. SCHNEIDER. *Retirement in American Society*. New York: Cornell University Press, 1971.

86. TOWNSEND, P. *The Family Life of Old People*. Glencoe, Ill.: Free Press, 1957.

87. TURNER, H. "Promoting Understanding of Aged Patients," *Social Casework*, 34 (1953), 428–435.

88. VERWOERDT, A. *Communication With the Fatally Ill*. Springfield, Ill.: Charles C. Thomas, 1966.

89. WASSER, E. *Creative Approaches in Casework with the Aging*. New York: Family Service Assoc., 1966.

90. WAYNE, G. J. "Psychotherapy in Senescence," *Ann. West. Med. Surg.*, 6 (1952), 88–91.

91. WEINBERG, J. "Psychotherapy of the Aged," in J. H. Masserman et al, eds., *Progress in Psychotherapy, Anxiety and Therapy*, Vol. 2, pp. 103–109. New York: Grune & Stratton, 1957.

92. YALOM, I. D. *The Theory and Practice of Group Psychotherapy*, 1st ed. New York: Basic Books, 1970.

93. ZARSKY, E. L. and D. BLAU. "The Understanding and Management of Narcissistic Regression and Dependency in an Elderly Woman Observed over an Extended Period of Time," *J. Geriatr. Psychiatry*, 3 (1970), 160–176.

CHAPTER 43

THE TREATMENT OF
DRUG ABUSERS[*]

Edward C. Senay

⟨ Introduction

THE DEFINITION of drug abuse depends upon the vantage point of the person defining it. In the emergency room, drug abuse is a serious medical psychiatric problem. The proportion of cases with drug-related problems presenting in general hospitals is slowly and unquestionably growing, although it is not of the same order as that associated with alcoholism. In the classroom, drug abuse is a perplexing and unresolved problem in education and prevention. In the school, medical aspects are not prominent, but social features are, and the drug-abuse problem is closely related to the problem of delinquency. In the courtroom, drug abuse is a major legal problem; various estimates place the proportion of inmates with drug-related offenses in State and City prison systems somewhere between one and three quarters.[18] From the vantage point of a Mayor or a Gov-

* Prepared with the technical assistance of Richard J. Weinberg.

ernor, drug abuse is a political problem of serious dimensions because of its relationship to street crime. The drug crisis in U.S. troops during the Viet Nam war generated direct Presidential concern and major governmental response.[22] The legal, educational, and political problems associated with drug abuse should be understood by the psychiatrist, if he is to achieve maximum therapeutic results.

From every vantage point drug abuse should be defined as a social problem with major medical-psychiatric and legal aspects.[74] It is established that drug abuse begins as an affliction of adolescence, although since the late 1960s younger age groups are also becoming involved. Drug experimentation begins in adolescent groups and peer-to-peer transmission is responsible for epidemics.[30] Epidemics occur now in all strata of society but are most malignant when they occur in disadvantaged minority groups in the inner city.[41] In these groups it is particularly important to recognize the essentially social nature of this problem. For those caught in the frequent drug epidemics sweeping through inner-city neighborhoods, the prescription of a job is of greater ultimate import than the prescription of methadone or of any form of psychotherapy. It appears that although some progress has been made,[24] innovative social programs will be required if we are to make any real inroads into the problem of drug abuse.[61] Treating cases does nothing to alleviate the conditions responsible for creating the cases in the first instance, and if one defines the problem solely in medical-psychiatric terms, one is forced to watch the cycle of improvement through treatment followed by repeated relapse, because the medical model can achieve only limited success with what is essentially a social problem.

Before turning to the issues of treatment, it is also important to understand that there is a subtle and very important issue involved in the politics of drug abuse; namely, the relationship between the government and the mind and body of the citizen. Powerful politicians and professionals concerned with drug abuse call for compulsory testing of the urine of all school children with involuntary treatment for those detected. Indeed, such an approach has been the backbone of the Armed Forces strategy of drug abuse prevention and treatment.[88] Tennant states[80] that the approach was so successful that civilian application is justified. Heroin addicts are compared with smallpox carriers with the merits of "quarantine" in prison or on islands (both perhaps for life) debated. Federal registration of all addicts in treatment could become a reality. The social context in which treatment occurs then is changing as the balance between individual freedom and society's need for protection appears to be shifting in ponderous, uncertain, and some would say in ominous fashion.[23]

(Acute Treatment of Opiate and Polydrug Abuse

In this discussion we will follow the generally accepted division of clinical problems in drug abuse into those associated with opiates, e.g.,

heroin or demerol dependence, and those associated with so-called polydrug abuse. Such definitions are not precise, but a generally accepted nosology of drug problems does not exist.

In the treatment[42,75] of the drug dependent one must be prepared to deal with acute physiological and/or psychological crises, and also with long-term treatment of chronic problems. Acute treatment per se cannot cure a chronic drug abuser; its goals are to preserve life, to alleviate pain and suffering, and to encourage the person to seek long-term treatment. It has been said that it is absurd to expend effort on the acute management of a drug abuser who may return a week later with the same problem; but surely this is a legitimate function of the physician, just as much as providing cardiac care for the patient with irreversible atherosclerosis, or chemotherapy for the terminal-cancer patient. In the past, an attitude of moral judgment by society made it difficult for a drug abuser to get the necessary medical attention but this has improved as physicians and hospital administrators have become more aware of these problems and as treatment programs have expanded. Treatment efforts principally based on the work of Dole and Nyswander,[20,21] and Diederich, as cited by Casrield[6] and Yablonski,[89] have dispelled the apathy that once characterized the field.

General Considerations of Acute Treatment

The issue of trust is a problem in all phases of treatment of the drug abuser, but it is particularly important in the acute phase. The patient, being possibly liable for criminal prosecution, and possibly suspicious due to drug effects, may be understandably reluctant to tell the truth. However, a demonstration of understanding and helping the patient should elicit cooperation. If the patient is a juvenile, the psychiatrist may be required to notify the parents; there is much variation between States on this point. It is also necessary to understand that the current youth culture makes it difficult for its members to admit the need for help from other than its own members.[69] Furthermore, this culture puts a premium on "putting down" people in authority. In dealing with drug abusers, the physician will find it useful to focus on the job at hand and to avoid responding to provocations, while exhibiting a willingness to learn about the patient and his world.

After the history has been taken, it may be useful to examine the patient for old and fresh needle marks. If it appears that he has used drugs intravenously, he may have complications, such as skin abscesses or hepatitis. Less common disorders associated with the life style and mode of drug use include tuberculosis, venereal diseases, endocarditis, pulmonary granulomas, tetanus, malaria, ulceration of the nasal mucosa and emboli in lungs and eyes.[48,70]

Opiate Overdose

Overdose of narcotics has become a frequent problem in hospital emergency rooms. The question of whether death from overdose is directly caused by ingestion of a lethal dose of narcotics, or by some synergism of opioids and alcohol or sedatives, or by some little-known allergic phenomenon, has been the subject of controversy.[6] In any event, treatment involves the following procedures:

1. Clear airway, maintain respiration artificially, and administer oxygen.
2. Administer narcotic antagonists, e.g., Naloxone · HC_1, 0.4–1.2 mg. IV (pediatric dose 0.05 mg./kg); Levallorphan tartrate, 1–3 mg. IV (pediatric dose 0.075 mg./kg); Nalorphine · HC_1, 5–10 mg IV (pediatric dose 0.1 mg./kg.). Naloxone is the drug of choice,[27] with a high therapeutic margin of safety, but it has not yet been approved for administration to children and neonates. In uncomplicated overdose, response to administration of antagonists is dramatic and diagnostic. Failure to see prompt improvement in the respiratory rate implies that factors other than opiates are responsible for the respiratory depression which characterizes opiate overdose. The following considerations should be kept in mind when administering antagonists:

   a. Narcotic antagonists specifically antagonize opioids. They may aggravate respiratory depression if caused by other CNS (central nervous system) depressants, although Naloxone appears safe in this respect. In addition Naloxone appears to be effective in Pentazocine overdose, while other antagonists are not.

   b. Antagonists are effective for only about two hours and repeat doses may be necessary. Heroin may remain active for six hours, methadone for twenty-four hours, and L-alpha-acetylmethadol for forty-eight to seventy-two hours, so care must be taken not to release the patient prematurely. As a rule of thumb, one should observe all opiate overdose cases for at least twenty-four to forty-eight hours in the hospital. Even after discharge someone should be with the patient at all times for another one- to two-day period.

   c. In an active addict, antagonists can precipitate a very powerful withdrawal syndrome. They should be given in doses large enough to stimulate consciousness, but not so large as to cause severe withdrawal.

3. Manage pulmonary edema if present.
4. Treat for shock if indicated.
5. Treat secondary complications if present.

Opiate Withdrawal

The opiate-withdrawal syndrome, while seldom fatal, can cause great suffering, and should be treated medically.[43] There is no rationale for "cold turkey" withdrawals under any circumstances, because effective treatment is simple, inexpensive, and can be accomplished in any setting. The treatment of choice is to stabilize the patient on methadone and then to withdraw this drug gradually. The general principle in withdrawal is to provide the addict with sufficient drug to eliminate withdrawal signs without causing mental clouding or a "high," and then to reduce dosage gradually. In all withdrawal attempts, constant clinical monitoring is necessary, for it is common for heroin addicts to be also addicted to sedatives or to alcohol. In the instance of multiple dependencies the safest technique appears to be to withdraw one drug at a time, while stabilizing the patient on whatever other drugs he may be addicted to, e.g., chlordiazepoxide for alcohol, and barbiturates for barbiturate dependence, while methadone is withdrawn in a patient who is severely dependent on alcohol, barbiturates, and heroin. Since heroin addicts are notoriously manipulative, more attention should be paid to objective withdrawal symptoms, e.g., lacrimation, rhinorrhea, pupillary dilation, and piloerection, than to subjective reports. Frequently a single oral dose of 20 mg. methadone suppresses withdrawal. If 20 mg. fails to suppress symptoms, 5- or 10-mg. increments may be given until symptoms are suppressed; then the dose may be reduced approximately 1–5 mg. per day until abstinence is achieved.

If the addict was using methadone, he may require a higher initial dosage and more gradual reduction. In uncomplicated cases, that is, without coexisting major medical or psychiatric problems, detoxification from heroin can be achieved in seven to ten days, while detoxification from methadone may require more time, particularly if high doses were used. Withdrawal of methadone in patients who have been maintained on this drug for years is an area of research at present.[10] Clinical experience certainly indicates that the difficulties in achieving abstinence are substantial for many of these patients. Methadone-maintained patients requesting to be withdrawn should be counseled and their motivations reviewed prior to any attempt to achieve abstinence. As a rule of thumb, patients who attempt to withdraw because of external pressure, e.g., from peers or governmental regulations, do not appear to do well. The patient who has made steady progress and wants in his own right to become abstinent has the best prognosis.[19] The abstinence attempt should occur at a time in which other areas of the patient's life are relatively free of stress, and continued counseling should be provided on a

regular basis for at least one year following complete abstinence.

Before release from treatment for overdose or withdrawal, every effort should be made to encourage the addict to seek long-term treatment. It cannot be overstressed that the physician and the treatment team's ability to create at least minimal trust in the patient is significant in affecting the amount of drug required, the length of withdrawal, and in creating the conditions for a successful rehabilitation.

Sedatives and Minor Tranquilizers Overdose

An overdose of sedatives, as with opiates, is potentially life-threatening. Symptoms range from mild intoxication, similar to drunkenness, to deep coma and death. All CNS depressants, if taken in sufficient quantity, appear to produce a similar comatose state, although many investigators feel that opiate overdose produces a characteristic "shallow coma" with low respiratory rates (4–6 per min.). The CNS depressants are synergistic. Treatment is essentially symptomatic and medical in the acute phase. The following measures are recommended:

1. Gastric lavage only if drug was taken orally, recently, and the patient is conscious.
2. Use respiratory support such as intubation and mechanical ventilation if necessary. Administer oxygen in high concentrations, preferably at tidal volume of 12–15 cc./1 kg. body weight.
3. Treat shock with IV fluids and vasopressor if indicated. Monitor electrolyte balance.
4. Continue monitoring of vital functions until consciousness returns. Treat cardiovascular problems symptomatically.
5. If barbiturates are implicated, diuresis and alkalinization of urine is helpful. Dialysis may be useful. Analeptic drugs are probably contraindicated.
6. Upon recovery, care must be taken with respect to possible suicidal potential (CNS depressants are commonly used in

sucide attempts) and possible addiction to CNS depressants.

Sedative Withdrawal

All sedatives and minor tranquilizers are potentially addicting, particularly short-acting sedatives. Withdrawal is medically more serious than is the case with opiates; very abrupt withdrawal, for example, carries the risk of death.[86] It is thus imperative that such withdrawal be conducted under close supervision in a hospital setting. Recently outpatient withdrawal has been described, and there may be circumstances in which it may be the only approach possible.[78]

Withdrawal from short-acting sedatives begins within twenty-four hours, although the withdrawal syndrome from longer-acting sedatives may not occur for several days following abstinence. Nervousness, anxiety, insomnia, abdominal cramps, nausea and vomiting, disorientation, hallucinations, coarse tremors, hyperreflexia, and convulsions may be observed in variable subsets.

Treatment

The CNS depressants, including sedatives such as the barbiturates Methaqualone and Glutethimide, minor tranquilizers, and alcohol are cross-tolerant, and theoretically withdrawal syndromes may be treated identically with short-acting barbiturates. However, it is established practice that barbiturates are used for withdrawal from sedatives, while a minor tranquilizer, such as Chlordiazepoxide or Diazepam is used for alcohol withdrawal. Given the demonstrated effectiveness of these drugs in these conditions there is no compelling rationale for change.

Berle, Gamen, and Lowinson find that alcohol/sedative addicts can be detoxified safely with sodium amytal, according to the following schedule:[2]

Day 1: four doses of 250 mg. IM QID or eight doses of 125 mg. IM every three hours.
Day 2: four doses of 200 mg. orally QID.
Day 3: four doses of 100 mg. orally QID.
Day 4: three doses of 100 mg. orally TID.
Day 5: two doses of 100 mg. orally BID.
Day 6: two doses of 50 mg. orally BID.
Day 7: one dose of 50 mg. orally, twenty-four hours after previous dose.

Of course, the appearance of signs of withdrawal, such as restlessness or hyperreflexia, indicates that additional sodium amytal may be needed. Others have had similar success using secobarbital or phenobarbital.

Stimulant Abuse

Stimulants, including many amphetamine derivatives, phenmetrazine, methylphenidate, cocaine, and others, are more widely abused than generally recognized.[25] In view of their substantial danger of abuse, medically approved stimulants should be prescribed carefully and only when the benefits exceed the potential dangers implicit in these drugs. When grossly abused, all stimulants produce a similar clinical picture, including some or all of the following symptoms:[27]

1. Insomnia.
2. Anorexia, with possible malnutrition.
3. Hypertension, tachycardia, elevated body temperature.
4. Dilated pupils, muscular tremor.
5. If taken as snuff, possible damage to nasal mucosa; if taken IV, extensive needle scars and associated pathology.
6. Verbosity; constant, "rambling" talk.
7. Extreme nervousness, suspiciousness, and hostility which may develop into a characteristic stimulant-induced paranoid psychosis. This psychosis is very similar to that of paranoid schizophrenia, except that thought disorders are not prominent, and the short-term prognosis is good. Upon termination of the drug, psychotic manifestations usually disappear within a few days, although occasionally they may last for several weeks or months.

Acute treatment of stimulant abuse depends on the group of symptoms observed.

ACUTE OVERDOSE

This condition is rather uncommon, and is seen most commonly in cocaine abuse. It can include severe hyperthermia, convulsions, cerebrovascular accidents, and possible cardiovascular or respiratory collapse. Treatment must be rapid and appropriate to the symptomology, including respiratory or cardiac support if indicated, sedation, and aggressive treatment of hyperthermia.

CHRONIC-ABUSE SYNDROME

Treatment is primarily psychotherapeutic and in severe psychotic reactions, short-term psychiatric hospitalization may be indicated. Minor tranquilizers will control the anxiety seen in these states. Davis recommends haloperidol to alleviate psychotic symptomology;[11] phenothiazines are not indicated as they may retard the excretion of amphetamines.

STIMULANT WITHDRAWAL

Usually the chronic abuse syndrome is alleviated after a single sleep period (often twenty-four to forty-eight hours long). However, possibly due to depletion of brain catecholamines or other causes,[84] there is usually a withdrawal syndrome, which may need additional treatment. This syndrome, which may last weeks or months, is characterized by:

1. Moderate to severe depression, possible suicidal ideation.
2. Sleep disturbances.
3. Postpsychotic suspiciousness or hostility.
4. Mild tremor in extremities.
5. Possible malnutrition, liver damage, severe caries, mucosal irritation, etc.

Initially treatment should be oriented to restoration of biological health, including sedatives at night until the twenty-four-hour cycle is restored, ample diet, supplemented by vitamins, and an appropriate treatment of associated pathology, e.g., hepatitis. Major tranquilizers should be used only if psychosis persists. Antidepressants are contraindicated in the first week of treatment, as blood levels of stimulants may persist for some time, a situation which creates the possibility of undesirable interaction between the two classes of drugs.[11] After medical needs are met, there should be referral for long-term care.

VOLATILES

There is a current phenomenon of abuse of psychoactive volatile chemicals,[51] although few of these are considered drugs in the usual sense. The use of such substances is predominantly among youth between eleven and eighteen years of age, many of whom have difficulty getting access to common drugs of abuse.[64] Substances known to have been abused include gasoline, varnish, paint thinner, cleaning fluids, aerosol sprays, glue, chloroform, ether, amyl nitrite, nitrous oxide, toluene, and many others. In general, intoxication with such chemicals is short and is characterized by stuporous, hostile, "drunken" behavior. Often a chemical odor may be noticed on the breath. The most common clinical disorders involve a pneumonialike state due to irritant properties of the substances, and possible liver or kidney damage. Occasionally, there may be cardiac dysfunction, but the most common serious problem is anoxia. In general, volatiles do not appear to produce dependence or to be involved in chronic-abuse patterns although a few cases of a decade of continued use are known. The usual pattern observed is experimentation, abuse, and then cessation of use as the young person's age increases.

Hallucinogens

Hallucinogens[75] are widely available and subject to frequent experimentation.[56,77] Whether controlled use of these drugs over extended periods is possible for the average person is doubtful, but there is no question that a few individuals do appear to be able to control such use. For many, use cannot be controlled and sooner or later attempts to do so turn into negative and frightening experiences. Due to the variety of hallucinogens and the unpredictability of content of illicit drugs, the youthful abuser usually does not know what he is ingesting; this is particularly true of "street" drugs.[8]

The relatively rare serious physical reaction may consist of convulsions, elevated body temperature, severe vomiting, respiratory depression and/or cardiac dysfunction. Such disorders may be caused by phencyclidine (PCP), belladonna alkaloids and various other drugs.

CLINICAL SYMPTOMS

Patients who come to medical attention after using hallucinogenic chemicals may be disoriented, anxious, or panicky.[79] They may have sensory disturbances including abnormal sensitivity to or interpretation of stimuli. Hallucinations of course can be prominent and there may be ideas of reference and inappropriate affect.

Psychiatric syndromes resulting from hallucinogens can, at times, be distinguished from ordinary psychotic states by the history of drug use, by the presence of disorientation and by the relative preponderance of visual phenomena in the drug-related emergency. In addition the physician will sense that ego processes are not damaged to the degree to which they are damaged in the acute schizophrenic break. Patients on a "bad trip" are more likely to report that they see or hear "crazy" things, and their judgment and control appears to be more intact than is the case of the acute psychotic break. In addition the symptomology of the bad trip tends to be labile; delusional symptoms are transient, affect rapidly changes; often the patient can emerge suddenly from extreme confusion to complete rationality, only to return to confusion minutes later.

Physiological signs, such as dilated pupils, cramps, nausea, or mild tachycardia are common. It is not surprising that most individuals who have used hallucinogens report difficulty talking or communicating while intoxicated, or that many become frightened. Hallucinogens do not usually leave significant long-term pathology, but chronic psychosis has been reported. Although differing somewhat from drug to drug, most hallucinogens begin taking effect one to two hours after an oral dose. Intoxication is very powerful for about five hours, then declining over the next eight hours. Usually the individual is fully "normal" after twenty-four hours; although he may report unusual thoughts or feelings as much as a week later. The most common adverse reaction is panic, usually because the psychological factors involved in the use of the drug are pathological and because the social setting is not supportive.

TREATMENT

Typical reports of bad experiences include the following:

1. Extreme disorientation—"I must be losing my mind, I'll never come down"—and other similar feelings aggravated by disorientation in time.
2. Fearful, paranoid reaction—"Why are they looking at me that way?" This may be partially induced by the illegal nature of the experience; fear of police and other authorities is common, while anxiety and disorientation also inhibit ego function. Pathological group dynamics are also frequently associated with this syndrome.
3. Frightening hallucinations, or release of threatening unconscious material.
4. Severe ego disturbances—"I have just died," or "I am you" experiences.
5. Hypochondria, including feelings of asphyxiation or impending death.

Treatment must be performed in a nonthreatening fashion. After checking vital signs to eliminate possibility of physiological danger, the patient should be "brought down," i.e., treated in a place that is quiet and dimly lit. Low levels of sensory input are desirable because of the distractability involved.

If a friend of the patient is available, it is usually wise to keep him or her present, but only a small number of people should be involved. Direct contradiction of fantasies is not helpful; emphasis should be on alleviating anxiety ("Everything's going to be fine," "The drug will wear off in a few hours," "Are you feeling better now?" etc.), coupled with friendliness and assistance in orientation ("you're in a hospital," "you took a pill," "would you like some orange juice?" etc.) Quiet music, or even a TV, can be useful. At least one person should remain with the patient until the effects of the drug have worn off.

Chemotherapy should be reserved for refractory cases whose agitation is not reduced by psychological approaches. In such instances chlordiazepoxide, diazepoxide, or barbiturates can be helpful. Phenothiazines should not be used as they may interact with many hallucinogenic drugs to cause lability of blood pressure and/or worsening of the psychoticlike state. In some cases, short or long-term hospitalization may be necessary. Prognosis is variable; serious and chronic adverse reactions have been noted.

FLASHBACKS

Flashbacks develop in a significant percentage of hallucinogenic experiences.[76] Typically these are recurrent spells of a few seconds or minutes of acute depersonalization or hallucinosis reminiscent of the hallucinogenic experience. They are usually precipitated by fatigue or acute stress and may persist for many weeks. They ordinarily stop permanently after a few months, and reassurance is usually adequate treatment. In more severe cases, minor tranquilizers or psychotherapy may be indicated.

Cannabis

Cannabis products such as marijuana and hashish are widely used but only rarely produce reactions severe enough to require medical attention.[54] Occasionally acute panic develops and in such cases the general measures described above should be instituted. Cannabis use also can be associated with psychotic behavior. In such cases current knowledge suggests that treatment should be oriented to underlying personal problems, not to the drug per se.

⟨⟨ Chronic Treatment of Opiate Dependence and Polydrug Abuse

Long-term treatment may be conveniently divided into chemotherapeutic approaches in which a drug plays a major, though not exclusive, role in treatment, and sociotherapeutic approaches in which drugs play only a minor role.

General Comments on Chemotherapy

All major advances to date in the chemotherapy of drug abuse have centered around the problem of heroin dependence, or more generally opioid dependence. "Opioid" denotes the class of drugs including the analgesic alkaloids of opium, such as morphine and codeine, their derivatives, such as heroin and oxycodone, and purely synthetic chemicals, such as methadone and meperidine which are pharmacologically similar to morphine. Opioids share many features. They all induce tolerance—repeated doses give less response than the first dose, and they all act as positive reinforcers in animal experiments. In addition their repeated use produces physical dependence, a state in which cessation of drug use causes an "abstinence" syndrome, and they exhibit cross-tolerance, i.e., a dose of one relieves the abstinence syndrome related to the use of another.[39,43]

The British System

Until the Harrison Act of 1914 there were many opiate addicts in the United States, but they did not exhibit the kinds of pathology we see in heroin addicts today. After the Harrison Act, clinics opened which provided addicts with a medically supervised source of opiates. These clinics operated with reasonable success for a few years, but a scandal in 1920, in regard to some improperly managed opiate clinics, resulted in their closing.[5]

In 1924, a British committee headed by Sir Humphrey Rolleston examined the opiate policies of the United States. He concluded that our approach had not appreciably reduced the incidence of opiate addiction and had forced U.S. addicts to become criminals. On the basis of this finding, the Rolleston committee recommended the implementation of what is now called the British System, namely, greatly restricting availability of opiates, but permitting addicts to obtain opiates from physicians. This system did not pretend to cure addicts, but it attempted to maintain addicts as noncriminal and to prevent the recruitment of new addicts. By 1951 there were only 301 known addicts in Britain.

In the 1960s, a significant black market in opiates developed in Britain, and substantial numbers of new addicts developed. The country tightened its opiate laws to restrict the dispensation of opiates to addicts to only a few doctors and clinics, and to require more extensive registration. In 1970, there were 1430 known British addicts, the number was again apparently stable.

The British technique appears to have been successful. It was developed on a pragmatic basis, not using medical or legal models. It has been suggested that the United States should adopt the British policy, although the pressure for this has abated somewhat as more effective treatment techniques have been found here. The British experience appears to have limited applicability to the United States, since we have perhaps a thousand times as many addicts as Britain, and a problem of quite different cultural and social significance. The American addict, for example, is profoundly criminalized and could be expected to be far less compliant to rules and more likely to engage in black market practices. Moreover, the American addict is in much more need of rehabilitative services apart from addiction treatment per se to overcome the social gradient which distinguishes him from his British counterpart. For detailed discussion on these issues the reader should consult Brecher[5] and other references.[63]

Methadone Maintenance

Methadone maintenance, pioneered by Dole and Nyswander in the 1960's, is the current treatment of choice for many chronic opiate addicts.[7,20,21,35] The consensus of workers in the field is that drug-treatment programs using methadone in support of their efforts can be useful for some 40 to 60 percent of addicts in aiding them to achieve a socially desirable change in lifestyle.[31,33,47]

RATIONALE

Methadone, a synthetic opioid, is subjectively similar to morphine in that effective analgesia follows the injection of 5 to 10 mg. In sufficiently high dosage, it has euphorigenic effects comparable to those experienced from the use of heroin. However, as it is used in treatment, the dose is adjusted so that withdrawal does not occur while euphoria is avoided; the dosage range in which both purposes can be achieved is large. The duration of methadone-induced analgesia is similar to that of morphine (three to four hours,) but withdrawal discomfort in methadone-dependent users does not commence for eight to twenty-four hours, while morphine withdrawal occurs after four to six hours. The extended "holding" period of methadone plus the fact that methadone, unlike morphine, is orally effective, defines its usefulness in treating opiate addiction. Orally administered, one dose of methadone effectively prevents the appearance of the abstinence syndrome for twenty-four hours. Heroin, on the other hand, requires frequent parenteral and unsterile administration with its associated hazards. Heroin administration can also cause the addict to "see-saw" between euphoric stupor and incipient withdrawal.

Like other opioids, methadone is a respiratory depressant and antitussive agent. It produces mild hypothermia and hyperglycemia, and in general, has neurophysiological effects similar to morphine.[43] Methadone, as it is used in maintenance programs, has several common side effects, including sedation, constipation, excessive sweating, urinary retention, and changes in libido, i.e., usually a decrease but occasionally an increase. Pruritis, urticaria, nausea, or delirium have been rarely reported. Appetite may improve with the consequent development of a weight problem.

Clinical experience in the treatment of heroin addicts suggests that the psychophysiological changes attendant upon the addict's attempt to change his lifestyle are usually more significant than those pharmacologically induced by methadone. Tolerance to most side effects usually develops quickly, except for constipation and excessive sweating. No remedy is known to counteract these troublesome side effects but they usually disappear after a period of weeks or months.[73]

TREATMENT

Methadone maintenance, i.e., a treatment contract in which the patient expects to receive methadone daily for the indefinite future, is indicated for heroin addicts who are not strongly motivated to achieve abstinence. Methadone-maintenance therapy does not have the goal of "complete cure," if by this phrase we mean complete and permanent abstention from all opiate drugs and full social rehabilitation. In view of the poor prognosis of heroin addicts, goals of methadone maintenance are, at a minimum, reduction of illicit drug use, reduction of criminal activity, increase in productivity as reflected by employment in the legitimate job market and increase in self esteem.[72] In addition, improvement in family and community functioning is sought.

In the classic work of Dole and Nyswander methadone maintenance involved an initial period of induction, in which the patient was first given methadone sufficient to eliminate withdrawal symptoms.[20] Over a period of several weeks this dose was gradually raised to a "blocking" oral dose of approximately 100 mg./day. Reported side effects were minimal, and opiate "hunger" was eliminated. Not only did this dose eliminate opiate hunger, but tolerance to opioids was raised to such a degree that normal doses of "street" heroin had no effect. It was believed that loss of the positive reinforcement from heroin administration would lead to extinction of the habit. (However, many chronic addicts apparently do not have a "high" following self administration of heroin and take drugs solely to forestall the painful abstinence syndrome).

Dole and Nyswander's original studies limited admissions to male patients between twenty-one and thirty-nine years old with at least a five-year history of heroin addiction and a record of previous (nonmethadone) treatment failures. Excluded were psychotics, alcoholics, medically ill, and mentally deficient patients.

Results of these early studies were promising.[33] Approximately two-thirds of the patients were still in treatment after forty-two months, and many of the others had subsequently joined other treatment programs. Arrest rates declined, while social adjustment, as measured by return to school and legitimate employment, improved. It was noted that approximately 10 percent of the patients simply changed from drug abuse to alcohol, cocaine, barbiturates, or amphetamines, and many of these were expelled from treatment.[35]

On the basis of this and similar experiences, methadone maintenance has gained growing acceptance. More recent studies have indicated lower success rates in other programs, an effect no doubt attributable to more open admissions, i.e., accepting psychotics, alcoholics, and other high-risk addicts into treatment on the theory that while they cannot be expected to show a high degree of rehabilitation, nevertheless, methadone maintenance can provide significant help to many addicts.[72] Some of the differences, of course, may be explained by the poor quality of treatment. In addition, some of the differences in success between programs may be explained by the fact that they are treating people from different addict subcultures.

Appropriate dosage remains a controversial question. Goldstein,[36] and Jaffe et al.[45] have demonstrated that program outcome remains equally good regardless of dose, i.e., 40–50 mg. schedules in comparison to the original 100–120 mg. schedule of Dole and Nyswander. Apparently the ability of high doses to block the effects of heroin is not as important as the relief of opioid craving, which may be effectively achieved at the lower dose. Patients given 50 mg. daily may initially complain of discomfort beginning sixteen to eighteen hours after administration, but they seem to adapt readily to the twenty-four-hour schedule. In

1974 there were over 70,000 addicts in methadone programs. The remarkable growth in this modality of treatment resulted from Federal action which created the Special Action Office for Drug Abuse Prevention.[22]

Urinalysis for the detection of the use of methadone, heroin, and other drugs has became an integral part of maintenance treatment. Addicts are notoriously unreliable in reporting drug-related activities and this is a convenient technique for obtaining independent data. It may also serve a deterrent purpose, by increasing the likelihood that unreported drug use will be detected. When used as a technique for fostering honesty, urine monitoring can be helpful.[85] Tests positive for illicit drugs are an indication that the patient needs help, while negative tests indicate increased ability of the patient to control his behavior. Unfortunately, urine-test results are used also in a punitive "legalistic" fashion and such a practice may destroy a beneficial counselor–patient or doctor–patient relationship.[34]

A typical methadone maintenance clinic provides daily administration of oral methadone, plus such "ancillary" services as vocational, legal, and social counseling. Group therapy is normally provided, but is usually optional. Groups tend to be confrontational in nature, with an emphasis on honesty and direct reporting of feelings. This approach leads to intense emotional experiences, but many patients find the intensity of the groups so anxiety-provoking that they cannot derive benefit from them.

Although the provision of counseling and auxilliary social services in methadone treatment has not yet been conclusively proven to influence treatment outcome, few serious observers doubt that such services play a vital role.[7]

There are subgroups of addicts entering treatment; one subgroup is highly motivated and will improve regardless of treatment; another subgroup is so little motivated and so burdened with social and psychological pathology that no treatment will produce any change; outcome in a third intermediate group is probably strongly dependent on the availability and quality of "auxilliary" treatment services.

Exaddicts are often involved as counselors in drug treatment programs. They are usually highly motivated and uniquely knowledgeable with respect to the meaning of behaviors of patients from the addict subculture. Some believe that they provide an important role in mediating the sociocultural gap between physicians and addicts. They also serve as role models for new patients. For some exaddict workers, a job in a treatment program may be an important stabilizing force in maintaining progress in rehabilitation. The precise role of the exaddict worker in methadone maintenance clinics remains to be explored fully. Programs vary widely in the extent to which they employ ex-addicts and few studies have been carried out to help define the needs and potentials of this important class of workers.

It is unclear whether traditional psychotherapy is useful to most patients on methadone maintenance. Provision of chemical therapy and the general affiliation with a program seem to be more important, but psychotherapy is clearly indicated among those patients manifesting serious psychopathology.

Current FDA regulations[28] require detoxification of opiate addicts who have been addicted for less than two years; detoxification schedules for such patients are prescribed by FDA regulation and cannot extend beyond twenty-one days. Diagnosis is also complicated by the existence of "pseudo-junkies,"[32] i.e., youthful addicts who have all the stigmata of heroin addicts including positive urines for morphine and acute withdrawal syndromes but who prove to be intolerant to low doses of methadone.

COMMON CLINICAL PROBLEMS

In general, coexisting medical/psychiatric problems may be treated concurrently in methadone-maintained patients. Caution should be exercised in the administration of CNS depressants, e.g., phenothiazines or sedatives, because of the possibility of synergism. Clinical experience suggests that medical or surgical crises in methadone-maintained patients are best managed by continuing daily oral methadone administration at the normal dose. Should parenteral administration be necessary during such crises 10 mg. of methadone two or three times a day either IM or SC (subcutaneously) will almost always suffice regardless of previous oral dose levels. Analgesic needs do not change and are not covered by the methadone. If opiates are indicated, e.g., Demerol, they should be administered in normal doses concurrent with maintenance methadone. Pentazocine should not be used for analgesia in the methadone-maintenance patient as it may precipitate withdrawal symptoms.[53]

Pregnant addicts have been maintained on methadone through delivery.[3] Surprisingly few newborns of such patients exhibit withdrawal syndromes but such cases when they arise may be easily treated with small doses of paregoric or methadone. Possible teratogenic or abortifacient properties of methadone have not yet been conclusively ruled out, but one must bear in mind, when weighing the risks of maintaining pregnant patients on methadone, hazards to the fetus implicit in the lifestyle of the heroin addict and the fact that premature delivery is a common occurrence in the pregnant addict. Further experience is needed before guidelines can be set down with reference to these questions. Zelson[90] seriously questions whether methadone has any role in the treatment of the pregnant addict.

The most serious common complication of methadone maintenance therapy is alcoholism. O'Donnel reports that two-thirds of the addicts seen at Lexington have a history of alcoholic excess,[65] so it is not surprising that when opiate addiction is controlled by methadone therapy, many cases of alcohol abuse appear. A patient showing signs of acute alcohol intoxication should not receive methadone while he is intoxicated. Alcohol and methadone are synergistic, and if other CNS depressants have been taken, a lethal outcome is possible. A methadone program should offer support for this common complication whenever possible. This may involve alcohol detoxification, disulfiram therapy, and/or referral to Alcoholics Anonymous.

DISCUSSION

Some have attacked the basic premise of methadone maintenance,[52] pointing out that being an opiate, methadone does not cure opiate addiction, and that abstinence is the only meaningful criterion of cure. However, with increasing experience, it has become clear that a significant percentage of addicts will not become abstinent under the various treatment methods now known. In the light of this observation, it appears that methadone maintenance can provide help to a large number of addicts who would otherwise be returned to full-scale criminal activity and illicit drug use. It must be borne in mind that the typical addict normally uses illegal heroin, which is both expensive and impure. He faces arrest for using heroin and maintaining his habit becomes a full-time job, into which he pours all his energies. He remains in a criminal addict milieu. On the other hand, medically sponsored methadone administration is legal and safe; it permits the addict to seek employment, choose his friends, and lead a more stable life. Psychologically, the status associated with chronic heroin addiction is destructive to self-esteem. By being "on methadone," an addict can feel that he is taking medicine instead of "drugs," and can start to feel some socially sanctioned basis for self-esteem.[37] The treatment clinic can provide support and treatment for primary or secondary psychosocial problems. With community-based control of clinics the argument that methadone maintenance is used as a social control mechanism does not appear to be compelling.

It is too soon to make any definitive statements regarding the future role of methadone maintenance. At present, it appears that methadone maintenance has an important role in the development of a national treatment strategy for problems of drug dependence. It seems indisputable that a large number of people are now being helped in methadone programs. The evidence also suggests that for the average addict, treatment in a program is preferrable to treatment by an individual therapist.

Methadone Substitutes

The compound L-alpha acetylmethadol (LAAM), is a congener of methadone; it differs from methadone in that it suppresses the abstinence syndrome for two to three days, while methadone's effects in this regard last only twenty-four hours. Experience to date suggests that it is therapeutically identical to methadone.[46] Being active for several days, it provides a more convenient form of treatment in which it is possible to deemphasize chemical aspects of the treatment relationship.

From many perspectives, this drug would appear to be a major improvement over methadone. However, even if a very long-acting morphine substitute with minimal toxicity and side effects is perfected, there will still be problems in clinical use, namely, the irrevocable nature of ingestion of a very long-acting drug implies considerable hazard in the case of accidental drug ingestion, or in cases in which medical or clinical considerations indicate termination of opiate support therapy. Affiliation with a clinic such as is required by current methadone treatment may be of overriding importance, and this effect would be lost in the case of a substitute with a long-lasting effect. The significance of these and other reservations is unclear at this point; it appears that longer-acting opioids can make a meaningful contribution to chemotherapy, but it remains uncertain whether they will fully supplant methadone.

Other Morphine Substitutes

For many years scientists have attempted to develop an opioid with effective pain-killing properties, but minimal addiction liability, that is to find a drug which effectively alleviates opioid craving without significant addictive potential. Recent work with propoxyphene napsylate ("Darvon-N"),[81] suggests that this drug (chemically similar to methadone) may provide effective relief for opioid craving while having a low addiction potential. There is room for skepticism regarding such work. Animal experiments with many hundreds of opioids suggest that if a drug is effective as a pain-killer, its effectiveness to relieve abstinence is exactly the same, and also its addiction potential.[39] If propoxyphene napsylate or some other drug proves not to follow this rule, the implications are, of course, highly significant for treatment.

Narcotic Antagonists

There are many known chemicals which directly antagonize opioid effects in the human body, such as nalorphine, naloxone, and cyclazocine.[29,49] Recently, a good deal of research has been devoted to their possible utility in the treatment of opiate addiction.[38] This technique is roughly analogous to the use of disulfiram in the treatment of alcoholism, except that disulfiram creates a situation in which the use of alcohol is associated with negative subjective effects while narcotic antagonists simply block the effects of opiates. To date, effective antagonists are either prohibitively expensive, their effectiveness short-lived, or they are producing unpleasant side effects. Work continues on a cheap, long-acting, orally effective antagonist, free of major side effects.[59]

The best clinical results have been with cyclazocine. It is orally effective, and a dose of 4–8 mg. appears to block the effects of heroin for roughly twenty-four hours. Unfortunately, cyclazocine has several unpleasant side effects. If a therapeutically effective dose is given to a naive subject, such symptoms as irritability, insomnia, and tension are common. Many patients report feeling "unreal," and other subjective effects which they compare to the effects of marijuana or LSD. Side effects may be usually avoided by building up to a therapeutic dose in small increments over a period of weeks. Resnik et al. however, state that rapid induction over a period of a few days successfully avoids the major unpleasant effects of this drug.[67] Side effects that persist can usually be controlled by tranquilizers.

Cyclazocine does not reduce opiate craving, but since it blocks opiate effects there is no positive reinforcement from injecting heroin. Thus one expects to see typical "extinction" behavior in a patient treated with cyclazocine. Cyclazocine is itself an addictive drug, and withdrawal may be accompanied by muscle aches, rhinitis, and subjective discomfort.

Candidates for antagonist treatment must be completely free of drugs, since antagonists induce severe, and conceiveably lethal withdrawal syndromes if administered to opiate dependent patients. Cyclazocine is probably best suited for short-term treatment subsequent to detoxification as an adjunct to other abstinence regimens. It may also prove to have a role in assisting stabilized methadone-maintained patients in achieving abstinence.

Naloxone is an essentially "pure" antagonist, having minimal side effects or addiction potential. Unfortunately it is expensive, short-acting, and variably potent when taken orally. However, it too appears to be useful for a small group of patients attempting to maintain a drug-free status.

Work continues on developing a long-acting (or permanent) antagonist devoid of unpleasant side effects. Naltrexone is one of the newest drugs in this series. Its blocking effects last for twenty-four hours and its use is not accompanied by negative subjective effects; early results are promising.

Heroin Detoxification

While it has been asserted that heroin detoxification without coordinated long-term aftercare treatment is an exercise in futility,[65] others maintain that it can provide meaningful help in certain circumstances. Dole[18] finds that one-half of prisoners in the Manhattan House of Detention for Men are addicts on admission. He presents evidence that detoxification of these new admissions alleviates human suffering, improves prison morale, and reduces the number of incidents of violence and suicide. Lloyd et al. find that while only 3 percent of detoxified addicts remain in treatment, 18 percent are abstinent six months after detoxification.[55] While this is an appreciable success rate, he recommends that aftercare services should be provided. Others point out that in addition to the moderate percentage reporting long-term abstinence, a large percentage attain temporary abstinence, and that this reduces human suffering and heroin related crime, at least temporarily.

Coercive Treatment

Heroin addiction is uniquely tied to criminality and the criminal justice system. There is no psychopharmacological basis for this association; it occurs principally because the street cost of heroin is high and criminal activity is the only source of funds for the average addict.

As a consequence of the social concern over heroin addiction, many approaches to involuntary or semi-voluntary treatment have been proposed, ranging from offering treatment in lieu of prosecution to civil commitment for drug-related crime. Results of such approaches to date are inconclusive. The early addiction treatment center at Lexington, Ky., which used civil commitment extensively, has been criticized, but Vaillant in a number of long-term follow up studies reports rehabilitation rates of about 40 percent.[83] Wieland and Novack report some success in the Philadelphia Criminal Justice program, in which addicts are offered treatment in lieu of prosecution; however, outcome appears to be poorer than in a comparison group of patients without active relationship to the criminal justice system.[87]

There are many unresolved questions in such treatment approaches, including questions of efficacy, medical ethics, civil liberties, and social policy. The National Conference of Commissioners on Uniform State Laws has proposed guidelines for involuntary treatment including the following main points:[4]

1. No mandatory treatment should be provided except for those who have committed a criminal violation.
2. Mandatory treatment should not be imposed for a longer period than the maximum sentence of the criminal violation, or eighteen months, whichever is shorter.
3. The patient should at all times have the option to leave treatment and serve out his jail term.

4. The patient should always have the option of drug-free treatment.

Nonvoluntary treatment may become a major tool in drug-abuse rehabilitation, but experience to date indicates that where treatment opportunities exist, the majority of addicts will voluntarily seek treatment.[40]

Sociotherapy

We use the term "sociotherapy" to denote many different approaches to the treatment of drug abuse. Their underlying common element is that they put primary emphasis on social interaction. Some forbid all "chemicals" as a matter of policy, while others may use drugs quite extensively; however, chemotherapy is at most an adjunct to treatment, and does not itself constitute treatment.

THERAPEUTIC COMMUNITIES

The "therapeutic-community" technique* of drug-abuse rehabilitation (not to be confused with the milieu therapy of Maxwell Jones in psychiatric wards) was created by Charles Diederich in the late 1950s. Diederich, a "graduate" of Alcoholics Anonymous, began holding meetings for alcoholics. Several drug abusers started coming to these meetings and Diederich became interested in their problems. By the early 1960s the structure of Synanon, the archetypal therapeutic community, was completely developed.[12,89] Since then, therapeutic communities have flourished throughout the country.[6] Diederich's basic concept was that a person who uses drugs is emotionally immature and as a consequence cannot function in "straight" society.

"Treatment" in the typical therapeutic community lasts from one to two years, after which the person can reenter the community as a successfully functioning drug-free individual. During this treatment period psychological growth, measured in phases or steps in the various programs, proceeds until a client has acquired the ability to function autonomously.

In general, therapeutic communities are

* See references 5, 6, 12, 17, 35, 68, and 89.

based on the notion that an individual knows his feelings and that he can report his feelings if he desires to do so. There is an emphasis on honesty and a directness of approach which has unquestionable therapeutic value for many addicts. Typically, intake requires considerable initiative on the part of the prospective resident. During what is usually a stressful "acceptance interview" the candidate must actively and vigorously commit himself to the program. Such a situation serves the double purpose of screening out candidates of low motivation, for whom therapeutic communities are probably inappropriate, and providing a very explicit and self-defined reason for the successful candidate to enter treatment. Upon admission, social status is low. The new resident has no "privileges," i.e., there are restrictions on telephone calls, personal possessions, and visitors. Typically the neophyte is given rather poor living quarters. He is assigned a menial job function, e.g., washing dishes or sweeping floors, and he is expected to abstain from violating the house rules (e.g., no drugs, physical violence, or disobeying orders). He is expected to function well in his job, to manifest concern about his fellow residents, and to be active in group-therapy sessions. If these expectations are met the resident will progress through successful phases in which autonomy is given gradually.

A well-functioning therapeutic community could be compared to a very large and tightly-run family. Indeed the word "family" is often used to denote the entire membership of a therapeutic community. Punishment for inappropriate behavior in the form of verbal "haircuts," demeaning tasks, and peer contempt, can be quite severe in some therapeutic communities.

Encounter groups, led by staff and/or advanced residents, are held frequently. Typically a resident will participate in three groups each week. Honesty of expression and open verbal hostility are considered proper group behavior. Such groups are helpful in resolving personal problems in a psychotherapeutic sense and in providing an appropriate setting for "blowing off steam" for people living under conditions which are stressful.

Reentry into the community is usually divided into several steps. The patient progresses from being a regular resident with some personal freedom, e.g., weekend passes, visitors, etc., to living outside the therapeutic community while attending occasional groups. After considerable time in a basically outpatient status, the exaddict formally graduates from the therapeutic community (assuming he has not relapsed) and is formally considered rehabilitated. Whether or not addicts can ever graduate is still an unresolved question in the Synanon system.

In visiting a therapeutic community, one is struck by the high esprit de corps of the family, the personal friendliness of the residents, and the sense of order apparent in the cleanliness of the house. Certain aspects of the community, such as the tight control over the individual and the intolerance to minor deviance, may be disquieting. A new resident is traditionally expected to detoxify from heroin "cold turkey," i.e., without any chemical support. During withdrawal, he is expected to participate fully in house activities. One finds that subjective withdrawal symptoms under such circumstances, i.e., where passivity is not permitted, are far less unpleasant than when "kicking" in a hospital or jail.

The most serious problem in the therapeutic community approach is a very high premature termination of treatment or "split" rate.[5] Although accurate statistics are difficult to compile, it is estimated that slightly less than 10 percent of new members ever graduate. The majority of splits occur in the first few months of treatment, but splitting at a lower rate continues up to graduation. Observers have noted that residents who have stayed even for only a few months can derive benefit from their stay.[13] Therapeutic communities probably provide the highest "quality" of rehabilitation of any major treatment modality, in that their graduates are drugfree, have a low recidivism rate, and are gifted workers with the drug-dependent. A disproportionate number of graduates get jobs as exaddicts in drug-abuse programs.

The therapeutic community may be the treatment of choice for the very highly motivated drug abuser who has been deeply involved with drugs. It may be a dangerous form of treatment for some who are unable to identify and/or to report their feelings. The milieu is not generally supportive to people who are unable to function well, although there are some striking exceptions of psychotics making major recoveries after traditional treatment has proven ineffective.[14] The cost of treatment in this modality is higher than that of methadone maintenance, but there is a much greater chance to make long-term significant changes in the lifestyle of the drug abuser. Moreover, treatment can be provided for individuals for whom methadone support is inappropriate, such as polydrug abusers.

Although traditionally therapeutic communities have avoided interaction with professionals, this has changed in recent years. At this point, professionals can make significant contributions to therapeutic communities by acting as general consultants, by training staff, and by providing treatment for residents with significant psychiatric problems. The psychiatrist who works with a therapeutic community will do well if he regards himself as a student of the therapeutic community process and identifies himself as such.

Modified Therapeutic Communities

There have been many efforts to modify therapeutic communities to permit other subgroups of drug abusers to benefit from the therapeutic community experience. Jaffe developed the multimodality treatment system,[44] in which methadone support is incorporated into the therapeutic community structure. Due to early polarization between drugfree and drug-supported treatment, it was first thought that such a combination would not be feasible, but the experience of Jaffe has shown that abstinent and methadone supported patients can be successfully treated in the same unit both on an outpatient and a residential basis. Such "mixed" treatment provided significant programmatic flexibility, and the ability to tailor treatment to the specific needs of the individual patient. It is too early to make conclusions regarding comparative results, but clinical impressions suggest that programs offering "mixed" treatment may reach many who would not succeed in outpatient methadone maintenance or in a traditional therapeutic community.[44]

In the modified therapeutic community one can observe considerable "loosening" of the rigid structure of the classical therapeutic community; this takes many forms, from shorter residence (in modified therapeutic communities length of stay may be in terms of weeks), to reducing the stressful aspects of treatment, and to increasing the personal freedom of residents. Early results indicate that such modifications may render therapeutic communities less suitable for the groups originally helped by them, but more suitable for other groups, particularly young polydrug users.

OTHER SOCIOTHERAPIES

Sociotherapeutic approaches include the various religion-oriented drug rehabilitation programs, such as Teen Challenge, a fundamentalist Christian program,[35,58] the Black Muslims, who base their work on the teachings of Elijah Mohammed,[62] and several small sects using various Eastern philosophies. Many such organizations provide significant help to substantial groups of drug abusers. There are also programs such as The Seed[60] which, while not based on religion, centers its efforts on the charisma of a single person. Probably much of their success stems from the same process which enables therapeutic communities to be successful in a drug free environment, i.e., they provide structure, affiliation, and hope for their members.

There have been several types of treatment designed specifically for young polydrug abusers. Hotlines, for example, are telephone services offering crisis intervention and various types of other services.[16,82] These services, which appeared in large numbers in the late 1960s, were originally set up to handle "bad trips" (see p. 835). They are typically staffed by young volunteers. Professional supervision of such efforts is desirable as they have probably suffered in the past from a lack of professional interest.

Drop-in centers may also provide crisis intervention, but they are usually medium-term treatment centers. Many people, particularly youths, are reluctant to seek formal treatment, as they are reluctant to consider themselves "sick," and drop-in centers provide an acceptable alternative. The typical drop-in center avoids all medical jargon. An attempt is made to provide recreation and friends, "rap groups" and individual conversations with staff.

It is noteworthy that both drop-in centers and hotlines tend to be operated by very young people with few ties to the medical establishment. This occurs because many young people are alienated from the medical establishment, and often will not trust medical personnel to help them.[82]

The Role of Professionals in Drug Rehabilitation Programs

The psychiatrist working in a drug rehabilitation program faces a unique challenge. Professional training seldom provides experience with the world of criminality and violence surrounding the opiate addict or with the world of the counter-culture surrounding the young polydrug user. Both worlds place a negative value on physicians of any speciality, often on well justified grounds. Drug-dependent persons, like alcoholics, are in fact discriminated against in our medical-care system and many patients can recall vivid and moving experiences in which they have been demeaned, if not endangered, by medical discrimination. Many psychiatrists are not prepared to understand that the positive image they enjoy in ordinary practice turns to a negative one in the drug world. The situation is rendered more complex because the basic psychiatric techniques of individual or group psychotherapy have not been particularly successful with addicts.

Optimal contributions from psychiatrists appear to be associated with team functioning in which the psychiatrist works side by side with exaddicts or paraprofessionals who serve as interpreters of the drug subculture and as primary counselors for patients in treatment. Although the psychiatrist can contribute by assuming primary care of patients in drug treatment programs, his expertise can have maximum effect if he shares his skills with other members of the treatment team and if he assumes administrative responsibilities, not the least of which is resolution of staff conflict. Once through a basic learning experience focused on the unique aspects of drug abuse, he will find that the status he enjoys in the "straight" world will be also accorded to him in the drug world and new and challenging demands will be made on his leadership.

⟦ Bibliography

1. AMERICAN MEDICAL ASSOCIATION, Council on Mental Health. "Treatment of Morphine-Type Dependence by Withdrawal Methods," *JAMA*, 219 (1972), 1611–1615.

2. BERLE, B. B., M. GANEM, and J. LOWINSON. "Detoxification of Multiple-Drug Abusers with Sodium Amytal," *N.Y. State J. Med.*, 72 (1972), 2971–73.

3. BLINICK, G., E. JEREZ, and R. C. WALLACH. "Methadone Maintenance, Pregnancy, and Progeny," *JAMA*, 225 (1973), 477–479.

4. BONNIE, R. J. and M. R. SONNEREICH. "Proposed Uniform Drug Dependence Treatment and Rehabilitation Act and Commentary," in National Commission on Marijuana and Drug Abuse, *Drug Use in America: Problems in Perspective*, Appendix 4. *Treatment and Rehabilitation*, pp. 827–856. Washington: U.S. Govt. Print. Off., 1973.

5. BRECHER, E. M. and the editors of *Consumer Reports*. *Licit and Illicit Drugs*. Boston: Little, Brown, 1972.

6. CASRIEL, D. and G. OMEN. *Daytop*. New York: Hill and Wang, 1971.

7. CHAMBERS, C. D. and L. BRILL. *Methadone: Experience and Issues*. New York: Behavioral Publications, 1973.

8. CHEEK, F. E., S. NEWELL, and M. JAFFE. "Deceptions in the Illegal Drug Market," *Science*, 167 (1970), 1276.

9. CHEIN, I., D. L. LEE, and E. ROSENFELD. *The Road to H: Narcotics, Delinquency and Social Policy*. New York: Basic Books, 1964.

10. CUSHMAN, P. and V. P. DOLE. "Detoxification of Rehabilitated Methadone Maintained Patients," *JAMA*, 226 (1973), 747–752.

11. DAVIS, J., J. SEKERKE, and D. JANOWSKI. "Drug Interactions Involving Drugs of Abuse," in National Commission on Marijuana and Drug Abuse, *Drug Use in America: Problem in Perspective*, Appendix 1. *Patterns and Consequences of Drug Use*, pp. 181–208. Washington: U.S. Govt. Print. Off., 1973.

12. DEITCH, D. A. "Treatment of Drug Abuse in the Therapeutic Community: Historical Influences, Current Considerations and Future Outlook," in National Commission on Marijuana and Drug Abuse, *Drug Use in America: Problem in Perspective*, Appendix 4. *Treatment and Rehabilitation*, pp. 158–175. Washington: U.S. Govt. Print. Off., 1973.

13. DELEON, G., S. HOLLAND, and M. S. ROSENTHAL. "Phoenix House: Criminal Activity of Dropouts," *JAMA*, 222 (1972), 686–689.

14. DELEON, G., A. SKODOL, and M. S. ROSENTHAL. "Phoenix House: Changes in Psychopathological Signs of Resident Drug Addicts," *Arch. Gen. Psychiatry*, 28 (1973), 131–135.

15. DELONG, J. V. "Treatment and Rehabilitation," in P. M. Wald and P. B. Hutt, eds., *Dealing with Drug Abuse: A Report to the Ford Foundation*, p. 195. New York: Praeger, 1972.

16. DELWORTH, V., E. H. RUDOW, and J. TAUB, eds. *Crisis Center/Hotlines: A Guidebook to Beginning and Operating*. Springfield, Ill.: Charles C. Thomas, 1972.

17. DENSEN-GERBER, J. *We Mainline Dreams: The Odyssey House Story*. Garden City, N.Y.: Doubleday, 1973.

18. DOLE, V. P. "Detoxification of Sick Addicts in Prison," *JAMA*, 220 (1972), 366–369.

19. ———. "Detoxification of Methadone Patients, and Public Policy," *JAMA*, 226 (1973), 780–781.

20. DOLE, V. P. and M. NYSWANDER. "A Medical Treatment for Diacetylmorphine Addiction," *JAMA*, 193 (1965), 646–650.

21. ———. "Heroin Addiction—A Metabolic Disease," *Arch. Intern. Medicine*, 120 (1967), 19–24.

22. DRUG ABUSE OFFICE AND TREATMENT ACT OF 1972. U.S. Code, Vol. 86 Stat. 66

(1972), 21 U.S.C. Sec. 1101 ff. Washington: U.S. Govt. Print. Off., 1972.

23. DUMONT, M. P. "Technology and the Treatment of Addiction," in S. Fisher and A. M. Freedman, eds., *Opiate Addiction: Origins and Treatment*. Washington: Winston & Sons, 1973.

24. DUPONT, R. L. and M. H. GREENE. "The Dynamics of a Heroin Addiction Epidemic," *Science*, 181 (1973), 716–722.

25. ELLINWOOD, E. H. "Emergency Treatment of Acute Reaction to CNS Stimulants," *J. Psyched. Drugs*, 5, (1972), 147–152.

26. ELLINWOOD, E. H. and S. COHEN, eds. *Current Concepts on Amphetamine Abuse*. Rockville, Md.: National Institute of Mental Health, 1970.

27. EVANS, L. E. J., C. P. SWANSON, P. ROSCOE et al. "Treatment of Drug Overdosage with Naloxone, a Specific Narcotic Antagonist," *Lancet*, 1 (1973), 452–455.

28. FEDERAL REGISTER, "Approved New Drugs . . . Listing of Methadone with Special Requirements for Use," 27, no. 242 (Dec. 15, 1972) 26790–26807.

29. FINK, M. "Narcotic Antagonists," in National Commission on Marijuana and Drug Abuse, *Drug Use in America: Problem in Perspective*, Appendix 4. *Treatment and Rehabilitation*, pp. 143–157. Washington: U.S. Govt. Print. Off., 1973.

30. FREEDMAN, D. X. and E. C. SENAY. "Heroin Epidemics," *JAMA*, 228 (1973), 1155–1156.

31. ———. "Methadone Treatment of Heroin Addiction," *Annu. Rev. Med.*, (1973), 153–164.

32. GAY, G. R., E. C. SENAY, J. A. NEWMEYER et al. "The Pseudojunkie: Evolution of the Heroin Lifestyle in the Non-addicted Individual," *Drug Forum*, 2 (1973), 279–290.

33. GEARING, F. R. "Successes and Failures in Methadone Maintenance Treatment of Heroin Addiction in New York City," Proc. 3rd Natl. Conf. Methadone Treatment, pp. 2–16. New York: National Association for the Prevention of Addiction to Narcotics, 1971.

34. ———. "People vs Urines," Proc. 4th Natl. Conf. Methadone Treatment, pp. 325–326. New York: National Association for the Prevention of Addiction to Narcotics, 1972.

35. GLASSCOTE, R. M., J. N. SUSSEX, J. H. JAFFE et al. *The Treatment of Drug Abuse: Programs, Problems, Prospects*. Washington: Joint Information Service of the Am. Psychiatr. Assoc. and the NIMH, 1972.

36. GOLDSTEIN, A. "Heroin Addiction and the Role of Methadone in Its Treatment," *Arch. Gen. Psychiatry*, 26 (1972), 291–297.

37. GOLDSTEIN, A. and B. A. TUDSON. "Efficacy and Side Effects of Three Widely Different Methadone Doses," Proc. 5th Natl. Conf. on Methadone, pp. 21–44. New York: National Association for the Prevention of Addiction to Narcotics, 1973.

38. HAMMOND, A. L. "Narcotic Antagonists: New Methods to Treat Heroin Addiction," *Science*, 173 (1971), 503–506.

39. HARRIS, R. T., W. M. MC ISAAC, and C. R. SCHUSTER, eds. *Drug Dependence*. Austin: University of Texas Press, 1970.

40. HUGHES, P. H., C. R. SAUNDERS, and E. SCHAPS. "The Impact of Medical Intervention in Three Heroin Copping Areas," Proc. 4th Natl. Conf. Methadone Treatment, pp. 81–83. New York: National Association for the Prevention of Addiction to Narcotics, 1972.

41. HUGHES, P. H., E. C. SENAY, and R. PARKER. "The Medical Management of a Heroin Epidemic," *Arch. Gen. Psychiatry*, 27 (1972), 585–593.

42. JACKSON, A. H. and R. I. SHADER. "Guidelines for the Withdrawal of Narcotic and General Depressant Drugs," *Dis. Nerv. Syst.*, 34 (1973), 162–166.

43. JAFFE, J. H. "Narcotic Analgesics," in L. S. Goodman and A. Gilman, eds., *The Pharmacological Basis of Therapeutics*. New York: Macmillan, 1965.

44. ———. "Multimodality Approaches to the Treatment and Prevention of Opiate Addiction," in S. Fisher and A. M. Freedman, eds., *Opiate Addiction: Origins and Treatment*, pp. 127–140. Washington: Winston & Sons, 1973.

45. JAFFE, J. H., S. DIMENZA, and E. C. SENAY. "Methadone Maintenance: Further Studies on the Role of Dosage," Rept. 33rd Annu. Sci. Meet., Committee on Problems of Drug Dependence, Toronto, 1971, pp. 1104–1132.

46. JAFFE, J. H., E. C. SENAY, C. R. SCHUSTER et al. "Methadyl Acetate vs. Methadone: A Double-Blind Study in Heroin Users," *JAMA*, 222 (1972), 437–442.

47. JAFFE, J. H., M. S. ZAKS, and E. N. WASH-
INGTON. "Experience with the Use of
Methadone in a Multi-Modality Program
for the Treatment of Narcotics Users," *Int.
J. Addict.*, 4 (1969), 481–490.

48. JOHNSON, R. B. and W. M. LUKASH, eds.
*Summary of Proceedings of the Washing-
ton Conference on Medical Complications
of Drug Abuse.* Washington: Committee
on Alcoholism and Drug Dependence of
the American Medical Association, 1972.

49. KLEBER, H. D. "Clinical Experiences with
Narcotic Antagonists," in S. Fisher and
A. M. Freedman, eds., *Opiate Addiction:
Origins and Treatment.* Washington: Win-
ston & Sons, 1973.

50. KNOX, J. W. and J. R. NELSON. "Permanent
Encephalopathy from Toluene," *N. Engl. J.
Med.*, 275 (1966), 1494.

51. KUPPERSTEIN, L. R. and R. M. SUSMAN. "A
Bibliography on the Inhalation of Glue
Fumes and Other Toxic Vapors—A Sub-
stance Abuse Practice among Adolescents,"
Int. J. Addict., 3 (1968), 177–197.

52. LENNARD, H. L., L. J. EPSTEIN, and M. S.
ROSENTHAL. "The Methadone Illusion,"
Science, 176 (1972), 881–884.

53. LEWIS, J. R. "Use and Misuse of Pentazocine:
A Follow-up," *JAMA*, 225 (1973), 1530–
1531.

54. LIEBERMAN, C. M. and B. W. LIEBERMAN.
"Marijuana—a Medical Review," *N. Engl.
J. Med.*, 284 (1971), 88–91.

55. LLOYD, R. L., R. N. KATON, R. L. DuPONT
et al. "Detoxification: What Makes the
Difference?" Proc. 5th Natl. Conf. Metha-
done Treatment, pp. 275–283. New York:
National Association for the Prevention of
Addiction to Narcotics, 1973.

56. LOURIA, D. B. *Overcoming Drugs: A Program for Action.* New York: McGraw-Hill,
1971.

57. LOWINSON, J. and J. LANGROD. "Detoxification of Long-Term Methadone Patients,"
Proc. 5th Natl. Conf. Methadone Treatment, pp. 256–261. New York: National
Association for the Prevention of Addiction to Narcotics, 1973.

58. McDONNEL, K. "The Pentecostals and Drug
Addiction," *America*, 118 (1968), 402–
406.

59. MAUGH, T. H. "Narcotic Antagonists: The
Search Accelerates," *Science*, 177 (1972),
249–250.

60. MILLER, J. "The Seed: Reforming Drug

Abusers with Love," *Science*, 182 (1973),
40–42.

61. MILLMAN, R. B., E. T. KLUIRI, and M. E.
NYSWANDER. "A Model for the Study and
Treatment of Heroin Addiction in an Ur-
ban Adolescent Program," Proc., 4th Natl.
Conf. Methadone Treat., pp. 47–50. New
York: National Association for the Preven-
tion of Addiction to Narcotics, 1972.

62. MUHAMMED, E. *Message to the Black Man
in America*, no. 2. Chicago: Muhammed's
Mosque of Islam, 1965.

63. MUSTO, D. *The American Disease: Origins
of Narcotic Control.* New Haven: Yale
University Press, 1973.

64. NATIONAL COMMISSION ON MARIJUANA AND
DRUG ABUSE. "Inhalants," in *Drug Use In
America: Problem in Perspective*, pp. 78–
82. Washington: U.S. Govt. Print. Off.,
1973.

65. O'DONNELL, J. A. *Narcotic Addicts in Kentucky*, Public Health Serv. Pub. no. 1881,
pp. 135–142. Washington: U.S. Govt.
Print. Off., 1969.

66. O'MALLEY, J. E., W. H. ANDERSON, and
A. LAZARE. "Failure of Outpatient Treat-
ment of Drug Abuse: I. Heroin," *Am. J.
Psychiatry*, 128 (1972), 99–101.

67. RESNICK, R. B., B. KISSIN, H. KLEBER et al.
"Clinical Experiences with Narcotic Antagonists: Cyclazocine and Naloxone,"
Proc., 5th Natl. Conf. Methadone Treatment, pp. 447–451. New York: National
Association for the Prevention of Addiction to Narcotics, 1973.

68. ROSENTHAL, M. S. and I. MOTHNER. *Drugs,
Parents, and Children: The Three-Way
Connection.* Boston: Houghton Mifflin Co.,
1972.

69. ROSZAK, T. *The Making of a Counter-Culture.* Garden City, N.Y.: Doubleday, 1968.

70. SAPIRA, J. D. "The Narcotic Addict as a Medical Patient," *Am. J. Med.*, 45 (1968),
555–588.

71. SCHULTE, N. and J. V. DeLONG. *Heroin
Maintenance: The Issues.* Washington:
Drug Abuse Council, 1973.

72. SENAY, E. C., J. H. JAFFE, J. N. CHAPPEL
et al. "IDAP—5 Year Results," Proc., 5th
Natl. Conf. Methadone Treatment, pp.
1437–1464. New York: National Association for the Prevention of Addiction to
Narcotics, 1973.

73. SENAY, E. C. and P. F. RENAULT. "Treatment Methods for Heroin Addicts: A Re-

view," *J. Psyched. Drugs*, 3 (1971), 47–54.

74. SENAY, E. C. and M. WRIGHT. "The Human Needs Approach to the Treatment of Drug Dependence," Paper presented at the International Council on Alcoholism and Addictions, Amsterdam, 1972.

75. SHICK, J. F. E. and D. X. FREEDMAN. "Research in Non-narcotic Drug Abuse," in S. Arieti, ed., *American Handbook of Psychiatry*, Vol. 6, 2nd ed., pp. 552–623. New York: Basic Books, 1975.

76. SHICK, J. F. E. and D. E. SMITH. "An Analysis of the LSD Flashback," *J. Psyched. Drugs*, 3 (1970), 13–19.

77. ———. "The Illicit Use of the Psychotomimetic Amphetamines with Special Reference to STP (DOM) Toxicity," *J. Psyched. Drugs*, 5 (1972), 131–138.

78. SMITH, D. E. and D. R. WESSON. "Phenobarbital Techniques for Treatment of Barbiturate Dependence," *Arch. Gen. Psychiatry*, 24 (1971), 56–60.

79. TAYLOR, R. L., J. I. MAURER, and J. R. TINKLENBERG. "Management of 'Bad Trips' in an Evolving Drug Scene," *JAMA*, 213 (1970), 422–425.

80. TENNANT, F. S., JR. "Drug Abuse in the U.S. Army, Europe," *JAMA*, 221 (1972), 1146–1149.

81. TENNANT, F. S., JR., M. TISCHER, B. RUSSEL et al. "Treatment of Heroin Addicts with Propoxyphene Napsylate," Paper presented at the Committee on Drug Dependence of the National Academy of Science, Chapel Hill, N.C., May 23, 1973.

82. TOROP, D. and K. TOROP. "Hotlines and Youth Culture Values," *Am. J. Psychiatry*, 129 (1972), 106–109.

83. VAILLANT, G. E. "A Twenty Year Follow-Up of New York Narcotic Addicts," Rept. 34th Annu. Sci. Meet. Comm. Problems of Drug Dependence of the National Academy of Sciences, Ann Arbor, Mich., May 1972, pp. 63–71.

84. WATSON, R., E. HARMANN, and J. J. SCHILDKRAUT. "Amphetamine Withdrawal: Affective State, Sleep Patterns, and MHPG Excretion," *Am. J. Psychiatry*, 129 (1972), 263–269.

85. WEINBERG, J. A. and P. GREVERT. "A Controlled Study of the Clinical Effectiveness of Urine Test Results in a Methadone Maintenance Treatment Program," Proc., 5th Natl. Conf. Methadone Treatment, pp. 1052–1059. New York: National Association for the Prevention of Addiction to Narcotics, 1973.

86. WESSON, D. R. and D. E. SMITH. "Barbiturate Toxicity and the Treatment of Barbiturate Dependence," *J. Psyched. Drugs*, 5 (1972), 159–166.

87. WIELAND, W. F. and J. L. NOVACK. "A Comparison of Criminal Justice and Non-Criminal Justice Related Patients in a Methadone Treatment Program," Proc., 5th Natl. Conf. Methadone Treatment, pp. 116–122. New York: National Association for the Prevention of Addiction to Narcotics, 1973.

88. WILBUR, R. S. "How to Stamp Out a Heroin Epidemic—Army Style," *Today's Health*, 50 (July 1972), 9–10.

89. YABLONSKY, L. *Synanon: The Tunnel Back*. New York: Macmillan, 1965.

90. ZELSON, C. "Infant of the Addicted Mother," *N. Engl. J. Med.*, 288 (1973), 1393–1395.

PART SIX

Legal Psychiatry

CHAPTER 44

PSYCHIATRY AND THE LAW

Bernard Rubin

❨ Historical Background

IN ALL RECORDED HISTORY, societies have indicated the limits of the conduct of individuals with one another and have devised sanctions, primarily in law, as a response to those whose behavior seems to deviate from acceptable norms. Also throughout recorded history, certain persons and agencies have been designated as being responsible to apprehend, examine, mediate, and decide upon the formal institutional responses to those deviations. Such persons usually have a formal connection to a social system of sanctions. A second group of persons has also helped in decisions concerning sanctions (or the absence of them) by attempting to account for men's behavior with theological, biological, psychological, or social reasons, or some combination of these. This second group has included theologians, shamans, physicians, and, more recently, psychiatrists. Thus two institutions, that of legal justice and that of health care, together with the men empowered to represent the agencies that provide their services, came together about certain critical issues:

1. The capacity of a person to be responsible for his act(s) or act responsibly in certain settings.
2. The distinctions between deviant behavior due to biological, psychological, and social causes.
3. The prediction and treatment of dangerousness.
4. The rights of persons designated as patients.

Madness (insanity, unreason, mental illness) has been and continues to be a complex social phenomenon.[163,189] It is accepted that there are at least four different empirical systems for viewing human behavior: physicochemical, motivational, social, and cultural. Each of these is separate and understandable in its own terms. The motivational system is useful primarily in explaining certain kinds of behavior known as mental illness, regardless of whether mental illness can be explained in psychological terms alone.

During the Middle Ages the mad were segregated into two groups, the raving and the feeble-minded, primarily for the purpose of protecting the security of the citizens of a given society. The raving were further categorized as criminal or possessed, depending on whether their actions contravened legal or social conventions, respectively. If criminal, they were usually subjected to those sanctions reserved for criminal behavior. If possessed, they were either ritually excluded or sent on pilgrimages to seek cures at various holy places. Subjected in this way to the "test of the return"—travel in the Middle Ages was extremely dangerous and required the use of one's strength and wits—such persons were felt to be well if they returned. The feebleminded were a large, varied group composed of the wretched, infirm, senile, mentally retarded, and probably neurotic.

After the Middle Ages, once madness was unlinked from theology, other qualities were imputed to the mad: first, in the sixteenth century, shamefulness—from the English poor laws associating madness and pauperism; then, in the eighteenth century, the cencept of dangerousness and nonhuman qualities—a kind of social Darwinism. Finally, at the end of the eighteenth century and the Age of Reason, humanness was again imputed to the mad, and "modern" (humane) treatment began. (See Foucault[78] for a complex elaboration of the historical development of "madness" into the Age of Reason.)

However, beginning with the asylums and workhouses of the seventeenth century, segregation of the mad became so central and organized that, by the end of the nineteenth century, treatment was conceived of only within institutions, and confinement remained the rule. This practice became regulated by laws, with a view to protecting society and supporting treatment while avoiding too many abuses of individual liberty. The latter concerns (treatment and liberty) were decidedly secondary, based on erroneously held views of the dangerousness and untreatability of the mentally ill. One of the most common mental illnesses, dementia praecox, using the paradigm of general paralysis of the insane (CNS—central nervous system—syphilis), was seen as a hopelessly progressive deterioration of mental functioning. This was not

helped by the concept of "alienist" as developed by Auguste Forel, or the mystification about the mentally ill that seemed to characterize the work of Jean-Martin Charcot and Hippolyte-Marie Bernheim in their use of hypnosis with some forms of mental illness.

In England, the Lunacy Act became law in 1828, and in France, the Regimen of the Alienated was promulgated in 1838. Both provided for the protection of the rights of persons held and treated for mental illness. In the United States, the rapid growth of public asylums for the care of the mentally ill was the result of a crusade led by Dorothea Dix. This effort raised the numbers of persons in mental hospitals far beyond the bed capacities of the hospitals and ended their selective admissions policies; within a short time, patient turnover all but ceased. However, despite these increasing numbers of persons (a distinct and separate group for whom the government had broad responsibilities), procedures for commitment remained uncertain and undefined. Some increasing concern for the rights of individuals committed to such facilities began to develop. This interest was first stimulated by public concern over the wrongful detention of the sane rather than by a concern for the rights and liberty of the mentally ill.

In the 1860s, Mrs. E. P. W. Packard led a vigorous campaign for strict commitment laws. She had been confined in an Illinois mental hospital for three years under an Illinois law which stated:

Married women and infants, when in the judgment of the medical superintendent are evidently insane or distracted, may be received and detained in the hospital on the request of the husband, or the woman, or parent, or guardian of the infants, without the evidence of insanity or distraction required in other cases.[13]

Consequently, during the next decade, a number of states enacted fairly vigorous commitment laws, some of which included a jury determination of insanity.[72] This overly legalistic approach to civil commitment for mental illness contributed largely to the stigma already attached to mental illness. [p. 438][71] In addition, the use of a criminal-justice model promoted the public identification of civilly committed persons with criminals, significantly impeding any treatment approaches as well as increasing the anxiety and isolation of persons so designated.

Advances in psychiatric knowledge proceeded slowly into the twentieth century, with a major impetus being observed during and immediately following World War II. Because of the increased concern for social justice, stimulated in part by the purposes of the war, there was an increased desire to eradicate many social ills. Concern for the rights of the mentally ill was one aspect of this desire. Another, related concern had become intertwined as well: the public health interest in reducing the morbidity of mental illness and, if possible, eradicating and preventing mental illness altogether. Thus the quest for social justice and the concern for public mental health have remained bound together; freedom and treatment have become inseparable. There are some[182,191] who believe that the lack of freedom is incompatible with treatment.

Because of the enlargement of this field of concern from forensic psychiatry[68]—the practice of which was limited, for the most part, to the courtroom or prison (see Halleck[92] for an historical elaboration of this period)—into something variously called social–legal psychiatry[157] or simply psychiatry and the law, it has become more truly interdisciplinary, dealing with ethical, psychological, medical, and legal problems with a variety of components. The interest in education and research in these areas exists in an increasing number of law and medical schools in conjunction with different legal agencies. The literature[45,110,155] has correspondingly begun to show less emphasis on the older, tired distinctions between free will and psychic determinism and the nature of criminal responsibility.

(Psychiatry and Civil Law

When a person's freedom is abrogated or his civil liberties are denied him, this power should be exercised for compelling reasons, at the most propitious moment, and for a minimum period of time. It should be clear that such power is exercised only if the person is definitely mentally ill *and* a danger to others or himself. To compel another person for less than those reasons—as, for example, to help them, to do "good," or to tyrannize them because their behavior offends us—is insupportable.

Prediction of Dangerousness

Commitment of the mentally ill has always been closely associated with their purported dangerousness. In fact, the association has often been so close that to make these determinations separately has at times been difficult or impossible. In part this has been due to a combination of the notions that a "beast" is released in man by mental illness and that the doctor has a responsibility to exclude all possibilities of dangerousness before opting for release. Therefore the psychiatrist, rather than attempting to carefully assess dangerousness, usually takes a safe course—that is, commitment. The other reason for the difficulty in separating mental illness from dangerousness has been the use of commitment laws for other purposes: for example, the removal of public nuisances from the open community, and the provision of treatment under the guise of benevolence.

The law requires that the civil commitment of a mentally ill patient depend on psychiatric testimony: The patient must be held to be in need of mental treatment and dangerous to himself or others. The problem is not a small one. Although the number of civil commitments to mental hospitals has been markedly reduced since the late 1960s, approximately 50,000 mentally ill persons per year are still predicted to be dangerous and are preventively detained, both for their own and society's protection, and for their treatment. In addition, an average of about 5 percent of the total mental hospital population of the United States (approximately 390,000) are kept in maximum security sections on the basis of the assessment of their potential dangerousness.[164]

Szasz[181] has compellingly written that the

behavioral sciences have not yet been able to solve simple and operational definitions of eccentricity and dangerousness. Because of this, he[180] feels that psychiatrists have been motivated in large part to be counteraggressive to very provocative patients. Such aggressiveness can be related to the psychiatrist's identification with prevailing societal sanctions regarding the certain deviant behavior, to an unwillingness by the psychiatrist to share power, and to the psychiatrist's personal readinessto respond to provocative behavior. Szasz's answer is to reject the concept of dangerousness and to argue that the psychiatrist, in the conflict between the patient's and society's rights, should always side with the patient.

For some psychiatrists there is a naive certainty that prediction is an accomplished fact. This naive certainty has not been supported by empirical studies nor by the few evaluations of the results of such prediction. Even in the most careful, painstaking, laborious, and lengthy clinical approaches to the prediction of dangerousness, false positive evaluations may be at a minimum of 60 to 70 percent.[113] The ability to predict dangerousness is in fact related to the basic capacity to understand disordered behavior and to intervene in those circumstances in which the result will be an increase in social good—that is, where society's members will be reasonably protected, and where effective rehabilitative efforts can be made.

A myth and a misconception stand between the problem and its possible solution. The myth is that of individual clinical judgment, which demands that each case be taken in its own right. Nevertheless, many authors[75,93,113] who can recognize a need for the prediction of dangerousness insist on individual clinical judgment, intuition, and unexplained hunches. The misconception is that particular psychiatric disorders are dangerous per se, which is encouraged when certain mental disorders are characterized by some kind of confused, bizarre, agitated, threatening, frightened, panicked, paranoid, or impulsive behavior. That misconception and the view that impulse— that is, ideation—and action are interchange-

able support the belief that all mental disorder must, of necessity, lead to inappropriate, antisocial, or dangerous actions.

In a staff report to the Commission on the Causes and Prevention of Violence, Ervin and Lion[75] note that "Violence refers to assaultive or destructive acts of ideation. The term 'ideation' is included because patients with fears and fantasies of violence sometimes act them out." Later they make a very doubtful, unsubstantiated statement connecting violence with psychological disorder: ". . . our impression has been that the largest group of patients complaining of violence fall into the classification of 'borderline' or 'schizoid' personality types." [p. 1187][75] Another author, Muller,[135] while arguing that "more specific criteria need to be established for imposing involuntary mental hospitalization" and that the "degree of likely damage must be great," then states his criteria: "These [two kinds of criteria] are the psychoses, both functional and organic, and conditions in which there is permanent or temporary impairment of cerebral cortical functioning so that at the time the person is not considered fully responsible for his own behavior." Thus the author confuses psychosis (and/or the absence of responsibility) with dangerousness. The argument is not very compelling. The criteria remain vague and inaccurate.

Part of the problem may be that psychiatrists use mental disease as a concept that relates to treatment, as Shah[167] noted. Labeling deviancy as mental illness or predicting dangerousness is just a convention to get someone treatment. Once the person is in treatment, the concept of dangerousness is forgotten. It is a device that enlarges and thereby confuses the apparent size of the problem. The confusion of serious psychological impairment with dangerousness, and the dialogue of misunderstanding between the law and psychiatry about this, is best illustrated by the judge who asks the psychiatrist if the patient is dangerous, to which the psychiatrist responds, "Yes, she is psychotic."[12]

The United States Court of Appeals, District of Columbia Circuit, in a series of cases dating from 1958 to 1969, refined the character of danger as it relates to the dangerously mentally ill. The cases included persons accused or found guilty of violent crimes as well as those civilly committed. First, there was the concept of reasonable foreseeability; that is, the dangerous act must occur in "the community in the reasonably foreseeable future."[33] Not only must the dangerousness occur soon, it must also be based on a "high" probability of substantial injury. Thus, the term "dangerous to others" cannot simply be a way of singling out anyone whom we would prefer not to meet on the streets. Possibility of injury is not enough. It must be likely, and the threatened harm must be substantial. Thus the psychiatrist must define "likely" as meaning "virtual certainty" rather than mere chance.[8,23]

Given the present reality, it is unlikely that dangerousness can be predicted in a person who has not previously acted in a dangerous or violent way.[93,113,162] However, until statistical data and prediction tables allow for more reliable and accurate prediction, it is mandatory that a clinical examination be carried out. This examination should utilize all ancillary data from family, friends, police, and onlookers, as well as prior information from other physicians, psychologists, and hospitals. It should also include special tests (projective tests, EEGs, and so forth) to determine whether or not mental illness is present, and its nature if found. The diagnosis of mental illness is critical. There is some disagreement; indeed, controversy concerning diagnosis versus labeling has been an intermittent and useful commentary on the mental disorders. (Most recently, see Rosenhan and other commentators.)[160] But the preponderance of opinion seems to be that, for legal purposes, psychoses of all types and the more severe character disorders (borderline and narcissistic) constitute the mental illnesses. That, and the determination of dangerousness, provide the information that will allow a court to make a judicial determination of the need for treatment.

Civil Commitment

Within a psychiatric hospital, sanatorium, or psychiatric section of a general hospital, freedom is limited, both for those being treated voluntarily and those being treated against their will. For this reason, laws have been devised to balance the needs of the rest of society against the needs and civil rights of the mentally ill. These laws, at first preoccupied with protecting society, began in the 1950s to redefine and enlarge the protection of the rights of patients.[54,95,114] This shift in emphasis was stimulated, in part, by social concerns generated during World War II, and by the work of social scientists, who found that prolonged mental hospitalization was pernicious. In fact, new treatments were becoming available for the mentally ill that shortened hospitalization or made it unnecessary. In England, the Royal Commission on the Law Relating to Mental Illness and Mental Deficiency, which spent three years examining needed reforms, published its report in May 1957. This was followed by the Mental Health Act of 1959. By the middle of the 1960s, most of Western Europe and the many states of the United States had modified existing laws or brought about sweeping reforms.[59]

An example of this reform is the Mental Health Code of the State of Illinois, which went into effect in July 1964. It is "person and crisis oriented" and offers early and easy access to treatment and easy movement in and out of the treatment system. It includes:

1. Revised hospitalization procedures.
2. Protection of civil rights.
3. Protection from civil and criminal liability for persons signing petitions associated with commitment.
4. Periodic review of all persons under the care of the facilities licensed by the Illinois Department of Mental Health.

With some modifications,* the following administrative admission procedures were introduced between 1964 and 1971:[14]

1. *Informal admission.* An individual presents himself to a facility for treatment. If, after examination, the physician deems him suitable

---

* This Mental Health code has been modified since 1963. For comparison see Ill. Rev. Stat. Chap. 91 1/2, Sects. 1–17, 1952.

for admission, care and treatment, he is admitted without formal application or medical certification. The individual requesting treatment need only indicate a desire for help. No signature is required. Informal admission is simple, fast, inexpensive, with no court procedure needed. The individual is free to leave at any time during the hospital's normal business hours. This admission procedure is not available to minors. [Sect. 4]

2. *Voluntary admission.* For an individual of lawful age (in Illinois, 18 years), he or any relative or attorney with the individual's consent may file a verified application requesting voluntary admission for treatment. If the individual is a minor, his parent or guardian may file. He is admitted for treatment if, in the physician's judgment, he is suitable for voluntary admission. Voluntary admission is relatively fast and simple with no initial court procedure needed. The patient is free to leave after giving notice in writing of his desire to leave. The patient cannot be detained for further treatment unless he withdraws his notice to leave in writing or if a petition for hospitalization on court order is filed. If the court petition is filed, the patient may be kept for five days pending the outcome of court proceedings. [Sect. 5]

3. *Admission on the certificate of physician.* This is a formal admission in which the individual does not object to treatment. He is admitted for treatment upon his application (if 18 years or over) and the certificate of a physician who has examined the individual not more than 72 hours prior to admission. The individual is then examined within 24 hours at the hospital by a psychiatrist to confirm the need for hospitalization. Within five days such a patient may further request an informal judicial hearing, which must be held in five days. If the patient does not protest, he can remain for 60 days. At this time the physician may apply to the court for an order of continued hospitalization which the court can grant without a hearing unless the patient or someone on his behalf requests a hearing within ten days of the above application, which then must be held in five days. [Sect. 6]

4. *Emergency admission.* This procedure permits immediate and protested hospitalization for a mentally ill person 18 years or older for the protection from physical harm to such persons or others, on the basis of the petition of a concerned citizen alone. While a physician's certificate is eventually required, a person may be admitted on the basis of the written petition alone. If no certificate is available in 24 hours, the patient must be released. Within 24 hours, a psychiatrist must examine the patient and his examination [be] made part of the record. Proceedings for a court hearing must be made immediately and must be held within five days. [Sect. 7]

5. *Petition for examination and hearing upon court order.* When a person 18 years or older is asserted to be mentally ill, on petition the court may order an examination for which the person may be detained no more than 24 hours. If, as a result of that examination, a certificate by a physician asserts that person to be in need of treatment and that certificate filed with the court within 72 hours, a hearing is set. At least 36 hours before the time of the examination fixed by the court, the person must receive notice of such examination. If the court finds it is necessary in order to complete the examination that the person be compelled to be hospitalized, the court may order a peace officer or other person to transport the person to a hospital. [Sect. 8]

6. *Hospitalization upon court order.* After hearing any person thought to be mentally ill, who is represented by counsel and other witnesses, including psychiatrists and other mental health professionals, the court may order hospitalization. The patient, spouse, relative or friend may demand that the question of hospitalization be heard by a jury selected in the same manner as in other civil proceedings. [Sect. 9]

Under all of the above procedures, individuals retain their civil rights. In addition, their rights in relation to the code must be explained in simple and understandable language. Fair notice must be given to the patient and to others concerned with his welfare. A court hearing with a jury trial can be requested. Counsel must be made available. If necessary, a judicial review can be ordered. While hospitalization on court order is no presumption of competency and does not affect civil rights, a *separate* judicial hearing can be held concerning competency. Earlier versions of the Illinois Mental Health Code contained various provisions under which persons committed to facilities of the Department of Mental Health or the Department of Public Welfare automatically lost their civil rights. This was alien to the basic premise of a democratic society, which provides that civil rights be protected for all individuals except in the event of overwhelming circumstances.[111,152] At present, the court order states only that the person is "in need of mental treatment" and does not comment directly upon loss of civil rights, loss of sanity, or loss of competence.

It is important to note here that legal discrimination was made in the code[14] between the following interdependent but separable factors in an illness: (1) need for treatment; (2) treatment requiring hospitalization; (3) need for involuntary submission to examination; (4) need for involuntary submission to treatment; and (5) competency to make a will, enter into contracts, vote, drive a motor vehicle, and so forth. Balancing the usefulness of a crisis-oriented response to the need for mental treatment for any person, against the danger of someone maliciously or fraudulently having a person detained or treated as mentally ill, the code supports the action of any citizen who petitions, on the basis of his personal observations, for the detention of another person as mentally ill. The Code protects him from civil and criminal liability if he acted in good faith. [Sect. 7–3] However, the penalties for perjury still pertain. [Sect. 15–1] All cases that have been admitted or hospitalized, whether by medical certification or by court order, must be reviewed every six months, and that review must be made part of the record. A more extensive review, done once the first year and once every two years subsequently, provides for a physical examination, mental status examination, behavioral evaluation, and a general social and life situation review. The findings on general health, mental health, and need for continued hospitalization are evaluated and reported to the patient, his attorney, his nearest relative, two other persons designated by the patient, and the court. [Sect. 10]

The Illinois Mental Health Code, in some ways a model of reform legislation, provides three separate grounds for commitment: [Sect. 1–11] (1) dangerousness to others; (2) dangerousness to oneself; and (3) inability to meet one's physical needs. The first is based on a threat to society and the latter two on the concept of *parens patriae* (the state acting to protect the individual from the active or passive harm he may do himself). The threat to society is clearly the stronger justification. (Yet commitment standards, when read broadly, often allow mental illness and dangerousness to be used interchangeably. Thus the threat to society is not always supported by the evidence.) The right of the state to confine persons dangerous to themselves rests on different grounds. In spite of John Stuart Mill's maxim from his 1859 *Essay on Liberty*, the state frequently intervenes with the mentally ill who are dangerous to themselves:

That the only purpose for which power can be rightfully exercised over any member of a civilized community against his will, is to prevent harm to others. His own good, either physical or moral, is not a sufficient warrant.

The earliest American judicial statement that a person may be locked up for his own good came in the case of Josiah Oakes in the nineteenth century in Massachusetts.[20] The opinion stated, ". . . it is a principle of law that an insane person has no will of his own. In that case it becomes the duty of others to provide for his safety . . ."

When one cannot care for himself, commitment may have drastic consequences not only in relation to liberty but also in regard to the rights over one's body and the management of one's property. Therefore it seems best that the standard for commitment in this group be that the risk is substantial and that the person is so disabled as to render him almost incapable of objecting. The most difficult case is that of a threatened or an attempted suicide. Commitment may be justified for one reason; to provide time for reflection—so that, hopefully, the individual will accept the help he may have been seeking. If, after a short period equivalent to those for other emergencies, the individual wants to leave the hospital, there seems little justification for holding him. However, most mentally ill persons, when acutely troubled, will readily accept help when it is offered with dignity and without threats.

In 1972 a lower federal court held[19] for the first time, in a case concerning the Wisconsin Commitment Laws, that in addition to requiring notice, hearing, and the right to counsel, the Constitution mandated three other procedural protections for persons protesting involuntary commitment: (1) a beyond-a-reasonable-doubt standard of proof; (2) a warning ("Miranda"-type) to enforce Fifth Amendment rights to remain silent; and (3) a principle favoring the least restrictive alternative, with the burden on proponents of hospitalization to prove that necessity. The beyond-a-reasonable-doubt standard of proof has been further supported by a decision[150] of the Federal Appeals Court, District of Columbia. With this new delineation of rights and restrictions concerning the involuntary detention and treatment of the mentally ill, re-examination of the legality and scope of all mental health laws has continued.

In contrast to the United States, the European experience of commitment is medical.[87] That is, it tends to be informal, and it vests in the physician immense powers for involuntary hospitalization. It has been argued (in England, for example) that when dealing with potential hospital patients, the doctor should decide, without inquiry, who should be hospitalized. It has also been argued that safeguards can come into play at a later stage. This view seems to be supported in part by the fact that a high proportion of patients against whom compulsion is used do not object at a later state. Their civil liberties are felt to be protected by providing adequate machinery both for reviewing the need for continued detention and for securing release. Such reviews are generally carried out by tribunals or boards, which are usually a combination of medical, legal, and lay persons.

However, there are several problems inherent in giving the physician the power to limit freedom as well as the power to treat. First, the physician's role is to discover and treat illness, and often his decisions are made "for the patient's own good." Thus he may limit freedom in spite of the fact that the person does not want or need treatment. Second, the physician who is given the power to restrict freedom must implicitly struggle with the question of serving society versus serving the patient. This becomes a serious problem whenever any delinquent or antisocial behavior is known in the patient's history. The European experience, with easy access to hospitalization, has the further danger of denying the protesting patient his right *not* to be hospitalized. In addition, such ready access to hospitalization, which is supported by liberal mental health acts, causes alternatives to hospitalization to be the more easily ignored.

What seems clear is that neither the medical nor the legal approach to the problems of involuntary detention and treatment of the mentally ill answers all of the many questions raised. In any society, interventions are at times necessary during periods of crisis. But such power, when taken, should be exceedingly brief, providing medical and procedural safeguards at many points along the way. Only by continually re-examining the problems and the proposed answers for protecting society and the mentally ill can the limitations of freedom be minimal and the opportunities for treatment interventions be optimal.

Civil Commitment of Special Categories of Persons

From time to time, commitment categories have been broadened to include persons whose behavior was socially troublesome and felt to be treatable, but who were unable to voluntarily submit to treatment or were potential offenders and therefore dangerous. These special categories of persons enlarge or contract depending on: (1) public sentiments about certain kinds of behavior—for example, drunkenness, which is punished as illegal at certain times and treated as illness at others; and (2) the humanity and/or grandiosity of psychiatrists who are willing to treat the causes of any kind of deviant behavior and the resultant suffering it might cause.

The categories are broad and include groups termed as psychopaths, sexual psychopaths, defective delinquents, narcotics addicts, and chronic alcoholics. These special groups grew out of the history of the study of the criminal and were attempts to isolate a group of potential criminals and prevent or treat the incipient criminality. In the nineteenth century, the search for organic determinants of behavior led to the concept of a "criminal brain." This concept was supported by such terms as "inherited perversion of the moral senses" and "congenital feeblemindedness," which also fitted in well with certain moral attitudes about deviancy at that time. Lombroso's[119] concept of a criminal type of brain, which related physical characteristics, degeneracy, and crime, and was based on anatomical and physiological findings, was strongly adhered to in this country.

With the rejection of Lombroso's findings at the turn of the century, the attention of psychiatrists turned to mental defectives as a unitary factor explaining criminal behavior. In a classic paper, Fernald maintained that every feeble-minded person, particularly the high-grade defective, was a potential criminal needing only the proper environment and opportunity to manifest his criminality. The feeble-minded were given such labels as "moral imbecile" and "defective delinquent," and few disagreed with Fernald, who stated, "Feeble-mindedness is the mother of crime, degeneracy and pauperism."[76] With the introduction of the Simon-Binet Intelligence Test in this country, and the subsequent testing of criminals, the incidence of feeble-mindedness in various prison populations was reported at 25, then 50, then 98, and lastly 100 percent, going higher each time with the skill of the tester. Along with the doctrine of hereditary criminality came sterilization as a technique of prevention, control and punishment. In 1917 William Allison White,[186] as head of a study committee on the sterilization of criminals, concluded that there was insufficient evidence to continue the practice.

As the spotty methodological foundation of these studies became apparent and was devastatingly attacked by Murchison's[137] classic study comparing the intelligence of criminals with the general adult population, environmental theories began to grow. Psychopathic laboratories proliferated, and Benjamin Karpman[107] began his studies of that special

class of offenders in the decade of the 1920s. From his work there was adduced a personality type, the definition of which varied from a legal to a medical one. As recently as 1964, a text states that "most social scientists postulate a common core of psychopathy . . . An asocial, aggressive, highly impulsive person who feels no guilt and is unable to form lasting bonds of affection with human beings." [p. 3][125] The American Psychiatric Association,[47] in its *Diagnostic and Statistical Manual* of 1952, has a category called "Sociopathic [a term to replace the more pejorative one of psychopathic] Personality Disturbances":

Individuals to be placed in this category are ill primarily in terms of society, and of conformity with the prevailing cultural milieu, and not only in terms of personal discomfort and relation with other individuals.

The subheadings under this category are: (1) antisocial relations, which include cases previously classified as "constitutional psychopathic states" and "psychopathic personalities"; (2) dyssocial reactions, which include "psychopathic personalities with asocial and amoral trends"; (3) sexual deviations; and (4) drug and alcohol addictions. [pp. 38–39][47] In 1968, in *Diagnostic and Statistical Manual II*,[48] the category of "Sociopathic Personality" no longer exists. Under the major heading of "Personality Disorders," however, there is the following:

Antisocial personality. This term is reserved for individuals who are basically unsocialized and whose behavior pattern brings them repeatedly into conflict with society. They are incapable of significant loyalty to individuals, groups or social values. They are grossly selfish, callous, irresponsible, impulsive and unable to feel guilt or to learn from experience and punishment. Frustration tolerance is low. They tend to blame others or offer plausible rationalizations for their behavior. A mere history of repeated legal or social offenses is not sufficient to justify this diagnosis. [p. 43]

Sexual deviations, alcoholism, and drug dependence are now diagnostically separate categories, unrelated to those of psychopath, sociopath, and antisocial personality.

Most often psychopathy is diagnosed by entering the class of apprehended offender. Such labeling contains aspects of the discarded hereditary and constitutional theories of criminality. At other times the diagnosis seems to be simply name calling of persons whose behavior is troublesome to others. Thus almost any deviance becomes psychopathy. Yet in 1972, in an otherwise thoughtful and careful study of the problem of predicting dangerousness, Kozol[113] states:

Our concept of the dangerous person is nearly identical with the classical stereotype of the criminal or antisocial psychopath. These terms are synonyms with sociopath, character disorder or antisocial personality. [p. 379]

What is a psychopath? He is at one and the same time an abstraction, a generalization, and a specification. He is a member of a larger class of unique individuals. [p. 380]

The state of being a psychopath is neither static nor exclusive. [p. 380]

Not all nonconformists are psychopaths, whether they are single social offenders or admired geniuses, but it is undoubtedly true that all psychopaths are nonconformists. [p. 382]

The concept of sexual psychopath (sexually dangerous person, sexual offender) is even more vague and probably invalid from a scientific viewpoint. The terms embodied in law usually follow some outrageous sex crime. In the past three decades, thirty states and the District of Columbia have enacted special legislation for commitment of sex offenders who, although not insane, are defined as mentally abnormal. A careful study[66] of this category of offender indicates that they are often not dangerous, are minor deviates, are less recidivistic, and (contrary to popular belief) do not progress from minor sexual offenses to more serious offenses.

The "defective delinquent"—a term coined by Fernald[76] in 1909 to describe the feeble-minded offender—has broadened in use in Maryland and elsewhere to include a wide variety of deviants. The older definitions always included mental retardation and a substantial amount of moral content. Branham, in 1926, reported four well-defined groups of defective delinquents on the basis of progno-

sis: (1) community conscious types (social); (2) community indifferent types (asocial); (3) community antagonistic types (antisocial); and (4) community irresponsible types (which include drug and alcohol abusers). [pp. 201–203][60] In spite of Branham's work, subsequent studies emphasized the almost impossible task of arriving at meaningful definitions. Lurie and his associates[120] were almost alone in arguing that the defective delinquent was a distinct clinical entity. Even their data did not support their contention. Now most statutory definitions of defective delinquent are only related to the issue of legal control of offenders.

There has also been an increasing trend toward the civil commitment of persons designated as alcoholics and drug abusers. In spite of the Robinson decision[32] of the Supreme Court, that it was a violation of the Eighth Amendment to imprison a person for his status as a narcotics addict, a number of jurisdictions permit civil commitment.* Contrarily, in Powell versus Texas,[29] it was held that an alcoholic could be prosecuted if drunk in public. It is most often recommended that alcoholism not be considered a criminal offense and that detoxification procedures be developed that may become part of comprehensive programs of treatment. Hutt[102] recently pointed out, in the *Task Force Report on Drunkenness,* that compulsory treatment following commitment for alcoholism would be medically unethical. There is no more a constitutional basis for depriving a chronic alcoholic of his freedom to choose or reject medical treatment than there is for depriving any other ill person suffering from a noncontagious disease of his freedom of choice. Whether or not a medical model of intervention is useful—and the evidence is inconclusive—most data support the finding that forcing an alcoholic or drug abuser to submit to treatment is useless.

A 1967 review[67] of status crimes (narcotics and alcohol addiction, vagrancy, and sexual psychopathy) seemed to indicate an aban-

* See *The Narcotics and Drug Abuse Task Force Report,* in which civil commitment is tentatively recommended. [p. 17][147]

donment of the *mens rea* (criminal intent) concept in defining crime. The categories were so broad and vague as to make questionable the notion that treatment alone justifies commitment. Civil commitments based on uncritical and often untested criteria of dangerousness become quasicriminal, showing a serious disregard for the due process rights of the individuals involved. Special statutes relating to these categories generally fail, in that they neither protect society nor provide for the selection of persons on the basis of dangerousness. Rather, they encourage indeterminate commitment, often without sentencing or regard for due process. A better solution would be to select persons only *after conviction*, on the basis of dangerousness. These persons would then be sentenced to terms adequate for the protection of society, and they would also have the opportunity to be treated.[141]

The Right to Treatment

Law is interpreted, modified, expanded, and changed through statutes. As a rule, broad legal change is effected through legislation. Mental health laws are the result of such legislation. Judicial decisions also affect laws in a limited and remedial way, by determining the rights and obligations of particular persons or parties. While historically there have been decisions relating to the wrongful detention of patients in mental hospitals, the treatment of the mentally disabled has only more recently become a matter of judicial concern. It is now possible for the mentally disabled to use the judicial system as both a forum of expression for legitimate grievances and an effective and responsible vehicle for social change. The class action suit has emerged as a mechanism for accelerating these changes.[127]

A major new legal thesis is that adequate treatment for the institutionalized mentally ill and mentally retarded is a constitutional right.[194] The legal doctrines that: (1) persons in custody for mental illness have a right to treatment; (2) they may not be held without treatment; and (3) treatment can be legally defined, have been elaborated in several courts (principally the Second Federal Appeals Court and the Alabama Federal District Court).

The first major judicial concern over the treatment and rights of hospitalized patients began with the cases of Catherine Lake (1964 and 1966)[16,17] and Charles Rouse (1966).[34] Both were considered by the Second Federal Court of Appeals, with the opinions stated by Judge David Bazelon. Catherine Lake was committed to St. Elizabeth's Hospital in 1962, suffering from a chronic brain syndrome due to arteriosclerosis, with a psychotic reaction. She appealed a District Court denial of relief in habeas corpus. Psychiatrists said that Mrs. Lake was prone to "wandering away" and demonstrated "difficulty with her memory." Mrs. Lake, on the other hand, testified that she felt able to be at liberty to a certain degree. The District Court, in denying the appeal for relief in habeas corpus, noted the appellant's right to "make further application in the event that the patient is in a position to show that there would be some facilities available for her provision."[16] Mrs. Lake contended, in the appeal, that a *suitable alternative* to "total confinement" in a mental hospital was warranted. She was agreeable to some form of restraint, either at home or in another institution or hospital. At the habeas corpus hearing, a psychiatrist testified that Mrs. Lake did not need "constant medical supervision" but only "attention" and that there would be no objection if she were in a "nursing home or place where there would be supervision." The Appeals Court ruled that it did not appear "that the appellant's illness required complete deprivation of liberty that results from commitment to St. Elizabeth's as a person of 'unsound mind.'" The case was remanded to the lower court for an inquiry into an "alternative course of treatment."

Judge Bazelon's opinion,[17] in summary, was:

1. When the question arises as to whether full-time confinement is appropriate, the lower court must explore alternatives and request assistance from public agencies. It should not rely upon the patient to bring this information to its attention. . . . this is related also to the obligation of the state to bear the burden of explora-

tion of possible alternatives as an indigent cannot bear.

2. The court should attempt to find a course of treatment that would be acceptable to the individual. Among the alternatives available are public health nursing care, foster care, private care subsidized by welfare payments, community mental health day care, or even the simple requirement that the patient carry an identification card.

3. It was not an issue whether the constitution would prohibit a complete deprivation of a patient's liberty in the event that there were no treatment alternatives available.

In the other cited case, Charles Rouse was committed to St. Elizabeth's Hospital, Washington, D.C., as criminally insane. He sought release on the grounds that he was not receiving treatment. The District Court denied relief in habeas corpus on the grounds that it did not have a right to consider whether or not Rouse was getting enough treatment. The Appeals Court decision reversed the lower court and remanded the case for further proceedings.

Judge Bazelon's opinion[34] can be summarized as follows:

1. Hospitalization, after a finding of insanity, is treatment, not punishment.
2. Custody without treatment is similar to punishment.
3. Shortage of staff and facilities furnish no excuse for inadequate treatment.
4. When a patient claims his treatment program is inadequate, the courts have a responsibility to bring together pertinent evidence to determine what kinds of treatment would be adequate, and whether the treatment program supplied meets these standards. If the patient is indigent, it is up to the courts and the government to supply experts who can aid in the decision as to whether or not the treatment is adequate.
5. The permissible range of treatment alternatives in a given case depends upon the particular needs of the patient; i.e., adequate treatment for one might not be sufficient treatment for another.
6. If the lower court determines that a patient is not receiving adequate treatment, it should give the hospital a reasonable opportunity to develop a program.

7. The extent of the hospital's opportunity will depend upon such factors as the length of time adequate treatment has been withheld, the length of the custody, and the nature of the patient's mental illness.
8. In some cases, an order of conditional or unconditional release may be the appropriate remedy.

The American Orthopsychiatric Association entered the case of Rouse versus Cameron as *amicus curiae* (friend of the court).[34] The brief stated that the most promising method of upgrading the inadequate treatment afforded to persons involuntarily committed to mental institutions for the criminally insane was to recognize that such persons had a judicially enforceable right to adequate treatment. It was agreed that the criminally insane generally failed to receive adequate treatment and that substantial reform would not occur until a right to adequate treatment was recognized in that area. The political constituency of the mentally ill was nonexistent. Only a judicial recognition of their constitutional rights would afford them the hope that their ultimate reentry into society may be effected. The brief contended further that a right to treatment was guaranteed by the Constitution and that the recognition of such a right would not create undue problems of judicial administration. Since the deprivation of liberty without treatment is identical to criminal punishment, such an incarceration of a mentally ill person must constitute the infliction of cruel and unusual punishment upon him. In addition, unless treatment were guaranteed to those persons detained by the government as a result of their mental or physical status, their detention would violate the due process clause of the Constitution, in that they were denied access to the sole means of attaining their liberty.

Therefore, the brief concluded, in determining whether treatment is adequate, a court would be called upon to answer five questions, all capable of objective analysis:

1. Does the treatment involved fall within an accepted school of medical thought?
2. Does the mode of treatment comport generally

with the accepted procedures of the school of thought to which it belongs?

3. Do the procedures adhered to in administering the treatment in question reasonably insure an ordered and rational program of care?
4. Are adequate records kept concerning the care afforded the patient?
5. Are the physical facilities of the institution adequate to provide the treatment?

In 1971 a class action suit was filed in the Alabama Federal Court by the guardians of civilly committed patients at, and by certain employees of, the Bryce State Mental Hospital, against the Commissioner of Mental Health, members of the Alabama Mental Health Board, and others. These defendants were charged with providing inadequate treatment to the approximately 5000 patients who resided there. Later this action was amended to include Searcy Mental Hospital and the Partlow School for the Mentally Retarded. The court based its decision[43] on a constitutional guarantee of a right to treatment: "To deprive any citizen of his or her liberty upon the altruistic theory that the confinement is for humane therapeutic reasons and fail to provide adequate treatment violates the very fundamentals of due process," and ordered the State Department of Mental Health to provide an effective treatment program within six months. Dissatisfied with the state plan for the improvement of facilities required by the court in its first order, and utilizing contributions and suggestions of a panel of national mental health experts, the court issued an order[44] in April 1972 that detailed the criteria for adequate treatment: (1) a humane psychological and physical environment; (2) qualified staff with sufficient numbers to administer adequate treatment; and (3) individualized treatment plans. Most recently a federal district court in Florida assessed damages against two psychiatrists for holding a nondangerous patient fourteen years without treatment. A federal appeals court affirmed this on the principle that when a nondangerous patient is involuntarily hospitalized, the only constitutionally permissible purpose is to provide treatment, and that the patient has a constitutional right to such treat-

ment.* This was further affirmed in another decision by the same appeals court.†

All of the above cases involve patients involuntarily hospitalized. The increasing utilization of voluntary hospitalization substantially reduces the numbers of those involuntarily incarcerated. However, there is no justification for compromising quality of care and treatment because of the legal status of the recipient. Minimum standards for adequate treatment should apply equally to voluntary and involuntary patients.

Questions persist about the efficacy, as well as the wisdom, of the courts persisting in their effort to define and enforce adequate treatment standards. Psychiatrists, too,[156] often are at odds about defining treatment standards, and they frequently feel that those outside the field of mental health are more in the dark than they are. In addition, the courts themselves are not unanimous in this extension of their power. In the same federal circuit as Alabama, a district court[5] held that determinations of the quality of mental health services and the adequacy of treatment rests with the "elected representatives of the people" and not with the courts.

Perhaps the more basic problem is a dual—public and private—treatment system. Resources, while not abundant in the private area, unquestionably exceed those available to the public system. A single system of care is being developed in California, with the hope of closing out the public mental hospitals. This may end further class action suits by patients in that state's mental health system. In 1967–1968, Illinois introduced a state insurance plan for the indigent and medically indigent that guaranteed their treatment in community hospitals and day treatment programs by removing any financial barriers. This program shows promise of eventually reducing or eradicating the dual treatment system in those areas where quality care for any citizen can be purchased.

Regardless of whether treatment is ade-

* Donaldson v. O'Conner, 493 F2d 507, (5th circuit), 1974

† Wyatt v. Aderholt, 493 F2d 712, (5th circuit), 1974

quate, questions[109] concerning the usefulness of involuntary commitment continue. Given our present predictive capacities, it has been argued that commitment hearings that require a complete application of the beyond-a-reasonable-doubt standard would eliminate civil commitment, due to the impossibility of meeting that standard. The Lessard case[19] demonstrates another procedural reform necessary in view of the often contradictory views of a patient's capacities: the incorporation of the Fifth Amendment right, which protects the individual against self-incrimination. About to be committed because he is incompetent to decide whether to accept treatment, he is (once warned of the consequences) considered competent to decide, without the aid of an attorney, which of the psychiatrist's questions it is in his best interest to answer. The last Lessard procedural innovation, as in Lake versus Cameron, was to make hospitalization a last resort. In that context, the question of voluntary hospitalization can be reexamined. Sometimes the coercion applied to have persons voluntarily admit themselves, rather than be legally committed, results in an inadequate examination of the need for hospitalization and an insufficient exploration of the alternatives. Of necessity, these areas receive more thorough consideration in the case of involuntary hospitalization.

Right to Refusal of Treatment

In the matter of the choice of a type and method of treatment, patients' rights also continue to be reexamined and defined. It has been argued that a patient, even though committed involuntarily for treatment, should retain absolute right over the use of medication, electroconvulsive shock, and similar treatment. At the present time, separate informed consent is required in most states before electroconvulsive therapy can begin, no matter whether a person is voluntarily or involuntarily hospitalized. However, the right of a patient to stop electroconvulsive treatments, after having initially consented to them, has stirred strong debate in at least one case. In

that case a woman, voluntarily admitted and diagnosed as involutionally depressed, was informed in detail about the nature of ECT as prescribed. She consented, but after the first treatment she refused to permit a second. The hospital staff felt she could not withdraw her consent on the grounds that "once the patient consented she became the responsibility of the medical staff . . . [and] the permissions papers were legal and gave the staff the right to act in her interest." Jonas Robitscher, a lawyer and psychiatrist at Emory University (Georgia), charged that the manner in which the patient was forced to continue ECT "is not only a violation of the patient's legal rights (assault and battery), but also an example of how mental patients ought not to be treated." Robitscher felt that ECT posed special problems in that it "makes the patient increasingly incompetent and unable to exercise his legal rights."[148] In another case, one involving New York City's Bellevue Hospital, Justice Gellinoff decided that while the patient who refused electroshock therapy was "sufficiently mentally ill to require further detention," such a finding "does not imply she lacks the mental capacity to knowingly consent or withhold her consent to electroshock therapy."[142]

When persons have been hospitalized against their will for an examination, their right to refuse treatment—for example, drugs, physical restraints, and isolation—can be contravened if their maintenance (not treatment) requires the application of physical or chemical restraints or the use of isolation. Legal safeguards are then required to see that these procedures are used only minimally. In New York, a woman committed for observation for sixty days was forcibly treated with oral and intramuscular medications in spite of her objections based on religious beliefs. Upon release she brought suit, which resulted in relief for damages. The court[42] noted that, in forcing medication on the patient, there was grave doubt that the state was protecting the interests of third party or society.

Psychosurgery, which is experiencing a renaissance (particularly in relation to violent behavior),[124] poses an even more difficult problem. While there have always been proponents[79] of the use of lobotomy (a form of psychosurgery) for chronic mental problems from schizophrenia to alcoholism, it had become a discredited treatment for the most part. However, it is now returning to use as a means of curbing violence. It is being recommended for the control of violent behavior in persons considered dangerous, including those mentally ill and hospitalized, and those non-mentally ill or mentally ill and in prison. Disregarding for the moment both the imprecision of determining dangerousness and the absence of treatment for such persons, who are then labeled as intractable or untreatable, it is unlikely that an incarcerated person (whether an involuntarily hospitalized patient, indeterminately sentenced offender, or long-term prisoner), can give his informed consent to psychosurgery. This is particularly true when the patient is held involuntarily and is led to believe that consenting to be the subject of such a surgical procedure will result in his early or immediate release.[166]

Legal Competence

At the present time, in almost all legal jurisdictions, persons involuntarily hospitalized (legally committed) retain their rights, particularly those relating to their person, property, and civil liberties.[64] Explicit statutory recognition of the civil and personal rights of the mentally ill and mentally retarded constitutes a significant and needed reform. It also indicates the kind of discrimination and illegal restrictions that have been placed on the mentally disabled in the past. In recent legislation, various rights have been explicitly enumerated,[64,127] such as:

1. The right to communicate with persons outside the facility by telephone, correspondence, and visits.
2. The right to keep clothing and personal effects.
3. The right to religious freedom.
4. The right to vote.
5. The right to be employed, if possible.

6. The right to execute instruments, such as wills.
7. The right to enter contractual relationships.
8. The right to make purchases.
9. The right to education.
10. The right to habeas corpus.
11. The right to independent psychiatric examinations.
12. The right to civil service status.
13. The right to retain licenses, privileges, or permits established by law.
14. The right to marry.
15. The right to sue and be sued.
16. The right not to be subjected to unnecessary mechanical restraint.

Mental illness does not necessarily impute any incompetency in exercising one or more of these rights. To be found incompetent requires a special and separate judicial determination. A number of statutes clearly differentiate between mental illness and mental incompetency, and some states (Illinois and New York) make reference to that distinction in their catalog of patients' rights.

The right to legal representation has been incorporated into a number of new mental health statutes to protect the rights of patients in commitment hearings. Legal representation ensures that they will no longer be subjected to any legal, economic, or social difficulties as a consequence of their illness. It also allows patients to affirmatively and actively maintain control of their own lives. Mechanisms for review, appraisal, and explanation of patients' rights have been established in several states. The Mental Heath Information Service,[161] a court-affiliated service established in New York in 1965, has been a pioneer in attempting to safeguard patients' rights and enforce legal procedures for hospitalization and release. In Minnesota, review boards[24] examine admission and retention of mental patients in hospitals. California has instituted the use of a nonprofit legal services group[36] to apprise involuntarily hospitalized patients of their legal rights. In Illinois, a pilot project[65] of legal services (concerning a variety of civil matters) for hospitalized patients, has demonstrated a largely unserved legal need of all the hospitalized mentally ill.

At times the question of legal competence is raised concerning a person whose judgment about himself or his property seems faulty. It has been raised in regard to the execution of instruments (wills), the dissipation of property and money, and the inability or unwillingness of a person to allow lifesaving medical or surgical procedures. Such people may be found in the community, or as patients on medical or surgical services, as well as in mental hospitals.

Since the finding of legal incompetence is an adjudicatory process, data can be collected from a number of sources, including family, friends, business associates, lawyers, physicians, and psychiatrists. It is a mistaken notion that only—or even preeminently—the psychiatrist can give testimony that will decide legal competence or incompetence. Should power over his person or properties be taken from an individual, either temporarily (as for surgery) or permanently (as in the case of the estate of an elderly, senile person), that power is usually vested in another family member, a lawyer, or the court, rather than in the physician. It is this other person who then gives permission for a particular procedure or manages as a conservator. Unfortunately, the law in the matter of legal incompetency is an all-or-none affair. Either you are legally competent or legally incompetent. From our knowledge of mental functions, we know that some functions remain more intact than others and that a person's capacities may diminish or increase from time to time under differing conditions. Nevertheless, once an adjudication of incompetency has occurred, all rights are vested in another. Therefore such proceedings should be entered into with care, since for a person with some intact mental functions, the psychological consequences of being declared legally incompetent may be to accelerate the process of psychological debilitation. This is certainly an area in which lawyer and psychiatrist should confer before proceeding with incompetency hearings, in order to protect a person's psychological and physical integrity.

⟨ Psychiatry and Criminal Law

Psychiatrists have collaborated with the criminal law system in two ways: as expert witnesses in various trial phases; and as therapists, primarily within conventional penal institutions. To date, this collaboration has not been particularly productive or happy. Typically, psychiatrists have become involved at the request of members of the legal profession, yet the tasks to be performed have often been delineated by the legal system without effective or even adequate consultation with psychiatrists.[179]

Part of the problem has been a difficulty in communication characterized by different terminology, different purposes, and different frames of reference (that is, sociocultural versus motivational). To that has been added an almost caricatured view of the concepts of psychosis versus insanity, legal responsibility versus psychic determinism,[117] and the legal model (innocent until proven guilty) versus the medical model (suspicion of illness until proven innocent).[167] Nevertheless there has now developed a more meaningful and thoughtful dialog between criminal law and psychiatry. This in turn has resulted in an appreciation of the fact that the issue of "criminal responsibility," although it raises many interesting and complex moral and philosophical questions relating law and psychiatry, has not deserved the overwhelming preponderance of attention it has received.

The criminal law system, like any other legal system, is composed of a framework of legislation that represents a culture's or society's values and sentiments concerning abhorrent behavior, and the hierarchy of penalties assigned on the basis of the degree to which such behavior is abhorred. Within the framework of the laws, the police enforce the law, the courts attempt to determine culpability and punishment, and the correctional system provides confinement and community probation and parole. This system is complex, and the areas of possible interreaction between psychiatry and the laws are many.[146] Nonetheless psychiatry—perhaps at the insistence of lawyers and jurists—has attended to issues more philosophical than psychiatric, resulting in inattention to pressingly difficult but perhaps more valuable areas.

One such area is *crisis intervention* in the community, which may be accomplished through a variety of agencies, including the police. Such agencies use power as a crime-preventive measure, getting closest to the point of difficulty and remaining there for the shortest possible period of time. Another area of interaction involves working with legislative groups to modify existing laws and promulgate new ones regarding extended sentencing for mentally disturbed individuals found guilty of violent crimes. Psychiatrists may also examine defendants for pretrial and presentencing data collection and diagnosis, in order to offer the court help in deciding what course of action or setting would be most helpful before trial or after conviction. They could also do research in the prediction of dangerousness and its relationship to treatment programs for such persons, both within the correctional setting and in the open community.

The Police

There are about 16,000 police in Chicago—to take a sample big city—of which 9,000 to 10,000 are patrolmen. The policeman's everyday life requires that he make many decisions quickly under crisis circumstances, decisions that are later subjected to detailed review by many different people. There is an unfortunate conflict between his understanding of his role and his understanding of the usual observer's interpretation of his role. On the one hand he is expected to be bright, strong, and brave. On the other hand he is expected to be cowardly, on the take, bumbling, and oppressive to members of minority groups.

The official job description for policemen in Chicago lists twenty items of expected excellence. Among them are the ability to tolerate long periods of boredom and monotony while maintaining a readiness for quick, competent responses; the capacity to learn the behavior of the people and social institutions within a

territory; the ability to exercise mature judgment and discretion, making no error in police procedure that might subject the man or his police department to criticism; familiarity with the many procedures and reports of the police department; and the exhibition of a high level of personal integrity. Much of the policeman's time is spent filling out reports of his work and justifying his activities, following highly detailed police procedures. Indeed, training sessions reflect a heavy emphasis on reporting properly and managing events according to correct procedure. The policeman's social role is ambiguous and his psychological environment is complex and subject to scrutiny, and at the same time he is asked to behave in a procedurally correct and detailed manner. In spite of all this, he is allowed and encouraged to use a large amount of discretionary judgment.

The police are important social agents to the poor in poverty areas of the city. They are available twenty-four hours a day, seven days a week; they have no waiting list; and they are called about everything from broken elevators to stopped-up toilets. In certain districts, 80 percent of police calls are for miscellaneous services not associated with disturbances or commissions of crime.

The Chicago police make 6000 arrests per year in which the arresting policeman believes that the person is, or may be, mentally ill. A misdemeanor charge is used as a device to get the person to treatment. Thus, for these 6000 cases—mostly poor people—their life crises become associated with an arrest leading to a separation from family and local social network, a separation from job and income resulting in the family's loss of support, and a loss of self-esteem. A different management of these crises might result in more effective intervention and diversion[115] from the legal-justice to a health-care system. The police could benefit from a more open dialog about their beliefs, values, and roles, which would aid in their understanding of human behavior and the paradoxes between their own self-image and their day-to-day functions.[55]

Because of their enormous discretionary power in the area of crisis intervention, the police can act as agents who prevent crime and expedite treatment for persons showing early evidence of mental disturbance. In New York City's 30th Precinct, a project using a police team as specialists in family crisis intervention has innovatively demonstrated possibilities of crime prevention and early mental health intervention. (One of the most difficult police functions is that of intervention in family crises. It has been shown that police calls for family disturbances lead to 20 percent of police deaths and account for 40 percent of time lost due to disabilities resulting from injuries.) In conjunction with the police department, the City College of New York trained a selected group of police, known as the Family Crisis Intervention Unit (FCIU)[50] in interpersonal skills to attempt to effect constructive solutions for family situations requiring police intervention. In a two-year experimental period involving 1400 interventions with 950 families in a police patrol area of 85,000 population, no injuries were sustained by members of the FCIU, and their basic professional identity as police remained intact. More crisis calls were processed in the demonstration precinct, as compared with a control precinct; more repeat interventions occurred; and fewer assaults occurred in families and against police. Mental health problems of a wide range frequently manifest themselves in domestic disturbances, and police with knowledge of this can provide helpful insights and make appropriate referrals, without compromising their peace-keeping mission.

Legislation

Psychiatry generally has had little to do with the legislative process. Nevertheless, as a result of an interest in community mental health and a continuation of the quest for social justice that reemerged after World War II, increasing numbers of modern psychiatrists have played significant roles in the development of legislation concerning mental health codes. These codes concern themselves with: (1) the rights of persons held both voluntarily and involuntarily for mental treatment; (2)

laws relating to privilege and confidentiality; and (3) laws relating to determinations of dangerousness and indeterminate sentencing for treatment. Most recently, in Illinois, psychiatric data was used in the preparation of a Unified Code of Corrections, particularly in the areas of sentencing and community supervision.

The Trial

PRETRIAL REPORTS

After a person has been charged with a crime, facts can be gathered regarding his motivation, extenuating circumstances, past and present social history, and medical and mental health information, and allowance can be made for special testing. This information and data from other sources can be used by the court to determine: (1) whether there is sufficient cause to proceed with a trial; or (2) whether the case may be diverted from the legal-justice system to a health-care and/or social welfare system.

COMPETENCY TO STAND TRIAL

The psychiatrist has become increasingly involved in the area of whether a trial should or should not take place in the context of competency to stand trial. The concept of competency to stand trial originally was developed to help the defendant. It was felt to be unjust and even cruel to try a person who was so disturbed that he really did not know what was happening, or who could not cooperate meaningfully with his defense counsel. It was hoped that, with time and treatment, the accused individual would be able to make the *best* defense possible—something that could not be accomplished while he was acutely and distressingly mentally ill. In fact what occured was that, although not convicted of crimes or civilly committed, many incompetent criminal defendants had been, in effect, serving life sentences in mental hospitals. Among psychiatrists a bias exists against returning the mentally ill for trial, arising in part from the fact that the system of criminal justice is seen as punitive and antitherapeutic. In practical terms, this has led to considerable wasting of human life and unnecessary deprivation of freedom. A study[126] in Massachusetts found that, of all incompetent defendants committed to Bridgewater, more left by death than all other avenues combined.

The doctrine of mental incompetency has its roots deep in common law.[38,91] It means that the defendant, because of the existence of mental disease or defect or other reasons, does not understand the nature and object of the proceedings pending against him; or cannot appreciate or comprehend his own condition in relation to the proceedings; or is unable, for some other reason, to competently assist his attorney in his own defense. If the defendant is found to be incompetent, all criminal proceedings are suspended, and the state is denied the power to proceed against him. Prosecuting an incompetent has been held[27] to be a denial of his right to due process of law. Even if the mental defect is not discovered until after the defendant has been convicted and his time for appeal has expired, the issue of incompetency can be raised collaterally; if it is proven, the entire proceedings may be voided and set aside. Thus, one may also be found incompetent to serve his sentence or be executed. This principle is so fundamental that incompetency may not be waived even with the consent of the court. Consequently, incompetency proceedings are sometimes initiated by the prosecution or the trial judge. This can result in a major abuse of the incompetency procedure, for in most states, commitment of a defendant adjudicated as incompetent to stand trial is mandatory.[96] The prosecutor or the court may use incompetency proceedings as an expedient substitute for criminal prosecution and as a final disposition of the case.

There has been an absence of detail in statutory law regarding competency, and although psychiatrists are frequently delegated the responsibility for decision-making regarding competency, they demonstrate confusion and a lack of understanding of the issue. (It has been suggested[170] that lawyers might be better suited than psychiatrists to make such determination.) The psychiatrist should know the common-law criteria stated above. Psychiatric reports to the court commonly confuse issues of illness and competency, competency and commitability, and competency and dangerousness. The evidence seems to indicate that both psychiatrists and lawyers are weak in their knowledge of the law and in the application of psychological data to findings of competency.[159] In Illinois in the 1970s, the term "incompetence" has been replaced by the term "unfitness." [Sect. 1005–2–1; also including commentary, pp. 92–93][103] It was felt that "fitness" speaks only to the person's ability to function within the context of the trial, whereas the term "competence" is often used in establishing whether an individual should be committed to an institution as mentally ill and excludes considerations of physical fitness.

Two issues require further elaboration. The first, amnesia, presents the court with a special problem: the defendant who claims amnesia concerning the events of an alleged crime is at least theoretically unable to assist his counsel in the preparation of his defense. Nevertheless, case law indicates[193] that defendants suffering solely from amnesia, who are otherwise competent to stand trial, are adjudicated competent insofar as they can assist counsel in a number of other ways. It has been suggested,[112] however, that temporary amnesia should be distinguished from permanent amnesia, and that the temporary variety is distinguishable by knowledgeable psychiatrists and may warrant a finding of incompetency.

The second issue is that of the medicated mental patient, and whether a person in such a "drugged" state is, in fact, competent to stand trial or return to trial. In a number of jurisdictions, medicated patients with a prior incompetency finding have not been allowed to return for trial. A Louisiana trial judge noted that such a defendant was "only synthetically sane." In Illinois the same was the case, and patients returning for hearings of competency prior to trial had to have medication terminated at least seventy-two hours prior to court examination. The arguments for allowing defendants to stand trial while receiving medication are:

1. Psychotropic drugs make a mentally ill person *more*, not less, normal.

2. Other jurisdictions have allowed defendants to stand trial when found competent with medication.

3. Failure to allow them to stand trial violates the equal protection clause of the Fourteenth Amendment, in that, other than mentally ill defendants, persons requiring medication for chronic illnesses are allowed to stand trial.

4. The denial of a trial permits indefinite commitment.

The Supreme Court has concerned itself with this issue of indefinite commitment following a determination of incompetency. In 1968 Theon Jackson was arrested for two purse snatchings involving a total of $9.00. He was a deaf mute with almost no capacity to communicate, and he was found incompetent to stand trial on the basis of a moderately severe mental deficiency. In reversing the State Supreme Court's affirmation of a denial of a new trial, the court stated, with reference to the due process issue: [p. 738, note 13][15]

We hold, consequently, that a person charged by a state with a criminal offense who is committed solely on account of his incapacity to proceed to trial cannot be held more than the reasonable period of time necessary to determine whether there is a substantial probability that he will attain that capacity in the foreseeable future. If it is determined that this is not the case, then the state must either institute the customary civil commitment proceeding that would be required to commit indefinitely any other citizen, or release the defendant. Furthermore, even if it is determined that the defendant probably soon will be able to stand trial, his continued commitment must be justified by progress toward that goal.

In 1973, in an extension of the Jackson decision, the Supreme Court affirmed a decision[151] by a three-judge appeals court in New York that a criminal defendant, judged incompetent to stand trial because of mental illness, could not be committed to a New York State mental hospital operated by the Department of Corrections unless a jury also determined him to be dangerous. Burt and Morris,[63] in a 1973 proposal for the abolition of the incompetency plea, argued that in the wake of the Jackson decision we will be tempted to resort to civil commitment proceedings rather than dismiss charges against and permanently release incompetent defendants. This, they say, may serve to continue or increase the damage of the results of incompetency proceedings in the past. Rather, they argue, incompetency should be grounds for obtaining a trial continuance, during which time the state must provide resources to assist the defendant toward greater trial competence. If trial competence is not achieved within six months, the state should be required to dismiss charges or to proceed to a trial governed, where necessary, by procedures designed to compensate for the incompetent defendant's trial disabilities. The risk to society posed by such rapid disposition of these offenders, whether by trial or release, seems to be no greater (and possibly even less great) than that posed by other groups of offenders.

THE DEFENSE OF INSANITY

It has been felt that the insanity defense serves an important symbolic role in our legal system. It long preceded the development of psychiatry; the first recorded insanity acquittal in English law occurred about 1000 years ago. However, it was not until after the famous M'Naghten Rule was enacted by the House of Lords that this defense came to be so closely tied to psychiatry.

In the seventeenth century, among the papers of Sir Matthew Hale, Chief Justice of the Court of King's Bench, was the following: "Human beings are naturally endowed with these two great faculties, understanding and liberty of will. . . . The consent of the will is that which renders human actions commendable or culpable. . . . And because the liberty or choice of the will presupposeth an act of understanding to know the thing or action chosen by the will, it follows that where there is a total defect of the understanding there is no free act of the will . . ." [pp. 14–16][91] Hale was explicitly aware of the difficulty of devising rules for the practical application of his test, in that the problem was not only *what* to excuse, but *how much*. Meanwhile, judges had begun to charge juries that a defendant was not to be held responsible for his actions unless he possessed the capacity to distinguish good from evil.[30] In May 1800, James Hatfield fired a shot at George III, believing he was commanded by God to sacrifice himself for the world's salvation. His counsel argued that in spite of his not having a raving madness, his delusion was a true characteristic of madness. The trial was stopped and the jury urged to return a verdict of not guilty by reason of insanity. Hatfield's case[31] settled only what to do with Hatfield, until January 20, 1843, when Daniel M'Naghten shot Daniel Drummond, Secretary to Prime Minister Robert Peel. The testimony and arguments[25] eventuated in the M'Naghten Rule.

Notwithstanding public satisfaction, the M'Naghten test was criticized almost from its inception as nothing more than a restatement of the "right and wrong" test. As early as 1838, Isaac Ray, in his *Medical Jurisprudence of Insanity*, called the right and wrong test "fallacious," because "the insane mind is not entirely deprived of [the] power of moral discernment, but in many subjects is perfectly rational, and displays the exercise of a sound and well balanced mind."[153] Ray attempted to formulate his own rule for a defense of insanity. He was pleased with the results of a New Hampshire State Supreme Court decision in which Chief Justice Perley instructed the jury:[35]

That, if the killing was the offspring or product of mental disease in the defendant, the verdict should be 'not guilty by reason of insanity;' That neither delusion nor knowledge of right and wrong, nor design or cunning in planning and executing the killing, and escaping or avoiding detection, nor ability to recognize acquaintances, or to labor, or transact business, or manage affairs is, as a matter of law, a test of disease; but that all symptoms and all tests of mental disease are purely matters of fact to be determined by the jury.

This resulted in a rule* in New Hampshire in which acquittal by reason of insanity would

* Also see State v. Jones, 50 N.H. 69, 1871.

follow if the felonious act were the "offspring" of a mental disease.

Although most American jurisdictions approved M'Naghten, an increasing number of states began to supplement the M'Naghten language as time went by with: "If he had a mental disease that kept him from controlling his conduct." This rule, often called the "irresistible impulse test," quieted psychiatric criticism, but only temporarily. The earliest decision[37] of the Supreme Court of the United States on the subject of the criminal responsibility of persons allegedly insane was made in 1895. This decision departed substantially from the M'Naghten Rule, holding that if all the evidence does not exclude beyond a reasonable doubt the hypothesis of insanity, the accused was entitled to acquittal.

In an attempt to deal with psychiatric criticism by allowing a less restrained use of psychiatric testimony, the Second Federal Appeals Court held, in the case of Durham versus United States in 1954, that "an accused is not criminally responsible if his unlawful act was the *product* of mental disease or mental defect."[9] This broadened the concept of the defense of insanity to a point where it appeared meaningless. Except for the District of Columbia, Maine, and the Virgin Islands, there were no jurisdictions that accepted the Durham test. The American Law Institute, in its Model Penal Code of 1962,[46] stated that "a person is not responsible for criminal conduct if at the time of such conduct, as a result of disease or defect, he lacked substantial capacity either to appreciate the wrongfulness of his conduct or to conform his conduct to the requirements of the law." This modification of the M'Naghten rule has been accepted in most jurisdictions, including most federal ones. The Second Federal Appeals Court in the United States versus Brawner case[39] decided in 1972, repudiated its own Durham stance. The American Psychiatric Association (APA), filing an *amicus curiae* brief in the case, favored the American Law Institute test of criminal responsibility because it allowed psychiatric testimony to elucidate more fully and clearly the history, development, adaptation, and function of the patients' behavioral processes and the results of all other medical tests, in order to evaluate the clinical symptoms of the disease in relation to the alleged criminal acts. Further, the APA argued[149] that it did not recommend that the testing of criminal responsibility distinguish between psychological, emotional, social, and cultural sources of impairment.* Lastly, the APA favored (with appropriate safeguards) the ultimate abolition of the insanity defense.

ARGUMENTS FOR ABOLISHING THE INSANITY DEFENSE

The defense of insanity, notwithstanding arguments for its abolition or enlargement, has always centered on what the appropriate definition can be of legal insanity. Essentially it has excluded from punishment those who, by definition, could not be deterred by punishment or those who, because of mental illness, were unable to distinguish between right and wrong. The feeling was that it would be unjust as well as futile to punish them.

Beginning with the M'Naghten case and continuing with Durham and then the American Penal Code, each attempt at a definition has been subjected to vigorous and continuing criticism. Some have seen the defense of insanity as providing a loophole in the law, while others have felt it should be broadened to include as exculpatory a variety of social and cultural factors. The M'Naghten test held that there was a criminal insanity when a person was laboring under such *defect of reason*, from disease of the mind, as not to know the nature and quality of the act he was doing—or if he did know it, he did not know he was doing wrong. The concept of "defect of reason" is difficult to define in psychiatry as well as in law. In fact, attempts by psychiatry to define defect of reason have simply confused the issue. The concept of responsibility cannot be translated into psychiatric terms, and these same psychiatric terms are very often used to attack people who are deviant rather than to explain their responsibility, or lack of it, in relation to some particular behavioral act.

* See also "APA Favors ALI Test of Criminal Responsibility," *Psychiatr. News*, 6 (1971).

Psychiatry has not even yet comfortably defined mental illness.

For these reasons, there has been a strong case made for the exclusion of the defense of insanity. An argument has also been made for the use of psychological insights in pre-trial and pre-sentencing information to the court. A number of authors such as Barbara Wooton, Norval Morris, Chief Justice Weintraub of New Jersey, Seymour Halleck, H. L. A. Hart and Thomas Szasz all argue for the abolition of the defense of insanity. (The positions for abolition are summarized by Morris.)[133] A few authors, most notably Kadish[105] and Fingarette,[77] insist that innocence and mental illness continue to have a very close relationship.

The arguments for abolition are persuasive. First, the defense of insanity has often led to indeterminate incarceration in a mental hospital, which makes the notion of exculpation seem hollow. Second, rather than serving to reduce stigmatization, the defense of insanity doubles it, as the person is seen as both "mad" and "bad." Third, it is a rare defense since the absence of the death penalty, used more as a sop to conscience than because of the presence or absence of psychopathology in the accused. And last, why should psychological factors be more exculpatory than sociological ones that have been shown to be much more likely to lead to crime? What should be relevant is the accused's mental condition at the time of the act. Did he or did he not have the prohibited *mens rea* of the crime with which he is charged? The answer to this question would be relevant to his sentence, and to his correctional treatment in the event of conviction.

Rather, what seems to have happened is that the psychiatrist's role has become prominent because he has been seduced into being an expert in the insanity defense. It has become a public ritual in which he is used to help deal with society's guilt about punishment. This may explain the development of certain folklore about the psychiatrist's capacity to know the psychic states and their causal relationships at the time of a criminal act. The limitations of psychiatry and the misuse of psychiatric testimony, of course, do not invalidate areas in which that testimony can be helpful. Nevertheless, it seems likely that the limitations of psychiatry will persist in the area of determining responsibility, and that most evidence seems to support the impossibility of a psychiatrist's determining whether or not an individual was responsible at the moment of a particular criminal act.[185] The commonsense view that has persisted over 2000 years—that the mad are unreasonable and therefore innocent of intent to do harm— ignores other data that have accumulated in that same period of time and have modified some of the same folk views of madness and the degree of exculpation they afford. Therefore, it seems more sensible to make available to the court all relevant social, psychological, and biological data. The court could then use that information in the determination of accountability for the crime and the determination of the best and most effective sentence if the accused is found guilty. Even if the concept of criminal insanity were understandable, it would not necessarily ensure an accurate or even adequate separation of groups of persons whose lack of reason makes their innocence clear and certain.

Paraphrasing one commentator,[53] if fault cannot be eliminated from the criminal process, then the defense of insanity can be considered but one aspect of the general problem of fault. It is one of a number of devices that allow the accused to show either that he did not know the true state of affairs or that he did not intend the consequences of his actions. The defense of insanity forces the institutions of criminal law to examine the validity of assumptions about responsibility and blameworthiness.

Treatment of the Offender

Criminality and the criminal mind have always intrigued the psychiatrist. The criminal often bears a resemblance to those called mentally ill, and incarceration (that is, punishment) causes distress and suffering similar to that experienced by the institutionalized mentally ill. Psychological mechanisms have been sought that could explain and, by intervention, attenuate criminal behavior. A humane desire to help improve conditions for the incarcerated criminal has drawn the psychiatrist to his treatment.

The nineteenth century was characterized by attempts to isolate biological determinants of crime and separate the ordinary offender from the insane criminal. Hospitals for the criminally insane were constructed in Illinois (Chester), Massachusetts (Bridgewater), Michigan (Ionia), and New York (Auburn, later moved to Matteawan). Isaac Ray considered[153] problems of mental illness and motivation as they related to law. In 1909, William Healy began a court clinic for juvenile offenders in Chicago. His experiences led to the development of new theories and techniques —principally the use of the case study method[97,98] for the individual delinquent, which had a profound impact on the field. Bernard Glueck[83] examined a large population of prisoners at Sing Sing in New York and reported that 58 percent demonstrated some form of nervous or mental disease.

By the second decade of the twentieth century, the monistic theories of crime and criminality began to change, leading to the employment of a variety of organic and environmental theories. This interest persisted and increased, characterized by the work of William Allison White,[187] Benjamin Karpman[106] and Winfred Overholser.[144] Particular interest in the psychopathic personality—as being useful in explaining and understanding criminal behavior—grew with the many comprehensive studies of this special group of offenders. In 1921 the Briggs law passed in Massachusetts required psychiatric examination of offenders charged with capital offenses and those charged with felonies who had previously been convicted of felonies. In 1927, Karl Menninger recommended the following to the American Bar Association:[92]

1. That a psychiatrist be available to every court.
2. That psychiatric reports be made available before sentencing any felon.
3. That there be psychiatric services in every correctional institution.
4. That a psychiatric report be done on every felon before release.

5. That a psychiatric report be available before any parole or transfer between institutions.

These recommendations were accepted in 1929, and the agreement between the legal and psychiatric professions was excellent. However, it was not destined to be maintained. Although psychiatric criminology was exciting, and eighty-three full- or part-time psychiatrists were reported to be working in American prisons in 1934, interest unfortunately began to decline by 1939 and failed to revitalize after World War II. Two issues probably accelerated this loss of interest: (1) a strong emphasis on diagnosis and disposition, with little or none on treatment, resulting in the psychiatrist doing little more than supporting the operations of the correctional institutions; and (2) the rise of psychoanalytic theory as a basis for psychotherapy with motivated individuals. How to apply this theory to an unmotivated person, who had to learn to conform to the law, was not understood. Hallek presents[92] a good summary of the history leading to and following this change in interest in treating offenders.

The major development after World War II centered around specialized programs for certain classes of offenders. The possibility of releasing prisoners after treatment and recovery appealed to psychiatrists. Indeterminacy had particular appeal when applied to behavior that could be labeled as dangerous. The first laws involving such indeterminate sentencing were passed without sufficient regard to defining dangerousness (see below) or developing sufficient legal safeguards. In addition, no provisions for treatment were offered. When these rarely-utilized laws were used, they frequently dealt with social nuisances rather than with persons who seriously endangered others. By 1955, prison psychiatry in Maryland (Defective Delinquent Law), Wisconsin (Sex Crime Law), California (Vacaville Medical Facility), and the Federal Bureau of Prisons had developed to try and treat the most difficult offenders.

The problems have been and continue to be immense. The issue of defining "deviant" and "dangerous" offenders grows more difficult.

The mentally retarded offender poses special problems for treatment. First, the data on the numbers, problems, and treatment of such offenders in penal and correctional institutions in the United States are either inaccurate or insufficient. Brown and Courtless[62] estimated 20,000 prison inmates with IQ scores below 70, with 3300 of that group having IQ scores below 55. The authors recommended:[62]

1. Collection of data on the magnitude of the retardates' involvement with criminal law, epidemiologic data, and knowledge of offense patterns.
2. Elucidation of the relationship between intelligence and antisocial behavior.
3. Clarification of responsibility for retarded offenders.
4. Clarification of terminology used for retardates, in order that some appropriate strategies regarding intervention might be accomplished.

Systems of indeterminate sentencing can be abused if full legal rights through due process are denied and treatment is not available. In the absence of an adequate definition of the group to be treated, and in the absence of legal safeguards and realistic facilities for treatment, such programs use psychiatry for questionable preventive detention and punishment.

DANGEROUSNESS

Treatment interventions depend on predictions of the likely consequences of such interventions. The prediction of dangerousness is expected of the psychiatrist. This belief in the psychiatrist's capacity to make such predictions is firmly held and constantly relied on, in spite of a lack of empirical support.

Of the approximately 600,000 persons who are apprehended and accused of index crimes against persons (homicide, aggravated assault, forcible rape, and robbery) in a year, about 5 percent to 10 percent (30,000 to 60,000) will be examined (pretrial or presentence) to advise the court of their potential future dangerousness and to determine appropriate intervention (prison or hospital, and so forth). About 10,000 of these will be designated as mentally ill offenders and will be committed. Two thirds of them will be in special hospitals for the criminally insane, one sixth will be in ordinary mental hospitals, and one sixth will be in correctional institutions. These include persons who are: (1) charged with a crime and held, pending determination of their competency to stand trial; (2) charged with a crime and found incompetent to stand trial; (3) found not guilty by reason of insanity; (4) convicted of a crime and found mentally ill at the time of sentencing; (5) found to be mentally ill while serving a sentence; and (6) sex offenders, not included in the above. Of these categories, those in the last five require yearly or more frequent examinations or reviews to determine whether their state of potential dangerousness has altered, been modified, or disappeared.[164]

Morris and Hawkins [pp. 185-192][134] note that the American Law Institute's Model Penal Code provides that a criminal sentence may be extended if the person is a "dangerous mentally abnormal person." In the Model Sentencing Act of the Advisory Council of Judges of the National Council on Crime and Delinquency,[140] dangerous offenders are defined as those who have committed or attempted certain crimes of physical violence and who are found to be "suffering from a severe personality disorder indicating a propensity toward criminal activity." The Durham decision in the District of Columbia has led to the commitment of those acquitted by reason of insanity until (1) their sanity is recovered and (2) they will not in the foreseeable future be dangerous to themselves or others. The authors insist that the above requires an operable concept of dangerousness, and they correctly conclude that not until such predictions can be made can policy questions be answered concerning the degree of risk that the community should bear.

In Hough versus the United States,[12] the psychiatrist testifies, states that he can, and yet cannot, predict dangerousness:

[Dr. Karpman]: I urged her father to hospitalize her, but of course he wouldn't do it. I predicted, I told him personally, that we never can tell what measures of what a person of this type of psychosis might do. It may be something very drastic. But I didn't think of murder, because I am not an astrologer and I couldn't predict in advance; but I said something drastic might happen.

Q: You thought she had a psychosis at that time?

A: Yes.

Q: What psychosis?

A: Paranoid schizophrenia.

Q: In your opinion, is Edith L. Hough the aggressive type of paranoid?

A: Yes, she is the aggressive type—as evidenced by the fact that she took measures of her own in killing the man. That is aggressiveness.

Q: In your opinion, is an aggressive paranoid potentially dangerous?

A: It is conceded universally that an aggressive paranoid is dangerous. I would say that universally we think that any paranoid schizophrenic is potentially dangerous, because one can never tell when the meekness and submissiveness may suddenly turn around and become aggressive.

Q: Would you say that Edith L. Hough at this time is dangerous because she has schizophrenia, paranoid type?

A: I would rather not answer this question directly. Ask me whether a paranoid schizophrenic is potentially dangerous and I would say yes.

Q: You would say yes?

A: Yes.

Arguments about dangerousness are frequently circular, and so, before proceeding, there should be some agreement as to what kinds of behavior are sufficiently threatening and damaging to be called dangerous. The National Commission on the Causes and Prevention of Violence defined violence as "overtly threatened or overtly accomplished application of force which results in the trying or destruction of persons or property or reputation or the illegal appropriation of property."[139] A narrower and more specific definition of dangerousness is used in the new Illinois Unified Code of Corrections, which describes it as [Sec. 1005-8-2][103] inflicting or attempting to inflict serious bodily injury, using a firearm in the commission of an offense (or fleeing from an offense), and continuing to cause apprehension of physical harm to the public.

TRYING TO PREDICT DANGEROUSNESS

Given the present reality, it is unlikely that dangerousness can be predicted in a person who has not already acted in a dangerous or a violent way. What information is available about such dangerous behavior and its genesis that might be helpful in making valid predictions about its reoccurrence? What are the characteristics of danger, and what are their relative weights in assessing the probabilities of dangerous behavior?

Violent crime is primarily a phenomenon of the youth of larger cities who are, for the most part, male, uneducated, and black. There are certainly criminogenic forces—poverty, inadequate housing, overcrowded living conditions, poor employment opportunities, reduced family functions, and broken homes —that can be implicated as forces in making the young, inner-city population a risk. Yet these demographic characteristics, while indicating some direction that can be pursued to reduce or remove criminogenic factors, do not help in developing subpopulations in which predictions of dangerousness (as defined above) have any reliability, much less validity. Sociological concepts such as criminal subcultures, opportunity, deviant role models, and a lack of "stake" have no predictive value, just as anthropological explanations related to territoriality and the frustration-rage continuum also fail to be useful. Violence is a form of social interaction, and attitudes to it are learned. For that reason, culture provides the triggering mechanism for human aggressive response to frustration, just as it provides the inhibiting mechanisms.[58,192] The data[85] showing that the United States has a culture that celebrates violence may help to explain the comparatively larger numbers of violent crimes in this country. But this in itself has no predictive value.

The reports associating violent crimes with biological defects have not been persuasive. Episodic dyscontrol with violent behavior has been associated with minimal brain damage and temporal lobe disorder and seizures.[49,123,131] Chromosomal defects (XYY)[101] and even testosterone overproduction[75] have been implicated. In these cases, the presence of these defects in known criminals has no predictive value in terms of their possible future violent behavior. At best, they are found only in from 10 to 50 percent of the known criminal population samples studied— that is, those apprehended and found guilty.

Psychiatry and psychoanalytic theory and studies have given very conflicting evidence* having no predictive value. Hypotheses concerning a "destructive drive" are used to develop models to explain human development, in particular the effect of aggressive fantasies on intrapsychic conflict. This has provided retrospective explanations about some mechanisms of inhibition, but little or nothing about predicting violent behavior. Notions such as "destructiveness is probably at its most perfect in early childhood and all later manifestations are, for most people, dilutions or mitigations,"[183] which describes the theoretical civilizing of destructive impulses, and "there is one representative of the destructive instincts that is accessible to observation, mainly sadism,"[143] as well as, "the destructive instinct appears most clearly in negativism," seem to be describing either violent fantasy, or action which is not truly violent. The nature of innate aggressiveness in man (if it exists) has yet to be fully explored, and the vicissitudes of such a drive and its possible relations to violence have yet to be described and understood. Operational relationships between the concepts of anger, hate, rage, and violence are poorly differentiated. It is repeatedly noted[73,122,136,176] that violence and violent crimes are associated with childhood familial brutality and violence. A number of authors[99,122] have reported that the triad in children of enuresis, fire setting, and cruelty to animals is predictive of adult crime.

The abuse of alcohol and drugs (amphetamines in particular) have been implicated in violent behavior,[74,90,136] and some have sought to prove that those particular drugs are the cause of violent crime. While their use

---

* See references 82 [pp. 347–351], 129, 143 [pp. 84–88, 218], 154 [pp. 778–798], and 183 [p. 151].

may be associated with persons who engage in violence and violent crime, it is more likely that a particular predisposing personality is necessary. And the nature of that personality (and of what triggers violence in it) is unknown. Blum,[57] in a compelling study of drugs and violence for the Commission on the Causes and Prevention of Violence, finds that one cannot link amphetamines to crimes of violence, sexual crimes, or accidents. Drugs do act as releasers or facilitators and in that sense can trigger violence in a person predisposed to it. Megargee,[129] in a critical review of theories of violence, shows that (as seen above) few studies test theories of human violence. What is strikingly clear is that there is no unidimensional topology of violence.

What about the possible relationship between mental illness and violent acts? Certainly a strong relationship is implied. Nevertheless, epidemiological data indicate that (1) the major mental illness rates are not comparable to violence rates, and (2) the distribution of major mental illness is not the same as the distribution of violence. Negative data support Morris and Hawkins,[134] who correctly state that "at present there is no operable concept of dangerousness, and when it is used it usually is for retributive purposes."

Because social labeling makes the prediction of dangerousness self-fulfilling,[56,94,163] prior prediction seems to have dangers that outweigh its usefulness. What is needed is the design of morbidity-experience prediction tables, which can be systematically tested to determine the possibilities of dangerousness in various subpopulations. Predictions of violence in mentally ill criminals will have importance in the rehabilitation programs of the criminal justice system, should they be in terms of various prison subpopulations.

The first quantitative data on a significant subpopulation considered to be a risk in the sense of engaging in violent behavior concerns a group of prisoners, all designated as "dangerous," who were released in New York because of a Supreme Court decision.[3] In this case, the Supreme Court declared unconstitutional the New York State practice of administratively committing offenders to Dannemora and Matteawan (Department of Corrections hospitals for the criminally insane). They declared that offenders such as Johnnie K. Baxstrom, who became mentally ill while serving a sentence, or others who at the end of their sentences were retained as dangerously mentally ill, were denied equal protection under the Fourteenth Amendment. As a result of that decision, 967 prisoners were transferred from Dannemora and Matteawan to state mental hospitals. During the first three months, six times the number of Baxstrom patients were released to the community as were retransferred to a security institution as dangerous, even though they were all alleged to be dangerous prior to the Supreme Court decision and release.

A four-year follow-up was conducted, asking: (1) Where were the Baxstrom patients and what were the circumstances of their locations? (2) What was the level and type of criminal activity of the released prisoner-patients? The sample consisted of all 47 of the Baxstrom women and a 22 percent (199) random sampling of the 920 Baxstrom men.

The major findings[175] of the study substantiated the initial impression that these prisoners were less dangerous and posed fewer problems than initially expected. Over the four-year period, twenty-three patients (2 percent) of the 967 were retransferred to high-security institutions for the mentally ill, indicating a 98 percent false positive prediction[174] of these men and women as dangerously mentally ill. Of the sample, 117 (47.6 percent) remained in public mental hospitals, ten (4.1 percent) were in contact with community clinics, and twenty-nine (11.7 percent) had died.

The conclusion of nondangerousness was further borne out by the fact that only thirty-nine (19.6 percent) men and twelve (25.5 percent) women had any assaultive behavior in mental hospitals after transfer. In looking at the criminal activity of the sample after release, we find that 121 of the sample of 246 were released to the community and that twenty-one patients were arrested forty-six times, twenty-three of which were felonies.

These patients had been in the community an average of two and a half years each. There were sixteen convictions involving only nine patients, with only two convictions for felonies.

Several factors are responsible for the low incidence of dangerousness among these patients. First, the Baxstrom population was middle-aged at the time of their transfers (average age of sampled men, 49.8 years; average age of women, 51.9 years). The second—major—factor is that the bulk of Baxstrom patients became mentally ill while serving sentences. The original crime could have been innocuous; it was the mental illness that was felt to render them dangerous. Once prisoners were in mental hospitals, their prior crime had no value as an indicator to the examining psychiatrist of their dangerousness. If they were assaultive in the mental hospital, the psychiatrist tended to retain them as dangerous—which raises serious questions about the role of the psychiatrist and his application of unarticulated criteria for release. The major conclusion that can be drawn from this study is that the subsequent behavior patterns of the hospitalized and released Baxstrom prisoners cast serious doubts upon the classification of the "dangerous mentally ill offender" and the extended or indefinite sentence resulting from that classification. Further data may be useful in correlating violence with personality factors as well as with precipitating factors.

A second set of data has been provided by eighteen prisoners in the Illinois penitentiary system who were retained in prison by "administrative error" beyond the time when they were to be transferred from prison to the mental health system. The author[162] studied seventeen of these prisoners who had spent a cumulative 425 years in prison. From the data, it was impossible to establish a connection between mental illness and the nature of the crimes committed by these men. Their cases indicated that dangerousness is overpredicted in the presence of mental illness and/or by the nature of the crime. There was little evidence in the men (with one exception) to support continued prediction of dangerousness after two years of imprisonment.

POSSIBLE DEFINITIONS OF DANGEROUSNESS

Various legal definitions of dangerousness have been used and implemented through special institutions for the care and treatment of dangerous offenders. Since all penal codes have been moving in the direction of extended sentences for the persistent offender, the professional criminal, and the dangerous and mentally abnormal offender, it may be useful to examine some different tests for dangerousness and the practical results of confinement and/or treatment, both in the United States and Europe. The rationale for identifying the dangerous offender is that (1) others can then be given shorter terms or probation, and (2) the dangerous offender would be easier to treat if separated from the ordinary prison population and placed in special institutions. Although the second of these premises is still in some doubt, there is no question that the quality of life in the United States would improve if fear of bodily harm from violent behavior were substantially reduced by being able to adequately define, predict and modify such behavior.

As succinctly stated[172] in *Standard Minimum Rules for the Treatment of Prisoners:* "The purpose and justification of a sentence of imprisonment or a similar measure of deprivation of liberty is ultimately to protect society against crime. This end can only be achieved if the period of imprisonment is used to ensure, so far as possible, that upon his return to society the offender is not only willing but able to lead a law-abiding and self-supporting life."

The Model Penal Code[46] defines the abnormal offender by having a psychiatrist show that the offender:

a. possesses a gravely abnormal mental condition;
b. has engaged in criminal conduct which has been characterized by a pattern of repetitive or compulsive behavior or by persistent aggressive behavior with heedless indifference to consequences; and

c. as a result of the above two conditions, is a serious danger to others.

If the judge concurs in the diagnosis of dangerousness, the offender is labelled a dangerous, mentally abnormal person. Two problems are immediately apparent. Too much responsibility is shifted to the psychiatrist, and there is no provision for the mentally normal violent offender.

The Proposed Federal Criminal Code[*138] provides for "dangerous special offenders." Extended sentences up to twenty-five years may be imposed on a number of special groups, including a separate category for the dangerous, mentally abnormal offender. This category requires a finding that:

a. the offender possess an abnormal mental condition,
b. such mental condition makes him a serious danger to the safety of others, and
c. he committed a felony as an instance of aggressive behavior with heedless indifference to consequences.

A psychiatric report is required but is only advisory to the court. Another category of dangerous special offender includes those who use firearms or destructive devices in the commission of an offense or flight therefrom. No abnormal mental state is required to satisfy this criterion. There is also a special category that presumes dangerousness of criminals involved in a conspiracy. In general, the proposed Federal Code develops a diffuse, overly large concept of dangerousness.

The Model Sentencing Act[140] developed by the National Council on Crime and Delinquency extends the maximum sentence to thirty years for dangerous offenders. Specifically, an offender can be sentenced as dangerous if:

a. he inflicted or attempted to inflict serious bodily harm, and has a propensity to commit crime as indicated by a severe mental or emotional disorder; [and]
b. he committed a crime which, intended or not,

seriously endangered the life or safety of another, he was previously convicted of a felony, and he had a propensity to commit crime as indicated by a severe mental or emotional disorder. [Sect. 5]

There is an optional Sect. 8, which deals with certain atrocious† crimes for which the defendant, if convicted and failing to fall under the "dangerous person" section, may nonetheless be sentenced up to ten years without meeting the psychiatric and other criteria of Sect. 5. This act defines dangerousness more narrowly than the previous ones discussed, in that only assaultive offenders (mentally normal and abnormal) may be defined as dangerous.

The Illinois Unified Code of Corrections[103] provides for doubling the ordinary maximum sentence for convicted felons, who:

a. must be at least 17 years old and have been convicted of a felony in which he inflicted or attempted to inflict serious bodily injury, or in which he used a firearm in the commission of an offense or flight therefrom; [and]
b. must present a continuing risk of physical harm to the public. [Sect. 1005-8-2]

Unlike any of the preceding codes, the Illinois Code specifically defines serious bodily harm to mean risk of death, disfigurement, or impairment of health. The most striking feature is that the Illinois Code requires no mental abnormality or defect to classify an offender as dangerous. This approach makes it clear that the first priority of defining dangerousness is the protection of society. The second step is to determine what sort of therapy, if any, the offender shall receive during confinement. Psychiatric help is felt to be useful in predicting dangerousness, but the presence or absence of mental illness alone, aside from its predictive value, is irrelevant in Illinois in deciding which assaultive offender to confine for extended periods.

Greenland's Criminal Code[86] was written in 1954 as a practical testing of progressive penological ideas. There are no sentences at-

---

* As of early 1975: S 1-1975, Report by Committee on the Judiciary of the United States Senate. Federal Criminal Code, Chapt. 23, Sect. 2302 (b).

† Murder, second degree; arson; forcible rape; robbery while armed with a deadly weapon; mayhem; bombing of an airplane, vehicle, vessel, or other structure.

tached to individual crimes. Instead, every offender is treated according to his particular personal make-up. The judge has a wide range of different sanctions available. However, placement in an institution, the severest measure, is only used "when regard for public safety or general respect for the law renders it necessary and no other measure is found suitable." [Sect. 107] The offender's degree of dangerousness is the only justification for segregating a person from contact with others. [Sect. 108] There are no special provisions for "dangerous offenders," but dangerousness is considered an important element in the process of deciding every case.

TREATMENT SETTINGS

The empirical evidence on the correct diagnosis and successful treatment of dangerous offenders is varied, but it gives some reasons for optimism concerning the rehabilitation of a class of criminals who, until recently, were thought to be untreatable.[190]

The European experience can be characterized by three institutions, each headed by a psychiatrist. Two of these are prisons. The third is a curious mixture of prison and mental hospital.

The Herstedvester Detention Centre at Alberslund, Denmark, following a new Danish Penal Code established in 1930, allowed for the detention and treatment of certain male prisoners not susceptible to punishment, in the interest of public safety. (A sister institution, Horsens, now closed, took women prisoners for detention and treatment.) It was opened in 1935, first with a psychiatric consultant and later with a psychiatric superintendent. But it was not until 1942, when Georg K. Stürup succeeded to the superintendency, that a treatment program[177] evolved for chronic criminals (excluding psychotics and severe mental retardates). This prison has accepted and treated prisoners on the basis of the chronicity of their deviant or dangerous behavior (20 percent are deemed dangerous) and their inability to respond to usual prison life. The prison has a population of approximately 170 prisoners, 170 guard staff, and 60 clinical staff. Using a psychosocial therapeutic approach that is one-to-one and individualized, such prisoners are treated principally by the guard staff (who are not considered custodial); the Stürup innovation was to decide that the guards were the key to successfully changing deviant behavior.

While it is a prison, Herstedvester possesses a humane atmosphere. The overall stay of prisoners is two years, with home visits, furloughs, and work release providing a graduated stepwise return to the open community. Anxious prisoners may return either early from visits or during their parole. After ten years, 95 percent of any cohort will have finished with criminal behavior. Formerly a law of indeterminate sentencing, the law was changed to fixed sentencing as of July 1, 1973. Political changes in Denmark, plus Stürup's retirement, then left Herstedvester in a state of flux in relation both to leadership and to mission. The treatment organization became more group-oriented and decentralized, with a greater emphasis on social and individual strengths.

There is obviously some controversy over the Danish practice of voluntary castration in the treatment of some sexual offenders—"persons for whom the sexual drive entails considerable psychic suffering or social devaluation."[178] A summary of the rationale and findings of castration by Stürup indicated that over a thirty-year period, only twenty of 900 sex offenders so treated were recidivists.

The Dr. H. van der Hoeven Kliniek, founded in 1955 and situated in the center of the town of Utrecht, the Netherlands, is one of seven institutions for the care of criminal psychopaths in that country. Housing seventy prisoners (called patients)—seven men to one woman—the institution provides treatment by eighty-five nonuniformed, fulltime staff and approximately ten part-time staff, in an equal mix of men and women. Treatment is in small groups, with emphasis on (1) frustration-aggression, (2) self-confidence, and (3) self-image. Highly organized in groups, with vocational and study opportunities, the largely dangerous (approximately 50 percent) and repetitive criminals stay an average of two years and are reported to lead less criminal lives after returning to the open community. Opportunities for furlough and work release are excellent and well-supervised. Eighty percent of the prisoner-patients are indeterminately sentenced.[130] The setting, staff, and prisoners are innovative and creative in their approach to problems of architecture, staffing, and prisoner rehabilitation. A. M. Roosenburg, the superintendent, summarized the treatment position of the van der Hoeven Kliniek as follows:[158]

To make the criminal realize his responsibility for his deeds, it is necessary to make him bear his responsibility throughout the whole criminal procedure. He should participate in the discussion and evaluation of his criminal behaviour, and the harm he has caused—not only material but also psychological—through not having acted in consonance with the expectations of society as regards respect for human rights and fundamental freedom. He should also participate in the discussion of the consequences of his deeds and what he could do to alleviate them. Last, but not least, he should be involved in consideration of how to prevent recidivism and what he could do now towards a reconciliation with the victim or his family or other person affected. He should then have the opportunity to make himself as worthy as possible of that reconciliation.

H. M. Prison Grendon Underwood[145] was opened in 1962 in England under the direction of a full-time psychiatrist, W. J. Gray, as the long-delayed outcome of The 1939 East-Hubert Report, *The Psychological Treatment of Crime*. Housing 200 males, one half of whom are juveniles, it provides for a therapeutic community with intense and frequent large and small group meetings. The staff of approximately sixty-five (including guards) is responsible for treatment, with a staff–prisoner ratio of 1:3.5. Stays last approximately eighteen months. For political reasons the prison, although recommended to be built in London, is a long trip of one and a half hours away. This poor location makes prison industries poor and graduated release difficult.

None of these three prisons has any clinically controlled evaluation. There are no base-expectancy failure rates to support belief that felons, as a result of these prison experiences,

live better and less criminal lives in which less harm is done to themselves and others. Yet certain facts are inescapable. These prisons allow difficult prisoners to live in a humane setting in which less harm is done to themselves and others and in which an opportunity for change is available. Many do seem to change. Compared to institutions with similar purposes in the United States, they seem to be philosophically, politically, and practically far ahead of us.

The Patuxent Institution was established in 1955 in Maryland as an institution to treat, under indeterminate sentence, convicted offenders designated as "defective delinquents" under a 1951 Maryland law. The defective delinquent was defined as "an individual who by the demonstration of persistent aggravated antisocial or criminal behavior evidences a propensity toward criminal activity and is found to have either some intellectual deficiency or emotional imbalance or both as to clearly demonstrate an actual danger to society."[1] The institution, built to hold 600, has a prisoner population of approximately 500. Besides the director, a psychiatrist, there are approximately thirty-five mental health professionals (psychiatrists, psychologists, and social workers). Inmates remain an average of four and a half years. Treatment consists of small groups and a "graded tier" system that uses the behavioral hypothesis of operant conditioning.

Although broad categories of offenders are eligible for examination at Patuxent, the trend over time has been toward the referral of predominantly violent offenders (from 41 percent in 1955 to 71 percent in 1972). Controversy[100] has increased regarding the usefulness of indeterminate sentencing and the methods and efficacy of treatment at Patuxent. In a report[70] dated January 9, 1973, recidivism rates were reported of a sample of prisoners who passed through the institution. It should be added that this report of the Department of Public Safety and Correctional Services of Maryland resulted in the withdrawal of a Maryland House Bill that called for the abolition of Patuxent Institution. The report discusses recidivism rates of 577 patients referred for diagnosis (see Table 44–1). If these statistics are correct, it is clear there is a direct relationship between the amount of treatment a patient receives at Patuxent and his recidivism rate on release. One problem in assessing the statistics is that the recidivism rates for each category include convictions for all sorts of crimes. When compared with the careful study by Kozol [p. 392],[113] in which a general recidivism of 32 percent was reported, the 7 percent rate at Patuxent is remarkable. In examining the data, however, the patient who receives full treatment receives in-care for an average of four years and parole delinquency status for another three years. Only then is he finally released. If a patient commits a crime at any time during his parole status, he does not appear on the recidivism statistics of the fourth category. After three years of unviolated parole, when the patient is released from delinquency status, the odds that he will enter the last category as a success rather than a recidivist are greatly increased. This is supported by the statistics for the period 1959–1969, which show that 45 percent of the parolees violated their parole— 26 percent by committing a new crime. If we add the 26 percent to the 7 percent rate shown, we arrive at 33 percent, a figure approximately that of the Bridgewater Study by Kozol. Lastly, it has been reported in support of indeterminate sentencing that only 3 percent of the first 638 patients have not experienced some form of release. Actually, Schreiber[165] reports that of 348 inmates presently committed, 151 are beyond their original terms. Because the effects of treatment are not as broad or clearcut as represented in the report, serious questions arise as to the propriety of indefinitely sentencing an offender, given the limited predictive ability of the psychiatrist and the questionable success of the treatment.

In addition to the above questions, a federal and a Maryland state court challenged the institution's theoretical justification on practical grounds. First, a federal court[22] ruled that a prisoner who was convicted of assault and sentenced to five years imprisonment, but who was sent instead to Patuxent indeterminately, refused psychiatric examination, and remained beyond his original sentence, *had* to be released, because: (1) continued confinement was unlawful in that the petitioner was no longer in the class eligible for commitment; and (2) his refusal to submit to a psychiatric examination did not justify his continued confinement. Supreme Court Justice Douglas

TABLE 44–1.   Recidivism Rates—Comparing Four Groups of Patuxent Patients and the National Recidivism Rate*

	NUMBER	RECIDIVISM RATE, PERCENT
Patients recommended for commitment but not committed by the courts (not treated, subjected to regular correctional system programs)	156	81
Patients released at rehearing against staff advice, in-house treatment only	186	46
Patients released at rehearing against staff advice, in-house treatment, plus conditional release experience	100	39
Patients released at recommendation of staff of Institutional Board of Review, in-house and continued treatment for three years on parole	135	7

* Statistics are for 1955–1964. [p. 3][70]

made much of the second point, supporting the petitioner's claim to a Fifth Amendment right against self-incrimination. Second, a lower two-judge court[21] ruled in favor of inmates concerning the terrible conditions of solitary confinement—in fact, some of the conditions were worse than those proscribed by the American Correctional Association for Prisons—the lack of rules governing conduct of prisoners and staff, the diet, the censorship of mail, and the number and training of the staff. The court concluded that the "maintenance of prisoners in cells in a prison-like setting with the offering of group therapy and limited rehabilitative vocation training is not a total rehabilitative effort."[21] This may account for the mostly poor response of the press[173] to this prison.

The Center for the Care and Treatment of Dangerous Persons at Bridgewater, Massachusetts, was established in 1959 to implement a 1958 state law providing for the indefinite detention and treatment of dangerous offenders. Dangerousness is narrowly defined as a potential for inflicting serious bodily harm on another person. A prerequisite for such a finding is a past history of violent acts. Those offenders remanded to the Center are given a most extensive and meticulous examination made independently by at least two psychiatrists, two psychologists, and a social worker. Each diagnostic study includes a clinical ex-

amination, psychological testing, and a reconstruction of the life history, elicited from many sources. Table 44–2 gives a statistical examination of a sample of offenders processed by the Center, for serious assaultive crimes committed by the total of 435 patients released. [p. 390][113] The mean age of all 435 patients released was 35.6 years, unlike the Baxstrom population, which was middle-aged at the time of transfer to civil hospitals. It then seems unlikely that the recidivism rate was affected by the aging process.

As the Table 44–2 indicates, the Center's success in predicting dangerousness was good as to offenders recommended for release both before treatment and after commitment for treatment. Of 386 patients released upon the Center's recommendations, only thirty-one (8 percent) committed crimes. Since the number of patients (forty-nine) released against the Center's recommendations is rather small, the recidivism rate may not be generalizable to larger samples. Nevertheless, this group had a combined recidivism rate of 34.7 percent. Although this figure exceeds the rate of the group of patients recommended for release, what is striking is that the Center was only 34.7 percent successful in predicting dangerousness in this group. That is, 65.3 percent proved to be false postives, that is, found to be not dangerous after release, in spite of predictions to the contrary. What is distressing is

TABLE 44–2.   **Recidivism: A Comprehensive Study of All Patients Released**

		RECIDIVISTS	
	NUMBER	NUMBER	PERCENT
Recommended for Release			
At time of initial diagnostic study	304	26	8.6
After commitment and treatment	82	5	6.1
Total	386	31	8.0
Not Recommended for Release			
At time of initial diagnostic study	31	12	38.7
After commitment and treatment	18	5	27.8
Total	49	17	34.7
Total of all patients released	435	48	11.0

that even with a very narrow definition of dangerousness, the Center massively overpredicted dangerousness in the group it recommended against releasing.

There are a few other American institutions that try to treat the disturbed offender. Among these are Vacaville (California) and Springfield (Missouri) in the federal system. For the most part, they are said[84] to range from a cheap version of Patuxent to just plain awful.

The role of the psychiatrist in the "treatment" of the chronic and/or dangerous offender is still being defined, as are the determinants of criminal behavior. As with the mentally ill, labeling of the offender (mentally ill or not) without some kind of resources for treatment or rehabilitation is a mockery at best and pernicious at worst. Certainly the psychiatrist has a role to play in the areas of prediction of dangerousness and the testing of the efficacy of various modes of intervention, if only to determine the narrowness of that role. The relationship between frustration and aggression, the genesis of violent behavior, the interaction between biological, psychological, and social variables in criminality with or without violence, and the role of prisons and extramural services in treatment and resocialization are still being developed. The psychological areas of poor self-image, genesis of aggression, and narcissistic rage show some promise of delineating certain motivational factors that interdigitate with social situations in triggering violence toward other persons.

Most of the evidence points toward the necessity of developing small, specialized prisons for only the narrowest segment of convicted offenders. Such concepts as the use of space for developing optimal closeness and distance; stepwise increases of perimeter, stimulation, and responsibility; and the use of group supports and therapy can be tested there. It may well be that in such a setting the negative response to dangerous offenders can be minimized and less harm done to them.[84,94,118] Ways of doing this can be gleaned from the methods used by the three European treatment prisons described above. Some of these methods are the prisons' small size, the importance of the first four to six weeks of a prisoner's stay, the use of intense group experiences,[104] the sharing of responsibility by prisoners and staff with prisoners voluntarily[51] involved to a larger degree, and the use of graduated release. All of the prisons[132] that successfully treat offenders have these characteristics, and they also have an average stay of eighteen months. The failure of American experiments along the same line may result from not using those criteria noted, as well as from attempting to care for our entire class of offenders, once defined, rather than an optimal number. Thus the programs have been overwhelmed.

If, in addition, we can begin to predict dangerousness so that the truly dangerous can be segregated and given an opportunity to change, then the fear as well as the danger of harm to the ordinary citizen may be substantially reduced. The dangerous felon can return to the open community to live a better and less criminal life.

(Psychiatric Reports and Testimony

In order to collect data effectively, make recommendations, and be of help to the client, patient, offender, prisoner, or parolee, or to the lawyer, court, or treatment staff, the following are areas that should generally be understood.

1. A psychiatric expert should be qualified and experienced in the diagnosis and treatment of persons with various mental disorders. He should have some knowledge of offender and normal populations. He should know the law pertaining to the area of difficulty being discussed and should confer with the lawyer, the court, or other persons asking for his expertise, to determine if he can play a role, and if so what kind.

2. The psychiatrist must clarify his role (as previously defined) with the person being examined, explaining such issues as confidentiality or the lack of it, possible consequences of the revelation of information,

and how data will be used by the lawyer, court, or any agency involved.

3. A clinical examination should be carried out, usually in two to six hours in one half hour segments divided over days or weeks. An anamnestic history should be taken, with careful attention paid to facts and attitudes about alleged crimes and violence, attitudes about self and others, feelings about relationships to others (family and community), and prospects for the future. Unlike an examination of a person who seeks psychiatric help, these examinations should seek to establish facts as well as fantasy, which must be carefully differentiated.

4. Special tests should be run, including: (a) other medical examinations, e.g., neurological, endocrine, and so forth; (b) electroencephalograms; and (c) psychological tests to corroborate clinical findings, including organicity, and to reveal any less apparent psychopathology.

5. Data from other sources should be included. Information from family, friends, employers, police, witnesses, arrest records, and hospital or correctional records should be used, when available, to produce a composite picture of the individual's personality, alleged offense(s), and possible responses to punishment and treatment.

The data are then summarized and used to answer questions concerning illness, dangerousness, competence, accountability, and treatability in the form of correspondence, reports, depositions, or testimony.

In 1967 the Federal Appeals Court, District of Columbia, in attempting to help psychiatrists understand their role there, developed instructions[40] to ensure the collection of adequate information in cases involving insanity defenses. As stated below, these instructions provide an excellent description of what is expected of a psychiatrist in court:

Court's Instruction to Expert Witness in Case Involving the "Insanity Defense"

Dr. _____, this instruction is being given to you in advance of your testimony as an expert witness, in order to avoid confusion or misunderstanding. The instruction is not only for your guidance, but also for the guidance of counsel and the jury.

Because you have qualified as an expert witness your testimony is governed by special rules. Under ordinary rules, witnesses are allowed to testify about what they have seen or heard, but are not always allowed to express opinions and conclusions based on these observations. Due to your training and experience, you are allowed to draw conclusions and give opinions in the area of your special qualifications. However, you may not state conclusions or opinions as an expert unless you also tell the jury what investigations, observations, reasoning, and medical theory led to your opinion.

As an expert witness you may, if you wish and if you feel you can, give your opinion about whether the defendant suffered from a mental disease or defect. You may then explain how defendant's disease or defect relates to his alleged offense, that is, how the development, adaptation and functioning of defendant's behavioral processes may have influenced his conduct. This explanation should be so complete that the jury will have a basis for an informed judgment on whether the alleged crime was a "product" of his mental disease or defect. But it will not be necessary for you to express an opinion on whether the alleged crime was a "product" of a mental disease or defect and you will not be asked to do so.

It must be emphasized that you are to give your expert diagnosis of the defendant's mental condition. This word of caution is especially important if you given an opinion as to whether or not the defendant suffered from a "mental disease or defect" because the clinical diagnostic meaning of this term may be different from its legal meaning. You should not be concerned with its legal meaning. Neither should you consider whether you think this defendant should be found guilty or responsible for the alleged crime. These are questions for the court and jury. Further, there are considerations which may be relevant in other proceedings or in other contexts which are not relevant here; for example, how the defendant's condition might change, or whether there are adequate hospital facilities, or whether commitment in the courtroom is the kind of opinion you would give to a family which brought one of its members to your clinic and asked for your diagnosis of his mental condition and a description of how his condition would be likely to influence his conduct. Insofar as counsel's questions permit, you should testify in this manner.

When you are asked questions which fall within

the scope of your special training and experience, you may answer them if you feel competent to do so; otherwise you should not answer them. If the answer depends upon knowledge and experience generally possessed by ordinary citizens, for example questions of morality as distinguished from medical knowledge, you should not answer. You should try to separate expert medical judgments from what we may call "lay judgments." If you cannot make a separation and if you do answer the question nonetheless, you should state clearly that your answer is not based solely upon your special knowledge. It would be misleading for the jury to think that your testimony is based on your special knowledge concerning the nature and diagnosis of mental conditions if in fact it is not.

In order that the jury may understand exactly what you mean, you should try to explain things in simple language. Avoid technical terms whenever possible. Where medical terms are useful or unavoidable, make sure you explain these terms clearly. If possible, the explanation should not be merely general or abstract but should be related to this defendant, his behavior, and his condition. Where words or phrases used by counsel are unclear, or may have more than one meaning, you should ask for clarification before answering. You should then explain your answer so that your understanding of the question is clear. You need not give "yes or no" answers. In this way any confusion may be cleared up before the questioning goes on.

Some final words of caution. Because we have an adversary system, counsel may deem it is his duty to attack your testimony. You should not construe this as an attack upon your integrity. More specifically, counsel may try to undermine your opinions as lacking certainty or adequate basis. We recognize that an opinion may be merely a balance of probabilities and that we cannot demand absolute certainty. Thus you may testify to opinions that are within the zone of reasonable medical certainty. The crucial point is that the jury should know how your opinion may be affected by limitations of time or facilities in the examination of this defendant or by limitations in present psychiatric knowledge. The underlying facts you have obtained may be so scanty or the state of professional knowledge so unsure that you cannot fairly venture any opinion. If so, you should not hesitate to say so. And again, if you do give an opinion, you should explain what these facts are, how they led to the opinion, and what if any, are the uncertainties in the opinion.

In an earlier report[88] on psychiatric testimony, the Group for the Advancement of Psychiatry noted the limitations of the psychiatrist as expert witness:

1. He cannot fit any scientifically validated entity of psychopathology into present legal formulae of insanity. He cannot determine by scientific method the existence of "knowledge" as explained in legal tests, excepting in cases of disturbed consciousness or profound mental deficit.
2. He cannot testify in any manner in terms of moral judgement.
3. He cannot within the framework of present court requirements determine degree of legal responsibility calibrated to medical degrees of psychopathology.

As for competence, it was stated:[88]

1. He can predict behavior of the mass statistically and determine with fair accuracy the classes of undeterrable persons. He can predict the tendency of behavior in the individual and with fair accuracy determine his deterrability.
2. He can with fair accuracy determine the degree of disorder of the accused relating to: (a) the present mental state of the accused as it is relevant to his capacity to appreciate the significance of the charge and to cooperate in the preparation of his defense; and (b) the causal connection of the mental state and the act charged.
3. He can make advisory recommendations for suitable disposition of the convicted.

Twenty years later it would appear that the competence of the psychiatrist was exaggerated. Only now are the problems beginning to be understood, as the legal and psychiatric professions examine the questions together.

Rights of Patients

During the Age of Reason, two principles were articulated that expressed the sentiments of society regarding the treatment of persons designated as patients. The first, the right to be treated humanely, was applicable to the physically as well as the mentally ill and, in psychiatry, was expressed in the work of a group of men known as "moral" psychiatrists: Pinel, Tuke, and Chiarugi. Since "moral psychiatry" argued that the location of the problem and its possible correction lay in the higher (moral) faculties, the second principle supported the right of a patient to participate —that is, share responsibility—in the treatment.

These two rights slowly evolved into the patient's right to be treated as responsible and, as circumstances permitted, free. Public health laws, including mental health codes, shifted from concern for the protection of society to concern for the rights of individuals. This resulted in a gradual lessening of the doctor's power over a patient's body and mind. The rights of patients have been increasingly broadened and clarified, while the rights of physicians have been narrowed to agreements for specified interventions at agreed-upon times. Civil and criminal charges relating to breach of contract, false imprisonment, invasion of privacy, assault and battery, and negligence, can be brought against the psychiatrist. Freud[80] emphasized that the psychoanalyst must not take advantage of the transference. Undue influence and advantage taken by the psychiatrist in relation to the patient's transference has been perceived in two cases,[11,18] with findings for the plaintiff in both. Prudence is required to be certain that suggestions are suggestions and prescriptions only prescriptions.

Lastly, the patient's conduct outside of the physician's office, if criminal, should raise questions concerning the physician's involvement. Certainly, should the patient indicate the possibility of future dangerous behavior, (and if he is not certifiable as legally mentally ill), then serious questions of the doctor's posture vis-à-vis privilege and public policy, can be raised. This allocation of a greater share of responsibility to the individual for his destiny in regard to behavior, illness, and death has put a larger burden on the physician in terms of accountability. It has also demanded of the physician a greater concern with ethics and public policy as regards the nature and extent of his interventions with other citizens. As developing technology allows attempts to be made to prolong life and to modify and control behavior, serious discussions of the implications for the limiting of liberty and choice ought to be continuing. And psychiatrists, lawyers, and jurists should be leading the way.

Privilege

Four criteria are universally accepted for judging any privilege's appropriateness:

1. The communication must originate in a confidence that they will not be disclosed.
2. The element of confidentiality must be essential to the full and satisfactory maintenance of the relationship to the parties.
3. The relation must be one which, in the opinion of the community, ought to be sedulously fostered; and
4. The injury that would inure to the relation by the disclosure of the communication must be greater than the benefit thereby gained for the correct disposal of the litigation. [Sect. 2285][188]

Such privilege has been granted the attorney-client, physician-patient, and clergyman–penitent relationships. But all professional–client privileges contain exceptions, usually in relation to criminal rather than civil laws. The exceptions usually relate to the fourth item above—that is, when the "benefit gained for the correct disposal of the litigation" outweighs the "injury that would inure to the relationship by the disclosure." The attorney–client privilege covers all civil actions and criminal actions *except* where the attorney has knowledge (or ground to believe) that his client (1) was contemplating the commission of a crime (future crime exception) or (2) was attempting to suppress the discovery of a crime already committed. [Sect. 2298][188]

The physician–patient privilege is only applicable to civil actions. However, the clergy-penitent covers all communications in all kinds of actions. The nature of the psychiatrist-patient relationship—because of the intense, probing character of the communication, the desirability of expressing things not acceptable to society at large, and the concern for feelings and fantasy as well as facts—seems to make it closer to the clergy–penitent relationship, which alone remains unhampered. Historically, however, psychiatrists, as physicians, have used the physician–patient privileges when available. Only California[28] has sought to distinguish between physician–patient and psychiatrist–patient. A probable mistake was the proposal[89] of a model statute by the Group for the Advancement of Psychiatry, which in 1960 stated, "The confidential relationship and communication between psychiatrist and patient shall be placed on the same basis as regards privilege as provided by law between attorney and client." Neither the physician–patient nor lawyer–client privilege can provide the protection needed for a full psychotherapeutic relationship. An Illinois trial court recognized that a psychotherapist–patient relationship was worthy of more extensive privilege than a physician–patient relationship. The reasons are worth noting:[4]

1. A thorough examination for mental illness and more important, a thorough cure, cannot take place unless the patient reveal his thoughts. A therapist cannot ferret out secrets of the mind in the way a physician can ferret out secrets of the body.
2. Whereas an organic illness can be treated without trust between a physician and patient, a mental illness cannot.
3. If the patient feels betrayed by one analyst, chances are that he will mistrust the whole profession—and thus negate his chances for future treatment. On the other hand, patients frequently seek out new doctors.

In criminal actions, the conflict between injury and benefit is more of concern to the accused and to society as a whole. It is not helpful to say that psychiatrists do not treat criminals, as they may, and it cannot be ignored in relation to the entire area of the treatment of offenders, dangerous or not. Such persons are more in need of privilege—to talk without fear that their therapist will testify against them in court—than is the civil litigant.[121,169,171]

Informed Consent

The physician's duty to inform his patients is derived from his duty to obtain the patient's consent to the proposed treatment. Consent consists of awareness and assent. Battery was the older theory of recovery in relation to this concept, but since the late 1950s a second ground—negligence—has been developing. The classic case where consent is not required is an emergency situation where the life and health of the person is in immediate danger. Consent is held to be implied.

Consent can be imposed by the law—for example, inoculations. Upon application of a physician or hospital, a few courts have ordered medical treatment for a nonconsenting adult on the grounds that the state, as *parens patriae*, has an interest in protecting the patient's life. This is especially true if the patient has children who would become wards of the state on his incapacity or death.[2] A few cases appear to condone the withholding of information when a disclosure of collateral risks to a treatment may unduly alarm an already apprehensive patient. Arguments tend to be paternalistic, usually based neither on law nor logic. The problem of innovative treatment, the results of which are not fully known or explored, is informing the patient and getting his consent. In response to this, Waltz[184] states:

If a physician acted improperly by going ahead with an innovative technique as to which there were too many unplumbed questions involving its potential risks, liability will flow from the physician's unreasonable consent. If, on the other hand, he acted reasonably in going forward on the basis of existing knowledge, the patient's consent even to the possibility of unanticipated risks is again irrelevant, since the physician had no legal duty to disclose risks about which he neither knew nor should have known, and for that reason alone he is immune from liability.

This leaves the position of consent intact, and does not thwart the development of new ideas for medicine. Three court decisions in California,[7] the District of Columbia,[6] and Rhode

Island[41] in the 1970s together more clearly define the legal position in relation to informed consent in medical malpractice. That position is:[61]

Respect for the patient's rights of self-determination on particular therapy demands a standard set by law for physicians rather than one which physicians may or may not impose upon themselves. Unlimited discretion of the physician is irreconcilable with the basic right of the patient to make the ultimate informed decision regarding the course of treatment to which he knowledgeably consents to be subjected.

In Cobbs versus Grant, the court[7] indicated that the patient had an abject dependence upon and trust in his physician for education in regard to his condition. That is, the relationship between physician and patient was a fiduciary one. It was further stated that "adults of sound mind have a right to determine whether to submit to lawful medical treatment." And in Canterbury versus Spence, it[6] was emphasized that ". . . the decision whether or not to undertake treatment is vested in the party most directly affected: the patient." There were no exceptions except for emergency or incompetency. The most important element in obtaining informed consent is discussion of death, bodily harm, recovery and recuperation, and the possible complications. The patient should know all his options.

In the area of mental illness, how may consent be properly obtained when the mental illness of the patient is severe enough to render the patient incapable of consent? The standard used by the courts is the same as that for competency to stand trial—that is, to be able to understand the seriousness of the information that the doctor is required to give him and to make a decision based on that knowledge. If a patient is not competent to give consent, it can be given by the person *legally* responsible for the patient.[10] In a pair of decisions the U.S. district court in Alabama held as unconstitutional a statute which allowed sterilization of mentally retarded inmates at the behest of the superintendent and assistant superintendent of the institution, and set down guidelines for informed consent in such a situation, and for the review of that consent.*

Medicine, Psychiatry, and Liberty

Progress in the physical sciences and medicine has resulted in increased freedom, due to technological innovations, that make the quality of life less harmful and more enjoyable with the decline in sickness and premature death. Equally serious dangers have become more apparent in recent years, with resulting concern about overpopulation, pollution, surveillance, and behavior control.

PARTICIPATION IN MEDICAL RESEARCH

Such studies fall into two categories: (1) therapeutic experiments conducted in the context of the traditional doctor–patient relationship; and (2) experiments that are aimed at acquiring knowledge of potential value to others but of no benefit to the research subjects themselves. The first category is covered by malpractice and contract law, as noted above. The second category of research, carried out to serve the scientific interests of the investigator, raises more difficult problems, with many uncertain ethical and legal questions. In 1971 the Public Health Service produced new guidelines,[69] including a sophisticated discussion of the types of risk that may occur (such as physical, psychological, and social dangers), and it lucidly defined the differences between therapy and experimentation. Detailed criteria for informed consent were provided and exculpatory clauses were expressly prohibited.

Yet a number of problems about research remain unresolved. One is that of research on civil prisoners. Inmates often are enthusiastic about participation because they get paid, it relieves monotony, and it implies earlier release. It is doubtful whether truly noncoerced consent can be obtained from prisoners. A prisoner in Michigan, diagnosed as dangerous and chosen as a subject for psychosurgery,

* Wyatt v. Aderholt, 368 F Supp. 1382, 1973
Wyatt v. Aderholt, 368 F Supp. 1383, 1974.

was *not* allowed to be a subject although he himself was strongly in favor of it. In this case, a panel of experts and the state agreed that there could be no true consent to this procedure for this prisoner.[166] One argument for research on prisoners is that society needs to understand and control dangerous and/or repetitive criminal behavior. Many and at times extreme approaches have been suggested, including lithium therapy,[168] in-depth electrode placement, and ablation of parts of the brain.[123,124,166] This is all being proposed on the basis of a behavioral complex characterized by episodic "violent" behavior.[123,124,131] As discussed above, it remains theoretically possible and practically valid to have therapeutic experiments aimed at controlling violent behavior so that offenders might lead more free and satisfying lives. Nevertheless, there should be absolute freedom from coercion. Methods by which acceptable research can be carried out in this area are still being devised.

More subtle are the ethical questions[128] raised concerning the use of long-acting medications or electrode implantation in the control of psychosis, epilepsy, and other behavior. Such medication, once injected, can affect the individuals for weeks and possibly months. How, and when and to what extent such medications should be used experimentally or therapeutically requires continuing discussions of public policy.

Another set of unresolved problems concerns research on subjects who are incapable of giving informed consent. This includes children and the mentally incompetent. Should any hazardous research be carried out on these groups? If so, who should provide consent and under what limitations? What standards should govern nonhazardous but painful studies? Still further, to what extent has the burden of research participation been lifted from the indigent hospitalized? What about mass testing of drugs by American companies in countries other than the United States?

Lastly, what threats to civil liberties are inherent in the medical process of organ transplantation? Serious questions regarding the definition of death, the choice of subjects, and the equitable distribution of scarce biological resources are raised. The newest development in medicine is the possibility of producing human beings through a type of asexual reproduction known as "cloning." If it becomes feasible to produce such individuals, what are the consequences for them as well as for the rest of us?

FREEDOM TO BE WRONG, FREEDOM TO DIE

As medical science progresses and its technological assets increase, there is an increasing illusion that the power of the physician over illness and death is absolute. Because of this the physician, when confronted with not knowing what to do, usually responds with a massive use of technological supports as a means of handling his own anxiety. This often results in a maintenance of metabolism but of little else that resembles life as we ordinarily experience it. Patients who do not wish to be treated or saved should have the right to make that decision. Each person should be able, when possible, to die in his own way and in his own place, as long as he brings no harm to others.[116] As populations live longer, physicians have an increasing proximity to death as a part of life.[52]

To insure a dignified death, the patient should have the right to know the truth, to experience human company and caring, to share in the decisions, and to be unmolested if that is his wish. Should the patient be incapable of communication, comatose, senile, or mute, it is suggested that the physician act in a way that he believes would be consistent with the patient's wishes.[108] Since euthanasia,[81] in relation to the hopeless and terminal patient, has become more of an issue as the number of such individuals increases, there have been renewed discussions of its ethical and moral implications. The more we know, the more difficult the questions become. In attempting to determine the possible limits of human behavior, concern with maintaining optimal freedom should be central. In that regard, the words of Supreme Court Justice Louis Brandeis are instructive:[26]

Experience should teach us to be most on guard to protect liberty when the government's purposes are beneficent. Men born to freedom are naturally alert to repel invasion of their liberties by evil-minded rulers. The greatest danger to liberty lurks in insidious encroachment by men of zeal, well-meaning but without understanding.

⟮ Bibliography

CITATIONS

1. The Annotated Code of the Public General Laws of Maryland, Art. 31D, par. 5 (1951).
2. Application of the President and Directors, Georgetown Colleges, Inc., 331 F2d 1000, cert. denied 377 U.S. 978 (1964).
3. Baxstrom v. Herold, 383 U.S. 107 (1966).
4. Binder v. Ruvell, Civil Docket 52 C 25 35 Cir. Ct. Cook (1952).
5. Burnham v. Dept. Pub. Health, State Ga., Civil Action No. 16385, ND Ga. (1972).
6. Cantebury v. Spence, 464 F2d 772 (1972).
7. Cobbs v. Grant, 8 Cal. 3d 229 (1972).
8. Cross v. Harris, 418 F2d 1095 (1969).
9. Durham v. United States, 214 F2d 862 (1954).
10. Faber v. Olkon, 40 Cal. 2d 503, 254 P2d 520 (1953).
11. Hammer v. Rosen, 198 NYS 2d 65 (1960).
12. Hough v. United States, 217 F2d 458 (1959).
13. Illinois Laws, par. 10 (1851).
14. Illinois Rev. Stat., Chap. 91½, 1–20, effective 1968, amended 1969–71 (1972).
15. Jackson v. Indiana, 406 U.S. 715 (1972).
16. Lake v. Cameron, 331 F2d 771 (1964).
17. Lake v. Cameron, 364 F2d 657 (1966).
18. Landau v. Werner, 105 Sol J 257, on appeal 105 Sol J 1008, C.A. (1961).
19. Lessard v. Schmidt, 349 F. Supp. 1078, E.D. Wisc. (1972).
20. Matter of Josiah Oakes, 8 Mass. Law Rep. 123, Sup. Ct. (1845).
21. McCray v. Maryland, Misc. Pet. 4363, Cir. Ct. Montgomery County (1971).
22. McNeil v. Director, Patuxent Institution, 40 L.W. 4743 (1972).
23. Millard v. Harris, 406 F2d 964 (1968).
24. Minnesota Stats. s 253A.16 (1972).
25. M'Naghten's Case, House of Lords, 10 Cl & F 200, 8 Eng. Rep. 718 (1843).
26. Olmstead v. United States, 277 U.S. 438, 479 (1928).
27. Pate v. Robinson, 383 U.S. 375 (1966).
28. People v. Scheer, 272 Cal. 2 165, 77 Cal. Rep. 35 (1969).
29. Powell v. Texas, 392 U.S. 514 (1968).
30. Rex v. Arnold, 16 How. St. Tr. 695 (1724).
31. Rex v. Hatfield, 27 How. St. Tr. 1281, 1312–1314 (1800).
32. Robinson v. California, 370 U.S. 660 (1962).
33. Rosenfield v. Overholser, 262 F2d 34 (1958).
34. Rouse v. Cameron, 373 F2d 451 (1966).
35. State v. Pike, 49 N. H. 399 (1869).
36. Thorn v. Sup. Ct. San Diego County, 464 P2d 56 (1970).
37. United States v. Davis, 160 U.S. 469 (1895).
38. United States v. Chisholm, 149 F 284, SD Ala. (1906).
39. United States v. Brawner, 471 F2d 979 (1972).
40. Washington v. United States, 390 F2d 444 (1967).
41. Wilkenson v. Vesey, 295 A2d 676 (1972).
42. Winters v. Miller, 446 F2d 65 (1971).
43. Wyatt v. Stickney, 325 F Supp. 781, MD Ala. (1971).
44. Wyatt v. Stickney, 344 F Supp. 373, MD Ala. (1972).

BOOKS AND PERIODICALS

45. ALLEN, R. C., E. Z. FERSTER, J. G. RUBIN. *Readings in Law and Psychiatry.* Baltimore: The Johns Hopkins Press, 1968.
46. AMERICAN LAW INSTITUTE. *Model Penal Code, Proposed Official Draft.* Philadelphia: Am. Law Institute, 1962.
47. AMERICAN PSYCHIATRIC ASSOCIATION. *Diagnostic and Statistical Manual I of Mental Disorders.* Washington: Am. Psychiatric Assoc., 1952.
48. ———. *Diagnostic and Statistical Manual II of Mental Disorders.* Washington: Am. Psychiatric Assoc., 1968.
49. BACH-Y-RITA, G., J. R. LION, C. E. CLIMENT et al. "Episodic Dyscontrol: A Study of 130 Violent Patients," *Am. J. Psychiatry,* 127 (1971), 1473–1478.
50. BARD, M. *Training Police as Specialists in Family Crisis Intervention.* Washington: U.S. Govt. Print. Off., 1970.
51. BARR, N. I. "Voluntary Imprisonment: Its Usefulness in the Rehabilitation of Crimi-

nal Offenders," *Am. J. Psychiatry*, 124 (1967), 170–179.

52. BARTON, D. and M. H. HOLLANDER. "Death Takes a Holiday—Reconsidered," *Pharos*, 36 (1973), 20–22.

53. BECKER, L. E. "Durham Revisited: Psychiatry and the Problem of Crime, Part 2," *Psychiatr. Ann.*, 3 (1973), 54–60.

54. BELLAK, L. "The Need for Public Health Laws for Psychiatric Illness," *Am. J. Public Health*, 61 (1971), 119–121.

55. BITTNER, E. *The Functions of the Police in Modern Society*. Washington: U.S. Govt. Print. Off., 1970.

56. BLAKE, R. R. and J. S. MOUTON, "Conformity, Resistance and Conversion," in I. A. Berg and B. M. Bass, eds., *Conformity and Deviation*. pp. 1–2. New York: Harper & Row, 1961.

57. BLUM, R. "Drugs and Violence," in D. J. Mulvihill and M. M. Tumin, eds., *Crimes of Violence, A Staff Report to the National Commission on the Causes and Prevention of Violence*, Vol. 13, Append. 32, pp. 1461–1523. Washington: U.S. Govt. Print. Off., 1969.

58. BOHANNON, P. "Cross-cultural Comparison of Aggression and Violence," in D. Mulvihill and M. Tumin, eds., *Crimes of Violence, A Staff Report to the National Commission on the Causes and Prevention of Violence*, Vol. 13, Append. 25, pp. 1189–1239. Washington: U.S. Govt. Print. Off., 1969.

59. BRAKEL, S. J. and R. S. ROCK. *The Mentally Disabled and The Law*, rev. ed. Chicago: University of Chicago Press, 1971.

60. BRANHAM, V. C. "The Classification and Treatment of the Defective Delinquent," *J. Crim. Law Criminol.*, 17 (1926), 183–217.

61. BRECKLER, I. A., E. M. PRICE, and S. SHORE. "Informed Consent: A New Majority Position," *J. Legal Med.*, 1 (1973), 15–17.

62. BROWN, B. S. and T. F. COURTLESS. *The Mentally Retarded Offender*. Washington: U.S. Govt. Print. Off., 1971.

63. BURT, R. A. and N. MORRIS. "A Proposal for the Abolition of the Incompetency Plea," *Univ. Chicago Law Rev.*, 81 (1973), 454–573.

64. CHAYET, N. L. "Legal Neglect of the Mentally Ill," *Am. J. Psychiatry*, 125 (1968), 785–792.

65. COOK COUNTY LEGAL ASSISTANCE FOUNDA-

TION. Personal communication, June 1972.

66. CRAIG, R. *Sexual Psychopath Legislation*. Submitted to the President's Commission on Law Enforcement and the Administration of Justice. Washington: U.S. Govt. Print. Off., 1967.

67. CUOMO, A. A. "Mens Rea and Status Criminality," *S. Calif. Law Rev.*, 40 (1967), 463–526.

68. DAVIDSON, H. A. *Forensic Psychiatry*, 2d ed. New York: Ronald, 1965.

69. DEPARTMENT OF HEALTH, EDUCATION, AND WELFARE. *The Institutional Guide to DHEW Policy on Protection of Human Subjects*, Publ. no. 72-102. Washington: U.S. Govt. Print. Off., 1971.

70. DEPARTMENT OF PUBLIC SAFETY AND CORRECTIVE SERVICES, MARYLAND. *Maryland's Defective Delinquent Statute: A Progress Report*. Baltimore: Dept. Pub. Safety and Correctional Service, 1973.

71. DEUTSCH, A. *The Mentally Ill in America: A History of Their Care and Treatment from Colonial Times*, 2d rev. ed. New York: Columbia University Press, 1949.

72. DEWEY, R. "The Jury Law for the Commitment of the Insane in Illinois (1867–1893) and Mrs. E. P. W. Packard, Its Author (Modern Persecution, 1887), also Later Developments in Lunacy Legislation in Illinois," *Am. J. Insanity*, 69 (1913), 571–584.

73. DUNCAN, J. W. and G. M. DUNCAN. "Murder in the Family: A Study of some Homicidal Adolescents," *Am. J. Psychiatry*, 127 (1971), 1498–1502.

74. ELLINWOOD, E. H., JR. "Assault and Homicide Associated with Amphetamine Abuse," *Am. J. Psychiatry*, 127 (1971), 1170–1175.

75. ERVIN, F. R. and J. R. LION. "Clinical Evaluation of the Violent Patient," in D. J. Mulvihill and M. M. Tumin, eds., *Crimes of Violence, A Staff Report to the National Commission on the Causes and Prevention of Violence*, Vol. 13, Append. 24, pp. 1163–1188. Washington: U.S. Govt. Print. Off., 1969.

76. FERNALD, W. E. "The Imbecile with Criminal Instincts," *Am. J. Insanity*, 65 (1909), 731–747.

77. FINGERETTE, H. *The Meaning of Criminal Insanity*. Berkeley, Calif.: University of California Press, 1972.

78. FOUCAULT, M. *Madness and Civilization: A*

History of Insanity in the Age of Reason. New York: Pantheon, 1965.

79. FREEMAN, W. "Letter," *Am. J. Psychiatry,* 128 (1972), 1315–1316.

80. FREUD, S. (1938) "An Outline of Psycho-Analysis," in J. Strachey, ed., *Standard Edition,* Vol. 23, pp. 144–207. London: Hogarth, 1964.

81. FURLOW, T. W., JR. "A Matter of Life and Death," *Pharos,* 36 (1973), 84–90.

82. GLOVER, E., *The Roots of Crime.* New York: International Universities Press, 1970.

83. GLUECK, B. "A Study of 608 Admissions to Sing Sing Prison," *Ment. Hyg.,* 2 (1918), 85–151.

84. GOLDFARB, R. L. and L. R. SINGER. *After Conviction: A Review of the American Correction System.* New York: Simon & Schuster, 1973.

85. GRAHAM, H. D. and T. R. GURR, eds. *Violence in America: Historical and Comparative Perspectives: A Staff Report to the National Commission on the Causes and Prevention of Violence,* Vols. 1 and 2. Washington: U.S. Govt. Print. Off., 1969.

86. *The Greenland Criminal Code.* The American Series of Foreign Penal Codes, no. 16. South Hackensack, N.J.: Fred B. Rothman, 1970.

87. GREENLAND, C. "Appealing against Commitment to Mental Hospitals in the United Kingdom, Canada and the United States: An International Review," *Am. J. Psychiatry,* 126 (1969), 538–542.

88. GROUP FOR THE ADVANCEMENT OF PSYCHIATRY. *Criminal Responsibility and Psychiatric Expert Testimony,* Report no. 26. Topeka, Kan.: Group Adv. Psychiatry, 1954.

89. ———. *Confidentiality and Privileged Communications in the Practice of Psychiatry,* Report no. 45, New York: Group Adv. Psychiatry, 1960.

90. GUZE, S. B., V. B. TUASON, P. D. GATFIED et al. "Psychiatric Illness and Crime with Particular Reference to Alcoholism: A Study of 223 Criminals," *J. Nerv. Ment. Dis.,* 134 (1962), 512–521.

91. HALE, SIR M. *Historia Placitorum Coronae: The History of the Pleas of the Crown,* pp. 14–16, 29–37. London: Sollom Emlyn, Lincoln's-Inn, Esq., 1778.

92. HALLECK, S. "American Psychiatry and the Criminal: A Historical Review," *Am. J.*

Psychiatry (Suppl.), 121 (1965), i–xxi.

93. ———. *Psychiatry and the Dilemmas of Crime,* pp. 301–318. New York: Harper & Row, 1969.

94. ———. *The Politics of Therapy,* pp. 99–118, 157–174. New York: Science House, 1971.

95. HARVARD LAW REVIEW. "Civil Commitment of the Mentally Ill: Theories and Procedures," 79 (1966), 1288–1298.

96. ———. "Incompetency to Stand Trial," 81 (1967), 454–473.

97. HEALY, W. *The Individual Delinquent: A Textbook of Diagnosis and Prognosis for All concerned in Understanding Offenders.* Boston: Little, Brown, 1915.

98. HEALY, W. and A. F. BRONNER. *Delinquents and Criminals, Their Making and Unmaking: Studies in Two American Cities.* New York: Macmillan, 1926.

99. HELLMAN, D. S. and N. BLACKMAN. "Enuresis, Firesetting and Cruelty to Animals: A Triad Predictive of Adult Crime," *Am. J. Psychiatry,* 122 (1966), 1431–1435.

100. HODGES, E. F. "Crime Prevention by the Indeterminate Sentence Law," *Am. J. Psychiatry,* 128 (1971), 291–295. (Includes a discussion by A. A. Stone.)

101. HOOK, E. B. "Behavioral Implications of the Human XYY Genotype," *Science,* 179 (1973), 139–150.

102. HUTT, P. B. "The Recent Court Decisions on Alcoholism," in *Drunkenness: Task Force Report to the President's Commission on Law Enforcement and the Administration of Justice.* Append. 11, pp. 109–119. Washington: U.S. Govt. Print. Off., 1967.

103. ILLINOIS UNIFIED CODE OF CORRECTIONS, 1001–1008. St. Paul, Minn.: West Publ., 1972.

104. JEW, C. C., T. L. CLANON and A. L. MATTOCKS. "The Effectiveness of Group Psychotherapy in a Correctional Institution," *Am. J. Psychiatry,* 129 (1972), 602–605.

105. KADISH, S. H. "The Decline of Innocence," *Cambridge Law J.,* 26 (1968), 273–290.

106. KARPMAN, B. "Psychotherapy and the Criminal Insane," *Psychiatr. Q.,* 3 (1929), 370–383.

107. ———. "The Problem of Psychopathies," *Psychiatr. Q.,* 3 (1929), 495–525.

108. KASS, L. R. "Man's Right to Die," *Pharos,* 35 (1972), 73–77.

109. KATZ, J. "The Right to Treatment—An En-

chanting Legal Fiction?" *Univ. Chicago Law Rev.*, 36 (1969), 755–783.

110. KATZ, J., J. GOLDSTEIN, and A. DERSHOWITZ. *Psychoanalysis, Psychiatry and Law.* New York: Free Press, 1962.

111. KITTRIE, N. N. *The Right To Be Different: Deviance and Enforced Therapy.* Baltimore: The Johns Hopkins Press, 1972.

112. KOSON, D. and A. ROBEY. "Amnesia and Competency to Stand Trial," *Am. J. Psychiatry*, 130 (1973), 588–592.

113. KOZOL, H. L., R. J. BOUCHER and R. F. GAROFALO. "The Diagnosis and Treatment of Dangerousness," *J. Crime. Delinq.*, 18 (1972), 371–392.

114. KUMASAKA, Y., J. STOKES, and R. K. GUPTA. "Criteria for Involuntary Hospitalization," *Arch. Gen. Psychiatry*, 26 (1972), 399–404.

115. LEMERT, E. M. *Instead of Court: Diversion in Juvenile Justice.* Washington: U.S. Govt. Print. Off., 1971.

116. LERNER, M. "When, Why and Where People Die," in O. G. Brim, H. E. Freeman, S. Levine et al., eds., *The Dying Patient*, pp. 5–29. New York: Russell Sage Found., 1970.

117. LEWY, E. "Responsibility, Free Will and Ego Psychology," *Int. J. Psychoanal.*, 42 (1961), 260–270.

118. LION, J. R. and S. A. PASTERNAK. "Countertransference Reactions to Violent Patients," *Am. J. Psychiatry*, 130 (1973), 207–210.

119. LOMBROSO, C., *Le Crime: causes et remèdes.* Paris: Schleicher Frères, 1899.

120. LURIE, L. A., S. LEVY, and F. M. ROSENTHAL. "The Defective Delinquent: A Definition and a Prognosis," *Am. J. Orthopsychiatry*, 14 (1944), 95–103.

121. MACCORMICK, A. "A Criminologist Looks at Privilege," *Am. J. Psychiatry*, 115 (1959), 1068–1070.

122. MACDONALD, J. M. "The Threat to Kill," *Am. J. Psychiatry*, 120 (1963), 125–130.

123. MALETSKY, B. M. "The Episodic Dyscontrol Syndrome," *Dis. Nerv. Syst.*, 34 (1973) 178–185.

124. MARK, V. H. and F. R. ERVIN. *Violence and the Brain.* New York: Harper & Row, 1970.

125. MCCORD, W. and J. MCCORD. *The Psychopath: An Essay on the Criminal Mind.* Princeton, N.J.: Van Nostrand, 1964.

126. MCGARRY, A. L. "The Fate of Psychotic Offenders Returned for Trial," *Am. J. Psychiatry*, 127 (1971), 1181–1184.

127. MCGARRY, A. L. and H. A. KAPLAN. "Overview: Current Trends in Mental Health Law," *Am. J. Psychiatry*, 130 (1973), 621–630.

128. MEDICAL TRIBUNE. "Brain Pacers for Epileptics Raise Ethical Considerations," 14 (1973), 1, 23.

129. MEGARGEE, E. I. "A Critical Review of the Theories of Violence," in D. J. Mulvihill and M. Tumin, eds., *Crimes of Violence, A Staff Report to the National Commission on the Causes and Prevention of Violence*, Vol. 13, Appen. 22, pp. 1037–1115. Washington: U.S. Govt. Print. Off., 1969.

130. MINISTRY OF JUSTICE, THE NETHERLANDS. *Detention at the Government's Pleasure: Treatment of Criminal Psychopaths in the Netherlands.* The Hague: The Prison Service, 1971.

131. MONROE, R. R. *Episodic Behavioral Disorders.* Cambridge: Harvard University Press, 1970.

132. MORRIS, N. "Prison in Evolution," *Fed. Probation*, 29 (1965), 20–32.

133. ———. "Psychiatry and the Dangerous Criminal," *S. Calif. Law Rev.*, 41 (1968), 514–547.

134. MORRIS, N. and G. HAWKINS. *The Honest Politician's Guide to Crime Control.* Chicago: University of Chicago Press, 1970.

135. MULLER, D. J. "Involuntary Mental Hospitalization," *Compr. Psychiatry*, 9 (1968), 187–193.

136. MULVIHILL, D. and M. TUMIN, eds. *Crimes of Violence: Staff Report to the National Commission on the Causes and Prevention of Violence.* Washington: U.S. Govt. Print. Off., 1969.

137. MURCHISON, C. "American White Criminal Intelligence," *J. Crim. Law Criminol.*, (1924), 239–3160.

138. NATIONAL ADVISORY COMMISSION ON CRIMINAL JUSTICE STANDARDS AND GOALS. *Proposed Federal Criminal Code.* Washington: U.S. Govt. Print. Off., 1973.

139. NATIONAL COMMISSION ON THE CAUSES AND PREVENTION OF VIOLENCE. *To Establish Justice, To Insure Domestic Tranquility.* Final Report. Washington: U.S. Govt. Print. Off., 1969.

140. NATIONAL COUNCIL ON CRIME AND DELIN-

QUENCY. *Model Sentencing Act, Advisory Council of Judges.* New York: Natl. Council on Crime and Delinquency, 1963.

141. NATIONAL INSTITUTE FOR MENTAL HEALTH. Center for Studies of Crime and Delinquency. *Civil Commitment of Special Categories of Offenders.* Washington: U.S. Govt. Print. Off., 1971.

142. NEW YORK TIMES, "Patient Upheld in Refusing Shock," by W. H. Waggoner. 15 July, 1972, p .7.

143. NUNBERG, H. *Principles of Psychoanalysis.* New York: International Universities Press, 1962.

144. OVERHOLSER, W. "Psychiatric Service in Penal and Reformatory Institutions and Criminal Courts in the United States," *Ment. Hyg.,* 12 (1928), 801–838.

145. PARKER, T. *The Frying Pan: A Prison and Its Prisoners.* London: Hutchinson, 1970.

146. PRESIDENT'S COMMISSION ON LAW ENFORCEMENT AND THE ADMINISTRATION OF JUSTICE. *The Challenge of Crime in a Free Society.* Washington: U.S. Govt. Print. Off., 1967.

147. ———. *Narcotics and Drug Abuse Task Force Report.* Washington: U.S. Govt. Print. Off., 1967.

148. PSYCHIATRIC NEWS. "Right to Stop ECT after Initial Consent Stirs Debate in N.Y.," 7 (1972), 7.

149. ———. "U.S. Appeals Court Junks Durham Rule on Insanity," 7 (1972), 1, 12.

150. ———. "Ballay v. United States," [482 F2d 648, 1973] 8 (1973).

151. ———. "Metesky et al. v. W. C. Johnston, Superintendent Matteawan State Hospital," [Gomez v. Miller, 341 F Supp. 323, 412, U.S. 914, 1973] 8 (1973), 5.

152. RAWLS, J. *A Theory of Justice.* Cambridge: Harvard University Press, 1971.

153. RAY, I. *A Treatise on the Medical Jurisprudence of Insanity,* 5th ed. Boston: Little, Brown, 1871.

154. REDLICH, F. C. and D. X. FREEDMAN. *The Theory and Practice of Psychiatry.* New York: Basic Books, 1966.

155. ROBITSCHER, J. *Pursuit of Agreement: Psychiatry and the Law.* Philadelphia: Lippincott, 1966.

156. ———. "Courts, State Hospitals and the Right to Treatment," *Am. J. Psychiatry,* 129 (1972), 298–304.

157. ———. "The New Face of Legal Psychia-

try," *Am. J. Psychiatry,* 129 (1972), 315–321.

158. ROOSENBURG, A. M. "Mental Health Aspects of the Prevention of Crime." Paper presented to Third U.N. Congress on the Prevention of Crime and Treatment of Offenders, Stockholm, August 9–18, 1965.

159. ROSENBERG, A. H. and A. L. McGARRY. "Competency for Trial: The Making of an Expert," *Am. J. Psychiatry,* 128 (1972), 1092–1096.

160. ROSENHAN, D. L. "On Being Sane in Insane Places," *Science,* 179 (1973), 250–258. (Letters in Response, *Science,* 180 (1973), 356–369.

161. ROSENZWEIG, S. "Compulsory Hospitalization of the Mentally Ill," *Am. J. Public Health,* 61 (1971), 121–126.

162. RUBIN, B. "Prediction of Dangerousness of Mentally Ill Criminals," *Arch. Gen. Psychiat.,* 27 (1972), 397–407.

163. SCHEFF, T. S. "The Role of the Mentally Ill and the Dynamics of Mental Disorder," *Sociometry,* 26 (1963), 436–453.

164. SCHEIDMANDEL, P. L. and C. K. KANNO. *The Mentally Ill Offender: Survey of Treatment Programs.* Washington, D.C.: Joint Information Service (APA-NAMH), 1969.

165. SCHREIBER, A. M. "Indeterminate Therapeutic Incarceration of Dangerous Criminals: Perspectives and Problems," *Va. Law Rev.,* 56 (1970), 602–634.

166. RAWLS, L. *A Theory of Justice.* Cambridge: Harvard University Press, Belknap Press, 1971.

167. SHAH, S. A. "Crime and Mental Illness: Some Problems in Defining and Labeling Deviant Behaviour," *Ment. Hyg.,* 53 (1969), 21–33.

168. SHEARD, M. H. "Effect of Lithium on Human Aggression," *Nature,* 230 (1971), 113–114.

169. SLOVENKO, R. "Psychiatry and a Second Look at the Medical Privilege," *Wayne Law Rev.,* 6 (1960), 175–203.

170. ———. "The Psychiatric Patient, Liberty, and the Law," *Amer. J. Psychiatry,* 121 (1964), 534–539.

171. SLOVENKO, R. and G. L. USDIN. *Psychotherapy, Confidentiality, and Privileged Communication,* Springfield, Ill.: Charles C. Thomas, 1966.

172. *Standard Minimum Rules for the Treatment of Prisoners.* Report by the International Commission of Jurists to 4th United Nations Congress on the Prevention of Crime and the Treatment of Prisoners, Kyoto, Aug. 17–26, 1970.

173. STANFORD, P. "A Model Clockwork-Orange Prison," *New York Times Magazine*, Sept. 17, 1972.

174. STEADMAN, H. J. "Follow-up on Baxstrom Patients Returned to Hospitals for the Criminally Insane," *Amer. J. Psychiatry*, 130 (1973), 317–319.

175. STEADMAN, H. J. and G. KEVELES. "The Community Adjustment of the Baxstrom Patients: 1966–1970," *Amer. J. Psychiatry*, 129 (1972), 304–310.

176. STEELE, B. F. and C. B. POLLOCK. "A Psychiatric Study of Parents Who Abuse Children," in R. E. Helfer and C. H. Kempe., eds., *The Battered Child*, pp. 103–147. Chicago: Chicago University Press, 1968.

177. STÜRUP, G. K. *Treating the "Untreatable": Chronic Criminals at Herstedvester.* Baltimore: Johns Hopkins Press, 1968.

178. ————. *Treatment of Sexual Offenders in Herstedvester, Denmark: The Rapists.* Copenhagen: Munksgaard, 1968.

179. SUAREZ, J. M. "Psychiatry and the Criminal Law System," *Amer. J. Psychiatry*, 129 (1972), 293–297.

180. SZASZ, T. S. "Commitment of the Mentally Ill: 'Treatment' or Social Restraint?" *J. Nerv. Ment. Dis.*, 125 (1957), 293–307.

181. ————. "Civil Liberties and Mental Illness: Some Observations of the Case of Miss Edith L. Hough," *J. Nerv. Ment. Dis.*, 131 (1960), 58–63.

182. ————. *Law, Liberty and Psychiatry.* New York: Collier Books, 1968.

183. WAELDER, R. *Basic Theory of Psychoanalysis*, p. 151. New York: Schocken Books, 1966.

184. WALTZ, J. R. and T. W. SCHEUNEMAN. "Informed Consent to Therapy," *N.W. Law Rev.*, 64 (1970), 628–650.

185. WEINTRAUB, J. "Criminal Responsibility: Psychiatry Alone Cannot Determine It," *Amer. Bar. Assoc. J.*, 49 (1963), 1075–1079.

186. WHITE, W. A. "Report of Chairman, Committee on Sterilization of Criminals, Amer. Inst. Crim. Law & Criminol.," *J. Crim. Law & Criminol.*, 8 (1917), 499–501.

187. ————. *Insanity and the Criminal Mind.* New York: Macmillan, 1923.

188. WIGMORE, J. H. *Code of the Rules of Evidence in Trials at Law*, Vol. 8. Boston: Little, Brown, 1961.

189. WILKINS, L. T. *Social Deviance.* London: Tavistock, 1964.

190. ————. "Evaluation of Penal Treatments," in R. M. Carter, D. Glaser, and L. T. Wilkins, eds., *Correctional Institutions*, pp. 509–523. Philadelphia: Lippincott, 1972.

191. WOLLHEIM, R. "The Role of the State: Perspectives of Culture and Philosophy." Presented at the International Conf. Ment. Illness and the State. N.W. Univ. Law School, Chicago, Aug. 2, 1966.

192. WOOTEN, B. *Social Science and Social Pathology.* London: Allen & Unwin, 1955.

193. *Yale Law Journal.* "Notes and Comments: Amnesia: A Case Study in the Limits of Particular Justice," 71 (1967), 109–136.

194. ————. "Notes and Comments: Civil Restraint, Mental Illness, and the Right to Treatment," 77 (1967), 87–116.

CHAPTER 45

PSYCHIATRIC MALPRACTICE*

William A. Bellamy

* In 1975, at the time that the second edition of the Handbook is being prepared, the increase in psychiatric malpractice suits gives cause for alarm. The factors leading to this rapid change are presented in Part B of this chapter.

However, the basic situation described in the chapter Psychiatric Malpractice in the first edition in 1966 still applies, and it is republished here unchanged as Part A. Footnotes, set in italics, have been added to unfinished cases or issues which have been terminated or stabilized in the meantime.

A. A Study of Twenty-eight Appellate Court Cases

WHILE THE OCCASIONAL DISAGREEMENTS between medicine and law tend to make the headlines, cooperative efforts continue, quietly, toward improving the laws that govern medical practice and bringing them up to modern concepts of medicine. Both psychiatry and the law have made their contributions to these collaborations: the model commitment law drawn up by the National Institute of Mental Health,[46] or *The Mentally Disabled and the Law*,[42] drawn up by the American Bar Foundation, are but two examples. Many disciplines participate in these study groups, and broad benefits accrue to society, medicine, and law from continuing collaborations.†

† It is noteworthy that such outstanding jurists as professor Henry Weihofen and Judges John Biggs and David Bazelon have won the coveted Isaac Ray Award for distinction in the field of psychiatry and law.

❰ The Law of Torts

Every professional practitioner carries certain legal duties of care; lacking violation of these, there can be no malpractice.

The law of torts* liability embraces three divisions: (1) negligent tort; (2) intentional tort; and (3) absolute liability. Only the first two apply to the practice of medicine.

1. Nearly all malpractice claims are tried under the law of negligent tort. Under this law the plaintiff's attorney must prove: (a) that a legal duty of care existed, (b) which the defendant (physician or hospital) fulfilled negligently, (c) as a result of which damages accrued to the plaintiff patient (or estate), and (d) that these damages were substantial.

Often, proving the claim is difficult. Year after year the defendant physicians win more cases than they lose, in spite of the fact that in most cases the jury feels sympathetic to the plaintiff.[39] The pleas of plaintiffs' attorneys, stressing the difficulty of bearing the burden of proof, should be tempered with awareness that unmeritorious claims are also encountered.

The plaintiff's burden of proof is lessened when res ipso loquitur† is utilized. Objectively, when this principle is admitted and properly utilized by the court, it constitutes no more than circumstantial evidence, a "mere inference of negligence"[47] which should be weighed along with all the other evidence. Under these conditions, the medical profession has no objection to its use.

However, in recent years the principle has been misused as a presumption of negligence (rather than an inference of negligence) so that the burden of proof is shifted from the plaintiff to the physician. Unless the physician can come up with a factually convincing explanation of the cause of the damages to the patient, the physician may find himself held liable for an unusual complication, just because it is rare and not explainable. Prosser, former Dean of the University of California Law School, found the misuse of res ipsa loquitur sufficient to state:

> The Latin catchword is an obstacle to all clear thinking. . . . There is no case in which it has been anything but a hindrance. The present state of affairs in California, as elsewhere, is a reproach to the law. This, at least, speaks for itself.[48]

In addition, Harper has stressed that the doctrine is unfair to the physician, in view of the fact that the plaintiff wins most of the cases in which res ipsa loquitur is ruled admissible.[39]

2. In rare instances, a malpractice claim will be tried under the law of intentional tort, implying an intent to touch injuriously, as in a fight, or as in administering electroshock therapy (EST).

A claim based upon unenlightened consent is a case in point. The physician holds a legal duty of care to explain to the patient, relative, or guardian, the possible complications of EST, sufficient to form an enlightened consent. Without sufficient explanation, the consent is considered to be unenlightened, which amounts to signing no consent at all, and the physician has "assaulted" his patient.

Since witnesses usually are not present when the complications of EST are discussed, the case of alleged unenlightened consent boil down to the word of the patient against that of the physician. Thus, the plaintiff's attorney is relieved of the necessity to produce an expert witness of the same school of thought as the defendant-physician, willing to testify on behalf of the plaintiff. Understandably, plaintiff's attorneys base their claim upon unenlightened consent whenever possible.

Warranty of cure is somewhat similar to unenlightened consent. When a physician allegedly has said, "You accept this or that treatment and you will be all right," he has "promised a cure." Here, too, the case becomes the word of the patient against that of the physician, and no expert witness is needed on behalf of the patient. The physician who utters such a careless statement makes himself

---

* In civil law, a tort is a wrongful action of commission or omission not involving breach of contract.

† Literally, the thing or fact speaks for itself. If a burn on the skin appears at the site of a heating pad, it constitutes circumstantial evidence that someone was negligent—the patient, the doctor, the manufacturer, or others.

a warranter of cure—something the law would never do. Specifically, the law does not hold a medical service to be always safe. On the contrary, the law does hold the pharmaceutical manufacturer to be the warranter of a safe product, as exemplified by the $3,145,000 judgments against Cutter Laboratories—with a few more minor suits still outstanding*—for manufacturing, admittedly nonnegligently, polio vaccines according to government specifications. It would have made as much sense for the plaintiff's attorneys to sue the federal government for faulty specifications as to sue the pharmaceutical manufacturing company which produced this highly complex attenuated vaccine product.

3. As an example of absolute liability, consider the owner of a reservoir, which overflows from a storm, and a neighbor suffers damage. The owner of the reservoir holds an absolute liability even though he maintained his reservoir nonnegligently. Absolute liability is not applicable in forensic medicine.

Legal Duty of Care

The existence of a legal duty of care is basic to all malpractice. As regards the practice of medicine, a legal duty can be formed either by law or by "common sense."

Our laws consist of both *statutory law* (enacted by legislative bodies) and *case law* (precedent established via case decisions).† The judiciary are well aware of the danger of stultification of the law,[34] and it is quite appropriate for medicine and psychiatry to help

in bringing about changes, via either statute or case law, so that the law may stay abreast of modern psychiatric principles of diagnosis, treatment, and management of the mentally ill.

Statutory Law

Recently, in Connecticut, psychiatric interests were successful in uniting with the Bar Association in fostering enactment of a new psychiatric disclosure law dealing with privileged communication. By this law, psychotherapists in Connecticut now have greater protection in maintaining confidentiality, as well as precise delineation of the circumstances under which confidential communication from a client may, or shall, be broken for the benefit of society.‡

To prepare the way for eventual enactment of the disclosure law, psychiatrists collected information, documented by case illustrations,[53] to demonstrate the need for confidentiality in psychotherapy, organized committees and study groups in collaboration with the Bar Association, and gave advance information to many members of the legislature as to the significance of the proposed bill.[38] Proper preparation may save years of aimless discussion in the wrong committees, reaching the wrong ears.

Case Law

Modification of the law by establishing new precedents takes place constantly, but these changes generally occur over a longer period of time and are less spectacular than statutory changes. Also, modification by precedent can scarcely be planned, or debated in study groups, nor can forces be mobilized toward the intended goal. Nevertheless, by carefully defending all defensible malpractice claims, medicine and psychiatry can gradually mold the precedents thus established. An outstanding example of this is a suicide case presented below.

That "common sense" can also be used as a

---

* Mr. Edward Cutter stated that since 1966, two more cases have been completed for a total of $25,500 additional awards or $3,170,000 liability as of the end of 1974.

There are two final cases outstanding which may not be determined for several years. For children, the statute of limitations may not begin to toll until the age of eighteen or twenty-one years; various states allow one to seven years after that. The "prayer" need not be declared at the time the claim is filed initially in twelve states, and this happens to apply in the two cases outstanding. However, Mr. Cutter stated that there was reason to believe that the prayer was moderate.

† Probably we may now recognize law by a third process, administrative law (established by codes or regulations administratively created), which is discussed below (see p. 919).

‡ By the time of the second edition of the Handbook, 1975, the Connecticut State Legislature already had weakened the formerly exemplary State Commitment Law.

yardstick of reasonable duty of care may come as a surprise to some professional practitioners. We are more familiar with "the standard of practice in the community by practitioners of the same or similar school of thought"* so often used in malpractice cases. Actually, the measure of "what a man of reasonably prudent mind would do under circumstances" may be employed at the discretion of the judge and jury. Thus, in another case of suicide presented below, a plaintiff won a favorable verdict although the precautionary care provided the patient compared well with "standard practice" in psychiatric wards in that community.

⟨ The Vulnerability of the Psychiatric Profession

It is evident from the foregoing study of laws bearing on malpractice that good laws facilitate good medicine. But there are limitations,

* *Standard of practice in the community has been made to conform to the standard of practice in that state or in the nation. Thus the courts are ruling on admissible testimony of an expert witness from a distance of several hundred miles (Sinz v. Owens, 33 C2d 749, 1949; Huffman v. Lindquist, Cal S Ct, 1952.*

As to "practitioner of the same school of thought," this philosophy has been expanded (Brown v. Colm, 11 Cal 3d 639, 1931). For example, a defendant surgeon had performed a rare and stipulatedly difficult surgical procedure many years before the case came to trial. The pathologist who testified for the plaintiff had done no surgery, but from countless autopsies performed in a distant community had presented himself as knowledgable about the issue at bar. The appellate court sustained the admissibility of his testimony.

In a second case, a judge allowed testimony from an expert witness who had minimal experience but extensive reading on the issue at bar. If carried to a ridiculous extreme, a psychiatrist could find his testimony opposed by a professional assistant whom he was training in his clinic, if she had read the literature. More seriously, in Magit v. Board of Medical Examiners (57 C2d 74, 1961), an anaesthetist was held liable for hiring an anaesthetist who did not yet have his license in California.

The philosophy "what a man of reasonable prudent mind would do under circumstances," is still not overly utilized. However, there is evidence of this philosophy being embraced covertly and juries seem to be getting the message.

and although psychiatry and the law have come a long way toward more humane handling of the mentally ill, malpractice claims cannot be eliminated entirely. First, discretionary powers must be allowed the professional practitioner or his activities cease to be professional and he becomes a tradesman. Thus, "good practice" cannot and should not be too rigidly codified, either by the law, or by medicine or psychiatry through too detailed codes of ethics or brochures delineating "standards of care."† Secondly, progress cannot be made without the occurrence of periods of flux. Changes, either in social attitude, legal maneuvers, or treatment concepts do affect malpractice claims, both as to incidence or outcome (for instance, size of award). It has taken time to work out the ground rules for adjudicating alleged damage to patients from innovations such as EST, introduced in 1938; the legal maneuver of alleged "unenlightened consent" which expanded rapidly in malpractice cases during the 1950's; or the current concepts of treatment by which the more serious forms of mental illness, such as suicidal tendencies, are being treated increasingly in the home, on open wards, or in day centers in the community closer to the patient's familiar surroundings, with admittedly greater risks, but with more patients getting well.

If malpractice claims cannot be eliminated, it is good preventive medicine to familiarize oneself with the nature of those risks that have been encountered.

The American Medical Association from time to time publishes accurate information on malpractice.‡[40,41,45,49,52,54] Psychiatry constitutes a low-risk group within the practice of medicine and consequently the American Medical Association has not given special attention to psychiatric risks. There are few papers dealing directly with psychiatric malpractice,[29,30,32,43] although the subject arises tangentially in many publications.

A malpractice claim may be dropped by the plaintiff, weeded out as unmeritorious in pretrial hearing, settled out of court, or adjudi-

† See the section on Preventive Measures, p. 909.

‡ By contrast, many popular magazines tend to sacrifice accuracy for sensationalism.

cated in trial courts. Finally, a claim may be appealed; it is estimated that only about one out of every hundred claims reaches the appellate court,[52] and no reliable information is available about the other ninety-nine. However, all appellate court cases in the nation are abstracted and published as permanent documents, so they constitute one reliable source of information about the more serious primary malpractice risks in psychiatry. Out of 600 to 700 medical and surgical appellate court cases nationwide, twenty-eight were psychiatric cases in the eighteen years from 1946 to 1964.

([Primary Psychiatric Malpractice Risks

The twenty-eight psychiatric cases that reached appellate courts between 1946 and 1964 suggest five main areas of risk: (1) problems of treatment, twelve cases (43 percent); (2) problems of commitment, eight cases (29 percent); (3) problems of suicide, four cases (14 percent); (4) patient's assaultiveness, two cases (7 percent); and (5) problems of psychic injury ("mental anguish"), two cases (7 percent).

Problems of Treatment

Of the twelve cases based upon alleged negligent treatment, eight are concerned with shock therapies, and four with other forms of treatment.

Shock Therapies

Unauthorized Consent. The father of a schizophrenic patient signed consent for EST. The patient, after he improved, felt that he should have had the exclusive right to say whether or not he consented to the treatment. The psychiatrist was absolved of blame in this case, which occurred in California.[3]

When mental competency is an issue, the signed authorization for treatment should be obtained from the legal guardian, if one has been appointed. Otherwise, it is better to obtain the signature of both the patient and the nearest relative, if possible, or to arrange to have a legal guardian appointed. It is fallacious for the psychiatrist to presume that if he proceeds with EST and improvement follows that is gratifying to the patient, no malpractice claim will be filed.

Unenlightened Consent.* The law recognizes that if the physician were required by legal code to relate all the alarming details as to possible complications, the patients or relatives might refuse to sign their consent and useful treatment would be obstructed. Legal authorities advise the physician to inform the patient of potential hazards of the treatment "insofar as possible."[44] Thus, discretionary powers are allowed the professional practitioner—which is as it should be.

The physician who conscientiously writes in the patient's record what complications were discussed and with whom (patient, relative, guardian), will have strong evidence that he fulfilled his legal duty of care to his patient. Of course, these notations must be made at the time of the discussions.

Alternatively, the patient or guardian may be asked to read a printed account of EST and its possible complications, and to sign to the effect that he has read and understands the contents of the account.[50] There is no foolproof method, however, of ensuring that consent is sufficient.

Three of the eight EST cases were tried on the basis of unenlightened consent; two were won by the defendant physician. In the third case[12] a trial jury in New Mexico awarded $5,889.59, not against the psychiatrist who administered EST which allegedly resulted in vertebral compression fracture and deafness, but against the diagnosing and referring psychiatrist who allegedly did not explain to the patient that complications might occur in connection with EST. The defendant referring psychiatrist appealed, and a new trial was held, and the psychiatrist was absolved.

Warranty of Cure.† Psychiatrists generally

---

* *The courts have tightened up in this respect, as discussed in Part B. (see p. 916).*

† *With the rapid expansion of new psychiatric methods—often discussed in popular magazines, complete with promises of cure—this may become a serious malpractice risk.*

understand the insecurity that can be engendered by sickness. Wishful thinking, bolstered by distortions in perception and/or memory, may serve a useful, dynamic purpose in the insecure, or even in the mentally competent relative, guardian—or physician. The physician who reveals godlike attitudes is prone to malpractice.[31]

There is no direct defense against an allegation of warranty of cure. The physician will not have written in the record, "I did not promise to cure this patient!" However, the presence of an accurate record, showing an overtone of due modesty in the healer, generally has been sufficient to win these cases. Such was the result in the two cases considered here.

Shock Therapy Negligently Administered. When a fracture or other significant complication of shock therapy occurs, the patient may claim that the shock was negligently administered, that the extremities were not held securely enough, or that they were held too securely, and so forth. The patient needs a physician to testify to the alleged negligence. These cases were won by the defendant psychiatrist, except for two cases in which EST was continued after a fracture had occurred. In one case[2] a New York trial jury awarded $5000; the defendant appealed and retrial was granted. Before the second trial was held, the case was settled out of court for an undisclosed amount.

In the second case,[11] a North Carolina trial judge ruled involuntary nonsuit. The plaintiff appealed, and a full trial was ordered by the appellate court. This trial ended in a mistrial due to a hung jury. The defendant then made an out-of-court settlement, amount held in confidence.

Plaintiffs' attorneys have attempted to introduce *res ipsa loquitur*—the contention being that fracture or other serious complication would not occur without the inference of negligence. However, the courts generally hold that if it is well known that complications frequently occur in connection with such procedures as shock therapies, then the fact that a complication did occur does not warrant an inference of negligence. Thus, *res ipsa loquitur* thus far has been ruled inadmissible in cases involving EST.

OTHER TREATMENT SITUATIONS

Wet Pack, Allegedly Cruelly Applied. In a Pennsylvania case,[9] the defendant psychiatrist and state hospital demonstrated that the wet pack was applied in accordance with "standard practice in the community," as described in a military manual, and was not cruelly applied. Both were absolved.

Psychiatrist's Assault upon the Patient. In a New York case,[5] the mother of a schizophrenic patient brought suit because her daughter had been seen to emerge from treatment sessions with ecchymoses. The mother testified that the psychiatrist had claimed either (1) self-defense, or (2) that assault was part of the treatment. The mother also testified that the patient was not assaultive. However, the mother's own diary contained entries describing the daughter's assaults upon relatives or servants. The trial judge dismissed the case at the conclusion of the plaintiff's presentation.

Upon appeal, the appellate court in New York granted a full trial, on the basis that if the psychiatrist's alleged assaults were claimed to be part of the treatment, this would be prima-facie malpractice. Through failure to prosecute, this case now probably is as good as closed.*

Multiple Allegations. In another New York case,[4] a claim was filed naming several alleged acts of negligence, one of which was that the physician had given prolonged psychiatric treatment costing a few thousand dollars without obtaining a psychiatric consultation. The physician was absolved of all allegations.

This case occurred in 1949, but it may still be important in view of the current trend toward encouraging the family physician to treat increasing numbers of the mentally ill in our nation. The law does not hold a physician to the same duty of care under all circumstances—for example, emergency treatment on the highway. On the other hand, some

---

* Case has been closed for this reason.

physicians tend to underestimate the value of psychiatric skill, and articles appearing in leading medical journals outline criteria for referral of a patient to a psychiatrist which are essentially the criteria of a psychotic episode! This would deprive a patient of earlier treatment by the specialist in psychiatry.

The emergency treatment of the mentally ill is an important trend by which the number of patients in some of our state hospitals is being decreased. As physicians are encouraged and trained to institute early treatment, they may also be informed of the value of psychiatric consultative and/or referral and treatment services, along with the potential jeopardy of a malpractice claim if they do not avail themselves of these services under proper circumstances. The benefits from early treatment of the mentally ill by the psychiatrist are too great to risk their being curtailed through faulty application of useful principles of treatment.

Wrongful Death. In a Pennsylvania case[1] a patient was admitted to a private sanatorium for intermittent quadriplegia and other hysterical symptoms. About six or seven hours following the first EST, and after having had lunch and a nap, the patient fell down a flight of stairs. He was unattended at the time, and the fall was not observed. He immediately complained that his neck was broken. On the fourth day following the accident the patient died. During these four days there developed several typical signs of cervical cord injury, such as pain, distended abdomen, projectile vomiting, and quadriplegia. Diagnostic and treatment procedures customary in cases of spinal cord injury had not been instituted either by the psychiatrist or by his medical consultant. Post-mortem X-ray revealed an anterior dislocation of the fourth cervical vertebra, 8 mm., on the fifth cervical vertebra. The jury awarded $60,000 ($25,000 in wrongful death and $35,000 in survival action).

The above case is of further interest in that only the laymen hospital owners were named as defendants. The psychiatrist who was employed part-time by the hospital was not named as a defendant, nor was he called to testify as a witness. As a general medicolegal trend, owners of a hospital are assuming increased jeopardy because they are held responsible for the actions of their employees even though they may exercise no direct supervision.

In summary, of the twelve cases concerning problems of treatment, the trial court rendered a judgment against the defendant in seven. Upon appeal, five of the judgments either were reversed or retrial granted. In the final result, a judgment for the plaintiff was won in three cases: (1) EST continued after a fracture had occurred, approximately $5000; (2) wrongful death, $60,000; and (3) EST "negligently administered," out-of-court settlement, amount held in confidence.

Problems of Commitment and Hospitalization

The most frequent basis for claims of illegal confinement is that the patient was *committed* on the basis of examination(s) performed perfunctorily or with ulterior motive—for example, to "dispose" of a patient who had proven refractory to treatment efforts.[13]

In commitment cases the examining physician generally is exonerated. The courts hold that it is the judge, not the physician, who commits a patient, and that a witness must be free to testify as to his findings without fear of reprisal such as by suit for libel, or suit for negligent examination. It is a case of competing rights: the right of the individual witness to be protected against false statement, and the right of the public to be protected. The latter is considered the more important, according to an old legal principle worked out at the turn of the century.

However, for a physician to testify on the basis of cursory examination, or no examination at all, always has been a criminal offense punishable by fine, imprisonment, or both. The law generally has not seen fit to prosecute in these infrequent instances.

In one case, the two examining physicians allegedly made no examination at all, but the district attorney did not prosecute. In a 1963 New York case,[18] the two examining physicians made twenty-minute examinations, allegedly negligently performed, and the trial judge allowed the defendants to be tried under the law of negligence; an award of $20,000 was made, upheld through two appeals to both appellate courts.

In both of these cases, the four physicians involved were not psychiatrists—but it is psychiatry that gets the "black eye" for these alleged felonies! In many jurisdictions the superior court holds the legal right to appoint medical examiners on the "lunacy commission." The psychiatric profession stands ready to advise the superior court as to reliable psychiatrists willing to serve as appointees of the courts within reasonable salary or fee schedules, and hopes that its advisory committees will be more fully utilized by the judiciary in connection with these appointments.

Hospitalization other than by commitment is exemplified by the following case. (Problems of hospitalization overlap with problems of suicide discussed further in the next section.)

In a California case[19] a psychiatrist examined a patient who was acutely incompetent, obtained additional history from the patient's husband, administered sedative intravenously to the patient, and upon authorization signed by the husband for hospitalization and EST, had the patient taken to a hospital (of which the psychiatrist was part owner), and a course of EST was started. The patient made a very good recovery, but brought suit for assault and battery, claiming that when she "came to her senses" in the hospital and asked to leave, she was detained and, further, that EST was continued against her will. The psychiatrist would have been on safe ground had he followed any one of three or four legal codes for involuntary hospitalization. As one example, he could have filed a report of his examination to designated authorities within twenty-four hours, along with an examination and report by a second psychiatrist.

The trial court awarded $78,000 to the patient, and the defendant psychiatrist appealed. The appellate judges granted a new trial, but

included, for consideration of the new trial court, the fact that the patient had benefited by hospitalization and treatment, and that such benefit could be given consideration in assessing damages as alleged. The case was retried, and $60,000 was the final judgment.

In summary, of eight cases, six were won by the defendant. In one case a judgment of $60,000 was awarded to the patient for false imprisonment, and in a second case a judgment of $20,000 for negligent mental examination was rendered.

Problems of Suicide

The referring physician, the treating physician-psychiatrist, or the hospital owners carry certain risks attendant to locked-ward and to open-ward types of treatment facilities.

In a Georgia case,[24] a woman committed suicide by jumping from her unbarred window in a large university hospital. The referring physician was absolved. Evidently, back in 1948, if a hospital accepted mental patients it was considered to be reasonably prudent for the referring physician to admit a patient in that hospital. The hospital was absolved because the plaintiff made a general claim of inadequate attendance, but failed to show that the patient was not guarded at the critical moment.

In a Missouri case,[23] a woman committed suicide in her room on a locked ward by hanging herself with a rope fashioned from torn strips of nightgowns. The nurse had checked only one-half hour before the suicide and found the woman apparently sleeping comfortably on her bed with the safety belt presumably locked. The trial jury awarded $9000 damages and the appellant court sustained this judgment, claiming that one-half hour was too long a period to leave a patient unattended.

Hospital costs surely would become astronomical if hospitals were required to maintain constant attendance upon patients presumably sleeping in locked safety belts! This precedent must be reversed in subsequent cases for the benefit of law, justice, and the mentally ill trying to recover.*

In a Spokane, Washington, case,[21] a woman sustained serious injuries from her dash for freedom or suicide from an open ward. On Christmas Eve the patient had tried to commit suicide by swallowing her nightgown and breaking off her toes. The family physician called in a physician-psychiatrist at once, but the psychiatrist was not told that the patient was actively suicidal either by the referring physician, the psychiatrist who had treated her three months earlier in a state hospital in a neighboring state, or by the husband —otherwise the open-ward facility would not have been selected as appropriate for this patient. The treating psychiatrist was absolved.

However, the trial jury awarded $11,226 against the hospital owners. A nurse testified that the patient alternated between periods of depression and moods in which she was cheerful and sociable. The patient, with permission, had gone off the ward to the bathroom several times unattended during her five days in the hospital, and this time when the patient asked the nurse for permission to go to the bathroom she gave no telltale sign whatever of her intended dash for freedom, or suicide—otherwise, the nurse testified, she surely would have accompanied the patient to the bathroom.

The appellate court upheld absolution of the treating psychiatrist, but because nurses in this hospital customarily guarded the corridor leading outdoors, and because the nurse on duty in the nurse's station did not have unobstructed visibility up and down the corridor, a new trial against the defendant hospital was ordered. The case was then settled out of court at a figure slightly smaller than $11,226.

Evidently, if by custom an area has once been guarded, it must always thereafter be guarded. Furthermore, another nurse had talked to the patient immediately prior to the incident, and the patient gave no sign of her intention to flee or attempt suicide.

The open ward is too valuable a treatment method to be endangered through unjust litigation. Perhaps psychiatrists can (as anaesthesiologists have) get across to judges and juries the complex nature of managing potentially or actively suicidal patients and get reasonable justice back into a very difficult field of professional treatment endeavors. Just this was done in the next case.

In another Missouri case,[22] as a treating psychiatrist was leaving a locked door of a locked ward, a patient dashed from his bed fifteen feet distant, pushed through the door, and jumped through an unbarred window in a stairway and sustained serious injuries, miraculously short of death. This very complicated medicolegal case has been presented in detail elsewhere.[30] It suffices here to demonstrate a proper way for psychiatrists, through their defense attorneys, to present their complex findings and philosophies of proper treatment to the judiciary. The trial jury had awarded $40,000 against the hospital, but the appellate court established a favorable precedent by absolving the hospital on the basis of the following deliberation, developed from court testimony:

The modern concept of treatment in such cases is to allow patients as much freedom as possible, to treat them as individuals, and to try to "resocialize" them; therein the physicians knowingly take a calculated risk; better safeguards could be afforded by strict confinement, but few patients would be cured; there is potential for suicide or for harming others in all acutely depressed mental cases, and in some patients this may increase when they begin to improve, but certainly not in all; patients such as plaintiff are being cured regularly by modern treatment; care in entering or leaving such a ward becomes a sort of automatic reflex and specifically, it was shown here, it was a constant procedure for the doctors and attendants in this hospital to be careful on entering or leaving the ward. . . . At the time of the trial he [plaintiff] had apparently recovered completely from his mental illness

---

* By 1974, the highly useful concept of "dangerousness" has been developed, referable to suicide, murderousness, and the place of diagnosis. See references from Part B: 9, 11, 12, 18, 23, 26, 31–33, 36, 39, 41, 47, 51, 57, 69, and 70.

and he was working, though at a less remunerative position.[22]

Note the great clarity of the opinion expressed by the judiciary. This is an example of defending a difficult case, from which a favorable precedent was established for the benefit of law and medicine alike.

In summary, of four cases, the trial jury awarded judgments in three cases and appellate courts absolved the defendant hospital in one case but upheld the judgments against hospitals in the other two cases ($9000 in one case and less than $11,226 in the second case). Thus 50 percent of the suicidal cases were awarded judgments; the highest incidence of risk in psychiatry.

Problems of Patient's Assaultiveness

In these two cases, a patient suddenly became assaultive to relatives and attendants caring for the patient.

Both the physician and the psychiatrist defendants were acquitted in these two cases. However, the wording of the deliberations strongly suggests that if a physician does know that a patient has assaultive tendencies, he carries a legal duty of care to give warning of potential assaultiveness to those persons who may be involved in custodial care of that patient, in the home or elsewhere. Also, the duty of care is higher for the psychiatrist than for the nonpsychiatric physician.

Problems of Psychic Injury

This is potentially a dangerous and unjust psychiatric risk. Thus far only one award has been sustained (against a treating roentgenologist). However, the judgment evidently rested largely upon psychiatric testimony, and consequently psychiatrists may well study the following two cases. In a New York case,[27] $25,000 was awarded against a roentgenologist of which a portion, $15,000, was for "mental anguish." X-ray treatment, administered to the shoulder for bursitis, was followed by a skin lesion that did not heal. After two years the patient's attorney directed the patient to a dermatologist who allegedly advised her to "have her shoulder checked every six months inasmuch as the area of burn might become cancerous." Whereupon, she asserted, she developed a fear of cancer. The psychiatrist testified that the patient had "cancerophobia."[*]

In their deliberations, the appellate judges spoke of (1) "autosuggestibility," and (2) "iatrogenic disease," as though these were a true explanation of the phobia. Thus, the deliberation: "It is common knowledge (from physical-culture lectures and newspaper articles) among laymen and even more widely among laywomen that wounds which do not heal over long periods of time frequently become cancerous." Nevertheless, the dermatologist's statement "it might become cancerous" is held to be a form of "iatrogenic disease" and the damages accrue to the first "negligent person," the roentgenologist. This was a four-to-three split decision which carried a strongly worded minority opinion, but the $15,000 for "mental anguish" was sustained.

In other words, the roentgenologist is liable when the dermatologist tells the patient something she already knew from the newspapers. It would make as much sense to sue the newspapers for "newspaperogenic disease." It falls to the psychiatrist testifying in such a case to state clearly that (1) "suggestibility" is a universal function of every mind, normal or "neurotic," and (2) "cancerophobia" is a complex psychological mechanism not arising from any single cause but of necessity stemming from multiple causality. In any event, a start toward a dangerous precedent was made by the majority decision in this case.

In another New York case,[28] although the preceding case[27] was cited as a reference, the defendant family physician was absolved from a charge of alleged "mental anguish" from "tuberculophobia." The trial judge believed the case was of little merit and, upon the conclusion of the plaintiff's testimony, gave a directed verdict absolving the physician. The appellate court upheld the directed verdict of absolution.

[*] I do not know what additional details the psychiatrist may have included in his testimony.

Thus a dangerous precedent was reversed, but other cases in other jurisdictions surely will follow, and the psychiatrist had best be well prepared. We must remember that the judiciary are highly dependent upon expert medical testimony in order to formulate their deliberations in medical cases. Of course, the expert testimony must be accurate, well thought out in advance of appearance in court, and able to withstand the impeachment attempts allowed by law in the trial courts in the interest of discovering the truth—or falsity—of testimony rendered under oath.

In summary, these twenty-eight psychiatric malpractice cases comprise a low-risk group within the practice of medicine. Yet this low-risk group reflects nearly every important mediocolegal trend observed in high-risk groups.

⟨ Potential Psychiatric Risks

Reportable Diseases

Failure to report a reportable disease (epilepsy), which later figured in a serious auto accident, brought an out-of-court settlement of $230,000, of which $200,000 was against eight physicians who had failed to report their knowledge that this patient had epilepsy.*

Drug-Induced Diseases†

Diseases attendant on the administration of drugs, such as agranulocytosis following psychopharmaceutical prescriptions, have brought awards in the quarter-million-dollar bracket. Psychiatrists are prescribing relatively new drugs to countless patients over prolonged periods of time. Although periodic physical and laboratory examinations are a notoriously

poor preventive measure in cases of dyscrasia, nevertheless a patient should not continue on psychoactive drugs for years without an examination either by the psychiatrist or the family physician in the team on the case.

Treatment Innovations

In England, a psychiatrist had a judgment of £6000 brought against him for a new form of psychotherapy, namely, agreeing to innocent socializing with a female patient in a final effort to resolve a "transference love" that had resisted all usual psychoanalytic techniques for many months before the final socializing innovation was instituted. The patient finally committed suicide.

Research

Manufacture, testing, and research on new drugs now is carried on under new rulings by the Food and Drug Administration. Atrocities to civilians perpetrated under the guise of "medical experiments" (for example, at the Buchenwald concentration camp) resulted in the Nuremberg laws, which are fairly adequate.[35] Many physician-psychiatrists are unhappy with the restrictions passed. These laws have not yet been tested in our courts and we must reserve judgment. In the meantime, excellent articles have covered the anticipated pros and cons quite adequately.‡[35,36,37]

⟨ Preventive Measures

The Individual Psychiatric Practitioner

1. Know your laws. Know your rights as well as your duties under the law.
2. Purchase adequate malpractice insurance

---

* Battered child syndrome is now a legally reportable disease in several states (see reference 34 in Part B). This is almost certain to become a nation-wide legal duty of care for the psychiatrist.

† This malpractice risk of potentially large monetary award is now compounded by questionable supervision of treatment regimes—e.g., who gives injections and cursorily signs prescriptions in some instances?—requires detailed appraisal (see Part B, pp. 918–919).

‡ The FDA has tightened the conditions required in research such that it is difficult or impossible, especially in child research projects, for the researcher to feel secure that he has obtained an informed consent (see reference 50 from Part B). Furthermore, the Review Boards passing judgment on proposed research projects have more members who are laymen—the latter sometimes holding a majority vote.

coverage from an insurance carrier known to defend all defensible cases.

3. Do not overlook the value of a consultation under appropriate circumstances.

4. Keep adequate records, and keep them current.

5. If you repeatedly find yourself in trouble, consider obtaining psychiatric treatment.

The American Psychiatric Association

In one case, the plaintiff's attorney relied heavily upon the evidence of a statement from *Standards of Electroshock Treatment,* prepared by Committee on Therapy and approved by the Council of the American Psychiatric Association, May 1953: "If the patient should complain of pain or impairment of function, he should receive a physical examination, including X-rays, to ascertain whether he has suffered accidental damage."[11]

Even though in this particular case the clinical picture may have warranted taking X-rays, such a statement deprives the physician of his discretionary powers. Should every patient who complains of headache or backache following EST be X-rayed? Certainly not.

Consequently, the officials of the APA and other organizations of psychiatry and psychoanalysis should review their canons of ethics and their manuals of standard practice,* changing mandatory language to permissive language (or including a qualifying clause) whenever appropriate, and secondly, officials of all psychiatric organizations should make it their policy to screen all future official statements with that principle in mind.

⟨ Ethical Considerations

Since the professional practitioner must be granted discretionary powers in order that his activities may remain professional, and since good judgment cannot be legislated, it follows that ethics must pick up where the law leaves

* *In 1959 the Board of Trustees of APA rescinded the manual on EST on the basis that it was a stabilized procedure.*

off. To possess the highest ethical considerations is as important to the political and legal practitioner as it is to the medical practitioner.

Judge Jerome Frank said, in introducing Justice William O. Douglas: "Empathy constitutes his central virtue. He has discovered that the finest wisdom stems from emotionally understanding what one knows."[34] Justice Douglas said, "The work of a court may send a whole economy in one direction, or help shape the manifest destiny of an era." Therefore, one must be ready to acknowledge his mistakes. Thus: "My convictions of yesterday I now see were wrong; to adhere to them, out of prideful consistency would be foolish, wicked. . . . It is a healthy practice . . . for a court to reexamine its own doctrines. . . . Responsible government should entail the undoing of wrongs."[34]

Such is the high ethical awareness possessed by leaders of medicine and the judiciary. Ethical goals are like ideals that we strive toward but rarely, if ever, achieve. Yet we should be as unafraid to proclaim ideals as we would truths, and we should not be like those persons of whom Samuel Butler wrote: "Some men love truth so much that they seem to be in constant fear that she should catch cold from overexposure."

Consequently, to shirk our duty to speak our psychological truths by defending all defensible malpractice cases would be to foster stultification, rigidity, and injustice through case law. Equally, it is the duty of physicians, attorneys, judges, and political leaders to be worthy of the discriminatory powers bestowed upon them by tradition and by law.

In the vast majority of instances in the cases briefly reviewed above, the quality of performance of the medical witnesses, the attorneys, and the judges was of superbly high quality. (Those few exceptions have already been presented in greater detail.)

Turning briefly to another area, that of criminal law, physician-psychiatrists, when testifying as to the assumed mental status of a criminal at the time he performed the alleged crime, are of necessity testifying to opinions based upon a high degree of inference.[33] The public generally, and the judiciary occasionally, do not fully appreciate this fact and the image of psychiatry suffers accordingly, condemned by newspaper headlines.

On the other hand, in the above cases physician-psychiatrists were testifying to clinical observations and opinions carrying a much lower degree of inference, and their testimony, now written into case law, was generally excellent. It is the latter area of testimony that resides on open library shelves as public documents—which, ironically, the public does not read!

The superb performance of the judiciary is the more remarkable considering that some degree of prejudice is universal, a fact that prompted Voltaire to say, "We must make intolerance intolerable, but we must respect prejudice," or, as Erikson put it, "The only unprejudiced person is one who is prejudiced against being prejudiced." I can perceive how the judiciary could have obtained such excellent empathy and understanding of the problems which physician-psychiatrists encounter in dealing with patients. But it is highly remarkable that the judiciary put aside their prejudices so well during their deliberations, which consequently stand up well under the test of time.

I should like to conclude with a statement of ethical principles for the professional practitioner, the law, and the social milieu, as forged by our professional statesmen.

1. Of the professional man (physician, attorney, statesman), it is reasonable to expect that he develop those arts and skills necessary to effectively carry out his professional duties; that he acquire that degree of knowledge necessary to have something to profess; that he profess it with discretion; and that he develop that degree of moral fiber necessary to profess it with sincerity, integrity, and good conscience (ethics).

2. Of the law it is reasonable to expect that the lawmakers continue their search for better laws, toward our constitutional ideal of equal rights to everyone under the law, and that practitioners of the law strive toward the ideal of the "professional man" as delineated above, in order to better implement these laws in the interest of justice.

3. It is reasonable to expect society to provide an optimum social milieu for the ideals expressed under 1. and 2. and that the political leaders maintain that political climate in which what the professional man has to profess will be heeded as at least one of the multiple alternative choices in planning our social order.

Our late President John F. Kennedy said, "Give me multiple choices," operating under a sound psychological principle expressed by Macaulay, "Men are never so likely to settle a question rightly as when they discuss it freely."

⟨[Bibliography

DECISIONS

Problems of Treatment

1. Brown v. Moore, 143 F Supp. 816 (1956).
2. Eisele v. Malone, 157 N.Y.S. 2d 155 (1956).
3. Farber v. Olkon, 254 P. 2d 520 (1953).
4. Gasperini v. Manganelli, 92 N.Y.S. 2d 575 (1949).
5. Hammer v. Rosen, 181 N.Y.S. 2d 805 (1959); 198 N.Y.S. 2d 376 (1960).
6. Johnston v. Rodis, 251 F. 2d 917 (1958).
7. Mitchell v. Robinson, 334 S.W. 2d 11 (1960); 360 S.W. 2d 673 (1961).
8. O'Rourke v. Halcyon Rest, 118 N.Y.S. 2d 693 (1953).
9. Powell v. Risser, 99 A. 2d 454 (1953).
10. Quinley v. Cooke, 192 S.W. 2d 992 (1946).
11. Stone v. Proctor, 131 S.E. 2d 297 (1963).
12. Woods v. Brumlop, 377 P. 2d 520 (1962).

Problems of Commitment and Hospitalization

13. Bailey v. McGill, 100 S.E. 2d 860 (1957).
14. Bartlett v. Weimer, 268 F. 2d 860 (1959).
15. Daniels v. Finney, 262 S.W. 2d 431 (1953).
16. Dunbar v. Greenlaw, 128 A. 2d 218 (1956).
17. Hawley v. Towne, 156 A. 2d 377 (1959).
18. Kleber v. Stephens, 242 N.Y.S. 2d 497 (1963).
19. Maben v. Rankin, 55 Cal. 2d 139; 358 P. 2d 681 (1961).
20. Mezzullo v. Molitz, 118 N.E. 2d 356 (1954).

Problems of Suicide

21. Benjamin v. Havens, 373 P. 2d 109 (1962).

22. Gregory v. Robinson, 338 S.W. 2d 88 (1960).
23. Stallman v. Robinson, 260 S.W. 2d 743 (1953).
24. Tisinger v. Wooley, 50 S.E. 2d 122 (1948).

Patients' Assaultiveness

25. Bullock v. Parkchester Hospital, 160 N.Y.S. 2d 117 (1957).
26. Sealey v. Finkelstein, 206 N.Y.S. 2d 512 (1961).

Psychic Trauma

27. Ferrara v. Galluchio, 176 N.Y.S. 2d 996; 152 N.E. 2d 249 (1958).
28. Krause v. Spielburg, 236 N.Y.S. 2d 143 (1962).

BOOKS AND PERIODICALS

29. BELLAMY, W. A. "Malpractice Risks Confronting the Psychiatrist: A Nationwide Fifteen-Year Study of Appellate Court Cases, 1946 to 1961," *Am. J. Psychiatry*, 118 (1962), 769–780.
30. ———. "Malpractice in Psychiatry," *Dis. Nerv. Syst.*, 26 (1965), 312–320.
31. BLUM, R. H. *Management of the Doctor–Patient Relationship.* New York: McGraw-Hill, 1960.
32. DAVIDSON, H. A. *Forensic Psychiatry.* New York: Ronald Press, 1952.
33. DIAMOND, B. L. "Criminal Responsibility of the Mentally Ill," *Stanford Law Rev.*, 14 (1961).
34. DOUGLAS, W. O. *Law and Psychiatry.* With an introduction by Judge Jerome Frank. New York: The William Alanson White Institute of Psychiatry, Psychoanalysis and Psychology, 1956.
35. DRAGSTEDT, L. D., ed., "Special Review of the National Conference on the Legal Environment of Medical Science (Including the Nuremberg Code)," *Bull. Med. Res. Natl. Soc. Med. Res.*, May 27–28, 1959.
36. FURST, W. and W. FURST. "The Medico–Legal Aspects of Psychiatric Research," *Dis. Nerv. Syst.*, 21 (1960), No. 2, Part 2.
37. GILDER, S., ed., "Symposium on Human Experimentation," *World Med. J.*, 7 (1960), No. 2.
38. GOLDSTEIN, A. S. and J. KATZ. "Psychiatrist-Patient Privilege. The Group for the Advancement of Psychiatry Proposal and the Connecticut Statute," *Am. J. Psychiatry*, 118 (1962), 733–739.
39. HARPER, F. W. and J. FLEMING. *The Law of Torts*, Vol. 2. Boston: Little, Brown, 1956.
40. HASSARD, H. "Professional Liability Claims Prevention," *JAMA*, 163 (1957), 1267–1269.
41. HOLLOWAY, J. W. "Put It in Writing, Doctor!" *JAMA*, 163 (1957), 657–659.
42. LINDMAN, F. T. and D. M. McINTYRE, eds., *The Mentally Disabled and the Law.* The American Bar Foundation. Chicago: University of Chicago Press, 1961.
43. LOUISELL, D. and H. WILLIAMS. *Trial of Medical Malpractice Cases.* New York: Matthew Bender, 1960.
44. McCOID, A. H. "A Reappraisal of Liability for Unauthorized Medical Treatment," *Minn. Law Rev.*, 41 (1957), 381.
45. MORRIS, R. C. "Res Ipsa Loquitur–Liability Without Fault," *JAMA*, 163 (1957), 1055–1071.
46. NATIONAL INSTITUTE OF MENTAL HEALTH. Public Health Serv. Publ. no. 51. Washington: U.S. Govt. Print. Off., 1951.
47. PROSSER, W. L. *Handbook of the Law of Torts.* 2nd ed. St. Paul, Minn.: West Publishing, 1955.
48. ———. *Selected Topics on the Law of Torts.* The Thomas M. Colley Lectures. Ann Arbor, Mich.: University of Michigan Law School, 1953.
49. REGAN, L. J. "Malpractice and the Physician," *JAMA*, 147 (1951), 54–59.
50. RODIS, I. and R. H. GROH. "One Aspect of the Medico-Legal Implications of Shock Therapy," *South. Med. J.*, 51 (1958), 219–221.
51. SADUSK, J. F. "Hazardous Fields of Medicine in Relation to Professional Liability," *JAMA*, 163 (1957), 953–958.
52. SANDOR, A. A. "The History of Professional Liability Suits in the U.S.," *JAMA*, 163 (1957), 456–466.
53. TERHUME, W. B. "Confidentiality," *Conn. Med.*, 25 (1961), 258–259.
54. TUCKER, D. and R. WATERSON. "Professional Liability Insurance–Amount of Coverage," *JAMA*, 163 (1957), 1159–1162.

B. New Malpractice Risks in Current Psychiatry*

THE NINE YEARS elapsed since the first edition is too brief a span of time for basic psychiatric malpractice risks to have changed substantially with respect to case law. The basic findings presented there were gathered from appellate court cases which have been deliberated in depth and then published weekly in legal documents. Thus they "stand still," and since the appellate-court deliberations stood the test of time well, so did Part A of this chapter.

By contrast, the new risks are, indeed, too new to have been tried in trial court (unpublished), or to have gotten beyond a court settlement, or perhaps are looming only as a threat. Anecdotes, newspaper accounts, and assessments published but highly speculative, all leave much to be desired as source material and make this review highly speculative as well.

The new psychedelic vogue has brought many innovations. Treatment methods are tried without control studies. Innovations are to be encouraged, but control studies are difficult. Important dilemmas never have singular or simple solutions. However, the obvious malpractice risk mandates vigorous study for solutions.

Blum† analyzed the godlike attitude in the

malpractice-prone physician. More of the current indiscretions of psychiatrists and their professional assistant (PA) supervisees will be discussed in depth (see page 918).

From the point of view of the patient, a lawsuit is more likely if he is dissatisfied with the treatment results. Thus there are several forces at work, e.g. the cruel hoax of false promises which lead the mentally ill to disillusionment, frustration and perhaps mental depression.[54] This source of increase in malpractice claims is obvious. Consequently, physicians have cautioned the legislators that it would be ill advised to enact laws that promise today what will take perhaps a decade or more of research to find; i.e., methods by which the professional practitioner reasonably will be able to deliver the desired benefits to the patient.‡

Furthermore, within statutory law inequities exist. For example, in each of two California cases a patient discharged from a mental hospital committed murder shortly thereafter.

In one case the next of kin could not sue the doctor and/or the hospital because a statute proscribed this type of suit against a government facility. Had it been a public hospital or private practitioner (PP) what size award, if any, might have accrued?

In researching the second case, Tarasoff v.

* I express my deep appreciation to C. Delos Puty, Dean of the School of Law, University of San Francisco, for allowing me to use the Kendrick Law Library for more than two decades.
† See reference 31 of Part A of this chapter.

‡ A patient is not a "consumer," as in the consumer-product relationship. The professional "provider" of a "service" does so to a "recipient," or "benefactor."

Regents of University of California[3] the author found "publication delayed," or words to that effect, on an otherwise blank page. The law librarian advised that this meant the California Supreme Court was not entirely satisfied with the deliberation and/or decision of the California Appellate Court, and that in a few weeks or months the case might or might not be published. I consulted two attorneys who stated that the University of California physician involved stipulated that before being discharged the patient verbalized to him his active murderous intentions. The district attorney did not bring charges against this physician, basing his decision on a humanitarian principle—that should it become known that a physician could not protect the patient's privileged communication, then hardly any actively murderous or suicidal patient could be expected to disclose his inner thoughts in the psychotherapist-patient relationship. Thus, this district attorney showed more empathy with the critically mentally ill than did the Congress of the United States when in 1973 it voted down five rules of evidence dealing with privileged communication for relationships such as that of husband-wife, priest-penitent, psychotherapist-patient. In this action, Congress went against the recommendation of the United States Supreme Court.[4] The year before, however, the Supreme Court took a first step toward totalitarianism by reversing the privilege traditionally held by the newsman as to the source of his information.* (See Bellamy[10] for a discussion in depth.)

It seems clear to this author that if we are to refute the allegation that psychiatry is dying, we must learn to understand ourselves and our science of psychiatry; learn to cooperate in fruitful debate with all subspecialties within psychiatry; and collaborate with statesmen, legislators, the judiciary, attorneys, and all others interested in equal opportunity for good quality medical care for all. If so, then let us make public the charges brought against psychiatry to better enable us to refute them publicly.

* Bransburg v. Hayes, 92 S.C. Rep. 2646 (1972).

(Medical Malpractice Trends

Case-finding, Incidence, Rate of Change, and Size of Awards

It is common knowledge that, although it is hard to find "cases" in the "pre-appellate court" stages of inception of malpractice threats or claims filed, nevertheless the incidence is increasing at an escalating rate and bringing larger awards approaching geometrical progression.

A report of the Secretary's Commission of Health, Education and Welfare (HEW)[62] admits this—only to refute it:

Magnitude and Impact of the Medical Malpractice Problem: Analysis of Claims Paid

The total number of claims paid does not appear to be as important a factor in the overall problem as does the number that give rise to large settlements or awards. These relatively few claims (the 6.1 percent above $40,000) appear to be the ones that most alarm health-care providers. As depicted in Table 7 [Table 45–1], more than half of the claimants who receive payment get less than $3,000, the other half receive more. Less than one out of every 1,000 claims paid is for $1 million or more, and there are probably not more than seven such payments each year. There is little doubt that the number of large awards or settlements has been increasing dramatically within the recent past. [page 10][62]

HEW refuted their above opinion by the following:

The Magnitude in Perspective

(1) Despite the publicity resulting from a few large malpractice cases, a medical malpractice incident is a relatively rare event; claims are even rarer and jury trials are rarer still.

(2) In 1970, a malpractice incident was alleged or reported for one out of every 158,000 patient visits to doctors.

(3) In 1970 a claim was asserted for one out of every 226,000 patient visits to doctors. . . .

(11) If the average person lives 70 years, he will have, based on 1970 data, approximately 400 contacts as a patient with doctors and dentists. The chances that he will assert a medical malpractice claim are one in 39,500. [p. 12][62]

TABLE 45–1. **Distribution of Amounts Paid on Medical Malpractice Claims Closed in 1970**

TOTAL SETTLEMENT COSTS OF INCIDENTS, IN DOLLARS	PERCENT OF INCIDENTS	CUMULATIVE PERCENT OF INCIDENTS
1–499	21.1	21.1
500–999	16.0	37.1
1,000–1,999	12.3	49.4
2,000–2,999	10.1	59.5
3,000–3,999	3.0	62.5
4,000–4,999	2.7	65.2
5,000–9,999	13.4	78.6
10,000–19,999	10.0	88.6
20,000–39,999	5.3	93.9
40,000–59,999	1.3	95.2
60,000–79,999	1.0	96.2
80,000–99,999	0.8	97.0
100,000 and up	3.0	100.0
	100.0	

Source: Commission Study of Claim Files Closed in 1970. [p. 11][62]

Physician-attorney Rubsamen[60] presents the situation more concisely and informatively by the simple expedient of counting actual cases* rather than by extrapolating:

This month a 5-year old Santa Clara County girl obtained a $1.1 million settlement for severe brain damage arising from a complication of her birth. This is the 12th million plus malpractice award in California's history and the seventh in the past 18 months.

What price *is* right for human life? Gates, as reported by Hoffer† in his government study, estimated that it cost about $400,000 to train a jet fighter pilot and therefore it was considered uneconomical to exceed that value for safety devices on the plane. Would that the government place that ceiling on malpractice awards.

* Another good source of early case reporting is "Citation," prepared by the Office of The General Counsel of the American Medical Association.[46]
† W. Hoffer "What Price Is Right for Human Life," *PRISM* (published under the direction of the Board of Trustees of The American Medical Association, August 1974.

Geographical Distribution of Malpractice Claims

The Secretary's Commission of HEW calculates by extrapolation that the national average was 6.54 malpractice claims closed per 100 practicing physicians in 1970. Of three possible impressions—the figure is representative, is understated, or is overstated—it is noteworthy that HEW chose the latter:

The gross rate of 6.54 closed claims per 100 practicing physicians somewhat overstates the situation since some claims are made solely against hospitals, dentists, and others, but this gross rate does provide a fairly uniform comparison among the states. Only two of the western states are below the average, whereas the states with the highest rates are New Jersey, California, Montana, Arizona, Washington and Nevada. Although the average rate in some of the smaller states may be influenced by the fact that some carriers do not collect claims data for every state (Delaware may be mixed with some of Pennsylvania, for instance), the state groupings do suggest a western versus eastern bias in the number of claims per 100 practicing physicians. [p. 8][62]

Figure 45–1 illustrates the geographic distribution of malpractice claims.

Cost of Medical Malpractice Insurance

HEW's report indicated that malpractice insurance premiums rose from $7,051 in 1960 to $37,610 in 1972. [p. 13][62]

Rubsamen[58,59] and Hitchings[25] reported that several insurance companies in California raised their premiums for malpractice insurance between 5 and 20 percent in the early 1970s; that some insurance companies have discontinued malpractice coverage because it is unfair to spread over the large group of insured physicians the very high awards granted against a few physicians; and that awards were increasing in size so rapidly as to render it impossible to actuarially appraise reasonable premium rates.

Physicians have had to form their own malpractice insurance companies to insure them-

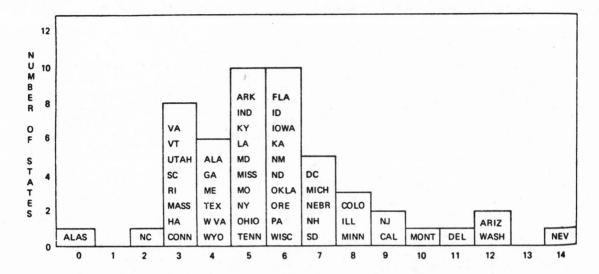

Figure 45–1. State to state differences in number of claims closed in 1970 per 100 physicians providing patient care (U.S. average = 6.54).[62]

selves against their own risks, which proves conclusively that the problem is substantial.

Pharmaceutical Problems in Relation to Unenlightened Consent

The reader may recall from Part A that the manufacturers of pharmaceuticals have a legal duty of absolute warranty as to safety of their products. To make sure that the manufacturer will have no loophole, in some states this "warranty liability" has been expanded to the "strict liability" rule, which is a somewhat higher duty of care.

As a consequence of cases decided against them,[1,2] such as Gottsdanker v. Cutter, the pharmaceutical manufacturers are now listing every possible complication of a given drug in the annual *Physicians Desk Reference* and circulating it to all physicians. This puts another burden on the physician. If he cannot impress on the jury that he adequately explained to

TABLE 45–2.   **National Price and Index for Hospital Medical Malpractice Coverage, 1960, 1966, 1970, 1972**

YEAR	PREMIUM COST FOR CONSTANT DEGREE OF COVERAGE*	INDEX FOR MEDICAL MALPRACTICE INSURANCE (1966 = 100)	MEDICAL SERVICES PRICE INDEX
1960	$ 7,051	86.5	92.8
1966	8,153	100.0	100.0
1970	25,546	313.3	116.4
1972	37,610	461.3	n.a.

* The National Daily Average of occupied hospital beds was 217 in 1960, 207 in 1966, and 193 in 1970. Outpatient visits were 188, 226, and 322, respectively. The 1970 figures were used for 1972.

Sources: Insurance Services Office, New York (1960–1972), and Economic Report of the President (1971), p. 249.

the patient the potential risk in connection with the use of a given drug, he may be sued for "unenlightened consent." The discretionary powers mentioned in Part A (see p. 903) technically are still granted the physician, but recent court rulings indicate that the courts are demanding more discourse with the patient concerning the potential risks and have tightened up the need for "proof" that such discussion took place.

Awards obtained from negligence in medication tend to be very large. Although no cases involving psychiatrists have as yet come to this author's attention, the customary use of medications in the treatment of the mentally ill, often multiple and extended over long periods, makes psychiatrists vulnerable. One or two large awards and insurance rates are certain to increase precipitously.

Informed consent has replaced *res ipsa loquitur* as the basis of claim to place the physician in jeopardy through legal ambiguity.[42] This has implications for psychiatry because the syndromes of mental illness are less precise than those of most physical illnesses.

Cobbs v. Grant[5] outlines the problem, and the California Medical Association (CMA)[17] presents guidelines. Malpractice vulnerability is such as to prompt readers to study the case citations and law(s) governing informed consent in the state(s) in which they practice.

(Psychiatric Malpractice Trends

So much for the above documentation of general trends. In the following we must revert to anecdotes. Certain categories of risk-inducing trends are suggested. There is considerable overlap among categories.

Phasing-Out of State Hospitals

Treatment in state mental hospitals has been called "warehousing." But now that these facilities are less available, we recall the usefulness of the state hospital for certain types of mentally ill who could not be managed as well in local facilities. Two factors should be taken into consideration: (1) the overloading of local facilities; and (2) injudicious administrative practices. Details are presented by Robbins[55] and Peszke.[53]

In any event, such patients are now being treated in outpatient facilities, e.g. clinics, or the offices of private practitioners. These are the patients who had been considered too sick for treatment outside of a hospital.[45]

Hospitalization Difficulties

In California the Lanterman-Petris-Short Act has eliminated all commitment procedures. The patient is seen by a psychiatrist employed by a local mental-health facility, partly funded by the state.* The bases for holding a patient involuntarily are that the patient is dangerous to himself or others and/or that he is so disabled as to be incapable of feeding or clothing himself. The psychiatrist may then sign a hold order for three days, followed by fourteen-day hold periods, while informing the patient of his right of habeus corpus, which, if exercised, brings the patient to judicial review to see if his civil rights have been infringed. The difficulty with this procedure is that it makes the psychiatrist both judge and jury. Also, all full-time PP's have no say in these cases.

The intent of this provision for holding a patient is that mentally ill persons can have voluntary admission to local facilities, such as community mental-health centers (CMHC). In actual practice, most local facilities— although fully funded (e.g., in California)— are overloaded. The police seem to know this, and refuse to take to a CHMC any but the nearly totally incapacitated so the more costly method of private ambulance often has to be utilized—round trip when there is no available bed—and the patient who knows by heart his way to his state hospital is turned away with "you aren't sick enough yet," or "your psychi-

* Thus the private practitioners in psychiatry are totally disenfranchised, perhaps because psychiatrists seem to be increasingly under suspicion. Bazelon[8] examines the issues; Szasz[71] (leading the Anti-Mental-Health Movement) and anti-intellectuals[61] also have been heard on this issue.

atrist ought to know better," or words to that effect.

One result is that voluntary admissions are possible in theory but not in fact. The very ill must fall back on a hold order, so the hospital is *forced* to admit the patient. We have taken a giant step back to the Middle Ages, treating patients as prisoners rather than as sick people. Auerbach[6] described the Anti-Mental Health Movement, led by Thomas Szasz, which has spread far. One wonders how people can be influenced to believe that mental illness does not exist except in the minds of psychiatrists, the motive of the myth being to protect the psychiatrist against loss of his occupation.

The Influence of the Community Mental Health Center

We turn now to undesirable practices found in some CMHC's. The private practitioner of psychiatry (PP) also is imprudent at times, but the shortcomings and dangers are more readily detected in the former. In addition, some risks are peculiar to the CMHC, e.g., administrative problems and the increasing use of the professional assistant (PA)—an innovation too new to have the problems worked out as yet.

Problems of Hospital Administration

According to hearsay, in some CMHC's in California, a patient-client may be admitted, have his history taken, be examined, diagnosed, and have a treatment prescribed, the discharge conference may be conducted, and a follow-up plan of management of the patient undertaken without the patient-client ever seeing a licensed or certified person on the staff of the center, whether that person be the director of the center, or a leader assigned to direct a subgroup of patients.[13,20]

The hospital's position on this management, and critiques and suggestions, are presented below.

HOSPITAL'S POSITION	CRITIQUES AND SUGGESTIONS
1. The case load is too high.	More certified professional assistants (PA's) should be employed, authorized to establish a diagnosis.
2. Funding is insufficient.	Centers should be fully funded.
3. Full time is committed to psychiatric administration:	This applies only to very large centers.
(a) to promote good will in the community, and	Schedule luncheon and/or evening meetings.
(b) in the interest of economy, psychiatrists are competing to establish or continue their programs that may not fulfill psychiatric standards.	It is false economy to institute substandard programs.

If under the circumstances of the management defended above, a patient should sustain substantial damages, e.g., loss of his estate through having been prevented the opportunity to adequately supervise and manage it, this would be *prima facie* malpractice.

The Professional Assistant

Community mental-health centers and other mental-health facilities are increasingly using the professional assistant (PA). Training large numbers of PA's holds advantages, such as being able to treat more of the mentally ill (often in their homes, with their families), earlier case finding, and often at lower cost.*

However, the laws regarding the PA are sketchy.[16] The physician is the only person on the team who can sign a prescription. When a PA brings a prescription for him to sign, he has been known to sign without knowing

---

* See references 13, 30, 38, 43, and 56.

about, or inquiring into, the patient's condition. Certified clinical psychologists in some states are authorized to make a diagnosis, yet they may leave this to a subordinate. Many PA's, both certified and uncertified,* oftentimes are uncertain as to what their respective duties and responsibilities are. Clinicians in charge of a clinic or a group of patients within the clinic, often assign work to their subordinates without having assessed what their particular talents, reliability and practical abilities are. These clinicians are highly vulnerable to malpractice claims if substantial damage to a patient or client accrues therefrom. For example, not infrequently the person carrying legal sanction to diagnose does not do so through inadvertance or refusal to "label" anyone. Upon discharge, however, the laws almost universally require an *official* diagnosis. To comply with the law, the clerk in the chart room, who sometimes has been known to graduate from school without the ability to read or write more than simple words, "chooses" a diagnosis without asking anyone. Obviously such a claim would be *prima facie* malpractice. There are dozens of subtle applications of this principle. Don't underestimate the ability of attorney(s), jury, and/or judge to bring these out—under oath.†

The AMA code has been adopted by the APA.[15]

In the above situation the prima facie malpractice rests on the legal principle *respondeat superior* (the superior is responsible for the negligence of his subordinates). Simonaitim[66]

wrote reassuringly to surgeons that the judiciary understood the complexity of surgery, that a surgeon could not reasonably be expected to supervise, e.g., the anesthesiologist, and so the surgeon is no longer held responsible—unless he *chose* his *surgical team negligently*. The psychiatrist or any PA in charge of a treatment team, let alone a chart room clerk, is *not* so taken up with infinite details (as is a surgeon performing an operation) and most likely the judge would rule *respondeat superior* applicable. To the best of my knowledge the way to remain on a sound legal and ethical basis is to: (1) recruit capable employees; (2) observe good business methods governing tables of organization as to lines of authority *and* responsibility, including definition of terms and job analysis (duties *expected* and job *limitations*).[35,7] These rules should be followed with constant vigilance to prevent the inevitable relaxation that customarily follows any reorganization period.‡

Finally, inservice training should include areas usually overlooked, e.g., laws, medical ethics, and the value of carrying individual malpractice liability insurance.§ As to preventive measures, see Part A, p. 909.

(Administrative Law

Some practices which may hold risk have become established as standard practice in community mental-health programs subsidized by local, state, or federal governments. The enabling legislation limits itself to defining services that are to be provided and the appropriation of public funds to pay for these services.

Enabling legislation, e.g., The National Mental Health Act of 1963 and The California Mental Health Act, spell out provisions for *establishing* mental-health programs. How-

---

* We should press for legislation to make PA training standards such that every graduate cannot practice until he has been granted certification.

† Consider the Nork Case, "Why the Lawyers Caught Nork and the Doctors Didn't"[64] (see also references 15, 46, 48, and 49). The malpractice award totaled $3,710,447 of which 2 million dollars was punitive damages. Perhaps better peer review might have prevented this malpractice. Section 4 of the AMA Principles of Medical Ethics states:

> The medical profession should safeguard the public and itself against physicians deficient in moral character or professional competence. Physicians should observe all laws, uphold the dignity and honor of the profession and accept its self-imposed disciplines. They should expose, without hesitation, illegal or unethical conduct of fellow members of the profession.

‡ See references 19, 21, 28, 29, 63, and 69.

§ Insurance varies with age, type of practice, size and age of family, and size of estate to be protected. For those of high risk, e.g., EST administrators, some professional risk underwriters offer a million dollar umbrella provided the basic coverage is $300,000/-$600,000 and there is no prior malpractice claim.

ever, these acts do not spell out (1) a definition of terms, e.g., "psychiatrist," "psychologist," or "nurse"; (2) job qualifications; (3) job analyses; or (4) how to practice community psychiatry, counseling, etc.

In order to translate such enabling legislation into practice it is necessary to adopt, promulgate, and publish official guidelines. In California the guidelines are developed and then public hearings are held. The guidelines are finally adopted as part of the administrative code, which is a part of the Statutory Laws of California. This concept of administrative law gives a form of legal sanction to practices in the field of psychiatry which are not necessarily consonant with traditional medical ethics or standards of practice of medicine. Thus what may be administratively sound may be malpractice. It is my opinion that once a practice is established on the basis of enabling legislation promoting mental-health programs, there results a set of precedents which, if unchallenged, become "established standard practice" in the community for CMHC's, while traditional standards still hold for PP's. Consider the PP who works mornings in a CMHC and sees private patients in his own office afternoons. He well may be practicing a double standard, often supplying a lower level of care for the (usually) economically disadvantaged patient attending the clinic and applying a higher standard for the middle and upper class patient paying a full fee. If this be true, then would he be engaged in malpractice in the morning? Would it not be better for psychiatry to clarify these issues before they may be adjudicated in the courts? This is a dilemma of substantial proportion for the ethical psychiatrist.

❨ **Concluding Remarks**

The author agrees with Talkington that:[72,73]

1. Our shortcomings notwithstanding, psychiatry in the United States has attained eminence and some world-wide recognition.

2. The belief prevalent today that "most anyone can do psychotherapy" is false, and that high quality psychiatric treatment requires years of vigorous training.[30,43]

3. Erosion of high quality clinical psychiatry already has lowered the quality of psychiatric efforts and shows no promise of subsiding in the foreseeable future;

4. Nevertheless psychiatry holds by far the best means of:

(a) Selection of the mentally stalwart;

(b) prevention of mental illnesses;

(c) evaluation of all aspects of each person including external forces, such as culture, environment, family constellation, and the like; and

(d) therefrom to formulate psychiatric and medical treatment plans best suited for each individual among the physically and mentally ill.

5. And that it is time that psychiatrists unite in concerted efforts to hold for psychiatry the position of eminence that we have won during the present century.

Malpractice suits are steadily on the increase in this country. High ethical standards are a good protection for the psychiatrist or physician, but he should carry insurance because patients have become more prone to sue for malpractice.

❨ **Bibliography**

Decisions

1. Davis v. Wyeth Lab., 399 Fed. 2d 121 (1968).
2. Gottsdanker v. Cutter, 182 Cal. Ap. 2d 602 (1960).
3. Tarasoff v. Regents of U.C., 33 Cal. Ap. 3d 373.
4. Rules of Evidence, 93 S. 1 (1973).
5. Cobbs v. Grant, 8 Cal. 3d 229; 502 P. 2d 1 (1972).

Books, Periodicals, and Tape Recordings

6. AUERBACH, A. "The Anti-Mental Health Movement," *Am. J. Psychiatry*, 120 (1963).

7. BARTEMEIER, L. H. "The William C. Menninger Memorial Lecture," *J. Natl. Assoc. Priv. Psychiatr. Hosp.*, 2 (1970), 5–7.

8. BAZELON, D. L. "Psychiatrists and the Adversary Process," *Sci. Am.*, 230 (1974), 18–23.

9. BECK, A. et al. *Prediction of Suicide.* Bowie, Md.: Charles Press, 1973.

10. BELLAMY, W. A. "Forensic Psychiatry: Privileged Communication and Confidentiality." Unpublished.

11. BENJAMIN, S. P. "Drug Coma Profile," *J. Leg. Med.*, 2 (1974), 30–40.

12. BLACKMAN, N., J. M. WEISS, and J. W. LAMBERTI. "The Sudden Murderer, Clues to Preventive Interaction," *Arch. Gen. Psychiatry*, 8 (1963), 289.

13. BOURNE, P. G. "Human Resources: A New Approach to the Dilemmas of Community Psychiatry," *Am. J. Psychiatry*, 131 (1974), 666–669.

14. BRADFORD, R. T. "Medical Specialists in Legal Medicine," *J. Leg. Med.*, 2 (1974), 24–28.

15. BRANCH, C. H. H. et al. "The Principals of Medical Ethics: With Annotations especially Applicable to Psychiatry (Official Actions of APA)," *Am. J. Psychiatry*, 130 (1973).

16. BURTON, S. J. "Tort Liability and the California Health Care Assistant," *So. Cal. Law Rev.*, 45 (1972), S768.

17. CALIFORNIA MEDICAL ASSOCIATION. *Special Report: Some Advice on Informed Consent*, pp. 1–3. San Francisco: California Medical Association, 1973.

18. DANTO, B. L. "Becoming on Effective Suicidologist," in *Suicide*, Audio Digest, Vol. 3. Glendale, Cal.: Audio Digest Found., 1973. (Tape recording.)

19. DILLON, C. "Staff Stress When a Public Agency Changes," *Psychiatr. Ann.*, 3 (1973), 42–60.

20. DuMAE, F. M. "Medical, Nonmedical, or Antimedical Models for Mental Health Centers?" *Am. J. Psychiatry*, 131 (1974).

21. FREY, L. "Organizational and Emotional Change," *Psychiatr. Ann.*, 3 (1973), 16–44.

22. GELB, L. A. "Private and Community Psychiatry: Contrast between the Two Practices," *Bull. N.Y. State Am. Psychiatr. Assoc.*, 13 (1971).

23. GOLDZBAND, M. G. "The Dangerous Patient," in *Managing the Potentially Dangerous Patient*, Audio Digest, Vol. 2. Glendale, Cal.: Audio Digest Found., 1972. (Tape recording.)

24. HARDIN, G. "Lifeboat Ethics: The Case against Helping the Poor," *Psychol. Today*, 8 (1974), 38–43.

25. HITCHINGS, B. "New Ways to Cope with Malpractice: Medical Malpractice Insurance Rates Aren't Going up: They're Running away," *Physicians Manag.*, 14 (1974), 31–36.

26. HOLLISTER, L. E. "Safeguards of Drugs Prescribed for the Suicidal Patient," *JAMA*, 229 (1974), 1517.

27. HORSLEY, J. E. "How to Prepare Yourself for Cross-Examination," *J. Leg. Med.*, 2 (1974), 21–23.

28. HUME, P. B. "Searchlight on Community Psychiatry," *Community Ment. Health J.*, 1 (1965), 109–112.

29. ———. "General Principles of Community Psychiatry," in S. Arieti, ed., *American Handbook of Psychiatry*, 1st ed., Vol. 3, pp. 515–541. New York: Basic Books, 1966.

30. KARNO, M., J. G. KENNEDY, and S. LIPSCHULTZ. "Community Psychiatry at UCLA: A Decade of Training," *Am. J. Psychiatry*, 131 (1974), 601–604.

31. KIEV, A. "Prognostic Factors in Attempted Suicide," *Am. J. Psychiatry*, 131 (1974), 987–990.

32. KLEIN, D. F. and J. M. DAVIS. *Diagnosis and Drug Treatment of Psychiatric Disorders.* Baltimore: Williams & Wilkins, 1969.

33. ———. "Diagnosis for What?" in *The Future of Psychiatric Diagnosis*, Audio Digest, Vol. 3. Glendale, Cal.: Audio Digest Found., 1974. (Tape recording.)

34. KOHLMAN, R. J. "Malpractice Liability for Failing to Report Child Abuse," *West. J. Med.*, 121 (1974), 244–248.

35. LEAKE, C. D. "Percival's Medical Ethics: Promise and Problems," *Calif. Med.*, 114 (1971), 68–70.

36. LEIFER, R. *In the Name of Mental Health: Social Functions of Psychiatry.* New York: Science House, 1969.

37. ————. "Psychiatric Diagnosis and the Social Function of Psychiatry," in *The Future of Psychiatric Diagnosis*, Audio Digest, Vol. 3. Glendale, Cal.: Audio Digest Found., 1974. (Tape recording.)

38. LIPOWSKI, Z. J. "Consultation-Liaison Psychiatry," *Am. J. Psychiatry*, 131 (1974), 623–630.

39. MALMQUIST, C. P. "Preliminary Signs of Homicidal Aggression in Juveniles," *Am. J. Psychiatry*, 128 (1971), 93.

40. McCABE, J. J. "What to do if You Are Sued for Malpractice," *J. Leg. Med.*, 2 (1974), 11–15.

41. MILLER, D. "The Prediction of Murder by Adolescents," in *Managing the Potentially Dangerous Patient*, Audio Digest, Vol. 2. Glendale, Cal.: Audio Digest Found., 1973. (Tape recording.)

42. MILLS, D. H. "Whither Informed Consent?" *JAMA*, 229 (1974), 305–310.

43. MORRISON, A. P., M. F. SHORE, and J. GROBMAN. "On the Stresses of Community Psychiatry, and Helping Residents to Survive Them," *Am. J. Psychiatry*, 130 (1973), 1237–1241.

44. NATIONAL COMMISSION ON THE CAUSES AND PREVENTION OF VIOLENCE. *Progress Report to President Lyndon B. Johnson.* Washington: U.S. Govt. Print. Off., 1969.

45. OZARIN, L. D. and C. A. TAUBE. "Psychiatric Inpatients: Who, Where, and Future," *Am. J. Psychiatry*, 131 (1974), 98–101.

46. OFFICE OF THE GENERAL COUNCIL. "Legal Aspects of Mental Illness. The Citation," *JAMA (Spec. Issue)*, 25 (1972), 97–112.

47. PASNAU, R. O. "Suicide of Psychiatric Residents: Analysis of Five Cases," in *Suicide*, Audio Digest, Vol. 3. Glendale, Cal.: Audio Digest Found., 1974. (Tape recording.)

48. PAXTON, H. T. "What You Haven't Read about the Nork Case," *Med. Econom.* (1974), 37–109.

49. ————. "Making Your Practice more Malpractice Proof," *Med. Econom.* (1974), 69–130.

50. PERLMAN, J. L. "Human Experimentation," *J. Leg. Med.*, 2 (1974), 30–40.

51. PEER, I. N. "Suicide and Civil Litigation," *J. Forensic Sci.*, 19 (1974), 261–265.

52. ————. "The World of Humor, Medicine, Psychiatry, and the Law," *J. Psychiatry Law* (1973), 493–498.

53. PESZKE, M. A. and R. M. WINTROB. "Emergency Commitment—A Transcultural Study," *Am. J. Psychiatry*, 131 (1974), 36–40.

54. POSNER, J. "The Other Side of Swedish Medicine," *PRISM (Socoieconom. Mag. AMA)* (1974), 13–67.

55. ROBBINS, E. and L. ROBBINS. "Charge to the Community: Some Early Effects of a State Hospital System's Change of Policy," *Am. J. Psychiatry*, 131 (1974), 641–645.

56. ROGAWSKI, S. "The New Paraprofessional's Role in Mental Health," *Psychiatr. Ann.*, 4 (1974), 59–71.

57. ROSS, M. "Suicide among Physicians: A Psychological Study," *Dis. Nerv. Syst.*, 34 (1973), 145–150.

58. RUBSAMEN, D. S. *Profess. Liability Newsl.*, 3 (1971).

59. ————. *Profess. Liability Newsl.* 4 (1972).

60. ————. *Profess. Liability Newsl.* 6 (1974).

61. SANVILLE, J. L. " 'Army of Spirits,' Black Magic and the Devil Face Psychiatrist," *Clin. Psychiatry News*, 2 (1974), 1.

62. SECRETARY'S COMMISSION ON MEDICAL MALPRACTICE, Dept. of Health, Education, and Welfare. *Medical Malpractice Report*, pp. 1–12. Washington: U.S. Govt. Print. Off., 1973.

63. SELIG, A. "Change in a Psychiatric Ward," *Psychiatr. Ann.*, 3 (1973), 66–85.

64. SHERIDAN, B. "Why the Lawyers Caught Nork and the Doctors Didn't," *Med. Econom.* (1974), 91–109.

65. SHORE, M. F. "The Five Principles of Change," *Psychiatr. Ann.*, 3 (1973), 8–15.

66. SIMONAITIM, J. E. "Does the 'Captain of the Ship' Doctrine still Apply legally to Hospital Care of Patients?" *JAMA*, 229 (1974), 205.

67. SMALL, S. M. and P. F. REGAN. "An Evaluation of Evaluations," *Am. J. Psychiatry*, 131 (1974), 51–55.

68. SPITZER, R. L. "Quantification of Agreement in Psychiatric Diagnosis," *Arch. Gen. Psychiatry*, 17 (1967), 85–88.

69. STEADMAN, H. J. *The Prediction of Dangerousness*, pp. 1–24. Albany, N.Y.: Mental Health Research Unit, N.Y. State Dept. of Mental Hygiene, 1973.

70. STOLLER, R. "Psychiatric Diagnoses Do Not Work," in *The Future of Psychiatric Diagnosis*, Audio Digest, Vol. 3. Glendale, Cal.:

Audio Digest Found., 1974. (Tape recording.)

71. SZASZ, T. S. "Might Makes the Metaphor," *JAMA*, 229 (1974).

72. TALKINGTON, P. C. "The Presidential Address: A Time for Action," *Am. J. Psychiatry*, 130 (1973), 745–747.

73. ⸺. "View from the Top," in Audio Digest, Vol. 2. Glendale, Cal.: Audio Digest Found., 1973. (Tape recording.)

74. WECHT, C. H. "What the Medical Expert Can Expect from the Trial Lawyer," *J. Leg. Med.*, 2 (1974), 21–23.

PART SEVEN

Psychiatry for the Seventies

CHAPTER 46

THE ORGANIZATION OF PSYCHIATRIC SERVICES IN THE UNITED STATES: PAST, PRESENT, AND FUTURE

Robert S. Daniels

THE ORGANIZATION of psychiatric services in the United States has evolved from a system based on large mental hospitals, for the most part under state and/or federal auspices,[36] to a complicated combination of public and private services operated by a wide variety of governance mechanisms. This increased complexity of services has paralleled the increasing complexity of society, with its rapid population growth and urbanization. Society's recent stance that at least some minimum quantity and quality of human services is its right suggests that the public will expect that minimum, at least, to be available for all citizens, irrespective of geographic location, socioeconomic status, or ethnic or racial origin. As a part of this "right-to-service" development, the public is raising questions about financial or other criteria for eligibility. Should our current mental illness and medical care delivery systems become a one-class system rather than the two-class system now prevalent, based primarily on socio-economic status and income?

Current interest in a system for delivering service to maladaptive and mentally ill persons is a natural culmination of changes that took place after World War II. These changes included a reduction in the size of large mental hospitals; the establishment of psychiatric units in general hospitals; the increasing availability of effective psychotropic drugs; the development of academic departments of psychiatry; the rapid expansion of a psychiatric manpower pool; the discovery of the effect of the therapeutic community, with its "open door" and "total push" methods of treatment; the development of the multidisciplinary team, with its increasing diversity of professional and nonprofessional manpower; and the growth of services located geographically close to and effectively in tune with the populations they serve. A first attempt to assess these advances and to plan for the development of a better and more effective system appeared in 1961 in *Action for Mental Health*.[21] It was legislatively encouraged by the community mental health and mental retardation legislation of the early 1960s.

After several years of experience with community mental health center programs, it is once again a time for reassessment. A number of questions may be raised about the improvement of the system of mental health and illness services. Among these questions are the following:

1. What is the minimum acceptable quantity and quality of service?
2. What varieties of organization of service will prove most effective under what circumstances in what geographic area?
3. Who will govern and administer the services?
4. How will they be financed?
5. Under what conditions should services be mainly separate, and when should they be mainly a part of other human service systems—for example, educational, legal, medical, and social services?
6. What are the optimum number, mix, and functions of manpower?
7. Should there be a national policy about mental illness services that establishes certain guidelines, requirements, and constraints?

Answers to these and related questions are not yet available; the data from research and evaluation are thus far inconclusive. However, discussions are taking place of major reorganizations of medical services such as the health maintenance organization,[11,12,17,18] the health care corporation,[1] and the physician's foundation.[12] Modification of methods of finance such as universal health insurance, catastrophic insurance, and others are also possible. As a result the public, its political representatives, and the professions and agencies and institutions cannot long delay inputs into planning and development now under way.

(Origins of Psychiatric Service Systems

The development of psychiatry as a medical discipline or specialty in the United States began with Benjamin Rush (1745–1813), a physician with broad social, medical, and scientific interests. These interests gradually became centered in the diagnosis and treatment of mental illness; Rush published the first book in the United States that related to these matters.[32] Following his lead, a small number of physicians began to specialize in these disorders, and a number of institutions that treated mental illness came into existence along the Eastern seaboard. The institutions were under both public and private auspices. Their diagnostic and treatment programs may be thought of as prescientific, but they evolved an effective form of psychiatric treatment called moral treatment. Moral treatment emphasized kind, humane, and nonpunitive interventions, with emphasis on good living conditions and general support measures such as proper diet, exercise, environment, regulation of body processes, and interpersonal relationships. Since the young nation was primarily agricultural in its orientation, the location of these new institutions in pleasant rural surroundings followed as a natural consequence of the existent social organization, philosophic ideals, and treatment regimens.

Not all institutions were of this nature. Many were overcrowded, understaffed, and underfinanced. The mentally ill were regarded by some as criminal, immoral, weak, and inadequate, requiring controlled and punitive circumstances for any effective treatment to occur. Dorothea Dix (1802–1887),[26] recognizing these deficiencies, led a social and political movement that promoted change in the institutions and in their therapeutic programs. She stimulated state legislatures to accept greater programmatic and financial responsibility for the treatment of the mentally ill and the emotionally maladaptive.

This first reorganization of services led to a period during which psychiatric treatment was improved. Social change, including industrialization and urbanization, quickly disrupted the equilibrium, however, and overcrowding and social isolation began to be the rule once more in the late 19th century. The tranquil and idyllic settings for moral treatment that had joined the patient with his family and the community were replaced by the warehousing and custodial care typical of large institutions, a process that was to persist and grow more extreme for the next fifty years. Treatment optimism often gave way to treatment nihilism, and the view prevailed of mental illness as chronic, irreversible, and having a worsening downhill course. The public support provided by state legislatures was not able to maintain pace with the increased need, and personnel and physical structures gradually became inadequate in quantity and quality. As a concomitant to these developments, public attitude shifted. The predominant tendency was to want to have the mentally ill put away in these large and usually distant institutions, out of sight of and contact with society.

◖ The Development of Psychiatry as a Science

In the late 19th and early 20th century psychiatry became established as a science. Important contributions to this development were: an improved diagnostic nomenclature; the differentiation of organic from nonorganic disorders; advances in neuropathology; a better understanding of infectious disease processes as they affect the central nervous system; and the beginnings of different and improved psychologies[28] for understanding both adaptive and maladaptive human behavior.

Although these contributions did not result in any immediate alteration of the human service system, they formed a theoretical and practical base for such changes to occur later. Physician psychiatrists began to enter fee-for-service outpatient practice as well as to work in mental hospitals, and psychiatry gradually became a recognized medical specialty, with both outpatient and inpatient functions. Although the majority of psychiatrists continued to practice in public and private institutional settings, an increasing number of professionals came to deal with the less severe disorders and with the adaptive states of the relatively more severe disorders.

The psychiatrists who functioned mainly in outpatient settings were somewhat more likely to be psychodynamic and psychoanalytic in their orientation, while those psychiatrists who functioned in public mental hospitals were more likely to be organic and biological. These two groups of professionals and their associated institutions marked the beginning of two somewhat separate systems. One of these systems was more likely to deal with outpatients with less severe disorders on a fee-for-service payment basis, utilizing a psychotherapeutic approach based on a psychodynamic-psychoanalytic psychology. The other system was more likely to be hospital-based and financed by public tax money, dealing with a group of patients who were more severely ill, and conceptualizing disease states in biological and/or genetic terms.

In the period from 1890 to 1940, these groups of practitioners and their associated facilities and resources grew steadily but slowly. (These dates correspond roughly with the productive scientific lifetimes of Bleuler,[5] Freud,[23] Kraepelin,[25] Meyer,[27] Pavlov,[30] and other contributors of stature.) Then, in the 1940s, this gradual change and growth was transformed into a rapid expansion of manpower and institutions. Perhaps the most significant stimulus came as a consequence of World War II. The United States was shocked at the amount and extent of psychiatric disability seen at the induction points and training centers and in combat. The public turned to leading psychiatrists to assist in managing these actual or potential casualties. Most psychiatrists had been functioning up until then within relatively separate and isolated settings, either in public or private hospitals or in individual offices. Entry into military service catapulted them suddenly onto the public scene in ways that probably could not have occurred except for World War II. They became responsible for psychiatric treatment units within military medical facilities; and they began, in many instances, to advise military command about psychological functioning and morale issues.[16]

A number of important principles were rediscovered during World War II and in the subsequent Korean War. Among them were the determination that: (1) the social system and its interpersonal relationships could provide emotional supports, during periods of stress, that decreased the number of casualties and the length of the disability; (2) immediate intervention at the time of crisis, so as to maintain the casualty close to his unit and his friends, reduced the length of disability; (3) evacuation to facilities that were geographically or emotionally more distant, on the other hand, increased disability; (4) opportunities to talk about and deal with frightening experiences were helpful; and (5) programs of extended treatment and rehabilitation were more effective when careful attention was paid to the therapeutic milieu—the social system in which the casualty found himself. This last principle led to the development of the therapeutic community,[10,23] the open hospital, the day hospital,[4] group methods of treatment, the multidisciplinary-treatment team, and improved techniques of self help.

On their return to civilian life following World War II, psychiatric leaders were influential in modifying the treatment philosophies of a large number of institutions and agencies. As a result of these changes and of public, professional, and political recognition of the shortage of personnel and treatment resources, the National Institute of Mental Health was developed as an instrument of the federal government to promote change in education and research. Initial programs were established to train more psychiatrists and personnel and to do research into the etiology and treatment of mental illness and maladaptation. The moneys made available through this channel encouraged most medical schools to establish psychiatry departments.

Training opportunities became more widespread in university departments, private and public mental hospitals, and consortia of training facilities (including inpatient and outpatient settings). Psychiatry enjoyed a special advantage over the rest of medicine in developing these training opportunities and resources, because there was substantial federal financial support for faculty and trainee salaries. Also, trainees were better paid through federal stipends than were trainees in the remainder of medicine. Psychiatry moved from a relatively minor position among medical specialities to become the third largest medical specialty.

The development of research capacity to some extent paralleled the increasing training capacity, but it occurred somewhat later and more slowly. Again, this change was most evident in departments of psychiatry in medical schools. Since the bodies of knowledge that underpin psychiatry—that is, the social, psychological, and biological sciences—are complex and diverse, these research developments were also complex and diverse.

During the 1940s and 1950s, the discovery of chemical compounds that had effects on human behavior and on disease states—including both natural and synthetic[9] and somatic treatments—further increased the capacity of mental illness personnel to deal with maladaptive behavior. These drugs reduced the length of time of hospitalization, and (if continued when indicated) the frequency of episodes of disturbed behavior that required hospitalization. Eventually drugs were available for both the excited, agitated, or anxious states and the slowed, depressed states. They enabled the treatment team to respond promptly and more effectively and they reduced the need for keeping patients locked up or highly protected. For the first time the number of psychiatric beds in hospitals began to decrease, a trend that then continued every year since 1957. During the same period admissions increased each year, so hospitalizations also tended to be brief. The overall result was that the number of beds needed for the mentally ill was reduced, and chronically ill psychiatric patients, on the average, spent much more time out of the hospital in their own communities.

These advances in the understanding of social, psychological, and biological factors in psychiatric disability fostered the development of psychiatric units in general hospitals. There was a reawakening of professional and public interest in outpatient treatment settings that were closer to where the patient lived and/or worked and to the social fields in which his disability occurred. (The origins of psychiatry outpatient clinics date to the 1920s, with the child guidance movement and with publicly sponsored and financed adult outpatient clinics. Growth in these services paralleled and was enhanced by the developments described above.)

The community mental health center development was a logical next step and a natural outgrowth of these advances. President Eisenhower commissioned a series of studies in 1956 that eventuated in the 1961 report, *Action for Mental Health*.[21] As a result of the changes and the report, guidelines for services and legislation for construction and staffing grants emerged in a model called the community mental health center, a system[3,20] for mental illness care. Formally, the system was to include inpatient, outpatient, partial hospitalization, emergency, and consultation and education services. Also—and for the first time —actual prevention of mental illness was considered to be a possibility.[7]

The appropriations were channeled through the National Institute of Mental Health. Over the next ten years the granting agency gradually became more interested and experienced in and knowledgeable about such associated issues as: (1) methods of governance; (2) the availability of services for broad age groupings, particularly the aged, adolescents, and children; (3) the availability of services for special problems like addiction; (4) the needs of inadequately served populations; and (5) relationships with other human service systems such as health, social, education, and legal services.

Concomitant with these changes, the availability of fee-for-service psychiatric services was also increasing. More psychiatrists were in practice and there were more facilities available for the care of their patients. Although there are many junctional points of service, the public and the private fee-for-service systems tended to be separate and distinct, with the main differentiation occurring on a socioeconomic basis. As a result, psychiatric services developed into two systems, much as did the rest of health and illness services. Psychiatric services, however, continue to be weighted more heavily in the direction of the public sector than do the services of the rest of medicine.

([A Systems View of Mental Health Services Delivery Systems

An examination and evaluation of the ways in which mental health and illness services developed in the United States suggests that there are three major service delivery systems currently in use. They are in the public sphere: (1) hospital- and institution-based delivery systems such as exist in state hospitals or in the Veterans Administration system; (2) community mental health centers; and (3) the private fee-for-service system based on individual and group outpatient activity, together with the system based on general hospitals and dependent on individual financial responsibility and third-party payment. These systems are often separated from other service systems, although they may be a part of the medical service delivery system; they have rarely been a part of the educational, legal, and social service systems.

The older public system—the large hospital system—derives from the original state hospitals built in the first half of the 19th century. During the following 100 years increased needs were met primarily by expanding existent mental hospitals or by constructing new ones, usually in rural or semirural settings.

Resources for development did not keep pace with the need, and institutional treatment programs in time became overburdened by the numbers of very sick patients. Public support for resources for these institutions and their treatment programs was limited, so they gradually became more custodial in their orientation. Their population of long-stay patients consisted mainly of chronic schizophrenics and the aged. Some patients became so well adapted to the institution that they came to be more or less permanent residents.

Gradually, fewer and fewer psychiatrists were willing to work in this kind of setting. The hospitals became dependent on general (and often foreign-trained) physicians and on other mental illness treatment personnel such as social workers, psychologists, and nurses. These personnel were also often in short supply, so that most staff–patient contact occurred with technical assistants such as mental health aides and attendants. These nonprofessional staffs often had limited training and supervision, and their capacity to deal with patient problems was frequently based only on their natural capacities. Incomes for these categories of personnel were low, and the jobs often were not competitive with other employment opportunities. Furthermore, at least during the earlier years of this period, jobs were part of a state political spoils system, so that many jobs turned over with each change in state government administration.

Outpatient facilities associated with these large state hospitals were rarely under the same management auspices as the hospital. At times they were under separate state control, but more often they were funded by combinations of city, county, community chest, or other charitable funds and were governed either by separate agencies under local political unit control or by community boards. Although typically there was some patient flow between these facilities, admission to the hospital was usually in situations of acute crisis and was often the result of commitment proceedings. Aftercare was usually limited. Patients were also occasionally seen, before or after hospitalization, by other sections of the medical-care or social-agency systems. However, the patient flow was rarely easy or smooth, and most patients were not seen in continuity. The system, then, was incomplete and fragmented, and the services were physically and emotionally distant from those who were served.

This state-funded state hospital system remains an important part of the U.S. mental illness delivery system—a situation that will continue for the foreseeable future. The development of newer delivery systems such as the community mental health center has led some people to believe that the state hospital-based system could be phased out. However, ten years of experience with a newer system have not yet eliminated the need for the older service delivery system, and there are no indications that this situation will change in the immediate future. Several states, including California, have embarked on experimental financial incentive programs to encourage local communities to avoid sending patients to state hospitals. These experimental programs have resulted in a sharper decrease in utilization and bed requirements and a more rapid closing of such facilities.

Another major, publicly funded system for the treatment of mental illness is the Veterans Administration system of outpatient care: hospitalization in general medical and surgical hospitals (equivalent to community general hospitals); large hospitals for the mentally ill (equivalent to state hospitals); and various types of rehabilitation services. This range of resources more nearly forms a coherent system. There are, however, problems about eligibility in various parts of the system, with service-connected disability being the most important criterion. Other difficulties in the system include the physical distance between client and service, difficulties in communication among various portions of the system, and difficulties in interconnections and patient flow.

The most recently developed publicly supported system for mental health and illness care is the community mental health center. Typically, the centers provide five services— inpatient, outpatient, emergency, partial hospitalization, and consultation and education— to a geographically defined population of

75,000 to 200,000 people. Legislation originally made provision for both construction and staffing grants, but more recently most of the available money has been allocated for staffing. Community mental health center systems are under various governance auspices, including existent institutions and agencies, consortia of existent resources, and new community or other types of corporations. Federal support is on a diminishing matching basis over a five- or eight-year period, with the expectation that local funding will be provided for the increasing local share.

The above systems have several advantages: a defined population; a comprehensive set of services; location in the community to be served; a service system under single organizational, administrative, and management auspices and more responsive to local community needs and wishes; a common record system, with ease of flow of information and of clients; and universal eligibility. However, there are also major deficiencies: difficulties in reaching objectives; the complexity of the political and governance issues; and the problem of acquiring suitable personnel. The systems have sometimes been divided by political forces in local communities, with the struggle for control of resources becoming more important than the needs of clients. Depending on local conditions and on choice, these systems may be more or less connected with health, social service, educational, and legal systems or with the other mental illness service delivery systems.

A major part of current mental illness service delivery is within the fee-for-service system, which may be either a part of or separate from the medical care system. This service system consists of individual professionals, alone or in group practice with other psychiatrists, and/or medical practitioners providing ambulatory services. The inpatient services are usually provided in psychiatric units of community general hospitals or in privately operated psychiatric hospitals. The more usual mode of intervention in the outpatient setting is psychoanalytically-oriented psychotherapy, although there is also a widespread use of other techniques.

There has been only limited experience with modes of payments other than fee-for-service[*] —i.e., capitation, or uniform tax—or with other forms of organization such as the health care corporation or the health maintenance organization.[6,14,15] Populations thus served must be able to finance their own care, either through their own payments or through third-party payers.

([The Problem of National Policy

In the late 1960s and early 1970s it was commonly recognized that desires and needs for all human services were very great but that resources were finite. Questions of gaps and overlaps in services became more urgent, and there were increasing pressures to make certain that high-quality services were being efficiently delivered. These issues became most apparent in medical care delivery, where there were serious organizational, manpower, and financial problems. The public and Congress began to examine these problems and to consider various types of universal health insurance and the possible influence of new forms of medical service organization. There were also major attempts to influence the production of manpower and sway the direction of its activities toward primary care. Thus, in the early 1970s a national policy on health services remains undefined, both as to their organization and as to their financing.

Congress and the national administration are unclear as to whether mental health and illness services need to be included within the proposed reorganization of medical care delivery. There has been even greater confusion about the more specific issue of services for the mentally ill. Congress is concerned about the potential cost of such services; it also wishes to maintain local responsibility wherever possible—historically, mainly at the state level. Thus the early proposals for universal health insurance were remarkable for their absence of coverage for the mentally ill or the emotionally maladaptive.

[*] See references 2, 6, 13, 19, 29, and 31.

Further, the late 1960s saw little increase in the federal moneys available for mental health and illness services through the community mental health center model. Essentially stable amounts of money reflected both monetary shortages and uncertainty whether the community mental health center model was the best one available. As yet there is no clearcut public decision about the methods of financing and organizing mental health and illness services, and the degree of their connectedness to medical services.

❨ The Future Organization of Services for the Mentally Ill

The organization of services for the mentally ill is likely to remain pluralistic in the United States for a while. Financing will also probably continue to be from multiple sources, both public and private, with combinations of personal, third party, and local, state, and federal money. However, there will be increasing pressure for a national policy for these as well as other services, and for financing. This national policy will probably establish some guidelines for and constraints on the expected diversity, quantity, and quality of services, as well as suggestions about ownership, governance, evaluation, finance, manpower, and their relationship to other human services.

Ownership, Governance, and Administration

Very little is known about the comparative advantages of various ownership arrangements. Typically, in the past, the ownership of mental health and illness services has been vested in a not-for-profit agency or institution oriented to service and/or education; a public political body such as a city, county, state, or federal structure; or a group of professionals. There has been relatively little experience with consumer, community, union, industrial, or business ownership. Recent developments

have fostered community or consumer ownerships. The advocates of this model claim that such ownership will be more responsive to community needs, more innovative in the types of service delivered and the types of manpower utilized, and less bound by traditional bureaucratic constraints. The balance between these advantages and the inputs of knowledgeable, responsible, and sensitive professionals and institutions is not yet clear. As a result there have been many tensions and conflicts in some of the new community-based systems.

Governance is closely related to ownership and many of the issues are similar. The balance between the professionals, the professional administrator, the institution, and the inputs from the lay community and consumer is critical if one wishes to establish a sensitive and sensible governance and administrative system that is flexible, responsive, responsible, and able to change.

Ownership, governance, and administrative structures must somehow be developed that balance the advocacy positions among the interested parties. These parties could well include such diverse groups as local communities and their organizations, professionals from a number of disciplines, agencies and institutions such as clinics and hospitals, educational institutions such as medical colleges and universities, the larger community with its formal and informal political organizations, and various agencies that may have roles and functions concerned with planning, development, funding, and evaluation. Clearly this is a complex, important, and relatively untapped area for careful investigation and evaluation. A current danger is that there would be premature closure of the investigation with public regulations that made a final choice among one or another of the possible mechanisms to deal with these important functions.

Organization of Services

Current models for mental health service delivery include the large mental hospital-oriented system, the community mental health service system, the private practice–commmuity general hospital system, and various combinations of these. These current systems have been largely separate from one another. When combined with other human service delivery systems, the health delivery system has been the most common choice. Only in recent years has there been serious consideration of combinations with educational services, legal services, or social services.

The community mental health service model will probably continue to expand its geographic and population coverage slowly. A possible competitive and potentially collaborative model would be the health care corporation, the health maintenance organization, or the physician foundation. In these delivery systems, mental health and illness services would become a part of comprehensive health services for a population defined by voluntary enrollment. Personnel could then be a part of the health and illness treatment system, or that system could purchase certain services from the nearby community mental health service system or other mental illness service systems. The likelihood of this development depends, of course, on current discussions in Congress about national health and illness insurance and service organization possibilities. Also, it is as yet unclear to what extent mental health and illness services will be included within such systems.

The extension of mental health and illness services into other human service systems such as educational, legal, and social services has occurred in a few instances, usually utilizing a consultation model.[7] The mental health professionals share knowledge and expertise with the primary professionals from the other service systems. The mental health and illness interventions are mainly indirect.

A somewhat different model has occasionally been used. i.e., the mental health professionals and their services becoming a primary part of the other human service systems. Still another variant is the multiservice human service system, in which many or all of these services are available in a single organizational framework, often in a single location.[34,35]

These several possibilities for organization of services have not been evaluated comparatively. Under current arrangements, however, most professionals and most funding and payment agencies favor either the separatist model or the health system model. The other models are almost always financed by programmatic research moneys.

Manpower

The mental health and illness service systems have been experimenting with the types and mixes of manpower necessary to deliver optimum service. Frequently the experimentation has been based on extreme shortages of manpower and the need to make an effective delivery system operative with these limited quantities. The major disciplines involved continue to be medicine, nursing, psychology, and social work. Perhaps the most striking and the most uncertain of the new developments is the use of mental health technicians. These individuals may come from a variety of educational levels (from less than high school to four years of college) and with varying degrees of training (from specialized training programs of some duration to mainly on-the-job training). There has also been considerable experimentation with individuals having special life experiences or qualities, such as persons having origins in the indigenous community, college students, persons having successfully raised children, or middle-aged housewives. The use of these types of manpower has been largely left to local option, as has been the mix of professionals involved in a particular program. Again, the optimum arrangements are not clear, and there is no convincing evidence for a particular composition of mental health and illness service system staff.

Finance

The methods of finance are unclear, particularly for the future. The two major methods of financing services have been fee-for-service and public subsidy, usually through state and federal tax moneys. Professionals have been paid by fee-for-service and salaried arrangements. Part of the lack of clarity about method arises out of a controversy concerning what level of government is responsible for financing what service. There has been a tendency on the part of political units to displace responsibility to other levels, thereby saving a particular level's tax dollars. However, this struggle frequently results in the consumer being caught between various public groups, none of which wish to accept responsibility.

Developments at the national level brought new means of financing services during the 1960s. The mental health center moneys from the federal level supported staff salaries. Medicare and Medicaid[33] have frequently supported fee-for-service payments. In current discussions of universal health insurance, still another method of finance—the capitation method—is being considered. In this type of financing a payment is agreed upon in advance for a specified time period and for specified services. There is evidence, with medical care payments, that such a system decreases cost by decreasing the use of certain physician and hospital services without decreasing the quality of care or the health status of the population served. Evidence on the relationship between method of finance and the quantity, quality, and cost of mental health and illness services is not yet available, although there is some suggestion that appropriate use of psychiatric consultation and services may reduce the overall use of medical services.

Finance becomes an extremely important factor in the quantity and quality of service provided, because service may be limited or defined by the extent of financial elibibility for service. Therefore the current and legislative activity on universal health insurance and the question of inclusion of psychiatric and mental illness coverage become extremely important factors in determining the organization of the mental illness service intervention system and the overall service system in which it will reside. Some data are available to suggest that the inclusion of service in any benefit package is socially and economically feasible.

(Bibliography

1. AMERICAN HOSPITAL ASSOCIATION. *Report of a Special Committee on the Provision of Health Services*, E. Perloff, Chairman. Chicago: Am. Hospital Assoc., 1970.
2. AMERICAN PSYCHIATRIC ASSOCIATION. *A.P.A. Guidelines for Psychiatric Services Covered under Health Insurance Plans*, 2nd ed. Washington: Am. Psychiatric Assoc., 1968.
3. BERTALANFFY, L. VON. "General Systems Theory and Psychiatry," in S. Arieti, ed., *American Handbook of Psychiatry*, Vol. 3, 1st ed., pp. 705–721. New York: Basic Books, 1966.
4. BIERER, J. *The Day Hospital*. London: H. K. Lewis, 1951.
5. BLEULER, E. *Dementia Praecox or the Group of Schizophrenias*. New York: International Universities Press, 1950.
6. BURNELL, G. M. "Financing Mental Health Care," *Arch. Gen. Psychiatry*, 25 (1971), 49–55.
7. CAPLAN, G. *Principles of Preventive Psychiatry*. New York: Basic Books, 1964.
8. COLE, J. O. "Evaluation of Drug Treatments in Psychiatry," *Psychopharmacol. Serv. Cen. Bull.*, 2 (1962), 28–38.
9. ———. "Phenothiazine Treatment in Acute Schizophrenics: Effectiveness," *Arch. Gen. Psychiatry*, 10 (1964), 246–261.
10. EDELSON, M. *Ego Psychology, Group Dynamics, and the Therapeutic Community*. New York: Grune & Stratton, 1964.
11. ELWOOD, P. "Concept and Strategy of Health Maintenance Organizations," *Hospitals*, 45 (1971), 53–56.
12. FELDSTEIN, P. *Prepaid Group Practice: An Analysis and a Review*. Ann Arbor, Mich.: School Public Health, 1971.
13. GLASSER, M. and G. DUGGAN. "Prepaid Psychiatric Care: Experience with U.A.W. Members," *Am. J. Psychiatry*, 126 (1969), 675–681.
14. GOLDENSOHN, S., R. FINK, and S. SHAPIRO. "Referral, Utilization, and Staffing Patterns of a Mental Health Service in a Prepaid Group Practice Program in New York," *Am. J. Psychiatry*, 126 (1969), 689–697.
15. GREEN, E. L. "Psychiatric Services in a California Group Health Plan," *Am. J. Psychiatry*, 126 (1969), 681–688.

16. GRINKER, R. R. and J. SPIEGEL. *Men Under Stress*. New York: McGraw-Hill, 1945.

17. "Health Maintenance Organizations: A Reconfiguration of the Health Services System," in Proc. 13th Annu. Symposium on Hospital Affairs. Chicago: University of Chicago Press, 1971.

18. HEALTH SERVICES AND MENTAL HEALTH ADMINISTRATION. *Health Maintenance Organizations: The Concept and Structure*. Rockville, Md.: Health Services and Mental Health Administration, March 1970.

19. HESS, A. E. "Medicare and Mental Illness," *Am. J. Psychiatry*, 123 (1966), 174–176.

20. HOLDER, H. D. "Mental Health and the Search for New Organizational Strategies: A Systems Proposal," *Arch. Gen. Psychiatry*, 20 (1969), 709–717.

21. JOINT COMMISSION ON MENTAL ILLNESS AND HEALTH. *Action for Mental Health*. Final Report of the Joint Commission on Mental Illness and Health. New York: Basic Books, 1961.

22. JONES, E. *The Life and Work of Sigmund Freud*, Vols. 1–3. New York: Basic Books, 1953.

23. JONES, M. *The Therapeutic Community*. New York: Basic Books, 1953.

24. KALINOWSKY, L. and P. HOCH. *Somatic Treatments in Psychiatry*. New York: Grune & Stratton, 1961.

25. KRAEPELIN, E. *Clinical Psychiatry: A Textbook for Students and Physicians*. Translated and adopted from the 7th German edition by A. R. Deifendorf. New York: Macmillan, 1921.

26. MARSHALL, H. *Dorothea Dix: Forgotten Samaritan*. Chapel Hill: University of North Carolina Press, 1937.

27. MEYER, A. *Collected Papers of Adolph Meyer*, Vols. 1–3, E. E. Winters, ed. Baltimore: The Johns Hopkins Press, 1951.

28. MUNROE, R. *Schools of Psychoanalytic Thought*. New York: Holt, Rinehart and Winston, 1955.

29. NATIONAL ASSOCIATION FOR MENTAL HEALTH. *Action Guidelines: Health Insurance Coverage for Mental Illness*. New York: National Assoc. Mental Health, 1969.

30. PAVLOV, I. P. *Experimental Psychology and Other Essays*. New York: Philosophical Library, 1957.

31. REED, L. S., E. S. MEYERS, and P. L. SCHEIDMANDEL. *Health Insurance and Psychiatric Care: Utilization and Cost*. Washington: Am. Psychiatric Assoc., 1972.

32. RUSH, B. *Medical Inquiries and Observations Upon Diseases of the Mind*. New York: Hafner, 1962.

33. SOMERS, H. M. and A. R. SOMERS. *Medicare and the Hospitals*. Washington: The Brookings Institution, 1967.

34. WILLIAMS, E., ed. *Delivery Systems for Model Cities: New Concepts for Serving the Urban Community*. Chicago: University of Chicago, Center for Policy Study, 1969.

35. THE WOODLAWN ORGANIZATION. *Woodlawn's Model Cities Plan: A Demonstration of Citizen Responsibility*. Northbrook, Ill.: Whitehall, 1970.

36. ZILBOORG, G. and G. HENRY. *A History of Medical Psychology*. New York: Norton, 1941.

CHAPTER 47

EVALUATION OF BEHAVIOR CHANGE AND THERAPEUTIC EFFECTIVENESS

Eberhard H. Uhlenhuth

⟦ Introduction

E VALUATION is the new bon mot in mental health. We share this preoccupation with social programmers[127] on the one hand and with physicians in general[14,131] on the other hand. The status of the issue in our field is reflected by the recent appearance of several monumental overviews that are rich sources for the serious student.[8,43,92,103]

The growing interest in evaluating treatments in psychiatry signals a developing concensus that we now have real therapeutic alternatives requiring choices among a variety of effective procedures, probably even differentially effective in different problem situations. So the focus is shifting gradually from a reductionistic search for the common element in psychiatric therapy to ferreting out clinically significant differences between treatment tactics.[41,90,140]

Among the burgeoning variety of new pharmacological agents and psychological techniques, presumably only a few will offer significant advances. This provides another motive for careful evaluation, which the public deems so pressing that it finds institutional representation in such governmental agencies as the Food and Drug Administration. The high cost of health care, including psychiatric care, is another public concern generating pressure to justify therapeutic interventions on the basis of relative benefit and expense. The increasing support of psychiatric care through public (governmental) and private (insurance) organizations accelerates this trend.

Current social values and economic conditions seem to promote an emphasis on accountability throughout the social structure.

Under these pressures it is important to distinguish clearly, as Suchman does, between "... *evaluation* as the general process of judging the worthwhileness of some activity regardless of the method employed, and *evaluative research* as the specific use of the scientific method for the purpose of making an evaluation."[142] In the past, we often have taken the position that only the clinician's intuitive, impressionistic evaluation of the effects of his interventions can do justice to the richness and subtlety of human function in the social context. In such highly complex situations, unfortunately, even professional observation and judgment, unaided by the signposts of a systematic plan, all too frequently seem to lose their way.[100]

A pertinent example concerns our persistent tendency to confuse treatment effects and patients' inherent potential for change: we continue to select candidates for *treatment* on the basis of characteristics that predict *spontaneous* improvement. From the start of our clinical training we learn to select patients with an eye to their probable (gratifying) response, which powerfully reinforces us in our daily practice. Unfortunately, this process takes place under complex circumstances that consistently and without our awareness prevent us from sorting out specific *effects* that contribute to a patient's *response*.

The rest of this discussion deals with evaluative research: substantive knowledge, principles, and procedures useful in minimizing such unwitting errors of observation and judgment in evaluating treatment effects. The distinction between evaluating the effects of a program and evaluating the effects of a variable is an important issue.[142] The results of program evaluation may be valid only for the special circumstances of that program. Properly designed evaluations of the effect of a clearly defined variable often have more general validity and contribute understanding of pathological and restorative processes. The unique potential of this entry point to basic knowledge about human function is itself a justification for evaluative research.[87]

Discussions of evaluative research usually list several principal areas of interest:[31,158] (1) effort—the accounting of services rendered and resources employed; (2) outcome—the results of the effort expended; (3) process—the mechanism by which the effort produces the outcome; and (4) cost—the expense entailed. Meaningful evaluation of treatments probably requires some attention to each of these closely interwoven topics. The present discussion emphasizes especially outcome as the central point of departure for the evaluation of treatments.

⟦ Criteria of Outcome, Change, and Effectiveness

Over the past several decades, criteria of outcome, change and therapeutic effectiveness have received the enormous amount of attention they deserve.* Whereas investigators often must concern themselves especially with precision of measurement (reliability), clinicians' interest centers on adequately representing the range of human functions that are the object of therapeutic influence (validity). The measurement of "intrapsychic processes" or "character structure" is a particular issue. The Menninger Foundation's Psychotherapy Research Project[83,130] well illustrates the current potentials and limitations in this area. Clearly, highly skilled observers can make direct, quantitative estimates of such global, highly conceptualized dimensions as ego strength.

Psychometricians approach the same problem in a more empirical, atomistic fashion with formal test measures of personal "traits"[19] and pathological personality trends.[26] Unfortunately, these measures often seem rather insensitive to differential treatment effects.

A less ambitious framework for criteria grows rather pragmatically from roots in the

* See references 8, 29, 37, 56, 68, 98, 99, 103, 151, and 152.

medical model. The final criteria of therapeutic effectiveness become reductions in discomfort and ineffective function.[111] Other criteria that are often proposed, such as continuation in treatment or development of insight, take their places as possible mediating variables in the process of treatment. This framework underscores the relationship of psychiatric treatment to general health care, spans the pharmacotherapeutic agents and the "proprietary" psychotherapies with an atheoretical bridge,[140] and points toward specific measures to make the criteria operational. Finally, many of the measures derived from this framework do indeed discriminate treatment effects.

Discomfort, in particular the states of anxiety and depression, is essentially a subjective phenomenon. The patient's verbal reports constitute the principal source of data, although the skillful observer integrates these with the patient's concomitant nonverbal behavior. Measurement of this domain merits particular emphasis in patients with neurotic and affective disturbances. In addition measurement of the broader symptom picture is essential in any evaluation of treatment.

Ineffective function refers to social-role performances that, at least in principle, are forms of behavior open to direct observation by others. These include occupational productivity, effectiveness as a spouse and parent, adequacy in social relations, and such basics as hospitalization vs. community tenure, self-care in the hospital, etc. Although some of these functions may be measurably impaired by any psychiatric disturbance requiring treatment, role-performance criteria are central in therapeutic studies of severe, especially psychotic, conditions.

Both comfort and effectiveness may be viewed by various observers, and each has had advocates: patient, therapist, nurse or other professional, relatives. The therapist's assessment of the patient's clinical condition is the major factor in evaluation by reason of his skill and his knowledge of the patient. The patient's assessment is an important addition in work with adult neurotics, who have predominantly subjective complaints and are relatively reliable observers. Nurses, relatives, and other outside observers can contribute valuable assessments in studies of young, old, psychotic, addicted, and psychopathic individuals.

The "independent research assessor"[62] represents a viewpoint of special interest in certain situations. He can bring to the assessment professional skills without therapeutic investment; and he may be kept blind with regard to the details of treatment. The cost is less familiarity with the patient.

Curiously enough, assessments by different observers (e.g., therapist and patient) using the same measuring instrument differ more than assessments by the same observer using different instruments.[111] Assessments by multiple observers in an evaluative study provide broader coverage of relevant changes and tend to compensate for the unique biases of each.

A plethora of instruments have been developed for all types of observers, rating every facet of comfort and effectiveness. Comprehensive efforts to sort out this bewildering array of outcome measures are now under way by the Clinical Research Branch, NIMH, for application to psychotherapy,[68,151] and by the Bureau of Drugs, FDA, for application to pharmacotherapy.[29,37,98,152] We may anticipate substantial overlap between the efforts of the two groups. Also available and under continuing development by the Psychopharmacology Research Branch, NIMH, are comprehensive batteries of well-established instruments linked to a complete data-processing system.[61,97]

Despite the effort that has been expended in developing highly specific measuring instruments, the simple seven-point global rating of status or change by the therapist remains one of the most sensitive methods of discriminating treatment effects.[93] Unfortunately, it offers no information as to the nature of the therapeutic effect. In a strict sense, this measure may not provide comparable information about different patients, as the rater is free to accent the most relevant features in each individual.

Highly structured measures of clinical condition can be criticized on the grounds that they may be irrelevant to many patients. An approach to this problem is to rate "target symptoms" defined individually with each patient.[6] This concept applies quite naturally to behavior modification with its emphasis on changing specific behavior.

The timing of assessments is as critical as the instrument and the observer in discerning certain treatment differences. Chlorpromazine is preferable to lithium in treating acute, highly active manics partly because of its rapid action:[118] assessments after the first week of treatment do not reveal this difference in the time of onset of action. Assessments repeated at regular intervals have the particular advantages of permitting trend fitting to study the course of change over time[30] and to provide a more stable estimate of the individual's response based on all this data. Repeated measurements over time also offer an approach to assessing character traits, defined as characteristic tendencies to exhibit recurrent states or behavior.

On the other hand, assessment over extended periods, as in follow-up studies, presents special problems in interpretation since treatment during the interim cannot be controlled.[101,138] In such cases only criteria applied before uncontrolled treatment are useful, typically the occurrence of relapse or the decision to reinstitute treatment.

(The Patient

The patient's own characteristics remain perhaps the most potent determinants of outcome or prognosis.[94] In the comparative evaluation of treatments it is crucial that patients in different groups be equivalent so that effects due to treatment and to prognostic factors can be separated. Equivalence with respect to unknown prognostic factors—and this is still an important issue—can be assured only by assigning patients to treatments at random (possibly with some restrictions to allow for matching on certain characteristics).

Prognostic factors may influence outcome

independently of treatment. Even more significant are patient characteristics that affect outcome differentially in relation to the treatment employed (interaction). These patterns provide the differential indications for treatment that clinicians seek.[146]

Details of the patient's clinical condition contain basic prognostic information. A high level of current disturbance, particularly affective disturbance, seems to be a favorable sign.[57,58,83,140] The favorable outlook for episodes of the major affective disorders and acute schizophrenia is well known.[136]

On the other hand, a healthy characteristic level of function (traits, character style) seems to be prognostically favorable.[*] Competent function relates to such variables as high intelligence, educational and occupational levels, verbal ability, ego strength, low neuroticism, and satisfactory interpersonal relations, including marriage.

Direct studies of these as prognostic variables in psychotherapy, however, have produced surprisingly conflicting results.[47,103] The same is true for age, sex, race, and prior treatment. There is more general agreement that the patient's expectations upon entering treatment influence the outcome.[†]

The situation is more promising with pharmacotherapy, where prognostic variables of both general significance and specific significance in the choice of drug (interaction) are beginning to emerge. Psychiatric diagnosis and other features of the clinical picture offer useful indications for the choice of medication,[87] and diagnostic refinements are proceeding apace.[155] Among patients with major affective disorders, differential indications for treatment are relatively clear: in bipolar patients lithium prevents affective episodes but in unipolar patients imipramine prevents affective episodes at least as effectively as lithium.[119] Among schizophrenics, patients with good premorbid adjustment and no paranoid symptoms carry the best prognosis[35] and benefit least from phenothiazines.[36,78] Among anxious psychoneurotic patients, those with higher anxiety levels, more chronic distur-

* See references 35, 47, 48, 83, 103, and 149.
† See references 39, 41, 42, 46, 49, 67, 123, and 147.

bance, and better response to previous drug treatment benefit most from medication.[123]

Consensus on the prognostic significance of other variables is building gradually as the data accumulate.[120,123,146] For example, neurotic patients with higher indices of social advantage seem to benefit more from antidepressants[32] or antianxiety agents.[123] Older depressed patients respond better than younger ones to antidepressants.[120]

What accounts for the apparently more rapid advance of prognostic discrimination related to pharmacotherapy than to psychotherapy? The positive indicators for response to psychotherapy, for spontaneous remission[54] and for response to placebo are similar in many respects. Curiously, many of the positive indicators for pharmacotherapy seem to stand at the opposite pole: beneficial medication effects are manifest especially in patients who would be less likely to improve otherwise.

Much of the information on prognostic indicators for psychotherapy derives from studies of a single group of subjects, all treated with the therapy of interest. In such a situation the observed responses include some unspecifiable mixture of nonspecific effects and effects attributable specifically to therapy. Differential indications for different treatments, including "no treatment," emerge clearly only from comparative studies designed to separate treatment effects from other effects on outcome. A survey of therapeutic outcomes by Saenger[129] illustrates that even relatively crude approximations to this design highlight differential prognostic effects. His results also suggest that the specific benefits of treatment, contrary to popular opinion, emerge in patients who have a relatively poor prognosis without treatment.

⟨ The Treatment

Psychotherapeutic procedures generally have not been well specified. This tendency, surprisingly, is perhaps stronger among investigators than among clinicians and teachers. In the psychoanalytic setting considerable attention

has been paid to technical detail as illustrated, for example, by Bibring's[9] classification of interventions. There is growing recognition that "psychotherapy" is not a unitary process, so that questions about "the effects of psychotherapy" carry meaning only on a very gross level.[7] Many investigators are joining Paul[115] in his call for specification: "What treatment by whom, is most effective for this individual with that specific problem, under which set of circumstances, and how does it come about?" Note also, however, May's[100] argument for our need to be concerned with the effectiveness of "average psychotherapy."

Pharmacotherapy can serve as a model for the specification of treatment in psychiatry. The precision of chemical specification doubtless helps to account for the rapid development of evaluative research in pharmacotherapy during the past two decades. The ideal presented by this model probably is unattainable in studies of psychotherapy, even in the area of behavior modification, since the inherent difficulties are substantially greater.

The "central therapeutic ingredients"[144] of psychotherapy have not yet been identified clearly. Indeed, the analogy to medication, despite its attractiveness, eventually may prove inadequate for conceptualizing psychotherapeutic influence. For the time being the notion is useful, partly because it highlights the still unresolved issue between specific procedures (skills) and less tangible personal qualities as the principal therapeutic tools.[140] The final common pathway of both, of course, must be therapist's specific behavior.

Granted the importance and the difficulty of specifying psychotherapeutic treatment, then what significant dimensions can be specified at our present level of understanding? Some studies have shown differential effects related to *general treatment technique*—psychoanalysis, expressive therapy, supportive therapy, behavior therapy—when patient characteristics also are considered. For example, desensitization seems to be more effective and more rapidly effective than other psychotherapies for specific phobias of moderate or less severity.[94] The relative effects on general adjustment, however, are less clear. The most comprehensive comparative study of psychoanalysis and related treatments[83] suggests (1) that psychoanalysis is more effective than supportive or expressive therapies with persons who have high ego strength, and (2) that an intermediate supportive-expressive therapy is more effective than psychoanalysis or primarily supportive therapy with persons who have low ego strength.

At present, there is no convincing evidence of differences in effectiveness among practitioners of different *theoretical orientations*—psychoanalytic, Rogerian, behavioral—except for those already mentioned in regard to the behavioral approach.[94,103] This area, however, has received relatively meager attention.

From the patient's viewpoint, the *persons included in treatment*—patient, family, group of unrelated persons—are part of the treatment setting (see below). Currently available reports provide little evidence for differential effectiveness associated with this aspect of the setting,[94,103,121] although the issue certainly is not closed, especially with regard to certain forms of group therapy with schizophrenic patients.[103,107]

Differences among *settings*—office, clinic, day hospital, full-time hospital—and between different settings in the same class are observed commonly in controlled treatment studies.[123] Some schizophrenics respond better to day-hospital than to outpatient treatment[63] and also respond differently to differences in milieux among hospital wards.[79] Instruments for measuring dimensions of ward atmosphere are available.[79,104]

Since random assignment of patients to settings generally is not feasible, the confounding of patient characteristics, which often differ among settings, and intrinsic differences among settings cannot be undone. A recent study of pharmacotherapy and group psychotherapy with ambulatory depressed patients addressed itself specifically to this issue by employing the same study team in two clinics serving patients of differing social class status.[25] The highly significant response contrasts in favor of imipramine and against diazepam (compared with placebo) were contributed primarily by the clinic with patients of higher social class.

The *therapist's style* can be viewed as some combination of his personality, orientation, and procedures. For present purposes this variable is of interest insofar as it can be specified. The Rogerian school has developed the most comprehensive body of work in this direction, well summarized by Truax and Carkhuff[144] and Truax and Mitchell.[145] They report that different therapists characteristically provide different "levels of core interpersonal skills" along scaled dimensions of accurate empathy, nonpossessive warmth, and genuineness.

Another series of investigations center around the therapist's type as originally defined by Whitehorn and Betz[153] according to success (Type A) or failure (Type B) in treating schizophrenic patients. These types showed different patterns on the Strong Vocational Interest Blank, and subsequent work was based on the types as differentiated by this test index. Despite fifteen years of research, the value of this discrimination remains controversial.[103]

The *therapist's experience* is another factor that intuitively seems important in therapeutic results. Although the weight of the evidence favors this idea,[103] it is much less conclusive than might be expected.[100]

It is equally surprising to find a lack of definitive studies and conclusive results relating treatment outcome to *amount of therapeutic contact*—duration, frequency, number, and regularity of sessions.[103] Most of the available evidence suggests that therapeutic gains increase with the number of sessions up to some limit probably determined by other factors, but lower than generally supposed, say twenty.

A major study on the amount of treatment indicates that minimal contact (thirty minutes every two weeks) provides about the same relief as weekly individual (one hour) or group (one and one-half hour) sessions. Improvement in social function, however, is more rapid in the individual or group modalities.[40]

Most of these studies suffer from the difficulty of disentangling the several time-related dimensions. Another problem is the possible confounding effect of both patient and therapist expectations.[145]

The behavioral approaches offer a model for the specification of *particular technical maneuvers*. Although behavioral techniques as a class already have compiled an encouraging record of effectiveness,[116,94] the promise of differentiation among technical variations remains largely unfulfilled in this young field.

Investigations of differential effects due to other specific tactics also show considerable promise. Therapists who lose lower-class patients and therapists who retain them in treatment differ markedly on such maneuvers as addressing their patients by name.[73] Patients prepared for psychotherapy with detailed information about the procedures and their anticipated results benefit more than unprepared patients.[67]

As noted earlier, medication lends itself to detailed specification more readily than other aspects of treatment. Nevertheless, even in studies of pharmacotherapy, problems regarding the therapeutic agent do arise, including the regimen followed by the patient as distinct from the regimen prescribed by the investigator. These issues are discussed comprehensively in Levine et al.[92] The critical point here is that many studies of psychotherapy fail to control or even to take account of medications used by the patients. In an era when, each year, 22 percent of the population ingest psychotropic prescription drugs of established potency,[102] this oversight can have disastrous consequences for a study.[100]

The patient's environment beyond the treatment setting is another greatly neglected area that bears on outcome. External events, for example, can diminish drug-placebo contrasts, since unfavorable events differentially reduce drug response whereas favorable events differentially increase placebo response.[122] In the only controlled study of psychotherapy that paid explicit attention to environmental variables, no association with outcome was noted.[83]

([Cost

The cost of health care is a subject of such concern that it finds expression in the public press almost daily. Cost-benefit concepts and their importance have been discussed in the psychiatric literature for some time.[40] Nevertheless, controlled studies on the effectiveness of treatment leave the reader to draw his own inferences on the issue. There are no data, with the striking exception of May's report on the treatment of schizophrenia.[99] He shows that ataraxic drugs markedly reduce and psychotherapy markedly increases the cost of treatment, absolutely and in relation to effectiveness.

The cost of treatment usually is tallied under direct and indirect expenses. Indirect expenses generally include items such as maintenance of the facility, room and board, basic nursing care, and clerical functions. These are charged in direct proportion to the length of hospital stay or the number of outpatient visits. Direct expenses usually include procedures that are costly and individually ordered, such as tests, psychotherapy, ECT, and medications. The cost of outpatient care is largely attributable to the special procedures that the therapist personally prescribes and performs and so should be easily within reach of the clinical investigator in many outcome studies.

The cost of psychiatric illness itself can be modified by treatment, but its estimation presents some almost insurmountable difficulties. It includes items such as welfare; pensions or disability compensation; loss of productivity, income and taxes; and human losses in function as a spouse or parent. Even long-delayed and tenuously related consequences like increased susceptibility among the children of ill parents could involve significant costs. Despite the acknowledged problems, partial accounting of the costs of illness should be possible now with data from individual patients on days of work lost, income, and its sources, and certain criteria of ineffective functioning.

(Design

For present purposes the design of a study is a plan of procedure that will allow the investigator to make causal inferences from his data by separating the sources of variation in outcome among patients. In its broadest sense, this plan specifies all details of the research, including criteria for selecting patients and therapists, treatments to be compared and their mode of delivery, allocation of patients to treatments and therapists, criteria of treatment effect and the timing of their application, management of deviations from protocol, analysis and interpretation of the data. In a more limited sense, design refers to the manner in which patients enter and pass through the experimental treatment framework.

Specialists in design with an extensive statistical background have developed in the field of psychology.[17] An alternative pattern of close collaboration between a clinical investigator and a biomedical statistician is emerging in the field of psychiatry.[30,59,148]

The importance of statistical skills in design now seems to be generally recognized. Since adequate design depends primarily on keen logical analysis of the real treatment situation, the very active participation of a person with substantive and logistic knowledge of the field, i.e., a clinician, is equally critical. In the absence of a strong empirical influence from the clinician-investigator, a tendency may develop to deal with issues by carrying deduction well beyond the point of support by data. A pertinent example in psychopharmacologic evaluation is the current rather uncritical rejection of patient-own-control designs, specifically "intensive design,"[20] based on the *possibility* that a treatment effect may carry over into a subsequent phase of the study. The current press for ever larger sample sizes— with their increasing possibilities for error—as a solution for the problem of error variation within treatment groups may prove to be another example.[28,109,124]

Designs incorporate controls for a variety of errors, both random and systematic (bias).[55] These controls include clear conceptualization, specification of all aspects of procedure, appropriate sampling techniques, treatment-comparison groups, and the structure of the informational context within which the study takes place. The most familiar example of the last is the "double blinding" of patient and investigator as to the specific treatment received by an individual patient at a particular time. Limitations in double blinding present a special problem in evaluating nonmedicinal treatments in psychiatry that can be resolved only partly by using an "independent research assessor."[62]

In any event, the double blind is too narrow a concept. All of the information transmitted in connection with a study, either verbally or nonverbally, must be carefully considered and structured in view of its probable effects on patients and therapists.[108,126] These effects probably are mediated by activation of patients' and therapists' expectations (see pp. 941 and 944). The expectations activated, however, often bear no simple relation to the information supplied by the investigator.[110]

Designs in the strictest sense are for experiments in which the investigator manipulates the variable of causal interest, the treatment. The basic strategy is to distribute unintended and especially unidentifiable effects on outcome equally among treatment groups in order to disassociate such effects from the treatment effects under study. The usual tactic employed is to assign patients to treatments at random, sometimes with certain systematic restrictions (stratification, matching) to assure balance with respect to variables of known importance.

There are, however, many situations where random assignment is not ethically justifiable. The issue arises when one of the experimental treatments is inferior or essentially a dummy. Complete assurance that a particular study is sensitive to treatment differences unfortunately requires the inclusion of a standard treatment and a dummy treatment in addition to the treatment being evaluated. This conflict between experimental and ethical requirements is likely to increase as more effective treatments are discovered.

Many investigators of psychotherapy advocate "naturalistic" studies.[15] The basic strategy here is the careful, systematic observation of existing situations with correlational analysis of the resulting data. This approach can comprehend many of the variables found in such complex situations as psychotherapy and their relationships.[85] It does not encounter the ethical problems mentioned above. Because it requires minimal interference with the way treatment is prescribed and delivered, the naturalistic approach may offer the only practical hope of evaluating the effectiveness of ongoing treatment programs of immediate public interest. The large data banks that are gradually accumulating by virtue of computer technology require similiar approaches for their full utilization.

Statisticians for some time have considered the problems of nonexperimental research in general.[11,23] Survey research is based on nonexperimental techniques that, in part, are applicable to outcome studies.[132] The growing interest in this area among psychopharmacologists was manifested by a workshop in January 1973 to discuss "Approaches to the Use of Observational Data in Psychopharmacology."

Critical consideration of the nonexperimental approach in the light of some of these materials reveals some problems that are shared by the experimental approach, but are often overlooked. The major issues concern confounding the effects of the treatment under study and the effects of other variables. Covariance techniques can be used to account for identified sources of confounding if they are not too severe. Unidentified sources of confounding that are intrinsically related to treatment (conceivably some effects of treatment settings) are clearly unmanageable in either experimental or nonexperimental research. This technical problem can be reformulated as a substantive question about the mechanism of treatment effects.

Unidentified sources of confounding that are not intrinsically related to treatment (conceivably some prognostic characteristics of patients who tend to be selected for some treatment) can be controlled by the random assignment of patients to treatments. The particular weakness of nonexperimental research lies in its inability to account for this type of confounding. The consensus nevertheless seems to regard observational research as a fruitful source of hypotheses that should be and usually can be confirmed by supplementary experiments.[75]

An important problem encountered with increasing frequency in treatment evaluations stems partly from growing public sophistication about psychiatry. More patients come with more definite wishes for a specific form of treatment. In samples where most patients favor one of the experimental treatments, random assignment to treatments is likely to create rather than control bias since the evenly allocated expectations are likely to enhance response in the favored treatment group and inhibit response in the other groups. Additional complications may ensue if patients selectively drop from the treatments that are not favored. If these trends gain strength, it may be useful to consider studies not concerned with the direct comparison of treatment effects, but rather with the factors prognostic of benefit among patients who presented themselves for a particular treatment.

(Analysis

The analysis of results from evaluative research, of course, is closely related to the design employed. Analyses of variance, covariance, and regression are the procedures commonly applied in comparing independent treatment groups. Extensions of the basic methods to include multiple independent variables, as in multiple regression[24] and discriminant function analyses, and to include also multiple dependent variables, as in multivariate analyses of variance and covariance offer elegant approaches to understanding complex sets of correlated data.[12,105] Several well-documented, flexible computer programs are now available to implement these procedures at different levels of complexity.* At least one data processing system complete from measuring instruments through analyses is operational.[97]

The application of these methods in experiments, where increased precision is the main objective, is relatively straightforward. In nonexperimental studies, where the removal of bias due to imbalance of confounding factors among treatments is a prime objective, the use of these methods remains controversial.[23,76,132]

As interest grows in processes of change, the time dimension gains importance in evaluative research. The analysis of repeated measures for trends is a useful device in this connection. Such analyses provide a dynamic picture of treatment effects, increase precision by employing all the data from every patient, and may be less affected by an occasional missing value.[30]

Analyses of data from patient-own-control designs, especially those extending over multiple time periods, also deserve special mention. They encounter the problems of internal correlation common to all time series, but generally do not provide enough data to take advantage of such special methods as auto- and cross-correlation. Chassan[20] offers a simple, but controversial, approach.

With the vast power of modern electronic computers so readily available, it is easy to act as if sufficiently sophisticated statistical manipulations could solve most of the problems of evaluative research. It is tempting to carry out massive searches through the data to uncover effects that may confound, interact with, or be even more striking than the treatment effects under study. The amounts of data required for such efforts to produce replicable results are difficult to appreciate.[13,75] It is also tempting to try endless variations on the same analytic theme to wring one more sufficient F ratio ($p < 0.05$) from the data. Unfortunately, close practical (computational) similarities sometimes lurk under hotly argued theoretical differences separating some of

these analytic approaches. There is evidently no substitute for a carefully conceived, designed and executed study, with results that are clear on inspection of the raw data and confirmable with simple statistics.

⟦ Concluding Remarks

Evaluative research in psychiatry has had an interesting history—even exciting, especially in psychopharmacology, where experimental methods could be developed, applied, and refined most readily. With interest growing in the question of what works, the future promises further development of evaluative research. Hopefully, the pressures to evaluate particular programs will not compromise the design of studies to provide information about specific variables valid beyond the immediate context of the particular programs.

More detailed specification of psychological variables surely is a keystone in the future development of evaluative research in psychiatry. Pertinent specification in turn depends partly on the emergence of additional substantive knowledge about the very effects we wish to study, including the effects of psychological interventions. Promising new chemical entities with distinctly different structures would serve as a similar stimulus for research on the effects of psychopharmacological treatments.

Advances in methods also are needed. Some basic statistical developments seem indicated, for instance, in reference to interpreting results from procedures that "search" stepwise a pool of independent variables for relations to a dependent variable.

Improved measurement and vastly increased sample size have received much emphasis as a means of coping with variation within treatment groups ("error"). Although further improvement is always desirable, great strides in measurement have been made. Logistic problems in assembling large samples probably disproportionately escalate error. Statistically significant differences between treatments in large samples also may not be large enough to be clinically meaningful.

* See references 1, 2, 21, 38, 106, 135, and 148.

Improved design has received less attention in the search for greater experimental precision. Investigators tend to fall into the routine of comparing treatments in parallel independent groups while focusing debate on whether six or eight weeks duration is more appropriate. The imaginative development and application of more fundamental modifications in design now seem to hold promise for increasing the sensitivity of evaluative studies in psychiatry and also meeting ethical requirements. One possible direction is variation on the patient-own-control theme.

There is a notable tendency to employ deductive debate, sometimes at astonishing length, rather than experiment, to resolve methodologic uncertainties. For example, only one empirical study—and this is not comparative—has seriously addressed the question of the value of employing an initial placebo washout period in clinical psychopharmacologic research.[77] This stance among evaluators seems incongruous, to say the least, since empirical evaluative research contains within itself the means for its own improvement, should we choose to employ them.

⟨ Bibliography

1. ANDREWS, F. M., J. M. MORGAN, and J. A. SONQUIST. *Multiple Classification Analysis: A Report on a Program for Multiple Regression Using Categorical Predictors.* Survey Research Center, Institute for Social Research. Ann Arbor, Mich.: University of Michigan Press, 1967.

2. ARMOUR, D. J. and A. S. COUCH. *The Data-Text Primer: An Introduction to Computerized Social Data Analysis Using the Data-Text System.* New York: Free Press, 1972.

3. ARNOLD, M. F. "Evaluation: A Parallel Process to Planning," in M. F. Arnold, L. V. Blankenship, and J. M. Hess, eds., *Administering Health Systems*, pp. 263–282. Chicago: Aldine-Atherton, 1971.

4. ASTRUP, C., A. FOSSUM, and R. HOLMBOE. *Prognosis In Functional Psychoses.* Springfield, Ill.: Charles C. Thomas, 1963.

5. BAHN, A. K. and C. A. THRALL. "Impairment of Psychiatric Outpatients and Change with Treatment," *Ment. Hyg.*, 48 (1964), 217–242.

6. BATTLE, C. C., S. D. IMBER, R. HOEHN-SARIC et al. "Target Complaints as Criteria of Improvement," *Am. J. Psychother.*, 20 (1966), 184–192.

7. BERGIN, A. E. "The Evaluation of Therapeutic Outcomes," in A. E. Bergin and S. L. Garfield, eds., *Handbook of Psychotherapy and Behavior Change: An Empirical Analysis*, pp. 217–270. New York: Wiley, 1971.

8. BERGIN, A. E. and S. L. GARFIELD, eds. *Handbook of Psychotherapy and Behavior Change: An Empirical Analysis.* New York: Wiley, 1971.

9. BIBRING, E. "Psychoanalysis and the Dynamic Psychotherapies," *J. Am. Psychoanal. Assoc.*, 2 (1954), 745–770.

10. BINNER, P. R. "Operational Problems of Program Evaluation." Presented at S. Reg. Conf. Ment. Health Statis. Workshop, Norman, Okla., August 1968.

11. BLALOCK, H. M., JR. *Causal Inferences in Nonexperimental Research.* Chapel Hill: University of North Carolina Press, 1964.

12. BOCK, R. D. "Multivariate Analysis of Variance of Repeated Measures," in C. W. Harris, ed., *Problems in Measuring Change*, pp. 85–103. Madison: University of Wisconsin Press, 1967.

13. BOSTON COLLABORATIVE DRUG SURVEILLANCE PROGRAM. "Clinical Depression of the Central Nervous System Due to Diazepam and Chlordiazepoxide in Relation to Cigarette Smoking and Age," *N. Engl. J. Med.*, 288 (1973), 277–280.

14. BROOK, R. H. and F. A. APPEL. "Quality-of-Care Assessment: Choosing a Method for Peer Review," *N. Engl. J. Med.*, 288 (1973), 1323–1329.

15. BUTLER, J. M., L. N. RICE, and A. K. WAGSTAFF. "On the Naturalistic Definition of Variables: An Analogue of Clinical Analysis," in H. H. Strupp and L. Luborsky, eds., *Research In Psychotherapy*, Vol. 2, pp. 178–205. Washington: Am. Psychological Assoc., 1962.

16. CAMPBELL, D. T. "From Description to Experimentation: Interpreting Trends as Quasi-Experiments," in C. W. Harris, ed.,

Problems In Measuring Change, pp. 212–242. Madison: University of Wisconsin Press, 1967.

17. CAMPBELL, D. T. and J. C. STANLEY. *Experimental and Quasi-Experimental Designs for Research*. Chicago: Rand McNally, 1966.

18. CARO, F., ed. *Readings in Evaluation Research*. New York: Basic Books, 1971.

19. CATTELL, R. B. *The Scientific Analysis of Personality*. Chicago: Aldine, 1965.

20. CHASSAN, J. B. *Research Design in Clinical Psychology and Psychiatry*. New York: Appleton-Century-Crofts, 1967.

21. CLYDE, D. J. *Manova: Multivariate Analysis of Variance on Large Computers*. Miami: Clyde Comput. Serv., 1969.

22. COCHRANE, A. L. *Effectiveness and Efficiency: Random Reflections on Health Services*. London: Nuffield Provincial Hospitals Trust, 1972.

23. COCHRAN, W. G. "The Planning of Observational Studies of Human Populations," *J. R. Statis. Soc. Ser. A*, 128 (1965), 234–265.

24. COHEN, J. "Multiple Regression as a General Data-Analytic System," *Psychol. Bull.*, 70 (1968), 426–443.

25. COVI, L., R. LIPMAN, and L. R. DEROGATIS. "Drugs and Group Therapy in Neurotic Depression." Presented at 126th Annu. Meet. Am. Psychiatr. Assoc., Honolulu, May 8, 1973.

26. DAHLSTROM, G., G. S. WELSH, and L. E. DAHLSTROM. An MMPI Handbook. Vol. 1. *Clinical Interpretation*. Minneapolis: University of Minnesota Press, 1972.

27. DENT, J. K. *A Bibliographic Index of Evaluation in Mental Health*. U.S. Public Health Service Pub. no. 1545. Washington: U.S. Govt. Print. Off., 1966.

28. DEROGATIS, L. R., R. R. BONATO, and K. C. YANG. "The Power of IMPS in Psychiatric Drug Research: As a Function of Sample Size, Number of Raters, and Choice of Treatment Comparison," *Arch. Gen. Psychiatry*, 19 (1968), 689–699.

29. DIMASCIO, A., B. WARSHAVER, and A. RASKIN. "Ward Behavior and Psychiatric Rating Scales." *Mimeo.*, 1972.

30. DIXON, W. J. and P. R. A. MAY. "Process Analysis in the Assessment and Prediction of Psychiatric Outcome," in P. R. A. May and J. R. Wittenborn, eds., *Psychotropic Drug Response: Advances In Prediction*, pp. 228–267. Springfield, Ill.: Charles C. Thomas, 1969.

31. DONABEDIAN, A. "Evaluating the Quality of Medical Care," *Milbank Mem. Fund Q.*, 44 (1966), 166–206.

32. DOWNING, R. W. and K. RICKELS. "Predictors of Response to Amitriptyline and Placebo in Three Outpatient Treatment Settings," *J. Nerv. Ment. Dis.*, 156 (1973), 109–129.

33. ENDICOTT, J. and R. L. SPITZER. "Current and Past Psychopathology Scales (CAPPS)," *Arch. Gen. Psychiatry*, 27 (1972), 678–687.

34. ENGELHARDT, D. M., B. ROSEN, N. FREEDMAN et al. "Phenothiazines in Prevention of Psychiatric Hospitalization," *Arch Gen. Psychiatry*, 16 (1967), 98–101.

35. EVANS, J. R., M. J. GOLDSTEIN, and E. H. RODNICK. "Premorbid Adjustment, Paranoid Diagnosis, and Remission," *Arch. Gen. Psychiatry*, 28 (1973), 666–672.

36. EVANS, J. R., E. H. RODNICK, M. J. GOLDSTEIN et al. "Premorbid Adjustment, Phenothiazine Treatment, and Remission in Acute Schizophrenics," *Arch. Gen. Psychiatry*, 27 (1972), 486–490.

37. FEDERAL DRUG ADMINISTRATION. "FDA Guidelines for Psychotropic Drugs (Draft —June 1974)," *Psychopharmacol. Bull.*, 10 (1974), 70–91.

38. FINN, J. D. *Multivariance: Univariate and Multivariate Analysis of Variance, Covariance and Regression: A Fortran IV Program*, Version 5. Ann Arbor: Natl. Educational Resources, 1972.

39. FISKE, D. W., H. F. HUNT, L. LUBORSKY et al. "Planning Research on Effectiveness of Psychotherapy," *Arch. Gen. Psychiatry*, 22 (1970), 22–32.

40. FOX, P. D. and J. M. KULDAU. "Expanding the Framework for Mental Health Program Evaluation," *Arch. Gen. Psychiatry*, 19 (1968), 538–544.

41. FRANK, J. D. *Persuasion and Healing: A Comparative Study of Psychotherapy*, rev. Baltimore: The Johns Hopkins University Press, 1973.

42. FRANK, J. D., L. H. GLIEDMAN, S. D. IMBER et al. "Patients' Expectancies and Relearning as Factors Determining Improvement in Psychotherapy," *Am. J. Psychiatry*, 115 (1959), 961–968.

43. FRANKS, C. M., ed. *Behavior Therapy: Appraisal and Status.* New York: McGraw-Hill, 1969.

44. FREEMAN, H. E. "Outcome Measures and Social Action Experiments: An Immodest Proposal for Redirecting Research Efforts," *Am. Sociol.,* 7 (1972), 17–19.

45. FRIED, M. "Evaluation and the Relativity of Reality," in L. M. Roberts, N. S. Greenfield, and M. H. Miller, eds., *Comprehensive Mental Health: The Challenge of Evaluation.* Madison: University of Wisconsin Press, 1968.

46. FRIEDMAN, H. J. "Patient Expectancy and Symptom Reduction," *Arch. Gen. Psychiatry,* 8 (1963), 61–67.

47. GARFIELD, S. L. "Research on Client Variables in Psychotherapy," in A. E. Bergin and S. L. Garfield, eds., *Handbook of Psychotherapy and Behavior Change: An Empirical Analysis,* pp. 271–298. New York: Wiley, 1971.

48. GELDER, M. G., I. M. MARKS, and H. H. WOLFF. "Desensitization and Psychotherapy in the Treatment of Phobic States: A Controlled Inquiry," *Br. J. Psychiatry,* 113 (1967), 53–73.

49. GOLDSTEIN, A. P. *Therapist–Patient Expectancies in Psychotherapy.* New York: Pergamon, 1962.

50. GOLDSTEIN, A. P. and S. J. DEAN, eds. *The Investigation of Psychotherapy: Commentaries and Readings.* New York: Wiley, 1966.

51. GOLDSTEIN, A. P., K. HELLER, and L. B. SECHREST. *Psychotherapy and the Psychology of Behavior Change.* New York: Wiley, 1966.

52. GOTTSCHALK, L. A. "Some Problems in the Evaluation of the Use of Psychoactive Drugs, with or without Psychotherapy, in the Treatment of Non-psychotic Personality Disorders," in D. H. Efron, J. O. Cole, J. Levine et al., eds., *Psychopharmacology: A Review of Progress 1957–1967,* pp. 255–269. U.S. Public Health Service Pub. no. 1836. Washington: U.S. Govt. Print. Off., 1968.

53. GOTTSCHALK, L. A. and A. H. AUERBACH. *Methods of Research in Psychotherapy.* New York: Appleton-Century-Crofts, 1966.

54. GOTTSCHALK, L. A., P. MAYERSON, and A. A. GOTTLIEB. "Prediction and Evaluation of Outcome in an Emergency Brief Psychotherapy Clinic," *J. Nerv. Ment. Dis.,* 144 (1967), 77–96.

55. GROUP FOR THE ADVANCEMENT OF PSYCHIATRY. *Some Observations on Controls in Psychiatric Research,* Rep. no. 42. New York: GAP, 1959.

56. ———. *Psychiatric Research and the Assessment of Change,* Rep. no. 63. New York: GAP, 1966.

57. ———. *Psychotherapy and the Dual Research Tradition,* Rep. no. 73. New York: GAP, 1969.

58. ———. *Pharmacotherapy and Psychotherapy: Paradoxes, Problems and Progress,* Rep. no. 93. New York: GAP, 1975.

59. GURLAND, B. J., N. J. YORKSTON, K. GOLDBERG et al. "The Structured and Scaled Interview to Assess Maladjustment (SSIAM); II. Factor Analysis, Reliability, and Validity," *Arch. Gen. Psychiatry,* 27 (1972), 264–267.

60. GURLAND, B. J., N. J. YORKSTON, A. R. STONE et al. "The Structured and Scaled Interview to Assess Maladjustment (SSIAM); I. Description, Rationale, and Development," *Arch. Gen. Psychiatry,* 27 (1972), 259–264.

61. GUY, W. and R. R. BONATO. *Manual for the ECDEU Assessment Battery,* 2nd rev. ed. Washington: NIMH, 1970.

62. GUY, W., M. GROSS, and H. DENNIS. "An Alternative to the Double-Blind Procedure," *Am. J. Psychiatry,* 123 (1967), 1505–1512.

63. GUY, W., M. GROSS, G. E. HOGARTY et al. "A Controlled Evaluaton of Day Hospital Effectiveness," *Arch. Gen. Psychiatry,* 20 (1969), 329–338.

64. HALPERT, H. P., W. J. HORVATH, and J. P. YOUNG. *An Administrator's Handbook on the Application of Operations Research to the Management of Mental Health Systems,* Publ. no. 1003. Washington: National Clearinghouse for Mental Health Information, 1970.

65. HARRIS, C. W., ed. *Problems In Measuring Change.* Madison: University of Wisconsin Press, 1967.

66. HERZOG, E. *Some Guide Lines for Evaluative Research: Assessing Psycho-Social Change in Individuals.* DHEW, Children's Bureau Pub. no. 379-1959. Washington: U.S. Govt. Print. Off., 1959.

67. HOEHN-SARIC, R., J. D. FRANK, S. D. IM-

BER et al. "Systematic Preparation of Patients for Psychotherapy: I. Effects on Therapy Behavior and Outcome," *J. Psychiatr. Res.*, 2 (1964), 267–281.

68. Hogarty, G. E. "Selected Measures of Community Adjustment following Outpatient Psychotherapy: Ratings from Significant Others." Mimeo.

69. Hogarty, G. E., S. C. Goldberg, and the Collaborative Study Group. "Drug and Sociotherapy in the Aftercare of Schizophrenic Patients: One Year Relapse Rates," *Arch. Gen. Psychiatry*, 28 (1973), 54–64.

70. Holt, R. R. "Experimental Methods in Clinical Psychology," in B. B. Wolman, ed., *Handbook of Clinical Psychology*, pp. 40–77. New York: McGraw-Hill, 1965.

71. Honigfeld, G. "Non-Specific Factors in Treatment," *Dis. Nerv. Syst.*, 25 (1964), 145–239.

72. Hornstra, R. K. and T. S. McPartland. "Aspects of Psychiatric After-Care," *Int. J. Soc. Psychiatry*, 9 (1963), 135–142.

73. Howard, K., K. Rickels, J. E. Mock et al. "Therapeutic Style and Attrition Rate from Psychiatric Drug Treatment," *J. Nerv. Ment. Dis.*, (1970), 102–110.

74. Imber, S. D., E. H. Nash, R. Hoehn-Saric et al. "A Ten-Year Follow-up Study of Treated Psychiatric Outpatients," in S. Lesse, ed., *An Evaluation of the Results of the Psychotherapies*, pp. 1–12. Springfield, Ill.: Charles C. Thomas, 1968.

75. Jick, H., O. S. Miettinen, S. Shapiro et al. "Comprehensive Drug Surveillance," *JAMA*, 213 (1970), 1455–1460.

76. Johnson, L. C. and A. Lubin. "On Planning Psychophysiological Experiments," in N. S. Greenfield and R. A. Sternbach, eds., *Handbook of Psychophysiology*, pp. 125–158. New York: Holt, Rinehart and Winston, 1972.

77. Jones, M. B. and J. D. Ainslie. "Value of a Placebo Washout," *Dis. Nerv. Syst.*, 27 (1966), 393–396.

78. Judd, L. L., M. J. Goldstein, E. H. Rodnick et al. "Phenothiazine Effects in Good Premorbid Schizophrenics Divided into Paranoid-Nonparanoid Status," *Arch. Gen. Psychiatry*, 29 (1973), 207–211.

79. Kellam, S. G., S. C. Goldberg, N. R. Schooler et al. "Ward Atmosphere and Outcome of Treatment of Acute Schizo-phrenia," *J. Psychiatr. Res.*, 5 (1967), 145–163.

80. Kellner, R. "The Evidence in Favour of Psychotherapy," *Br. J. Med. Psychol.*, 40 (1967), 341–358.

81. ———. "Part 1. Improvement Criteria in Drug Trials with Neurotic Patients," *Psychol. Med.*, 1 (1971), 416–425.

82. ———. "Part 2. Improvement Criteria in Drug Trials with Neurotic Patients," *Psychol. Med.*, 2 (1972), 73–80.

83. Kernberg, O. F., E. D. Burstein, L. Coyne et al. "Psychotherapy and Psychoanalysis: Final Report of the Menninger Foundation's Psychotherapy Research Project," *Bull. Menninger Clin.*, 36 (1972), 1–275.

84. Kiesler, D. J. "Some Myths of Psychotherapy Research and the Search for a Paradigm," *Psychol. Bull.*, 65 (1965), 16–136.

85. ———. "Experimental Designs in Psychotherapy Research," in A. E. Bergin and S. L. Garfield, eds., *Handbook of Psychotherapy and Behavior Change: An Empirical Analysis*, pp. 36–74. New York: Wiley, 1971.

86. Kiresuk, T. J. and R. E. Sherman. "Goal Attainment Scaling: A General Method for Evaluating Comprehensive Community Mental Health Programs," *Community Ment. Health J.*, 4 (1968), 443–453.

87. Klein, D. F. and J. M. Davis. *Diagnosis and Drug Treatment of Psychiatric Disorders*, p. 436. Baltimore: Williams & Wilkins, 1969.

88. Klein, Z. E. "Research in the Child Psychiatric and Guidance Clinics: A Bibliography (1923–1970)." Mimeo.

89. Klerman, G. L., A. DiMascio, M. Weissman et al. "Treatment of Depression by Drugs and Psychotherapy." Presented at 126th Annu. Meet. Am. Psychiatr. Assoc. Honolulu, May 8, 1973.

90. Klett, C. J. and E. C. Moseley. "The Right Drug for the Right Patient," *J. Consult. Psychol.*, 29 (1965), 546–557.

91. Krasner, L. "The Therapist as a Social Reinforcement Machine," in H. H. Strupp and L. Luborsky, eds., *Research In Psychotherapy*, Vol. 2, pp. 61–94. Washington: Am. Psychological Assoc., 1962.

92. Levine, J., B. C. Schiele, and L. Bouthilet. *Principles and Problems in Establish-*

ing the Efficacy of Psychotropic Agents. U.S. Public Health Service Publ. no. 2138. Washington: U.S. Govt. Print. Off., 1971.

93. LIPMAN, R. S., J. O. COLE, L. C. PARK et al. "Sensitivity of Symptom and Nonsymptom-Focused Criteria of Outpatient Drug Efficacy," Am. J. Psychiatry, 122 (1965), 24–27.

94. LUBORSKY, L. "Comparative Studies of Psychotherapies: Is It True that 'Everybody Has Won and All Must Have Prizes'?" Presented at 3rd Annu. Meet. Soc. Psychother. Res. Nashville, June 16, 1972. Unpublished.

95. LUBORSKY, L. and H. H. STRUPP. "Research Problems in Psychotherapy: A Three-Year Follow-Up," in H. H. Strupp and L. Luborsky, eds., Research In Psychotherapy, Vol. 2, pp. 308–329. Washington: Am. Psychological Assoc., 1962.

96. LYERLY, S. B. and P. S. ABBOTT. Handbook of Psychiatric Rating Scales (1950–1964). U.S. Public Health Service Pub. No. 1495. Washington: U.S. Govt. Print. Off., 1966.

97. McGLASHAN, T., A. CAMPBELL, P. CLEARY et al. The Documentation of Clinical Psychotropic Drug Trials. Washington: NIMH, 1973.

98. McNAIR, D. M. "Self-Evaluations of Antidepressants." Unpublished.

99. MAY, P. R. A. Treatment of Schizophrenia: A Comparative Study of Five Treatment Methods. New York: Science House, 1968.

100. ———. "Psychotherapy and Ataraxic Drugs," in A. E. Bergin and S. L. Garfield, eds., Handbook of Psychotherapy and Behavior Change: An Empirical Analysis, pp. 495–540. New York: Wiley, 1971.

101. MAY, P. R. A., A. H. TUMA, and W. KRAUDE. "Community Follow-up of Treatment of Schizophrenia—Issues and Problems," Am. J. Orthopsychiatry, 35 (1965), 754–763.

102. MELLINGER, G. D., M. B. BALTER, H. J. PARRY et al. "An Overview of Psychotherapeutic Drug Use in the United States." Presented at Conf. Epidemiology of Drug Use. San Juan, Puerto Rico, Feb. 12–14, 1973. Unpublished.

103. MELTZOFF, J. and M. KORNREICH. Research in Psychotherapy. New York: Atherton, 1970.

104. MOOS, R. H. Revision of the Ward Atmosphere Scales (WAS): Technical Report.

Stanford: Stanford University Press, 1971.

105. MORRISON, D. F. Multivariate Statistical Methods. New York: McGraw-Hill, 1967.

106. NIE, N., D. H. BENT, and C. H. HULL. Statistical Package for the Social Sciences. New York: McGraw-Hill, 1970.

107. O'BRIEN, C. P., K. B. HAMM, B. A. RAY et al. "Group vs. Individual Psychotherapy with Schizophrenics," Arch. Gen. Psychiatry, 27 (1972), 474–478.

108. ORNE, M. T. "On the Social Psychology of the Psychological Experiment: With Particular Reference to Demand Characteristics and Their Implications," Am. Psychol., 17 (1962), 776–783.

109. OVERALL, J. E., L. E. HOLLISTER, and S. N. DALAL. "Psychiatric Drug Research: Sample Size Requirements for One vs. Two Raters," Arch. Gen. Psychiatry, 16 (1967), 152–161.

110. PARK, L. C .and L. COVI. "Non-Blind Placebo Trial: An Exploration of Neurotic Patients' Responses to Placebo when Its Inert Content Is Disclosed," Arch. Gen. Psychiatry, 12 (1965), 336–345.

111. PARK, L. C., E. H. UHLENHUTH, R. S. LIPMAN et al. "A Comparison of Doctor and Patient Improvement Ratings in a Drug (Meprobamate) Trial," Br. J. Psychiatry, 111 (1965), 535–540.

112. PARLOFF, M. B., H. C. KELMAN, and J. D. FRANK. "Comfort, Effectiveness and Self-Awareness as Criteria of Improvement in Psychotherapy," Am. J. Psychiatry, 111 (1954), 343–351.

113. PASAMANICK, B., F. R. SCARPITI, and S. DINITZ. Schizophrenics in the Community: An Experimental Study in the Prevention of Hospitalization. New York: Appleton-Century-Crofts, 1967.

114. PAUL, G. L. Insight vs. Desensitization in Psychotherapy: An Experiment in Anxiety Reduction. Stanford: Stanford University Press, 1966.

115. ———. "Behavior Modification Research: Design and Tactics," in C. M. Franks, ed., Behavior Therapy: Appraisal and Status, pp. 29–62. New York: McGraw-Hill, 1969.

116. ———. "Outcomes of Desensitization II: Controlled Investigations of Individual Treatment, Technique Variations, and Current Status," in C. M. Franks, ed., Behavior Therapy: Appraisal and Status, pp. 105–159. New York: McGraw-Hill, 1969.

117. POLLACK, E. S. "Monitoring a Comprehensive Mental Health Program: Methodology and Data Requirements," in L. M. Roberts, N. S. Greenfield, and M. H. Miller, eds., *Comprehensive Mental Health: The Challenge of Evaluation.* Madison: University of Wisconsin Press, 1968.

118. PRIEN, R. F., E. M. CAFFEY, JR., and C. J. KLETT. "Comparison of Lithium Carbonate and Chlorpromazine in the Treatment of Mania," *Arch. Gen. Psychiatry,* 26 (1972), 146–153.

119. PRIEN, R. F., C. J. KLETT, and E. M. CAFFEY, JR. *A Comparison of Lithium Carbonate and Imipramine in the Prevention of Affective Episodes in Recurrent Affective Illness,* Prepubl. Rep. no. 94. Perry Point, Md.: VA Central Neuropsychiatric Research Laboratory, 1973.

120. RASKIN, A. "Factors Affecting Response to Drug Treatment in Depressed Patients." Mimeo., 1972.

121. REID, W. J. and A. W. SHYNE. *Brief and Extended Casework.* New York: Columbia University Press, 1969.

122. RICKELS, K., R. CATTELL, A. MACAFEE et al. "Drug Response and Important External Events in the Patient's Life," *Dis. Nerv. Syst.,* 26 (1965), 782–786.

123. RICKELS, K. and R. W. DOWNING. "Minor Tranquilizers in Anxiety: Some Prognostic Indicators." Presented at Int. Symp. on Relaxation Therapy for Psychosomatic Disorders, St. Moritz, Switzerland, Jan. 11–13, 1971. Unpublished.

124. RICKELS, K. and B. E. McLAUGHLIN. "Sample Size in Psychiatric Drug Research," *Clin. Pharmacol. Ther.,* 9 (1968), 631–634.

125. ROBERTS, L. M., N. S. GREENFIELD, and M. H. MILLER, eds. *Comprehensive Mental Health: The Challenge of Evaluation.* Madison: University of Wisconsin Press, 1968.

126. ROSENTHAL, R. *Experimenter Effects in Behavioral Research.* New York: Appleton-Century-Crofts, 1966.

127. ROSSI, P. and W. WILLIAMS, eds. *Evaluating Social Programs.* New York: Seminar Press, 1972.

128. RUBINSTEIN, E. A. and M. B. PARLOFF, eds. *Research in Psychotherapy.* Washington: Am. Psychological Assoc., 1959.

129. SAENGER, G. "Patterns of Change among 'Treated' and 'Untreated' Patients Seen in Community Mental Health Clinics," *J. Nerv. Ment. Dis.,* 150 (1970), 37–50.

130. SARGENT, H. D. "Intrapsychic Change: Methodological Problems in Psychotherapy Research," *Psychiatry,* 24 (1961), 93–108.

131. SCHULBERG, H. C., A. SHELDON, and F. BAKER, eds. *Program Evaluation in the Health Fields.* New York: Behavioral Pub., 1969.

132. SCHWARTZ, C. C., J. K. MYERS, and B. M. ASTRACHAN. "The Outcome Study in Psychiatric Evaluation Research: Issues and Methods," *Arch. Gen. Psychiatry,* 29 (1973), 98–102.

133. SHAPIRO, S. "End Result Measurements of the Quality of Medical Care," *Milbank Mem. Fund Q.,* 51 (1967), 49–72.

134. SHLIEN, J. M., H. F. HUNT, J. D. MATARAZZO et al., eds. *Research in Psychotherapy,* Vol. 3. Washington: Am. Psychological Assoc., 1968.

135. SONQUIST, J. A. and N. J. MORGAN. *The Detection of Interaction Effects.* Ann Arbor: University of Michigan Press, 1964.

136. STEPHENS, J. A. and C. ASTRUP. "Treatment Outcome in 'Process' and 'Nonprocess' Schizophrenics Treated by 'A' and 'B' Types of Therapists," *J. Nerv. Ment. Dis.,* 140 (1965), 449–456.

137. STOLLAK, G. E., B. G. GUERNEY, and M. ROTHBERG, eds. *Psychotherapy Research: Selected Readings.* Chicago: Rand McNally, 1966.

138. STONE, A. R., J. D. FRANK, E. H. NASH et al. "An Intensive Five-Year Follow-up Study of Treated Psychiatric Outpatients," *J. Nerv. Ment. Dis.,* 133 (1961), 410–422.

139. STRUPP, H. H. and A. E. BERGIN. *Research in Individual Psychotherapy: A Bibliography.* U.S. Public Health Service Pub. no. 1944. Washington: Govt. Print. Off., 1969.

140. ———. "Some Empirical and Conceptual Bases for Coordinated Research in Psychotherapy: A Critical Review of Issues, Trends, and Evidence," *Int. J. Psychiatry,* 7 (1969), 18–90.

141. STRUPP, H. H. and L. LUBORSKY, eds. *Research In Psychotherapy,* Vol. 2. Washington: Am. Psychological Assoc., 1962.

142. SUCHMAN, E. A. *Evaluative Research:*

Principles and Practice in Public Service and Social Action Programs, pp. 31; 77. New York: Russell Sage Foundation, 1967.

143. Thompson, C. P. and N. W. Bell. "Evaluation of a Rural Community Mental Health Program, *Arch. Gen. Psychiatry*, 20 (1969), 448–456.

144. Truax, C. B. and R. R. Carkhuff. *Toward Effective Counseling and Psychotherapy: Training and Practice*. Chicago: Aldine, 1967.

145. Truax, C. B. and K. M. Mitchell. "Research on Certain Therapist Interpersonal Skills in Relation to Process and Outcome," in A. E. Bergin, and S. L. Garfield, eds., *Handbook of Psychotherapy and Behavior Change: An Empirical Analysis*, pp. 299–344. New York: Wiley, 1971.

146. Uhlenhuth, E. H., L. Covi, and R. S. Lipman. "Indications for Minor Tranquilizers in Anxious Outpatients," in P. Black, ed., *Drugs and the Brain: Papers on the Action, Use and Abuse of Psychotropic Agents*, pp. 203–221. Baltimore: The Johns Hopkins Press, 1969.

147. Uhlenhuth, E. H. and D. B. Duncan. "Subjective Change with Medical Student Therapists: II. Some Determinants of Change in Psychoneurotic Outpatients," *Arch. Gen. Psychiatry*, 18 (1968), 532–540.

148. Uhlenhuth, E. H., D. B. Duncan, and L. C. Park. "Some Nonpharmacologic Modifiers of the Response to Imipramine in Depressed Psychoneurotic Outpatients: A Confirmatory Study," in P. R. A. May and J. R. Wittenborn, eds., *Psychotropic Drug Response: Advances in Prediction*, pp. 155–197. Springfield, Ill.: Charles C. Thomas, 1969.

149. Vaillant, G. E. "Prospective Prediction of Schizophrenic Remission," *Arch. Gen. Psychiatry*, 11 (1964), 509–518.

150. Wartski, S. A. and D. S. Green. "Evaluation in a Home Care Program," *Med. Care*, 9 (1971), 352–364.

151. Waskow, I., ed. *The Evaluation of Psychotherapy Outcome*, forthcoming.

152. Weissman, M. M. "The Assessment of Social Adjustment: Measures Suitable for Antidepressant Trials." Mimeo., 1972.

153. Whitehorn, J. C. and B. J. Betz. "A Study of Psychotherapeutic Relationships between Physicians and Schizophrenic Patients," *Am. J. Psychiatry*, 111 (1954), 321–331.

154. Wittenborn, J. R. *The Clinical Pharmacology of Anxiety*. Springfield, Ill.: Charles C. Thomas, 1966.

155. Woodruff, R. A., D. W. Goodwin, and S. B. Guze. *Psychiatric Diagnosis*. New York: Oxford University Press, 1974.

156. Zolik, E. S., E. M. Lantz, and R. Sommers. "Hospital Return Rates and Prerelease Referrals," *Arch. Gen. Psychiatry*, 18 (1968), 712–717.

157. Zusman, J., V. Hannon, B. Z. Locke et al. *Bibliography on Epidemiology of Mental Disorders*, Publ. no. 5030. Washington: National Clearinghouse for Mental Health Information, 1970.

158. Zusman, J. and E. R. R. Ross. "Evaluation of the Quality of Mental Health Services," *Arch. Gen. Psychiatry*, 20 (1969), 353–357.

NAME INDEX

Note: Bold face figures indicate chapter pages.

SUBJECT INDEX

126; school phobia and, 759; speech disorders and, 245; therapeutic communities in drug addiction and, 843, 844; transference and, 747; traumatic neurosis and, 433; urban class and, 613; verbal statements about, 56; violence and, 577, 578

Stretch reflex, 47

Strokes, 581, 813

Strong Memorial Hospital, 610

Strong Vocational Interest Blank, 943

Structural family therapy, 378–380

Structural model of psychic functioning, 169

Structured exercises, in group therapy, 351, 353

Strychnine, 409

Students, see College students; Graduate students

Study of Brief Psychotherapy, A (Malan), 255

Stupor: electro-convulsive therapy and, 542; hypnosis and, 241

Stuttering: carbon dioxide and, 516; conditioning and, 322; hypnosis and, 245; metranome for, 309; operant conditioning and, 301; violence and, 577

Subconvulsive petit-mal response, 534

Subdural hematomas, 584

Sublimation, in school, 648

Sublimination: convalescent stage of disease and, 794, 795; medical psychotherapy and, 785

Submission, in communist beliefs, 36

Substance P, 797

Suburbs, and hospitals, 612

Success, fear of, 242

Succinimide drugs, 72

Succinylcholine: aversion treatment and, 307; electro-convulsive therapy and, 536, 539

Sucking behavior, and sexual behavior, 414

Sudden death, and phenothiazines, 460

Suggestibility: hysterical personality and, 788; psychotherapy and, 104–105

Suggestion: brief psychotherapy and, 260; conversion reactions and, 798; definition of, 260; hypnosis and, 165, 237, 238, 239–245, 248, 249, 251, 254; hypochondriasis and, 198; placebo effect and, 6, 7; psychotherapy and, 97, 180; sex therapy and, 416; sickness and, 514; treatment of illness with, 7, 8; youthful suicide and, 758

Suicide, 44, 620; anger and, 822; child psychiatry and, 757, 758–759; college students and, 398;

emergency services and, 571, 575, 576, 578; family and, 285; heroin detoxification and, 842; malpractice and, 903, 906–909; old age and, 819; schizophrenia and, 77

Suicide attempts: anorexia nervosa and, 760; antianxiety drugs and, 430, 437; brief psychotherapy and, 265; civil commitment and, 859; college students and, 398; conjoint therapy and, 224; depression and, 484; doctor-patient relationship and, 914; electroconvulsive therapy and, 476–477, 540; emergency services for, 567, 570, 571, 573, 574–576, 580; foster-home care and, 696; general hospitals and, 614; homicides and, 578–580; hospitalization for, 608; hypnotherapy and, 246; hypochondriasis and, 198; parent-child relationship and, 219; preadolescent, 215; primary-care-physician psychotherapy and, 753; psychotherapy with children and, 146, 147; rescue factor in, 575–576; residential treatment and, 640; sedative overdose and, 832–833; stimulant drug withdrawal and, 834

Sullivanian school, 183, 703

Sundowner syndrome, 799

Superego: deprivation and, 79; development and, 758; ego functions and, 169; impulsive personality and, 789; internal dialogue and, 54; obsessive-compulsive personality and, 786; old age and, 814; paradoxes in psychoanalysis and, 59; psychoanalytic psychotherapy and, 185, 189, 194; psychological development and, 213; psychotherapy with children and, 136; structural metaphors in, 13; Transactional Analysis and, 274; youthful suicides and, 758

Superintendents, of state mental hospitals, 594, 597

Supernatural forces, and women, 207

Support, in sex therapy, 417

Suppression: action and communication and, 220; medical psychotherapy and, 785

Supreme Court, 862, 872, 873, 879, 914

Surgery: chlorpromazine and, 441; conversion reactions and, 795; frontal-lobe, 548–552; future outlook for, 556–558; grief and, 794; historical overview of, 548–549; hypnosis and, 243, 244; limbic-system, 552–554; old age and, 819; psychiatric nursing and, 656; psychiatric training and, 87;

psychiatric treatment with, 548–563; sex therapy and, 415; temporal-lobe, 554–556

Surrogate partners, in sex therapy, 417

Survival, and old age, 816, 818

Survival guilt: old age and, 816; psychoanalytic psychotherapy and, 194

Suspiciousness: paranoid personality and, 787; phenothiazines and, 446; stimulant abuse and, 833

Swinging (sexual behavior), 410

Sydenham's chorea, 71–72, 239

Symbiosis, and dying process, 803

Symbolic thinking: animal studies of behavior and, 298; neonatal period and, 51; timetables of, 51–52

Symptom Distress Check List, 350

Symptom formation: behavior therapy and, 20, 22, 292; conversion reactions and, 796–798; demoralization and, 120; dynamic therapy and, 22; hypnosis and, 241–242; infancy and, 213–214; internalization of conflict and, 214; preadolescent, 215; psychodynamic therapy and, 10, 28

Symptom scheduling, in existential psychotherapy, 281

Synanon, 286, 364, 843

Synchrony in dance therapy, 706

Syphilis, 89, 90, 595

Springomyelia, 238

Systemic desensitization, see Desensitization

Systems theory, see General systems theory

Tabes, 238

Taboos: childhood and, 62; sexual behavior and, 413; voodoo curses and, 239

Tabula rasa concept, 207

Tachycardia: antidepressant drugs and, 483; hallucinogens and, 835; hypnotherapy and, 238; phenothiazines and, 460; stimulant abuse and, 833

Tactile stimulation, and orienting reflex, 48

Tahiti, 57

Tai Chi, 701

Talmud, 59

Talwin, 800

Taractan, 449

Tarasoff v. Regents of University of California, 913–914

Tardive dyskinesia: antipsychotic drugs and, 462–463; lithium and, 480

TAT, see Thematic Appperception Test (TAT)

Teachers: behavior therapy and, 291; child-behavior therapy and,